Alan Rogers

France

Quality camping & caravanning sites

Alan Rogers

2008

INSPECTED CAMPSITES & SELECTED

Compiled by: Alan Rogers Guides Ltd

Designed by: Paul Effenberg, Vine Design Ltd

Maps created by Customised Mapping (01769 540044)
contain background data provided by GisDATA Ltd
Maps are © Alan Rogers Guides and GisDATA Ltd 2007

Published by: Alan Rogers Guides Ltd,
Spelmonden Old Oast, Goudhurst, Kent TN17 1HE
www.alanrogers.com Tel: 01580 214000

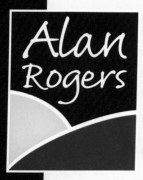

British Library Cataloguing-in-Publication Data:
A catalogue record for this book is available from the
British Library.

ISBN-13 978-1-906215-00-2

Printed in Great Britain by J H Haynes & Co Ltd

Contents

 4 Introduction

 6 How To Use This Guide

 10 Alan Rogers Awards

 12 Alan Rogers Travel Service

 17 Brittany

 75 Normandy

 95 Northern France

 106 Paris & Ile de France

 116 Eastern France

 133 Vendée & Charente

 169 Loire Valley

 194 Burgundy

 207 Franche Comté

 215 Savoy & Dauphiny Alps

 236 Atlantic Coast

 272 Dordogne & Aveyron

 317 Limousin & Auvergne

 336 Rhône Valley

 362 Provence

 378 Midi-Pyrénées

 395 Mediterranean West

 441 Mediterranean East

 473 Corsica

 480 Mobile Homes & Chalets

 513 Parc Résidentiels de Loisirs

 517 Open All Year

 517 Dogs

 518 Dogs, Naturist Sites

 519 Travelling in Europe

 537 Maps

 556 Town and Village Index

 562 Campsite Index by Number

 569 Campsite Index by Region and Name

the Alan Rogers
approach

Alan Rogers

Last year we celebrated the publication of the fortieth editions of the Alan Rogers Guides. Since Alan Rogers published the first campsite guide that bore his name, the range has expanded to six titles covering 27 countries. No fewer than 20 of the campsites selected by Alan for the first guide are still featured in our 2008 editions.

There are over 11,000 campsites in France of varying quality: this guide contains impartially written reports on 950 (70 more than last year), including some of the very finest, each being individually inspected and selected. All the usual maps and indexes are also included, designed to help you find the choice of campsite that's right for you. We hope you enjoy some happy and safe travels – and some pleasurable 'armchair touring' in the meantime!

A question of quality

The criteria we use when inspecting and selecting sites are numerous, but the most important by far is the question of good quality. People want different things from their choice of campsite so we try to include a range of campsite 'styles' to cater for a wide variety of preferences: from those seeking a small peaceful campsite in the heart of the countryside, to visitors looking for an 'all singing, all dancing' site in a popular seaside resort. Those with more specific interests, such as sporting facilities, cultural events or historical attractions, are also catered for.

The size of the site, whether it's part of a chain or privately owned, makes no difference in terms of it being required to meet our exacting standards in respect of its quality and it being 'fit for purpose'. In other words, irrespective of the size of the site, or the number of facilities it offers, we consider and evaluate the welcome, the pitches, the sanitary facilities, the cleanliness, the general maintenance and even the location.

" ...the campsites included in this book have been chosen entirely on merit, and no payment of any sort is made by them for their inclusion."

Alan Rogers, 1968

INSPECTED & SELECTED SINCE 1968

INSPECTED CAMPSITES & SELECTED

Expert opinions

We rely on our dedicated team of Site Assessors, all of whom are experienced campers, caravanners or motorcaravanners, to visit and recommend sites. Each year they travel some 100,000 miles around Europe inspecting new campsites for the guide and re-inspecting the existing ones. Our thanks are due to them for their enthusiastic efforts, their diligence and integrity.

We also appreciate the feedback we receive from many of our readers and we always make a point of following up complaints, suggestions or recommendations for possible new sites. Of course we get a few grumbles too – but it really is a few, and those we do receive usually relate to overcrowding or to poor maintenance during the peak school holiday period. Please bear in mind that, although we are interested to hear about any complaints, we have no contractual relationship with the campsites featured in our guides and are therefore not in a position to intervene in any dispute between a reader and a campsite.

HIGHLY RESPECTED BY SITE OWNERS AND READERS ALIKE, THERE IS NO BETTER GUIDE WHEN IT COMES TO FORMING AN INDEPENDENT VIEW OF A CAMPSITE'S QUALITY. WHEN YOU NEED TO BE CONFIDENT IN YOUR CHOICE OF CAMPSITE, YOU NEED THE ALAN ROGERS GUIDE.

✓ Sites only included on merit

✓ Sites cannot pay to be included

✓ Independently inspected, rigorously assessed

✓ Impartial reviews

✓ Over 40 years of expertise

Independent and honest

Whilst the content and scope of the Alan Rogers guides have expanded considerably since the early editions, our selection of campsites still employs exactly the same philosophy and criteria as defined by Alan Rogers in 1968.

'telling it how it is'

Firstly, and most importantly, our selection is based entirely on our own rigorous and independent inspection and selection process. Campsites cannot buy their way into our guides – indeed the extensive Site Report which is written by us, not by the site owner, is provided free of charge so we are free to say what we think and to provide an honest, 'warts and all' description. This is written in plain English and without the use of confusing icons or symbols.

Written in plain English, our guides are exceptionally easy to use, but a few words of explanation regarding the layout and content may be helpful. Regular readers will see that our site reports are grouped into 19 'tourist regions' and then by the various départements in each of these regions in numerical order.

The Site Reports – *Example of an entry*

Site Number Site name
Postal Address (including département)
Telephone number. Email address

A description of the site in which we try to give an idea of its general features – its size, its situation, its strengths and its weaknesses. This section should provide a picture of the site itself with reference to the facilities that are provided and if they impact on its appearance or character. We include details on pitch numbers, electricity (with amperage), hardstandings etc. in this section as pitch design, planning and terracing affects the site's overall appearance. Similarly we include reference to pitches used for caravan holiday homes, chalets, and the like. Importantly at the end of this column we indicate if there are any restrictions, e.g. no tents, no children, naturist sites.

Facilities
Lists more specific information on the site's facilities and amenities and, where available, the dates when these facilities are open (if not for the whole season). Off site: here we give distances to various local amenities, for example, local shops, the nearest beach, plus our featured activities (bicycle hire, fishing, horse riding, boat launching). Where we have space we list suggestions for activities and local tourist attractions.

Open: Site opening dates.

Directions
Separated from the main text in order that they may be read and assimilated more easily by a navigator en-route. Bear in mind that road improvement schemes can result in road numbers being altered.

GPS: references are provided as we obtain them for satellite navigation systems (in degrees and minutes).

Charges 2008

Regions and départements

For administrative purposes France is actually divided into 23 official regions covering the 95 départements (similar to our counties). However, these do not always coincide with the needs of tourists. For example the area we think of as the Dordogne is split between two of the official regions. We have, therefore, opted to feature our campsites within unofficial 'tourist regions', and the relevant départements are stated in our introduction to each region with their official number (eg. the département of Manche is number 50) included. We use these département numbers as the first two digits of our campsite numbers, so any campsite in the Manche département will start with the number 50, prefixed with FR.

Indexes

Our three indexes allow you to find sites by their number and name, by region and site name or by the town or village where the site is situated.

Campsite Maps

The maps relate to our tourist regions and will help you to identify the approximate position of each campsite. The colour of the campsite number indicates whether it is open all year or not. You will certainly need more detailed maps and we have found the Michelin atlas to be particularly useful.

Facilities

Toilet blocks

We assume that toilet blocks will be equipped with a reasonable amount of British style WCs, washbasins with hot and cold water and hot showers with dividers or curtains, and will have all necessary shelves, hooks, plugs and mirrors. We also assume that there will be an identified chemical toilet disposal point, and that the campsite will provide water and waste water drainage points and bin areas. If not the case, we comment. We do mention certain features that some readers find important: washbasins in cubicles, facilities for babies, facilities for those with disabilities and motorcaravan service points. Readers with disabilities are advised to contact the site of their choice to ensure that facilities are appropriate to their needs.

Shop

Basic or fully supplied, and opening dates.

Bars, restaurants, takeaway facilities and entertainment

We try hard to supply opening and closing dates (if other than the campsite opening dates) and to identify if there are discos or other entertainment.

Children's play areas

Fenced and with safety surface (e.g. sand, bark or pea-gravel).

Swimming pools

If particularly special, we cover in detail in our main campsite description but reference is always included under our Facilities listings. Opening dates, charges and levels of supervision are provided where we have been notified. There is a regulation whereby Bermuda shorts may not be worn in swimming pools (for health reasons). It is worth ensuring that you do take 'proper' swimming trunks with you.

Leisure facilities

For example, playing fields, bicycle hire, organised activities and entertainment.

Dogs

If dogs are not accepted or restrictions apply, we state it here. Check the quick reference list at the back of the guide.

Off site

This briefly covers leisure facilities, tourist attractions, restaurants etc. nearby.

Charges

These are the latest provided to us by the sites. In those few cases where 2007 or 2008 prices are not given, we try to give a general guide.

Reservations

Necessary for high season (roughly mid-July to mid-August) in popular holiday areas (ie beach resorts). You can reserve via our own Alan Rogers Travel Service or through tour operators. Or be wholly independent and contact the campsite(s) of your choice direct, using the phone or e-mail numbers shown in the site reports, but please bear in mind that many sites are closed all winter.

Telephone numbers

All numbers assume that you are phoning from within France. To phone France from outside that country, prefix the number shown with the relevant International Code (00 33) and drop the first 0, shown as (0) in the numbers indicated.

Opening dates

Are those advised to us during the early autumn of the previous year – sites can, and sometimes do, alter these dates before the start of the following season, often for good reasons. If you intend to visit shortly after a published opening date, or shortly before the closing date, it is wise to check that it will actually be open at the time required. Similarly some parks operate a restricted service during the low season, only opening some of their facilities (e.g. swimming pools) during the main season; where we know about this, and have the relevant dates, we indicate it – again if you are at all doubtful it is wise to check.

Some French site owners are very laid back when it comes to opening and closing dates. They may not be fully ready by their stated opening dates – grass and hedges may not all be cut or perhaps only limited sanitary facilities open. At the end of the season they also tend to close down some facilities and generally wind down prior to the closing date. Bear this in mind if you are travelling early or late in the season – it is worth phoning ahead.

The Camping Cheque low season touring system goes some way to addressing this in that participating campsites are encouraged to have all key facilities open and running by the opening date and to remain fully operational until the closing date.

Mobile homes ▶ page 480

Our Accommodation Section

Over recent years, more and more campsites have added high quality mobile home and chalet accommodation. In response to feedback from many of our readers, and to reflect this evolution in campsites, we have now decided to include a separate section on mobile homes and chalets. If a site offers this accommodation, it is indicated above the site report with a page reference where full details are given. We have chosen a number of sites offering some of the best accommodation available and have included full details of one or two accommodation types at these sites. Please note however that many other campsites listed in this guide may also have a selection of accommodation for rent.

Whether you're an 'old hand' in terms of camping and caravanning or are contemplating your first trip, a regular reader of our Guides or a new 'convert', we wish you well in your travels and hope we have been able to help in some way. We are, of course, also out and about ourselves, visiting sites, talking to owners and readers, and generally checking on standards and new developments.

We wish all our readers thoroughly enjoyable Camping and Caravanning in 2008 – favoured by good weather of course!

THE ALAN ROGERS TEAM

Regions

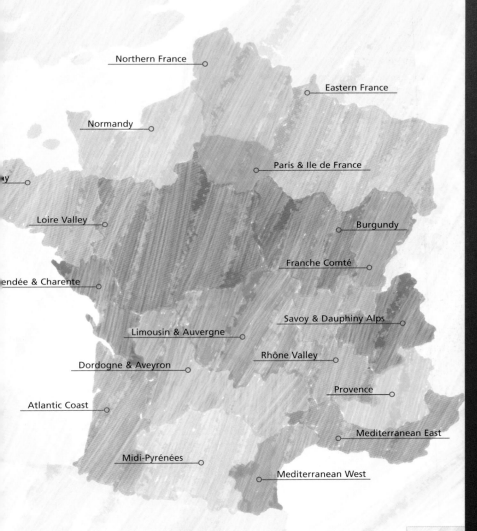

Northern France

Eastern France

Normandy

Paris & Ile de France

y

Loire Valley

Burgundy

Franche Comté

endée & Charente

Savoy & Dauphiny Alps

Limousin & Auvergne

Rhône Valley

Dordogne & Aveyron

Provence

Atlantic Coast

Mediterranean East

Midi-Pyrénées

Mediterranean West

Corsica

the Alan Rogers awards

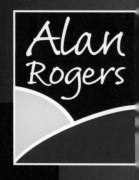

In 2004 we introduced the first ever Alan Rogers Campsite Awards.

Before making our awards, we carefully consider more than 2000 campsites featured in our guides, taking into account comments from our site assessors, our head office team and, of course, our readers.

Our award winners come from the four corners of Europe, from southern Portugal to the Czech Republic, and this year we are making awards to campsites in 14 different countries.

Needless to say, it's an extremely difficult task to choose our eventual winners, but we believe that we have identified a number of campsites with truly outstanding characteristics.

In each case, we have selected an outright winner, along with two highly commended runners-up.

Listed below are full details of each of our award categories and our winners for 2007.

Alan Rogers Progress Award 2007

This award reflects the hard work and commitment undertaken by particular site owners to improve and upgrade their site.

WINNER
AU0060 Natterersee, Austria

RUNNERS-UP	
BE0712	Ile de Faigneul, Belgium
DE3672	Elbsee, Germany

Alan Rogers Welcome Award 2007

This award takes account of sites offering a particularly friendly welcome and maintaining a friendly ambience throughout reader's holidays.

WINNER
FR24090 Soleil Plage, France

RUNNERS-UP	
IR9610	Mannix Point, Ireland
UK4640	Goosewood, England

Alan Rogers Active Holiday Award 2007

This award reflects sites in outstanding locations which are ideally suited for active holidays, notably walking or cycling, but which could extend to include such activities as winter sports or water sports

WINNER
DK2170 Klim Strand, Denmark

RUNNERS-UP	
FR09060	Pre Lombard, France
DE3450	Munstertal, Germany

Alan Rogers Motorhome Award 2007

Motorhome sales are increasing and this award acknowledges sites which, in our opinion, have made outstanding efforts to welcome motorhome clients.

WINNER
PO8210 Campismo Albufeira, Portugal

RUNNERS-UP	
IR9650	Woodlands Park, Ireland
FR29180	Les Embruns, France

Alan Rogers Rented Accommodation Award 2007

Given the increasing importance of rented accommodation on many campsites, we feel that it is important to acknowledge sites which have made a particular effort in creating a high quality 'rented accommodation' park.

WINNER

ES8480	Sanguli, Spain

RUNNERS-UP

NL5575	Scheldeoord, Netherlands
CR6736	Valdaliso, Croatia

Alan Rogers Unique Site Award 2007

This award acknowledges sites with unique, outstanding features – something which simply cannot be found elsewhere and which is an important attraction of the site.

WINNER

FR78040	Huttopia Rambouillet, France

RUNNERS-UP

FR80070	Ferme des Aulnes, France
UK1590	Exe Valley, England

Alan Rogers Family Site Award 2007

Many sites claim to be child friendly but this award acknowledges the sites we feel to be the very best in this respect.

WINNER

NL5985	Beerze Bulten, Netherlands

RUNNERS-UP

UK0170	Trevella, England
ES8540	Torre del Sol, Spain
IT6014	Villaggio Turistico Internazionale, Italy

Alan Rogers 4 Seasons Award 2007

This award is made to outstanding sites with extended opening dates and which welcome clients to a uniformly high standard throughout the year.

WINNER

CH9570	Eienwaldi, Switzerland

RUNNERS-UP

AU0440	Schluga, Austria
IT6814	Flaminio, Italy

Alan Rogers Seaside Award 2007

This award is made for sites which we feel are outstandingly suitable for a really excellent seaside holiday.

WINNER

ES8030	Nautic Almata, Spain

RUNNERS-UP

FR85210	Les Ecureuils, France
IT6036	Ca Pasquali, Italy

Alan Rogers Readers' Award 2007

In 2005 we introduced a new award, which we believe to be the most important, our Readers' Award. We simply invited our readers (by means of an on-line poll at **www.alanrogers.com**) to nominate the site they enjoyed most. The outright winner for 2007 is:

WINNER

ES8530	Playa Montroig Resort, Spain

Alan Rogers Country Award 2007

This award contrasts with our former award and acknowledges sites which are attractively located in delightful, rural locations.

WINNER

UK1020	Oakdown, England

RUNNERS-UP

CZ4896	Camping Country, Czech Republic
NL5980	De Roos, Netherlands

Alan Rogers Special Award 2007

A special award is made to acknowledge sites which we feel have overcome a very significant setback, and have, not only returned to their former condition, but has added extra amenities and can therefore be fairly considered to be even better than before. In 2007 we acknowledged two campsites, which have undergone major problems and have made highly impressive recoveries.

CH9510	Aareg, Switzerland
IT6845	San Nicola, Italy

Alan Rogers. trave

The Alan Rogers Travel Service was set up to provide a low cost booking service for readers. We pride ourselves on being able to put together a bespoke holiday, taking advantage of our experience, knowledge and contacts. We can tailor-make a holiday to suit your requirements, giving you maximum choice and flexibility: exactly what we have been offering for some 8 years now.

Whether you book on-line or book by phone, you will be allocated an experienced Personal Travel Consultant to provide you with personal advice and manage every stage of your booking. Our Personal Travel Consultants have first-hand experience of many of our campsites and access to a wealth of information. They can 'paint a picture' of individual campsites, check availability, provide a competitive price and tailor your holiday arrangements to your specific needs.

- Discuss your holiday plans with a friendly person with first-hand experience

- Let us reassure you that your holiday arrangements really are taken care of

- Tell us about your special requests and allow us to pass these on

- Benefit from advice which will save you money – the latest ferry deals and more

- Remember, our offices are in Kent not overseas and we do NOT operate a queuing system!

THE AIMS OF THE TRAVEL SERVICE ARE SIMPLE

- To provide convenience - a one-stop shop to make life easier.

- To provide peace of mind - when you need it most.

- To provide a friendly, knowledgeable, efficient service – when this can be hard to find.

- To provide a low cost means of organising your holiday – when prices can be so complicated.

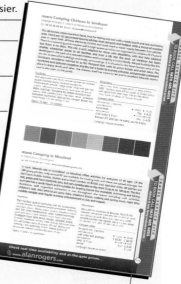

HOW IT WORKS

1 Choose your campsite(s) – we can book around 500 across Europe. Look for the yellow coloured campsite entries in this book. You'll find more info and images at www.alanrogers.travel.

Please note: the list of campsites we can book for you varies from time to time.

2 Choose your dates – choose when you arrive, when you leave.

3 Choose your ferry crossing – we can book most routes with most operators at extremely competitive rates.

Then just call us for an instant quote

01580 214000

or visit
www.**alanrogers.travel**

LOOK FOR A CAMPSITE
ENTRY LIKE THIS TO INDICATE
WHICH CAMPSITES WE CAN
BOOK FOR YOU.

THE LIST IS GROWING SO
PLEASE CALL FOR UP TO THE
MINUTE INFORMATION.

Book The Best, **With The Best**

This Premier Selection is designed to offer a hand-picked range of sites, well-known to us, where you will find the best of everything that makes a great holiday.

PITCHES AND MOBILE HOMES

FREE BROCHURE
01580 214000
www.**alanrogers.travel/premier**

Leave The Hassle To Us

- All site fees paid in advance (nominal local tourist taxes may be payable on arrival).
- Your pitch is reserved for you – travel with peace of mind.
- No endless overseas phone calls or correspondence with foreign site owners.
- No need to pay foreign currency deposits and booking fees.
- Take advantage of our expert advice and experience of camping in Europe.

Already Booked Your Ferry?

We're confident that our ferry inclusive booking service offers unbeatable value. However, if you have already booked your ferry then we can still make a pitch-only reservation for you (minimum 5 nights). Since our prices are based on our ferry inclusive service, you need to be aware that a non-ferry booking may result in slightly higher prices than if you were to book direct with the site.

book
on-line
and save money

www.alanrogers.travel is a website designed to give you everything you need to know when it comes to booking your Alan Rogers inspected and selected campsite, and your low cost ferry.

Our friendly, expert team of travel consultants is always happy to help on **01580 214000** – but they do go home sometimes!

Visit www.alanrogers.travel and you'll find constantly updated information, latest ferry deals, special offers from campsites and much more. And you can visit it at any time of day or night!

www.alanrogers.travel

Campsite Information

☑ Details of all Travel Service campsites - **instantly**

☑ Find latest special offers on campsites - **instantly**

☑ Check campsite availability - **instantly**

Ferry Information

☑ Check ferry availability - **instantly**

☑ Find latest ferry deals - **instantly**

☑ Book your ferry online - **instantly**

☑ Save money - **instantly**

Crossing the Channel

One of the great advantages of booking your ferry-inclusive holiday with the Alan Rogers Travel Service is the tremendous value we offer. Our money-saving Ferry Deals have become legendary. As agents for all major cross-Channel operators we can book all your travel arrangements with the minimum of fuss and at the best possible rates.

Just call us for an instant quote

01580 214000

or visit
www.alanrogers.travel
Book on-line AND SAVE

Let us price your holiday for you
instantly!

The quickest and easiest way is to call us for advice and an instant quote. We can take details of your vehicle and party and, using our direct computer link to all the operators' reservations systems, can give you an instant price. We can even check availability for you and book a crossing while you're on the phone!

Please note we can only book ferry crossings in conjunction with a campsite holiday reservation.

MAP 1

Rolling sandy beaches, hidden coves, pretty villages and a picturesque coastline all combine to make Brittany a very popular holiday destination. Full of Celtic culture steeped in myths and legends, Brittany is one of the most distinctive regions of France.

DÉPARTEMENTS: 22 CÔTES D'ARMOR, 29 FINISTÈRE, 35 ILLE-ET-VILAINE, 56 MORBIHAN, 44 LOIRE ATLANTIQUE

MAJOR CITIES: RENNES AND BREST

Brittany's 800 miles of rocky coastline offers numerous bays, busy little fishing villages and broad sandy beaches dotted with charming seaside resorts. The coastline to the north of Brittany is rugged with a maze of rocky coves, while to the south, the shore is flatter with long sandy beaches. Inland you'll find wooded valleys, rolling fields, moors and giant granite boulders, but most impressive is the wealth of prehistoric sites, notably the Carnac standing stones.

Breton culture offers a rich history of menhirs, crosses, cathedrals and castles. Strong Celtic roots provide this region with its own distinctive traditions, evident in the local Breton costume and music, traditional religious festivals and the cuisine, featuring crêpes and cider. Many castles and manor houses, countless chapels and old towns and villages provide evidence of Brittany's eventful history and wealth of traditions. The abbey fortress of Mont-St-Michel on the north coast should not be missed and Concarneau in the south is a lovely walled town enclosed by granite rocks.

Places of interest

Cancale: small fishing port famous for oysters.

Carnac: 3,000 standing stones (menhirs).

Concarneau: fishing port, old walled town.

Dinan: historical walled town.

La Baule: resort with lovely, sandy bay.

Le Croisic: fishing port, Naval museum.

Guérande: historic walled town.

Perros-Guirec: leading resort of the 'Pink Granite Coast'.

Quiberon: boat service to three islands: Belle Ile (largest of the Breton islands), Houat, Hoedic.

Rennes: capital of Brittany, medieval streets, half timbered houses; Brittany Museum.

St Malo: historical walled city, fishing port.

Cuisine of the region

Fish and shellfish are commonplace; traditional *crêperies* abound and welcome visitors with a cup of local cider.

Agneau de pré-salé: leg of lamb from animals pastured in the salt marshes and meadows.

Beurre blanc: sauce for fish dishes made with shallots, wine vinegar and butter.

Cotriade: fish soup with potatoes, onions, garlic and butter.

Crêpes Bretonnes: the thinnest of pancakes with a variety of sweet fillings.

Galette: can be a biscuit, cake or pancake; with sweet or savoury fillings.

Gâteau Breton: rich cake.

Poulet blanc Breton: free-range, quality, white Breton chicken.

FR22000 Camping des Vallées

Chemin des Vallées, Parc de Brézillet, F-22000 Saint Brieuc (Côtes d'Armor)

Tel: **02 96 94 05 05**. Email: **campingdesvallees@wanadoo.fr**

Previously run by the municipality, this site is now privately managed. Neat and tidy, it has 106 good size pitches, 70 with electrical connections (10A), set mainly on flat terraced grass and separated by shrubs and bushes. There are 14 pitches with hardstanding and electricity, water and sewage connections. Mature trees are plentiful, providing shade if required, and a small stream winds through the middle of the site creating a quiet, peaceful atmosphere. A key system operates the access gate (closed 22.30-07.00 hrs).

Facilities

The two main toilet blocks include some washbasins in cabins, facilities for disabled people and baby room. Laundry facilities. Motorcaravan services. Two further smaller blocks are at the bottom of the site. Shop with basic provisions. Compact bar with snacks. Play area. Volley and basketball, arcade games. Bicycle hire. Animation organised in peak season. Weekly pony days. Off site: Aquatic centre, gym and fitness centre (part of a holiday village). Saint Brieuc 800 m. Beach 10 km.

Open: Easter - 15 October.

Directions

From the east, on entering St Brieuc, look for the sign to the railway station and from there, signs for Brézillet or site.

Charges 2007

Per pitch incl. car, 1 person and electricity	€ 13,50 - € 15,90
extra person	€ 3,70 - € 4,60
child (under 7 yrs)	€ 2,40 - € 3,00
animal	€ 1,90 - € 2,50

No credit cards.

FR22010 Camping les Capucines

Kervourdon, F-22300 Tredrez-Locquémeau (Côtes d'Armor)

Tel: **02 96 35 72 28**. Email: **les.capucines@wanadoo.fr**

A warm welcome awaits at Les Capucines which is quietly situated about a kilometre from the village of Saint Michel with its good, sandy beach and also very near Locquémeau, a pretty fishing village. This attractive, family run site has 100 pitches on flat or slightly sloping ground. All are well marked out by hedges, with mature trees and with more recently planted. There are 70 pitches with electricity, water and drainage, including 10 for larger units. A good value restaurant/crêperie can be found at Trédrez; others at Saint Michel. A 'Sites et Paysages' member.

Facilities

Two modern toilet blocks, clean and very well kept, include washbasins mainly in cabins, facilities for babies and disabled people. Laundry with washing machines and dryer. Small shop for essentials (bread to order). Takeaway, bar with TV and a general room with table tennis and table football. Covered swimming and paddling pools. Playground. Tennis. Minigolf. New multisport area. Chalets and mobile homes to rent. Off site: Fishing 1 km. Riding 2 km. Golf 15 km. Beach 1 km.

Open: 15 March - 30 September.

Directions

Turn off main D786 road northeast of St Michel where site is signed, and 1 km. to site.

Charges 2007

Per unit incl. 2 persons	€ 14,00 - € 19,90
incl. electiricty (7A) and water	€ 18,50 - € 26,60
extra person	€ 3,90 - € 5,40
child	€ 2,80 - € 3,50

FR22020 Camping Rostrenen

Kerandouaron, route de Silfiac, F-22110 Rostrenen (Côtes d'Armor)

Tel: **02 96 29 16 45**. Email: **contact@fleurdebretagne.com**

With British owners, this small, rural site is set in the heart of the Brittany countryside, only one kilometre from the small town of Rostrenen. Well kept pitches are laid out in groups of seven or eight and these groups are separated by small trees and shrubs. The site is terraced and slopes gently down to a fishing lake. This site lends itself to a quiet holiday spent with friends and it is particularly suitable for campers using tents.

Facilities

Two well kept toilet blocks provide showers and washbasins, some in cubicles. Facilities for disabled visitors. Small bar which serves snacks and has a terrace overlooking a grassy area where children can play. Bread to order. Small unheated swimming pool. Football field. Boules. Fishing.

Open: All year.

Directions

Rostrenen is in the heart of Brittany, about halfway between St Brieuc and Quimper. From N164 Loudéac - Carhaix-Plouguer road, turn south to Rostrenen and take D764 Route de Pontivy to site on the southeast edge of the town.

Charges 2008

Per person	€ 1,50 - € 3,00
child (5-16 yrs)	€ 1,50 - € 2,00
pitch incl. electricity	€ 4,00 - € 11,00
dog	€ 1,00 - € 2,00

FR22030 **Camping Nautic International**

Route de Beau-Rivage, F-22530 Caurel (Côtes d'Armor)

Tel: **02 96 28 57 94**. Email: **contact@campingnautic.fr**

This friendly family site is on the northern shore of the Lac de Guerledan. The lake is popular for all manner of watersports and there are some pleasant walks around the shores and through the surrounding Breton countryside and forests. The site is terraced down to the lake shore and offers 100 large pitches, all with electrical connections. A number of 'super pitches' (160-200 sq.m.) are also available. There is an imaginatively designed swimming pool and smaller children's pool, both heated by a wood burning stove. Small boats can be launched from the site, and other boating activities are available on the lake. A member of 'Sites et Paysages'.

Facilities

There are two toilet blocks providing adequate facilities and well placed on the site. The slopes probably make the site unsuitable for disabled people. Washing and drying machines. Small shop and takeaway (7/7-31/8). Swimming pools (15/5-25/9). Gym. Giant chess. Play area. Fishing. Tennis. Games room. Mobile homes for rent. Off site: Restaurants and crêperie nearby. Watersports. Sailing school. Riding. Canal from Nantes to Brest. Sea 50 minutes by car.

Open: 15 May - 25 September.

Directions

From N164 Rennes - Brest road, turn off between Mur-de-Bretagne and Gouarec to the village of Caurel. Site is well signed from there.
GPS: N48:12.30 W03:03.03

Charges 2007

Per person	€ 3,30 - € 6,00
child (0-7 yrs)	€ 1,90 - € 3,30
pitch incl. car	€ 7,00 - € 12,50
electricity (10A)	€ 4,30 - € 4,50

FR22040 **Camping le Châtelet**

Rue des Nouettes, F-22380 Saint Cast-le-Guildo (Côtes d'Armor)

Tel: **02 96 41 96 33**. Email: **chateletcp@aol.com**

Carefully developed over the years from a former quarry, Le Châtelet is pleasantly and quietly situated with lovely views over the estuary from many pitches. It is well laid out, mainly in terraces with fairly narrow access roads. There are 216 good-sized pitches separated by hedges, all with electricity and 112 with water and drainage. Some pitches are around a little lake (unfenced) which can be used for fishing. Used by three different tour operators (73 pitches).

Facilities

Four toilet blocks with access at different levels include washbasins in cabins and facilities for children. Three small toilet blocks on the lower terraces. Some facilities are closed outside July/Aug. Motorcaravan services. Heated swimming and paddling pools. Shop for basics, takeaway, bar lounge and general room with satellite TV and pool table. Games room. Play area. Organised games and activities in season. Dancing (June, July and Aug). Off site: Beach 200 m. Bicycle hire, riding and golf 1.5 km.

Open: 24 April - 9 September.

Directions

Best approach is to turn off D786 road at Matignon towards St Cast; just inside St Cast limits turn left at sign for 'campings' and follow camp signs on C90.

Charges 2008

Per person	€ 4,30 - € 6,50
child (under 7 yrs)	€ 3,00 - € 4,30
pitch	€ 12,50 - € 20,50
electricity (6/8A)	€ 4,60 - € 5,60
animal	€ 3,60 - € 4,60

FR22050 **Camping le Vieux Moulin**

14 rue des Moulins, F-22430 Erquy (Côtes d'Armor)

Tel: **02 96 72 34 23**. Email: **camp.vieux.moulin@wanadoo.fr**

Le Vieux Moulin is a family run site, just two kilometres from the little fishing port of Erquy on Brittany's Emerald Coast on the edge of a pine forest and nature reserve. It is about 900 metres from a beach of sand and shingle. Taking its name from the old mill opposite, the site has 173 pitches all with electricity (6/9A) and some with electricity, water and drainage. One section of 39 pitches is arranged around a pond. Most pitches are of a fair size in square boxes with trees giving shade.

Facilities

Two good quality toilet blocks have mostly British style toilets and plenty of individual washbasins, facilities for disabled people and babies. A further small block provides toilets and dishwashing only. Washing machines and dryer. Motorcaravan service point. Shop. Pizzeria and takeaway. Bar and terrace. Heated, covered pool complex with jacuzzi and paddling pool. Play areas. Tennis. Fitness gym. TV room (with satellite) and games room with table tennis. Bicycle hire. No electric barbecues. Off site: Beach 900 m. Fishing 1.2 km. Golf and riding 7 km.

Open: 30 April - 10 September.

Directions

Site is 2 km. east of Erquy. Take minor road towards Les Hôpitaux and site is signed from junction of D786 and D34 roads.

Charges 2007

Per person	€ 4,50 - € 5,70
child (under 7 yrs)	€ 3,20 - € 4,30
pitch incl. electricity	€ 23,00 - € 29,70
dog	€ 3,00 - € 4,00

No credit cards.

FR22060 Camping Municipal la Hallerais

6 Bourg de Taden, F-22100 Taden (Côtes d'Armor)

Tel: **02 96 39 15 93**. Email: **camping.la.hallerais@wanadoo.fr**

As well as being an attractive old medieval town, Dinan is quite a short run from the resorts of the Côte d'Armor. This useful municipal site, open for a long season, is just outside Dinan, beyond and above the little harbour on the Rance estuary. There is a pleasant riverside walk where the site slopes down towards the Rance. The 226 pitches, all with electricity (6A) and most with water and drain, are mainly on level, shallow terraces connected by tarmac roads, with trees and hedges giving a park-like atmosphere. This is a clean efficiently run and well organised site.

Facilities

Two traditional toilet blocks, of good quality and heated in cool weather, have some private cabins with shower and washbasin. Unit for disabled people. Laundry. Shop. Bar/restaurant with outside terrace and takeaway. Swimming and paddling pools (15/5-30/9). Tennis. Minigolf. Games room. TV room with satellite. Fishing. Playground. Mobile homes for rent. Off site: Bus in Taden. Riding 2 km. Bicycle hire 5 km. Beach 20 km.

Open: 15 March - 4 November.

Directions

Taden is northeast of Dinan. On leaving Dinan on D766, turn right to Taden and site before reaching large bridge and N176 junction. From N176 take Taden/Dinan exit.

Charges guide

Per person	€ 3,20 - € 3,80
child (under 7 yrs)	€ 1,35 - € 1,65
pitch incl. electricity	€ 6,90 - € 11,90

FR22080 Yelloh! Village le Ranolien

Ploumanach, F-22700 Perros Guirec (Côtes d'Armor)

Tel: **02 96 91 65 65**. Email: **leranolien@yellohvillage.fr**

Le Ranolien has been attractively developed around a former Breton farm – everything here is either made from, or placed on or around the often massive pink rocks. The 560 pitches are of a variety of sizes and types, mostly large and flat but some are quite small. Some are formally arranged in rows with hedge separators, but most are either on open ground or under trees, amongst large boulders. With many holiday caravans and tour operator tents around the site (318 pitches), there are 70 pitches for tourists, all with electricity and some with water and drainage.

Facilities

The main toilet block, heated in cool weather, is supplemented by several other more open type blocks around the site. Washbasins in cabins, mostly British style WCs and good showers. Dishwashing facilities. Laundry. Motorcaravan services. Supermarket and gift shop (1/5-18/9). Restaurant, crêperie and bar (open over a long season). Disco some nights in high season. Minigolf. Games room. Play area. Cinema. Gym and steam room. Mobile homes for hire. Off site: Beach 150 m. Bicycle hire 1 km. Riding 3 km. Golf 10 km.

Open: 7 April - 17 September.

Directions

From Lannion take D788 to Perros Guirec. Follow signs to 'Centre Ville' past main harbour area and then signs to Ploumanach, La Clarté. Pass through village of La Clarté and around sharp left hand bend. Site is immediately on the right.

Charges 2008

Per unit incl. 2 persons and electricity	€ 13,00 - € 30,00
with water and drainage	€ 17,00 - € 40,00
extra person	€ 5,00 - € 8,00
child (2-7 yrs)	free - € 6,00

FR22090 Castel Camping le Château de Galinée

La Galinée, F-22380 Saint Cast-le-Guildo (Côtes d'Armor)

Tel: **02 96 41 10 56**. Email: **chateaugalinee@wanadoo.fr**

Situated a few kilometres back from St Cast and owned and managed by the Vervel family, Galinée is in a parkland setting on level grass with numerous and varied mature trees. It has 273 pitches, all with electricity, water and drainage and separated by many mature shrubs and bushes. The top section is mostly for mobile homes. An attractive outdoor pool complex has swimming and paddling pools and two pools with a water slide and a 'magic stream'. A new indoor complex has now also been added and includes a swimming pool, bar, restaurant and large entertainment hall.

Facilities

The large modern sanitary block includes washbasins in private cabins, facilities for babies and a good unit for disabled people. Dishwashing area. Laundry. Shop, bar and takeaway (all 1/7-26/8). Heated pool complex (12/5-7/9) with swimming and paddling pools. New covered complex with heated pool, bar, restaurant, entertainment hall and internet. Play area. Fishing. Field for ball games. Off site: Beach and golf 3.5 km. Riding 6 km.

Open: 12 May - 9 September.

Directions

From D168 Ploubalay - Plancoet road turn onto D786 towards Matignon and St Cast. Site is very well signed 1 km. after leaving Notre Dame de Guildo.

Charges 2007

Per person	€ 4,00 - € 6,00
child (under 7 yrs)	€ 2,50 - € 4,20
pitch incl. water and drainage	€ 8,50 - € 15,00
electricity (10A)	€ 4,80
Camping Cheques accepted.	

FR22110 Camping les Madières

Le Vau Madec, F-22590 Pordic (Côtes d'Armor)

Tel: **02 96 79 02 48**. Email: **campinglesmadieres@wanadoo.fr**

Les Madières is well placed for exploring the Goëlo coast with its seaside resorts of St Quay-Portrieux, Binic and Etables-sur-Mer – ports used in the past by fishing schooners and now used by pleasure boats and a few coastal fishing boats. The young and enthusiastic owners here have already made their mark on this quiet campsite. With plenty of open spaces and set in the countryside, yet near the sea (800 m), it has 83 pitches of which 10 are used for mobile homes. There are no tour operators. The site has an outdoor swimming pool and some entertainment is organised in July and August by the welcoming and helpful owners.

Facilities

Two refurbished heated toilet blocks include facilities for disabled visitors. Basic provisions are kept all season. Bar, takeaway (all season) and newly refurbished restaurant. Swimming pool (1/6-20/9). Some entertainment (high season). Off site: Beach 800 m. Bus service nearby. Riding 2.5 km. Bicycle hire 3 km.

Open: 1 April - 31 October.

Directions

From St Brieuc ring-road (N12), turn north on D786 signed Paimpol (by the coast). Les Madières is at Pordic, 3 km. from the ring-road. Site is well signed from the D786. GPS: N48:34.944 W02:48.288

Charges 2007

Per person	€ 4,80
child 90-10 yrs)	€ 3,00
pitch incl. electricity (10A)	€ 11,00
dog	€ 2,00

Discounts outside July and August.

Camping Caravaning
Les Madières

- 93 pitches
- 800 m from the beach, quietly situated with shadow pitches
- Heated swimmingpool
- Heated sanitary blocks

Open from 1st April till 30th October 2008

Le Vau Madec - 22590 Pordic - Bretagne
Tel: 0033 296 790 248
www.campinglesmadieres.com

FR22100 Camping l'Abri Côtier

Ville Es Rouxel, F-22680 Etables-sur-Mer (Côtes d'Armor)

Tel: **02 96 70 61 57**. Email: **camping.abricotier@wanadoo.fr**

L'Abri Côtier is a well cared for, family run site 500 metres from a sandy beach. Small and tranquil, it is arranged in two sections separated by a lane. The pitches are marked out on part level, part sloping grass, divided by mature trees and shrubs with some in a charming walled area with a quaint, old-world atmosphere. The second section has an orchard type setting. The evening bar forms a good social centre. In total there are 140 pitches, all with electrical connections (long leads useful) and 60 fully serviced.

Facilities

Good clean sanitary facilities, heated in low season, include some washbasins in cabins, two units for disabled visitors and a baby bath/shower. Dishwashing under cover. Laundry room. Well stocked shop, set menu and simple takeaway service. Bar (with TV) and outdoor terrace area. Sheltered, heated swimming pool with paddling pool and outdoor jacuzzi. Playground. Games room. Some entertainment in peak season. Off site: Restaurants and indoor pool in the village. Riding 1 km. Fishing 2 km. Bicycle hire 4 km. Golf 10 km. Beach 500 m.

Open: 6 May - 15 September.

Directions

From N12 (Saint Brieuc bypass) take D786 towards St Quay Portrieux. After 12 km. pass Aire de la Chapelle on the right and take second left on D47 towards Etables-sur-Mer. Take second right to site at crossroads in 100 m.

Charges 2007

Per person	€ 4,20 - € 4,70
child (under 7 yrs)	€ 2,50 - € 3,00
pitch	€ 6,50 - € 7,50
serviced pitch	€ 7,50 - € 8,50

TRAVEL SERVICE SITE
TO BOOK CALL 01580 214000
Advice & low ferry-inclusive prices

FR22120 Camping du Port

3 chemin des Douaniers, Landrellec, F-22560 Pleumeur-Bodou (Côtes d'Armor)

Tel: 02 96 23 87 79. Email: renseignments@camping-du-port.com

Camping du Port is situated beside the beach at Landrellec with magnificent views of the estuary and islands. It is a well maintained, family run site with 103 pitches of varied size, 80 of which are for touring. The pitches are marked and numbered on level grass with hedging and most have electricity, water and drainage. The site is within ten minutes of the village Pleumeur-Bodou and centrally located for visiting the Pink Granite Coast at Perros-Guirec, Ploumanach, Trégastel and Trébeurden.

Facilities

Sanitary facilities are centrally located in one large block with modern toilets, washbasins in cabins and showers. Small toilets and basins for children. Excellent facilities for babies. Provision for disabled people. Laundry and dishwashing facilities. Motorcaravan service point. Shop for basics. Restaurant. Takeaway. Bar with TV. Small play area. Children's club and organised entertainment in high season.

Open: 1 April - 30 September.

Directions

From Lannion head north to Pleumeur-Bodou, then follow signs to Landrellec. Site is signed.

Charges 2007

Per pitch incl. 2 persons	€ 13,50 - € 16,50
extra person	€ 4,50 - € 5,50
child (2-7 yrs)	€ 2,00 - € 3,00
electricity	€ 2,60

FR22130 Camping de Port l'Epine

Venelle de Pors Garo, F-22660 Trélévern (Côtes d'Armor)

Tel: 02 96 23 71 94. Email: camping-de-port-lepine@wanadoo.fr

Port l'Epine is a pretty little site in a unique situation on a promontory. There is access to the sea, therefore, on the south side of the site, with views across to Perros Guirec. The area covered by the site is not large but there are 160 grass pitches, all with electricity, which are divided by pretty hedging and trees. Some are used for mobile homes. Access is a little tight in parts. This site is ideal for families with young children (probably not for teenagers).

Facilities

The original toilet block is well equipped and a second block has been refurbished in modern style. Unusual dishwashing sinks in open air stone units. Shop and bar/restaurant (1/4-22/9) with takeaway (1/7-31/8). Small heated swimming pool and paddling pool (May-Sept). Fenced play area near the bar/restaurant. Table tennis and video games. Bicycle hire. Off site: Riding or golf 15 km. Useful small supermarket up hill from site. Many coastal paths to enjoy.

Open: 5 April - 19 September.

Directions

From roundabout south of Perros Guirec take the D6 towards Tréguier. Pass through Louannec, then left turn at crossroads for Trélévern. Go through village following camp signs – Port l'Epine is clearly marked as distinct from the municipal site.

Charges 2007

Per pitch incl. 2 persons and electricity	€ 14,50 - € 29,00
serviced pitch	€ 2,50 - € 3,00
extra person	€ 5,00 - € 7,00
Camping Cheques accepted.	

TRAVEL SERVICE SITE
TO BOOK CALL 01580 214000
Advice & low ferry-inclusive prices

FR22140 Camping de Port la Chaine

F-22610 Pleubian (Côtes d'Armor)

Tel: 02 96 22 92 38. Email: info@portlachaine.com

The Suquet family has worked hard to establish this comfortable, quiet, family site. In a beautiful location on the 'Untamed Peninsula' between Paimpol and Perros Guirec, attractive trees and shrubs provide a balance of sun and shade, edging the central road and the grassy bays or fields which branch off on the gradual decline towards the bay and the sea (a sandy bay with rocks). Most of the bays have a slight slope, so those with motorcaravans will need to choose their pitch carefully. More open, level pitches nearer the sea are useful for tents.

Facilities

Two traditional style toilet blocks are comfortable and fully equipped, both now completely renovated. Washbasins in cabins, British and Turkish style toilets. Cabins for families or disabled visitors. Bar/restaurant with terrace and takeaway (23/6-25/8). Heated swimming pool (17/5-9/9). Play area. Games room. Petanque. Children's entertainer in July/Aug. Beach, fishing and sailing. Off site: Bus 1 km. Village 2 km. for market, shops and restaurants. Good fishing and diving. Boat launching 1 km. Bicycle hire 2 km. Riding 6 km. Golf 18 km.

Open: 5 April - 13 September.

Directions

Leave D786 between Lézardrieux and Tréguier to go north to village of Pleubian (about 8 km). Continue on D20 towards Larmor Pleubian and site signed on left, 2 km. from Pleubian.
GPS: N48:51.333 W03:07.966

Charges 2008

Per person	€ 3,50 - € 5,70
child (under 7 yrs)	€ 3,00 - € 3,70
pitch	€ 5,50 - € 10,00
electricity	€ 3,50 - € 4,10
dog	€ 2,90

Check real time availability and at-the-gate prices...

www.alanrogers.com

FR22200 Camping Au Bocage du Lac

Rue du Bocage, F-22270 Jugon-les Lacs (Côtes d'Armor)
Tel: **02 96 31 60 16**

This well kept former municipal site has been updated over the past few years by the current owners M. and Mme. Riviere. It is on the edge of the village beside a lake, 25 km. from the sea. It offers 181 good size pitches, all with electrical connections, set on gently sloping grass and divided by shrubs and bushes, with mature trees providing shade. Some 40 wooden chalets and mobile homes are intermingled with the touring pitches. On-site facilities include a good pool with children's section and sunbathing patio. There is also a small animal park.

Facilities

Two main sanitary blocks include facilities for disabled visitors. British and Turkish style WCs and some washbasins in cabins. Washing machine. Small shop. Bar. Swimming pool (15/6-10/9). Table tennis, tennis, football. Play area. Activity programmes July/Aug. Fishing. Bicycle hire. Off site: Supermarket in village 1 km. River 1 km.

Open: 1 April - 31 October.

Directions

From N176 (E401) Lamballe - Dinan road, about 15 km. from Lamballe take turning for Jugon-les-Lacs. Site is signed shortly after.

Charges 2007

Per person	€ 3,70 - € 4,70
child (under 7 yrs)	€ 2,70 - € 3,20
pitch	€ 13,10 - € 17,40
electricity (5A)	€ 3,00

FR22150 Camping Domaine du Launay

11 route Toul Veing, F-22470 Plouézec (Côtes d'Armor)
Tel: **02 96 20 63 15**. Email: **domainedulaunay@wanadoo.fr**

Domaine de Launay is an unspoilt, rural site of 23 hectares. Wooded and spacious, there are many flowers and shrubs. It is situated 4 km. from the costal resort of Plouézec with its beaches and 6 km. south of Paimpol. It is a quiet retreat for those wishing to escape city life. However, it is also well placed for visiting the resorts of Goëlo coast, the Ile de Bréhat, the Emerald Coast, the Pink Granite Coast and the Seven Islands. There are 90 mainly level, hedged and shady grass pitches with 60 for touring (with 16A electricity connections).

Facilities

One large toilet block is looking rather elderly but it is well mantained and clean. Motorcaravan services. Small shop (all season). Bar and snack bar (1/6-15/9). Heated swimming pool (1/7-15/9). Minigolf. Swing golf. Volleyball. Boules. English bowls. Play area. Bicycle hire. Entertainment 3 evenings a week (July/Aug). Off site: Fishing, sailing and boat launching 2 km. Beach 4 km. Riding and golf 5 km.

Open: 1 April - 30 September.

Directions

From N12, Saint-Brieuc ringroad, head north on the D786 Paimpol (Par la Côte). 6 km. before Paimpol, at Plouézec, look for a sign left to Domaine de Launay. GPS: N48:44.119 W03:00.221

Charges 2007

Per person	€ 3,60 - € 4,00
child (0-7 yrs)	€ 2,25 - € 2,50
pitch	€ 7,00 - € 7,80
electricity (16A)	€ 3,00

FR22160 Camping le Neptune

Kerguistin, F-22580 Lanloup (Côtes d'Armor)

Tel: **02 96 22 33 35**. Email: **contact@leneptune.com**

Situated on the Côte de Goëlo at Lanloup, Le Neptune offers a peaceful, rural retreat for families. The friendly new owners, M. and Mme. Camard, keep the site neat and tidy and there is a regular programme of renovation. There are 84 level, grass pitches (65 for touring units) separated by trimmed hedges providing privacy and all with electricity. There are also 18 mobile homes to rent. A heated swimming pool has a retractable roof so can be open for a long season. Within walking distance is the local village, with a restaurant and shop, and sandy beaches. The site is also a good base for cycling and walking.

Facilities

Motorcaravan services. The modern toilet block is of a good standard, clean and well maintained. Laundry room with washing machine and dryer. No restaurant but good takeaway (all season). Small shop well stocked for basic needs. Bar with indoor and outdoor seating. Heated swimming pool (Easter - end Oct). Petanque. Volleyball. Table tennis, table football. Animation in season. Off site: Tennis 300 m. Fishing and beach 2 km. Golf 4 km. Riding 8 km. Restaurant and shop within walking distance. Beach 2.5 km.

Open: 1 April - 31 October.

Directions

From Saint Brieuc (N12) take D786 Paimpol ('par la Côte'). After 28 km. on approaching Lanloup, site is well signed. GPS: N48:42.490 W02:58.000

Charges 2007

Per person	€ 4,00 - € 5,30
child (under 7 yrs)	€ 2,50 - € 3,40
pitch	€ 6,40 - € 8,50
electricity (6A)	€ 3,50
dog	€ 1,60 - € 2,20

Camping Cheques accepted.

FR22190 Les Roches

Caroual Village, F-22430 Erquy (Côtes d'Armor)

Tel: **02 96 72 32 90**. Email: **info@camping-lesroches.com**

Among several very good campsites in Erquy, this is a little gem. It has magnificent, panoramic views over the Bay of Erquy and is situated 900 metres from sandy beaches and 2 km. from the seaside resort of Erquy. You will receive a warm and genuine reception from the owners to their immaculately kept site. Although rather limited in amenities (no pool, restaurant or bar), nearby Erquy offers a full range of shops, restaurants and activities. The site itself offers a takeaway service in high season. Limited entertainment is also provided at that time.

Facilities

One large and two small toilet blocks are attractive and clean providing good facilities. Provision for children, babies and disabled visitors is also good. Well equipped laundry area. Small shop in reception (all season). Snack bar and takeaway (1/7-31/8), also some entertainment. Lounge area with TV. Minigolf. Play area. Off site: Erquy 2 km. Bicycle hire 100 m. Golf 2 km. Riding 5 km.

Open: 31 March - 15 September.

Directions

From the N12 southeast of Saint Brieuc take D786 northeast to Erquy. Site is well signed on approaching the town.

Charges 2007

Per person	€ 3,80
child (2-7 yrs)	€ 2,80
pitch incl. car	€ 6,60
electricity (6A)	€ 2,80

FR22230 Camping Bellevue

68 boulevard du Littoral, F-22410 Saint Quay-Portrieux (Côtes d'Armor)

Tel: **02 96 70 41 84**. Email: **campingbellevue@free.fr**

With magnificent coastal views, this attractive and well cared for site lives up to its name. Family-owned for many years, it is situated on the outskirts of the popular seaside resort of Saint Quay-Portrieux and you will be made to feel most welcome by the owners. The 173 numbered touring pitches vary in size and 140 have 6A electricity. Some are separated by hedges, whilst others are in groups of four. Entertainment on site is limited but there is plenty to do and see around the area and a great opportunity for exploring the Goëlo coast.

Facilities

Two clean sanitary blocks provide both open and cubicled washbasins and controllable showers. Facilities for disabled visitors and babies. Laundry and dishwashing facilities. Motorcaravan service point. Shop for basics. Simple snack bar (1/7-16/9). Outdoor pool (1/6-16/9; no Bermuda shorts). Paddling pool. Volleyball. Boules. Play area. Off site: Shops, bars, restaurants and casino. Bicycle hire 1 km. Riding 8 km. Golf 10 km.

Open: 26 April - 16 September.

Directions

From N12 St Brieuc by-pass, take D786 north towards Paimpol. Site is well signed north west of St Quay-Portrieux, 13 km. from the bypass.

Charges 2008

Per person over 7 yrs	€ 4,00 - € 5,00
child	€ 3,00 - € 3,20
pitch	€ 5,80 - € 7,80
electricity (6A)	€ 3,00

24

FR22210 Camping Bellevue

Route de Pléneuf Val-André, F-22430 Erquy (Côtes d'Armor)

Tel: **02 96 72 33 04**. Email: **campingbellevue@yahoo.fr**

Situated a mile from the beaches between Erquy and Pléneuf Val-André, Camping Bellevue offers a quiet country retreat with easy access to the cliffs of Cap Fréhel, Sables d'Or and St Cast. There are 140 pitches of which 120 are available for touring units, most with electricity (6/10A) and 15 with water and drainage. The site also has 20 mobile homes, chalets and bungalows to rent. Children are well catered for at this campsite – there are heated swimming and paddling pools, three play areas and minigolf, petanque and volleyball. Indoor entertainment for all includes theme evenings, Breton dancing and visits to a local cider house. There are numerous walks in the area and a vast range of aquatic sports at nearby Erquy. A 'Sites et Paysages' member.

Facilities

Two modern, unisex toilet blocks are of a high standard. Some washbasins in cubicles. Facilities for disabled visitors. Dishwashing and laundry facilities. Shop and bar (15/6-10/9). Restaurant and takeaway (12/6-31/8). Swimming and paddling pools (10/5-10/9). Play areas. Pool table. TV room. Table football, video games and library. Minigolf. Petanque. Volleyball. Entertainment and organised activities in high season. Off site: Beach and fishing 2 km. Golf 3 km. Bicycle hire and boat launching 5 km. Riding 6 km.

Open: 31 March - 30 September.

Directions

From St Brieuc road take D786 towards Erquy. Site is adjacent to the D786 at St Pabu and is well signed.

Charges 2007

Per unit incl. 2 persons	€ 15,20 - € 18,80
extra person	€ 4,00 - € 5,00
child (2-13 yrs)	free - € 4,40
electricity	€ 3,30
dog	€ 1,30 - € 1,70

FR22250 Camping Municipal de Cruckin

Rue de Cruckin, F-22500 Paimpol (Côtes d'Armor)

Tel: **02 96 20 78 47**. Email: **contact@camping-paimpol.com**

A neat and well managed municipal site situated close to the historical fishing port of Cité des Islandais and within easy reach of the Ile de Bréhat. This is an ideal location for many interesting walks. The site has 130 well maintained, mostly level pitches set in both wooded and open areas and all have electricity connections (5-12A). A very large area has been provided for field sports, a play area and picnic tables. Although the site does not have its own swimming pool, the beach is just a short walk away.

Facilities

One modern and heated toilet block (a second block is planned). Washbasins in cabins and showers. Facilities for babies and disabled visitors. Laundry and dishwashing facilities. Bread and milk (high season). Snack bar/takeaway (July/Aug). Motorcaravan service point. Large field for football and volleyball. Petanque. Table tennis. Fenced play area. Internet access on request. Off site: Beach. Kérity village with shops, restaurants and cafés. Riding 2 km. Golf 10 km.

Open: 1 April - 31 October.

Directions

From N12 St Brieuc bypass, take D786 north towards Paimpol. Village of Kérity is about 3 km. south of Paimpol. Site is signed.

Charges guide

Per pitch incl. 2-3 persons	€ 12,35 - € 12,90
extra person	€ 2,85 - € 3,00
child (under 7 yrs)	€ 1,45 - € 1,50
electricity	€ 2,50 - € 3,05
dog	€ 1,05 - € 1,10

FR22260 Camping Vert le Vallon aux Merlettes

Route de Lamballe, F-22550 Matignon (Côtes d'Armor)

Tel: 02 96 41 11 61. Email: giblanchet@wanadoo.fr

Le Vallon aux Merlettes is situated on the edge of the town and has a quiet, simple and rural ambience. The friendly owners are very welcoming and take care to maintain the site well. There are almost 100 grass touring pitches which are level and numbered and all have electricity (6A). Many shrubs and trees provide shade to some areas. Although there are limited leisure facilities on site, there are several sporting opportunities adjacent. The magnificent beaches of Saint Cast and a swimming pool with sea water are within 5 km.

Facilities

One modern and centrally located toilet block includes washbasins both open style and in cabins and pre-set showers. Facilities for disabled visitors. Dishwashing area and laundry facilities. Motorcaravan service point. Small shop in reception for basics. Bar and basic snack bar. TV. Small unfenced play area. Internet access. Off site: Leisure facilities adjacent. Beach and swimming pool 5 km.

Open: 1 May - 30 September.

Directions

From the N12 take the D786 northeast to Erquy. Matignon is 16 km. east of Erquy still on the D786. Site is well signed in the town.

Charges 2007

Per person	€ 3,60
child (under 7 yrs)	€ 1,80
pitch	€ 5,50
electricity (6A)	€ 3,10

FR22270 Camping Les Blés d'Or

La Chapelle, F-22380 Saint Cast-le-Guildo (Côtes d'Armor)

Tel: 02 96 41 99 93. Email: camping-les-bles-dor@wanadoo.fr

This comfortable and relaxing site is situated on the outskirts of St Cast-le-Guildo and is just 700 m. from its magnificent beaches. The 79 grass pitches are numbered and of average size. Electricity (10A) is available to all. A rare feature is the provision of individual wooden cabins with private sanitary facilities for 30 of the pitches, although stays of twelve days or longer are required for these. This is a simple and quiet site which, with the exception of the swimming pool, has limited recreational provision.

Facilities

Two toilet blocks include washbasins (some in cabins) and pre-set showers. Private sanitary facilities on some pitches (stays of 12 days or longer). Facilities for disabled visitors. Washing machines and dryers. Bar (July - Sept). Heated outdoor swimming pool and paddling pool (15/6-15/9). Games room and TV. Small unfenced play area. Evening entertainment for all ages in high season. Off site: Beach 700 m. Fishing 800 m. Supermarket 900 m. Golf and riding 1 km. Bicycle hire 2 km.

Open: 1 April - 30 October.

Directions

From the N12 southeast of St Brieuc take the D786 towards Côte de Pontievre and Erquy. From Erquy continue on D786 to Matignon then the D13 to St Cast-le-Guildo. Site is well signed on entering the town.

Charges 2007

Per unit incl. 2 persons	€ 15,00
extra person	€ 3,50
child (1-7 yrs)	€ 2,00
electricity	€ 3,00

FR22280 Camping des Hautes Grées

Rue Saint Michel, les Hôpitaux, F-22430 Erquy (Côtes d'Armor)

Tel: 02 96 72 34 78. Email: hautesgrees@wanadoo.fr

This site is situated just 400 m. from the beaches and resort facilities of Erquy. You will receive a warm welcome from the owners who are keen gardeners and have created a beautiful and clean site with an abundance of flowers. There is a total of 170 grass pitches, 128 of which are for touring. They are well tended, divided by hedges and all have electricity connections. Whilst there are plenty of activities available on site including a children's club every morning in high season, it is also well positioned for fishing, diving, bathing and also for walking.

Facilities

Two toilet blocks provide modern facilities and include washbasins in cabins and pre-set showers. Laundry facilities. Motorcaravan services. Small shop (1/7-31/8). Bar and takeaway (1/7-31/8). Heated outdoor swimming pool and paddling pool (15/6-15/9). Small gym with good equipment. Sauna. Games room with TV. Adventure play area. Children's club every morning and evening entertainment once a week in high season. WiFi. Off site: Beach 400 m. Fishing and boat launching 500 m. Bicycle hire 1 km. Golf 2 km. Riding 4 km.

Open: 1 April - 30 September.

Directions

From the N12, southeast of Brieuc, take the D786 to Erquy. 2 km. before Erquy, follow signs for Frehél/Matignon. At Super U roundabout follow signs for Les Hôpitaux. Site is clearly signed in village.

Charges 2007

Per person	€ 3,10 - € 4,90
child (under 7 yrs)	€ 1,50 - € 3,50
pitch	€ 5,60 - € 10,00
electricity (10A)	€ 2,50 - € 3,60

FR22360 Yelloh! Village les Pins

Route du Guen, Le Guen, F-22430 Erquy (Côtes d'Armor)

Tel: **04 66 73 97 39**. Email: **info@yellohvillage-les-pins.com**

Erquy is a pretty holiday resort nestling between two promontories. There are plenty of great sandy beaches around here, and one of the best is just 900 m. from this wooded site. Les Pins is a member of the Yelloh! Village group and has been recommended. We plan to undertake a full inspection in 2008. There are 182 touring pitches here and a further 148 pitches are occupied by mobile homes and chalets. The site boasts some impressive amenities including a top class pool complex.

Facilities

Shop. Bar. Restaurant. Snack bar. Takeaway food. Large swimming pool complex with water slides and other features. Children's pool. Fitness centre. Sauna. Tennis. Activity and entertainment programme. Off site: Nearest beach 900 m. Fishing. Sailing. Sand yachting. Sea kayaking. Golf. Casino. Diving school.

Open: 26 April - 13 September.

Directions

From St Brieuc, take the northbound D786 to Erquy. Continue through the town following signs to Cap d'Erquy and the site is well indicated.

Charges 2008

Per unit incl. 2 persons and electricity	€ 17,00 - € 34,00
extra person (over 1 yr)	€ 4,00 - € 5,00

FR29000 Yelloh! Village les Mouettes

La Grande Grève, F-29660 Carantec (Finistère)

Tel: **02 98 67 02 46**. Email: **camping@les-mouettes.com**

Les Mouettes is a sheltered site on the edge of an attractive bay with access to the sea at the front of the site. In a wooded setting with many attractive trees and shrubs, the 434 pitches include just 70 for touring units, the remainder being taken by tour operators and around 131 site-owned mobile homes and tents (located together at the top of the site). The touring pitches, mostly arranged in hedged areas in the lower section, are of a good size and all have electricity. The focal point of the site is an impressive heated pool complex.

Facilities

Three clean unisex sanitary blocks include washbasins in cabins, mainly British toilets and baby bathrooms. Facilities for disabled people. Laundry. Motorcaravan services. Shop (limited hours outside the main season). Takeaway. Bar. Pool complex. Games and TV rooms. Play area. Volleyball, two half-courts for tennis and minigolf. Table tennis. Entertainment in main season. Large units should phone first. Dogs are not accepted after 26/6. Off site: Fishing 1 km. Golf 2 km. Riding 6 km. Bicycle hire, locally in July/August. Beach 2 km.

Open: 17 May - 7 September.

Directions

From D58 Roscoff - Morlaix road, turn to Carantec on D173. Site is 4 km. from here on the outskirts of the village, signed to the left at roundabout immediately after passing supermarket on right. GPS: N48:39.384 W03:55.484

Charges 2008

Per unit incl. 2 persons, electricity and water	€ 14,00 - € 44,00
extra person	€ 5,00 - € 7,00
child (under 1 yrs)	free
dog	€ 3,00 - € 5,00

FR29030 Camping du Letty

F-29950 Bénodet (Finistère)

Tel: **02 98 58 62 82**. Email: **reception@campingduletty.com**

The Guyader family have ensured that this excellent and attractive site has plenty to offer for all the family. The site on the outskirts of the popular resort of Bénodet spreads over 22 acres with 493 pitches, all for touring units. Groups of four to eight pitches are set in cul-de-sacs with mature hedging and trees to divide each cul-de-sac. Most pitches have electricity, water and drainage. Although there is no swimming pool here, the site has direct access to a small sandy beach.

Facilities

Six well placed toilet blocks are of good quality and include mixed style WCs, washbasins in large cabins and controllable hot showers (charged). One block includes a separate laundry and dog washing enclosures. Baby rooms. Separate facility for disabled visitors. Launderette. Motorcaravan service points. Mini-market. Extensive snack bar and takeaway (21/6-31/8). Bar with games room and night club. Library/reading room with four computer stations. Entertainment room with satellite TV. Fitness centre (no charge). Saunas, jacuzzi and solarium (all on payment). Tennis and squash courts (charged). Play area. Entertainment and activities (July/Aug).

Open: 5 April - 5 November.

Directions

From N165 take D70 Concarneau exit. At first roundabout take D44 to Fouesnant. Turn right at T-junction. After 2 km. turn left to Fouesnant (still D44). Continue through La Forêt Fouesnant and Fouesnant, picking up signs for Bénodet. Shortly before Bénodet at roundabout turn left (signed Le Letty). Turn right at next mini-roundabout and site is 500 m. on left. GPS: N47:52.020 W04:05.270

Charges 2008

Per person	€ 4,00 - € 6,50
child (under 7 yrs)	€ 2,00 - € 3,25
pitch with electricity	€ 10,50 - € 13,00
car or motorcaravan	€ 2,00

Check real time availability and at-the-gate prices...

www.**alanrogers**.com

FR29020 Camping le Club Saint-Laurent

Kerleven, F-29940 La Forêt-Fouesnant (Finistère)

Tel: 02 98 56 97 65. Email: info@camping-du-saint-laurent.fr

Saint Laurent is a well established site, situated on a sheltered wooded slope bordering one of the many attractive little inlets that typify the Brittany coastline. The 260 pitches are on level terraces, under tall trees. All are of average size (100 sq.m.) and divided by hedges and partly shaded, all with electricity connections. Around 50% of the pitches are occupied by tour operators or site owned mobile homes. Pitches with the best sea views tend to be adjacent to the cliff edge and may not be suitable for families with young children. Access to some places can be a little difficult, but the friendly site owners ensure that this is not a problem by offering to site any caravan using their own 4 x 4 vehicle. The swimming pool (complete with paddling pool and two water slides) is overlooked by the bar terrace. With organised activities and entertainment in high season, this site is an ideal choice for a lively family holiday, particularly for older children. There is direct access from the site to two small sandy bays, which empty at low tide to reveal numerous rock pools (ideal for children to explore), and the site is on the coastal footpath that leads from Kerleven to Concarneau.

Facilities

Two sanitary blocks provide combined shower and washbasin cubicles, separate washbasin cubicles, baby changing and facilities for disabled people. Washing machines, dryers and ironing. Small shop at reception. Bar, snack bar and takeaway. Swimming pools. Gym and sauna. Canoe and boat hire. Basketball. Two tennis courts (no charge). Table tennis. Play area. Entertainment in July/Aug. for adults and children (in English as well as in French), with discos in the bar each evening.

Open: 2 May - 9 September.

Directions

From N165 take D70 Concarneau exit. At first roundabout take first exit D44 (Fouesnant). After 2.5 km. turn right at T-junction, follow for 2.5 km, then turn left (Port La Forêt). Continue to roundabout, straight ahead (Port La Forêt) and after 1 km. turn left (site signed here). In 400 m. left turn to site. GPS: N47:53.770 W03:57.305

Charges 2007

Per unit incl. 1 or 2 persons,	
electricity and water	€ 17,00 - € 37,00
extra person	€ 3,00 - € 5,50
child (2-7 yrs)	free - € 3,50
dog	€ 2,00 - € 3,50

FR29040 Camping Ar Kleguer

Plage Ste Anne, F-29250 Saint-Pol-de-Léon (Finistère)

Tel: 02 98 69 18 81. Email: info@camping-ar-kleguer.com

Ar Kleguer is located 20 minutes from the Roscoff ferry terminal in the heart of the Pays du Léon in north Finistère. The site is in two sections – one is in a quiet woodland setting which incorporates a small domestic animal and bird park. The other section is divided into several more open areas at the edge of the sea with spectacular views overlooking the Bay of Morlaix. There are 173 large and well kept pitches, all with 10A electricity connections. Of these, 125 are for touring units.

Facilities

Three modern, tiled toilet blocks are bright, clean and heated when required. Facilities for babies, children and disabled visitors. Laundry room. Shop, bar and takeaway (all July/Aug). Heated pool complex. Bicycle hire. Animal park. Play area. Activities and entertainment in high season. Beach adjacent with fishing and sailing. Off site: Restaurant at entrance. Riding 3 km. Golf 5 km.

Open: Easter - 30 September.

Directions

From Roscoff take D58 to Morlaix. From Morlaix follow signs to Saint-Pol-de-Léon (centre). In the centre follow white 'campings' signs or Plage de Sainte Anne until site signs appear.

Charges 2007

Per person	€ 3,80 - € 4,90
child (2-7 yrs)	€ 2,20 - € 3,30
pitch with electricity	€ 8,40 - € 10,30

FR29010 Castel Camping le Ty-Nadan

Route d'Arzano, F-29310 Locunolé (Finistère)

Tel: 02 98 71 75 47. Email: infos@camping-ty-nadan.fr

Mobile homes ▶ page 482

Ty-Nadan is a well organised site set amongst wooded countryside along the bank of the River Elle. The 183 pitches for touring units are grassy, many with shade and 99 are fully serviced. The pool complex with slides and paddling pool is very popular as is the large indoor pool complex and an indoor games area with a climbing wall. There is also an adventure play park and a 'Minikids' park for 5-8 year olds, not to mention tennis courts, table tennis, pool tables, archery and trampolines. This is a wonderful site for families with children. Several tour operators use the site. An exciting and varied programme of activities is offered throughout the season – canoe and sea kayaking expeditions, rock climbing, mountain biking, aqua-gym, paintball, riding or walking – all supervised by qualified staff. A full programme of entertainment for all ages is provided in high season including concerts, Breton evenings with pig roasts, dancing, etc. Be warned, you will be actively encouraged to join in!

Facilities

Two older, split-level toilet blocks are of fair quality and include washbasins in cabins and baby rooms. A newer block provides easier access for disabled people. Washing machines and dryers. Restaurant, takeaway, bar and well stocked shop. Crêperie (July/Aug). Heated outdoor pool (17 x 8 m). New indoor pool. Small river beach (unfenced). Indoor badminton and rock climbing facility. Activity and entertainment programmes (high season). Bicycle hire. Boat hire. Fishing. Off site: Beaches 20 minutes by car. Golf 12 km.

Open: 1 April - 7 September.

Directions

Make for Arzano which is northeast of Quimperlé on the Pontivy road and turn off D22 just west of village at camp sign. Site is about 3 km.

Charges 2007

Per unit with 2 persons and electricity	€ 19,90 - € 45,90
child (under 7 yrs)	€ 1,70 - € 5,40
dog	€ 1,70 - € 5,40

Less 15-20% outside July/Aug.

Camping Cheques accepted.

Camping "Le Ty Nadan" ★★★★

from the 31st of march for unforgettable holidays!

www.tynadan-vacances.fr

CAMPING PLUS

LES CASTELS
CAMPING & CARAVANING

FR29050 Castel Camping l'Orangerie de Lanniron

Mobile homes ▶ page 482

Château de Lanniron, F-29336 Quimper (Finistère)
Tel: **02 98 90 62 02.** Email: **camping@lanniron.com**

L'Orangerie is a beautiful and peaceful, family site set in 10 acres of a XVIIth century, 42 acre country estate on the banks of the Odet river, formerly the home of the Bishops of Quimper. The site has 199 grassy pitches (156 for touring units) of three types varying in size and services. They are on flat ground laid out in rows alongside access roads with shrubs and bushes providing pleasant pitches. All have electricity and 88 have all three services. With lovely walks within the grounds, the restaurant and the gardens are both open to the public and in spring the rhododendrons and azaleas are magnificent. The site is just to the south of Quimper and about 15 km. from the sea and beaches at Bénodet. The family owner's five year programme to restore the park, the original canal, fountains, ornamental 'Bassin de Neptune', the boathouse, the gardens and avenues is very well advanced. The original outbuildings have been attractively converted around a walled courtyard. Used by tour operators (30 pitches). All facilities are available when the site is open.

Facilities

Excellent heated block in the courtyard and second modern block serving the top areas of the site. Facilities for disabled people and babies. Washing machines and dryers. Motorcaravan services. Shop (15/5-9/9). Gas supplies. Bar, snacks and takeaway, plus restaurant (open daily). Swimming pool (144 sq.m.) with paddling pool. New pool complex. Small play area. Tennis. Minigolf. Golf (9-hole) with academy and driving range. Fishing. Archery. Bicycle hire. General reading, games and billiards rooms. TV/video room. Karaoke. Outdoor activities. Large room for indoor activities. New putting green. Off site: Two hypermarkets 1 km. Historic town of Quimper under 3 km. Activities in the area include golf, cycling, walking, fishing, canoeing, surfing and sailing. Beach 15 km.

Open: 15 May - 15 September.

Directions

From Quimper follow 'Quimper Sud' signs, then 'Toutes Directions' and general camping signs, finally signs for Lanniron.

Charges 2008

Per person	€ 4,25 - € 7,10
child (2-9 yrs)	€ 2,75 - € 4,50
pitch (100 sq.m.)	€ 10,25 - € 17,70
with electricity (10A)	€ 13,25 - € 22,20
special pitch (120/150 sq.m.)	
with water and electricity	€ 17,00 - € 27,70
Less 15% outside July/Aug.	

Camping Cheques accepted.

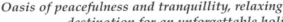

L'Orangerie de Lanniron

Castel Camping ★ ★ ★ ★

Oasis of peacefulness and tranquillity, relaxing destination for an unforgettable holiday

Situated on the banks of the river Odet, this former residence of the bishops of Cornouaille welcomes you to its 90 acres botanical park where you can take advantage of several fun and sporting activities.

This is an ideal spot for discovering this part of Brittany, so rich in historical sites, monuments and folklore.

New in 2008: extraordinary heated water park (500 m² water + terrace and solarium) with 4 waterslides hidden in a rock formation, heated bath and beds, waterfall, fountains, geyser, paddling pool with water slide, Golf practice and putting green - introduction to golf.

More information or to book:
www.lanniron.com
camping@lanniron.com

Château de Lanniron Allée de Lanniron 29000 Quimper
Tel. 0033 (0) 298 90 6202 - Fax 0033 (0) 298 52 1556

 La Clef Verte

 QUALITE TOURISME

 ADAC 2007

 CASTELS

FR29080 Camping le Panoramic

Mobile homes ⏵ page 482

Route de la Plage-Penker, F-29560 Telgruc-sur-Mer (Finistère)
Tel: 02 98 27 78 41. Email: info@camping-panoramic.com

This medium sized traditional site is situated on quite a steep, 10 acre hillside with fine views. It is personally run by M. Jacq and his family who all speak good English. The 200 pitches are arranged on flat, shady terraces, in small groups with hedges and flowering shrubs and 20 pitches have services for motorcaravans. Divided into two parts, the main upper site is where most of the facilities are located, with the swimming pool, its terrace and a playground located with the lower pitches across the road. Some up-and-down walking is therefore necessary, but this is a small price to pay for such pleasant and comfortable surroundings. This area provides lovely coastal footpaths. A 'Sites et Paysages' member.

Facilities

The main site has two well kept toilet blocks with another very good block opened for main season across the road. All three include British and Turkish style WCs, washbasins in cubicles, facilities for disabled people, baby baths, plus laundry facilities. Motorcaravan services. Small shop (1/7-31/8). Bar/restaurant with takeaway (1/7-31/8). Barbecue area. Heated pool, paddling pool and jacuzzi (1/6-15/9). Playground. Games and TV rooms. Tennis. Volleyball. Bicycle hire. Off site: Beach and fishing 700 m. Riding 6 km. Golf 14 km. Sailing school nearby.

Open: 1 June - 15 September.

Directions

Site is just south of Telgruc-sur-Mer. On D887 pass through Ste Marie du Ménez Horn. Turn left on D208 signed Telgruc-sur-Mer. Continue straight on through town and site is on right within 1 km. GPS: N48:13.428 W04:22.382

Charges 2008

Per person	€ 4,00 - € 5,00
child (under 7 yrs)	€ 2,40 - € 3,00
pitch	€ 9,60 - € 12,00
electricity (6-10A)	€ 3,10 - € 4,50
dog	€ 1,60

Less 20% outside July/Aug.

Camping LE PANORAMIC ★★★★ BRITTANY

On the Crozon penninsular and the Bay of Douarnenez, this is a family campsite bordering the sea, where english is spoken and everything is well-maintened. There are many holiday activities available, including a swimming pool, childrens' play area, tennis, bathing, sailing, mountain biking etc., and a further choice of cultural activities in the Armorique Regional Park - the coast, the local ports, museums and of course the richness of the Breton culture itself.

Mr et Mme JACQ
29560 Telgruc-sur-Mer - France
Tel. 0033 298 27 78 41 - Fax: 0033 298 27 36 10
Email : info@camping-panoramic.com / www.camping-panoramic.com

---

FR29060 Flower Camping le Pil-Koad

Route de Douarnenez, F-29100 Poullan-sur-Mer (Finistère)
Tel: 02 97 74 42 11. Email: info@pil-koad.com

Pil-Koad is an attractive, family run site just back from the sea near Douarnenez in Finistère. It has 190 pitches on fairly flat ground, marked out by separating hedges and of quite good quality, though varying in size and shape. With 88 pitches used for touring units, the site also has a number of mobile homes and chalets. All pitches have electrical connections and the original trees provide shade in some areas. A large room, the 'Woodpecker Bar', is used for entertainment with discos and cabaret in July/Aug. Weekly outings and clubs for children are organised in high season.

Facilities

Two main toilet blocks in modern style include washbasins mostly in cabins and facilities for disabled visitors. Laundry facilities. Motorcaravan service point. Gas supplies. Small shop for basics (1/4-30/9). Bar, new restaurant and takeaway (all 1/6-5/9). Heated swimming and paddling pools (1/4-30/9, no Bermuda-style shorts). Tennis court. Table tennis. Minigolf. Volleyball. Fishing. Bicycle hire. Playground. Off site: Restaurants in village 500 m. Riding 4 km. Nearest sandy beach 5 km. Douarnenez 6 km.

Open: 1 April - 30 September.

Directions

Site is 500 m. east from the centre of Poullan on D7 road towards Douarnenez. From Douarnenez take circular bypass route towards Audierne; if you see road for Poullan sign at roundabout, take it, otherwise there is a camping sign at turning to Poullan from the D765 road. GPS: N48:04.560 W04:24.250

Charges 2007

Per pitch incl. 2 persons	€ 16,00 - € 30,80
extra person	€ 3,60 - € 5,10
child (2-7 yrs)	€ 2,30 - € 3,40

FR29090 Camping le Raguenès-Plage

Mobile homes ▶ page 483

19 rue des Iles, F-29920 Névez (Finistère)

Tel: **02 98 06 80 69**. Email: **info@camping-le-raguenes-plage.com**

Madame Guyader and her family will ensure you receive a warm welcome on arrival at this well kept and pleasant site. Le Raguenès-Plage is an attractive and well laid out campsite with many shrubs and trees. The 287 pitches are a good size, flat and grassy, separated by trees and hedges. All have electricity, water and drainage. The site is used by one tour operator (60 pitches), and has 46 mobile homes of its own. A pool complex complete with water toboggan is a key feature and is close to the friendly bar, restaurant, shop and takeaway. From the far end of the campsite a delightful five minute walk along a path and through a cornfield takes you down to a pleasant, sandy beach looking out towards the Ile Verte and the Presqu'île de Raguenès.

Facilities

Two clean, well maintained sanitary blocks include mixed style toilets, washbasins in cabins, baby baths and facilities for disabled visitors. Laundry room. Motorcaravan service point. Small shop (from 15/5). Bar and restaurant (from 1/6) with outside terrace and takeaway. Reading and TV room, internet access point. Heated pool with sun terrace and paddling pool. Sauna (charged). Play areas, table tennis, games room and volleyball. Various activities are organised in July/Aug. Off site: Beach, fishing and watersports 300 m. Supermarket 3 km. Riding 4 km.

Open: 1 April - 30 September.

Directions

From N165 take D24 Kerampaou exit. After 3 km. turn right towards Nizon and bear right at church in village following signs to Névez (D77). Continue through Névez, following signs to Raguenès. Continue for 3 km. to site entrance on left (entrance is quite small and easy to miss).

Charges 2008

Per unit incl. 2 persons	€ 16,50 - € 28,80
extra person	€ 4,40 - € 5,80
child (under 7 yrs)	€ 2,20 - € 3,40
electricity (2-10A)	€ 3,20 - € 4,80
dog	€ 1,50 - € 2,50

FR29070 Camping Plage de Trez Rouz

Route de Camaret á la Pointe des Espagnol, Camaret sur Mer, F-29160 Crozon (Finistère)

Tel: **02 98 27 93 96**. Email: **contact@trezrouz.com**

If you are looking for a restful holiday without swimming pools, televisions and noisy games, Trez Rouz could be just the place for you. Yannick and Isabelle Trouplin aim to keep their campsite, to use their own words, calm and peaceful. The 80 pitches vary in size, trees give shade on many and electricity is a generous 16A. Some are hedged, others have superb views across the bay to Camaret. The site has a comfortable, rural feel. There is a small bar and terrace where Yannick will be pleased to make you a crêpe or a pizza.

Facilities

One toilet block with British style toilets, showers and washing cubicles. Separate building for disabled campers. Washing machine and dryers. Fridges for hire. Bread can be ordered. Very basic groceries from reception. Small bar with snacks lunch and evening. TV room. Minigolf. Bicycle hire. Play area with trampoline. Kayak hire. Off site: Camaret 3 km. Riding 5 km. Beach 20 m.

Open: 15 March - 15 October.

Directions

From the RN165 (Brest - Quimper) turn west on D971 at Le Frou towards Corzon. Continue to Camaret and just before town turn right on D355 coast road. Site is signed to right after 3 km. GPS: N48:17.190 W04:33.570

Charges 2008

Per person	€ 4,00 - € 5,00
child (2-7 yrs)	€ 2,20 - € 3,00
pitch	€ 3,20 - € 4,50
electricity (10A)	€ 3,50

FR29110 Yelloh! Village la Plage

F-29730 Le Guilvinec (Finistère)

Tel: 02 98 58 61 90. Email: info@yellohvillage-la-plage.com

La Plage is a spacious site located beside a long sandy beach between the fishing town of Le Guilvinec and the watersports beaches of Penmarc'h on the southwest tip of Brittany. It is surrounded by tall trees which provide shelter and is made up of several flat, sandy meadows. The 410 pitches (100 for touring units) are arranged on either side of sandy access roads, mostly not separated but all numbered. There is less shade in the newer areas. Electricity is available on most pitches. Like all beach-side sites, the facilities receive heavy use. Used by tour operators (176 pitches). There is plenty to occupy one at this friendly site but the bustling fishing harbour at Le Guilvinec and the watersports of Penmarc'h and Pointe de la Torche are within easy travelling distance.

Facilities

Four sanitary blocks are of differing designs but all provide modern, bright facilities including washbasins in cabins, good facilities for children and disabled people. Laundry facilities. Motorcaravan service point. Shop with gas supplies. Bright, airy well furnished bar, crêperie and takeaway. Heated swimming pool with paddling pool and slide. Sauna and fitness complex. Play area. TV room. Tennis courts. Volleyball, basketball, minigolf, badminton, petanque, table tennis, giant chess/draughts. Bicycle hire. Beach. Off site: Fishing and watersports near. Riding 5 km. Golf 20 km.

Open: 5 April - 16 September, with all facilities.

Directions

Site is west of Guilvinec. From Pont l'Abbé, take the D785 road towards Penmarc'h. In Plomeur, turn left on D57 signed Guilvinec. On entering Guilvinec fork right signed Port and camping. Follow road along coast to site on left. GPS: N47:48.150 W04:18.430

Charges 2007

Per unit incl. 2 persons	
and electricity (5A)	€ 17,00 - € 38,00
extra person	€ 5,00 - € 7,00
child (under 10 yrs)	free - € 5,00
electricity (10A)	free - € 1,00
dog	€ 3,50

FR29120 Yelloh! Village le Manoir de Kerlut

F-29740 Plobannalec-Lesconil (Finistère)

Tel: **02 98 82 23 89**. Email: **info@yellohvillage-manoir-de-kerlut.com**

Le Manoir de Kerlut is a comfortable site in the grounds of a manor house on a river estuary near Pont l'Abbé. The campsite itself has neat, modern buildings and is laid out on flat grass providing 240 pitches (90 for touring units). All have electricity connections, some also have water and drainage and around ten pitches have hardstanding. One area is rather open with separating hedges planted, the other part being amongst more mature bushes and some trees which provide shade. Site amenities are of good quality. A 'Yelloh! Village' member.

Facilities	Directions
Toilet facilities in two good blocks (each with several rooms, not all open outside July/Aug), include washbasins all in cabins, and facilities for babies and disabled people. Laundry. Small shop. Takeaway. Large modern bar with TV (satellite) and entertainment all season. Two heated swimming pools, paddling pool and water slide. Sauna, solarium and small gym. Fitness centre. Play area. Games room. Bicycle hire. Off site: Beach 2 km. Fishing 2 km. Riding 5 km. Golf 15 km.	From Pont l'Abbé on D785, take D102 towards Lesconil. Site is signed on the left, after Plobannalec village. GPS: N47:48.733 W04:13.316

Charges 2007

Per unit incl. 2 persons and electricity (5A)	€ 17,00 - € 37,00
extra person	€ 5,00 - € 7,00
electricity (10A)	€ 1,00

Open: 5 May - 16 September, with all services.

See advertisement on page 33.

FR29130 Camping des Abers

Dunes de Sainte Marguerite, F-29870 Landéda (Finistère)

Tel: **02 98 04 93 35**. Email: **camping-des-abers@wanadoo.fr**

The location of this delightful 12 acre site is beautiful and the setting is ideal for those with younger children. Camping des Abers is set just back from the beach, the lower pitches sheltered from the wind by high hedges or with panoramic views from the higher places and the new orientation table. There are 180 pitches arranged in distinct areas, many partly shaded and sheltered by mature hedges, trees and flowering shrubs, all carefully tended over 30 years by the Le Cuff family.

Facilities	Directions
Three toilet blocks (recently refurbished) are very clean, providing washbasins in cubicles and roomy showers (token from reception € 0.80). Facilities for disabled visitors and babies. Dishwashing sinks. Laundry facilities. Motorcaravan services. Mini-market (25/5-22/9). Simple takeaway (1/7-31/8). Pizzeria and restaurant next door. Play area. Games room. Hairdresser. Massage. Live music. Breton dancing and cooking classes, and guided walks arranged. Direct access to beach with fishing and windsurfing. Torch useful. Gates locked 22.30-07.00 hrs. Off site: Miles of coastal walks. Riding 10 km. Golf 30 km. L'Aber Wrac'h with many restaurants.	From Roscoff (D10, then D13), cross river bridge (L'Aber Wrac'h) to Lannilis. Go through town taking road to Landéda and from there signs for Dunes de Ste Marguerite, 'camping' and des Abers. GPS: N48:35.584 W04:36.183

Charges 2008

Per person	€ 3,40
child (1-7 yrs)	€ 1,90
pitch with electricity	€ 8,50
dog	€ 1,80
Less 10% outside 15/6-31/8.	

Open: 28 April - 30 September.

FR29140 Siblu Camping Domaine de Kerlann

Land Rosted, F-29930 Pont-Aven (Finistère)

Tel: **02 98 06 01 77**. Email: **kerlann@siblu.fr**

Siblu have, with careful and imaginative planning, ensured that their mobile homes pitches (of which there are over 700) blend naturally into this well kept and landscaped holiday village. There are 20 touring pitches of medium size and quality, all with water and electricity. Much evening holiday camp style entertainment (with a French flavour) takes place on the bar terrace with its raised stage which overlooks the complex.

Facilities	Directions
The main large toilet block includes washbasins in cubicles. Laundry. Mini supermarket. French style restaurant, snack restaurant, takeaway and bar. Indoor and outdoor pool complex with lifeguards. Play areas. All weather multisport court, tennis, minigolf. Video games room. Satellite TV in bar. Children's clubs. Gas barbecues are not permitted. Off site: Pont-Aven with art galleries and museums. Small ports and villages. Beach 5 km.	From Tregunc - Pont-Aven road, turn south towards Névez and site is on right. GPS: N47:50.40 W03:47.21

Charges 2007

Per pitch incl. up to 6 persons with electricity	€ 14,00 - € 40,00

Open: 1 April - 29 October.

FR29150 Camping les Sables Blancs

Avenue Le Dorlett, F-29900 Concarneau (Finistère)

Tel: **02 98 97 16 44**. Email: camping.les-sablesblancs@libertysurf.fr

This is a steeply terraced site on the outskirts of Concarneau and overlooking the sea. Most of the 100 touring pitches are shaded by large mature trees and shrubs. They are level but tend to be small and access to some could prove difficult for large units. A traditional style bar and restaurant opens out onto a new terrace with swimming pool overlooking the bay of De La Forêt. The climb from the bottom of the site to the top is via some very steep steps, so those with walking difficulties would be advised to choose one of the higher pitches. The site is run by young owners who work very hard and make you feel welcome. An advantage of the site's position is its close proximity to Concarneau, which is said to be the second largest fishing port in France.

Facilities

One new modern toilet block provides very good facilities. Washbasins are both open and in cubicles. Showers. Facilities for babies and disabled visitors. Dishwashing and laundry facilities. Bar. (1/6-1/9). Restaurant in bar (1/7-1/9). Heated outdoor swimming pool (1/6-15/9). Play area. Evening entertainment (July/Aug). Off site: Concarneau with shops, bars and restaurants. Riding 1 km. Bicycle hire, boat launching 1.5 km.

Open: 1 April - 30 September.

Directions

Leave the N165 for Concarneau on D70. Site is situated on the northern edge of town on the coast road. Well signed. GPS: N47:52.55 W03:55.43

Charges 2007

Per unit incl. 2 persons	€ 12,00 - € 16,00
extra person	€ 3,00 - € 4,50
child	€ 1,00 - € 3,50
electricity (10A)	€ 3,50

Camping Les Sables Blancs***

Avenue de Dorlett - 29900 Concarneau
internet : www.camping-lessablesblancs.com
E-mail: camping.les-sablesblancs@libertysurf.fr
Tel : 0033 (0)298 971 644

Les Sables Blancs is a lovely family campsite, in green surroundings, 200 m away from Concarneau's largest beach. The sheltered, white sandy beach is perfect for sports and aquatic activities. At 15 minutes walk from the campsite: the historical city of Concarneau, its shop and city walls. Also to discover: the islands of Glénan, at 20 minutes by boat. The campsite has: marked pitches (sunny / shady), cottages and chalets to let, new sanitary blocks equipped with individual, family and disabled cabines, baby bath, heated swimming pool. Also on the site : bread, ice cream, bar, snack, children's playground, table tennis, washing machine, dryer, spa, padding pool.

FR29160 Camping les Genets d'Or

Kermerour, Pont Kereon, F-29380 Bannalec (Finistère)

Tel: **02 98 39 54 35**. Email: Enquiries@holidaybrittany.com

A jewel of a small site, Les Genets d'Or is situated in a tiny country hamlet at the end of a road from Bannalec, 12 km. from Pont-Aven in Finistère. The spacious surroundings offer a safe haven for young children and a rural, tranquil environment for adults. The gently sloping, grassy site is edged with mature trees and divided into hedged glades with the odd apple tree providing shade. There are only 52 pitches (42 for touring units), all of a good size – some of over 100 sq.m. – and most pitches have electricity, each glade having a water point.

Facilities

The good quality toilet block provides all the necessary amenities and washing facilities, including a shower for disabled campers. Washing machine and dryer. Shop (15/6-30/9). Bar area. Bread delivered in season. Ice pack service. Indoor room with snooker and table tennis. Bicycle hire. Play and picnic area. Caravan storage. Off site: Riding 3 km. Beach 12 km. The village is 15 minutes walk with bars, shop, baker, etc.

Open: Easter/1 April - 30 September.

Directions

Take exit D4 from N165 towards Bannalec. In Bannalec turn right into Rue Lorec (Quimperlé) and follow camp signs for 1 km. GPS: N47:55.30 W03:41.20

Charges 2007

Per person	€ 3,50
child (under 6 yrs)	€ 2,50
pitch	€ 6,00
electricity (6A)	€ 3,00
animal	€ 1,50
Less 10% for over 7 nights.	

FR29180 Camping les Embruns

Mobile homes ▶ page 483

Rue du Philosophe Alain, le Pouldu, F-29360 Clohars-Carnoët (Finistère)

Tel: **02 98 39 91 07**. Email: **camping-les-embruns@wanadoo.fr**

This site is unusual in that it is located in the heart of a village, yet is only 250 metres from a sandy cove. The entrance with its code operated barrier and wonderful floral displays, is the first indication that this is a well tended and well organised site, and the owners have won numerous regional and national awards for its superb presentation. The 180 pitches (100 occupied by mobile homes) are separated by trees, shrubs and bushes, and most have electricity (10A), water and drainage. There is a covered, heated swimming pool, a circular paddling pool and a water play pool. It is only a short walk to the village centre with all its attractions and services. It is also close to beautiful countryside and the Carnoët Forest which are good for walking and cycling.

Facilities

Two modern sanitary blocks, recently completely renewed, include mainly British style toilets, some washbasins in cubicles, baby baths and good facilities for disabled visitors. Family bathrooms. Laundry facilities. Motorcaravan service point. Mini-market and restaurant by site entrance. Bar and terrace (1/7-31/8). Takeaway (20/6-5/9). Covered, heated swimming and paddling pools. Large games hall. Play area. Football field, volleyball and minigolf. Communal barbecue area. Daily activities for children and adults organised in July/Aug. Off site: Nearby sea and river fishing and watersports. Bicycle hire 50 m. Beach 250 m. Riding 2 km.

Open: 4 April - 13 September.

Directions

From N165 take either 'Kervidanou, Quimperlé Ouest' exit or 'Kergostiou, Quimperlé Centre, Clohars Carnoët' exit and follow D16 to Clohars Carnoët. Then take D24 for Le Pouldu and follow site signs in village.

Charges 2008

Per unit incl. 2 persons	€ 10,50 - € 15,50
fully serviced pitch	€ 15,50 - € 29,90
extra person	€ 3,95 - € 5,50
child (under 7 yrs)	€ 2,60 - € 3,50
animal	€ 3,90

Less in low seasons.
Use of motorcaravan services € 4.

Les Embruns ★★★★

250 m from one of Brittany's sandy beaches Mr & Mrs Leguennou welcome you in their particularly well maintained campsite where you are assured of a good holiday.
• First class facilities and amenities in a green and floral environment • Mobile homes to let
• Motorcaravan service point • Covered heated swimming pool right from the opening •

LE POULDU - F-29360 CLOHARS-CARNOET
TEL: 0033 298 39 91 07 - FAX: 0033 298 39 97 87
www.camping-les-embruns.com
E-mail: camping-les-embruns@wanadoo.fr

FR29170 Camping de la Piscine

Kerleya B.P.12, Beg-Meil, F-29170 Fouesnant (Finistère)

Tel: **02 98 56 56 06**. Email: **contact@campingdelapiscine.com**

There are many campsites in this area but La Piscine is notable for the care and attention to detail that contributes to the well-being of its visitors. Created by the Caradec family from an apple orchard, the 185 level, grass pitches are of generous size and are separated by an interesting variety of hedges and trees. Water, waste and electricity points are provided, normally one stand between two pitches. A quiet site, set back from the sea, La Piscine will appeal to families looking for good quality without too many on site activities.

Facilities

Two refurbished toilet units include British and Turkish style toilets and washbasins in cabins. Facilities for disabled people. Laundry facilities. Motorcaravan service point. Shop. Takeaway (high season). Pool complex with three slides, waterfall and jacuzzi. Sauna and solarium. Play area. BMX track. Football pitch, volleyball, half-court tennis and table tennis. TV room. Entertainment organised in high season. Off site: Beach 1 km. Bicycle hire, fishing and riding within 4 km. Golf 7 km.

Open: 15 May - 15 September.

Directions

Site is 5 km. south of Fouesnant. Turn off N165 expressway at Coat Conq signed Concarnau and Fouesnant. At Fouesnant join D45 signed Beg Meil and shortly turn left on D145 signed Mousterlin. In 1 km. turn left and follow signs to site. GPS: N47:51.941 W04:00.932

Charges 2008

Per pitch with 2 persons and electricity	€ 18,80 - € 29,40
extra person	€ 3,60 - € 5,90
child (2-7 yrs)	€ 1,80 - € 2,95

FR29190 Camping les Prés Verts

B.P. 612, Kernous-Plage, F-29186 Concarneau Cedex (Finistère)

Tel: **02 98 97 09 74.** Email: **info@presverts.com**

What sets this family site apart from the many others in this region are its more unusual features which include its stylish pool complex with Romanesque style columns and statue, and its plants and flower tubs. The 150 pitches are mostly arranged on long, open, grassy areas either side of main access roads. Specimen trees, shrubs or hedges divide the site into smaller areas. There are a few individual pitches and an area towards the rear of the site where the pitches have sea views. Concarneau is just 2.5 km. and there are many marked coastal walks to enjoy in the area, plus watersports or boat and fishing trips available nearby. A 'Sites et Paysages' member.

Facilities

Two toilet blocks provide unisex WCs, but separate washing facilities for ladies and men. Pre-set hot showers and washbasins in cabins for ladies, both closed 21.00 - 8.00 hrs. Some child-size toilets. Laundry facilities. Pizza service twice weekly. Heated swimming pool (1/7-31/8) and paddling pool. Playground (0-5 yrs only). Minigolf (charged). Off site: Path to sandy/rocky beach (300 m.) and coastal path. Riding 1 km. Supermarket 2 km. Bicycle hire 3 km. Golf 5 km.

Open: 1 May - 22 September.

Directions

Turn off C7 road, 2.5 km. north of Concarneau, where site is signed. Take third left after Hotel de l'Océan.

Charges 2008

Per unit incl. 2 persons	€ 17,50 - € 22,00
extra person	€ 5,20 - € 6,50
child (2-7 yrs)	€ 3,40 - € 4,30
electricity (2-10A)	€ 3,20 - € 7,00
dog	€ 1,30 - € 1,60

FR29210 Camping Municipal Bois de la Palud

F-29250 Plougoulm (Finistère)

Tel: **02 98 29 81 82**

This delightful, small municipal site is on the edge of the little village of Plougoulm, about 10 km. southwest of Roscoff. It sits on the brow of a hill with lovely views across the Guillec valley and the sandy bay and estuary to which there is access by footpath. There are 34 reasonably level, numbered pitches grouped in small hedged bays and most have access to 6A electricity (although long leads may be necessary). A small building near the entrance houses reception and sanitary facilities. The season is short – only 1 June - 9 September.

Facilities

All necessary toilet facilities are provided. Play area. Off site: Fishing, bicycle hire and riding, all within 4 km.

Open: 1 June - 9 September.

Directions

On leaving Roscoff, follow signs for Morlaix. After 6 km. take D10 (westward) signed Plouescat and after 3 km. watch for clear camp signs in the village of Plougoulm.

Charges guide

per person	€ 3,00
child (under 7 yrs)	€ 2,00
pitch	€ 3,50
electricity	€ 2,50
No credit cards.	

FR29220 Camping Municipal de Kerisole

Kerisole, F-29390 Scaër (Finistère)

Tel: **02 98 57 60 91**. Email: **mairie@ville-scaer.fr**

Within walking distance of the pleasant little town of Scaër, Kerisole is an attractive and well kept site, ideal for exploring inland Brittany and yet only 32 km. from the coast. There are 80 mostly level, grass pitches, not hedged, but individually numbered (28 have electricity). Throughout the season the managers, in conjunction with the local council, organise walks, local visits and various activities, many of which are free of charge. With its delightful park-like setting, reasonable charges, and proximity to both town facilities and countryside walks, this site makes an ideal base.

Facilities

Central, clean and tidy sanitary blocks include washbasins in cubicles (separate facilities for men and ladies). Facilities for disabled people. Laundry. Dishwashing sinks. Library. Bread to order. Adjacent play area. Woodland footpath, with a range of 'assault course' obstacles. Access to the pool is no longer free of charge. Off site: Tennis and indoor swimming pool (free for campers). Shops, bars and restaurants a few minutes walk in Scaër. Beach 25 km.

Open: 15 June - 15 September.

Directions

From N165 take D70 to Rosporden, then D782 to Scaër. Drive through town centre, following signs for Faouet, and site is on left at traffic lights on leaving town centre.

Charges 2007

Per unit with 2 persons and electricity	€ 12,30
child (under 7 yrs)	€ 1,90

No credit cards.

FR29240 Camping de Kéranterec

Route de Port la Forêt, F-29940 La Forêt-Fouesnant (Finistère)

Tel: **02 98 56 98 11**. Email: **info@camping-keranterec.com**

A well established family run site with a very French ambience (unlike some of the neighbouring sites which have a much higher UK presence), Keranterec has 265 grassy pitches in two distinct areas. The upper part of the site is more open and has little shade, and is also largely taken up by private mobile homes. The lower and more mature area is predominantly for tourers, with terraced pitches set in a former orchard. Spacious and divided by mature hedging, all pitches have electrical connections (25 m. cable advised) and most also offer water and drainage.

Facilities

Two modern, fully equipped toilet blocks kept very clean include washbasins in cubicles, baby baths and facilities for disabled visitors. Laundry facilities. Small shop and bar (15/6-10/9) and takeaway (1/7-31/8). TV room with satellite. Heated swimming pool (1/6-10/9) with paddling pool, jacuzzi and three slides. Tennis court, boules, volleyball and basketball, table tennis. Play area. In July/Aug. organised events and activities for all the family, and a free children's club. Off site: Attractive sandy beach of Kerleven 10 minutes walk. Golf 0.8 km. Riding 2 km.

Open: 5 April - 21 September.

Directions

From N165 take D70 Concarneau exit. At first roundabout take D44 (Fouesnant). After 2.5 km. turn right at T-junction, follow for 2.5 km. and turn left (Port La Forêt). Continue to roundabout and take second exit, signed Port La Forêt. After 1 km. turn left (site signed), then in 400 m. turn left to site on left. GPS: N47:53.930 W03:57.375

Charges 2007

Per person	€ 7,00 - € 8,00
child (under 7 yrs)	€ 3,00 - € 4,00
pitch incl. electricity	€ 13,00 - € 17,00

No credit cards.

FR29260 Camping les Genêts

Rue de Gouesnac'h Nevez, F-29760 Penmarc'h (Finistère)

Tel: **02 98 58 66 93**. Email: **nohartp@wanadoo.fr**

The present owners of Les Genêts, Bridgette and Pascal Rohart, bought this old, rural campsite a few years ago and have transformed it beyond recognition. The modem reception is in front of a modestly sized swimming pool that has a section for small children. The toilet block although old but adequate, is to be replaced by two new blocks. There are 100 pitches which are divided by trees and hedges and vary in both size and quality. Some in one corner of the site appear to have poor drainage. Around 40 pitches are used for mobile homes which are placed to one side of the campsite.

Facilities

One old but very clean toilet block (with no facilities for disabled visitors) has both British and Turkish style toilets, showers and wash cubicles. This is to be replaced by two new blocks. Laundry room. Bar and snack bar (July/Aug). Bread (July/Aug). Swimming pool. Play area and trampoline. Off site: Shops and restaurants 1.5 km. Beach, fishing, boat launching, riding 1.5 km. Golf 3 km.

Open: 1 April - 31 October.

Directions

From Pont l'Abbé, take the D785 southwest towards Penmarc'h. Before the town turn left eastwards on the D53 (Loc Tody) and site is on left in about 2 km. GPS: N47:49.05 W04:18.32

Charges 2007

Per unit incl. 2 persons	€ 11,20 - € 14,60
extra person	€ 3,00 - € 3,80
electricity (10A)	€ 2,90

FR29290 Camping Village le Grand Large

48 route du Grand Large, Mousterlin, F-29170 Fouesnant (Finistère)

Tel: **02 98 56 04 06**. Email: **info@yellohvillage-grand-large.com**

Le Grand Large is a beach-side site situated on the Pointe de Mousterlin in natural surroundings. The site is separated from the beach by the road that follows the coast around the point. It is also protected from the wind by an earth bank with trees and a fence. There are 260 pitches with just 51 places used for tourers. Some pitches are taken by one tour operator and the site itself has tents and mobile homes to rent. Electricity is available everywhere (long leads useful) and some pitches have drainage. A small river runs through the site but it is fenced. The ground is rather sandy in places with some shrubs and mature trees. Benodet (7 km.) and Fouesnant (5 km.) are near in different directions and the sandy beach is just up the steps and across the road. A family site, Le Grand Large would also suit nature lovers in low season as it is next to a large tract of protected land, Marais de Mousterlin, ideal for walking, cycling and birdwatching. The beach itself looks over the bay towards the Isles de Glénan.

Facilities

Two neat toilet blocks, the largest only opened in high season, include plenty of washbasins in cabins. Facilities for children in the larger block, for disabled people in both. Laundry facilities. Shop. Bar overlooking the sea with attractive terrace. Crêperie/grill restaurant including takeaway. Swimming pool with paddling pool, water slides in separate pool. Tennis court and multisport court. Small play area. TV and games rooms. Bicycle hire. Off site: Beach, fishing 100 m. Golf and riding 5 km.

Open: 31 March - 16 September (with all services).

Directions

Site is 7 km. south of Fouesnant. Turn off N165 expressway at Coat Conq, signed Concarneau and Fouesnant. At Fouesnant take A45 signed Beg Meil, then follow signs to Mousterlin. In Mousterlin turn left and follow camping signs. GPS: N47:50.520 W04:02.120

Charges 2007

Per unit incl. 2 persons and electricity (5A)	€ 17,00 - € 37,00
extra person	€ 5,00 - € 7,00
child (under 10 yrs)	free - € 5,00
electricity (10A)	€ 1,00

FR29270 Camping des Dunes

67 rue Paul Langevin, F-29740 Lesconil (Finistère)

Tel: **02 98 87 81 78**

On the edge of the sand dunes near the village of Lesconil, this campsite has the great advantage of providing direct access to an excellent sandy beach. The 120 sandy and grassy pitches have little shade, but are quite spacious and all have electricity. The site is only 800 m. from the village of Lesconil, an unspoilt fishing port where you can still see the little fishing fleet return each day. There is a good choice of restaurants and cafés, and a 'Centre Nautique' offering a range of watersports.

Facilities

Two central, unisex toilet blocks have predominantly British style toilets and washbasins, both open and in cubicles. Baby area. Two toilet/shower rooms for disabled people. Laundry and dishwashing sinks. Washing machine and dryer. Baker's van visits every morning in high season. Play area for younger children. Two trampolines, bowling alley game, volleyball and table tennis. Off site: Tennis. Beach 100 m.

Open: 1 June - 15 September.

Directions

From Pont L'Abbé follow D102 to Lesconil. Just before village (sports stadium on right) – site signed just past stadium. Site is 1.5 km. on the right, just past Camping de la Grande Plage. GPS: N47:47.49 W04:13.42

Charges 2007

Per unit incl. 2 persons and electricity	€ 23,55
extra person	€ 4,60
child (under 7 yrs)	€ 2,95

FR29280 La Pointe Superbe Camping

Route de St Coulitz, F-29150 Châteaulin (Finistère)

Tel: **02 98 86 51 53**. Email: **lapointecamping@aol.com**

La Pointe, just outside Châteaulin, has been lovingly and impressively brought back to life by its delightful English owners Colin Grewer and Sue Dodds. Châteaulin is a bustling market town, 15 km. from the beach at Pentrez and within easy reach of Quimper, mediaeval Locronan and the Crozon peninsula. Although not endowed with a great deal in terms of amenities, this very tranquil site does boast particularly large, grassy pitches in a quiet valley leading down to the River Aulne, which makes up part of the Nantes - Brest canal. The 60 pitches all have electricity (10A) with water close by.

Facilities	Directions
The first class toilet block, kept very clean at all times, has many washbasins in cubicles. Shower cubicles are somewhat small but have full adjustable hot and cold taps. Large room with facilities for disabled visitors. Baby bathroom. Motorcaravan service point. Play area. Table tennis, volleyball and large activity room with basketball, badminton and children's corner. Off site: Châteaulin 700 m. Riding and tennis nearby. Fishing in the Aulne (permit needed). Beach 9 km.	Site is just southeast of Châteaulin. From the bridge over the river in town centre follow signs for St Coulitz and Quimper. Shortly turn left signed St Coulitz. Site is clearly signed at this point and is 100 m. on the right. GPS: N48:11.15 W04:05.05

Open: 6 March - 31 October.

Charges 2007

Per unit incl. 2 persons and electricity	€ 17,50
extra person	€ 3,00

No credit cards.
Camping Cheques accepted.

FR29330 Camping la Corniche

F-29710 Plozévet (Finistère)

Tel: **02 98 91 33 94**. Email: **infos@campinglacorniche.com**

A well presented site, La Corniche is conveniently placed for both coast – with some sandy beaches – and the delights of inland Brittany. The owners speak minimal English, but are good at sign language! Large level fields are divided into smaller areas by mature hedging and there is some shade from trees. There are 120 grass pitches with 6A electricity available to touring units, with some mobile homes as well. Plozévet is a ten minute stroll away with several restaurants, bars and a small supermarket. This site would be ideal for those wishing to get away from the busiest tourist areas.

Facilities	Directions
Toilet facilities are excellent, one block having been completely rebuilt. Comprehensively equipped, they include individual wash cubicles. Roof lights create a light and airy feel. Provision for those with disabilities. Small shop (from May). Bar (from May) and takeaway (July/Aug). Swimming pool and paddling pool. Off site: Village within walking distance. Beach 2 km.	Head west from Quimper and pick up the D784 towards Landudec and Plozévet. After 26 km, where the road makes a sharp right in the centre of Plozévet, take a left (caravan site sign partially obscured on the corner) towards the coast (Plage). The site is on the right after 1 km.

Open: 31 March - 30 September.

Charges 2007

Per pitch with electricity	€ 8,40 - € 9,20
person	€ 3,80 - € 4,50
child (under 7 yrs)	€ 2,20 - € 3,00

FR29340 Camping de la Côte des Légendes

Keravezan B.P. 36, F-29890 Brignogan-Plages (Finistère)

Tel: **02 98 83 41 65**. Email: **camping-cote-des-legendes@wanadoo.fr**

Located just behind a safe, sandy beach on the Bay of Brignogan and adjacent to a Centre Nautique (sailing, windsurfing, kayak), this site is ideal for a family seaside holiday. It is a quiet site with 147 level pitches arranged in rows and protected by hedges. There are a few mobile homes and chalets for rent but no tour operators. A shop, bar and takeaway are open in high season when activities are arranged for adults and children by the helpful owner (good English is spoken). The beach of fine sand can be reached directly from the site.

Facilities	Directions
Main toilet facilities are at the rear of the site in a large block that provides washbasins in cubicles, baby baths and facilities for disabled visitors. Dishwashing and laundry sinks. Motorcaravan service point. Games room. Further toilet facilities are at the reception building, also a laundry. Bar, small shop and takeaway (July/Aug). Playground and playing field. Off site: Watersports centre adjacent. Village 700 m. Bicycle hire 1 km. Riding 6 km.	From Roscoff take the D58 towards Morlaix and after 6 km. turn right on the D10 towards Plouescat and then Plouguerneau. Turn right on the D770 to Brignogan-Plages. In the main street go straight on following signs for site and Club Nautique.

Open: Easter - 1 November.

Charges guide

Per unit incl. 2 persons	€ 9,90 - € 12,50
extra person	€ 3,05 - € 3,75
electricity	€ 1,00 - € 3,10

FR29380 Yelloh! Village Port de Plaisance

7 route de Quimper, F-29950 Bénodet (Finistère)

Tel: **02 98 57 02 38**. Email: **info@campingbenodet.fr**

Sometimes larger campsites can lack ambiance, but it is not so with Port de Plaisance. This is a delightful, family run site with 340 pitches of which 105 are for touring campers. The pitches are mostly in two areas, where they are hedged and positioned in small groups amongst the many mature trees and flowering shrubs. Although there are five holiday tour operators on site, their presence is unobtrusive because of careful positioning amongst the trees. This is truly a campsite with something for everybody, with a wide range of entertainment and activities provided over a long season. The restaurant that overlooks the pool complex boasts a very good menu. There is entertainment suitable for all ages, from up-to-date films to taster aquadiving lessons in the pool. An additional covered pool was planned when we visited. The marina at the mouth of the Odet river is 500 m. away, and from here you can enjoy a boat trip up to Quimper. The large seaside town of Bénodet, with all the shops, bars and restaurants that you could wish for is just 1 km.

Facilities

Three toilet blocks, older and simple in style, include British style toilets, showers and washing cubicles. Baby room. Facilities for disabled visitors. Laundry room. Shop (15/5-15/9). Bar. Restaurant and takeaway (21/3-30/9). Swimming pool complex with flumes and toboggan. Games room. Programme of entertainment. Taster diving lessons in the pool. Multisports court. Bicycle hire. Off site: Bénodet 1 km. Fishing 1 km. Riding 2 km. Golf 3 km. Beach 1 km.

Open: 21 March - 28 September.

Directions

Take the D34 south from Quimper. Site is on the left just as you enter Bénodet. GPS: N47:52.560 W04:06.120

Charges 2008

Per unit incl. 2 persons and electricity (6A)	€ 14,00 - € 38,00
extra person	€ 4,00 - € 7,00
child (0-7 yrs)	free - € 3,50

Open from 21 march 2008 to 28 september 2008

www.benodet.co.uk

Camping **Yelloh! Village** PORT DE PLAISANCE ★ ★ ★ ★

yёlloh! VILLAGE

29950 BENODET-**Tél :** **00 33 (0)2 98 57 02 38** fax : 00 33 (0)2 98 57 25 25 info@campingbenodet.fr

FR29410 Camping Domaine de Ker Ys

Pentrez Plage, F-29550 Saint Nic (Finistère)

Tel: **02 98 26 53 95**. Email: **camping-kerys@wanadoo.fr**

Domaine de Ker Ys is a site especially suited to families with young children. Here there are many imaginative play areas on the site and miles of wide sandy beach 20 metres away. The site has no bar or restaurant, but the pool complex is very good with its slides, fountains and paddling pools, and a little entertainment is organised in high season. The 121 touring pitches vary in size, some being in open groups of four or five, others being divided by hedges. The site is pleasantly laid out with many varieties of trees giving shade. This site's main attraction is its close proximity to magnificent beaches.

Facilities

Three unisex toilet blocks have British style toilets, showers and washbasins in cabins. Facilities for disabled visitors. Washing machines and dryers. Some groceries in reception, bread (July/Aug). Play area. Mini tennis. TV and games rooms. Off site: Shops, bars and restaurants nearby (but not many). Riding 15 km. Beach 20 m.

Open: 1 May - 24 September.

Directions

From the N165 (Quimper - Brest) take exit west at Châteaulin on D887 towards Crozon. Turn left to Saint Nic, then follow signs for Penthez Plage and site. At the promenade turn left and site is 300 m. on the left. GPS: N48:11.32 W04:18.04

Charges 2007

Per unit incl. 1 or 2 persons	€ 12,00 - € 23,00
extra person	€ 3,60 - € 6,00
child (2-7 yrs)	€ 2,10 - € 3,50
electricity	€ 3,20

Check real time availability and at-the-gate prices...

www.**alanrogers**.com

FR29470 Camping les Deux Fontaines

Feunteun Vilian, Raguenèz, F-29920 Névez (Finistère)

Tel: **02 98 06 81 91**. Email: **info@les2fontaines.fr**

Les Deux Fontaines is a large site with 288 pitches. Of these 115 are for touring, 118 are used by tour operators, and the remainder for mobile homes. The well cared for pitches are on grass, level and attractively laid out amongst mature trees and shrubs. All have 6/10A electricity connections. Trees have been carefully planted creating one area with silver birch, one with apple trees and another with palms and tropical plants. The pool complex is an excellent feature complete with chutes, flumes and waterfalls. There are numerous daytime activities for all the family to enjoy and a variety of entertainment in the evening. A short drive away you can experience some of the most scenic coastline of Brittany. Further afield you can visit the old walled town of Concarneau with its fishing port, the town of Nevez or Pont Aven, home to the painter Gauguin.

Facilities

Two modern toilet blocks are of good quality and provide washbasins in cabins and pre-set showers. Separate facilities for disabled visitors. Dishwashing sinks, washing machines and dryers. Well stocked shop. Bar. Restaurant (1/7-31/8). Takeaway (1/6-31/8). Basic motorcaravan services. Large swimming pool complex. Fitness and pamper room. Play area. Skateboard Park. 6-hole golf course. Driving range. Rollerblade hire. Off site: Fishing 1 km. Bicycle hire, riding 5 km.

Open: 15 May - 6 September.

Directions

Travel south from Nevez on the D1. The site is on the left after 3 km. and is well signed. GPS: N47:47.57 W03:47.26

Charges 2007

Per unit incl. 2 persons	€ 17,50 - € 30,40
extra person	€ 3,70 - € 5,80
child (2-7 yrs)	free - € 3,90
electricity (6A)	€ 3,50

FR29450 Camping le Helles

55 rue du Petit Bourg, Sainte Marine, F-29120 Combrit (Finistère)

Tel: **02 98 56 31 46**. Email: **contact@le-helles.com**

This is a delightful site with a very French feel. Out of its 130 pitches, 100 are used for touring. The pitches are grassy, level and generous in size, but with little division by hedges. Mature trees offering shade surround large open areas of numbered pitches. Mobile homes are in an area of their own. Facilities on this site are excellent and the swimming pool with surrounding terrace provides a main feature. A gate at the back of the touring area leads to the beach, which is just 300 m. away. The village of Sainte Marine is close by and a little further is the port of Combrit with shops, bars and restaurants. The large seaside resort of Bénodet is a 10 minute drive away.

Facilities

Excellent sanitary facilities include washbasins in cabins and controllable showers (some also with washbasin). Baby room and facilities for disabled visitors. Dishwashing and laundry facilities. Bread van delivers daily. Takeaway (July/Aug). Swimming pool. Play area. Boules. Off site: Beach, fishing 300 m. Bicycle hire, riding 4 km. Golf 5 km.

Open: 1 April - 30 September.

Directions

Travelling west on D44 from Benodet turn south on to C18 signed Combrit Ste Marine. Site is well signed at entry to village. GPS: N47:52.08 W04:07.42

Charges 2007

Per unit incl. 2 persons	€ 15,00 - € 20,50
extra person	€ 3,90 - € 5,00
child (under 7 yrs)	€ 2,90 - € 3,40
electricity (6A)	€ 3,50

FR29480 Domaine de Kervel

Kervel, F-29550 Plonevez-Porzay (Finistère)

Tel: 02 98 92 51 54. Email: camping.kervel@wanadoo.fr

This is a large, well maintained site with many mature trees providing shade and colourful landscaping with shrubs and flowers. Marked by faint lines on the ground, the grassy pitches are level and well kept. Arranged in enclosures of five to six units, each group is surrounded by trees. The excellent pool complex provides indoor and outdoor pools, sunbathing terraces, paddling pools and a slide. Nearby are a comfortable bar and separate restaurant and for youngsters on a rainy day, a large, well equipped games room. The beach of Douarnenez Bay is 1 km. and is wide, safe and popular with sail-boarders. Douarnenez itself is 15 minutes by car and offers shops, bars and restaurants. There is a variety of accommodation for rent.

Facilities	Directions
One large and one small toilet block provide toilets, showers and washbasins in cabins. Baby room. Washing machines and dryers (at the large block). Bar. Restaurant. Snack bar. Shop. Swimming pools, indoor and outdoor. Games room. Multisport court. Minigolf. Off site: Beach 1 km. Douarnenez 15 minutes by car. **Open:** 31 March - 30 September.	From Plonevez-Porsay travel southwest on the D107 for about 3 km. Turn west on CD107 signed Kervel and site is signed from here. GPS: N48:06.59 W04:16.05

Charges 2007

Per person	€ 4,00 - € 5,50
child (2-7 yrs)	€ 2,50 - € 3,00
pitch	€ 7,50 - € 12,50
electricity (10A)	€ 3,50

FR29490 Camping de Trologot

Grève du Man, F-29250 Saint Pol de Léon (Finistère)

Tel: 02 98 69 06 26. Email: camping-trologot@wanadoo.fr

This small and attractive riverside site has a comfortable ambience and is only a short drive from the port of Roscoff. There are 100 pitches, 85 for touring, all level, grassy and hedged and with electricity (10A). Many small trees give a little shade. A comfortable bar opens onto a large terrace that surrounds the swimming and paddling pools. There is little in the way of sports provision other than table tennis and boules. Young children are catered for with an excellent play area and, for the not so young, there is entertainment in the bar during high season.

Facilities	Directions
One central toilet block includes facilities for campers with disabilities. Washing machine and dryer. Heated swimming and paddling pools (15/6-10/9). Small shop and bar (July/Aug). Play area. Table tennis. Boules. Billiards. Visiting food vans (July/Aug). Little organised activities (July/Aug). Off site: Pebble and sandy beaches, shell fishing and sea angling (close by). St Pol de Léon with shops, bars, restaurants 2 km. Port of Roscoff 7 km. **Open:** 1 May - 30 September.	From Morlaix go north on D58 to St Pol de Léon. Follow signs for Plage/Port. Site is well signed. GPS: N48:41.600 W03:58.167

Charges 2007

Per person	€ 3,40 - € 4,50
child (under 7 yrs)	€ 1,00 - € 2,70
pitch	€ 5,70 - € 8,20

43

FR29500 Camping de la Plage Bénodet

20 rue du Poulquer, F-29950 Bénodet (Finistère)

Tel: **02 98 57 00 55**. Email: **info@campingdelaplagebenodet.com**

This is a large well organised site that has a rural feel, although it is only 300 m. from the beach and 800 m. from the popular seaside town of Bénodet. It has a very short season for touring. There is a great variety of shrubs and trees offering ample shade and privacy for the 300 grassy pitches. There are 190 for touring (electricity 6/10A), all attractively and informally laid out on one side of the site. Access for large units may be difficult. A splendid pool complex has a retractable cover, flumes, a toboggan and a jacuzzi. Most of the organised entertainment takes place in the bar and on a traditional style terrace. A short walk away is the beach and promenade of Bénodet with shops, bars, restaurants and the mouth of the river Odet. There are organised river trips to the town of Quimper and to the islands in the bay.

Facilities

Four large adequate toilet blocks with facilities for campers with disabilities although access is not easy. Motorcaravan services. Shop. Bar with TV and takeaway (all season). Heated swimming and paddling pools (one can be covered), flumes, toboggan, Jacuzzi (July/Aug). Multisports court. Boules. Exercise bikes. Good play areas. Games room. Miniclub and entertainment (July/Aug). Bicycle hire. Off site: Beach 300 m. Seaside resort of Bénodet, bars, restaurants, shop, cinema 800 m. Boat trips.

Open: 1 July - 31 August (for touring).

Directions

From Fouesnant take D44 west towards Bénodet. After 10 km. take Le Letty road south. Site is well signed. GPS: N47:52.067 W04:05.850

Charges 2008

Per person	€ 6,20
child (2-10 yrs)	€ 3,30
pitch with electricity	€ 13,30 - € 14,10
dog	€ 2,60

CAMPING DE LA PLAGE IN BENODET AND ITS STAFF ARE VERY HAPPY TO WELCOME YOU AND YOUR FAMILY ON OUR CAMPSITE IN SOUTH BRITTANY . OUR CAMPSITE IS LOCATED IN A VERY PRETTY SEASIDE RESORT CLOSE TO THE SEAFRONT (ABOUT 300M) AND FROM BENODET TOWN-CENTER (ABOUT 800 M) . YOU WILL ENJOY THE OUTSTANDING NATURAL LANDSCAPE OF OUR CAMPSITE ! IT IS A REAL TREAT FOR YOUR EYES ! GREEN AND RELAXING CAMPSITE AS MOST OF OUR REGULAR CUSTOMERS SAY !

SPECIAL OFFER :

● **5% DISCOUNT** FOR CARAVANING-TOURERS (MINIMUM 7 NIGHTS) FROM 15 /6 TO 19/7 AND FROM 15/8 TO 13/9

● **5% DISCOUNT** FOR 3 WEEKS' RENTAL OF A MOBIL-HOME OR CHALET

29950 Benodet - France - tel : 0033 (0)298 570 055 - fax : 0033 (0)2 98 57 12 60 e-mail : laplagebenodet@wanadoo.fr - website: www.campingdelaplagebenodet.com

FR29510 Camping Baie de Térénez

Moulin de Térénez, F-29252 Plouézoc'h (Finistère)

Tel: **02 98 67 26 80**. Email: **campingbaiedeterenez@wanadoo.fr**

There are masses of flowers and a warm welcome awaiting at this site. The owners M. & Mme. Lucienne have owned this site for three years and their hard work has made it well worth visiting. There are 114 well cared for and attractive grass pitches with 98 for touring units. Separated by hedges with trees giving some shade, some are quite small. There are 50 with 8A electricity. The area is renowned for its coastal walking and scenery. Scuba diving lessons commence in the pool and afterwards in the sea. A variety of entertainment is organised in the bar, including music groups, sea shanties and traditional Breton songs.

Facilities

Two old but clean toilet blocks include facilities for campers with disabilities. Shop (July/Aug). Bar with TV. Restaurant (evenings). Takeaway. Unheated swimming and paddling pools (15/6-15/9). Minigolf. Boules. Small play area. Horse and carriage rides (high season). Off site: Fishing 1 km. Beach, sailing, boat launching 1.5 km. Riding 3 km. Bicycle hire 4 km. Golf 10 km. Town of Plouezoc'h nearby shops, bars, restaurants. A little further is the large town of Morlaix.

Open: 1 April - 30 September.

Directions

From Morlaix take the D76 north towards Térénez. Site is well signed, on right just before village. GPS: N48:39.567 W03:50.867

Charges 2007

Per person	€ 3,40 - € 4,80
child (2-7 yrs)	€ 1,00 - € 3,00
pitch	€ 4,50 - € 6,20
electricity (8A)	€ 3,00

FR29520 Camping le Cabellou Plage

Avenue du Cabellou, F-29185 Concarneau (Finistère)

Tel: 06 33 76 93 82. Email: info@le-cabellou-plage.com

Le Cabellou Plage is a recently developed site located close to Concarneau, parts of which overlook the old walled town and which has been recommended by our agent. There are 200 pitches here, some of which are occupied by mobile homes. The pitches all have electrical connections (6A) and some also offer water and drainage. The nearest beach is 500 m. distant and the attractive walled town of Concarneau is a short distance away. Le Cabellou Plage is well located for those wishing to explore Finistère, and the impressionist town of Pont Aven and the cathedral city of Quimper are both within easy reach.

Facilities	Directions
Toilet blocks include facilities for babies and disabled visitors. Washing machines and dryers. Play area. Mobile homes for rent. Off site: Supermarket, shops and restaurants in Concarneau. Riding 5 km. Tennis 3 km. Golf 15 km. Swimming pool 3 km.	Site is south of Concarneau's centre. Head south on the D783 towards Tregunc and turn right to join the Avenue Cabellou before crossing the estuary. Site is well signed from here.

Open: 12 May - 16 September.

Charges 2007

Per person	€ 5,50
child (0-12 yrs)	€ 1,50
pitch	€ 4,00
electricity (6A)	€ 3,00

Campsite **le Cabellou Plage**
South Britany

a peninsula
in Front of Concarneau

Tél : 00 33 2 98 97 37 41   www.le-cabellou-plage.com

FR35010 Camping le Bois Coudrais

F-35270 Cuguen (Ille-et-Vilaine)

Tel: 02 99 73 27 45. Email: info@vacancebretagne.com

This gem of a campsite, owned and run by a delightful couple from Jersey, is the kind of small, rural site that is becoming a rarity in France. It has 25 medium to large, well kept, grassy pitches, some divided by young shrubs, others by mature trees. They are spread over three small fields, one of which has an area set aside for ball games and is also home to a group of friendly goats and some chickens – a magnet for children. Electrical connections are possible in most areas. In the small bar, Claire is happy to prepare and serve a selection of homemade meals.

Facilities	Directions
The toilet block beside the house provides washbasins in cubicles, showers and sinks for dishwashing and laundry, plus facilities for disabled visitors. Bar with meals (May-Sept). Small heated swimming pool. Play area on grass. New sporting activites and childrens entertainments. Animal enclosure. Table tennis. Bicycle hire. Games field. Internet access. Off site: Shop in village 500 m. Combourg 5 km. Fishing 5 km. Golf and riding 15 km. Beach 20 km.	From St Malo take the N137 (in the direction of Rennes) to Combourg. Follow signs on D83 for Fougères and Mont St Michel. Site is 500 m. past Cuguen on the left, well signed. GPS: N48:27.237 W01:39.080

Open: 1 May - 30 September.

Charges 2007

Per person	€ 2,75
child (0-12 yrs)	€ 2,35
pitch	€ 9,00
electricity	€ 3,00
No credit cards.	

FR35000 Camping le Vieux Chêne

Mobile homes ▶ page 483

Baguer-Pican, F-35120 Dol-de-Bretagne (Ille-et-Vilaine)

Tel: **02 99 48 09 55**. Email: **vieux.chene@wanadoo.fr**

This attractive, family owned site is situated between Saint Malo and Mont Saint Michel. Developed in the grounds of a country farmhouse dating from 1638, its young and enthusiastic owner has created a really pleasant, traditional atmosphere. In spacious, rural surroundings it offers 199 good sized pitches on gently sloping grass, most with 10A electricity, water tap and light. They are separated by bushes and flowers, with mature trees for shade. A very attractive tenting area (without electricity) is in the orchard. There are three lakes in the grounds and centrally located leisure facilities include a restaurant with a terrace overlooking an attractive pool complex. Some entertainment is provided in high season, which is free for children.

Facilities

Three very good, unisex toilet blocks, which can be heated, include washbasins in cabins, a baby room and facilities for disabled people. Small laundry. Motorcaravan services. Shop, takeaway and restaurant (15/5-15/9). Heated swimming pool, paddling pool, slides (15/5-15/9; lifeguard July/Aug). TV room (satellite) and games room. Tennis court. Minigolf. Giant chess. Play area. Riding in July/Aug. Fishing. Off site: Supermarket in Dol 3 km. Golf 12 km. Beach 20 km.

Open: 31 March - 22 September.

Directions

Site is by the D576 Dol-de-Bretagne - Pontorson road, just east of Baguer-Pican. It can be reached from the new N176 taking exit for Dol-Est and Baguer-Pican. GPS: N48:32.972 W01:41.050

Charges 2007

Per person	€ 4,50 - € 5,75
child (under 13 yrs)	free - € 3,90
pitch with electricity	€ 10,00 - € 21,50
dog	€ 1,50

FR35060 Camping la Touesse

171, rue Ville Gehan, F-35800 Saint Lunaire (Ille-et-Vilaine)

Tel: **02 99 46 61 13**. Email: **camping.la.touesse@wanadoo.fr**

This family campsite was purpose built and has been developed since 1987 by Alain Clement who is keen to welcome more British visitors. Set just back from the coast road, 300 metres from a sandy beach, it is in a semi-residential area. It is, nevertheless, an attractive, sheltered site with a range of trees and shrubs. The 142 level, grass pitches in bays (95 for touring units) have electricity and are accessed by circular tarmac roads. The plus factor of this site, besides its proximity to Dinard, is the fine sandy beach which is sheltered – so useful in early season – and safe for children. The owners speak English.

Facilities

The central toilet block is well maintained, heated in low season with all modern facilities. Part of it may not be open outside July/Aug. Baby bath and toilet for disabled people. Dishwashing sinks. Laundry facilities. Motorcaravan service point. Shop for basics (1/4-20/9). Pleasant bar/restaurant with TV. Volleyball, table tennis and video games for children. Sauna. Off site: Buses 100 m. Sandy beach, fishing 300 m. Riding 500 m. Bicycle hire 1 km. Golf 4 km. Many amenities near.

Open: 1 April - 30 September.

Directions

From Dinard take D786 coast road towards St Lunaire; watch for site signs to the left.

Charges 2007

Per person	€ 4,00 - € 5,10
child (under 7 yrs)	€ 2,40 - € 2,90
pitch with electricity	€ 8,20 - € 9,80
dog	€ 1,50

No credit cards.

FR35050 Domaine de la Ville Huchet

Route de la Passagère, Quelmer, F-35400 Saint Malo (Ille-et-Vilaine)

Tel: 02 99 73 53 00. Email: info@villehuchet.com

Domaine de la Ville Huchet is a friendly, former municipal site which has been taken over by the owners of FR35020 Les Ormes. It is being progressively overhauled by its new owners and is a useful site on the edge of St Malo, with easy access to the ferry terminal, old town and beaches. Some road noise is audible from the St Malo bypass. Pitches are on level ground set around the old manor house at the centre of the site. Most pitches have electricity (6A), and there is shade from mature trees in some areas. Amenities include a small, well-stocked shop and a bar. The large pool has a number of water slides and is attractively landscaped.

Facilities

The sanitary blocks are old and undergoing renovation but were clean when we visited. Facilities for disabled visitors. Bar and snack bar. Shop. Aqua park with water slides. Football pitch. Bicycle hire. Animation programme in peak season (including live bands). Play area. Mobile homes to rent. Off site: Aquarium 700 m. St Malo (beaches, ferry terminal and old town) 4 km.

Open: 1 May - 15 September.

Directions

From St Malo take D301 heading south. Join D165 signed Quelmer and the site is well signed (2 km).

Charges 2007

Per person	€ 3,45 - € 5,20
child (1-7 yrs)	€ 2,30 - € 3,10
pitch	€ 9,00 - € 12,40
electricity	€ 3,65 - € 4,40

FR35020 Castel Camping le Domaine des Ormes

Epiniac, F-35120 Dol-de-Bretagne (Ille-et-Vilaine)

Tel: 02 99 73 53 00. Email: info@lesormes.com

This impressive site is in the northern part of Brittany, about 30 km. from the old town of Saint Malo, in the grounds of the Château des Ormes. In an estate of wooded parkland and lakes it has a pleasant atmosphere, busy in high season but peaceful at other times, with a wide range of facilities. The 800 pitches are divided into a series of different sections, each with its own distinctive character and offering a choice of terrain – flat or gently sloping, wooded or open. Only 150 pitches, all with electricity, are used for touring units and there is a large variety of other accommodation available to rent.

Facilities

The toilet blocks are of fair standard, including washbasins in cabins and ample facilities for disabled people. Motorcaravan services. Shop, bar, restaurant, pizzeria and takeaway. Games room, bar and disco. Two traditional heated swimming pools and Aqua park. Adventure play area. Golf. Bicycle hire. Fishing. Equestrian centre with riding. Minigolf. Two tennis courts. Sports ground with volleyball, etc. Paintball, Archery. Cricket club.

Open: 19 May - 9 September, with all services.

Directions

Access road leads off main D795 about 7 km. south of Dol-de-Bretagne, north of Combourg.

Charges 2007

Per person	€ 4,25 - € 7,25
child (under 13 yrs)	free - € 4,00
pitch incl. vehicle	€ 17,75 - € 29,25
electricity 3/6A	€ 3,50 - € 4,30
water and drainage	€ 1,60 - € 2,00
Less 10% outside July/Aug.	

FR35040 Camping le P'tit Bois

Saint Malo, F-35430 Saint Jouan des Guerets (Ille-et-Vilaine)

Tel: **02 99 21 14 30**. Email: **camping.ptitbois@wanadoo.fr**

On the outskirts of Saint Malo, this neat, family oriented site is very popular with British visitors, being ideal for one night stops or for longer stays in this interesting area. Le P'tit Bois provides 274 large level pitches with 114 for touring units. In two main areas, either side of the entrance lane, these are divided into groups by mature hedges and trees, separated by shrubs and flowers and with access from tarmac roads. Nearly all have electrical hook-ups and over half have water taps. Behind reception, an attractive, sheltered terraced area around the complex of heated indoor and outdoor pools provides a focus during the day along with a bar and snack bar. There are site-owned mobile homes and chalets but this does mean that the facilities are open over a long season (if only for limited hours).

Facilities

Two fully equipped toilet blocks, include washbasins in cabins. Baby baths. Laundry facilities. Simple facilities for disabled people. Motorcaravan service point. Small shop (from 5/4). Bar with entertainment in July-Aug. Snack bar with takeaway (from 5/4). TV room. Games rooms. Heated swimming pool, paddling pool and two water slides (from 15/5). Heated indoor pool with Turkish Baths and Jacuzzi (from 5/4). Playground. Multisports court. Tennis court, minigolf. Charcoal barbecues not permitted. Off site: Beach, fishing 1.5 km. Buses 2 km. Bicycle hire or riding 5 km. Golf 15 km.

Open: 5 April - 13 September.

Directions

St Jouan is west off the St Malo - Rennes road (N137) just outside St Malo. Site is signed from the N137 (exit second exit St Jouan on the D4). GPS: N48:36.579 W01:59.270

Charges 2008

Per person	€ 5,00 - € 8,00
child (under 7 yrs)	€ 3,00 - € 6,50
pitch and car	€ 8,00 - € 19,00
electricity (10A)	€ 4,00
dog	€ 4,00 - € 6,00

Camping ★★★★
Le P'tit Bois
St Malo
35430 St Jouan des Guérêts

www.ptitbois.com

Saint Malo *City of the sea*

Booking :
Tel. 33 (0)2 99 21 14 30
Fax 33 (0)2 99 81 74 14
E-mail : camping.ptitbois@wanadoo.fr

FR35070 Camping Longchamp

Boulevard de Saint Cast, F-35800 Saint Lunaire (Ille-et-Vilaine)

Tel: **02 99 46 33 98**. Email: **contact@camping-longchamp.com**

Michel Roult is justifiably proud of his campsite which lies on the 'Emerald Coast', just 100 m. from a magnificent sandy beach. Set in a wooded area and divided into three sections, this site feels like being in a large landscaped garden. Pitches are large and well kept with 240 for touring. Some hedging and shade is provided by Cypress trees and 140 have electricity. The restaurant on site has a cosy atmosphere, an extensive menu and is run by a 'Michelin' recommended chef. Mr Roult's aim is to keep the site simple and peaceful and as a result many families return year after year.

Facilities

Two very clean toilet blocks with washbasins in cabins and open-style and large showers. Covered dishwashing area. Laundry facilities. Restaurant, bar and takeaway. Small shop. Games room and TV. Play area with bouncy castle (Juy/Aug). Minigolf and tennis. Boules. Some entertainment in high season. Torches useful. Off site: Golf 2 km. Riding 4 km. Bicycle hire 6 km.

Open: Easter - 10 September.

Directions

Leave St Maloon D301 and follow signs for Dinard. Turn west onto D168. Keep west onto D603 and in approx. 3 km. turn north on D503 (St Lunaire). Site signed from village. GPS: N48:31.01 W02:07.15

Charges guide

Per person	€ 5,20
child (under 7 yrs)	€ 3,00
pitch	€ 5,80
electricity (4/10A)	€ 2,70 - € 3,90
dog	€ 1,30

FR35080 Domaine du Logis

Le Logis, F-35190 La Chapelle-aux-Filtzméens (Ille-et-Vilaine)

Tel: **02 99 45 25 45**. Email: **domainedulogis@wanadoo.fr**

This is an attractive rural site, set in the grounds of an old château. The site's facilities are housed in converted barns and farm buildings, which although old, are well maintained and equipped. There are a total of 180 pitches, 90 of which are for touring. The grass pitches are level, of a generous size and divided by mature hedges and trees. All have 10A electricity connections. This site would appeal to most age groups with plenty to offer the active including a new fitness room with a good range of modern equipment or for those who prefer to relax, perhaps a quiet days fishing beside the lake. The site is well places for excursions to Mont Saint Michel, Dinard and Dinan.

Facilities

Two comfortable toilet blocks with washbasins and showers. Toilet and shower for disabled visitors. Dishwashing and laundry facilities. Shop in reception. Bar with TV (all season). Restaurant and takeaway (28/6-31/8). Outdoor swimming pool (15/5). Fitness and games rooms. BMX circuit. Bicycle hire. Lake fishing. Unfenced play areas. Children's club (high season). Internet access. Certain breeds of dogs are not accepted. Off site: Boating on the canal. Riding 10 km.

Open: 1 April - 27 October.

Directions

Turn south off N176 onto D795 signed Dol-de-Bretagne. Continue to Combourg and then take D13 to La-Chapelle-aux-Filtsmeens. Continue for 2 km. Site on right. GPS: N48:23.360 W01:50.080

Charges 2008

Per person	€ 4,50 - € 5,00
child (3-12 yrs)	€ 2,50 - € 3,50
pitch	€ 6,50 - € 18,00
electricity (10A)	€ 4,00

FR35090 Camping Pont de Laurin

La Vallée Gatorge, F-35800 Saint Briac-sur-Mer (Ille-et-Vilaine)

Tel: **02 99 88 34 64**. Email: **lepontlaurin@ouest-camping.com**

This site is within an urban area and gently slopes down to a tidal inlet. Although some of the buildings on site which house the facilities would benefit from some refurbishment, pitches are well cared for. There are 70 grass pitches available for touring out of a total of 167. They are small, hedged and mostly sloping with little shade (not suitable for large units). 6A electricity is available for which long leads may be required. A quiet and simple site with very limited facilities and activities available. There is access to a coastal path via a gate at the rear of the site.

Facilities

Single sanitary block with a mix of British and Turkish style toilets (no seats or paper). Washbasins and pre-set showers. Facilities for disabled visitors. Washing machine and dryer. Bread and ice from reception. Minigolf. Table tennis. Unfenced play area. Off site: Sports complex adjacent. Fishing 500 m. Beach 1 km. Golf 3 km.

Open: Easter - 30 September.

Directions

Turn north off N176 to Dinard, Then west on to D168. In approx. 1 km. turn right onto D603 signed Saint Lunaire. In approx. 3 km. turn left on to D3. Site on the right.

Charges 2007

Per person	€ 4,00
child (under 7 yrs)	€ 2,00
pitch	€ 6,80
electricity (6A)	€ 3,60

FR44040 Castel Camping le Parc Sainte-Brigitte

Domaine de Bréhet, F-44420 La Turballe (Loire-Atlantique)

Tel: **02 40 24 88 91**. Email: **saintebrigitte@wanadoo.fr**

Le Parc Sainte-Brigitte is a well established site in the attractive grounds of a manor house, three kilometres from the beaches. It is a spacious site with 150 good pitches, 110 with electricity, water and drainage. Some are arranged in a circular, park-like setting near the entrance, others are in wooded areas under tall trees and the remainder are on more open grass in an unmarked area near the pool. This is a quiet place to stay outside the main season, whilst in high season, it can become very busy. In high season it is mainly used by families with its full share of British visitors. One can walk around many of the areas of the estate not used for camping; there are farm animals to see and a fishing lake is very popular.

Facilities

The main toilet block, supplemented by a second block, is of good quality. They include washbasins in cabins and two bathrooms. Laundry facilities and lines provided. Motorcaravan services. Small shop. Pleasant restaurant/bar with takeaway (both 15/5-15/9). Heated swimming pool with retractable roof and paddling pool. Playground. Bicycle hire. Boules, volleyball, pool and 'baby-foot'. TV room and traditional 'salle de reunion'. Fishing. Off site: Riding 2 km. Nearest beach 2.5 km. Golf 15 km.

Open: 1 April - 1 October.

Directions

Entrance is off the busy La Turballe-Guérande D99 road, 3 km. east of La Turballe. A one-way system operates – in one lane, out via another.

Charges 2008

Per person	€ 6,00
child (under 7 yrs)	€ 4,90
pitch	€ 6,90
with water and electricity	€ 13,60
car	€ 3,20

No credit cards.

HEATED SWIMMING POOL

Close to the fishing village of LaTurballe and neighbouring beaches. 10 km from the well-known resort of La Baule. The charm of the countryside with the pleasures of the seaside. Sanitary facilities as in a first class hotel. Heated and covered swimming pool (approximately 200 m^2 water and 200 m^2 covered terrace around it). The cover can be retracted during warm weather. Children's pool.

campingsaintebrigitte@wanadoo.fr
www.campingsaintebrigitte.com

FR44020 Camping Municipal du Moulin

Route de Nantes, F-44190 Clisson (Loire-Atlantique)

Tel: **02 40 54 44 48**

This good value, small site is conveniently located on one of the main north - south routes on the edge of the interesting old town of Clisson. A typical municipal site, it is useful for short stays. There are 45 good sized, marked and level pitches with electricity and divided by hedges and trees giving a good degree of privacy and some shade. There is also an unmarked area for small tents. A barbecue and camp fire area is to the rear of the site above the river where one can fish or canoe (via a steep path). The warden lives on site in high season. The attractive old town is within walking distance.

Facilities

The fully equipped toilet block, cleaned each afternoon, includes some washbasins in cabins and others in a separate large room, with hot and cold water. Unit for disabled visitors. Dishwashing and laundry facilities. Bread delivered daily. Table tennis, volleyball, and small playground. No double axle or commercial vehicles accepted. Off site: Supermarket with cheap fuel just across the road. Bicycle hire, riding 5 km. Sailing 15 km. Golf 30 km.

Open: Mid April - mid October.

Directions

From N249 Nantes - Cholet road, take exit for Vallet and Clisson and D763 south for 7 km. then fork right towards Clisson town centre. At roundabout after passing Leclerc supermarket on your right take second exit (into site). GPS: N47:05.742 W01:16.965

Charges 2007

Per unit incl. 1 person and electricity	€ 7,77 - € 8,20
extra person	€ 2,42 - € 2,55
child (0-7 yrs)	€ 1,61 - € 1,70

No credit cards.

FR44050 Camping les Ecureuils

24 avenue Gilbert Burlot, F-44760 La Bernerie en Retz (Loire-Atlantique)

Tel: 02 40 82 76 95. Email: camping.les-ecureuils@wanadoo.fr

Just 350 metres from both the sea and the centre of the little town of La Bernerie, Les Ecureuils is a family run site. The sandy beach here is great for children; swimming is restricted to high tide, since the sea goes out a long way, but at low tide you can join the locals in collecting shellfish from the rocks. The site has 167 touring pitches, all with electricity (10A) close by and 19 with their own water tap and drain. There are also 80 mobile homes and chalets for rent and a further 70 privately owned. The site prides itself in its pool complex with heated leisure, swimming and paddling pools; water slides and a flume are only open when supervised in July and August. The fishing port of Pornic is worth a visit, as is the Ile de Noirmoutier, just 35 kilometres south.

Facilities

Four toilet blocks are in traditional French style; some have controllable showers and washbasins in cubicles. Facilities for disabled visitors are not all easily accessible. Very basic baby room. All is kept fairly clean but lacking attention to detail. Bar with terrace - also sells bread (15/6-31/8). Snack bar and takeaway (July/Aug). Swimming pools (15/5-15/9). Playground. Off site: Shops, restaurants and bars 350 m. Also beach, fishing, sailing and boat launching. Golf, riding and bicycle hire 6 km.

Open: 1 May - 15 September.

Directions

La Bernerie-en-Retz is 5 km. south of Pornic and 26 km. south of the Saint Nazaire bridge. From the D213/D13 (St Nazaire - Noirmoutier) turn west on D66 to La Bernerie. Site is signed to right by railway station before reaching town. GPS: N47:05.070 W02:02.200

Charges 2008

Per unit incl. 2 persons	€ 14,00 - € 29,00
extra person	€ 4,00 - € 6,50
child (2-10 yrs)	€ 3,00 - € 5,00
electricity (10A)	€ 4,00

CAMPING LES ECUREUILS***

24, Avenue Gilbert Burlot - 44760 La Bernerie-en-Retz
Tel: 0033(0) 240 82 76 95 - Fax: 0033(0) 240 64 79 52
E-mail: camping.les-ecureuils@wanadoo.fr - Internet: www.camping-les-ecureuils.com

FR44100 Sunêlia le Patisseau

Mobile homes ▶ page 484

29 rue du Patisseau, F-44210 Pornic (Loire-Atlantique)

Tel: 02 40 82 10 39. Email: contact@lepatisseau.com

Le Patisseau is situated in the countryside just a short drive from the fishing village of Pornic. It is a relaxed site with a large number of mobile homes and chalets, and popular with young families and teenagers. The 115 touring pitches all with electrical connections (6A), are divided between the attractive 'forest' area with plenty of shade from mature trees and the more open 'prairie' area some are on a slight slope and access to others might br tricky for lager units. A railway runs along the bottom half of the site with trains several times a day, (but none overnight) and the noise is minimal. The Morice family works very hard to maintain a friendly atmosphere.

Facilities

The modern heated toilet block is very spacious and well fitted. Good facilities for disabled visitors and babies. Laundry rooms. Shop (15/5-8/9). Bar, restaurant and takeaway (1/7-31/9). Indoor heated pool with sauna, jacuzzi and spa (all season). Small heated outdoor pools and water slides (15/5-3/9). Play area. Multisport court. Bicycle hire. Off site: Fishing and beach 2.5 km.

Open: 8 April - 6 November.

Directions

Pornic is 19 km. south of the St Nazaire bridge. Access to site is at junction of D751 Nantes - Pornic road with the D213 St Nazaire - Noirmoutier 'Route Bleue'. Avoid Pornic town centre. GPS: N47:07.183 W02:04.397

Charges 2007

Per unit incl. 2 persons and electricity (6A)	€ 24,00 - € 39,00
extra person	€ 3,00 - € 7,00
child (1-7 yrs)	€ 2,00 - € 5,00
animal	€ 5,00

51

FR44070 Camping Parc du Guibel

Route de Kerdrien, F-44420 Piriac-sur-Mer (Loire-Atlantique)

Tel: **02 40 23 52 67**. Email: **camping@parcduguibel.com**

This very large site, situated in an extensive wood, describes itself as 'un Hôtel de Plein Air' and prides itself on its spaciousness and its trees. A keen birdwatcher told the owner that he had seen 50 different species of birds. There are 450 pitches of which 307 are for touring scattered among the 14 hectares of woodland, mainly shaded but some in clearings. One section at the top of the site across a minor road is always quiet and peaceful. 110 pitches have electricity (3, 6 or 10A) of which 67 also have water tap and drainage. There are also 134 mobile homes and chalets for rent. A long room houses the bar, snack bar with takeaway and a small restaurant together with an electronic games area. A small shop sells bread and a few basics. There is a heated swimming pool and two paddling pools linked by a small water slide. A programme of activities and entertainment for children and adults is olrganised in high season. The sea is just over a kilometre away and nearby are the salt-marshes producing the famous 'Sel de Guérande'.

Facilities

Five sanitary blocks: the newest is smart and well equipped, with controllable showers and washbasins. Two others have been partially refurbished to the same standards. The others are rather old-fashioned, with preset showers and washbasins in cubicles. Facilities for disabled visitors. Baby room. Dishwashing and laundry facilities. Motorcaravan service point. Heated swimming and paddling pools (1/5-15/9). Bar, snack bar, takeaway and restaurant (July-Aug only). Off site: Riding 400 m. Fishing 1 km. Beach 1.2 km. Sailing 3.5 km. Golf 18 km.

Open: 1 April - 30 September.

Directions

On N165 from Vannes, leave at exit 15 towards La Roche Bernard, turn left to join D774 towards La Baule. 8 km. after Herbignac, turn right on D52 to St Molt and Mesquer towards Piriac. Do not take the coast road but turn left on D52. Site signed on right in 3 km. GPS: N47:23.177 W02:30.604

Charges 2007

Per person	€ 3,00 - € 4,95
child (under 7 yrs)	€ 2,00 - € 3,30
pitch	€ 3,00 - € 4,95
electricity (3-10A)	€ 2,85 - € 4,25

CAMPING CARAVANING ★★★★
Rental of mobiles homes and chalets

14 ha. wooded park
450 pitches

Route de Kerdrien - 44420 PIRIAC SUR MER
Tél. 02 40 23 52 67 - Fax 02 40 15 50 24
E-mail : camping@parcduguibel.com
www.parcduguibel.com

FR44150 Camping la Tabardière

F-44770 La Plaine-sur-Mer (Loire-Atlantique)

Tel: **02 40 21 58 83**. Email: **info@camping-la-tabardiere.com**

Owned and managed by the Barre family, this campsite lies next to the family farm. Pleasant, peaceful and immaculate, it will suit those who want to enjoy the local coast and towns but return to an 'oasis' for relaxation. It still, however, provides activities and fun for those with energy remaining. The pitches are mostly terraced and care needs to be taken in manoeuvring caravans into position – although the effort is well worth it. Pitches have access to electricity and water taps are conveniently situated. The site is probably not suitable for wheelchairs. A 'Sites et Paysages' member.

Facilities

Two good, clean toilet blocks are well equipped and include laundry facilities. Motorcaravan service point. Bar. Shop. Snacks and takeaway. Good sized covered swimming pool, paddling pool and slides (supervised). Playground. Minigolf. Table tennis. Volleyball and basketball. Half size tennis courts. Boules. Overnight area for motorcaravans (€ 13 per night). Off site: Beach 3 km. Sea fishing, golf, riding all 5 km.

Open: 1 April - 30 September.

Directions

Site is well signed, situated inland off the D13 Pornic - La Plaine sur Mer road. GPS: N47:08.280 W02:09.110

Charges 2008

Per unit incl. 2 persons	€ 13,20 - € 25,90
extra person	€ 3,60 - € 6,20
child (2-9 yrs)	€ 2,70 - € 4,20
electricity (3/8A)	€ 3,10 - € 4,60
Camping Cheques accepted.	

FR44090 Kawan Village du Deffay

Mobile homes ▶ page 484

B.P. 18 Le Deffay, Ste Reine de Bretagne, F-44160 Pontchâteau (Loire-Atlantique)
Tel: **02 40 88 00 57**. Email: **campingdudeffay@wanadoo.fr**

A family managed site, Château du Deffay is a refreshing departure from the usual formula in that it is not over organised or supervised and has no tour operator units. The 142 good sized, fairly level pitches have pleasant views and are either on open grass, on shallow terraces divided by hedges, or informally arranged in a central, slightly sloping wooded area. Most have electricity. The facilities are located within the old courtyard area of the smaller château (that dates from before 1400). With the temptation of free pedaloes and the fairly deep, unfenced lake, parents should ensure that children are supervised. The landscape is natural right down to the molehills, and the site blends well with the rural environment of the estate, lake and farmland which surround it. For these reasons it is enjoyed by many. The larger château (built 1880) and another lake stand away from this area providing pleasant walking. The reception has been built separately to contain the camping area. Alpine type chalets overlook the lake and fit in well with the environment. The site is close to the Brière Regional Park, the Guérande Peninsula, and La Baule with its magnificent beach (20 km).

Facilities

The main toilet block could do with some updating but is well equipped including washbasins in cabins, provision for disabled people and a baby bathroom. Laundry facilities. Maintenance can be variable and hot water can take time to reach temperature in low season. Shop, bar, small restaurant with takeaway and solar heated swimming pool and paddling pool (all 15/5-15/9). Play area. TV. Animation in season including children's miniclub. Torches useful. Off site: Golf and riding 5 km.

Open: 1 May - 30 September.

Directions

Site is signed from D33 Pontchâteau - Herbignac road near Ste Reine. Also signed from the D773 and N165. GPS: N47:26.270 W02:09.350

Charges 2007

Per person	€ 3,10 - € 5,00
child (2-12 yrs)	€ 2,10 - € 3,40
pitch	€ 7,40 - € 11,30
with electricity (6A)	€ 10,70 - € 15,20
with 3 services	€ 12,50 - € 17,20

Camping Cheques accepted.

Check real time availability and at-the-gate prices...
www.alanrogers.com

FR44130 Camping l'Hermitage

36 avenue du Paradis, F-44290 Guémené-Penfao (Loire-Atlantique)

Tel: **02 40 79 23 48**. Email: **contact@campinglhermitage.com**

L'Hermitage is a pretty wooded site set in the Vallée du Don and would be useful for en-route stops or for longer stays. The enthusiastic staff, even though their English is a little limited, provide a warm welcome and maintain this reasonably priced site to a good standard. There are 110 pitches of which 80 are a good size for touring and camping. Some are formally arranged on open, level grass pitches, whereas others are informal amongst light woodland. Electricity (6A) is available to all (a long lead may be useful). Both Nantes and Rennes are 30 minutes away, La Baule with its beaches is 40 minutes.

Facilities

A clean and well serviced toilet block includes some washbasins in cabins with warm water. Laundry and dishwashing sinks under cover (cold water but a hot tap is provided). Smallish pool, paddling pool and slide, nicely maintained and carefully fenced. Small play area. Table tennis. Petanque. Games room with video games. Off site: Leisure complex with indoor pool opposite. Fishing 500 m. Village 1 km. for all facilities. Riding 2 km. Many walking trails.

Open: 1 April - 31 October.

Directions

Exit N137 at Derval (signed Châteaubriant) but take D775 for Redon. Guémené-Penfao is about 13 km. Watch for site signs before village centre. Site is on the outskirts in a semi-residential area to the northeast. GPS: N47:37.330 W01:49.060

Charges 2007

Per unit incl. 2 persons	€ 12,00
extra person	€ 3,50
child (under 7 yrs)	€ 2,50
electricity	€ 2,90

FR44170 Camping les Ajoncs d'Or

Chemin du Rocher, F-44500 La Baule (Loire-Atlantique)

Tel: **02 40 60 33 29**. Email: **contact@ajoncs.com**

This site is situated in pine woods, 1.5 km. on the inland side of La Baule and its beautiful bay. A well maintained, natural woodland setting provides a wide variety of pitch types (just over 200), some level and bordered with hedges and tall trees to provide shade and many others that maintain the natural characteristics of the woodland. Most pitches have electricity and water nearby and are usually of a larger size. A central building provides a shop and open friendly bar that serve snacks and takeaways. The English speaking Bazillails family (the owners) who live on site will welcome you to their campsite.

Facilities

Two good quality sanitary blocks are clean and well maintained providing plenty of facilities including a baby room. Washing machines and dryers. Shop and bar (July/Aug). Snack bar (July/Aug). Good size swimming pool and paddling pool (1/6-5/9). Sports and playground areas. Bicycle hire. Reception with security barrier (closed 22.30 - 07.30 hrs). Off site: Beach 1.5 km. Fishing and riding 1.5 km. Golf 3 km.

Open: 1 April - 30 September.

Directions

From N171 take exit for La Baule les Pins. Follow signs for 'La Baule Centre', then left at roundabout in front of Champion supermarket and follow site signs. GPS: N47:17.370 W02:22.420

Charges 2007

Per unit incl. 2 persons	€ 20,00
with electricity	€ 23,00
with water and drainage	€ 25,00
extra person	€ 6,00

FR44160 Camping Armor-Héol

Route de Guérande, F-44420 Piriac-sur-Mer (Loire-Atlantique)

Tel: 02 40 23 57 80. Email: armor.heol@wanadoo.fr

Situated only 700 metres from Piriac town and the beach, and 14 km. from Guérande, this campsite makes an ideal base for a beach holiday or for touring this beautiful corner of southern Brittany. There are 97 good sized level pitches all with 5A electricity and a further 164 are occupied by mobiles and chalets, half privately-owned, the rest available for rent. As the site is attractively laid out with plenty of trees and hedges, these do not feel intrusive. With an impressive leisure complex and programme of activities and entertainment in high season, the site can be very lively, but it is very well run and becomes quiet after 23.00 hrs. With considerable recent investment, the site now offers excellent facilities for visitors of all ages. This is a friendly site with English speaking reception and good amenities.

Facilities

Two clean and well maintained toilet blocks include washbasins in cabins, baby rooms, facilities for disabled visitors and family rooms with shower, basin and toilet (free except July/Aug when they are for hire). At busy times facilities may be under pressure. Washing machines and dryers. Bar, takeaway and restaurant (1/6-15/9). Indoor pool with water movement. Outdoor heated pools and water slides (1/6-15/9). Multisports area, tennis, volleyball. Playground. Fitness rooms. Off site: Beach and town, fishing, boat launching, surfing and bicycle hire 700 m. Sailing 1 km. Golf and riding 2 km.

Open: 5 April - 21 September.

Directions

Piriac is 90 km. west of Nantes and 11 km. northwest of Guérande. Bypass Guérande and take D99 then D333 signed Piriac sur Mer. Site on left before Piriac. GPS: N47:22.481 W02:32.131

Charges 2008

Per unit incl. 2 persons	€ 16,00 - € 32,00
extra person	€ 4,00 - € 8,00
child (under 4 yrs)	€ 2,50 - € 4,60
electricity	€ 3,50
animal	€ 3,00 - € 4,50

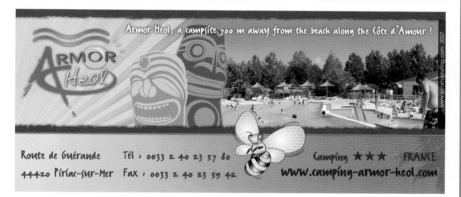

Armor Heol, a campsite 700 m away from the beach along the Côte d'Amour !

Route de Guérande 44420 Piriac-sur-Mer Tél : 0033 2 40 23 57 80 Fax : 0033 2 40 23 59 42 Camping ★★★ FRANCE www.camping-armor-heol.com

FR44240 Camping le Ranch

Les Hautes Raillères, F-44770 La Plaine-sur-Mer (Loire-Atlantique)

Tel: 02 40 21 52 62. Email: info@camping-le-ranch.com

This is a pleasant, family-run campsite with a friendly atmosphere, close to the beaches of the 'Jade Coast' between Pornic and St Brévin-les-Pins, yet not right on the seashore. The 99 touring pitches all have access to electricity (6A) although on some a long cable may be required; these occupy the central part of the site, with the fringe areas taken up by mobile homes and chalets, 21 for rent and 74 privately-owned (although 30 of these are also available for rent in high season). The rows of pitches are separated by well-kept hedges, and small trees mark the corners of most plots.

Facilities

The central sanitary block has pre-set showers, facilities for disabled visitors, washbasins in cubicles, a fairly basic baby room, and dishwashing and laundry sinks. Further small toilet block. Pool open 1/5-30/9 (heated 15/6-15/9). Bar has small shop selling bread, basics and camping gaz. Good takeaway (July - Aug). Activities for children and entertainment and sports events for families in high season. Off site: Beach 800 m. Bicycle hire 1.5 km. Boat launching 3 km. Fishing 5 km. Golf, riding and sailing 3 km.

Open: 1 April - 30 September.

Directions

La Plaine-sur-Mer is 16 km. south of the St Nazaire bridge. Site is on D96 5 km. northeast of the town. From D213 (Route Bleue) just south of St Michel-Chef-Chef turn southwest on D96 towards La Plaine. Site on left in about 2 km. GPS: N47:09.313 W02:09.894

Charges 2007

Per unit incl. 2 persons	€ 12,50 - € 22,00
extra person (over 7 yrs)	€ 3,00 - € 4,80
child (under 7 yrs)	€ 2,00 - € 3,00
electricity	€ 3,70

FR44180 Camping de la Boutinardière

Mobile homes ▶ page 484

Rue de la Plage de la Boutinardière, F-44210 Pornic (Loire-Atlantique)

Tel: **02 40 82 05 68**. Email: **info@laboutinardiere.com**

This is truly a holiday site to suit all the family whatever their age, just 200 m. from the beach. It has 250 individual good sized pitches, 100-120 sq.m. in size, many bordered by three metre high, well maintained hedges for shade and privacy. All pitches have electricity available. It is a family owned site and English is spoken by the helpful, obliging reception staff. Beside reception is the excellent site shop and across the road is a complex of indoor and outdoor pools, paddling pool and a twin toboggan water slide. On site there are sports and entertainment areas. Facing the water complex, the bar, restaurant and terraces are new and serve excellent food, be it a snack or in the restaurant or perhaps a takeaway. This campsite has it all – 2 km from the beautiful harbour town of Pornic and 200 m. from the sea, together with the very best of amenities and facilities.

Facilities

Toilet facilities are in three good blocks, one large and centrally situated and two supporting blocks. Washbasins are in cabins, dishwashing is under cover. Laundry facilities. Shop (15/6-15/9). New complex of bar, restaurant, terraces (1/4-30/9). Three heated pools, one indoor (1/4-15/9), a paddling pool and slides (15/5-22/9). Games room. Playground. Minigolf. Off site: Sandy cove 200 m. Golf, riding, sea fishing, restaurants, fishing harbour, sailing and windsurfing, all within 5 km.

Open: 1 April - 30 September.

Directions

From north or south on D213, take Nantes D751 exit. At roundabout (with McDonalds) take D13 signed Bemarie-eb-Retz. After 4 km. site is signed to right. Note: do NOT exit for Pomic Ouest or Centre. GPS: N47:05.490 W02:03.080

Charges 2007

Per unit incl. 2 persons	€ 14,00 - € 31,00
extra person	€ 3,00 - € 6,00
child (under 8 yrs)	€ 2,00 - € 4,50
electricity (6-10A)	€ 3,50 - € 5,00

FR44210 Camping de l'Océan

Mobile homes ▶ page 485

F-44490 Le Croisic (Loire-Atlantique)

Tel: **02 40 23 07 69**. Email: **camping-ocean@wanadoo.fr**

Camping de l'Océan is situated on the Le Croisic peninsula, an attractive part of the Brittany coastline. Out of a total of 400 pitches, just 80 are available for tourers with the remainder being taken by mobile homes either privately owned or for rent. Pitches are small, level and were rather worn when we visited. The leisure facilities however, which include a restaurant, bar and pool complex are of an excellent standard. This site, probably more suitable for families with young teenagers, can be very lively in high season with a wealth of activities and entertainment for all ages.

Facilities

Three toilet blocks are adequate although a little tired and include facilities for disabled visitors. Laundry facilities. Restaurant and bar. Takeaway. Shop. Motorcaravan service point. Swimming pool complex with indoor and outdoor pools and paddling pool. Tennis. Off site: Le Croisic for shops, bars and restaurants. Sailing, riding and golf.

Open: 9 April - 30 September.

Directions

From Le Pouliguen, travel west on N171 to Le Croisic. Site is well signed from here and found in approx. 1.5 km. GPS: N47:17.520 W02:32.090

Charges 2007

Per unit incl 2 persons and electricity (6A)	€ 16,50 - € 36,50
extra person	€ 3,00 - € 7,00

FR44220 Parc de Léveno

Mobile homes ▶ page 485

Route de Sandun, F-44350 Guérande (Loire-Atlantique)

Tel: **02 40 24 79 30**. Email: **domaine.leveno@wanadoo.fr**

There have been many changes to this extensive site over the past three years and considerable investment has been made to provide some excellent new facilities. The number of mobile homes and chalets has increased, leaving just 47 touring pitches. However, these are mainly grouped at the far end where there is more the feel of a real French campsite. Pitches are divided by hedges and trees which offer good shade and all have electricity (10A). Access is tricky to some and the site is not recommended for larger units. Twin axle caravans and American motorhomes are not accepted.

Facilities

Main refurbished toilet block offers pre-set showers, washbasins in cubicles and facilities for disabled visitors. Laundry facilities. Small shop selling basics and takeaway snacks. Restaurant and bar (all July/Aug). Indoor pool. Heated outdoor pool complex (15/5-15/9). Fitness room. Play area. Programme of activities and events (high season). Off site: Large hypermarket 1 km. Fishing 2 km. Beach, golf and riding all 5 km. Boat launching 7 km.

Open: 5 April - 30 September.

Directions

Site is less than 3 km. from the centre of Guérande. From D774 and from D99/N171 take D99E Guérande by-pass. Turn east following signs for Villejames and Leclerc Hypermarket and continue on D247 to site on right. GPS: N47:19.987 W02:23.478

Charges 2007

Per unit incl. 2 persons, electricity and water	€ 10,80 - € 18,00
extra person	€ 3,60 - € 6,00

mpsites with water park
the lovely region of south Brittany...

3 covered swimming pools with heated water and air.

www.Aquaticamp.com

r park l'Océan

NEW water park
in 2008 La Boutinardière

* Espace aquatique de Léveno

le Croisic

Pornic

la Brière

la Baule

Guérande

Domaine
de
éveno
mping - Locations
★★★★

La Boutinardière
Camping Village
★★★

l'Ocean
Camping Village ★★★

km from la Baule !
camping-leveno.com
de Sandun
CE
GUÉRANDE
00 33 2 40 24 79 30
00 33 2 40 62 01 23

only 200 m from the beach !
www.camping-boutinardiere.com
23, rue de la plage de la Boutinardière
44210 PORNIC
FRANCE
Tel. : 00 33 2 40 82 05 68
Fax : 00 33 2 40 82 49 01

Camping
Qualité
Clé
Airotel

only 150 m from the beach !
www.camping-ocean.com
15, route Maison Rouge - B.P. 15
44490 LE CROISIC
FRANCE
Tel. : 00 33 2 40 23 07 69
Fax : 00 33 2 40 15 70 63

Camping
Qualité

FR44190 Camping le Fief

Mobile homes ▶ page 485

57 chemin du Fief, F-44250 Saint Brévin-les-Pins (Loire-Atlantique)

Tel: **02 40 27 23 86**. Email: **camping@lefief.com**

If you are a family with young children or lively teenagers, this could be the campsite for you. Le Fief is a well established site only 800 metres from sandy beaches on the southern Brittany coast. It has a magnificent 'aqua park' with outdoor and covered swimming pools, paddling pools, slides, river rapids, fountains, jets and more. The site has 220 pitches for touring units (out of 413). Whilst these all have electricity (5A), they vary in size and many are worn and may be untidy. There are also 143 mobile homes and chalets to rent and 55 privately owned units. This is a lively site in high season with a variety of entertainment and organised activity for all ages. This ranges from a miniclub for 5-12 year olds, to 'Tonic Days' with aquagym, jogging and sports competitions, and to evening events which include karaoke, themed dinners and cabaret. There are plenty of sporting facilities for active youngsters.

Facilities

One excellent new toilet block and three others of a lower standard. Laundry facilities. Shop (15/5-15/9). Bar, restaurant and takeaway (15/4-15/9) with terrace overlooking the pool complex. Outdoor pools, etc. (15/5-15/9). Covered pool (all season). Play area. Tennis. Volleyball. Basketball. Pétanque. Table tennis. Archery. Games room. Internet access. Organised entertainment and activities (July/Aug). Off site: Beach, bicycle hire 800 m. Bus stop 1 km. Riding 1 km. Golf 15 km. Planète Sauvage safari park.

Open: 1 April - 15 October.

Directions

From the St Nazaire bridge take the fourth exit from the D213 signed St Brévin - L'Océan. Continue over first roundabout and bear right at the second to join Chemin du Fief. The site is on the right, well signed.

Charges 2007

Per pitch incl. 2 persons	€ 17,00 - € 37,00
extra person	€ 5,00 - € 9,00
child (0-7 yrs)	€ 2,50 - € 4,50
electricity	€ 5,00 - € 6,00
dog	€ 2,00 - € 5,00

FR44270 Camping le Château du Petit Bois

F-44420 Mesquer (Loire-Atlantique)

Tel: **02 40 42 68 77**. Email: **info@campingdupetitbois.com**

This pleasant campsite is located in the wooded grounds of a small château. The 125 good-sized touring pitches, all with electricity (3 or 6A) have varying degrees of shade and a few are in the open for those who like a sunny plot. Reception is housed in the converted outbuildings of the château, and is welcoming and informative. The Marin family and their staff are friendly and helpful, and the site is very well run. The sea is just over a kilometre away, as is the village of Mesquer and nearby are the salt marshes which produce the famous Sel de Guérande. On site there is an attractive swimming pool complex: a heated main pool and paddling pool, and a separate pool with two good water slides which is only open when the pool is supervised.

Facilities

The main sanitary block has pre-set showers and open style washbasins together with some cubicles with controllable shower and a washbasin. Dishwashing and laundry facilities. Facilities for disabled visitors. Combined bar, snack bar and takeaway (with TV, pool table and 'babyfoot'). Small shop selling bread and basics (July/Aug). Pool complex with heated main pool and paddling pool and pool with water slides (only open when supervised). Programme of activities (all July/Aug). Off site: Fishing, bicycle hire, riding and sailing all nearby. Golf 12 km.

Open: 1 April - 30 October.

Directions

Mesquer is 80 km. northwest of Nantes and 16 km. north of La Baule. From N165 Nantes - Vannes road, leave at exit 15 towards La Roche Bernard, turn left to join D774 towards La Baule. 8 km. after Herbignac, turn right on D52 to St Molt and Mesquer. Site is on D52 just west of village (do not go into village). GPS: N47:23.941 W02:28.279

Charges guide

Per unit incl. 2 persons	€ 15,40 - € 19,20
extra person	€ 4,90 - € 6,10
child (3-7 yrs)	€ 3,40 - € 4,20
electricity (3/6A)	€ 4,30 - € 5,40

FR44320 Camping La Pierre Longue

Rue Henri Danant B.P 13, F-44490 Le Croisic (Loire-Atlantique)

Tel: **02 40 23 13 44**. Email: **lapierrelongue@orange.fr**

Le Croisic can be found on a peninsula which stretches over 5 km. into the ocean. The friendly owners have a great sense of humour at this delightful site. There are a total of 52 grass touring pitches of ample size which are well tended and divided by small trees and young shrubs. There is a little but not much shade. A comfortable bar and restaurant with a comprehensive menu serving speciality seafood dishes, both open out onto a terrace and small swimming pool. This site is open all year and has a very pleasant ambience.

Facilities

The main modern toilet block is heated with washbasins both open and in cubicles. Large shower area. Facilities for disabled visitors. Dishwashing sinks and laundry facilities. Small shop (June - Sept). Bar, restaurant and takeaway (May - Sept). Outdoor heated swimming pool and paddling pool (May - Sept). Off site: Riding, golf, boat launching within 1.5 km. Medieval town of Guerande. Beaches of La Baule. Salt beds of the Salines.

Open: All year.

Directions

Take D774 from Guerande south to Pouliguen. Follow northwest to Le Croisic. Site is well signed and on left after 1.5 km. GPS: N47:17.32 W02:31.45

Charges 2007

Per unit incl. 2 persons	€ 11,50 - € 19,90
extra person	€ 3,00 - € 6,50
child (3-12 yrs)	€ 1,50 - € 4,50
electricity (6A)	€ 3,00 - € 3,50

FR44230 Camping EléoVic

Route de la Pointe St Gildas, Préfailles, F-44770 Pornic (Loire-Atlantique)

Tel: **02 40 21 61 60**. Email: **contact@camping-eleovic.com**

This is a delightful site overlooking the sea on the attractive Jade Coast west of Pornic. There are 80 touring pitches, some with wonderful views, and a similar number of mobile homes, many of which are available for rent. The site is well cared for and everything looks neat. All pitches have access to electricity (10A), though on some you may need a long cable. Much of the ground is sloping, so a really level pitch may not be available. Access for larger units to some pitches may be tricky.

Facilities

Central sanitary block has spacious pre-set showers and washbasins in cabins. Facilities for disabled visitors. Excellent room for dishwashing and laundry. Further facilities are in the pool building. Good restaurant (July-Aug) with small bar and terrace. Fitness room. Playground. Children's activities and entertainment and sporting events for families (high season). Off site: Sailing and boat launching 800 m. Bicycle hire and golf 7 km.

Open: 5 April - 28 October.

Directions

From north on D213 (Route Bleue) turn southwest just south of St Michel-Chef-Chef on D96 to La Plaine-sur-Mer and follow signs for Préfailles. Continue on D313 past village towards La Pointe Saint-Gildas and at 50 km. sign turn left, then left again to site on right. GPS: N47:07.957 W02:13.890

Charges 2008

Per unit incl. 2 persons	€ 15,90 - € 31,10
extra person	€ 4,90 - € 8,30
electricity (10A)	€ 4,70

FR44250 Camping Trémondec

48 rue du Château Careil, F-44350 Guérande (Loire-Atlantique)

Tel: **02 40 60 00 07**. Email: **camping.tremondec@wanadoo.fr**

This is a delightful site close to the sophisticated resort of La Baule, the more relaxed beaches of La Turballe, the salt marshes of the historic town of Guérande and the Natural Reserve of Brière. It is lovingly cared for by the very friendly Schgier family. There are 60 touring pitches on gently sloping ground, divided by hedges and with plenty of trees offering some shade to many; almost all have electricity (6A) nearby. A further 40 pitches are occupied by mobile homes, chalets and family tents either for rent or leased to individuals and a small tour operator.

Facilities

Two well-equipped and clean sanitary blocks with push button showers and some washbasins in cubicles. Facilities for disabled visitors. Dishwashing and laundry facilities. Bar, snack bar/takeaway and restaurant all July/Aug. Good heated pool (1/5-30/9). Small games room. Children's activities and evening events. Off site: Bicycle hire, sailing and beach all within 2.5 km. Riding 5 km. Fishing and golf 10 km.

Open: 1 April - 24 September.

Directions

Site is 5 km. southeast of Guérande and 2.5 km. north of La Baule. From east on N171 turn south at exit for La Baule Centre. Right at next roundabout signed to Château Careil and then right signed to château and site. GPS: N47:17.856 W02:23.998

Charges guide

Per person	€ 3,10 - € 5,50
child (2-7 yrs)	€ 1,50 - € 3,20
pitch incl. electricity	€ 9,30 - € 11,50

FR44300 Camping Les Pierres Couchées

L'Hermitage, F-44250 Saint Brévin-les-Pins (Loire-Atlantique)

Tel: **02 40 27 85 64**

In high season this is a lively and bustling site, just 300 metres from the beach and close to the 'Route Bleue' running south from St Nazaire towards the Vendée. Most of the site is devoted to mobile homes and chalets either privately-owned or for rent. There are 79 touring pitches on the hilly part of the complex, 53 with electricity available (5A) and access to some is not easy. There are no water taps, so a sometimes lengthy trek to the toilet block is necessary. There is a programme of activities for children, young people and families in July and August and good leisure facilities.

Facilities

Several sanitary blocks, but only one serving the touring pitches. It has pre-set showers, washbasins in cubicles and facilities for disabled visitors, although the latter would have great difficulty in getting there as it is on top of a hillock. Dishwashing and laundry facilities. Bar/restaurant. Shop, bakery and takeaway (July-Aug). Multisport court, tennis, boules. Bicycle hire. Children's play areas. Large covered amphitheatre. Off site: Shops, restaurants and bars nearby. Beach 300 m. Riding 1 km. Fishing, sailing and boat launching 4 km. Golf 12 km.

Open: 1 April - 8 October.

Directions

St Brévin is about 6 km. south of the St Nazaire bridge. The site is south of the town just off the D213 between St Brévin-l'Océan and St Michel-Chef-Chef, on a brief section where the road narrows - a difficult crossing from the south and the sign for Les Pierres Couchées is concealed until the last second from the north. GPS: N47:12.282 W02:09.091

Charges guide

Per unit with 2 persons and electricity	€ 20,00 - € 30,00
extra person	€ 4,00 - € 6,50

FR44340 Camping la Falaise

1 boulevard de Belmont, F-44420 La Turballe (Loire-Atlantique)

Tel: 02 40 23 32 53. Email: info@camping-de-la-falaise.com

La Falaise is a simple site enjoying direct access to a wide sandy beach. There are 160 pitches of which 75 are available to tourers. Other pitches are occupied by mobile homes or chalets (some available to rent). The pitches are of a reasonable size but are unshaded and tend to be very sandy. This is a quiet site in low season becoming much livelier in July and August. There are relatively few amenities on site but nearby La Turballe has a good selection of shops and restaurants. There is one main building housing reception and washing and toilet facilities. In high season, a takeaway food service is available. La Turballe is a bustling fishing port and nearby Guérande, on the edge of the Grande Brière natural park, merits a visit with its excellent market.

Facilities

Central toilet block (predominantly Turkish style toilets). Snack bar and takeaway food. Play area (unfenced). Mobile homes and chalets for rent. Direct access to the beach. Off site: Fishing. Boat launching 500 m. Golf 2 km. Riding 10 km. Walking and cycle trails. Shops and restaurants in La Turballe 2 km.

Open: 21 March - 5 November.

Directions

Take the D99 from Guèrande to La Turballe and then continue towards Piriac sur Mer. Bypass La Turballe and the site is on this road after a further kilometre. GPS: N47:21.233 W02:31.333

Charges 2008

Per unit incl. 2 persons, electricity and water	€ 20,10 - € 30,65
extra person (over 4 yrs)	€ 4,20 - € 4,80

Camping La Falaise

2 entrance to the beach, on 400 m distance from the fisher harbour and marina. The center is at 600 meters distance, you will find a supermarket at 400 meter distance. La Falaise is near various places of interest. The mediaeval city of Guérande, ferries to the islands, the Parc Naturel Régional de Brière and the Côte Sauvage.

1 Boulevard de Belmont - 44420 La Turballe - Tel: 0033 240 23 32 53 - Fax: 0033 240 62 87 07
E-mail: camping-de-lafalaise@orange.fr - www.camping-la-falaise.com

FR56040 Camping de Penboch

9 chemin de Penboch, F-56610 Arradon (Morbihan)

Tel: 02 97 44 71 29. Email: camping.penboch@wanadoo.fr

Penboch is 200 metres by footpath from the shores of the Golfe du Morbihan with its many islands, and plenty to do including watersports, fishing and boat trips. The site, in a peaceful, rural area, is divided into two – the main part, on open ground, with hedges and young trees, the other across a minor road in woodland with lots of shade. Penboch offers 175 pitches on flat grass, 95 are for touring and mostly divided into groups. Electricity (6/10A) is available on all pitches and most also have water and drainage. British tour operator (12 pitches). A 'Sites et Paysages' member.

Facilities

Three toilet blocks, two in the main part (one heated) and one in the annex, include washbasins in cabins. Facilities can be under pressure in peak season. Laundry facilities. Motorcaravan service point. Bar with satellite TV, snacks and takeaway, shop (all 20/5-11/9). Heated pool with water slide and children's pool (26/4-14/9). Good playground. Games room. Caravan storage. American motorhomes accepted in low season. Off site: Beach, fishing 200 m. Sailing, windsurfing 2 km. Bicycle hire 2 km. Golf and riding 6 km.

Open: 5 April - 20 September.

Directions

From N165 at Auray or Vannes, take D101 along northern shores of the Golfe du Morbihan; or leave N165 at D127 signed Ploeren and Arradon. Take turn to Arradon and site is signed. GPS: N47:37.336 W02:48.074

Charges 2007

Per unit incl. 2 persons	€ 10,50 - € 32,80
extra person	€ 3,00 - € 5,00
child (2-7 yrs)	€ 2,50 - € 4,20
electricity (6/10A)	€ 3,20 - € 4,20
dog	free - € 3,50

61

FR56020 Camping de la Plage

Plage de Kervilaine, F-56470 La Trinité-sur-Mer (Morbihan)

Tel: **02 97 55 73 28**. Email: **camping@camping-plage.com**

The Carnac/La Trinité area of Brittany is popular with British holiday makers. Camping de la Plage is one of two sites, close to each other and owned by members of the same family, with direct access to the safe sandy beach of Kervillen Plage. There are 198 grass pitches of which 112 are for touring (58 are used by tour operators). All are hedged and have electricity (6/10A), water and drainage. The site has a pronounced slope and some pitches reflect this. With narrow roads and sharp bends, it is not suitable for large units. The shop, restaurant and bar, 200 m. along the coast opposite Camping de la Baie, are used by local residents and provide excellent value. The restaurant and takeaway have extensive menus. A lively entertainment programme for all ages in high season makes this an attractive site for family holidays.

Facilities

Toilet blocks have washbasins in cubicles and facilities for disabled people and small children. Laundry facilities. Small swimming pool with water slides. Play areas including ball pool. Tennis, basketball, table tennis. TV. Entertainment programme in high season for all ages. Bicycle hire. Beach. Guided tours. Internet access. Communal barbecue areas (gas or electric only on pitches). Off site: Fishing 50 m. Shop with bakery. Bar, restaurant, crêperie, takeaway (all 200 m). Sailing 1.5 km. Riding 3.5 km. Golf 13 km.

Open: 30 April - 14 September.

Directions

From N165 at Auray take D28 (La Trinité-sur-Mer). On through town following signs to Carnac-Plage on D186. Site signed off this road to the south. Take care to take road signed to Kervillen Plage where it forks. At sea front turn right. Site is 300 m. on right. GPS: N47:34.538 W03:01.734

Charges 2008

Per unit incl. 2 persons	€ 17,10 - € 34,40
extra person	€ 5,10
child (2-17 yrs)	€ 3,00 - € 4,10
electricity (6/10A)	€ 2,40 - € 4,20
dog	free - € 1,30

www.camping-plage.com
our holiday at La Plage
56470 La Trinité sur Mer
Tel 33 2 97 55 73 28
Fax 33 2 97 55 88 31
email : contact@camping-plage.com
★★★★ CAMPING CARAVANING LA TRINITE SUR MER

FR56030 Camping de la Baie

Plage de Kervillen, F-56470 La Trinité-sur-Mer (Morbihan)

Tel: **02 97 55 73 42**. Email: **contact@campingdelabaie.com**

This site is one of two owned by members of the same family. It is situated on the coast overlooking the safe, sandy beach of Kervillen Plage, with its little rocky outcrops providing a naturally enclosed swimming area. This is a very friendly site, which is ideal for quiet or family holidays in an area with lots of local interest. There are 170 pitches, of which 60 are used by tour operators. The 91 touring pitches are all of good size, hedged and all have electricity (6/10A) water and drainage. Some shade is provided by mature and maturing trees.

Facilities

Two modern, very clean toilet blocks include well equipped baby rooms and full en-suite facilities for disabled visitors. Laundry facilities. Bar, restaurant and takeaway (open to the public - all season). Well stocked shop. Small (12 m.) swimming pool with slide. Play areas. Multisport pitches. TV room. Indoor games. Bicycle hire. Internet access. Off site: Beach, fishing and boat ramp 50 m. Tennis, minigolf 200 m. (shared with Camping de la Plage). Riding 3 km. Sailing school 1.5 km. Golf 5 km.

Open: 17 May - 14 September.

Directions

From the N165 at Auray take D28 signed La Trinité-sur-Mer. Keep on through the town following signs to Carnac Plage on D186. Site is well signed off this road to the south. Be careful to take the road signed to Kervillen Plage where it forks.

Charges 2008

Per person (over 2 yrs)	€ 2,90 - € 7,80
small pitch	€ 7,70 - € 11,95
serviced pitch	€ 11,55 - € 22,60
electricity (6/10A)	€ 2,25 - € 4,50

FR56010 Castel Camping la Grande Métairie

Route des Alignements de Kermario, B.P. 85, F-56342 Carnac (Morbihan)

Tel: **02 97 52 24 01**. Email: **info@lagrandemetairie.com**

La Grande Métairie is a good quality site situated a little back from the sea, close to the impressive rows of the famous 'menhirs' (giant prehistoric standing stones). The site has 575 individual pitches (108 for touring units), surrounded by hedges and trees. All have electricity (some long leads needed). The site is well known and popular and has many British visitors with 358 pitches taken by tour operators. It is ideal for families with children of all ages, but not suitable for those with walking difficulties. The site has a great deal to offer and is lively and busy over a long season. Outside amphitheatre for musical evenings and barbecues. Organised events. Occasional dances (pitches near these facilities may be noisy late at night – the bar closes at midnight). Paddocks with ponds are home for ducks, goats and ponies to watch and feed. There are also pony rides around the site. A super swimming pool complex comprises heated indoor and outdoor pools, water slides and toboggans and a jacuzzi. A local market takes place at Carnac on Wednesdays and Sundays.

Facilities

Three large well maintained toilet blocks, with washbasins in cabins. Facilities for babies and disabled people. Laundry facilities. Motorcaravan service points. Shops. Restaurant. Takeaway. Bar lounge and terrace. TV and games rooms. Pool complex with bar. Playgrounds and playing field. Tennis courts. Volleyball and basketball. Minigolf. BMX track. Bicycle hire. Fishing. Amphitheatre. Zip-wire. Paintball. Helicopter rides (July/Aug). Organised events. American motorhomes accepted up to 27 ft. Off site: Riding 1 km. Nearest beach 3 km. Golf 12 km.

Open: 1 April - 9 September (all services from 20/5).

Directions

From N165 take Quiberon/Carnac exit onto the D768. After 5 km. turn south onto D119 towards Carnac. At roundabout and after 4 km. turn left (north east) onto D196 to the site. GPS: N47:35.837 W03:03.646

Charges 2007

Per person	€ 4,00 - € 7,30
child (under 4-7 yrs)	€ 3,50 - € 5,40
pitch incl. car	€ 8,00 - € 23,90
electricity (6A)	€ 10,00 - € 27,40

Less 20% 22/5-29/6 and after 1/9.

La Grande Métairie
Des Vacances Uniques ★★★★

Route des Alignements de Kermario   Tél. 33(0)2 97 52 24 01
B.P. 85 - 56342 Carnac Cedex   Fax 33(0)2 97 52 83 58
www.lagrandemetairie.com

FR56050 Camping de Kervilor

F-56470 La Trinité-sur-Mer (Morbihan)

Tel: **02 97 55 76 75**. Email: **ebideau@camping-kervilor.com**

Kervilor may be a good alternative for those who find the beach-side sites in La Trinité too busy and lively. In a village on the outskirts of the town, it has 230 pitches on flat grass and is attractively landscaped with trees (silver birch) and flowers giving a sense of spaciousness. The pitches are in groups divided by hedges, separated by shrubs and trees and 200 have electricity (6/10A). Around 116 are used for touring units. Used by tour operators (10 pitches). The site has an inviting, well designed pool complex with swimming and paddling pools, slides and fountains. Activities and entertainment are organised in high season. The pleasant port is only 1.5 km. with sandy beaches within 2 km.

Facilities

Two modern toilet blocks of a good standard with further facilities in an older block. They include many washbasins in cabins, facilities for disabled people and babies. Dishwashing. Small laundry. Small shop and takeaway in season. Bar with terrace (28/5-9/9). Pool complex. Play area. Minigolf, pétanque, tennis and volleyball. Table tennis. Bicycle hire. Only charcoal barbecues are permitted. Off site: Town facilities 1.5 km. Sandy beach, fishing or riding 2 km. Golf 12 km.

Open: 1 May - 14 September.

Directions

Site is north of La Trinité-sur-Mer and is signed in the town centre. From Auray take D186 Quiberon road; turn left at camp sign at Kergroix on D186 to La Trinité-sur-Mer, and left again at outskirts of town.

Charges 2007

Per person	€ 4,90
child (under 7 yrs)	€ 3,20
pitch	€ 16,00
electricity	€ 3,40 - € 3,90
dog	€ 2,80

Less 25% outside high season.

camping **Kervilor** ★★★★

Near to the port and beaches, Camping de Kervilor will welcome you to its calm, shaded setting - with heated swimming pools, waterslides (including multi-track), spa bath, bar, entertainment tennis court, multi-sport terrain - divertissement room and billards, multi-sport terrain - everything on site. Mobile home rental.

© Photo Luc Vignaud

56470 La Trinité sur Mer - Tel. 0297557675 - Fax. 0297558726
www.camping-kervilor.com - ebideau@camping-kervilor.com

FR56080 Camping Municipal le Pâtis

3 chemin du Pâtis, F-56130 La Roche Bernard (Morbihan)

Tel: **02 99 90 60 13**

This is another of those excellent municipal sites one comes across in France. Situated beside the River Vilaine, a 5 minute walk from the centre of the very attractive old town of La Roche Bernard and beside the port and marina, it provides 69 level grass, part-hedged pitches in bays of four, with 7A electricity and water. 10 special pitches for motorcaravans have been created at the entrance (9.4 incl. 2 persons and elec.). Next door is a sailing school, boats to hire, fishing, tennis, archery, etc. A restaurant and bar are on the quay-side, with others uphill in the town.

Facilities

There are two fully equipped sanitary blocks, one new and very modern, the other fully refurbished. Laundry room behind reception with washing machine and dryer. Small play area. Bicycle hire. Off site: Bicycle hire and fishing 500 m. Riding 5 km. Golf 15 km.

Open: Easter/April - 30 September.

Directions

Go into town centre and follow signs for the Port around a one-way system and then a sharp turn down hill. GPS: N47:31.090 W02:18.190

Charges 2007

Per pitch with 2 persons and electricity	€ 13,00
extra person	€ 3,00
child (under 9 yrs)	€ 1,50
animal	€ 1,00

No credit cards.

FR56130 Camping Mané Guernehué

52 rue Mané er Groez, F-56870 Baden (Morbihan)

Tel: 02 97 57 02 06. Email: mane-guernehue@wanadoo.fr

Located close to the Morbihan Gulf, Mané Guernehué is a smart, modern site with excellent amenities and a variety of pitches. Some are terraced beneath pine trees, others in a former orchard with delightful views of the surrounding countryside. The 377 pitches are generally large, 200 being occupied by mobile homes and chalets. Most pitches have 10A electricity and a few also have water and drainage. Many are level but a few, particularly in the centre of the site, slope to varying degrees. There is a well stocked fishing lake on the edge of the site. The swimming pool complex here is of top quality with three large pools, a lazy river and no fewer than six water slides. An imaginative entertainment programme is on offer and includes childrens' clubs and a variety of daytime and evening activities. The Morbihan gulf is ideal for sailing, windsurfing and most other watersports, and numerous boat trips are available around the gulf and to its islands.

Facilities

Three modern toilet blocks include washbasins in cabins. The maintenance of the blocks does seem to be under some pressure. Facilities for disabled visitors. Washing machines and dryers. Small shop, bar and takeaway. Heated swimming pool, waterslide, jacuzzi and gym. Fishing. Minigolf. Pony trekking. Teenagers' room with table tennis, pool, billiards and TV. Play area. Tree top adventure area. Varied entertainment programme in high season, based around a large purpose built hall. Mobile homes to rent. Off site: Beach, golf 3 km.

Open: 1 April - 30 September.

Directions

From Auray or Vannes use the D101 to Baden and watch for signs to site.

Charges 2007

Per person	€ 3,10 - € 6,80
child (2-6 yrs)	€ 2,00 - € 4,80
pitch	€ 10,50 - € 19,20
electricity (10A)	€ 4,40
dog	€ 1,70 - € 3,60
Camping Cheques accepted.	

Situated in a 10 hectares wooded park
During the season: rental of chalets, cottages and mobile homes
Year-round: rental of gîtes

Morbihan
MANÉ GUERNEHUÉ
CAMPING ★★★★
Golfe du Morbihan
52 Rue Mané Er Groëz - 56870 BADEN
Tél. 33 (0)2 97 57 02 06
Fax 33 (0)2 97 57 15 43
www.camping-baden.com
E mail : info@camping-baden.com

INDOOR SWIMMING POOL COMPLEX

FR56100 Camping de Moulin Neuf

F-56220 Rochefort-en-Terre (Morbihan)

Tel: 02 97 43 37 52

This quiet family site is in wooded countryside, 600 m. from the town. Ian and Norma Hetherington have worked hard to develop Moulin Neuf into a neat, tidy and organised site. There are 72 pitches (60 for tourers, 44 with 10A electricity) of good size (120 sq.m.) on neat grass, with two levels. The top level, with a limited number of electrical hook-ups, is flat and pitches are divided by young shrubs. The entrance is here and reception is located just beyond the security gate. The lower level is partly sloping with mature trees, shade and electricity on all pitches.

Facilities

The modern heated sanitary block is kept very clean and includes large, comfortable showers, cabins with washbasins and British and Turkish style WCs. Provision for disabled people. Baby room. Laundry facilities with washing lines. Bread delivered each morning. Heated swimming pool (1/6-31/8). Tennis, basketball, football. Play areas. Off site: Lake 500 m. with watersports. Shop 600 m. Riding. Golf. The beaches of Golfe du Morbihan.

Open: 15 May - 16 September.

Directions

From Redon take D775 Vannes road west for 25 km. Branch north on D774 signed Rochefort en Terre. Follow road past the lake on left, in 800 m. Turn left and follow sign to site.

Charges 2007

Per unit incl. 2 persons	€ 14,00 - € 16,50
with electricity	€ 16,00 - € 19,60
extra person	€ 3,80 - € 4,80
child (under 8 yrs)	€ 1,60 - € 2,00

Check real time availability and at-the-gate prices...

www.alanrogers.com

FR56150 Camping du Haras

Aérodrome Vannes-Meucon, F-56250 Vannes-Meucon / Monterblanc (Morbihan)

Tel: **02 97 44 66 06**. Email: **camping-vannes@wanadoo.fr**

Close to Vannes and the Golfe du Morbihan in southern Brittany, Le Haras is a small, family run, rural site that is open all year. There are 140 pitches at the moment, although there are plans to extend the site. With a variety of settings, both open and wooded, the pitches are well kept and of a good size, all with electricity (4-10A) and most with water and drainage. Whilst M. Danard intends keeping the site quiet and in keeping with its rural setting, he provides plenty of activities for lively youngsters, including some organised games and evening parties. There is a good pool with waves, a long slide, fountains and plenty of sunbathing space. Small animals are kept at the animal park on site and there is a riding school nearby. The site is close to a small airfield, where there are opportunities for leisure flights over the Morbihan, Vannes and Carnac areas, all of which are also easily accessible by car. The beaches are 25 km.

Facilities

The small modern toilet block (heated in winter) provides a few washbasins in cabins and controllable showers. Facilities for babies and disabled visitors. Laundry facilities. No shop but basics are kept in the bar. Bar with snacks (May - Oct). Swimming pool with waves and slide (1/5-31/10). Play area. Animal park. Table tennis. Trampoline. Minigolf. Bicycle hire. Organised activities (high season). Off site: Riding 400 m. Fishing 3 km. Beach 15 km. Golf 25 km.

Open: All year.

Directions

From Vannes on N165 take exit signed Pontivy and airport on the D767. Follow signs for airport and Meucon. Turn right on the D778, follow airport and yellow campsite signs. GPS: N47:43.000 W02:43.000

Charges 2007

Per person	€ 3,00 - € 4,00
child (0-7 yrs)	€ 2,00 - € 3,00
pitch	€ 2,00 - € 3,00
electricity	€ 3,00 - € 6,00
dog	€ 3,00 - € 4,00

Camping du Haras
HOTELLERIE DE PLEIN AIR
Sur les hauteurs de Vannes
et du Golfe du Morbihan
http://campingvannes.free.fr

CHALETS AND MOBILE HOMES FOR RENT
02 97 44 66 06   56250 VANNES-MEUCON

FR56110 Kawan Village le Moustoir

Route du Moustoir, F-56340 Carnac (Morbihan)

Tel: **02 97 52 16 18**. Email: **info@lemoustoir.com**

Camping le Moustoir is a friendly, family run site situated about three kilometres inland from the many beaches of the area and close to the famous 'alignments' of standing stones. Pitches are grassy and separated by shrubs and hedges, with several shaded by tall pine trees. There is a popular pool area with slides, a separate swimming pool and a paddling pool with 'mushroom' fountain. The bar and terrace become the social centre of the site in the evenings. A high season entertainment programme includes a daily 'Kid's club' attracting children of several nationalities. Several small tour operators use the site.

Facilities

The substantial, traditional style toilet block is well maintained (outside peak season some sections may be closed). Motorcaravan service facilities. Shop. Bar and takeaway (from 20/5). Heated swimming pool (21 x 8 m), water slides, and paddling pool (from 20/5). Adventure playground. Tennis. Boules. Volleyball, football and basketball. Table tennis and pool. 'Kids Club'. Barrier deposit € 20. Off site: Watersports at Carnac Plage. Fishing, bicycle hire, riding 2 km. Beach 3 km. Golf 10 km.

Open: 6 June - 22 September.

Directions

From N165, take exit to D768 (Carnac and Quiberon). At second crossroads after 5 km. turn left (D119) towards Carnac. After 3 km. turn left (oblique turning) after a hotel. Site is 500 m. on left.

Charges 2007

Per person (over 2 yrs)	free - € 4,80
pitch incl. car	€ 14,60 - € 26,60
electricity	€ 4,00
water	€ 4,00

Camping Cheques accepted.

FR56180 Camping le Cénic

F-56760 Pénestin-sur-Mer (Morbihan)

Tel: **02 99 90 33 14**. Email: **info@lecenic.com**

Le Cénic is attractively set amidst trees and flowers, providing activities for all tastes. An attractive covered aquatic complex has water slides, bridges, rivers and a jacuzzi, whilst the outdoor pool comes complete with water slide, 'mushroom' fountain and sunbathing areas. You may fish in the lake or use inflatables, watched by the peacock, the geese and turkeys. There is a hall for table tennis and a range of indoor games. There are 310 pitches, 160 of which are for touring and 90 have electricity (6A), but long leads will be required. The area has much to offer from the beaches of La Mine d'Or, the harbour at Trébiguier-Pénestin, the Golf du Morbihan with its numerous islands, La Baule with its magnificent beach and the medieval city of Guérande to the unique Brière nature reserve.

Facilities

Good new toilet block includes washbasins in cabins, facilities for disabled visitors, baby room and laundry and dishwashing sinks. Separate laundry. Bar and shop (1/7-31/8). TV and games rooms (1/7-31/8). Indoor (15/4-15/9) and outdoor (1/7-31/8) swimming pools. Play area. Fishing. Off site: Riding 500 m. Bicycle hire 1 km. Sailing 2 km. Pénestin town 2 km. Sandy beaches 2.5 km. Golf 30 km.

Open: 1 May - 30 September.

Directions

From D34 (La Roche-Bernard), at roundabout just after entering Pénestin take D201 south (Assérac). After 100 m. take first turning on left. After 800 m. turn left and campsite is 300 m. on right down a narrow winding lane. GPS: N47:28.746 W02:27.386

Charges 2007

Per person	€ 4,50 - € 6,00
child (under 7 yrs)	€ 2,00 - € 3,00
pitch	€ 5,00 - € 15,00
electricity	€ 4,00
dog	€ 1,50 - € 2,50

Covered Aquatic Centre (heated swimming pool, balneotherapy area, children's pool), outdoor pool, water chute, games room, bar), fishing in the lake.
Le Cénic offers a range of accommodation : static caravans, chalets to rent.

www.lecenic.com
56760 Pénestin-sur-Mer   Tél : +33 (0)2 99 90 33 14   Fax : +33 (0)2 99 90 45 05
info@lecenic.com

FR56120 Camping les Iles

La Pointe du Bile, F-56760 Pénestin-sur-Mer (Morbihan)

Tel: **02 99 90 30 24**. Email: **contact@camping-des-iles.fr**

You will receive a warm and friendly welcome at this family run campsite. The owner, Madame Communal, encourages everyone to make the most of this beautiful region. Of the 189 pitches, 107 are for touring. Most are flat, hedged and of a reasonable size (larger caravans and American motorhomes are advised to book) and all have electricity. Some pitches have sea views and overlook the beach. All services are fully open 15/5-15/9, with a limited service at other times. There is direct access to cliff-top walks and local beaches (you can even walk to small off-shore islands at low tide).

Facilities

The new large central toilet block is spotlessly clean with washbasins in cabins and showers. Dishwashing and laundry facilities. Facilities for disabled people and baby room. Shop. Bar and restaurant with takeaway (15/5-15/9). Pool complex (15/5-15/9). Bicycle hire. Riding. Activities and entertainment in July/Aug. Across the road in Parc des Iles (mobile home section of site): TV room, multisport pitch, tennis court and motorcaravan service point. Off site: Windsurfing 500 m. Sailing school 3 km. Golf 3.5 km.

Open: 4 April - 18 October.

Directions

From D34 (La Roche-Bernard), at roundabot just after entering Pénestin take D201 south (Assérac). Take right fork to Pointe du Bile after 2 km. Turn right at crossroads just before beach. Site is on left. GPS: N47:26.735 W02:29.040

Charges 2008

Per unit incl. 2 persons and car	€ 35,00
extra person (over 7 yrs)	€ 5,00
child (2-7 yrs)	€ 2,50
electricity (6A)	€ 3,50
pet	€ 1,00

67

FR56200 Camping la Ferme de Lann-Hoëdic

Route du Roaliguen, F-56370 Sarzeau (Morbihan)

Tel: 02 97 48 01 73. Email: contact@camping-lannhoedic.fr

'Camping la Ferme' is an attractively landscaped site with many flowering shrubs and trees. The 108 touring pitches, all with electricity (10A) are large and mostly level, with maturing trees which are beginning to offer some shade. The 20 pitches with mobile homes are in a separate area. Families are welcome to visit the working farm which produces cereal crops and raises sheep. Mireille and Timothy Prouten, the owners, go out of their way to make this a welcoming and happy site. Located in the countryside on the Rhuys peninsula, Golfe du Morbihan, it is an ideal base for cycling, walking and water based activities.

Facilities

Two new, high quality toilet blocks with facilities for disabled people and babies. Washing machines and dryers. Playground with modern well designed equipment. Volleyball and petanque. Bread delivery. Ice creams and soft drinks available at reception. Takeaway meals and traditional Breton 'soirées' (high season). Bicycle hire. Off site: Beach, fishing and boating 800 m. Sarzeau 2 km. Riding 2 km. Golf 6 km.

Open: 1 April - 31 October.

Directions

East of Vannes on the N165, join the D780 in the direction of Sarzeau. Exit D780 at the 'Super U'; roundabout south of Sarzeau, following signs for Le Roaliguen. Campsite is signed. GPS: N47:30.447 W02:45.655

Charges 2007

Per person	€ 3,30 - € 4,20
child (under 7 yrs)	€ 1,60 - € 2,00
pitch	€ 6,10 - € 7,60
electricity	€ 2,20 - € 2,80
dog	€ 1,20 - € 1,70

No credit cards.

Camping Cheques accepted.

FR56140 Camping Municipal du Bas de la Lande

F-56120 Guégon-Josselin (Morbihan)

Tel: 02 97 22 22 20. Email: campingbasdulalande@wanadoo.fr

Bas de la Lande is a municipal site, ideally located for overnight stops. The Oust river, which makes up part of the Nantes - Brest canal, runs opposite the site and provides good fishing (permit needed). Bas de la Lande has 53 pitches, of which 49 are for touring and four are for mobile homes. 38 have electricity (6/10A). The pitches are on a number of flat terraces up a steep incline, and most are large, grassy and lightly shaded. As the site is situated close to the N24, a busy dual-carriageway, road noise can be audible in all parts of the site.

Facilities

The principal toilet block just behind reception has washbasins in cabins and large showers. Unit for disabled people (with shower, washbasin and toilet). Washing machine and dryer. A second, much older block is only used at peak periods. Motorcaravan service point. Play area. Fishing. Games and TV room. Table tennis. Off site: Minigolf (opposite site - free to campers). Nearest shops are in Josselin (2 km), where there is also bicycle hire and tennis.

Open: 1 April - 31 October.

Directions

Leave N24 Rennes - Lorient road to west of Josselin following signs to Guégon, then Josselin. Site is clearly signed from the N24.

Charges guide

Per person	€ 2,50 - € 3,00
child (under 7 yrs)	€ 1,30 - € 1,50
pitch	€ 2,10 - € 3,00
car or motorcaravan	€ 1,60 - € 2,00
motorcycle	€ 0,80 - € 1,00

Less 5% for stays over 5 nights, 10% for over 7 days. No credit cards.

FR56230 Camping Plijadur Park

94 route de Carnac, F-56470 La Trinité-sur-Mer (Morbihan)

Tel: 02 97 55 72 05. Email: parkplijadur@wanadoo.fr

Plijadur is Breton for pleasure. The owners of the campsite, M. and Mme. Prevosto, have spent many years developing the site to make an attractive, welcoming place for a quiet family holiday with the added benefits of being close to La Trinité-sur-Mer with its lively waterfront and the beaches along the coast. Of a total of 198 pitches 171 are touring pitches, all of good size, level, and separated by low hedges. Most have electricity (6/10A). The saltwater lake, controlled by sluices, makes a pleasant focal point – the bar overlooks it – and provides fishing. The adjacent woods have deer and there are views over the salt marshes to the sea.

Facilities

Four toilet blocks, three small and one more modern, heated large block, have washbasins in cabins, baby rooms and facilities for disabled visitors. Motorcaravan service point. Small shop (15/6-15/9). Bar with TV and terrace (1/7-31/8). Takeaway (5/7-24/8). Heated swimming and paddling pools (15/5-15/9). Indoor fitness facilities include multi-gym and sauna. Jacuzzi. Bicycle hire. Fishing. Minigolf. Boules. Play area. Off site: Port area, with shops, bars and restaurants, 1 km. Beach and sailing 1 km. Riding 4 km. Golf 12 km.

Open: 1 April - 30 September.

Directions

From La Trinité-sur-Mer take D781 to Carnac. Site is well signed on right 100 m. past the end of town sign for La Trinité-sur-Mer. GPS: N47:35.273 W03:02.613

Charges guide

Per person	€ 3,50 - € 4,30
child (2-7 yrs)	€ 2,00 - € 2,50
pitch	€ 5,50 - € 12,95
electricity (6/10A)	€ 2,50 - € 3,50

Camping PARK PLIJADUR

NOVELTIES: Sauna, Hammam, Jacuzzi, Fitness, TV room & Cinema

Heated Pool
Rent of appartments & mobil-homes

F-56470 la Trinité sur Mer · France · Tél. +33 (0)2 97 55 72 05
parkplijadur@hotmail.com · www.parkplijadur.com

FR56160 Camping la Vallée du Ninian

Le Rocher, F-56800 Taupont (Morbihan)

Tel: 02 97 93 53 01. Email: info@camping-ninian.com

M. and Mme. Joubaud have developed this peaceful family run site in central Brittany from a former farm and they continue to make improvements to ensure that their visitors have an enjoyable holiday. The level site falls into the three areas – the orchard with 100 large, hedged pitches with electricity, the wood with about 13 pitches more suited to tents, and the meadow by the river providing a further 35 pitches delineated by small trees and shrubs, with electricity. The bar has as its centre-piece; a working cider press with which M. Joubaud makes his own 'potion magique'.

Facilities

A central building houses unisex toilet facilities including washbasins in cubicles, large cubicle with facilities for disabled visitors and laundry area with washing machines, dryer and ironing board. Covered dishwashing area with hot water. Shop (July/Aug) selling freshly cooked bread. Small (7 x 12 m) heated swimming and children's pool with slide and fountain. Swings, slides and large trampoline. Fishing. Off site: Riding and bicycle hire 4 km. Golf 7 km.

Open: 15 April - 15 September.

Directions

From Plo'rmel follow signs to Taupont north on N8. Continue through Taupont and turn left (east) signed Vallée du Ninian. Follow road for 3 km. to site on left. From Josselin follow signs for Hellean. Through village, sharp right after river Ninian bridge. Site is 400 m. on right.

Charges 2008

Per person	€ 4,00
child (under 7 yrs)	€ 3,00
pitch and car	€ 6,00
electricity (3/6A)	€ 2,00 - € 3,50

Credit cards accepted in July/Aug. only.

FR56270 **Camping les Menhirs**

Allée Saint Michel, F-56340 Carnac (Morbihan)

Tel: 02 97 52 94 67. Email: contad@lesmenhirs.com

Although located within the built-up area of the popular resort of Carnac, and only 300 m. from the beach, this campsite feels much more rural. Catering for all ages, this is a friendly site and lively in high season with plenty of activities including evening entertainment and a club for children. There are 350 pitches; 154 touring pitches and the remainder used for mobile homes and chalets, of which the majority are used by tour operators. The touring pitches are in groups and are large, level and hedged. All have electricity (10A), water and drainage and 14 have hardstanding. The central complex containing the pools and games areas, all overlooked by the bar and its terrace, makes a convivial focal point. The town and seafront can be explored on foot and the Brittany coast and the Gulf of Morbihan are within easy reach by car or bicycle.

Facilities

Three spotless, modern, light toilet blocks with washbasins in cabins, facilities for children, babies and disabled people. A further en-suite unit for disabled people is by the pool complex. Laundry. Shop. Comfortable bar with satellite TV and takeaway (13/5-16/9). Heated indoor and outdoor swimming pools, the latter with slides (all season). Fitness complex with free massage, multi-gym, jacuzzi, sauna and solarium. Multisports pitch. Tennis. Boules. Riding (1/7-31/8). Play areas. Children's club and evening entertainment (July/Aug). Off site: Beach 300 m. Bicycle hire 500 m. Golf 800 m. Sailing 1 km. Town centre 1 km. Bars and restaurants within easy walking distance.

Open: 1 May - 30 September.

Directions

From Auray take D786 to Carnac and Quiberon. After 5 km. turn south on D119 towards Carnac at roundabout. 600 m. beyond next roundabout fork left, signed La Trinité-sur-Mer and Plages. Keep straight on at lights. Fork left at first roundabout. Turn left at next roundabout (T-junction) and site is signed at 250 m. on left.

Charges 2007

Per person	€ 7,69
child (0-6 yrs)	€ 5,71
pitch	€ 28,97
electricity	€ 3,60

No credit cards.

CAMPING LES MENHIRS

Situated 300 m from the sandy beach and close to the centre of Carnac Plage, the Camping des menhirs offers a variety of high standard facilities: heated outdoor swimming pool, heated indoor swimming pool, sauna, jacuzzi, etc...

Bp 167 - Allée St Michel - 56343 Carnac - France
Tel: 0033 (0)2 97 52 94 67 - Fax: 0033 (0)2 97 52 25 38

contact@lesmenhirs.com
www.lesmenhirs.com

FR56240 **Yelloh! Village Domaine d'Inly**

Route de Couarne, B.P. 24, Pénestin-sur-Mer F-56760 (Morbihan)

Tel: 02 99 90 35 09. Email: info@yellohvillage-domaine-inly.com

This very large site is mainly taken up with mobile homes and chalets, some belonging to the site owner, some private and some belonging to tour operators. Most pitches are arranged in groups of 10 to 14 around a central stone circle with a water point in the middle. Of the 500 pitches, 100 are for touring units and all are large (150-200 sq.m.) with a 10A electrical connection (Europlug). Most are sloping. There is an attractive lake where one can fish or canoe, and next to it the riding school.

Facilities

Two toilet blocks with facilities for disabled visitors and a baby room. Laundry. Shop, comfortable bar, with large screen satellite TV, and attractive restaurant (all 1/5-15/9). Heated swimming pool complex with slide (15/5-15/9). Games room. Play areas. Football pitch (weekly games organised in July/August). Lake for fishing/canoeing. Riding. Off site: Pénestin 2 km. Supermarket 1 km. Golf 2 km. Sailing and boat ramp 2.5 km. Beach 2 km.

Open: 5 April - 21 September.

Directions

From D34 from La Roche-Bernard, at roundabout just after entering Pénestin take D201 south, signed Assérac. After 100 m. take first turning on left (site signed) opposite Intermarché supermarket. After 650 m. turn right, again signed, and campsite is 400 m. on left. GPS: N47:28.289 W02:28.036

Charges 2008

Per unit with 2 persons and electricity	€ 17,00 - € 38,00
extra person (over 1 yr)	€ 5,00 - € 6,00

FR56280 Airotel les Sept Saints

B.P. 14, F-56410 Erdeven (Morbihan)

Tel: **02 97 55 52 65**. Email: **info@septsaints.com**

Mobile homes ▶ page 486

One is attracted to this campsite on arrival, with a well-tended shrubbery and reception to the left of the entrance and a landscaped pool complex on the right. The 200 pitches are divided equally between mobile homes and touring pitches, arranged in three separate groups; 60 normal touring pitches with electricity (10A), mobile homes, and an area under the trees across the play area for tents. Touring pitches are separated by manicured hedges and are level grass. The heated swimming pool complex, with its slides, jacuzzi and padding pool, and overlooked by the bar terrace, provides a focal point. In July and August there are separate children's clubs for younger children and teenagers and a variety of entertainment in the evenings. The site offers a complete holiday within itself as well as access to the Brittany coast.

Facilities

Two modern toilet blocks include en-suite facilities for disabled visitors and attractive baby rooms. Two laundry rooms. Bar, takeaway and shop (10/6-9/9). Heated swimming pool with slides, Jacuzzi,and paddling pool with mushroom and baby slide (15/5-15/9). Excellent play areas. Multisports pitch. Boules. Grass area for ball games. Bicycle hire. Games room. TV room. Gas supplies. Internet. Off site: Fishing 1.5 km. Riding 3 km. Golf 3 km. Beach and sailing 3 km.

Open: 15 May - 15 September.

Directions

From N165 at Auray take exit for D768 to Carnac and Quiberon. At roundabout entering Plouharnel turn west on D781, following signs to Erdeven and L'Orient. Continue through Erdeven, turn left where site is signed after 1.5 km. and site is 150 m. on the right. GPS: N47:39.317 W03:10.307

Charges 2008

Per person	€ 4,00 - € 7,00
child (under 7 yrs)	€ 3,00 - € 5,50
pitch	€ 10,00 - € 18,00
electricity	€ 5,50

Camping Les 7 Saints★★★★

Situated near the sea, in a region of rich heritage of the Brittany culture. Our 4-stars camping site offers the comfort of its marked, shaded camping spots and its high quality facilities.... Make the most of the swimming pool and toddlers' pool (both heated from the May 15th to Sept. 15th). And don't forget other facilities: color TV, video games, pool, crazy foot, table tennis, volley ball and toddlers' playground.

Live activities in July and August for the whole family (various games, sports, singers, bands, disco and karaoke).

Other facilities: washing machines, ironing room, bar and terrace, grocer, takeaway food, baby tubs and care room...
We will do our utmost to offer you quality holidays. In the vicinity : beaches 3 km away, sailing, wind-surfing, sail-karts, fishing, scuba diving, water skiing, tennis court, 18 hole golf course aero club, horse riding, enjoyable cycling and walking.

56410 Erdeven - Tel 0033 2 97 55 52 65
Fax 0033 2 97 55 22 67 - info@septsaints.com

www.sept-saints.com

FR56250 Domaine le Bohat

Route d'Arzon, F-56370 Sarzeau (Morbihan)

Tel: **02 97 41 78 68**. Email: **lebohat@campinglebohat.com**

Camping Le Bohat is a quiet site close to the Gulf of Morbihan and the medieval towns of Vannes and Auray. It is divided into two main parts by a wooded gully. The larger area by the entrance (some 120 pitches) was an orchard and some mature apple trees have been left to mark the pitches and provide some shade. On the other part, the 80 pitches are divided into small groups by hedges. There are 10 shaded pitches in the gully. All the pitches, except those in the gully, are flat and of good size, and most have electricity (10A).

Facilities

Three toilet blocks, one fairly new, with some washbasins in cabins, baby rooms and facilities for disabled visitors. Washing machines and dryer. Motorcaravan service point. Shop (25/4-13/9). Bar and takeaway (23/5-31/8). Heated swimming and paddling pools (25/4-13/9). Games room. TV room. Three graded play areas. Children's club (1/7-31/8). Off site: Supermarket and town centre 2 km. Bicycle hire 2 km. Riding 2 km. Fishing, Sailing 3 km. Beach 6 km. Golf 6 km. Daily market in Aurey.

Open: 25 April - 26 September.

Directions

East of Vannes on the N165, join the D780 in the direction of Sarzeau. Bypass Sarzeau, keeping on D780, following signs to Arzon. Turn left (south) at site sign after 2 km. and site is 300 m. on right. GPS: N47:31.350 W02:47.824

Charges 2008

Per pitch with 2 persons and electricity	€ 19,20 - € 31,20

FR56360 Camping Do Mi Si La Mi

31 rue de la Yierge, Saint Julien Plage, F-56170 Quiberon (Morbihan)

Tel: **02 97 50 22 52**. Email: **camping@domisilami.com**

Occupying a five hectare site on the Quiberon Peninsula just 100 metres from the sandy beaches, this campsite has plenty to offer. Of the 350 pitches, 194 are for touring and are set amongst high mature hedges giving plenty of shade and privacy; some have sea views. Long leads are required on a few pitches as hook-ups can be shared between three or four pitches. The excellent facilities for children are in a well-fenced area and include climbing frames, bouncy castles and multisport courts. Treasure hunts and other entertainment are organised daily. The well-managed reception gave us excellent customer service and we enjoyed our stay on this site which is ideally situated for exploring this fascinating area.

Facilities

Seven sanitary blocks, with good hot showers. Separate laundry. Shop. Bar. TV room. Table tennis. Bouncy castles. Multisport courts. Children's club. Off site: Bar, restaurant, supermarket 50 m. Beaches 100 m. Bicycle hire 100 m. Town centre 2 km. Golf, riding 3 km.

Open: 1 April - 31 October.

Directions

From the N165 Vannes-Lorient dual carriageway south of Auray, take the exit for Carnac/Ploemel. Continue southwest on D768 through the town of Plouharmel following signs for Quiberon. About 25 km. from the N165 but before reaching the town of Quiberon, the site is signed to the left at St. Julien Plage.

Charges 2007

Per person	€ 3,00 - € 4,10
child (under 7 yrs)	€ 1,80 - € 2,70
pitch	€ 7,80 - € 12,00
electricity (3/10A)	€ 2,70 - € 4,10

FR56310 Camping Municipal Beg Er Roch

Route de Lorient, F-56320 Le Faouët (Morbihan)

Tel: **02 97 23 15 11**. Email: **camping.lefaouet@wanadoo.fr**

Like many of today's Municipal campsites this one is immaculate and offers excellent value. There are 52 well kept grassy pitches with electricity (3/5A) available but long leads may be needed. There are also a few furnished tents and mobile homes for rent. For those campers that are anglers a river at the bottom of the site (fenced) provides salmon and trout fishing at a supplement. For the more energetic, the manager can provide details and maps of local walks. For shops and other amenities the town of Le Faouët is only 2 km. away.

Facilities

A single toilet block provides toilets, washbasins and showers. Facilities for the campers with disabilities. Washing machine and dryer. Play area. Minigolf. Boules. Fishing. Large games room with TV and bar billiards.

Open: 15 March - 30 September.

Directions

Take the D769 north from Lorient to Le Faouët. Site is well signed from this road.

Charges 2007

Per person	€ 3,00 - € 3,80
child (2-7 yrs)	€ 1,45 - € 1,70
pitch	€ 4,40 - € 5,50
electricity (5A)	€ 3,00
No credit cards.	

FR56300 Camping An Trest

Route de la Plage du Roaliguen, F-56370 Sarzeau (Morbihan)
Tel: 02 97 41 79 60. Email: letreste@campingletreste.com

This is a delightful site offering 198 touring pitches out of a total of 225. The small number of mobile homes are in a separate area. Pitches are of a good size for most but a limited number of larger ones are retained at one end of the site for larger units. The site is attractively laid out with grass pitches and hedged bays for between four and six units. A fair amount of shade is provided by a variety of trees and shrubs. There is no restaurant on site but a mobile takeaway visits six days a week with a different menu each day.

Facilities

The sanitary block is centrally located with mainly British style toilets and a few Turkish. Washbasins are open and in cubicles and showers are pre-set. Two excellent en-suite rooms provide for disabled visitors (key entry). Baby baths. Dishwashing sinks and laundry room with washing machines and dryers. Well stocked shop (July/Aug). Bar. Mobile takeaway. Heated swimming pool with slides and flume. Paddling pool. TV and games room. Off site: Beach 800 m. Supermarket in An Trest 3 km. Markets and shops in Sareau 3 km.

Open: 16 June - 10 September.

Directions

Take N165 from Vannes. Turn on to D780 signed Sarzeau. Turn left at roundabout by large supermarket. Site is 3 km. on left and is well signed. GPS: N47:30.20 W02:46.17

Charges 2007

Per person	€ 5,60
child (under 10 yrs)	€ 2,20
pitch	€ 9,85
electricity (10A)	€ 3,30

Less 20% in June and September.

FR56430 Camping Moulin de Cadillac

Route de Berric, F-56190 Noyal/Muzillac (Morbihan)
Tel: 02 97 67 03 47. Email: cadillac.camping@wanadoo.fr

Le Moulin de Cadillac is a riverside site, located 15 minutes from the beaches of the Morbihan. This site has been recommended by our French agent and we plan to undertake a full inspection in 2008. There are 130 shady pitches here, of which 87 are for tourers (all with electrical connections 10A). The balance of the pitches is occupied by mobile homes and chalets. Le Moulin de Cadillac has a good range of leisure amenities including a swimming pool with water slides and a separate children's pool. There are also two small fishing lakes and a children's zoo.

Facilities

Three toilet blocks are well equipped and have facilities for disabled people and for children. Small shop. Bar, snack bar, takeaway meals. Swimming pool with water slides. Children's pool. Play area. TV room. Two small fishing lakes. Children's zoo. All weather sports pitch. Tennis. Minigolf. Direct access to the river. Entertainment in high season. Mobile homes and chalets for rent. Off site: Nearest beaches 12 km. Golf 12 km.

Open: 25 April - 30 September.

Directions

From the N166 take exit for Questembert then the D7 towards Damgan. Shortly before Berric, turn left (site signed) and site is a further 2.5 km.

Charges 2007

Per person	€ 3,00 - € 4,50
child (under 7 yrs)	€ 1,80 - € 2,60
pitch	€ 4,50 - € 6,00
electricity (10A)	€ 1,00 - € 1,60

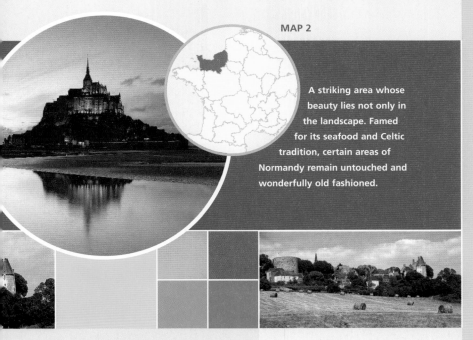

MAP 2

Normandy

A striking area whose beauty lies not only in the landscape. Famed for its seafood and Celtic tradition, certain areas of Normandy remain untouched and wonderfully old fashioned.

DÉPARTEMENTS: 14 CALVADOS, 27 EURE, 50 MANCHE, 61 ORNE, 76 SEINE MARITIME

MAJOR CITIES: CAEN AND ROUEN

Normandy has a rich landscape full of variety. From the wild craggy granite coastline of the northern Cotentin to the long sandy beaches and chalk cliffs of the south. It also boasts a superb coastline including the Cotentin Peninsula, cliffs of the Côte d'Albâtre and the fine beaches and fashionable resorts of the Côte Fleurie. Plus a wealth of quiet villages and unspoilt countryside for leisurely exploration.

The history of Normandy is closely linked with our own. The famous Bayeux Tapestry chronicles the exploits of the Battle of Hastings and there are many museums, exhibitions, sites and monuments, including the Caen Memorial Museum, which commemorate operations that took place during the D-Day Landings of 1944.

Known as the dairy of France you'll also find plenty of fresh fish, rich cream, butter, and fine cheeses such as Camembert and Pont l'Evêque. The many apple orchards are used in producing cider and the well known Calvados, Normandy's apple brandy.

Places of interest

Bayeux: home to the famous tapestry; 15th-18th century houses, cathedral, museums.

Caen: feudal castle, Museum of Normandy, Museum for Peace.

Omaha Beach: D-Day beaches, Landing site monuments, American Cemetery.

Deauville: seaside resort, horse racing centre.

Giverny: home of impressionist painter Claude Monet, Monet Museum.

Honfleur: picturesque port city with old town.

Lisieux: pilgrimage site, shrine of Ste Thérèse.

Mont St Michel: world famous abbey on island.

Rouen: Joan of Arc Museum; Gothic churches, cathedrals, abbey, clock tower.

Cuisine of the region

Andouillette de Vire: small chitterling (tripe) sausage.

Barbue au cidre: brill cooked in cider and Calvados.

Douillons de pommes à la Normande: baked apples in pastry.

Escalope (Vallée d'Auge): veal sautéed and flamed in Calvados and served with cream and apples.

Ficelle Normande: pancake with ham, mushrooms and cheese.

Poulet (Vallée d'Auge): chicken cooked in the same way as Escalope Vallée d'Auge.

Tripes à la Mode de Caen: stewed beef tripe with onions, carrots, leeks, garlic, cider and Calvados.

FR14010 Yelloh! Village la Côte de Nacre

Rue du Général Moulton, F-14750 Saint Aubin-sur-Mer (Calvados)

Tel: **04 66 73 97 39**. Email: **info@yellohvillage-cote-de-nacre.com**

La Côte de Nacre is a large, commercial site with many facilities, all of a high standard. This could be an ideal holiday location for families with older children and teenagers. Two thirds of the site is given over to mobile homes and there are five tour operators on the site. The touring pitches are reasonable, both in size and condition. With pleasant, well cared for flowerbeds, there is some hedging to the pitches, but not much, and a few trees, so little shade. There is a 'state of the art' pool complex which includes a covered pool (lifeguards in attendance).

Facilities

One open toilet block has showers and washbasins in cubicles. New block (completed in 2007). Laundry room. Bar, restaurant and takeaway. Pool complex with outdoor and indoor pools, slides, etc. Play area. Library. Games room. Children's club. Multisports area. Off site: Town 1 km.

Open: 21 March - 14 September.

Directions

Travel west from Ouistreham on D514 to St Aubin-sur-Mer. Site is well signed, just off the main road in a residential area. GPS: N49:19.566 W00:23.400

Charges 2008

Per unit incl. 2 persons and electricity	€ 17,00 - € 42,00
extra person	€ 5,00 - € 8,00
child (2-7 yrs)	free - € 5,00

FR14020 Camping Municipal du Bayeux

Boulevard Eindhoven, F-14400 Bayeux (Calvados)

Tel: **02 31 92 08 43**

Only a few kilometres from the coast and the landing beaches this site makes a very useful night stop on the way to or from Cherbourg, whether or not you want to see the tapestry. The 140 pitches are in two areas (many on hardstanding), well marked and generally of good size with electricity. The site is busy over a long season – early arrival is advised as reservations are not taken. There is a full time warden from 15/6-15/9, otherwise reception is open from 08.00-10.00 and 17.00-19.00 hrs. There may be some road noise on one side of the site.

Facilities

The two good quality toilet blocks have British and Turkish style WCs, washbasins in cabins in main block, and units for disabled people. Motorcaravan service point. Laundry room. Takeaway food and snacks. Two playgrounds. Volleyball. Reading room with TV. Games room. Off site: Large public indoor swimming pool adjoins site with children's pool and jacuzzi. Supermarket nearby (closes 8 pm). Bicycle hire 1 km. Riding 5 km. Beach, golf or fishing 8 km.

Open: 1 May - 30 September.

Directions

Site is on the south side of northern ring road (D613) to town, and just west of the junction with the D516 to autoroute. GPS: N49:17.037 W00:41.857

Charges guide

Per person	€ 3,10
child (under 7 yrs)	€ 1,65
pitch and car	€ 3,83
electricity	€ 3,14
Less 10% for stay over 5 days. No credit cards.	

FR14030 Castel Camping le Château de Martragny

F-14740 Martragny (Calvados)

Tel: **02 31 80 21 40**. Email: **chateau.martragny@wanadoo.fr**

Martragny is an attractive site in a parkland setting adjoining the château. Close to D-Day beaches, it is also convenient for the ports of Caen and Cherbourg, and has the facilities and charm to encourage both long stays and stopovers. The pleasant lawns surrounding and approaching the château take 160 units, with electricity for 140. Most pitches are divided by either a small hedge or a few trees. Bed and breakfast (en-suite) are available in the château all year (reservation essential). Madame de Chassey takes great pride in the site and takes care that peace and quiet is preserved.

Facilities

Three modernised sanitary blocks include washbasins in cabins, sinks for dishes and clothes and two baby baths. Disabled people are well catered for. Good laundry. Shop and takeaway food bar open 21/5-15/9. Bar. Swimming pool (20 x 6 m.) and paddling pool heated in poor weather. Play areas. Tennis courts. Minigolf. Games and TV room. Table tennis and billiards. Fishing. Bicycle and buggy hire. Off site: Riding 1 km. Beach 15 km. Golf 20 km.

Open: 1 May - 12 September.

Directions

Site is off N13, 8 km. southeast of Bayeux. Take Martragny exit from dual carriageway. GPS: N49:14.595 W00:36.348

Charges 2008

Per person	€ 5,50 - € 6,00
child (under 7 yrs)	€ 3,00 - € 3,50
pitch with electricity	€ 11,50 - € 12,10
Less 15% outside 1/7-31/8.	
Camping Cheques accepted.	

FR14070 Camping de la Vallée

Mobile homes ▶ page 486

88 rue de la Vallée, F-14510 Houlgate (Calvados)

Tel: **02 31 24 40 69**. Email: **camping.lavallee@wanadoo.fr**

Camping de la Vallée is an attractive site with good, well maintained facilities, situated on one of the rolling hillsides overlooking the seaside resort of Houlgate. The original farmhouse building has been converted to house a good bar and comfortable TV lounge and billiards room overlooking the pool. The site has 373 pitches with around 100 for touring units. Large, open and separated by hedges, all the pitches have 4 or 6A electricity. Part of the site is sloping, the rest level, with gravel or tarmac roads. Shade is provided by a variety of well kept trees and shrubs. The town and its beach are only 900 metres walk. This is a popular site which is busy in high season with entertainment provided. It is used by tour operators (104 pitches), there are 150 mobile homes on site and around 40 seasonal units. The site has attractive chalets to rent in two areas of the site. English is spoken in season.

Facilities

Three good toilet blocks include washbasins in cabins, mainly British style toilets, facilities for disabled people and baby bathrooms. Laundry facilities (no washing lines allowed). Motorcaravan services. Shop (from 1/5). Bar. Snack bar with takeaway in season (from 15/5). Heated swimming pool (15/5-20/9; no shorts). Games room. Playground. Bicycle hire. Volleyball, football, tennis, petanque. Entertainment in Jul/Aug. Internet access. Off site: Riding 500 m. Beach, town, fishing 1 km. Golf 2 km.

Open: 1 April - 30 September.

Directions

From A13 take exit for Cabourg following signs for Dives/Houlgate. Go straight on at two roundabouts, then four sets of traffic lights. Turn left along sea front. After 1 km. at lights turn right, after 1 km. go over mini-roundabout – look for sign and flag poles on right. GPS: N49:17.644 W00:04.097

Charges 2007

Per unit incl. 2 persons and electricity (4A)	€ 21,00 - € 29,00
extra person	€ 5,00 - € 6,00
child (under 7 yrs)	€ 3,00 - € 4,00

Credit card minimum € 50.
Camping Cheques accepted.

www.campinglavallee.com
Tél. : +33 (0)2 31 24 40 69
88, rue de la Vallée
14510 HOULGATE

La Vallée ★★★★

Authentic Normandy...
900 m away from the beaches

FR14060 Camping les Hautes Coutures

Route de Ouistreham, F-14970 Bénouville (Calvados)

Tel: **02 31 44 73 08**. Email: **camping-hautes-coutures@wanadoo.fr**

Les Hautes Coutures is a useful site for overnight stays and near the Caen - Portsmouth ferry terminal. It is beside the Caen ship canal, 2 km. from the sea (and ferry port) and 10 km. from Caen. Gates open at 06.00 hrs. for early ferries and there can be movement on site late into the evening. There are 120 grass touring pitches of 100 sq.m., clearly marked by mature hedges with tarmac roads. All have electrical connections (up to 10A). An area close to the canal is being developed to provide further pitches. There are also around 150 mobile homes.

Facilities

Two toilet blocks include showers, washbasins in cabins (warm water). Facilities can be under pressure at peak times with variable hot water supply. In low season only one block may be open. Dishwashing and laundry facilities. Motorcaravan service point. Small shop. Bar and takeaway. Small heated swimming pool (from June). Small lounge/TV area and games room. Play area. Tennis. Minigolf. Off site: Beach and riding 2 km. Golf 4 km.

Open: 1 April - 30 September.

Directions

Site is just off the D514 dual carriageway, north of Bénouville. From Caen, follow Ouistreham car ferry signs and take first exit from D514 after Bénouville. GPS: N49:15.003 W00:16.396

Charges 2007

Per person	€ 8,20
child (under 7 yrs)	€ 5,50
pitch	€ 8,20
electricity (4/10A)	€ 6,40 - € 8,50

FR14090 Castel Camping du Brévedent

Le Brévedent, F-14130 Pont-l'Evêque (Calvados)

Tel: **02 31 64 72 88**. Email: **contact@campinglebrevedent.com**

Le Brévedent is a well established, traditional site with 144 pitches (109 for touring units) set in the grounds of an elegant 18th century hunting pavilion. Level pitches are either around the fishing lake, in the lower gardens, or in the old orchard. Most have electricity. The site is used by a tour operator (31 pitches). It is an excellent holiday destination within easy reach of the Channel ports. Apart from the church bells ringing at 07.00 hrs, the otherwise peaceful, friendly environment makes it ideal for mature campers or families with younger children (note: the lake is unfenced).

Facilities

Three toilet blocks include washbasins in cubicles and facilities for babies and disabled people. Dishwashing and laundry facilities. Motorcaravan service point. Shop. Baker each morning. Bar open evenings (1/5-25/9). Restaurant (24/5-19/9). Takeaway (1/5-25/9). Clubroom. Internet access. TV and library. Heated swimming and paddling pools (unsupervised) (1/5-25/9). Playground. Minigolf. Boules. Volleyball. Games room. Fishing. Rowing. Bicycle and buggy hire. Dogs are not accepted. Off site: Golf. Discounted riding 1 km. Tennis. Beach 25 km.

Open: 28 April - 23 September.

Directions

From Pont-l'Evêque take D579 toward Lisieux for 4 km. then D51 towards Moyaux. At Blangy le Château turn right (still on D51) to Le Brévedent. GPS: N49:13.528 E00:18.342

Charges 2007

Per person	€ 5,20 - € 6,70
child (1-12 yrs)	€ 2,20 - € 4,50
pitch	€ 7,00 - € 9,00
electricity	€ 2,45

Camping Cheques accepted.

FR14100 Camping Municipal du Château

3 rue du Val d'Ante, F-14700 Falaise (Calvados)

Tel: **02 31 90 16 55**. Email: **camping@falaise.fr**

The location of this site is really quite spectacular, lying in the shadow of the Château de Falaise, in the old part of the town, in the 'coeur de Normandie'. The site itself is small, with only 66 pitches (all with 10A electricity). It has a rather intimate 'up-market' feel about it, different from the average municipal site. With good shade, tarmac roads and easy access, it was well recommended by the British campers we met there. Whatever this site lacks in size and facilities it makes up for in its situation. Charges are reasonable and the reception friendly.

Facilities

The quantity of sanitary facilities could be insufficient when the site is full - perhaps it never is and campers we met felt they were adequate. Although dated, quality is good and cleanliness reasonable. Unit for disabled visitors (shower room and separate WC). Motorcaravan service point. Play area. Boules. TV room. Fishing. Off site: Tennis adjacent. Bicycle hire 300 m. Riding 500 m.

Open: 1 May - 30 September.

Directions

Site on western side of town, well signed from ring road. From N158 heading south take first roundabout into Falaise (site signed), through suburb to site. GPS: N48:53.734 W00:12.288

Charges 2008

Per person	€ 3,30
pitch	€ 4,00
electricity	€ 2,50

FR14120 Camping les Ammonites

Auberville, route de la Corniche, F-14640 Villers-sur-Mer (Calvados)

Tel: **02 31 87 06 06**. Email: **camping.lesammonites@wanadoo.fr**

Les Ammonites is a friendly, family owned site with a total of 140 pitches in a location that slopes gently downwards towards the cliffs. On entering the site you pass through an area with about 100 mobile homes, 60 privately owned, and 40 to rent. The 40 tourist pitches are at the far end of the site with the most wonderful panoramic views over the Channel. All on grass with electric hook-ups (10A), most are slightly sloping, although the views do compensate for the inconvenience.

Facilities

The single sanitary unit is quite near the top of the site (so quite a walk from the touring pitches) with separate facilities for men and women at the front, some unisex facilities at the rear. Laundry facilities, plus facilities for disabled people are at one end. Motorcaravan service point. Reception has a small shop. Bar/brasserie and takeaway. Swimming pool (15m x 8 m). Playground. Small games room. Animation in July/August. Off site: Houlgate 4 km. and Villers-sur-Mer 3 km.

Open: 1 April - 31 October.

Directions

Auberville is on the D513 midway between Houlgate and Villers-sur-Mer. It is best approached from the D27, which is now the primary route from Deauville to Caen. Turn north on D163 to Auberville. At lights, turn left and almost immediately right towards coast, still on D163 signed Auberville. Site entrance is 500 m. on right.

Charges guide

Per unit incl. 2 persons	€ 8,00 - € 23,00
extra person	€ 3,00
electricity	€ 3,00

FR14140 Camping Municipal Pont Farcy

F-14380 Pont Farcy (Calvados)

Tel: 02 31 68 32 06

This well tended, riverside site is in a tranquil location within easy walking distance of the small village. Just off the A84 motorway it is within easy driving distance of Cherbourg or Caen. A warden lives on site. The 60 numbered pitches are on grass, some separated by small hedges, with electricity (5A) available to all (long leads may be needed). Activities either on-site or at the adjacent 'base plein air' include tennis, minigolf, volleyball, petanque, table tennis, canoe/kayak, pedaloes and cycle hire, walking and fishing. Swimming is not permitted and the river is fenced with access gates for anglers.

Facilities

A rather stylish modern building houses all the facilities, including some washbasins in cubicles and a suite for disabled campers. First floor 'salle' with dining tables for campers, table tennis and other games (ask the warden). There is a lift from the ground floor. Adventure style playground (5-12 yrs). Off site: Village garage with a small shop, bakery, butcher, post office. Bar/hotel. Nearby attractions include the Gorges de la Vire and opportunities for riding, climbing and parachuting.

Open: 1 April - 30 September.

Directions

Pont-Farcy is about 25 km. due south of St Lô. From A84, exit 39, take D21 south for 1 km. Site is on left at entrance to village. GPS: N48:56.395 W01:02.120

Charges 2007

Per unit incl.1 or 2 persons	€ 9,00
extra person	€ 2,15
child (under 7 yrs)	€ 1,00
electricity	€ 1,85

No credit cards.

FR14150 Sunelia Port'land

Chemin du Castel, F-14520 Port en Bessin (Calvados)

Tel: 02 31 51 07 06. Email: campingportland@wanadoo.fr

The Gerardin family will make you most welcome at Port'land, now a mature site lying 700 metres to the east of the little resort of Port en Bessin, one of Normandy's busiest fishing ports. The 300 pitches are large and grassy with 202 available for touring units, including 128 with 15A electricity. There is a separate area for tents without electricity. The camping area has been imaginatively designed into distinct zones, some overlooking small fishing ponds and another radiating out from a central barbecue area.

Facilities

The two sanitary blocks are modern and well maintained. Special disabled facilities. Heated swimming pool (covered in low season) and paddling pool. Bar, restaurant, takeaway (all open all season). Large TV and games room. Multisports pitch. Fishing. Play area. WiFi access. Off site: Nearest beach 4 km. 27-hole Omaha Beach International golf course adjacent. Fishing 600 m. Bicycle hire and riding 10 km. D-Day beaches. Colleville American war Cemetery. Bayeux.

Open: 29 March - 5 November.

Directions

Site is clearly signed off the D514 4 km. west of Port en Bessin. GPS: N49:20.829 W00:46.274

Charges 2008

Per unit incl. 2 persons and electricity	€ 25,00 - € 37,00
extra person	€ 4,80 - € 7,30
child (2-10 yrs)	€ 2,80 - € 4,20
dog	€ 3,00

Reductions for stays over 7 nights.

FR14160 Camping Bellevue

Mobile homes ▶ page 486

Route des Dives, F-14640 Villers-sur-Mer (Calvados)

Tel: 02 31 87 05 21. Email: contact@camping-bellevue.com

Bellevue is located just west of Villers-sur-Mer with its sandy beach, and 9.5 km. west of fashionable Deauville. A fairly large site with 249 pitches in total, but including 190 privately owned mobile homes and 20 units for rent, there are only 59 pitches left for tourists. Many of these are on terraces, individual and relatively small with restricted access, so suitable only for smaller units. Double axle caravans will have difficulty and will only be able to access pitches adjacent to the road.

Facilities

Two sanitary units provide unisex facilities, all in individual cubicles, with some wide door cubicles for disabled visitors. Baby changing room. Dishwashing and laundry facilities. Swimming pool complex (15/6-15/9). Bar (1/7-15/9). Takeaway van in July/Aug. Boules court. Video games machines. Pool table. Playground. Organised activities in peak season. Off site: Golf 4 km. Riding 2 km. Beach and town 1.5 km.

Open: 1 April - 31 October.

Directions

Villers-sur-Mer is about 8 km. west of Deauville. The site is 1.5 km. west of Villers on the D513. Be ready to turn right into lane (site signed) at the crest of a hill, where the road bends to the right. GPS: N49:18.562 W00:01.178

Charges 2007

Per person	€ 6,00
pitch	€ 7,00
electricity	€ 4,00

Check real time availability and at-the-gate prices...

www.alanrogers.com

FR14170 Camping la Capricieuse

2 rue Brummel, F-14530 Luc-sur-Mer (Calvados)

Tel: **02 31 97 34 43**. Email: **info@campinglacapricieuse.com**

La Capricieuse is situated on the edge of the delightful small seaside town of Luc-sur-Mer. It is an ideal location for those looking for a superb municipal site just a few minutes drive from the Ouistreham car ferry. This immaculate site has 204 touring pitches of varying size, on level grass with hedges and a variety of trees give some shade. 105 have electricity and 52 also have water and drainage. Although the site does not have its own shop, bar or restaurant, these can be found within walking distance in Luc-sur-Mer.

Facilities	Directions
Three modern toilet blocks with washbasins in cubicles and showers are kept very clean. Fully equipped facilities for disabled visitors. Laundry and dishwashing facilities. Motorcaravan service point. Large TV room. Games room. Adventure playground (unfenced). Tennis. Boules. Off site: Fishing and bicycle hire nearby. Riding 3 km. Golf 30 km. **Open:** 1 April - 30 September.	Take the D514 from Ouistreham car ferry and head west to Luc-sur-Mer. Campsite is well signed from the western end of St Luc.

Charges 2007

Per unit with 2 persons and electricity	€ 15,30 - € 19,62
extra person	€ 3,50 - € 4,36
child (0-7 yrs)	€ 1,84 - € 2,30

FR14180 Camping la Briquerie

Equemauville, F-14600 Honfleur (Calvados)

Tel: **02 31 89 28 32**. Email: **info@campinglabriquerie.com**

La Briquerie is a large, neat municipal site on the outskirts of the attractive and popular harbour town of Honfleur. Very well cared for and efficiently run by a family team, the site has 420 pitches, many of which are let on a seasonal basis. There are also 130 medium to large, hedged touring pitches. All have electricity (5/10A), water and drainage. One of the main attractions here is the close proximity to Honfleur where one can watch the fishing boats from the quay or browse the work of the artists who display their work in the galleries around the town.

Facilities	Directions
Two toilet blocks with washbasins in cubicles and showers. Good facilities for disabled visitors. Laundry room with washing machines and dryers. Large restaurant (July/Aug). Takeaway (1/6-15/9). Bar (1/6-30/9). Small shop (July/Aug). Large pool complex with two flumes (15/5-15/9). Sauna. Jacuzzi. Fitness room. Boules, table tennis and minigolf. TV and internet access. Off site: Supermarket adjacent. Riding and bicycle hire 1 km. Beach 2 km. Fishing 5 km. Golf 7 km. **Open:** 1 April - 30 September.	Site is well signed from Honfleur on the D579 road, beside the Intermarche on the D62. GPS: N49:23.868 E00:12.514

Charges 2007

Per pitch with 2 persons, electricity, water and drainage	€ 20,80 - € 26,80
extra person	€ 5,40 - € 7,40
child (2-7 yrs)	€ 3,00 - € 4,00
dog	€ 2,00 - € 3,00

FR14190 Camping les Peupliers

Allée des Pins, F-14810 Merville-Franceville (Calvados)

Tel: **02 31 24 05 07**. Email: **asl-mondeville@wanadoo.fr**

Les Peupliers is run by friendly, family managers who keep this site attractive and tidy. It is just 300 metres from a long, wide, sandy beach. The touring pitches, of which there are 85, are on level open ground, all with 10A electricity. Those in the newest part are hedged but, with just a few trees on the edge of the site, there is little shade. The campsite amenities are near the entrance, housed in neat modern buildings. An animation programme for children and various activities are organised in high season. This site is ideally located for visiting Caen, Bayeux and the traditional seaside towns of Deauville and Trouville.

Facilities	Directions
Two excellent heated toilet blocks with washbasins in cabins and showers. Good facilities for disabled visitors and for babies. Laundry room. Small shop, bar with terrace and takeaway (all July/Aug). Heated swimming pool and paddling pool (May-Sept). Play area. Games room. Entertainment in high season. Off site: Fishing, riding and golf all within 1 km. Bicycle hire 2 km. **Open:** 1 April - 30 October.	From Ouistreham take the D514 to Merville-Franceville. Site is well signed off Allée des Pins. From Rouen on A13 (exit 29B), take D400 to Cabourg then the D514 to Merville-Franceville.

Charges 2007

Per person	€ 6,50
child (0-7 yrs)	€ 3,85
pitch	€ 7,20
electricity (10A)	€ 5,10
animal	€ 2,80

FR14200 Camping la Vallée de Deauville

Avenue de la Vallée, F-14800 Saint Arnoult (Calvados)

Tel: 02 31 88 58 17. Email: campinglavalleededeauville@wanadoo.fr

Close to the traditional seaside resorts of Deauville and Trouville, this large, modern site is owned and run by a delightful Belgian couple. With a total of 450 pitches, there are many mobile homes, both for rent and privately owned, and 150 used for touring units. These pitches are level, of a reasonable size and mostly hedged, and 100 have 10A electricity connections. A brand new pool complex complete with flumes, lazy river, jacuzzi and fun pool makes an attractive focal point near the entrance and there is a large fishing lake. The bar and restaurant are large and comfortable and there is a very good shop on the site. The wide sandy beaches of this coast are 3 km. With the various new developments at this site, it promises to be a good choice in the Deauville and Caen area.

Facilities

Two new heated toilet blocks with showers and washbasins in cubicles. Good facilities for babies and disabled visitors. Laundry facilities. Small shop, bar and restaurant (high season). Takeaway (July/Aug). New swimming pool complex. Good play area and play room. Table tennis. Entertainment in high season. Off site: Golf and riding 2 km. Bicycle hire 3 km. Beach 3 km.

Open: 1 April - 31 October.

Directions

From the north, take the A29, then the A13 at Pont l'Eveque. Join the N177 (Deauville/Trouville) and after 9 km. take the D27 signed St Arnoult. Site is well signed on edge of village. GPS: N49:19.430 E00:05.100

Charges 2007

Per person	€ 5,40 - € 9,00
child (0-7 yrs)	€ 3,00 - € 5,00
pitch	€ 7,20 - € 12,00
electricity (16A)	€ 2,40 - € 4,00
animal	€ 2,40 - € 4,00

Camping La Vallee de Deauville

Avenue de la Vallée
14800 Deauville-St-Arnoult

Tél: (33) 02 31 88 58 57
Fax: (33) 02 31 88 11 57

Mail: contact@camping-deauville.com
Internet: www.camping-deauville.com

FR14220 Camping Loisirs Ariane

100, route de Cabourg, F-14810 Merville-Franceville-Plage (Calvados)

Tel: 02 31 24 52 52. Email: info@loisirs-arizne.com

You will get a warm welcome in English at this spacious, well laid-out site, just 300 metres from the beach. It has 144 good-sized pitches, all with 10A electricity, water and waste points close by. Roads and hedges are well maintained with easy access for larger units. The site is well lit and secure with gate-controlled entry. There are numerous beaches nearby and possible days out include the D-Day Beaches, Pegasus Bridge, Bayeux and its Tapestry, fashionable Deauville and picturesque Honfleur. The site is conveniently located for the ferry ports of Caen (Ouistreham 12 km) and Le Havre (65 km).

Facilities

Two bright, recently built sanitary blocks, heated with and tiled walls and floors. Controllable showers. Washbasins in cubicles. Special children's themed shower and toilets. Baby room. Facilities for disabled visitors. Washing machines and dryers. Motorcaravan service point. Shop, bar, snack bar and takeaway. Free use of internet. Bicycle hire. Games room. Children's club and entertainment for adults (July/Aug). Off site: Beach 300 m. Sailing 500 m. Golf and riding 1 km. Boat launching 2 km. Shops, bars and restaurants all close by in Merville.

Open: 1 April - 30 November.

Directions

Merville-Franceville-Plage is just 17 km. northeast of Caen. From A13 motorway exit 29/29b follow D400 north towards Cabourg (5 km); then bear west on D400A towards Cabourg Plage (3 km) and west on D514 to Merville-Franceville. Continue to site on right. From Ouistreham ferry port follow signs for Caen for about 4 km. then turn east and north on D514 to Merville and site on left.

Charges 2007

Per person	€ 4,05 - € 6,10
child (4-10 yrs)	€ 2,40 - € 3,50
electricity (10A)	€ 4,00

FR27010 Camping Caravaning des Etangs Risle-Seine

19 route des Etangs, Toutainville, F-27500 Pont-Audemer (Eure)

Tel: **02 32 42 46 65**. Email: **camping@ville-pont-audemer.fr**

This attractive and well maintained site is owned by the Pont-Audemer Council and run by an enthusiastic manager. It is well laid out with 61 hedged pitches on level grass and electricity connections for 28 of them. Fishing and watersports are possible as the site is positioned next to some large lakes, but swimming is not allowed. In high season a shuttle bus goes to Pont-Audemer where you will find shops, restaurants and a good swimming complex.

Facilities

Two well equipped and maintained toilet blocks with facilities for disabled visitors. They include washbasins in cabins and pre-set showers. Laundry and dishwashing facilities. Bar area with terrace (soft drinks only as there is no alcohol licence, visitors may bring their own). Bread and milk available. Paddling pool. Playing field. TV. Bicycle hire. Fishing. Takeaway food and courtesy bus (high season).

Open: 15 March - 15 November.

Directions

Approaching from north or south on D810, at the bridge over the River Risle, turn to the west on south side of river and travel 1.5 km. on Rue des Etangs. Site is well signed.

Charges guide

Per person	€ 2,81
pitch	€ 5,92
with water and drainage	€ 7,24
electricity (5/10A)	€ 2,65 - € 3,47

FR27020 Camping du Domaine Catinière

Route de Honfleur, F-27210 Fiquefleur-Equainville (Eure)

Tel: **02 32 57 63 51**. Email: **info@camping-catiniere.com**

A peaceful, friendly site, close to the Normandy coast, in the countryside yet in the middle of a very long village, this site is steadily achieving a modern look, whilst retaining its original French flavour. There are 17 rental and 23 privately owned mobile homes, but there should be around 90 pitches for tourists including a large open field for tents and units not needing electricity. Caravan pitches are separated, some with shade, others are more open and all have electricity hook-ups. The site is divided by well fenced streams, popular with young anglers.

Facilities

Toilet facilities include mostly British style WCs, some washbasins in cubicles, and facilities for disabled people and babies (cleaning can be variable). Dishwashing sinks. Washing machine and dryer. Reception with shop. Small bar/restaurant with regional dishes and snacks. Heated swimming pool (1/6-15/9). Two playgrounds, trampoline. Table tennis. Boules. Barrier (card deposit). Off site: Large supermarket close to southern end of the bridge. Smaller supermarket in Beuzeville 7 km. Beach 7 km.

Open: 5 April - 22 September.

Directions

From the Pont de Normandie (toll bridge). Take first exit on leaving bridge (exit 3, A29) signed Honfleur. At roundabout turn left under motorway in direction of Le Mans on D180. Take second exit on right after about 2.5 km, onto D22 towards Beuzeville. Site is on right after 1 km. GPS: N49:24.054 E00:18.365

Charges 2008

Per pitch incl. 1 or 2 persons	€ 15,00 - € 21,00
with electricity (4A)	€ 19,00 - € 25,00
extra person	€ 4,00 - € 6,00

FR27030 Camping Saint-Nicolas

F-27800 Le Bec-Hellouin (Eure)

Tel: **02 32 44 83 55**

This lovely site (formerly a municipal site and still run by the same resident wardens) is located on a forested hillside above the interesting and attractive small town of Le Bec-Hellouin. The town is quite photogenic, has the usual tourist shops, several bars and restaurants and horse drawn carriage rides. There are 90 marked grassy pitches, 30 used for seasonal units, leaving about 60 for tourists all with 10A hook-ups and some with water taps. There is limited shade from a few mature trees. A rather steep footpath leads down to the town and the imposing Abbey of Bec.

Facilities

A modern heated unit has good showers, British style WCs, open and cubicled washbasins, and a dishwashing area. Extra facilities in the old unit by reception, where you will find the laundry. Reception keeps soft drinks and ices. The baker calls each morning. Playground. Playing field and tennis courts. Off site: Le Bec-Hellouin and its Abbey 1.5 km. Fishing 1.5 km. Riding 2 km. Swimming pool at Brionne 6 km. Golf 7 km.

Open: 1 April - 30 September.

Directions

Le Bec-Hellouin is 24 km. southeast of Pont Audemer, just off the D130 between Pont Authou and Brionne. Turn east onto D39 to Le Bec-Hellouin, pass through edge of town. At far end of one-way section, turn left. Continue for about 1 km. Take left fork to site. GPS: N49:14.086 E00:43.519

Charges 2008

Per unit incl. 2 persons	€ 8,45
electricity	€ 3,15
No credit cards.	

FR27070 Camping de l'Ile des Trois Rois

Mobile homes ▶ page 487

1 rue Gilles Nicole, F-27700 Andelys (Eure)

Tel: 02 32 54 23 79. Email: campingtroisrois@aol.com

One hour from Paris and 30 minutes from Rouen, L'Ile des Trois Rois has an attractive setting on the banks of the Seine, with a private fishing lake and is a haven of peace. It is overlooked by the impressive remains of the Château-Gaillard and would be ideal as an overnight stop or for longer. The site has been owned by the Francais Family for the past four years and they live on site. Within walking distance of the town and shops, the site has 300 spacious and partly shady grass pitches, 150 with electricity (long leads may be required for some). Water taps are rather scarce. There are also four mobile homes for rent and 50 pitches occupied by private mobile homes/seasonal units. The Medieval Festival in Les Andelys takes place on the last weekend in June. Bread and cakes are available from a vending machine.

Facilities

Four small, unheated toilet blocks have British style toilets (no seats), showers and washbasins all in cubicles, diswashing and laundry sinks. One has facilities for disabled people and another has a laundry. Motorcaravan service point. Two heated swimming pools (15/6-15/9). Fishing in the Seine or in the private lake. Fenced play area. Animation. Bar and restaurant. Evening entertainment (4/7-30/8). Bicycles and barbecues for hire. Internet access and satellite TV. Off site: Day trips to Paris and Rouen. Cycling and walking trails. Riding 5 km. Golf 9 km.

Open: 15 March - 15 November.

Directions

From the A13 motorway, take exit 17 and join the D316 to Les Andelys. In Les Andelys follow signs to Evreux, and the campsite is located just off the island before passing the bridge over the Seine.

Charges 2007

Per unit incl. 2 persons and electricity	€ 16,00
extra person	€ 5,00
child (under 3 yrs)	free

L'Ile des Trois Rois

swimming pool opens during summer of 2007

The park Ile des Trois Rois is situated in the most beautiful bend of the Seine nearby Castle Gaillard in Normandy and is a haven of peace. Paris is situated of less than than an hour and Rouen is half an hour driving from the camp site.
Facilities: two heated swimming pools, ping pong, camper service, bar and restaurant (high season) and play area

1, Rue Gilles Nicole - F-27700 Les Andelys - France
Tel. 0033 (0) 2 32 54 23 79 - Fax 0033 (0) 2 32 51 14 54 - Email campingtroisrois@aol.com

FR27050 Camping Municipal Saint-Paul

2 route de St Paul, F-27480 Lyons-la-Foret (Eure)

Tel: 02 32 49 42 02. Email: camping-saint-paul@orange.fr

The village of Lyons-La-Foret, with its medieval covered market and magnificently preserved half-timbered buildings is regarded as one of the most beautiful in France. Within walking distance (900 metres), next to the stadium and public swimming pool, this quiet municipal campsite provides a pleasant respite. The site has 100 level grass, numbered pitches, separated by hedges or mature trees providing shade. 60 are available for tourists and each has access to electricity (6A), water and drainage. The site is edged by fast-flowing, shallow (unfenced) streams.

Facilities

Two reasonable toilet blocks include facilities for people with disabilities. These facilities could be stretched in peak season and cleaning may be variable. Laundry and dishwashing sinks. Washing machine. Drying lines. Play area. Separate tent area. Off site: All facilities in nearby village. Many walking and cycling routes.

Open: 29 March - 2 November.

Directions

Site is to the north of Lyons-La-Foret on the D921 road. GPS: N49:24.185 E01:28.693

Charges 2007

Per unit incl. 2 persons	€ 16,00
tent pitch incl. 2 persons	€ 13,50
extra person	€ 5,00
animal	€ 1,00
No credit cards.	

Normandy

83

FR27060 Domaine de Marcilly

Route de Saint-Andre-de-l'Eure, F-27810 Marcilly-sur-Eure (Eure)

Tel: **02 37 48 45 42**. Email: **domainedemarcilly@wanadoo.fr**

Just between Ile de France and Normandy, less than an hours drive from Paris, Domaine de Marcilly is beautifully located in a 15 hectare park, surrounded by pine, oak and birch trees. Although most pitches are dedicated to mobile homes, this park also welcomes motorcaravans and each pitch has a picnic table. Leisure facilities include a swimming pool and two tennis courts. There are paths and cycle routes through the parkland and surrounding countryside, as well as riding and fishing. It is well located for exploring the northern Loire Valley and both Chartres and Paris are within easy reach.

Facilities	Directions
The sanitary block provides hot showers, washbasins, laundry room and facilities for disabled visitors. Washing machine. Motorcaravan service point. Heated swimming pool (1/6-30/9). Boules. Tennis. Internet point. TV room. Animation and entertainment during high season. Off site: Local shops 900 m. Riding 3 km. Golf 10 km. Canoeing. Walking and cycling routes.	From Paris A13, A12 exit onto N12 for Houdan, take exit Goussainville, Havelu, Bu, then Marcilly. Site is on the D52 in the direction of St Andre. GPS: N48:49.513 E01:19.422

Open: All year.

Charges 2007

Per unit incl. 2 persons	€ 18,00 - € 21,00
child (3-10 yrs)	€ 2,50 - € 3,00
electricity	€ 3,00

FR50050 Kawan Village le Cormoran

Ravenoville-Plage, F-50480 Sainte-Mère-Eglise (Manche)

Tel: **02 33 41 33 94**. Email: **lecormoran@wanadoo.fr**

This welcoming, family run site, close to Cherbourg (45 km) and Caen (96 km), is situated just across the road from a long sandy beach and is also close to Utah beach. It is ideally located for those wishing to visit the many museums, landing beaches and remembrance gardens. The site has 100 good size pitches on level grass, separated by mature hedges and all with electricity (6A). Extra large pitches are available. A new shop, comfortable bar and takeaway are open all season. This is an ideal site which caters for both families and couples. There are many surrounding small towns and in early June, you may find groups re-enacting battles and the events of 1944-1945.

Facilities	Directions
Four toilet blocks of varying styles and ages but all maintained to a good standard. Dishwashing and laundry facilities. New shop, bar with snacks and takeaway. Swimming pool (heated 1/5-15/9, unsupervised). Play areas. Tennis. Boules. Entertainment, TV and games room. Bicycle and shrimp net hire. Communal barbecues. Off site: Beach 50 m. Golf 5 km.	From N13 take Ste Mère-Eglise exit and in centre of town take road to Ravenoville (6 km), then Ravenoville-Plage (3 km). Just before beach turn right and site is 500 m. GPS: N49:27.960 W01:14.104

Open: 1 April - 28 September.

Charges 2007

Per unit incl. 1 or 2 persons	€ 16,50 - € 27,00
extra person	€ 4,00 - € 7,00
child (3-10 yrs)	€ 2,00 - € 3,00
electricity (6A)	€ 4,00

Advanced booking advised in peak season.
Larger pitches available (extra charge).
Camping Cheques accepted.

Check real time availability and at-the-gate prices...

www.**alanrogers**.com

FR50000 Camping l'Etang des Haizes

43 rue Cauticotte, F-50250 Saint Symphorien-le-Valois (Manche)

Tel: **02 33 46 01 16**. Email: **info@campingetangdeshaizes.com**

This is an attractive and very friendly site with a swimming pool complex with four-lane slides, jacuzzi and a paddling pool. L'Etang des Haizes has 98 good size pitches, of which 60 are for touring units, on fairly level ground and all with electricity (10A). They are set in a mixture of conifers, orchard and shrubbery, with some very attractive, slightly smaller pitches overlooking the lake and 38 mobile homes inconspicuously sited. The fenced lake has a small beach (swimming is permitted), ducks and pedaloes, and offers good coarse fishing for huge carp (we are told)! Believe it or not, a turtle can sometimes be seen on a fine day! Just one kilometre away is La Haye-du-Puits with two supermarkets, good restaurants and a market on Wednesdays. A good sandy beach is within 10 km. and the Normandy landing beaches are 25 km.

Facilities

Two well kept and modern unisex toilet blocks have British style toilets, washbasins in cabins, units for disabled people and two family cabins. Small laundry. Motorcaravan services. Milk, bread and takeaway snacks available (no gas). Snack bar/bar with TV and terrace. Pool complex (all 20/5-10/9). Play areas. Bicycle hire. Table tennis, pool table, petanque and volleyball. Organised activities including treasure hunts, archery and food tasting (10/7-25/8). Off site: Beach 10 km.

Open: 1 April - 16 October.

Directions

Site is just north of La Haye-du-Puits on the primary route from Cherbourg to Mont St Michel, St Malo and Rennes. It is 24 km. south of N13 at Valognes and 29 km. north of Coutances: leave D900 at roundabout at northern end of bypass (towards town). Site signed on right.

Charges 2008

Per person (over 4 yrs)	€ 5,00 - € 7,00
pitch	€ 4,00 - € 17,00
electricity (10A)	€ 2,00 - € 4,00
dog	€ 1,00 - € 2,00

Camping Cheques accepted.

Check real time availability and at-the-gate prices...

www.alanrogers.com

FR50060 Camping le Grand Large

F-50340 Les Pieux (Manche)

Tel: 02 33 52 40 75. Email: le-grand-large@wanadoo.fr

Le Grand Large is a well established, quality family site with direct access to a long sandy beach and within a 20 kilometre drive of Cherbourg. It is a neat and tidy site with 147 touring pitches divided and separated by hedging giving an orderly, well laid out appearance. A separate area has 40 mobile homes for rent. The reception area is at the entrance (with a security barrier) and the forecourt is decorated with flower beds. To the rear of the site and laid out in the sand-hills is an excellent play area with swings, slides and climbing frame. Not surprisingly the sandy beach is the big attraction. Roads around the site are tarmac and there are pleasant views across the bay to the tip of the Cherbourg peninsula.

Facilities

Two well maintained toilet blocks. The main one is modern and includes washbasins in cubicles and some family rooms. WCs are mostly to the outside of the building. Provision for disabled people. Baby bathroom. Laundry area. Motorcaravan services. Shop for basics, bar (all season), snacks (12/4-21/9). WiFi. Swimming pool and children's pool. Play area. Tennis. Boules. TV room. Animation in July/Aug. Off site: Bicycle hire and riding 5 km. Golf 15 km.

Open: 12 April - 21 September.

Directions

From Cherbourg port take N13 south for about 2 km. Branch right on D650 (previously D904) signed Cartaret. Continue for 18 km. to Les Pieux. Take D4 in town and turn left just after 'Super U' supermarket. Follow site signs via D117/517. GPS: N49:29.665 W01:50.544

Charges 2008

Per unit incl. 2 persons	€ 17,00 - € 30,00
extra person	€ 4,00 - € 6,00
child (under 7 yrs)	€ 2,50 - € 3,50
electricity (6A)	€ 4,00

Less 20% in low seasons (excl. electricity).
Motorcaravan services € 6.10 - € 7.62 (free to guests).
Camping Cheques accepted.

FR50010 Camping la Gallouette

F-50550 Saint-Vaast La Hougue (Manche)

Tel: 02 33 54 20 57. Email: contact@camping-lagallouette.fr

Claudine and Jean Luc Boblin will give you a warm welcome at their seaside campsite which is ideally placed for visiting Barfleur, Sainte Mère-Eglise and the Normandy landing beaches. There are 192 level pitches in total, 132 of which are for touring and all have 6A electricity. Some are separated by hedges and there are many colourful flower beds, shrubs and trees but little shade. A light and airy bar faces onto a terrace and swimming pool and there is also a state-of-the-art multisports court.

Facilities

Three modern sanitary blocks, one open and two enclosed, have British style toilets, showers and washbasins (some in cabins). Area for disabled visitors and for babies. Laundry facilities. Small shop. Snack bar. Bar with terrace. Swimming pool. Multisports court. Play area. Petanque. Fishing. Internet access. Entertainment in high season. Off site: Beach 300 m. Shops and restaurant in Saint-Vaast. Riding 5 km. Golf 12 km.

Open: 1 April - 30 September.

Directions

The D902 runs between Barfleur and Valognes on the eastern side of the Cherbourg peninsula. About half way along at Quettehou take the D1 to Saint-Vaast. Site signed on right on entering town. GPS: N49:35.04 W01:16.07

Charges 2007

Per person	€ 4,50 - € 5,80
pitch	€ 6,20 - € 10,00
electricity (6/10A)	€ 3,70 - € 4,50

FR50070 Castel Camping Caravaning l'Anse du Brick

Route du Val de Saire, F-50330 Maupertus-sur-Mer (Manche)

Tel: 02 33 54 33 57. Email: welcome@anse-du-brick.com

A friendly, family site, l'Anse du Brick overlooks a picturesque bay on the northern tip of the Cotentin peninsula, 8 km. east of Cherbourg port. This quality site makes a pleasant night halt or an ideal longer stay destination for those not wishing to travel too far. Its pleasing location offers direct access to a small sandy beach and a woodland walk. This is a mature, terraced site with magnificent views from certain pitches. Tarmac roads lead to the 117 touring pitches (all with 10A electricity) which are level, separated and mostly well shaded by many trees, bushes and shrubs. Beyond the site lie miles of walking tracks through the gorse-covered hills which, together with a stark rock face, surround the site and make it a sheltered sun-trap. A gourmet restaurant is conveniently located just outside the site gates.

Facilities

Two sanitary blocks, although not ultra-modern, are kept spotlessly clean and are well maintained. British style toilets, washbasins mainly in cubicles and push button showers, provision for disabled visitors, laundry and dishwashing areas, motorcaravan service point. Heated swimming pool (1/5-15/9). Shop (1/4-30/9). Restaurant and bar/pizzeria (1/5-10/9). Tennis. Play area. Organised entertainment in season. Miniclub (6-12 yrs). Bicycle and kayak hire. Off site: Fishing 100 m. Riding 4 km. Golf 10 km.

Open: 1 April - 30 September.

Directions

From Cherbourg port follow signs for Caen and Rennes. After third roundabout, take slip road to right, under road towards Bretteville-en-Saire (D116). From southeast on N13 at first roundabout, take slip road to right towards Tourlaville (N13 car ferry), ahead at next roundabout, right at third lights on D116 to Bretteville. Continue for 7 km. Site signed to right. GPS: N49:40.044 W01:29.293

Charges 2007

Per pitch, 2 persons and electricity	€ 18,50 - € 33,00
extra person	€ 4,00 - € 7,00
child (3-12 yrs)	€ 3,00 - € 5,00

Camping Cheques accepted.

Beach at 100 m

L'Anse du Brick ★★★★

50330 MAUPERTUS/MER
Tel : 33 (0) 233 543 357
Fax :33 (0) 233 544 966
Internet : www.anse-du-brick.com
Mail : welcome@anse-du-brick.com

Mobile home and chalets to rent

FR50030 Castel Camping le Château de lez Eaux

Saint Aubin des Préaux, F-50380 Saint Pair-sur-Mer (Manche)

Tel: 02 33 51 66 09. Email: bonjour@lez-eaux.com

Set in the spacious grounds of a château, Lez Eaux lies in a rural situation just off the main route south, under two hours from Cherbourg. There are 229 pitches of which 113 are for touring, all with electricity (5/10A) and 70 fully serviced. Most of the pitches are of a very good size, partly separated by trees and shrubs on either flat or very slightly sloping, grassy ground overlooking Normandy farmland or beside a small lake (with carp and other fish). There is a considerable tour operator presence, but these units by no means dominate, being generally tucked away in their own areas.

Facilities

Three modern clean toilet blocks include hot showers and washbasins in cabins, facilities for children and babies, and for disabled people. Shop, small bar, snacks and takeaway (all from 1/5). Small heated swimming pool and indoor tropical-style pool (from 1/5, no Bermuda style shorts). Play area. Tennis. Football. Games and TV rooms. Bicycle hire. Lake fishing. Torches useful. Only one dog per pitch. Off site: Beach 4 km. Riding 5 km. Golf 7 km.

Open: 1 April - 15 September.

Directions

Lez-Eaux is just to the west of the D973 about 17 km. northwest of Avranches and 7 km. southeast of Granville. Site is between the two turnings east to St Aubin des Préaux and well signed. GPS: N48:47.764 W01:31.480

Charges 2007

Per unit incl. 2 persons	€ 14,00 - € 30,00
extra person	€ 8,50
electricity (5A)	€ 7,00

Check real time availability and at-the-gate prices...

www.alanrogers.com

FR50090 Camping la Gerfleur

Rue Guillaume Le Conquérant, F-50270 Barneville-Carteret (Manche)
Tel: **02 33 04 38 41**. Email: **alabouriau@aol.com**

La Gerfleur is a pleasant little site with a relaxed atmosphere and a warm welcome. It is a good holiday base, being an easy cycle ride from the sandy beach at Barneville Plage, or from the harbour and smaller cove at Carteret (both only 1.5 km). There are 40 mobile homes and chalets (13 to rent), but these are separated from 49 individual touring pitches. These are on grass with small dividing hedges and are arranged around a small lake which is used for fishing (and with a resident turtle). All the pitches have electricity hook-ups (6/10A; long leads needed in places) and some shade from mature trees. Day trips to the Channel Islands are possible from the nearby port. French and a little English are spoken by the friendly family owners.

Facilities

Clean and reasonable facilities include British style WCs, coin operated showers and some washbasins, all in unisex cubicles, units for disabled visitors. Laundry facilities. Motorcaravan service point. Bar, 'frites' and bread supplies (July/Aug). Heated swimming pool (6.5 x 14 m; 15/5-15/9) and paddling pool. Fishing lake. Boules. Games room. TV room. Small playground. Off site: Barneville 300 m. Beach 1.5 km. Golf 4 km. Riding 7 km.

Open: 1 April - 31 October.

Directions

Barneville-Carteret is 37 km. SSW of Cherbourg. From the north turn off the D904 Barneville-Carteret bypass, and use the old road to town. After 1 km. at roundabout, continue on D903E towards Barneville centre. Site is immediately on right. GPS: N49:22.974 W01:45.341

Charges 2007

Per person	€ 5,20
child (under 13 yrs)	€ 3,60
pitch	€ 6,20
electricity (6A)	€ 4,10

FR50110 Camping Saint-Michel

35 route du Mont Saint Michel, F-50220 Courtils (Manche)
Tel: **02 33 70 96 90**. Email: **infos@campingsaintmichel.com**

This delightful site is owned and run by an enthusiastic young couple, the Duchesnes. It is located in a peaceful, rural setting, yet is only 8 km. from busy tourist attraction of Mont St Michel. The site has 100 pitches which include 36 for touring units and 25 for mobile homes and chalets to rent. Electricity connections (6A) are available and many trees and shrubs provide shade to the pitches. From the restaurant and its terrace overlooking the pool, the site slopes gently down to a small enclosure of farm animals. The animals are kept to entertain children and adults alike. Meet Nestor and Napoléon, the donkeys, Linotte the pony and Dédé and Dedette, the Vietnamese potbellied pigs, as well as miniature goats, sheep, chickens and ducks. It is M. and Mme. Duschesne's intention to maintain a quiet and peaceful site, hence there are no discos or organised clubs.

Facilities

The modern, well maintained toilet block has washbasins in cubicles and showers. Separate laundry. Facilities for disabled visitors in the new reception building. All is of an excellent standard. Motorcaravan service point. Shop. Bar (15/3-15/10). Restaurant (15/6-10/9). Heated swimming pool (1/5-30/9). Animal farm. Play area. Games room. Bicycle hire. Off site: Fishing 2 km. Riding 3 km.

Open: 15 March - 15 October.

Directions

From St Malo take the N137 south and join the N176 east to Pontorson where it becomes the N175. In 20 km. turn northwest on D43 signed Courtils. Site is through village on left. GPS: N48:37.657 W01:24.960

Charges 2008

Per person	€ 4,00 - € 6,00
child (0-7 yrs)	€ 1,80 - € 2,50
pitch incl. electricity (6A)	€ 7,50 - € 9,00

Check real time availability and at-the-gate prices...

 www.**alanrogers**.com

FR50080 Kawan Village Haliotis

Chemin des Soupirs, F-50170 Pontorson (Manche)

Tel: **02 33 68 11 59**. Email: **info@camping-haliotis-mont-saint-michel.com**

The Duchesne family have achieved a remarkable transformation of this former municipal site. Situated on the edge of the little town of Pontorson and next to the river Couesnon, Camping Haliotis is within walking, cycling and canoeing distance of Mont Saint Michel. The site has 152 pitches, including 118 for touring units. Most pitches have electricity and 34 really large ones also have water and drainage. The large, comfortable reception area has been developed to incorporate a bar and restaurant. You will receive a warm welcome from the family in their comfortable reception area where there is a pleasant bar that opens onto the swimming pool terrace, A good local bus service is available from close to the site entrance.

Facilities

Very clean, renovated and well-equipped toilet block. Laundry facilities. Bar where breakfast is served. Bread to order. Heated swimming pool (cleaned daily) with jacuzzi, separate paddling pool. Sauna and solarium. Good fenced play area. Trampoline. Petanque. Archery. Large games room. Tennis court. Bicycle hire. Fishing in the River Couesnon. Japanese garden and animal park. Club for children. Off site: Local services including large supermarket, restaurants and takeaways in Pontorson within walking distance. Riding 3 km. Golf 4 km. Fishing 25 km. Beach 30 km.

Open: 22 March - 5 November.

Directions

Site is 300 m. from the town centre, west of D976, alongside the river, and is well signed from the town. GPS: N48:33.424 W01:30.670

Charges 2007

Per person	€ 4,50 - € 6,00
child (under 7 yrs)	€ 2,00 - € 3,50
pitch	€ 5,00 - € 7,00
electricity	€ 2,50 - € 3,00
dog	€ 0,50

Camping Cheques accepted.

FR50170 Camping le Lac des Charmilles

Route de Vire, F-50160 Torigni-sur-Vire (Manche)

Tel: **02 33 56 91 74**. Email: **contact@camping-lacdescharmilles.com**

The very friendly new owners Samuel and Delphine Grandidier have recently acquired this former municipal site and have already made some outstanding changes. Situated next to a lake on the outskirts of Torigni-sur-Vire (1 km) and surrounded by farmers' fields the 39 touring pitches are divided by mature hedges giving plenty of privacy. Additions have included an exceptional new bar and restaurant with an attractive wooden terrace, a new sanitary block providing the most modern facilities and a multisport court along with trampolines and bouncy castle. So, although still lacking some facilities, the first-class additions already installed make this a great choice if visiting this area. There are plans to increase the number of pitches and with so much unused land much more may be achieved over the coming months and years.

Facilities

Two sanitary blocks including one new central block with excellent facilities including those for disabled visitors. Bar/restaurant with full menu and takeaway. TV, table tennis, go-karts, petanque, multisport court, trampoline, bouncy castle. Motorhome service point. Large units accepted. Off site: Fishing 200 m. Village with shops, bars, banks etc. 1 km. Canoes 5 km. Riding 13 km. Golf 30 km. Beaches of Normandy 45 mins.

Open: 1 April - 31 October.

Directions

Exit the A84 Caen - Rennes motorway at junction 40 and head north on the N174 towards St Lô. The campsite is on your right just before you enter the town of Torigni-sur-Vire.

Charges 2007

Per unit incl. 2 persons and electricity	€ 10,00 - € 15,00
extra person	€ 2,00 - € 3,00
child (0-12 yrs)	€ 1,00 - € 2,00
dog	€ 1,00 - € 1,50

FR50180 Camping des Chevaliers

2 Impasse Pré de la Rose, F-50800 Villediieu-les-Poêles (Manche)

Tel: **02 33 61 02 44**. Email: **contact@camping-deschevaliers.com**

This pleasant site is situated less than a five minute walk from the attractive and interesting town of Villedieu-les-Poêles with its history of metalwork shops and foundries. There are five museums to visit, three of which are close by. This former municipal site is undergoing many modernisations and numerous further additions are planned. The 101 touring pitches are separated by low hedges and there are many mature trees giving plenty of shade. There are plenty of electrical hook-ups (4, 8 or 13A). A small river runs alongside the site which is safely fenced with gate access.

Facilities

Two sanitary blocks provide adequate facilities. One main block situated behind reception has all modern facilities, the other centrally located with toilets and sinks only. Bar and restaurant with terrace. Takeaway snacks and pizzas. Multisport court. Purpose-built skateboard park. Playground with trampoline and bouncy castle. Go-karts and bicycle hire. Fishing. Off site: Shops, bars, restaurants in town 500 m.

Open: 30 March - 31 October.

Directions

From the A84 Rennes-Caen motorway, take exit 37 and head east on the D524 to Villedieu-les-Poêles. Follow signs for the Office de Tourisme and continue on, keeping the Office and Post Office on your left. The campsite is 200 m. on your left.

Charges 2007

Per unit incl. 2 persons	€ 8,00 - € 13,00
with electricity	€ 10,00 - € 15,00
extra person	€ 2,00 - € 3,00
child (0-12 yrs)	€ 1,00 - € 2,00

FR50150 Camping la Route Blanche

F-50290 Breville-sur-Mer (Manche)

Tel: 02 33 50 23 31. Email: larouteblanche@camping-breville.com

La Route Blanche has a bright and cheerful atmosphere and Philippe and Corinne, the owners, are working continually to make an excellent site even better.The 140 pitches for touring are generous and numbered on well-cut grass and divided by young conifers. There are many shrubs and flowers and mature trees give shade to some areas. 67 pitches have 6/10A electricity and long leads may be necessary for some. Although the site does not have its own restaurant, there are five to choose from within a short distance and the beaches of Breville-sur-Mer are within a ten minute walk.

Facilities

Well maintained sanitary facilities with British style toilets, washbasins in cabins and showers. Good provision for disabled visitors. Laundry and dishwashing facilities. Bread available all season. Bar and takeaway (July/Aug). New large swimming pool complex with flumes, toboggan and bubble pool. Play area. Multisports court. Entertainment in high season. Off site: Golf (opposite). Fishing 500 m. Riding 1 km.

Open: 1 April - 31 October.

Directions

Take D971 that runs between Granville and Coutance. Then one of the roads west to Breville-sur-Mer. Site is well signposted.

Charges 2007

Per pitch incl. 2 persons	€ 16,00 - € 24,00
electricity (6/10A)	€ 2,60 - € 3,60
extra person	€ 3,50 - € 4,50
child (2-7 yrs)	€ 1,80 - € 2,20
dog	€ 2,00 - € 2,50

FR61010 Camping Municipal la Campière

Boulevard du Docteur Dentu, F-61120 Vimoutiers (Orne)

Tel: 02 33 39 18 86. Email: mairie.vimoutiers@wanadoo.fr

This small, well kept site is situated in a valley to the north of the town, which is on both the Normandy Cheese and Cider routes. Indeed the town is famous for its cheese and has a Camembert Museum, five minutes walk away in the town centre. The 40 pitches here are flat and grassy, separated by laurel hedging and laid out amongst attractive and well maintained flower and shrub beds. There is some shade around the perimeter and all pitches have electricity.

Facilities

The single central sanitary block is clean and heated, providing open washbasins, good sized, well designed showers, children's toilets and a bathroom for disabled visitors. Dishwashing and laundry facilities under cover. Off site: No shop but a large supermarket 300 m. Tennis courts and a park are adjacent. Water sports facilities or riding 2 km.

Open: March - October.

Directions

Site is on northern edge of town, signed from main Lisieux-Argentan road next to large sports complex. GPS: N48:55.954 E00:11.805

Charges guide

Per person	€ 2,30 - € 2,75
child (under 10 yrs)	€ 1,34 - € 1,60
pitch	€ 1,63 - € 1,95
extra car	€ 1,63 - € 1,95
animal	€ 0,92 - € 1,10

Reductions for 7th and subsequent days.

FR61040 Camping Municipal du Champ Passais

F-61700 Domfront (Orne)

Tel: **02 33 37 37 66**. Email: **mairie@domfront.com**

Situated on the edge of the fascinating fortified town of Domfront, this small site has 34 individual pitches on a series of level terraces and a separate open grassy area for tents. The nine pitches nearest the entrance are all hardstandings separated by grass and with 10A electricity. Grass pitches on the lower levels, divided by shrubs and hedges, have 5A electricity and most have water and waste water points. The site is cared for by a lady warden who keeps everything immaculate and is justifiably proud of the entries in her visitors' book.

Facilities

Excellent sanitary facilities include British style toilets, some washbasins in cubicles, facilities for disabled people, dishwashing and laundry facilities. Motorcaravan service point outside gate (small charge). No separate chemical waste disposal point, but a notice tells visitors where to empty toilet cassettes. Play area. Double axle caravans are not accepted under any circumstances; American RVs can be accommodated. Off site: Sports centre adjacent. Supermarket 800 m. Fishing 1 km.

Open: 1 April - 30 September.

Directions

Domfront is on the N176 Alençon - Mont St Michel road and site is just off this to the south of town; signed to the right up the hill towards town centre - or the left as you leave town heading west. GPS: N48:35.491 W00:39.146

Charges 2007

Per unit incl. 2 person	€ 5,70
electricity (10A)	€ 3,00
No credit cards.	

FR76040 Camping la Source

Petit Appeville, F-76550 Hautot-sur-Mer (Seine-Maritime)

Tel: **02 35 84 27 04**. Email: **info@camping-la-source.fr**

This friendly, attractive site with a new heated pool is just four kilometres from Dieppe and is useful for those using the Newhaven - Dieppe ferry crossing either as a one-night stop over or for a few days' break before heading on. The 120 pitches are flat and there is some shade. There are good hardstandings for motorcaravans and electricity is available. The site is quietly located in a valley with the only disturbance from the occasional passing train. A fast-flowing small river runs along one border (not protected for young children).

Facilities

A good, clean single toilet block (men - left, ladies - right) includes washbasins in cubicles and mainly British style WCs. En-suite unit for disabled people but the unmade gravel roads may cause problems. Laundry facilities. Small bar and terrace (15/3-15/10). Swimming pool. Playing field. TV and games rooms. Fishing. Bicycle hire. Off site: Riding 2 km. Beach 3 km. Golf 4 km.

Open: 15 March - 15 October.

Directions

From Dieppe follow D925 west to Fécamp. At foot of descent at traffic lights in Petit Appeville turn left. From west, turn right (signed D153 St Aubin). Just after railway, turn left under bridge and ahead on narrow road. Site is shortly on left. GPS: N49:53.925 E01:03.398

Charges 2007

Per person	€ 3,20 - € 4,80
pitch	€ 8,00
electricity (6A)	€ 2,50
Camping Cheques accepted.	

FR76090 Camping Municipal d'Etennemare

Hameau d'Etennemare, F-76460 Saint Valery-en-Caux (Seine-Maritime)

Tel: **02 35 97 15 79**

This comfortable, neat municipal site is two kilometres from the harbour and town, 30 km. west of Dieppe. Quietly located, it has 116 pitches of which 49 are available for touring units. The grassy pitches are all on a slight slope, all with electricity (6A), water and drain, but there is very little shade. Reception is open all day in July and August, but in low season is closed 12.00-15.00 hrs daily and all day Wednesdays: there is a card operated security barrier.

Facilities

Two modern, clean and well maintained sanitary buildings are side by side, one containing showers and the other, more recently refitted, has toilets, both open and cubicled washbasins and facilities for disabled people. Both blocks can be heated in winter. Dishwashing and laundry sinks. Washing machines. Small shop (July/Aug). Playground. Table tennis. Off site: Hypermarket 1.5 km. Harbour and beach (pebbles) 2 km.

Open: All year.

Directions

From Dieppe keep to D925 Fécamp road (not through town). At third roundabout turn right on D925E towards hypermarket. From Fécamp turn left on D925E as before. Take first right (site signed) to site on left in 1 km. GPS: N49:51.515 E00:42.279

Charges guide

Per unit incl. 2 persons and electricity	€ 13,40
extra person	€ 2,75
child (under 10 yrs)	€ 1,75

FR76130 Camping de la Forêt

Rue Mainberthe, F-76480 Jumieges (Seine-Maritime)

Tel: **02 35 37 93 43**. Email: **info@campinglaforet.com**

This is a pretty family site with a friendly laid back atmosphere. It is located just 10 km. from the A13 Paris – Caen autoroute. Cars and smaller motorcaravans can approach by ferry across the River Seine (not caravans). The site was formerly a municipal and has recently been taken on by the Joret family. The 111 grassy pitches (84 for tourers) are attractively located in woodland. Many pitches have some shade and all have 10A electrical connections. There is a separate area for tents. Jumieges is just 600 m. away. The site organises some activities in high season and these include treasure hunts and guided walks. The great abbey at Jumieges was founded in 654 by St Philibert, rebuilt by the Normans and consecrated in the presence of William the Conqueror – well worth a visit! A good range of shops, cafes, restaurants etc. can also be found here.

Facilities

Two toilet blocks, both of modern construction and maintained to a good standard with British toilets, some basins in cubicles and pre-set showers. Baby room. Facilities for disabled visitors. Laundry facilities. Shop. Baker calls daily and pizzas are available on Friday and Saturday evenings 18.30 hrs. Small swimming pool and children's pool (heated 15/6-15/9). Playground. Boules. Games room with TV. Cycle hire. Motorcaravan service point. Chalets and mobile homes to let.

Open: 5 April - 25 October.

Directions

Jumieges is around 10 km. north of A13 Paris - Caen autoroute (Bourg-Achard exit). Take D313 towards Caudebec-en-Caux. Then, either ferry across the Seine from Heurtauville to Jumieges (no caravans), or continue over Pont de Brotonne and double back on D982 to Jumieges. Site clearly signed. GPS: N49:26.092 E00:49.738

Charges 2008

Per unit incl. 2 persons	€ 16,00 - € 26,00
extra person	€ 4,00 - € 4,50
child (under 7 yrs)	€ 1,90
electricity	€ 4,00
Camping Cheques accepted.	

CAMPING DE LA FORÊT ★ ★ ★ ★

Rue Mainberte
76480 JUMIÈGES
Tél 02 35 37 93 43
Fax 02 35 37 76 48
www.campinglaforet.com
info@campinglaforet.com

FR76100 Camping Municipal Cany-Barville

Route de Barville, F-76450 Cany-Barville (Seine-Maritime)

Tel: **02 35 97 70 37**. Email: **mairie.cany-barville@cote-albatre.com**

This good quality site, first opened in 1997 next to the municipal sports stadium, has a floral entrance and tarmac roads. Of the 100 individual hedged pitches 75 are available for tourists. There are around 40 concrete hardstandings (awnings can be a problem) and the remainder are on grass: all are fully serviced with water, drain and electric hook-ups (10A). Shade from new specimen trees is still very limited. Cany-Barville, a bustling small town has a traditional Normandy market on Monday mornings.

Facilities

The modern, centrally located, sanitary unit can be heated and has British style toilets, controllable showers and washbasins in cubicles. Dishwashing and laundry sinks. Copious hot water. Separate suites for disabled people. Drive-over motorcaravan service point with chemical disposal facility. Table tennis, volleyball, boules. Games room with pinball machine and ski-simulator. Off site: Bakery, restaurants 600 m. Supermarket 1 km. Sailing and windsurfing centre 2 km. Beach 10 km.

Open: 1 April - 1 October.

Directions

Cany-Barville is 20 km. east of Fécamp on D925 to Dieppe. From traffic lights on east of town turn south on D268 towards Yvetot. Go under railway. Site is 600 m. from town on right, after stadium. GPS: N49:46.990 E00:38.546

Charges 2007

Per person	€ 2,95
child (under 14 yrs)	€ 1,25
pitch	€ 1,95 - € 2,95

FR76110 Camping Municipal les Boucaniers

Rue Pierre Mendès France, F-76470 Le Tréport (Seine-Maritime)

Tel: **02 35 86 35 47**. Email: **camping@ville-le-treport.fr**

This is a large, good quality, municipal site which has undergone redevelopment. It has an attractive entrance and some floral displays, tarmac roads and site lighting. The 260 pitches are on level grass, some with dividing hedges, and trees to provide a little shade. There are 22 good quality wooden chalets for rent, and some privately owned mobile homes, which leaves around 215 pitches for tourists, all with electric hook-ups (6A; some long leads are needed). A small unit acts as shop, bar and takeaway all season, the baker calls daily in high season, and every day except Monday in low season. The town centre is within walking distance with a choice of many good seafood restaurants.

Facilities

Three well equipped sanitary blocks (one can be heated) provide mainly British style WCs, washbasins in cubicles, pre-set hot showers, with new facilities for small children and disabled persons in one block. Multisport court. Minigolf. Boules. Off site: Tennis, football and gymnasium nearby. Fishing, golf and beach 2 km. Riding 3 km. Markets at Le Tréport (Mon and Sat) and at Eu (Fri).

Open: Easter weekend - 30 September.

Directions

From D925 Abbeville - Dieppe road take D1915 towards Le Tréport centre. At new roundabout take first exit to right and site entrance is 150 m. on the right in rue Pierre Mendès-France.
GPS: N50:03.463 E01:23.322

Charges 2007

Per person	€ 2,95
child (2-10 yrs)	€ 1,75
pitch	€ 2,85
incl. electricity	€ 6,95

FR76120 Camping Municipal Veulettes sur Mer

8 rue de Greenock, F-76450 Veulettes-sur-Mer (Seine-Maritime)

Tel: **02 35 97 53 44**

A good value, well kept municipal site in an attractive little coastal town, just 500 m. from the beach and all town services. There are 116 marked pitches on open level grass, 40 of which are seasonal pitches, which leaves 76 pitches for tourists, all with electric hook-ups, water and waste water drain. Reception keeps soft drinks and ices during July/August. Also on site is an attractive 'salle' (open all day in July/August) with a library and TV, a games area, table tennis, babyfoot and further toilet facilities. There is a traffic free cycle path to the next village 4 km. away.

Facilities

Three good modern sanitary units in traditional style buildings are of varying ages (one can be heated). These provide pre-set hot showers, washbasins in cubicles, and facilities for disabled people in the smallest unit on the far side of the site. Laundry room. Playground. Boules. TV, library and table tennis. Off site: Public park with tennis courts and large playground, beach (pebble), watersports centre and all shops and services are within 500 m.

Open: 1 April - 31 October.

Directions

Veulettes-sur-Mer is on the coast approx. 45 km. west of Dieppe. Site is central in town, lying about 500 m. back from the main promenade (signed).
GPS: N49:50.967 E00:35.791

Charges guide

Per person	€ 2,65
child (4-10 yrs)	€ 1,33
pitch with electricity	€ 6,00
car	€ 1,05
animal	€ 0,51

 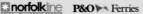
Check real time availability and at-the-gate prices...

 www.alanrogers.com

MAP 3

Northern France

Northern France, with its lush countryside and market towns, is much more than just a stop off en-route to or from the ports. The peaceful rural unspoilt charms of the region provide a real breath of fresh air.

NORD/PAS DE CALAIS: 59 NORD, 62 PAS-DE-CALAIS
MAJOR CITY: LILLE

PICARDY: 02 AISNE, 60 OISE, 80 SOMME
MAJOR CITY: AMIENS

This is a region where centuries of invaders have left their mark. At Vimy Ridge near Arras, World War One trenches have been preserved intact, a most poignant sight. Elsewhere almost every village between Arras and Amiens has its memorial. It is also the birthplace of Gothic architecture with six cathedrals, including Laon, Beauvais and Amiens, arguably the grandest in France.

The area however is predominately rural. Inland and south are long vistas of rolling farmland broken by little rivers and well scattered with pockets of forest woodland. The coastline is characterised by sandy beaches, shifting dunes and ports. It is a quiet and sparsely populated area with peaceful villages and churches that provide evidence of the glorious achievements of French Gothic architecture. Boulogne is home to Nausicaa, the world's largest sea-life centre and from Cap Griz-Nez you may be able to see the White Cliffs of Dover. There are also many huge hypermarkets where you may stock up on wine, beer and cheese.

Places of interest

Amiens: Notre Dame cathedral, monument to 1918 Battle of the Somme.

Chantilly: Château of Chantilly with a 17th century stable with a 'live' Horse museum.

Compiègne: Seven miles east of the town is Clairière de l'Armistice. The railway coach here is a replica of the one in which the 1918 Armistice was signed and in which Hitler received the French surrender in 1942.

Laon: 12th century cathedral, WW1 trenches, Vauclair Abbey.

Marquenterre: one of Europe's most important bird sanctuaries.

Cuisine of the region

Carbonnade de Boeuf à la Flamande: braised beef with beer, onions and bacon.

Caudière (Chaudière, Caudrée): versions of fish and potato soup.

Ficelles Picardes: ham pancakes with mushroom sauce.

Flamiche aux poireaux: puff pastry tart with cream and leeks.

Hochepot: a thick Flemish soup with virtually everything in it but the kitchen sink.

Soupe courquignoise: soup with white wine, fish, moules, leeks and Gruyère cheese.

Tarte aux Maroilles: a hot creamy tart based on Maroilles cheese.

Waterzooï: a cross between soup and stew, usually of fish or chicken.

FR02000 Camping Caravaning du Vivier aux Carpes

10 rue Charles Voyeux, F-02790 Seraucourt-le-Grand (Aisne)

Tel: **03 23 60 50 10**. Email: **camping.du.vivier@wanadoo.fr**

Vivier aux Carpes is a small quiet site, close to the A26, two hours from Calais, so is an ideal overnight stop but is also worthy of a longer stay. The 60 well spaced pitches, are at least 100 sq.m. on flat grass with dividing hedges. The 45 for touring units all have electricity (6A), some also with water points, and there are special pitches for motorcaravans. This is a neat, purpose designed site imaginatively set out with a comfortable feel. The enthusiastic owners and manager speak excellent English and are keen to welcome British visitors.

Facilities

The spacious, clean toilet block has separate, heated facilities for disabled visitors, made available to other campers in the winter. Laundry facilities. Motorcaravan service point (fresh water for large vans is charged). Large TV/games room. Small play area. Bicycle hire. Petanque. Fishing (about € 5.50 p/day). Gates close 22.00 hrs, office open 09.00-21.30. Rallies welcome. Off site: Village has post office, doctor, chemist and small supermarket. Riding 500 m. Golf 12 km.

Open: 1 March - 30 October.

Directions

Leave A26 (Calais - Reims) at exit 11. Take D1 left towards Soissons for 4 km. Take D8, on entering Essigny-le-Grand (4 km.) turn sharp right on D72 signed Seraucourt-le-Grand (5 km). Site signed. GPS: N49:46.915 E03:12.850

Charges 2008

Per unit incl. 2 persons and electricity	€ 18.00
extra person	€ 3.50

Monthly, weekly or weekend rates available. Discounts for students with tents. No credit cards.

FR02030 Caravaning la Croix du Vieux Pont

F-02290 Berny-Riviere (Aisne)

Tel: **03 23 55 50 02**. Email: **info@la-croix-du-vieux-pont.com**

Located on the banks of the River Aisne, La Croix du Vieux Pont is a very smart, modern 34 hectare site offering a high standard of facilities. Many pitches are occupied by mobile homes and tour operator tents, but there are 60 pleasant touring pitches, some on the banks of the Aisne. Maintained to a high standard, the excellent amenities include four heated swimming pools, one indoors with a waterslide and jacuzzi. At the heart of the site is a well-stocked fishing lake.

Facilities

The six toilet blocks are modern and kept very clean, with washbasins in cabins and free hot showers. Laundry facilities. Facilities for disabled visitors. Large supermarket. Bar, takeaway and good value restaurant (most amenities 1/4-30/9). Swimming pool complex (covered pool 1/4-30/10, outdoor 1/5-30/9). Play area. Fishing. Bicycle hire. Apartments to let. Off site: Riding 100 m. Golf 30 km.

Open: 8 April - 31 October.

Directions

From Compiegne take N31 towards Soissons. At Vic-sur-Aisne turn right, towards Berny-Riviere and site is on right after 400 m. GPS: N49:24.292 E03:07.704

Charges 2007

Per unit incl. 2 persons and electricity	€ 23.00
incl. 4 persons	€ 29.50 - € 32.00

Camping Cheques accepted.

FR59010 Camping Caravaning la Chaumière

529 Langhemast Straete, F-59285 Buysscheure (Nord)

Tel: **03 28 43 03 57**. Email: **camping.LaChaumiere@wanadoo.fr**

This is a very friendly, pleasant site, in the département du Nord with a strong Flanders influence. There is a real welcome here. Set just behind the village of Buysscheure, the site has 29 touring pitches separated by trees and bushes. Each pair shares a light, electricity connections, water points and rubbish container. Access from narrow site roads can be difficult. A small, fenced fishing lake contains some large carp (seen!) A bonus is that Bernadette works for the local vet and can arrange all the documentation for British visitors' pets. English is spoken.

Facilities

Modern unisex toilet facilities are simple and small in number, with two WCs, one shower and one washbasin cabin. Facilities for disabled visitors may also be used (a toilet and separate washbasin/shower room). Dishwashing and laundry facilities. Motorcaravan services. Basic chemical disposal. Bar (daily) and restaurant (weekends only, all day, in season). Dog exercise area. Heated outdoor pools. Play area. Gates closed 22.00-08.00 but parking by entrance. Off site: Local market (Monday) at Bergues. St Omer. Beach 30 km. Lille 60 km.

Open: 1 April - 30 September.

Directions

From Calais take N43 (St Omer) for 25 km. Just beyond Nordausques take D221 left (Watten). In Watten turn left for centre, then right on D26 (Cassel). Soon after Lederzeele site signed to right. On reaching Buysscheure turn left, then right, site signed. Single track road (1 km.) with bend.

Charges 2006

Per unit incl. 2 persons and electricity	€ 16.00
extra person	€ 7.00

No credit cards.

Check real time availability and at-the-gate prices...

www.alanrogers.com

FR59050 Camp Municipal du Clair de Lune

Route de Mons, F-59600 Maubeuge (Nord)

Tel: 03 27 62 25 48

This is an attractive site convenient for a night-stop or for longer stays close to the RN2 road. It is a neat and tidy municipal site with 92 marked pitches of fair size. Mainly on level ground and separated by trim hedges, most have electrical connections (6/10A) and some have hardstanding. A variety of broadleaf trees provides shade when needed. When inspected, reception staff were friendly and helpful. Although there are few amenities on the site, the interesting town centre of Maubeuge itself is only about 1 km.

Facilities

Two circular sanitary blocks provide good modern facilities. A new block should now be ready. Dishwashing sinks under cover and washing machines. The block used in winter can be heated. Motorcaravan service point. Small adventure-style playground. Fishing. Bicycle hire. Off site: Riding and bicycle hire 2 km. Golf 2.5 km.

Open: 1 February - 22 December.

Directions

Site is on the RN2 road (known as the N6 in Belgium) north of the town, on the right going towards Mons.

Charges 2008

Per person	€ 3.40
child (3-16 yrs)	€ 2.25
pitch	€ 3.30
electricity (3/10A)	€ 2.70 - € 5.15

FR60020 Aestiva Camping de Sorel

Rue Saint Claude, F-60490 Orvillers/Sorel (Oise)

Tel: 03 44 85 02 74. Email: contact@aestiva.fr

Aestiva Camping de Sorel is located north of Compiègne, close to the A1 motorway and may prove useful as an overnight stop. This site has been recommended by our French agent and we plan to undertake a full inspection in 2008. The site has 80 large grassy pitches, of which 60 are available for touring, all with electrical connections. The site is open for a long season but most amenities (bar, restaurant and takeaway) are only open from June to September. The site is, however, close to the village of Sorel with shops and restaurants available. Compiègne lies 15 km. to the south and its château is well worth a visit and houses a number of interesting museums. There is also an important golf course in the town. Closer to the site, the GR123 long distance footpath runs through Sorel, and offers the opportunity to explore the surrounding countryside on foot.

Facilities

Toilet block with facilities for disabled visitors. Small shop. Bar and snack bar. Takeaway meals. Play area. Games room. Hairdressing service. Motorcaravan service point. Bicycle hire. Off site: Fishing 5 km. Riding 5 km. Golf 8 km. Compiègne 15 km.

Open: 2 February - 14 December.

Directions

Take exit 11 from the A1 motorway (Lille - Paris) and join the northbound N17. Site is signed to the right on reaching village of Sorel after around 8 km.

Charges 2007

Per person	€ 6,00
child (under 7 yrs)	€ 5,00
pitch	€ 13,50 - € 15,00

FR62010 Castel Camping Caravaning la Bien-Assise

D231, F-62340 Guines (Pas-de-Calais)

Tel: 03 21 35 20 77. Email: castels@bien-assise.com

A mature and well developed site, the history of La Bien-Assise goes back to the 1500s. There are 198 grass pitches mainly set among mature trees with others on a newer field. Connected by gravel roads and of a good size (up to 300 sq.m.), shrubs and bushes divide most of the pitches. Being close to Calais, the Channel Tunnel exit and Boulogne, makes it a good stopping point en-route, but it is well worth a longer stay. The site can have heavy usage at times (when maintenance can be variable). Used by tour operators (40 pitches).

Facilities

Three well equipped toilet blocks provide many washbasins in cabins, mostly British style WCs and provision for babies, laundry and dishwashing. The main block is in four sections, two unisex. Motorcaravan service point. Shop. Restaurant. Bar/grill and takeaway (evenings from 1/5). TV room. Pool complex (1/5-20/9) with a toboggan, covered paddling pool and outdoor pool. Play areas. Minigolf. Tennis court. Bicycle hire. Off site: Fishing 8 km. Beach 9 km. Riding 10 km.

Open: 25 April - 20 September.

Directions

From ferry or tunnel follow signs for A16 Boulogne. Take exit 11 (Frethun, Gare TGV) and RD215 (Frethun). At first roundabout take third exit (Guines). Pass under the TGV. In Frethun take RD246 towards Guines and St Tricat and at roundabout take exit for Guines. Pass through St Tricat and Hames Boucres, and in Guines follow site signs turning right towards Marquise for 120 m.

Charges 2007

Per unit incl. 2 persons	
and electricity	€ 17.50 - € 28.50
extra person	€ 3.00 - € 5.00
child (under 13 yrs)	€ 2.00 - € 4.00
Less 10% in low seasons.	

FR62120 Camping l'Eté Indien

Hameau Honvault, F-62930 Wimereux (Pas-de-Calais)

Tel: 03 21 30 23 50. Email: ete.indien@wanadoo.fr

L'Eté Indien is a new site located near the resort of Wimereux, a little to the north of Boulogne. This site has been recommended by our French agent and we are planning a full inspection in 2008. Pitches are of a good size and grassy, all have electrical connections (10A). In keeping with its Wild West theme, there is a small village of Indian teepees available for rent, as well as more conventional mobile homes and chalets. A swimming pool and children's pool were added in 2007. Other amenities include a fishing pond and a snack bar, Le Jardin de l'Eté Indien. The site lies at the heart of the Côte d'Opale, which boasts over 130 km. of coastline. Wimereux is an old-fashioned resort with plenty of shops and restaurants, and is renowned as a centre for kite surfing and speed sailing.

Facilities

Toilet blocks include facilities for babies and disabled people. Laundry. Small shop. Bar. Snack bar. Takeaway food. Motorcaravan services. Fishing pond. Swimming pool. Children's pool. Playground. Off site: Wimereux. Boulogne and the Nausicaa museum. Cité de l'Europe complex at Calais. Sailing and windsurfing 2 km.

Open: All year.

Directions

From the A16 take exit 32 (Wimereux) and follow signs to Wimereux. Site is well signed from here and is located to the left, close to a riding centre.

Charges 2007

Per unit with 2 persons	
and electricity	€ 15,50 - € 20,00
extra person	€ 3,20 - € 4,00
child (under 13 yrs)	€ 2,00 - € 2,50

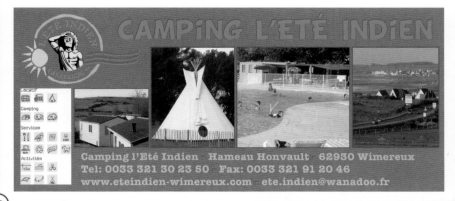

Camping l'Eté Indien · Hameau Honvault · 62930 Wimereux
Tel: 0033 321 30 23 50 Fax: 0033 321 91 20 46
www.eteindien-wimereux.com ete.indien@wanadoo.fr

FR62030 Kawan Village Château du Gandspette

F-62910 Eperlecques (Pas-de-Calais)

Tel: **03 21 93 43 93**. Email: **contact@chateau-gandspette.com**

This spacious family-run site, in the grounds of a 19th century château, conveniently situated for the Channel ports and tunnel, provides overnight accommodation and a range of facilities for longer stays. There are 100 touring pitches, all with electric hook-ups, inter-mingled with 50 French-owned mobile homes and caravans, and a further 18 for hire. Pitches are delineated by trees and hedging. Mature trees form the perimeter of the site, and there is access to woodland walks.

Facilities

Two sanitary blocks with a mixture of open and cubicled washbasins. Good facilities for disabled people and babies. Dishwashing sinks. Laundry facilities. Motorcaravan service point. Bar, grill restaurant and takeaway (all 15/5-15/9). Swimming pools (15/5-30/9). Playground and field. Tennis, petanque and a children's room. Entertainment in season. Off site: Supermarket 1 km. Fishing 3 km. Riding, golf 5 km. Bicycle hire 9 km. Beach 30 km.

Open: 22 March - 30 September.

Directions

From Calais follow N43 (St Omer) for 25 km. Southeast of Nordausques take D221 (east). Follow camp signs for 5-6 km. From St Omer follow N43 to roundabout at junction with D600. Turn right on D600 (Dunkirk). After 5 km. turn left on D221. Site is 1.5 km. on right. GPS: N50:49.137 E02:10.740

Charges 2008

Per unit incl. 2 persons	€ 13.00 - € 23.00
extra person (over 6 yrs)	€ 5.00 - € 6.00
electricity (6A)	€ 4.00

Camping Cheques accepted.

FR80010 Castel Camping le Château de Drancourt

B.P. 80022, F-80230 Saint Valéry-sur-Somme (Somme)

Tel: **03 22 26 93 45**. Email: **chateau.drancourt@wanadoo.fr**

This is a popular, busy and lively site within easy distance of the Channel ports, between Boulogne and Dieppe. There are 356 pitches in total, of which 220 are occupied by several tour operators; 30 units for rent, and 26 privately owned. The 80 touring pitches are on level grass, of good size, some in shade and others in the open, all with electricity. Fully-serviced pitches are available on reservation. The site is well landscaped and, in spite of the numbers in high season, does not feel over-crowded. It can be dusty around the reception buildings and the château in dry weather. English is spoken and the site is run personally by the energetic owner and his staff. Nearby medieval St Valéry-sur-Somme has a fête each year to celebrate William the Conqueror's embarkation in 1066. The reserve of Le Marquenterre is a must for bird enthusiasts. Pony riding is available in season (at other time there are stables 15 km. away).

Facilities

Three toilet blocks include washbasins in cubicles, family bathrooms and facilities for disabled visitors. Laundry facilities. Drainage difficulties can cause occasional problems. Shop, restaurant and takeaway. Several bars. TV rooms, one for children. Games room. Heated pools, one indoor, one outside and paddling pool. Tennis court, golf practise range and minigolf. Bicycle hire. Fishing. Off site: Beach 14 km.

Open: Easter - 5 November.

Directions

Site is 2.5 km. south of St Valéry and signed from the D940 Berck - Le Tréport road. Turn south on D48 Estreboeuf road. Turn immediately left to Drancourt and site. GPS: N50:09.228 E01:38.156

Charges 2007

Per unit incl. 2 persons	€ 12.00 - € 30.00
extra person	€ 5.00 - € 6.70
child (under 5 yrs)	€ 2.00 - € 4.70

Check real time availability and at-the-gate prices...

 www.**alanrogers**.com

FR62080 Camping la Paille Haute

145 rue de sailly, F-62156 Boiry-Notre-Dame (Pas-de-Calais)

Tel: **03 21 48 15 40**. Email: **la-paillehaute@wanadoo.fr**

Quietly situated in a small village overlooking beautiful countryside and easily accessed from the A1 and A26 autoroutes, this site makes an ideal overnight stop, whilst at the same time being a good base from which to explore the city of Arras and its surroundings. There are 100 pitches here, 65 for touring and all with 6/10A electricity. Some pitches are on open, level grass with lovely views over the countryside, and others are by the site's small fishing lake. You can be sure of a warm welcome here from the friendly owner, who is working hard still developing areas of the site.

Facilities

One modern, basic toilet block, unisex. Extra toilets by pool. One toilet/shower room for disabled visitors. Washing facilities under canopy. Motorcaravan service point. Bar and snacks. Swimming pool (15/6-15/9). Poolside bar and pizza oven. TV in bar. Fishing pond. Playground. Boules. Internet access. Entertainment. Off site: Supermarket 500 m. City of Arras with Flemish architecture and cellars and tunnels spreading beneath the town centre.

Open: 1 April - 31 October.

Directions

From A1 take exit 15 and D939 southeast. Follow signs for Boiry-Notre-Dame. From A26 take exit 8 and D939 northwest following signs for Boiry-Notre-Dame. From village follow camping signs to site. GPS: N50:16.412 E02:56.92

Charges 2007

Per unit incl 2 persons	€ 15.00 - € 18.00
extra person	€ 3.00 - € 3.50
electricity (6A)	€ 3.00

FR80020 Camping Caravaning le Champ Neuf

Rue du Champ Neuf, F-80120 Saint Quentin en Tourmont (Somme)

Tel: **03 22 25 07 94**. Email: **contact@camping-lechampneuf.com**

Part of a large farm, the campsite was started in 1995 and all the charming family are now involved (although Mama is firmly in charge). There are 157 pitches with 59 for touring, of which 30 are in a new field with the remainder scattered amongst more permanent mobile homes and caravans. All pitches are on level grass with 3 or 6A electricity. The site is only 75 minutes from Calais, 18 km. off the motorway. It is a quiet site with home-made cooking and soirées. The famous Marquenterre bird reserve is next door, bird-watching enthusiasts will appreciate the dawn chorus and migrating birds.

Facilities

Two toilet blocks have British style toilets, washbasins in cubicles, family cubicles and facilities for disabled visitors. Laundry facilities. Motorcaravan service point. Bar, entertainment area and snack bar. Games room. Tennis. Off site: Shops, restaurants, bars in Rue 7 km.

Open: 1 April - 1 November.

Directions

From A16 exit 24, take D32 towards and around Rue. At second roundabout take second exit on D940, then left on D4 for 1.5 km. before turning right on D204 to Le Bout des Crocs. Site is signed to the left.

Charges 2006

Per unit incl. 2 persons	€ 11.60
extra person	€ 4.10
electricity (3-6A)	€ 3.00 - € 3.60

FR80100 Camping Parc des Cygnes

111 rue de Montières, F-80080 Amiens (Somme)

Tel: **03 22 43 29 28**. Email: **camping.amiens@wanadoo.fr**

Formerly Camping de l'Ecluse, this is now a 3.2 hectare site which has been completely levelled and attractively landscaped. Bushes and shrubs divide the site into areas some 20 mature trees are planned to provide some shade. The 145 pitches are for touring, with plans for a handful of mobile homes for rent. All pitches are grassed with plenty of space on the tarmac roads in front of them for motorcaravans to park in wet conditions. There are 86 pitches with electricity (6-16A), water and drainage and further water points throughout the rest of the site.

Facilities

Two toilet blocks (one open only when site is busy) with separate toilet facilities but unisex shower and washbasin area. Baby bath. Facilities for disabled people. Dishwashing sinks. Reception building also has toilets, showers and washbasins (heated when necessary). Laundry facilities. Shop (open on request). New bar and takeaway (1/5-15/9; weekends only in low season). Games and TV room. Bicycle hire. Fishing. Off site: Golf and riding 5 km. Beaches 70 km.

Open: 1 April - 15 October.

Directions

From A16, leave at exit 20. Take the Rocade Nord (northern bypass) to exit 40, follow signs for Amiens Longpré. At roundabout take second exit to Parc de Loisirs, then right to site (signs all the way). GPS: N49:55.255 E02:15.53

Charges 2007

Per unit incl. 2 persons	€ 14.00 - € 19.50
extra person	€ 5.70
electricity	€ 3.50

Check real time availability and at-the-gate prices...

www.alanrogers.com

FR80060 Camping le Val de Trie

Mobile homes ▶ page 487

Rue des Sources, Bouillancourt-sous-Miannay, F-80870 Moyenneville (Somme)

Tel: **03 22 31 48 88**. Email: **raphael@camping-levaldetrie.fr**

Le Val de Trie is a natural countryside site in woodland, near a small village. The 100 numbered, grassy pitches are of a good size, divided by hedges and shrubs with mature trees providing good shade in most areas, and all have electricity (6A) and water. Access roads are gravel (site is possibly not suitable for the largest motorcaravans). It can be very quiet in April, June, September and October. If there is no-one on site, just choose a pitch or call at farm to book in. There are a few Dutch tour operator tents (5). This is maturing into a well managed site with modern facilities and a friendly, relaxed atmosphere. There are good walks around the area and a notice board keeps campers up to date with local market, shopping and activity news. English is spoken. The owners of Le Val de Trie have recently opened a new campsite nearby, Le Clos Cacheleux. This new site has 60 very large pitches (230 sq.m), all equipped with electricity (10A) and is located in the grounds of the 18th century Château de Bouillancourt. Visitors to this site are able to use the amenities at Le Val de Trie. We plan to undertake a detailed inspection of Le Clos Cacheleux during 2008.

Facilities

Two clean sanitary buildings include washbasins in cubicles, units for disabled people, babies and children. Laundry and dishwashing facilities. Motorcaravan services. Shop (from 1/4), bread to order and butcher visits in season. Bar with TV (1/4-15/10), snack-bar with takeaway (29/4-10/9). Room above bar for children Off site: Riding 14 km. Golf 10 km. Beach 12 km.

Open: 24 March - 15 October.

Directions

From A28 take exit 2 near Abbeville and D925 to Miannay. Turn left on D86 to Bouillancourt-sous-Miannay: site is signed in village. GPS: N50:05.038 E01:42.779

Charges 2008

Per unit incl. 2 persons	€ 14.60 - € 19.60
with electricity	€ 16.70 - € 23.60
extra person	€ 3.10 - € 4.90
child (under 7 yrs)	€ 1.90 - € 2.90
dog	€ 0.80 - € 1.30

Camping Cheques accepted.

Camping le Val de Trie ×××

Online reservation

Ideal spot for first or last night or longer stay
Situated at only 1 hour from Calais (A16) 12 km from the coast

Quiet and relaxing   Fishing pond   Swimming pools   Bar

BOUILLANCOURT sous MIANNAY   80870 MOYENNEVILLE
Tel : +33 3 22 31 48 88   Fax : +33 3 22 31 35 33
www.camping-levaldetrie.fr   raphael@camping-levaldetrie.fr

Camping le Clos Cacheleux   Route de Bouillancourt
80132 Miannay
raphael@camping-lecloscacheleux.com   tel.: +33 3 22 31 48 88
www.camping-lecloscacheleux.com   Online reservation

New

Ideal spot for first or last night or longer stay
1 hour from Calais (A16) 12 km from the coast

FR80040 Camping le Royon

1271 route de Quend, F-80120 Fort-Mahon-Plage (Somme)

Tel: **03 22 23 40 30**. Email: **info@campingleroyon.com**

This busy site, some two kilometres from the sea, has 300 pitches of which 100 are used for touring units. Of either 95 or 120 sq.m., the marked and numbered pitches are divided by hedges and arranged either side of access roads. Electricity (6A) and water points are available to all. The site is well lit, fenced and guarded at night (30 deposit for barrier card). Entertainment is organised for adults and children in July/Aug when it will be very full. The site is close to the Baie de l'Authie which is an area noted for migrating birds. Nearby there are opportunities for windsurfing, sailing, sand yachting, canoeing, swimming, climbing and shooting.

Facilities

Slightly dated toilet blocks provide unisex facilities with British WCs and washbasins in cubicles. Units for disabled people. Baby baths. Dishwashing and laundry sinks. Shop. Mobile takeaway calls evenings in July/Aug. Clubroom and bar. Heated, covered pool (16 x 8 m). Open air children's pool and sun terrace. Playground. Table tennis, multicourt, tennis court and boules. Bicycle hire. Off site: Fishing, riding, golf within 1 km.

Open: 7 March - 1 November.

Directions

From A16 exit 24, take D32 around Rue (road becomes D940 for a while)then continues as D32 (Fort-Mahon-Plage). Site is on right after 19 km. GPS: N50:19.980 E01:34.811

Charges 2007

Per pitch 95 sq.m. incl. caravan, car, water tap, electricity (6A) and 3 persons	€ 17.00 - € 27.50
extra person (over 1 yr)	€ 7.00
dog	€ 3.00

17€ PRIVILEGE CAMPING TICKET 17€

Present this Privilege Camping Ticket at reception and you will only pay 17 Euros per night for a pitch with electricity up to 3 people

Offer valid for year 2008, except in July and August

SUGGESTED BY AIROTEL CAMPING LE ROYON

Camping Qualité Picardie**** - 1271 Route de Quend - 80120 Fort-Mahon Plage
Tel: (33)3 22 23 40 30 - Fax (33)3 22 23 65 15 - www.campingleroyon.com

---

FR80090 Kawan Village Caravaning le Val d'Authie

20 route de Vercourt, F-80120 Villers-sur-Authie (Somme)

Tel: **03 22 29 92 47**. Email: **camping@valdauthie.fr**

In a village location, this well organised site is fairly close to several beaches, but also has its own excellent pool complex, small restaurant and bar. The owner has carefully controlled the size of the site, leaving space for a leisure area with an indoor pool complex. There are 170 pitches in total, but with many holiday homes and chalets, there are only 60 for touring units. These are on grass, some are divided by small hedges, with 6/10A electric hook-ups, and 10 have full services. A 'Sites et Paysages' member.

Facilities

Good toilet facilities include some shower and washbasin units, washbasins in cubicles, and limited facilities for disabled people and babies. Facilities may be under pressure in high season and cleaning variable. Shop (not October). Bar/restaurant (4/4-12/10; hours vary). Swimming and paddling pools with lifeguards in July/Aug). Playground, club room with TV. Weekend entertainment in season (discos may be noisy until midnight, once weekly). Multicourt, beach volleyball, football, boules and tennis court. Internet room. Fitness room including sauna (charged).

Open: 29 March - 12 October.

Directions

Villers-sur-Authie is about 25 km. NNW of Abbéville. From A16 junction 24 take N1 to Vron, then left on D175 to Villers-sur-Authie. Or use D85 from Rue, or D485 from Nampont St Martin. Site is at southern end of village at road junction. GPS: N50:18.815 E01:41.729

Charges 2007

Per unit incl. 2 persons	€ 18.00
extra person	€ 6.00
child (under 7 yrs)	free - € 3.00
electricity (6/10A)	€ 5.00 - € 8.00
Camping Cheques accepted.	

FR80070 Kawan Village la Ferme des Aulnes

Mobile homes ▶ page 487

1 rue du Marais, Fresne-sur-Authie, F-80120 Nampont-St Martin (Somme)

Tel: 03 22 29 22 69. Email: contact@fermedesaulnes.com

This peaceful site, with 120 pitches, has been developed on the meadows of a small, 17th century farm on the edge of Fresne and is lovingly cared for by its enthusiastic owner and his hard-working team. Restored outbuildings house reception and the facilities, around a central courtyard that boasts a fine heated swimming pool. A new development outside, facing the main gate, has 20 large level grass pitches for touring. There is also an area for tents. In the centre, a warden lives above a new facility building. The remaining 22 touring pitches are in the main complex, hedged and fairly level. From here you can visit Crécy, Agincourt, St Valéry and Montreuil (where Victor Hugo wrote Les Misérables). The nearby Bay of the Somme has wonderful sandy beaches and many watersports.

Facilities

Both sanitary areas are heated and include washbasins in cubicles with a large cubicle for disabled people. Dishwashing and laundry sinks. Shop. Piano bar and restaurant. Motorcaravan service point. TV room. Swimming pool (16 x 9 m; heated and with cover for cooler weather). Jacuzzi and sauna. Fitness room. Aqua gym and Balneo therapy. Playground. Beach volleyball, table tennis, boules and archery. Rooms with play stations and videos. Off site: River fishing 100 m. Golf 1 km. Riding 8 km.

Open: 22 March - 2 November.

Directions

From Calais, take A16 to exit 25 and turn for Arras for 2 km. and then towards Abbeville on N1. At Nampont St Martin turn west on D485 and site will be found in 2 km. GPS: N50:20.157 E01:42.740

Charges 2008

Per person	€ 7.00
child (under 7 yrs)	€ 4.00
pitch	€ 7.00
electricity (6/10A)	€ 6.00 - € 12.00

Camping Cheques accepted.

La Ferme des Aulnes ★★★

www.fermedesaulnes.com

Kawan   La Clef Verte   Camping Cheque   Camping Qualité   HOLIDAY CHEQUE

Check real time availability and at-the-gate prices...
www.alanrogers.com

FR80130 Flower Camping les Vertes Feuilles

25 route de la Plage Monchaux, F-80120 Quend Plage les Pins (Somme)

Tel: **03 22 23 55 12**. Email: **contact@lesvertesfeuilles.com**

Situated on the Picardy coast, three kilometres from the beach, this 1.5 hectare site provides 41 touring pitches out of a total of 106. The remainder contain a mix of mobile homes and semi-residential caravans. It is a charming campsite where a pleasant welcome awaits you. The site roads are slightly narrow, so larger units cannot be accommodated. This whole area is bustling in high season with many campsites and holiday villages but this makes for a wonderful French style seaside holiday. Don't forget to visit the nearby Aquaclub, the Abbey and Gardens of Valloires and the bird reserve of Le Marquenterre.

Facilities

One large toilet block, old but renovated, has unisex showers, washbasins in cubicles and 3 family rooms. Ramped facilities for disabled visitors. Snack bar in season. Covered heated swimming pool (10/4-30/9). Play areas. Bicycle hire. Off site: Beach 3 km. Golf 2 km. Riding 5 km. Local markets.

Open: 1 April - 1 November.

Directions

From A16 Rue exit, take D32 around Rue, when road becomes D940 for a while, then continues again as D32 towards Fort-Mahon-Plage. After left turn for Quend Plage, site on left.

Charges 2007

Per unit incl. 2 persons	€ 15.00 - € 24.00
incl. electricity	€ 17.00 - € 24.00
extra person	€ 4.00 - € 4.50
No credit cards.	

FR80120 Camping les Aubépines

Saint Firmin, F-80550 Le Crotoy (Somme)

Tel: **03 22 27 01 34**. Email: **contact@camping-lesaubepines.com**

This peaceful, family-run site is on the edge of the Parc Ornithologique du Marquenterre and is just 1 km. from a beach on the Baie de Somme, a river estuary famous for its resident population of seals. There are 196 pitches, although around 100 are occupied by privately-owned mobile homes with a few available for rent. Consequently there are just 76 touring pitches scattered throughout the site. All on level ground, they are of a reasonable to good size, separated by hedges and trees and with water taps and electricity (3-10A) close by.

Facilities

Two unisex toilet blocks, fairly basic but clean and in good order. British style toilets (seatless), washbasins in cubicles, push button showers and some larger cubicles with shower and basin. Baby bath and toilet. Facilities for disabled visitors are minimal (no grab-rails). Dishwashing sinks. Laundry room. Shop. Indoor games. Small play area. Bicycle hire. Off site: Riding adjacent. Beaches: 1 km. and 10 km. Fishing 2 km. Bird sanctuary, tennis 3 km. Golf 10 km.

Open: 30 March - 3 November.

Directions

Le Crotoy is on the D940 Berck - Le Tréport road. At roundabout for town, take D4 to St Firmin, turn right at next roundabout. After village sign, turn left to site (signed) on right in about 500 m. GPS: N50:15.004 E01:36.747

Charges 2007

Per unit incl. 2 persons and electricity (3A)	€ 19.00 - € 23.00
extra person	€ 4.50 - € 5.00
electricity 6/10A	€ 2.20 - € 5.00

FR80110 Camping le Ridin

Lieu-dit Mayocq, F-80550 Le Crotoy (Somme)

Tel: **03 22 27 03 22**. Email: **contact@campingleridin.com**

Le Ridin is a popular family site in the countryside just 2 km. from Le Crotoy with its beaches and marina, and 6 km. from the famous bird reserve of Le Marquenterre. The site has 162 pitches, including 47 for touring, the remainder occupied by mobile homes and chalets (for rent). There is some shade. The pitches and roads are unsuitable for large units. The site amenities are housed in beautifully converted barns across the road and these include a heated pool, fitness centre, bar/restaurant and bicycles for hire. Reception staff are helpful and will advise on local excursions.

Facilities

Toilet blocks are heated in cool weather and provide good showers and special facilities for children. Restaurant/bar. Small shop. Swimming and paddling pools. Fitness centre. Games room. Play area. TV room. Bicycle hire. Entertainment and activity programme. Off site: Birdwatching 6 km. Golf 10 km.

Open: 21 March - 5 November.

Directions

From A16 (Calais - Abbéville) take exit 24 and follow signs to Le Crotoy. At roundabout on arrival at Le Crotoy turn towards St Férmin, then second road on right. GPS: N50:14.364 E01:37.893

Charges 2008

Per unit incl. 2 persons	€ 16.00 - € 24.00
extra person	€ 5.00 - € 5.20
electricity (6-10A)	€ 2.50 - € 5.50
Camping Cheques accepted.	

Check real time availability and at-the-gate prices...

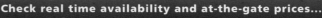 **www.alanrogers.com**

FR80150 Camping le Walric

Route d'Eu, F-80230 Saint-Valery-sur-Somme (Somme)

Tel: **03 22 26 81 97**. Email: **info@campinglewalric.com**

A clean, well-kept, managed site, Le Walric is about 75 minutes from Calais. A former municipal site, it has been completely up-dated with a new bar and snack bar, a pool complex, two play areas and entertainment in high season. There are 263 well laid out, large and level grass pitches. Of these, 105 with electricity connections are for touring with the remainder used for a mix of new mobile homes and semi-residential caravans. The site's situation on the outskirts of the town make it an ideal holiday location. Medieval Saint-Valéry is renowned for its association with William the Conqueror. The cathedral cities of Amiens, St Quentin and Laon are near. The Bay of the Somme is of especial interest to bird enthusiasts. Watersports abound in this area. There are two other sites in this group which you may also consider for a stay: Les Galets de la Molliere and Le Bois de Pins

Facilities

Two toilet blocks include British style WCs, washbasins in cubicles and showers. Facilities for disabled visitors. Laundry room with baby changing. Motorcaravan service point. Bar with snacks and TV. Heated outdoor pool. Off site: Shops, restaurants, bars in Saint-Valéry.

Open: 1 April - 1 November.

Directions

From A16 exit 24, follow D32 across N1. At roundabout take D235 to Morlay; turn left on the D940 and continue around Saint-Valéry until second roundabout where take first exit on D3 to site.

Charges 2008

Per unit incl. 3 persons and electricity	€ 17,00 - € 28,50
extra person	€ 7,00
dog	€ 3,00

Le Bois de Pins ★★★   Le Walric ★★★★   Les Galets de la Mollière ★★★

Privilege Camping Ticket € 18,- per night for a pitch

This offer is not valid for arrivals in July and August

FR80190 Camping les Galets de la Mollière

Rue Faidherbe La Mollière, F-80410 Cayeux-su-rMer (Somme)

Tel: **03 22 26 61 85**

Cayeux sur Mer is an attractive, traditional seaside resort close to the Somme estuary. Les Galets de la Mollière is located just to the north of the town and has undergone a recent renovation programme. This site has been recommended to us by our French agent and we plan to undertake a full inspection in 2008. The site extends over 6 hectares and has 198 pitches, of which 118 are reserved for touring, all with electrical connections and some with water and drainage. A fine sandy beach is adjacent to the site – a short walk across the sand dunes. Although there are limited amenities on site, Cayeux is just 3 km. away and has a good range of shops and restaurants.

Facilities

Toilet blocks include facilities for babies and disabled people. Laundry. Small shop. Bar. Snack bar.. Takeaway food. Motorcaravan services. Off site: Nearest beach 300 m. Cayeux sur Mer 3 km. Tennis 3 km. Riding 1 km. Sailing and windsurfing 1 km.

Open: 1 April - 1 November.

Directions

From the A16 take exit 24 (Le Crotoy) and join the D32 to Rue, and then the D940 to St Valery. Bypass St Valery on the D940 and then join the D3 signed Cayeux sur Mer. After a further 4 km you will arrive at La Mollière and site is well signed from here.

Charges 2007

Per unit incl. 2 persons and electricity	€ 14,32 - € 18,89
extra person	€ 2,97
child (under 7 yrs)	€ 1,37

105

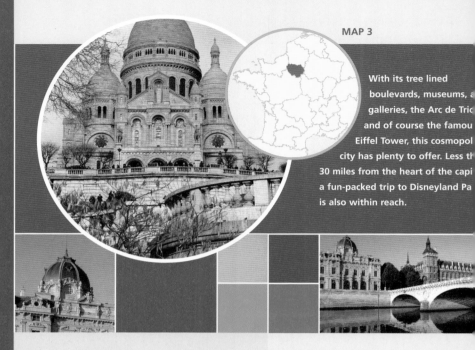

MAP 3

With its tree lined boulevards, museums, a galleries, the Arc de Trio and of course the famou Eiffel Tower, this cosmopol city has plenty to offer. Less th 30 miles from the heart of the capi a fun-packed trip to Disneyland Pa is also within reach.

DÉPARTEMENTS: 75 PARIS, 77 SEINE-ET-MARNE, 78 YVELINES, 91 ESSONE, 92 HAUTS-DE-SEINE, 93 SEINE-ST-DENIS, 94 VAL DE MARNE, 95 VAL D'OISE

MAJOR CITIES: PARIS, VERSAILLES, IVRY, MELUN, NANTERRE, BOBIGNY, CRETEIL AND PONTOISE.

One of the most chic and culturally rewarding cities in the world, Paris has something for everyone. The list of things to do is virtually endless and could easily fill many holidays - window shopping, the Eiffel Tower, Notre Dame, Montmartre, trips on the Seine, pavement cafés and the Moulin Rouge, the list goes on.

As a peaceful retreat, you can relax and enjoy the lush scenery of surrounding hills and secret woodlands of the Ile de France. Square bell towers in gentle valleys, white silos on endless plains of wheat; soft and harmonious landscapes painted and praised by La Fontaine, Corot and all the landscape painters. Paris is surrounded by forests, Fontainebleau, Compiègne, Saint-Germain-en-Laye and majestic châteaux such as Fontainbleau and Vaux-le-Vicomte.

Disneyland Resort Paris provides a great day out for all the family with two fantastic theme parks with over 70 attractions and shows to choose from. On the outskirts of Paris is Parc Asterix. with one of Europe's most impressive roller-coasters.

Places of interest

Fontainebleau: château and national museum, history of Napoléon from 1804-1815.

Malmaison: château and national museum.

Meaux: agricultural centre, Gothic cathedral, chapter house and palace.

Paris: obviously! The list of places is too extensive to include here.

St Germain-en-Laye: château, Gallo-roman and Merovingian archeological museum.

Sèvres: ceramics museum.

Thoiry: château and Parc Zoologique, 450-hectare park with gardens and African reserve containing 800 animals.

Versailles: Royal Castle, Royal Apartments, Hall of Mirrors, Royal Opera and French History Museum.

Cuisine of the region

Although without a specific cuisine of its own, Paris and Ile de France offer a wide selection of dishes from all the regions of France. Paris also has a wide choice of foreign restaurants, such as Vietnamese and North African.

FR91000 Camping Caravaning le Bois de la Justice

F-91930 Monnerville (Essonne)

Tel: **01 64 95 05 34**. Email: **picquetfredo@orange.fr**

La Bois du Justice is a conveniently located site close to Paris and Versailles. It is situated in a wood in the middle of farmland with a narrow, 1.2 km. approach road. The 150 pitches, of which 30 are for touring units, are laid out among the trees (60-100 sq. m.), well shaded but sloping, with 12 in a newer, open area. Electricity (5A) is available throughout and most pitches have a water tap. Access to some pitches would be difficult for larger units. The site is ideal as an overnight stop when travelling north or south or for touring the area southwest of Paris.

Facilities

The single large toilet block can be heated and has been refurbished with modern vanity units and controllable showers. Facilities for babies and disabled visitors. Washing machine. No shop. Bread and provisions van calls mornings (every day except Wed. in Apr - Oct; every day in July/Aug). Bar with snacks and takeaway (July/Aug). Medium sized pool (about15/6-15/9). Playground. TV. Table tennis and volleyball. Off site: Shops and restaurants in Mereville 3 km. Riding 1.5 km. Fishing 7 km.

Open: 1 February - 30 November.

Directions

Going south on the N20 (Paris-Orléans), take exit for Monnerville. Keep right over N20 into village, straight over crossroads and site is well signed.

Charges 2007

Per person	€ 6,00
child (under 10 yrs)	€ 3,00
pitch	€ 5,00
electricity (5A)	€ 2,50

FR91010 Camping Caravaning le Beau Village

1 voie des Prés, F-91700 Villiers-sur-Orge (Essonne)

Tel: **01 60 16 17 86**. Email: **le-beau-village@wanadoo.fr**

This is a pleasant, typically French campsite just 25 km. south of Paris and conveniently located at the centre of a triangle formed by the A6 motorway, the N20/A10 to Orleans and the N104 east/west link road 'La Francilienne'. Half of its 100 pitches are occupied on a seasonal basis by Parisians; the rest are touring pitches, all hedged and with 10A electricity. Trees provide some shade. Reception, in a traditionally-styled building, also has a pleasant little bar and an attractive terrace.

Facilities

The main toilet block has controllable showers and some washbasins in cabins. A second (older) block has adequate facilities for disabled visitors, the third (in a 'portacabin') has laundry facilities and a very tired unit for children. All three can be heated. Small bar. Games room with internet access (charged). Play area. Loan of canoes. Off site: Shops and restaurants. Golf, riding 2 km. River beach and sailing 3 km. Boat launching 4 km.

Open: All year.

Directions

From N20 at Ballainvillers take exit for La Ville du Bois on D35 southeast to Villiers-sur-Orge. In village (foot of hill), turn right on Voie des Prés along river bank to site on left. .

Charges 2007

Per person	€ 4,50
pitch	€ 3,50
electricity	€ 3,50

FR91020 Le Parc des Roches

La Petite Beauce, F-91530 Saint-Chéron (Essonne)

Tel: **01 64 56 65 50**. Email: **contact@parcdesroches.com**

This large site with 400 pitches occupying a wooded hill-top is principally dedicated to providing Parisians with somewhere to escape from city life, but also offers 80 touring pitches on gently sloping ground near the entrance. These are reasonably well tended and all have 5A electricity. A convenient location for a night's break if travelling north or south on the N20. A large heated swimming pool has a lifeguard at busy times and has plenty of space for sunbathing (no loungers!) The bar/restaurant is pleasant and offers basic food at reasonable prices.

Facilities

The main toilet block provides pre-set showers, washbasins in cabins (warm water only). Dishwashing and laundry facilities. Several separate toilets, washbasins in cubicles and showers (with detachable shower-heads) for disabled visitors. An older block is more basic with open style washbasins. Both can be heated. Swimming pool (1/6-15/9). Bar/restaurant and takeaway (15/6-15/9) also sells basics. Tennis. Football goals. Volleyball and basket-ball. Play area (in residential part). Off site: Station 3 km. (Paris, Versailles). Fishing 6 km. Riding 10 km. Golf 15 km.

Open: 15 April - 1 November.

Directions

From N20, 5 km. south of junction with N104 (La Francilienne) turn west at Arpajon on D97. At roundabout turn south on D116 (St Chéron and Dourdan). In St Chéron at first traffic lights turn left past railway, then left on D132 for 3 km. to la Petite Beauce. After hamlet turn left to campsite. GPS: N48:32.717 E02:08.22

Charges 2007

Per person	€ 6,60
pitch incl. car	€ 7,60
electricity	€ 2,60

FR75020 **Camping du Bois de Boulogne**

2 allée du Bord de l'eau, F-75016 Paris (Paris)

Tel: **01 45 24 30 00**. Email: **camping-boulogne@stereau.fr**

A busy site and the nearest to the city, set in a wooded area between the Seine and the Bois de Boulogne. The site is quite extensive but nevertheless becomes very full with many international visitors. There are 510 pitches (including mobile homes and a few chalets) of which 280 are marked, with electricity (10A), water, drainage and TV aerial connections. The site has undergone a huge improvement and re-development programme including the refurbishment of all toilet blocks. Reservations are made for pitches – if not booked, arrive early in season (mornings).

Facilities

Toilet blocks have British style WCs, washbasins in cubicles and showers with divider and seat (hot water throughout). All these facilities suffer from heavy use in season. Laundry facilities. Five motorcaravan service points. Mini-market. Bar and restaurant (1/4-15/10). Bar open 07.00 - midnight at most times and until 02.00 in peak season. Pizza bar and takeaway service. Playground. Information service. Off site: Fishing 1 km. Bicycle hire 2 km.

Open: All year.

Directions

Site is on east side of Seine between the river and the Bois de Boulogne, just north of the Pont de Suresnes. Easiest approach is from Port Maillot. Traffic lights at site entrance. Follow signs closely and use a good map. GPS: N48:52.060 E02:14.050

Charges 2007

Per unit incl. 2 persons with electricity,	€ 20,40 - € 28,30
water and drainage	€ 24,60 - € 35,70
tent incl. 2 persons	€ 11,00 - € 16,50
extra person	€ 4,50 - € 6,50
child (under 7 yrs)	€ 2,40 - € 3,20

FR77020 **Camping le Chêne Gris**   0 1746 785100

Mobile homes ▶ page 488

24 place de la Gare de Faremoutiers, F-77515 Pommeuse (Seine-et-Marne)

Tel: **01 64 04 21 80**. Email: **info@lechenegris.com**

This site is currently being developed by a new Dutch/Italian company. A new building which houses reception on the ground floor and an airy restaurant/bar plus a takeaway is of high quality. Of the 198 pitches, 65 are for touring many of which are on rough aggregate stone, the rest (higher up the hill on which the site is built) being occupied by over 100 mobile homes and 25 tents belonging to a Dutch tour operator. Terraces look out onto a heated leisure pool complex and an adventure play area for over-fives and the play area for under-fives is at the side of the bar with picture windows overlooking it. The site is next to a railway station with trains to Paris. Disneyland is 20 km.

Facilities

One basic toilet block with push button showers, washbasins in cubicles and a dishwashing and laundry area. At busy times these facilities may be under pressure. A second block is to be added. Facilities for disabled visitors. Children's area with toilets and baby bath but showers at adult height! Bar, restaurant and takeaway. Pool complex (all season). Off site: Shops, bars and restaurants within walking distance. Fishing and riding 2 km.

Open: All year.

Directions

Pommeuse is 55 km. east of Paris. From A4 at exit 16 take N34 towards Coulommiers. In 10 km. turn south for 2 km. on D25 to Pommeuse; site on right after level-crossing. Also signed from south on D402 Guignes - Coulommiers road, taking D25 to Faremoutiers. GPS: N48:48.514 E02:59.530

Charges guide

Per unit incl. 2 persons, electricity	€ 29,00 - € 35,00
extra person	€ 2,00 - € 3,50
child (3-11 yrs)	€ 2,00 - € 3,00
animal	€ 2,50

- *15 minutes drive from Disneyland® Resort Paris*
- *next to the train station at Pommeuse with a direct line to Paris*
- *rental of luxury mobile homes*
- *rental of luxury, fully furnished bungalow tents*
- *pitch reservation with 10 amp electrical hook up*
- *well shaded campsite*
- *situated on a gently sloping hillside*
- *English, Italian, Spanish, French, Dutch and German spoken*
- *open 26ᵗʰ April 2008 to 9ᵗʰ November 2008*

Camping **Le Chêne Gris**
24, Place de la Gare de Faremoutiers
77515 Pommeuse
T: (+33) 1640 42 180 F: (+33) 1642 00 589
E: info@lechenegris.com

- Snack bar
- Restaurant ▪ Bar
- Laguna pool (Children's Pool)
- Covered swimming pool
- Supermarket

Le Chêne Gris   **www.lechenegris.com**

FR77030 Camping International de Jablines

Base de Loisirs, F-77450 Jablines (Seine-et-Marne)

Tel: **01 60 26 09 37**. Email: **welcome@camping-jablines.com**

Jablines is a modern site which, with the accompanying leisure facilities of the adjacent 'Espace Loisirs', provides an interesting, if a little impersonal alternative to other sites in the region. Man-made lakes provide marvellous water activities. The 'Great Lake' as it is called, is said to have the largest beach on the Ile-de-France! The site itself provides 150 pitches, of which 141 are for touring units. Most are of a good size with gravel hardstanding and grass, accessed by tarmac roads and marked by fencing panels and shrubs. All have 10A electrical connections, 60 with water and waste connections also. The whole complex close to the Marne has been developed around old gravel workings. Water activities include dinghy sailing, windsurfing, canoeing, fishing and supervised bathing, plus a large equestrian centre. In season the activities at the leisure complex are supplemented by a bar/restaurant and a range of very French style group activities.

Facilities

Two toilet blocks, heated in cool weather, include push button showers, some washbasins in cubicles. Dishwashing and laundry facilities. Motorcaravan service (charged). Shop. Play area. Bar/restaurant adjacent at leisure centre/lake complex with watersports including 'water cable ski', riding activities, tennis and minigolf. Whilst staying on the campsite, admission to the leisure complex is free. Internet point. Ticket sales for Disneyland and Asterix. Off site: Golf 15 km.

Open: 29 March - 26 October.

Directions

From A4 Paris - Rouen turn north on A104. Take exit 8 on D404 Meaux/Base de Loisirs Jablines. From A1 going south, follow signs for Marne-la-Vallée using A104. Take exit 6A Clay-Souilly on N3 (Meaux). After 6 km. turn south on D404 and follow signs. At park entry keep left for campsite. GPS: N48:54.817 E02:44.051

Charges 2008

Per pitch incl. 2 persons	
and electricity (10A)	€ 21,00 - € 26,00
extra person	€ 6,00 - € 7,00
child (3-11 yrs)	€ 4,00 - € 5,00
Camping Cheques accepted.	

Base Régionale de Plein-Air et de Loisirs de Jablines-Annet

Covering more than 450 hectares, a leisure and relaxation area unique in the Île de France.

L'espace loisirs
Jablines-Annet
www.camping-jablimes.com

Camping ★★★

FR77040 Caravaning des 4 Vents

Rue de Beauregard, F-77610 Crèvecoeur-en-Brie (Seine-et-Marne)

Tel: **01 64 07 41 11**. Email: **f.george@free.fr**

This peaceful, pleasant site has been owned and run by the same family for over 35 years. There are around 200 pitches, with many permanent or seasonal units, however, there are 130 spacious grassy pitches for tourists, well separated by good hedges, all with 6A electricity and a water tap shared between two pitches. The site is well landscaped with flowers and trees everywhere. This is a great family site with pool and games located at the top of the site so that campers are not disturbed.

Facilities

Three modern sanitary units (heated in cooler weather) provide British style WCs, washbasins (mainly in cubicles) and push button showers. Facilities for disabled people. Laundry facilities. Motorcaravan service point. In high season (July/Aug) a mobile snack bar and pizzeria (open from 16.00-23.00), and a baker from 07.30-11.00. Well fenced, circular swimming pool (16 m. diameter; June - Sept). Playground. Riding (high season). Off site: La Houssaye 1 km. Fontenay Tresigny 5 km.

Open: 1 March - 1 November.

Directions

Crèvecoeur is just off the D231 between A4 exit 13 and Provins. From north, pass obelisk and turn right onto the C3 in 3 km. From south 19 km. after junction with N4, turn left at signs to village. Follow site signs. GPS: N48:45.044 E02:53.775

Charges 2008

Per unit incl. 2 persons and electricity	€ 25,00
extra person (over 5 yrs)	€ 5,00

FR77070 Kawan Village la Belle Etoile

Quai Joffre, la Rochette, F-77000 Melun (Seine-et-Marne)

Tel: **01 64 39 48 12**. Email: **info@campinglabelleetoile.com**

Alongside the River Seine, this site has an overall mature and neat appearance, although the approach road is somewhat off-putting with several industrial plants. However, you'll discover that La Belle Etoile enjoys a pleasant position with pitches to the fore of the site within view of the barges which continually pass up and down. The 170 touring pitches, with electricity connections (6/10A), are on grass and laid out between the many shrubs and trees. There are ten units for hire. A friendly, family run site with pleasant and helpful English speaking owners. Ideally situated for visiting Fontainebleau and Paris.

Facilities

The toilet blocks are not new but they are kept very clean and the water is very hot. Laundry room. Baby bath. Facilities for disabled visitors (shower, washbasin and WC). Motorcaravan service point. Small bar, snacks and shop (28/6-30/8). Takeaway (1/5-15/9). Swimming pool (1/5-15/9). Play area. Fishing. Bicycle hire. Tickets for Disney and Vaux le Vicomte are sold by the site. Off site: Fontainebleau and Paris. Golf 15 km.

Open: 1 April - 22 October.

Directions

Travelling north on N6 Fontainebleau - Melun road, on entering La Rochette, pass petrol station on left. Turn immediately right into Ave de la Seine. At end of road turn left at river, site on left in 500 m. GPS: N48:31.501 E02:40.164

Charges 2007

Per person	€ 4,90 - € 5,40
child (3-11 yrs)	€ 3,00 - € 3,40
pitch	€ 5,00 - € 5,40

Camping Cheques accepted.

Camping La Belle Etoile

* Familycampsite
* Many playfacilities
* Hirefacilities:
  - Tent bungalows with toilet and shower
  - Mobil homes and chalets

GPS. 48,52578/2,66911 (lat / long)
E-mail: info@campinglabelleetoile.com
Internet: www.campinglabelleetoile.com
Tel: ++33(0) 1 64 39 48 12
Fax: ++33(0) 1 64 37 25 55

We accept Camping-Cheque

FR77060 Le Parc de la Colline

Mobile homes ▶ page 488

Route de Lagny, F-77200 Torcy (Seine-et-Marne)

Tel: **01 60 05 42 32**. Email: **camping.parc.de.la.colline@wanadoo.fr**

This is a traditional and fairly basic campsite with just one advantage – its proximity to Paris and to Disneyland. There are shuttle buses to the Metro (RER) station just 3 km. away and also to Disneyland and Parc Asterix. For the energetic, there are two large sports and water parks nearby, with swimming, bicycle and pedalo hire and weekend fitness and aqua gym sessions on the beach (500 m. from site) and canoeing, windsurfing, tennis, squash, badminton, weight training, etc (2 km). The site itself is on the side of a hill with most pitches on level grass terraces. Those at the foot of the hill are separated by mature hedges and bushes. All have electricity (2/6A), but water has to be fetched from the toilet blocks. Access to the terraces is quite steep.

Facilities

Two elderly toilet blocks seem to be reasonably maintained; an attempt has been made to brighten them up. Mainly Turkish style toilets but a few British with the occasional seat! Controllable showers. Warm and cold water to washbasins (mainly in cubicles). En-suite facility for disabled visitors (stark but fully equipped). Washing facilities. Small shop for basics. Snack bar (mainly canned drinks and beers) with internet point, TV and some games. Off site: Disneyland 10 mins. (métro), central Paris 20 mins (métro), Parc Asterix 30 mins (car). Supermarket and restaurants nearby. Fishing and golf 400 m. Riding 1 km.

Open: All year.

Directions

From Paris and the Péripherique take A4 to the junction with the A104 (Charles de Gaulle - Lille). From A1 Paris - Lille take A104 (Marne la Vallée), leave at exit 10 and head west signed Parc de Loisirs de Torcy to campsite on left in 1 km. GPS: N48:51.510 E02:39.219

Charges 2008

Per person	€ 7,10
child (under 7 yrs)	€ 5,10
pitch incl. electricity	€ 14,50
dog	€ 4,60

FR77120 Camping le Soleil de Crécy

Route de Serbonne, F-77580 Crécy-La-Chapelle (Seine-et-Marne)

Tel: **01 60 43 57 00**. Email: **info@campinglesoleil.com**

Le Soleil de Crécy is very well positioned for accessing both Disneyland Paris and the city itself. The nearest station is just 100 m. from the site and there is also a good bus service. This site has been recommended to us and we plan to undertake a full inspection in 2008. There are separate areas for those using tents or those with either caravans and motor caravans, with 4/10A electrical connections available for the latter. A number of mobile homes are available for rent. This is a lively site in high season with an entertainment and activity programme, as well as some good amenities including a swimming pool and mini golf course. Inevitably, Paris and Disneyland are the strongest attractions here but Europe's largest shopping complex is also close at hand, Le Val d'Europe at Marne la Vallée. By way of contrast, there are some fine châteaux to visit, notably Vaux le Vicomte, Ferrières and Blandy-les-Tours.

Facilities

Shop. Restaurant. Snack bar. Takeaway. Swimming pool. Minigolf. Activity and entertainment programme. Bicycle hire. Games room. Mobile homes for rent.
Off site: Disneyland Paris 14 km. Vaux le Vicomte 16 km. Val d'Europe shopping complex 14 km. Bus stop at site entrance.

Open: 28 March - 3 November.

Directions

Take exit 16 from the A4 motorway and join the N34 towards Coulommiers. This road passes through Crècy-la-Chapelle. Shortly after passing the church, turn right and the site is signed from here.

Charges 2008

Per unit incl. 2 persons
and electricity   € 25,00 - € 38,00

FR77090 Camping les Etangs Fleuris

Route Couture, F-77131 Touquin (Seine-et-Marne)

Tel: **01 64 04 16 36**. Email: **contact@etangs-fleuris.com**

This is a pleasant, peaceful site which has a very French feel despite the presence of a fair number of tour operator mobile homes, since these occupy their own areas round the periphery. The 60 touring pitches are grouped on the level ground around the attractive lakes, all with electricity (10A) and water, separated by hedges and with shade from mature trees. The life of the site centres round a smart bar/function room which doubles as reception and a shop, as well as the lakes and an attractive, irregularly shaped pool.

Facilities

Basic toilet has push button showers, and open washbasins (with dividers and hooks) for men but mainly in cubicles for ladies. Cleaning can be variable at busy times. No facilities for disabled visitors. Another heated block is only opened in cold weather or when site is very busy. Laundry facilities. Motorcaravan service area. Shop for basics in bar. Heated pool with paddling section (1/4-15/9). Takeaway meals and snacks (15/5-10/9). Internet access and WiFi. Covered table tennis area. Multisports pitch. Minigolf. Off site: Riding 5 km. Golf 15 km. Zoo 5 km.

Open: 15 April - 15 September.

Directions

Touquin is off the D231, 21 km. from exit 13 of A4 motorway and 30 km. northeast of Provins. From D231 follow signs for Touquin, then Etangs Fleuris. Site is 2.5 km. west of village. GPS: N48:43.867 E03:02.845

Charges 2008

Per unit incl. 2 persons   € 16,00
incl. electricity   € 18,00
child (0-9 yrs)   € 3,50 - € 4,00
No credit cards.

FR77130 Camping les Courtilles du Lido

Courtilles du Lido, Veneux-Les-Sablons F-77250 (Seine-et-Marne)

Tel: **01 60 70 46 05**. Email: **lescourtilles-dulido@wanadoo.fr**

Les Courtilles du Lido is a well-established site located just outside the 14th century village of Moret-sur-Loing, on the edge of the Forêt de Fontainebleau. There are 180 well shaded pitches here dispersed throughout the site's five hectare terrain. All have electrical connections (10A) The site also offers a good range of amenities including a swimming pool and an 18-hole minigolf course, as well as a pizzeria and bar. There are a number of chalets and mobile homes available for rent. The close proximity of Fontainebleau, just 5 km. distant, is, of course, a major attraction and the town merits repeated visits. Fontainebleau's golf course is the second oldest in France and many other activities are possible in the area, including rock climbing and 300 km. of walking and cycle trails through the forest. Paris lies 55 km. to the north and can be accessed by either the A5 or A6 motorways.

Facilities

Toilet blocks include facilities for children and disabled people. Shop. Pizzeria. Bar. Takeaway meals. Swimming pool. Play area. Games room. Motorcaravan services. Minigolf. Tennis. Off site: Moret-sur-Loing (an attractive Gallo-Roman village) 2 km. Fishing. Riding. Golf. Fontainebleau 5 km. River cruises 5 km. Paris 55 km.

Open: 22 March - 22 September.

Directions

Site is close to the point where the Loing joins the Seine. From Fontainebleau take the southbound N6 (towards Sens). Upon arrival at Veneux les Sablons follow signs for Moret-sur-Loing and then St Mammès. Site is well signed.

Charges 2008

Per person	€ 3,75
child (under 7 yrs)	€ 3,00

Camping Les Courtilles du Lido - Chemin du Passeur - 77250 Veneux les Sablons
Tel: 0033 160 70 46 05 - Fax: 0033 164 70 62 65
E-mail: lescourtilles-dulido@wanadoo.fr - www.les-courtilles-du-lido.fr

FR77140 Yelloh! Paris/Ile-de-France

La Cerclière, F-77560 Louan Villegruis Fontaine (Seine-et-Marne)

Tel: **04 66 73 97 39**. Email: **info@yellohvillage-paris-iledefrance.com**

Formerly known as La Cerclière, this Yelloh! Village site, to the east of Paris, has been recommended to us and we plan to undertake a full inspection in 2008. The site lies at the heart of the Montaiguillon forest, around 50 km. from Disneyland Paris and 80 km. from the city itself. This 11 hectare site contains 150 touring pitches and 100 mobile homes and chalets for rent. The pitches are well shaded and of a good size, and most offer electrical connections (6A). The site boasts some impressive amenities including a swimming pool with water slides, as well as a balneotherapy centre. In peak season, there is plenty of activity on site, with nature workshops for children and themed entertainment evenings. The mediaeval town of Provins is close and well worth a visit – a horse drawn carriage is a particularly appealing way to view the town.

Facilities

Shop. Bar. Restaurant. Takeaway. Swimming pool complex with water slides. Balneotherapy centre. Multisports pitch. Volleyball. Bicycle hire. Tennis. Activity and entertainment programme. Off site: Disneyland Paris 50 km. Paris centre 80 km. Walking and cycle trails. Fishing.

Open: 26 April - 6 September.

Directions

Take exit 16 from the A4 motorway (Paris - Metz) and join the N34. Continue on this road as far as La Ferté Gaucher and then turn left to join the southbound. Upon reaching the N4 turn left and then right on to the D15 to Villiers St Georges. Continue to Louan Fontaine Villegruis, from where the site is well signed.

Charges 2008

Per unit incl. 2 persons and electricity	€ 14,00 - € 35,00
extra person (over 3 yrs)	€ 5,00 - € 7,00

FR95000 Parc de Séjour de l'Etang

10 chemin des Bellevues, F-95690 Nesles-la-Vallée (Val-d'Oise)

Tel: **01 34 70 62 89**. Email: **brehinier1@hotmail.com**

Parc de Séjour de L'Etang is small, informal site 33 km. northwest of Paris. It is situated on the southern outskirts of the village of Nesles-la-Vallée in a pretty, tree-lined river valley not far from L'Isle-Adam, which is a popular destination for Parisians at weekends. Many of the 165 pitches are occupied by seasonal caravans but there are 65 large, flat pitches available for touring all with electricity (3/9A) and 25 also have water and waste water drainage. The site is informally arranged around a duck pond with many trees to provide shelter and shade.

Facilities

The main, central toilet block (heated in cooler weather) includes washbasins in rather small cubicles and, in separate rooms, rather older style British and Turkish WCs. Dishwashing and laundry sinks. Washing machine. Smaller, much older unit includes fairly basic facilities for disabled visitors. Playground, volleyball and basketball areas, and play barn with table tennis. Off site: Village and restaurant within walking distance. Fishing permits for the river from village. Riding 500 m. Golf 7 km.

Open: 1 March - 15 November.

Directions

From A15 exit 10 take D915 (Pontoise), avoiding town centre, then D27 (Beauvais) which joins D927, then D79 to Nesles-la-Vallée. Site on left as you leave village on D64. From N1 or A16 (exit 11) take D922 southwest (L'Isle Adam), then D64 northwest (Nesles la Vallée). SGPS: N49:07.647 E02:11.047

Charges 2007

Per person	€ 4,50
pitch incl. electricity (3/9A)	€ 7,65 - € 8,60

No credit cards.

FR94000 Camping du Tremblay Paris Est

Boulevard des Alliés, F-94507 Champigny-sur-Marne (Val-de-Marne)

Tel: **01 43 97 43 97**. Email: **champigny@campingparis.fr**

This site is on flat land beside the River Marne with 450 pitches, 76 of which are occupied by mobile homes and chalets to rent. The 220 touring pitches are on gravel and are separated by hedges. All have electricity (10A) but water has to be fetched from the toilet blocks except for the 32 serviced pitches which have taps and waste water points. There is a large area of grass pitches for camping where there are water points but no electricity. It is very much a short-stay site but seems well run.

Facilities

Three toilet blocks are old-fashioned but apparently cleaned three times a day. Toilets are mainly segregated with many Turkish-style but some British (with occasional seat!) One block has unisex toilets (seat-less British-style). Showers are pre-set and washbasins in cubicles with warm and cold water. Facilities for disabled visitors (some en-suite) are basic and there are no grab rails. Dishwashing sinks. Laundry facilities. Small shop, bar and snack bar (15/3-15/10). Fishing.

Open: All year.

Directions

From A4 take exit 5 on D45 south (towards Champigny). At lights, turn right on N303 (St Maur). At next lights continue on (now N4 to Vincennes) and immediately turn right at next lights (Boulevard de Polangis). Before reaching motorway flyover, turn right on Boulevard des Alliés. Site on left (passing under motorway). GPS: N48:49.777 E02:28.624

Charges 2007

Per unit incl. 2 persons	€ 11,00 - € 31,90
extra person	€ 4,60 - € 6,00

FR78010 Camping Caravaning International

1 rue Johnson, F-78600 Maisons-Laffitte (Yvelines)

Tel: **01 39 12 21 91**. Email: **ci.mlaffitte@wanadoo.fr**

This site on the banks of the Seine is consistently busy, has multilingual, friendly reception staff and occupies a grassy, tree covered area bordering the river. There are 351 pitches, 57 occupied by mobile homes and 70 used by tour operators, plus two areas dedicated to tents. Most pitches are separated by hedges, are of a good size with some overlooking the Seine (unfenced access), and all 195 touring pitches have electricity hook-ups (6A). The roads leading to the site are a little narrow so large vehicles need to take care. Train noise can be expected.

Facilities

Three sanitary blocks, two insulated for winter use and one more open (only used in July/August). Facilities are clean with constant supervision necessary, due to volume of visitors. Provision for people with disabilities. Laundry and dishwashing areas. Motorcaravan service point. Self-service shop. Restaurant/bar. Takeaway food and pizzeria. TV room. SNCF rep each morning (15/6-15/8) for travel advice. Off site: Sports complex adjoining. Riding 500 m. Bicycle hire 5 km.

Open: 15 March - 31 October.

Directions

Best approached from A13 or A15 autoroute. From A13 take exit 7 (Poissy) and follow D153 (Poissy), the D308 (Maisons-Laffitte), then site signs on right before town centre. From A15 exit 7 take D184 towards St Germain, after 11 km. turn left on D308 (Maisons-Laffitte). Follow site signs. GPS: N48:56.394 E02:08.740

Charges 2008

Per unit incl. 2 persons	€ 24,50 - € 30,00
extra person	€ 5,50 - € 6,20

TRAVEL SERVICE SITE
TO BOOK CALL **01580 214000**
Advice & low ferry-inclusive prices

FR78040 Huttopia Rambouillet

Route du Château d'Eau, F-78120 Rambouillet (Yvelines)

Tel: **01 30 41 07 34**. Email: **rambouillet@huttopia.com**

This pleasant site has recently been taken over by the Huttopia group who will be developing it, starting with an outdoor, heated swimming pool. It is in a peaceful forest location beside a lake, with good tarmac access roads, site lighting and 190 touring pitches of varying size and surfaces. Some of the individual pitches are divided by hedges, others are more open and sunny. All have electricity, 83 also have water and drainage, with a few hardstandings. There are many good cycle and footpaths in the area. It is possible to visit Paris by rail; the Mobilis 'transport package' ticket is available from the railway station. Rambouillet itself is an interesting town and Chartres and Versailles are within reach.

Facilities

Two heated sanitary buildings include British and Turkish style WCs, washbasins (some in cubicles), dishwashing and laundry sinks, plus basic facilities for baby changing and for disabled persons. Washing machine and dryer. Motorcaravan service point. Café/bar and boutique. Good playground. Swimming pool. Off site: Large supermarket at southern end of the town.

Open: 29 March - 2 November.

Directions

Rambouillet is 52 km. southwest of Paris. Site is southeast of town: from N10 southbound take Rambouillet/Les Eveuses exit, northbound take Rambouillet centre exit, loop round and rejoin N10 southbound, taking next exit. Pass under N10, following site signs. GPS: N48:37.623 E01:50.727

Charges 2008

Per person	€ 5,00 - € 6,50
child (2-7 yrs)	€ 3,00 - € 3,80
pitch	€ 6,50 - € 18,00
electricity (6-10A)	€ 4,20 - € 6,20
dog	€ 3,00 - € 3,50
Camping Cheques accepted.	

FR78050 Camping le Val de Seine

Base de Loisirs, chemin du Rouillard, F-78480 Verneuil-sur-Seine (Yvelines)

Tel: **01 39 28 16 20**. Email: **sce-client@valdeseine78.com**

This is an excellent little site, completely refurbished to high standards and located in a large leisure and country park on the western outskirts of Paris. Campers have free access to the huge country park (800 m. from site) with its three large lakes, one with a beach for swimming, others for sailing and pedalo hire. The site has 87 pitches in two sections, one end for campers (mainly groups) with its own toilet block, the other for caravans and tents. Here there are 37 level pitches, all but four with electricity (6A), water and drainage. There is some aircraft and train noise.

Facilities

Two modern toilet blocks have controllable showers and some washbasins in cubicles. Facilities for disabled visitors (touring area). Dishwashing provision. Small block for children plus baby room (camping area). Laundry facilities. Motorcaravan service point. Reception sells bread to order and basics. Country park. Lakes, fishing, sailing, other sports facilities. Self-service restaurant and brasserie. 18-hole minigolf. Off site: Golf 7 km. Paris 30 mins by car.

Open: 15 April - 30 September.

Directions

From A13 take exit 8 (Meulan-les Mureaux). Follow signs for 'Base de Loisirs du Val de Seine'. Go through Les Mureaux and bear right on D154 towards Verneuil. At roundabout turn left (signed 'Base de Loisirs') to site. GPS: N48:59.762 E01:57.548

Charges 2007

Per person (4 yrs and over)	€ 3,25 - € 3,75
pitch incl. electricity	€ 8,45 - € 9,55

FR78060 Huttopia Versailles

31 rue Berthelot, F-78000 Versailles (Yvelines)

Tel: **01 39 51 23 61**. Email: **versailles@huttopia.com**

This Huttopia site is rather different. When the French owners visited Canada and experienced 'back to nature' camping, they were so impressed that they decided to introduce the idea to France. This is probably a little like camping as it used to be, but with some big differences. Gone are the formal pitches with neatly trimmed hedges and instead there are 145 places of ample size arranged informally amongst the trees. The terrain is as nature intended with very little grass and much of it steep and rugged (there are plans to introduce some terracing). Long electricity leads are required and be prepared to use blocks and corner steadies on many pitches, most of which have good shade. All the site buildings are designed and built to fit into the natural concept. Attractive wooden huts, tents and gypsy style caravans can be rented. This is a different but popular site that will suit campers who, while still wanting their creature comforts, would like to be in more natural surroundings.

Facilities

Three well designed toilet blocks (wood cabin style) are evenly dispersed and provide basic facilities. Restaurant with takeaway (1/7-31/8 and weekends). Bar. Games room. Simple swimming and paddling pools (June-Sept). Playground. Bicycle hire. Children's club. Off site: Versailles and its château. Fishing 1 km. Golf 3 km. Riding 5 km. Paris 20 minutes by RER express train.

Open: 28 March - 2 November.

Directions

From the front of the château of Versailles take the Avenue de Paris and the site is signed after 2 km. GPS: N48:47.380 E02:09.380

Charges 2007

Per person	€ 6,00 - € 7,90
child (2-7 yrs)	€ 3,00 - € 4,00
pitch	€ 10,00 - € 20,00
electricity (6/10A)	€ 4,00 - € 6,20

Camping Cheques accepted.

FR60010 Camping Campix

B.P. 37, F-60340 Saint Leu-d'Esserent (Oise)

Tel: **03 44 56 08 48**. Email: **campix@orangel.fr**

This informal site has been developed in a former sandstone quarry on the outskirts of the small town. The quarry walls provide a sheltered, peaceful environment and trees soften the slopes. Not a neat, manicured site, the 160 pitches are in small groups on the different levels with stone and gravel access roads (some fairly steep and muddy in poor weather). Electricity (6A) is available to about 140 pitches. There are secluded corners mostly for smaller units and tents and space for children to explore (must supervised – some areas, although fenced, could be dangerous). Torches are advised.

Facilities

A large building houses reception and two clean, heated sanitary units - one for tourers, the other (open July/Aug) usually reserved for groups. Two suites for disabled people double as baby rooms. Laundry area. Facilities may be congested at peak times. Motorcaravan services. Daily bread and milk. Pizza and other Italian food delivered in the evenings. Off site: Fishing 1 or 5 km. Riding, golf 5 km.

Open: 7 March - 30 November.

Directions

St Leu-d'Esserent is 11 km. west of Senlis, 5 km. northwest of Chantilly. From north on A1 autoroute take Senlis exit, from Paris the Chantilly exit. Site north of town off D12 towards Cramoisy, and signed in village. GPS: N49:13.509 E02:25.638

Charges 2007

Per person	€ 3,00 - € 5,50
pitch incl. electricity	€ 6.00 - € 9.00

Camping Cheques accepted.

MAP 4

Home to the Champagne region, the varied landscape of Eastern France include dense forests, vineyards and winding rivers. The who area is dotted with fascinating ancient churches and castles, towns and villages.

EASTERN FRANCE IS DEFINED AS:
CHAMPAGNE-ARDENNE: 08 ARDENNES, 51 MARNE, 10 AUBE, 52 HAUTE-MARNE. LORRAINE VOSGES: 54 MEURTHE-ET-MOSELLE, 55 MEUSE, 57 MOSELLE, 88 VOSGES. ALSACE: 67 BAS-RHIN, 68 HAUT-RHIN

Situated on the flatlands of Champagne are the most northerly vineyards in France where special processing turns the light, dry wine into 'le Champagne' and names such as Moet et Chandon and Veuve Clicquot spring to mind. Nowhere else in the world are you allowed to make sparkling wine and call it champagne. Travelling further east you come across spa towns such as Vittel, the birth place of St Joan of Arc at Domrémy and the beautiful lake and valley around Gérardmer in the Vosges mountains.

Today you can descend from the mountains into the Alsace vineyards and fairy tale wine villages. The 'Route des Vins' follows the vineyards along the Rhine valley from Mulhouse to Colmar and north almost to Strasbourg. Alsace and Lorraine have been frequently fought over and today there are many poignant reminders of the turbulent past, such as at Verdun. There are also many beautiful places to visit, such as the garden-city of Metz and the Art Nouveau capital of Nancy.

Places of interest

Épernay: home of champagne production.

Gérardmer and La Bresse: the main towns of the Vosges mountains with many opportunities for hiking.

Le Linge: trenches including rusty barbed wire have been left as they were.

Metz and Nancy: the capitals of Lorraine, known for their beautiful cultural heritage.

Reims: 13th century Gothic cathedral.

Riquewihr: traditional town, fortifications and medieval houses.

Verdun: hill forts such as Fort de Vaux and Fort de Douaumont, large military cemetery at Douaumont.

Cuisine of the region

Bar-le-Duc ('Lorraine caviar'): redcurrant jam de-seeded with a goose quill.

Madeleine de Commercy: small, shell shaped, buttery pastries with orange flavouring.

Quiche Lorraine: made only in the classical manner with cream, eggs and bacon.

Tarte (aux mirabelles): golden plum tart. Also made with other fruits.

Tarte à l'oignon Alsacienne: onion and cream tart.

*Credit photo: CRTL.
The Comité Régional du Tourisme de Lorraine's annual Passport brochure suggesting over 150 places to visit (with discounted entrance) is available free of charge from www.tourisme-lorraine.fr*

Lorraine Vosges

country holidays in wonderful nature

Enjoy fresh air and beautiful nature in the Lorraine-Vosges region and stay on the numerous Camping Qualité" sites in this area offering quality-service for unforgettable holidays.

www.tourisme-lorraine.fr
www.tourismevosges.fr

FR51020 Camping Municipal en Champagne

Rue de Plaisance, F-51000 Châlons-en Champagne (Marne)

Tel: **03 26 68 38 00**. Email: **camping.mairie.chalons@wanadoo.fr**

The location of Châlons, south of Reims and near the A4 and A26 autoroutes, about 200 miles from Calais and Boulogne, makes this an ideal stopover. This site on the southern edge of town is an example of a good municipal site. The wide entrance with its neatly mown grass and flower beds sets the tone for the rest of the site; 96 of the 148 pitches, accessed from tarmac roads, are on a gravel base with the rest on grass. All have electricity (10A). The generously sized gravel pitches are separated by hedges. The newest area of pitches overlooks the small lake.

Facilities

Two toilet blocks (one can be heated) include washbasins in cabins, baby room and hairdressing station. Facilities for disabled visitors. Laundry and dishwashing facilities. Refuse bins. Bread to order. Bar, snack bar and takeaway (20/5-31/9 evenings, lunchtime July/Aug). Gas supplies. Games and TV rooms. Playground. Minigolf, tennis, volleyball, boules, mini-football. Motorcaravan service point. Off site: Bus stop. Fishing.

Open: 1 April - 31 October.

Directions

From north on A4, take La Veuve exit (27) onto N44 which by-passes town. Leave at last exit (St Memmie), follow camping signs. From south on A26, take exit 18 on N77 and towards town. Site well signed 'Camping', (south of town on D60). GPS: N48:56.156 E04:22.994

Charges 2007

Per person	€ 4,80
pitch incl. electricity	€ 8,00
vehicle	€ 3,20

FR54000 Camping le Brabois

Avenue Paul Muller, F-54600 Villers les Nancy (Meurthe-et-Moselle)

Tel: **03 83 27 18 28**. Email: **campeoles.brabois@wanadoo.fr**

This former municipal site is within the Nancy city boundary and 5 km. from the centre. Situated within a forest area, there is shade in most parts and, although the site is on a slight slope, the 185 good-sized, numbered and separated pitches are level. Of these, 160 pitches have electrical connections (5/15A) and 30 also have water and drainage. Being on one of the main routes from Luxembourg to the south of France, Le Brabois makes a good night stop. However, Nancy is a delightful city in the heart of Lorraine and well worth a longer stay.

Facilities

Six sanitary blocks (old and due for refurbishment over the next few years) with a mix of British and Turkish style WCs and some washbasins in cubicles. One can be heated in cool weather. Units for disabled visitors. Laundry facilities. Motorcaravan service point. Shop. Bread to order. Restaurant with bar and small shop (15/6-31/8). Library. Playground. Ball games. Table tennis. Off site: Restaurants, shops 1 km. Walking and cycling. Regular buses to Nancy.

Open: 1 April - 15 October.

Directions

Take exit 2b 'Brabois' from autoroute A33, continue for 500 m. to 'Quick' restaurant on left. Turn left, pass racetrack to T-junction, turn right and after 400 m. turn right on to site entrance road.

Charges 2008

Per unit incl. 2 persons and electricity	€ 15,00 - € 18,20
extra person	€ 4,00 - € 5,50
electricity	€ 4,00

FR54010 Camping de Villey-le-Sec

34 rue de la Gare, F-54840 Villey-le-Sec (Meurthe-et-Moselle)

Tel: **03 83 63 64 28**. Email: **info@campingvilleylesec.com**

This neat campsite is a popular overnight stop, but the area is worth a longer stay. Villey-le-Sec has its own fortifications, part of the defensive system built along France's frontiers after the 1870 war, and a long cycle track passes near the site. On a bank of the Moselle river, there are 75 level grassy marked touring pitches, with electricity (6A) and plenty of water taps. There are also individual water taps and waste water drainage for 8 of these pitches. Another area accommodates 11 tents (no electricity). Just outside the site is an overnight stopping place for motorcaravans.

Facilities

Two modern toilet blocks (one heated) contain British style WCs, washbasins in cabins and controllable showers. Facilities for disabled people and babies. Motorcaravan services. Washing machine and dryer. Gas supplies. Shop. Bar/restaurant. Snack bar and takeaway. Games room. Playground. Playing field. Table tennis. Boules. Fishing. Off site: Riding 2 km. Rock climbing 4 km. Golf 15 km.

Open: 1 April - 30 September.

Directions

Villey-le-Sec is 7 km. east of Toul. Leave A31 west of Nancy at exit 15 and after 1 km. at roundabout (Leclerc supermarket) take D909 to Villey-le-Sec. In village follow signs 'Camping, Base de Loisirs' to the right. At bottom of hill turn left to site in 300 m.

Charges 2007

Per person	€ 3,00
child (0-7 yrs)	€ 1,90
pitch	€ 2,30 - € 3,60
electricity (6-10A)	€ 3,50 - € 4,50

FR55010 Camping les Breuils

Allée des Breuils, F-55100 Verdun (Meuse)

Tel: **03 29 86 15 31**. Email: **contact@camping-lesbreuils.com**

Thousands of soldiers of many nations are buried in the cemeteries around this famous town and the city is justly proud of its determined First World War resistance. Les Breuils is a neat, attractive site beside a small fishing lake and close to the town and Citadel. It provides 166 flat pitches of varying sizes on two levels (144 for touring units), many with shade. Separated by trees or hedges, they are beside the lake and 120 offer electricity connection (6A; long leads will be necessary for some).

Facilities

Two sanitary blocks are a mixture of old and new, including washbasins in cabins for ladies. Laundry facilities. Facilities for the disabled and babies. Dishwashing sinks. Cleaning variable. Motorcaravan services. Shop (1/5-30/9). Guide books on sale at reception (1/5-31/8). Restaurant (1/6-20/8), bar (evenings 1/5-30/9). Pool (200 sq.m.) and children's pool (1/6-31/8). Fenced gravel play area. Multisports complex. Off site: Bicycle hire, town 1 km. Riding 5 km.

Open: 1 April - 30 September.

Directions

The RN3 forms a sort of ring road round the north of the town. Site is signed from this on the west side of the town (500 m. to site). GPS: N49:09.222 E05:21.938

Charges 2007

Per person	€ 5,50
child (2-10 yrs)	€ 3,50
caravan or motorcaravan	€ 4,50
double axle caravan	€ 20,00
tent	€ 3,00

Discounts for low season and longer stays.
Credit cards accepted for minimum of € 15.

FR57080 Camping la Croix du Bois Sacker

F-57220 Burtoncourt (Moselle)

Tel: **03 87 35 74 08**. Email: **camping.croixsacker@wanadoo.fr**

This very attractive site is quiet and child-friendly and has been run for the last few years by a young and enthusiastic couple who have made many improvements to this former municipal site. For example, the terrace has been enlarged, a small shop added and the facilities for disabled visitors improved. There are 60 pleasant, open pitches, some with shade and all with electricity and water taps. The site is not far from Metz and is well suited for travellers going south to Germany, Switzerland or Italy. Forming part of the site, a lake is good for fishing (carp).

Facilities

The seasonal and touring parts of the site have separate facilities. Showers are on payment (token). Turkish style toilets outnumber British style. Washbasin, some in cabins. Sports field and tennis court. Play area. Lake swimming (July/Aug). Fishing. Off site: Woodland walks.

Open: 1 April - 31 October.

Directions

From the A4 take exit 37 (Argancy) and follow signs for Nalroy, Chieulles and Vany on RD3 towards Bouzonville. Then take D53 to Burtoncourt and site.

Charges 2007

Per unit incl. 2 persons and electricity	€ 15,00

No credit cards.

FR57050 Camping Municipal de Metz-Plage

Allée de Metz-Plage, F-57000 Metz (Moselle)

Tel: **03 87 68 26 48**. Email: **campingmetz@mairie-metz.fr**

As this site is just a short way from the autoroute exit and within easy walking distance for the city centre, it could make a useful night stop if travelling from Luxembourg to Nancy or for a longer stay if exploring the area. By the Moselle river, the 151 pitches are on fairly level grass and most are under shade from tall trees. 65 pitches are fully serviced and 84 have electricity (10A). Tent pitches have a separate place beside the river.

Facilities

The two sanitary blocks, one newer than the other, are acceptable if not luxurious. Facilities for disabled visitors. Baby room. Laundry and dishwashing facilities. Motorcaravan service point. Shop. Bar, restaurant and takeaway. Hardstanding pitches for over night stops for motorcaravans without electricity. Off site: Indoor pool adjacent. Fishing. Riding 5 km. Golf 8 km.

Open: 5 May - 23 September.

Directions

From autoroute take Metz-Nord - Pontiffray exit (no. 33) and follow camp signs. GPS: N49:07.430 E06:10.135

Charges guide

Per person	€ 2,50
child (4-10 yrs)	€ 1,20
pitch incl. electricity	€ 6,00
with water and drainage	€ 7,00
tent and vehicle	€ 2,50

FR67010 Camping l'Oasis

3 rue du Frohret, F-67110 Oberbronn (Bas-Rhin)

Tel: **03 88 09 71 96**. Email: **oasis.oberbronn@laregie.fr**

This is an attractively situated, inexpensive site, amidst the mountains and forests of northern Alsace, not far from the German border. There are good views over the valley to one side and the pretty village with trees sheltering the other. The circular internal road has pitches around the outside (120 for touring units, 30 for seasonal units), and space in the centre where there is a playground. The solar-heated swimming pool and children's pool are of excellent quality. A 'Centre de Vacances' was added for 2004, with a covered swimming pool, sauna and fitness room.

Facilities	Directions
The first well appointed toilet block, heated in cool weather, has some washbasins in cabins for ladies, washing machines and dryers, a baby room and facilities for disabled people. The second block is unisex and small. Small shop. General room with table football and air hockey. Swimming pool and children's pool (July/Aug). Indoor pool next to site. Playground. Tennis court. Off site: Riding 700 m. Supermarket 1 km. Fishing 3 km.	South of Niederbronn turn left on D28 for Oberbronn-Zinswiller - site is signed from here. From A4 take exit 42 to Sarreguemines, then N62 and D620 towards Haguenau and as above. GPS: N48:55.746 E07:36.244

Open: 14 March - 12 November.

Charges guide

Per person	€ 3,70
pitch incl. electricity	€ 8.10

No credit cards.

FR67040 Camping la Ferme des Tuileries

F-67860 Rhinau (Bas-Rhin)

Tel: **03 88 74 60 45**. Email: **camping.fermetuileries@neuf.fr**

Close to the German border, this 10 hectare, family run site has 150 large open pitches, hardstanding for 15 motorcaravans and room for 50 seasonal caravans. The site buildings have a traditional external appearance but all have modern interiors. Welcoming reception staff will provide information about the site and the local area. A small lake with two water slides is used for swimming, fishing and boating (divided into two areas) and there is also a small unsupervised swimming pool (hats compulsory). A newly built restaurant and bar are at the lakeside.

Facilities	Directions
Three modern, bright and cheerful blocks with the normal facilities. Two washing machines and two dryers. Controllable showers. Family bathroom at no extra charge. Fully equipped facilities for disabled visitors (no key, no coins). Motorcaravan services. Newly built restaurant and bar. Small lake for swimming, fishing, boating, two water slides. Swimming pool (unguarded) open July/August. Tennis. Petanque. Minigolf. Off site: Supermarket 300 m. Ferry across the Rhine.	Coming from Colmar (A35) take exit 14 (Kogenheim-Benfeld-Erstein) then the N83 to exit for Benfeld-Rhinau, following site signs. From Strasbourg on A35 take exit 7 (Erstein-Fegersheim) then the N83.

Open: 1 April - 30 September.

Charges 2007

Per person	€ 3,30
pitch	€ 3,30
electricity (2-6A)	€ 1,40 - € 3,20

No credit cards.

FR57070 Camping Centre de Loisirs et Culture

Route de Luttange, F-57940 Volstroff (Moselle)

Tel: **03 82 56 93 40**. Email: **campingvol@aol.com**

This site is located in a fairly remote, rural setting but does have a full range of services and activities in July and August. Outside this period it may feel rather too empty and quiet for some. There are 26 chalet style gites on-site and a fair number of seasonal caravans. Set in one corner of what is a very large park with a lake, the camping area is fan shaped, with 134 individual pitches divided by hedges and shrubs. These are in rows back to back between fairly narrow gravel access roads which can be very dusty in dry weather.

Facilities	Directions
Two modern toilet blocks (not heated) are fairly stylish, clean and well appointed; some cubicles and corridors are cramped in the smaller block. Facilities for babies and disabled campers. Washing machine and dryer. Bar. Shop and takeaway. Outdoor swimming pool (25 x 18 m.) and children's pool (July/Aug). Sauna. Tennis. Minigolf. Play area. Fishing. Pedaloes. Animation. Internet access. Off site: Golf 15 km. Riding 10 km. Bicycle hire 10 km.	Best approached from A31 junction 37. Cross first river bridge on D8, at second (blue bridge) turn right on D8bis. After 2 km. turn left on D1 to Bousse. At Bousse take D8 for about 7 km. and turn left towards Volstroff on D2bis. Site is signed. GPS: N49:17.905 E06:16.329

Open: 12 April - 26 October.

Charges 2008

Per unit incl. up to 4 persons and electricity (3A)	€ 15,20 - € 17,30

Check real time availability and at-the-gate prices...

www.**alanrogers**.com

FR67050 Camping Municipal Wasselonne

Route de Romanswiller, F-67310 Wasselonne (Bas-Rhin)

Tel: **03 88 87 00 08**. Email: **camping-wasselonne@wanadoo.fr**

A good quality municipal site with a resident warden. Facilities include a well stocked small shop, a crêperie in season and the added bonus of free admission to the superb indoor heated swimming pool adjacent to the site. There are 80 tourist pitches and around 20 seasonal units, on grass with a slight slope, all with electricity hook-ups (10A). Four new rental chalets are in a separate fenced area and there are six new private chalets. This could be an excellent base from which to visit Strasbourg. A full programme of events is offered in the town by the Tourist Office, including welcome evenings, guided tours, concerts, musical festivals, food tasting evenings.

Facilities

The single, large and well maintained sanitary unit has unisex facilities with ample sized showers and washbasins in cubicles. Laundry facilities and covered dishwashing sinks. No specific facilities for disabled visitors but the rooms are spacious and should be accessible to many. Excellent drive-over motorcaravan service point. Off site: Heated pool, hotel with restaurant, tennis courts, plus athletics stadium all adjacent. Supermarket 500 m. Fitness trail, riding 1 km.

Open: 15 April - 15 October.

Directions

Wasselonne is 25 km. west of Strasbourg. Site lies southwest of town centre on D224 towards Romanswiller, and is well signed. GPS: N48:38.264 E07:25.907

Charges 2007

Per unit incl. 1 person	€ 7,30 - € 7,70
extra person	€ 3,40 - € 3,60
child (0-10 yrs)	€ 1,80 - € 1,90
electricity	€ 3,00
animal	€ 0,50 - € 0,60

FR68030 Camping de Masevaux

3 rue du Stade, F-68290 Masevaux (Haut-Rhin)

Tel: **03 89 82 42 29**. Email: **camping-masevaux@tv-com.net**

Masevaux is a pleasant little town in the Haut-Rhin département of Alsace, just north of the A36 Belfort - Mulhouse motorway. The neatly mown 120 pitches for tourists are on level grass, of reasonable size, marked by trees and hedges, and all have electricity (3/6A). Most are well shaded with good views of the surrounding hills. The pleasant and helpful Scottish managers, who take pride in the site, would like to welcome more British visitors. A good choice for one night or a longer stay to explore this interesting region, and an ideal destination for serious walkers. The site is situated in a quiet edge of town next to the sporting complex which has a good indoor pool and other sporting opportunities. A network of walking routes complete with overnight shelter cabins has been set up in the mountains around the area. These overnight cabins are free of charge.

Facilities

A modern, well designed and well equipped sanitary block has most washbasins in private cabins. Baby room. Laundry and covered dishwashing area. Café/bar serving snacks. Baker calls in high season. Ice-creams and soft drinks available at reception. TV room, small library. Boules. Children's play area. Tennis courts (extra charge), volleyball, table tennis. Off site: Supermarket, restaurants and indoor pool. Fishing. Market in Masavaux Wednesdays.

Open: 15 February - 31 December.

Directions

From D466 in Masevaux follow signs for Belfort and then 'Camping Complexe Sportif'. GPS: N47:46.677 E06:59.462

Charges 2007

Per person	€ 3,50
child (under 2-12 yrs)	€ 1,50
pitch	€ 3,00
electricity (3/6A)	€ 3,00 - € 3,60
dog	€ 0,80

Camping Masevaux*
Rue du Stade
68290 Masevaux
Tel/fax: 0033 389 82 42 29
E-mail: contact@camping-masevaux.com
Internet: www.camping-masevaux.com

FR68040 **Camping Municipal les Trois Châteaux**

10 rue du Bassin, F-68420 Eguisheim (Haut-Rhin)

Tel: **03 89 23 19 39**. Email: **camping.eguisheim@wanadoo.fr**

The village of Eguisheim is on the Alsace 'Rue du Vin' to the west of Colmar. The three châteaux from which the site gets its name are clearly visible on the distant hills. Being close to the village, Les Trois Châteaux is busy and popular. Flowers, shrubs and trees, and well tended grass areas make this a very pleasant place. The 121 pitches, 115 with electricity (6/10A), are either on a slight slope or a terrace, and are marked and numbered, most with good shade. Around 80% of pitches have some gravel hardstandings, most of irregular shape and size. The facilities of the fascinating village of Eguisheim are close and the site is well located for exploring this delightful part of Alsace.

Facilities

The single sanitary block in the centre of the site has hot showers and warm water only to washbasins. Some washbasins in cubicles and facilities for disabled people. Playground. Motorcaravan service point. Bicycle hire. Off site: Fishing 3 km. Golf, riding 10 km.

Open: 1 April - 30 September.

Directions

Eguisheim is just off the N83 and the site is well signed in the village.

Charges 2007

Per unit incl. 2 persons	€ 11,50 - € 13,00
extra person	€ 3,50 - € 4,00
child (0-12 yrs)	€ 0,10 - € 2,50
electricity (6/10A)	€ 4,00 - € 5,50
dog	€ 1,50

No credit cards.

FR68050 **Camping Municipal Pierre de Coubertin**

23 rue de Landau, F-68150 Ribeauvillé (Haut-Rhin)

Tel: **03 89 73 66 71**. Email: **camping.ribeauville@wanadoo.fr**

The fascinating medieval town of Ribeauvillé on the Alsace Wine Route is within walking distance of this attractive, quietly located site. Popular and well run, it has 226 tourist pitches, all with electricity hook-ups (2/6A) and some separated by shrubs or railings. There are tarmac or gravel access roads. This is a site solely for tourists – there are no mobile homes or seasonal units here. The small shop is open daily for most of the season (hours vary) providing bread, basic supplies and some wines. Only breathable groundsheets permitted.

Facilities

Large, heated block provides modern facilities with washbasins in cubicles. Baby changing facilities. Large laundry and dishwashing rooms with a generous supply of sinks. A smaller unit at the far end of the site is opened for July/Aug. Very good facilities for disabled campers at both units. Shop (Easter - October). Recycling. Excellent adventure style playground with a rubber base. Tennis court. Boules. Table tennis. TV room. Off site: Outdoor pool (June-Aug). Sports complex.

Open: 15 March - 15 November.

Directions

Ribeauvillé is about 13 km. southwest of Sèlestat. Site is well signed, turn north off D106 at traffic lights by large car park, east of town centre. GPS: N48:11.697 E07:20.198

Charges 2007

Per person	€ 3,80
child (0-7 yrs)	€ 1,90
pitch	€ 4,00
electricity (2/6A)	€ 2,50 - € 4,00

FR68080 Camping Clair Vacances

Route de Herrlisheim, F-68127 Saint Croix-en-Plaine (Haut-Rhin)

Tel: 03 89 49 27 28. Email: clairvacances@wanadoo.fr

Clair Vacances, extended in 2003, is a very neat, tidy and pretty site with 130 level pitches of generous size which are numbered and most are separated by trees and shrubs. All have electricity connections (8-13A) and 10 are fully serviced with water and drainage. The site has been imaginatively laid out with the pitches reached from hard access roads. This is a quiet family site. The friendly couple who own and run it will be pleased to advise on the attractions of the area. The site is 1 km. from the A35 exit, not far from Colmar. Alsace is a popular and picturesque area of lovely villages, large vineyards, mountains and forests, and is also on the route taken by many heading for Switzerland or Italy.

Facilities

Two excellent, modern toilet blocks include washbasins in cabins, well equipped baby rooms and good facilities for disabled visitors. Laundry and dishwashing facilities. Shop with limited supplies. Swimming pool and children's pool (heated) with large sunbathing area (15/6-15/9). Playground. Table tennis. Volleyball. Community room. Archery in high season. Camping Gaz stocked. Dogs are not accepted. No barbecues or football. American motorhomes and twin axle caravans are not accepted. Off site: Colmar with restaurants and shops is not far away.

Open: Week before Easter - 15 October.

Directions

Site is signed from exit 27 of the A35 south of Colmar on the Herrlisheim road (D1).
GPS: N48:00.957 E07:20.989

Charges 2008

Per unit incl. 2 persons	
and electricity	€ 15,50 - € 25,00
extra person	€ 5,00 - € 7,00
child (0-7 yrs)	€ 0,20 - € 3,00
child (8-12 yrs)	€ 4,00 - € 6,00

ClairVacances is located near tourist attractions in a green setting with a great variety of bushes and flowers. The camping site is known for its excellent facilities which are maintained with great care. Bungalows can be rented. ClairVacances will enchant you.

ClairVacances
68127 Sainte Croix en Plaine
Tel.: + 33 3 89 49 27 28
www.clairvacances.com

FR68060 Camping Intercommunal Riquewihr

Route des Vins, F-68340 Riquewihr (Haut-Rhin)

Tel: 03 89 47 90 08. Email: camping.riquewihr@tiscali.fr

Surrounded by vineyards and minutes from the delightful village of Riquewihr, this is a well run site which has earned its good reputation. Situated in the heart of the Alsace wine region the site covers three hectares with views across the open countryside. To the right of the security barrier stands a modern, part-timbered building housing reception and information. Close by is a small summer house and both are heavily garlanded with flowers. The 161 spacious individual pitches, many with shade and divided by hedging, have electrical connections (6/10A). Most are on grass but there are also a few with hardstandings. Wine caves are just 200 m. away.

Facilities

Three sanitary blocks, one of a more modern design (not all open in low season). Facilities include private cabins with basins, good nursery room with baby bath, child's WC and changing mat, and excellent facilities for disabled people. Dishwashing and laundry areas. Motorcaravan service point. Campers' room with tables and chairs. Shop for basic necessities, drinks and papers (from 1/7-31/8). TV room. Playground. Off site: Ball games area and sports field nearby. Fishing 3 km. Swimming pool 4 km. Bicycle hire 5 km.

Open: Easter - 31 December.

Directions

From N83 north of Colmar take D4 westwards (Bennwihr). Turn north on D1bis for 2 km. towards Ribeauvillé. Site signed off roundabout at southern end of Riquewihr bypass. Do not enter village.
GPS: N48:09.731 E07:19.014

Charges 2007

Per person	€ 3,25 - € 3,60
child (under 7 yrs)	€ 1,55 - € 1,70
pitch with electricity	€ 7,10 - € 8,00
dog	€ 1,10 - € 1,20

FR68100 Parc de la Fecht

Route de Gunsbach, F-68140 Munster (Haut-Rhin)

Tel: 04 99 57 21 21. Email: contact@village-center.com

This campsite has been recommended by our agent in France and we intend to undertake a full inspection in 2008. Parc de la Fecht is a popular site located close to Colmar and Munster and is attractively sited along the famous Alsace wine route. The site has 260 pitches, some of which are occupied by mobile homes and chalets. Touring pitches are partly shaded and all have electrical connections. The site has direct access to the River Fecht and a good range of leisure facilities including a sports field and children's play area. Parc de la Fecht is well located for those wishing to explore the region on foot or by mountain bike with many walking and cycle routes close at hand. A member of Village Center group.

Facilities

Heated toilet blocks include facilities for babies and disabled visitors. Small shop. Snack bar. Sports pitch. Play area. Miniclub and entertainment programme (July/Aug). Mobile homes for rent. Off site: Supermarket, shops and restaurants in Munster. Riding 5 km. Swimming pool with water slides. Extensive walking and cycle (mountain bike) opportunities. Many picturesque Alsatian villages.

Open: 12 May - 15 September.

Directions

Site is east of Munster on D417 (Gérardmer - Colmar). From Munster take the D417 towards Turkheim, then head for Colmar on the D10. The site is 2.2 km. from Munster.

Charges 2007

Per unit incl. 2 persons and electricity	€ 8,00 - € 16,00
extra person	€ 2,00 - € 4,00
child (under 7 yrs)	€ 1,50 - € 3,25

FR68120 Camping les Lupins

Rue de la Gare, F-68580 Seppois-Le-Bas (Haut-Rhin)

Tel: 03 89 25 65 37. Email: leslupins@wanadoo.fr

Only ten kilometres from the Swiss border and within walking distance of the small village (800 m), this is a very attractive site. It has 142 grass touring pitches, which are not separated and 25 chalets to rent. Attractive trees have been planted throughout the site. The main site building houses reception, a small shop, two pool tables and a television and used to be the old local railway station (1910-1970). A very pleasant, small, fenced swimming pool is guarded in July and August, as is a playground for small children. The site is a member of the Villagecenter group.

Facilities

One good toilet provides plenty of facilities in a traditional style. A second block is older but with similar facilities. Cabins for disabled visitors. Free hot water. Small shop. bar and terrace. Swimming pool. Play area. Internet access. Off site: Village 800 m. Restaurant across the road. Forest walks.

Open: 7 April - 15 October.

Directions

Leave Belfort - Basel (CH) autoroute at Grandvillars. From Colmar/Strasbourg to Altkirch-Férette and Seppois-le-Bas. Leave A36 at Burnhaupt (exit 14) and take D103 towards Dannemarie, then the D7b to Seppois. From there follow signs to site.

Charges 2007

Per unit incl. 2 persons	€ 9,00 - € 18,00
extra person	€ 2,00 - € 3,00

FR88020 Camping de Belle-Hutte

1 bis Vouille de Belle-Hutte, Belle-Hutte, F-88250 La Bresse (Vosges)

Tel: 03 29 25 49 75. Email: camping-belle-hutte@wanadoo.fr

Belle-Hutte is a pleasant family-run site in the heart of the Vosges mountains on one of the southern routes to the Col de la Schlucht. Attractively situated surrounded by mountains and trees, it occupies an open hill slope (900 m. above sea level) with 125 numbered grass pitches (95 for touring) on six terraces. Pitches of about 120 sq.m. (some are larger) are divided by hedges and all have electrical connections. To reach the site you would have to depart from the usual main through routes but access is easy via good roads.

Facilities

The well built, central sanitary block is of excellent quality. Heated in cool weather, it also has facilities for disabled people and babies. Laundry facilities. Motorcaravan service point. Shop for gifts and basic food supplies. Takeaway and bar (hours vary). Rest room with TV. New swimming pool complex (June-Sept; no Bermuda shorts). Playground and play room with table tennis. Fishing. Ski storage room. Internet access. Off site: Ski lift 100 m. Village 400 m. Fishing 4 km. Riding 10 km.

Open: All year.

Directions

Site is about 9 km. from La Bresse on the D34 road towards the Col de la Schlucht.
GPS: N48:02.095 E06:57.758

Charges 2008

Per unit incl. 2 persons	€ 11,00 - € 19,50
extra person	€ 3,70 - € 6,20
child (under 7 yrs)	€ 2,30 - € 3,20
electricity (2/10A)	€ 2,00
Higher prices are for winter.	

FR88030 Camping de Noirrupt

5 chemin de l'Etang, F-88530 Le Tholy (Vosges)

Tel: **03 29 61 81 27**. Email: **info@jpvacances.com**

This attractive, modern, family run site has a commanding mountainside position with some stunning views especially from the upper terraces. This is a very comfortable and high quality site and one that is sure to please. The tarmac site road winds up through the site with pitches being terraced and cars parked in separate small car parks close by. The 70 lawn-like tourist pitches are generally spacious, and the whole site is beautifully landscaped and divided up with many attractive shrubs, flower beds, decking and trees. Paved paths and steps take more direct routes between levels.

Facilities

Two very modern buildings at different levels, plus a small unit behind reception, all immaculate with modern fittings. Washbasins in cubicles, facilities for babies, children and disabled campers. Washing facilities. Shop. Bar, snack bar and takeaway (4/7-20/8). Swimming pool (15 x 10 m. 1/6-15/9). TV room (1/6-15/9). Tennis. Animation in season. No double axle caravans or American RVs. Off site: Riding 300 m. Fishing 2 or 5 km. Golf 30 km. Le Tholy with its supermarket banks and other services 2 km. Gérardmer 10 km.

Open: 15 April - 15 October.

Directions

From Gérardmer take D417 west towards Remiremont. In Le Tholy turn right on D11, continue up hill for 2 km., and site is signed to your left. GPS: N48:05.334 E06:43.709

Charges 2008

Per person	€ 5,50
child (under 7 yrs)	€ 3,20
pitch	€ 8,90
electricity (2/6A)	€ 3,00 - € 5,00

FR88040 Kawan Village Lac de Bouzey

Mobile homes ▶ page 489

19 rue du Lac, F-88390 Sanchey (Vosges)

Tel: **03 29 82 49 41**. Email: **camping.lac.de.bouzey@wanadoo.fr**

Camping-Club Lac de Bouzey is eight kilometres west of Épinal, overlooking the lake, at the beginning of the Vosges Massif. The 125 individual 100 sq.m. back-to-back grass pitches are arranged on either side of tarmac roads with electricity (6-10A); 100 are fully serviced. They are on a gentle slope, divided by trees and hedging and some overlook the 130 ha. lake with its sandy beaches. Units can be close when site is busy. In high season there is lots going on for all ages, especially teenagers. Open all year, the site is much quieter in low season. English is spoken.

Facilities

Sanitary block includes a baby room and one for disabled people (there is up and down hill walking). In winter a small, heated section in main building with toilet, washbasin and shower is used. Laundry and dishwashing facilities. Motorcaravan service point. Shop. Bar and restaurant. Heated pool (1/5-30/9). Fishing, riding, games room, archery and bicycle hire. Internet access. Sound-proof room for cinema shows and discos (high season). Off site: Golf 8 km.

Open: All year.

Directions

Site is 8 km. west of Épinal on D460 and is signed from some parts of Épinal. Follow signs for Lac de Bouzey and Sanchey. GPS: N48:10.015 E06:21.594

Charges 2007

Per unit incl. 2 persons	€ 15,00 - € 25,00
extra person	€ 5,00 - € 9,00
child (4-10 yrs)	free - € 6,00
electricity (6-10A)	€ 5,00 - € 6,00
Camping Cheques accepted.	

FR88050 Domaine de Champé

14 rue des Champs-Navés, F-88540 Bussang (Vosges)

Tel: **03 29 61 61 51**. Email: **info@domaine-de-champe.com**

Bordered by the Moselle river and located just off the town square, this site is open all year making it a good base from which to explore in summer, and ideal for skiing in winter, when you might be tempted to rent one of the 12 chalets. Domaine de Champé is a level site with 110 touring pitches, all with electricity (4-12A), spread over a fairly large area on both sides of a tributary stream, so some are quite a distance from the facilities. An improving site and you will receive an hospitable welcome.

Facilities

Two sanitary units, one behind reception, with a smaller one in a more central position, are adequate rather than luxurious. Facilities for disabled campers. Motorcaravan services. Bar (all year). Restaurant and takeaway (weekends only in low season). Swimming pool (1/5-30/9). Sauna, steam room, jacuzzi and massage. Tennis. Small play area. Fishing. Internet access and WiFi. Off site: Shops and all other services in town. Lake fishing 3.5 km. Riding 4 km. Skiing 3 km.

Open: All year.

Directions

Bussang is about midway between Remiremont and Mulhouse on N66, almost due north of Belfort. Site is signed from town centre. GPS: N47:53.317 E06:51.429

Charges 2007

Per person	€ 4,60 - € 6,00
child (4-10 yrs)	€ 2,40 - € 3,20
pitch	€ 5,20 - € 7,10
electricity (4A)	€ 3,40 - € 4,50

Check real time availability and at-the-gate prices...

www.**alanrogers**.com

FR88080 Yelloh! en Vosges Domaine des Bans

Rue James Wiese, F-88430 Corcieux (Vosges)

Tel: 03 29 51 64 67. Email: info@yellohvillage-domaine-des-bans.com

Domaine des Bans is a large, busy campsite with 630 pitches in a country setting, with plenty of opportunities to be active. There is a very high percentage of static and tour operator units, but room for about 80 tourist units. Pitches (with electricity, water and drainage), numbered and separated by hedges, vary in size with some on low terraces. There is good shade. Some are tucked away in quiet areas with others nearer to where activities take place. This is not really a site for short stays, but is a base for exploring the varied and interesting countryside.

Facilities

Three functional toilet blocks. Some washbasins are in cabins. Shop (30/5-30/9). Bar (1/6-15/9). Restaurant (1/5-15/9). Takeaway (30/4-15/9). Swimming pools (outdoor 1/6-15/9, indoor 1/5-15/9). Playground and area for ball games. Tennis, minigolf, volleyball and archery. Bicycle hire. Riding. Lakes for fishing and boating. High season entertainment including discos (sound-proof room). 'Goats Castle' with about two dozen goats. Off site: Restaurant outside site. Others nearby in village.

Open: 26 April - 6 September.

Directions

From D8 St Dié - Gerardmer road, turn west on D60 just north of Gerbepal to Corcieux. GPS: N48:10.142 E06:52.817

Charges 2008

Per unit with 2 persons and electricity	€ 14,00 - € 39,00
extra person (over 3 yrs)	€ 5,00 - € 7,00

FR88090 Base de Loisirs du Lac de la Moselotte

Les Amias, B.P. 34, F-88290 Saulxures-sur-Moselotte (Vosges)

Tel: 03 29 24 56 56. Email: lac-moselotte@ville-saulxures-mtte.fr

This neat, well run, spacious lakeside site, part of a leisure village complex, has 75 generously sized, grassy and individual hedged pitches. All have electrical hook-ups (10A) and 25 of these are multi-serviced with electricity, water and waste water drainage. The trees currently provide no more than a little shade. The site is fully fenced with security barrier and key for the gates (to site and lakeside). All facilities are modern and well maintained. The adjacent 'Base de Loisirs' has a wide variety of activities on offer, and the area is very good for walking and cycling.

Facilities

The heated toilet block has controllable hot showers, some washbasins in cubicles and good facilities for babies and disabled campers. Laundry facilities. Shop (July/Aug). Bread to order all year. Bar/snack bar and terrace. Bicycle hire. Play area. Outdoor skittle alley. 30 chalets for rent. Off site: Town an easy walk. The 'Base de Loisirs' with lake (supervised swimming July/Aug), sandy beach, a climbing wall, fishing, archery and hire of pedalos, canoes and kayaks.

Open: All year.

Directions

Saulxures-sur-Moselotte is 20 km. east of Remiremont. From Remiremont take D417 east (St Ame), then right (east) on D43 towards La Bresse for 10.5 km. Turn left into Saulxures (site signed), entrance on right after 500 m. by lake. GPS: N47:57.164 E06:45.127

Charges guide

Per person	€ 4,00 - € 5,00
child (4-10 yrs)	€ 2,40 - € 3,00
pitch incl. electricity	€ 9,00 - € 11,00

FR88100 Camping le Barba

45 le village, F-88640 Rehaupal (Vosges)

Tel: 03 29 66 21 17. Email: camping.barba@wanadoo.fr

Located in the refreshing and beautiful Haute-Vosges region, this small, very pleasant campsite is owned and run by a dedicated couple. There is room for 50 units on well tended, unmarked grass where you pitch where you like. This creates a very relaxed, natural environment with hedges and mature trees providing shelter and shade. The site is in the heart of the village with an auberge next door for fine wines and good food, including local specialties. The surrounding hills offer 150 km. of marked walking and bike trails. Gérardmer and the Valley of the Lakes are just 15 minutes away, with the mountains of the Vosges and Alsace just a little further.

Facilities

The single toilet block, built in chalet style, is of a high standard and should be sufficient. Washing machine and dryer. Bread delivered. Auberge next door for meals and takeaway (to order) and small shop. Dogs are not accepted. Off site: Supermarket 5 km. Walking, cycling, skiing and fishing.

Open: 1 May - 1 October.

Directions

From Gérardmer follow signs to Rehaupal. Site is very well signed. GPS: N48:07.135 E06:43.878

Charges 2007

Per person	€ 4,30
child (under 7 yrs)	€ 2,90
pitch	€ 4,20
electricity (3/6A)	€ 2,50 - € 3,50

FR88120 Camping le Clos de la Chaume

21 rue d'Alsace, F-88430 Corcieux (Vosges)

Tel: **03 29 50 76 76**. Email: **info@camping-closdelachaume.com**

This pleasant site is within walking distance of the town, on level ground with a small stream adjacent. The friendly family owners live on site and do their best to ensure campers have an enjoyable relaxing stay. There are 100 level grassy pitches of varying sizes, with some holiday homes (private and rental) leaving 70 pitches for tourists. All have electricity hook-ups (6/10A) and some are divided by shrubs and trees. Access roads are sandy and people with large units or American RVs should phone first to check pitch availability. The site boasts an attractive, well fenced, small swimming pool and an excellent small adventure style playground. The site has some excellent and informative leaflets (available in several languages) which give details of walks and mountain biking routes in the surrounding countryside. Corcieux is in the heart of the 'Ballons des Vosges' and this site would make a good base to explore the area.

Facilities

Two units provide well maintained facilities including a laundry with washing machines and dryers, a dual purpose family/disabled room and dishwashing sinks. Motorcaravan service point. Recycling. Reception keeps basic supplies (July/August). Campingaz stocked. Swimming pool (13 x 7m. June-Sept). Games room with table football and a pool table. Table tennis, boules and volleyball. Off site: Bicycle hire 800 m. Riding 2 km. Fishing 3, 10 km. Golf 30 km. Corcieux market (Mondays).

Open: 15 April - 20 September.

Directions

Corcieux is about 17 km. southwest of St Dié des Vosges. Site is on D60, east of town centre, by the town boundary sign. GPS: N48:10.094 E06:53.401

Charges 2007

Per unit incl. 2 persons	€ 11,80
extra person	€ 3,40
child (0-7 yrs)	€ 1,80
electricity	€ 2,90
animal	€ 1,25

Camping le Clos de la Chaume***

Le Clos de la Chaume - 21 rue d'Alsace - F-88430 Corcieux - France
Tél.: (33) 03 29 50 76 76 - Fax: (33) 03 29 50 76 76

info@camping-closdelachaume.com
www.camping-closdelachaume.com

FR88110 Camping la Sténiole

1 Le Haut Rain, F-88640 Granges-sur-Volonge (Vosges)

Tel: **03 29 51 43 75**. Email: **steniole@wanadoo.fr**

Set in a lovely rural area in the heart of the Vosges massif, this attractive site is run by a dedicated young couple who are constantly improving the site and its facilities. There are 70 pitches, either separated by hedges or beside the water. A small river has been used to form a small lake for fishing and swimming and a series of separate ponds (water quality is checked regularly). An atmosphere of relaxation is encouraged and the whole family can have a good time here. At an altitude of 720 m. there is easy access to 160 km. of paths and tracks for walking and cycling.

Facilities

One toilet block together with further facilities in the main building provide all necessities including 4 private cabins. Washing machines and dryers. Small shop. Bar and restaurant. Internet access on the terrace. Lake swimming. Fishing. Games room with TV and library. Play area. Tennis. Apartments and mobile homes to rent. Off site: Woods and hills for walking and cycling.

Open: 1 May - 30 September.

Directions

Take the N420 from Epinal to Gérardmer then the D423 to Granges. There are two sites not far away from each other. GPS: N48:07.272 E06:49.717

Charges 2007

Per person	€ 2,50
child (01-0 yrs)	€ 1,80
pitch	€ 3,20
electricity (4A)	€ 2,90

FR88140 **Camping les Lacs**

F-88110 Celles-sur-Plaine (Vosges)

Tel: **03 29 41 28 00**. Email: **camping@sma-lacs-piette-percee.fr**

This is a well organised site with its own pool, close to the town centre, with many water-based and sporting activities available at the nearby Base Nautique and adjacent Lac de la Plaine. There are 129 hedged touring pitches and 10 chalets and, unlike many sites in the area, there are virtually no seasonal caravans. Some shady pitches border the tiny Plaine river, some pitches have gravel hardstanding, others are on grass, but all are surrounded by well trimmed mature hedges.

Facilities

Three good sanitary units are equally spaced along the length of the site, providing adequate facilities including some Turkish toilets. Facilities for disabled visitors. Swimming pool (25 x 10 m.) and paddling pool. Small shop. Bar, snack bar and takeaway (all season, varied hours). Entertainment in high season. Off site: Many activities at Base Nautique adjacent to site and Adventure Parc at nearby Lake Pierre-Percée (8 km). Riding 22 km.

Open: 1 April - 30 September.

Directions

From Nancy take N59 southeast towards St Dié, turning into Raon l'Etape, then take D392a northeast for 10 km. to Celles-sur-Plaine, and follow camping signs. GPS: N48:27.296 E06:56.835

Charges 2007

Per person	€ 4,80 - € 6,00
child (under 7 yrs)	€ 3,00 - € 3,50
pitch incl. electricity (4/10A)	€ 18,00 - € 26,00

FR88150 **Camping de Ramberchamp**

21 chemin du Tour du Lac, F-88150 Gérardmer (Vosges)

Tel: **03 29 63 03 82**. Email: **boespflug.helene@wanadoo.fr**

A long established, family run site in a beautiful location on the southern side of Lake Gérardmer, de Ramberchamp is very peaceful. It benefits from a bar and restaurant adjacent to reception, which is on one side of the D69, with mostly long stay units on the pitches around it. Most of the 200 touring pitches are on the opposite side of the road by the lakeside, with the larger sanitary building. Pitches here vary in size, larger ones being further from the lake, all with electricity (4A) and quite level. Those by the lakeside are mostly on gravel and are very popular.

Facilities

The main sanitary unit is fairly central and has been refurbished with modern fittings, whilst retaining some of its old French style and character. Baby room. Unit for disabled campers. Laundry. Motorcaravan service point. A second smaller older unit serves pitches on the other side of the road. Bar/restaurant with takeaway (15/4-15/9). Small play area. Max length of unit 8.5 m. Off site: Fishing, riding and bicycle hire 500 m. Town centre with shops, banks, buses and station 1.5 km.

Open: 15 April - 15 September.

Directions

Site is west of Gérardmer, on D69 on southern side of the lake. Best approached from N417 towards Le Tholy, turning on D69, passing Lido. Site reception on right hand side, site entrance opposite. GPS: N48:03.860 E06:51.222

Charges 2008

Per unit incl. 2 persons	€ 16,00
extra person	€ 5,00
electricity (4A)	€ 3,50
No credit cards.	

FR88130 **Kawan Village Vanne de Pierre**

Mobile homes ▶ page 489

5 rue du camping, F-88100 Saint Dié-des-Vosges (Vosges)

Tel: **03 29 56 23 56**. Email: **vannedepierre@wanadoo.fr**

La Vanne de Pierre is a neat and attractive site with 118 pitches, many of which are individual with good well trimmed hedges giving plenty of privacy. There are 13 chalets and mobile homes (for rent) and a few seasonal units, leaving around 101 tourist pitches, all multi-serviced with water, drain and electricity hook-up (6/10A). The reception building has been recently refitted and provides a well stocked small shop plus a restaurant/bar with a takeaway facility (all year but opening hours may vary). A 'Sites et Paysages' member.

Facilities

Main unit is heated with good facilities including washbasins in cubicles. Three family rooms each with WC, basin, and shower and two similar units fully equipped for disabled campers. A second, older unit (opened July/Aug). Shop. Bar/restaurant and takeaway. Swimming pool (1/4-30/9, weather permitting). Internet terminal. Gas supplies. Bicycle hire. Nordic walking is organised. Off site: Golf course, tennis courts, archery, riding all 1 km. Fishing. Supermarkets (some have 2.5 m. height barriers).

Open: All year.

Directions

St Dié is south east of Nancy. Site is east of town on north bank of river Meurthe and south of D82 to Nayemont les Fosses. Site well signed. GPS: N48:17.160 E06:58.199

Charges 2007

Per unit incl. 2 persons	€ 15,00 - € 22,00
extra person	€ 4,00 - € 6,00
child (4-10 yrs)	free - € 4,00
electricity	€ 4,00 - € 5,00
Camping Cheques accepted.	

FR88160 Camping les Jonquilles

Route du Lac, F-88400 Xonrupt-Longemer (Vosges)

Tel: **03 29 63 34 01**

Les Jonquilles is a traditional, family run, lakeside site with a friendly reception and some terrific views of the surrounding countryside and lake. The site has an overall slope (blocks advised), with 240 pitches entirely for tourists and no mobile homes, chalets or rental units. All the pitches are marked, many by very small trees and have access to electricity hook-ups (6A), but the site is generally quite open. There are a number of special pitches for motorcaravans by the lakeside, with a full 'aire de service' facility alongside and this area is very popular.

Facilities

Two traditional buildings, modernised at various times, give a good provision and include some Turkish toilets, washbasins in cubicles and spacious showers. Baby bath in ladies. Facilities for disabled campers. Washing machines and dryer. Playground. Petanque. Off site: Opposite reception is a food shop, bar, snack bar and creperie, with takeaway, all operated by the site owner's brother. Bar has internet terminal and satellite TV.

Open: 15 April - 10 October.

Directions

Xonrupt-Longemer is just to the east of Gérardmer. From centre of town take D67a that runs around the southern side of the lake and site is on left opposite a bar/restaurant. GPS: N48:04.057 E06:56.944

Charges 2008

Per unit incl. 2 persons	€ 9,00 - € 12,00
extra person	€ 2,00 - € 3,00
child (under 7 yrs)	€ 1,30 - € 1,50
electricity (6A)	€ 3,00

FR88170 Camping les Pinasses

215 route de Bruyères, F-88600 La Chapelle-Devant-Bruyères (Vosges)

Tel: **03 29 58 51 10**. Email: **pinasses@dial.oleane.com**

Les Pinasses is an orderly, well run family site with a small outdoor swimming pool. Traditional in style, the site is long and narrow with pitches on two levels. The sanitary facilities are good. However the site is fronted by a fairly busy road and a railway track runs immediately behind it, and this is quite close to some pitches. There are around 125 grassy, individual, hedged pitches of varying sizes, all with 4/6A electricity under trees plus 14 units to rent. There are also a number of seasonal units on site. The site organises a little low key animation in July and August.

Facilities

Four blocks of varying styles, upgraded at different times, include a mix of seated and Turkish style toilets, some washbasins in cubicles. Facilities for disabled campers at one block only (ramped entrance). Washing machines, dryers and spin dryer. Small shop (15/4-15/9). Bar and restaurant (July/Aug). Swimming and paddling pools (1/6-15/9). Playground. TV room. Boule. Minigolf. Tennis. Fishing. Some entertainment in high season. American RVs not accepted. Off site: Golf 30 km. Bicycle hire 8 km.

Open: 15 April - 15 September.

Directions

La Chapelle-devant-Bruyères is about 25 km. southwest of St Dié. Site is beside D60 Corcieux to Bruyeres road, 2 km. east of its junction with D423. GPS: N48:11.399 E06:46.538

Charges 2007

Per unit incl. 2 persons	€ 17,80
extra person	€ 4,90
child (under 7 yrs)	€ 2,50
electricity (4/6A)	€ 3,50 - € 4,50

FR08010 Camping Municipal du Mont Olympe

Rue des Paquis, F-08000 Charleville-Mezieres (Ardennes)

Tel: **03 24 33 23 60**. Email: **camping-charlevillemezieres@wanadoo.fr**

Attractively situated alongside the Meuse River, within easy walking distance across a footbridge to the centre of the pleasant large town, this site was completely rebuilt in 2002. It now offers excellent facilities, with 129 grass pitches, all with electricity (10A), water and waste water connections. There are 66 from 108 to 219 sq.m. in size, 49 up to 106 sq.m. and 7 hardstandings for motorcaravans.

Facilities

Two heated buildings provide first class showers, private cabins, baby rooms and facilities for the disabled, plus inside dishwashing (including one for the disabled) and a well-equipped laundry room. Motorcaravan service point. Shop (July/Aug). Play area. TV and games room. Barbecues allowed at communal area only. Off site: Municipal pool next door. Boat trips on the river. Attractive town centre close by. Bicycle hire 1 km. Golf 20 km.

Open: 1 April - 15 October.

Directions

Site north of Charleville on island of Montcy St Pierre. From north D988/D1 follow river, over bridge, then immediately left. From southeast (A203/N51/N43) take 'centre' exit, head for 'Gare' then follow Avenue Forest north and sharp left after bridge. Site is 150 m. on from old site. GPS: N49:46.741 E04:43.246

Charges 2007

Per unit with 2 persons and electricity	€ 16,00
extra person	€ 3,20
child (2-10 yrs)	€ 1,60 - € 5,80
dog	€ 1,45

FR08040 Camping la Samaritaine

F-08240 Buzancy (Ardennes)

Tel: **03 24 30 08 88**. Email: **info@campinglasamaritaine.com**

A delightful new site in the heart of the Ardennes. It is peacefully situated just outside the village beside a stream. There may be some high season noise from a nearby lake where you can swim or fish. Flowers decorate the entrance and bushes and saplings separate the pitches. The 101 numbered touring pitches all have electricity (10A) and are on level grass off hard access roads. They vary in size up to 130 sq.m. 55 have water and waste water, and there are small wooden containers for waste. There are also 10 mobile homes and 9 chalets for rent.

Facilities

Sanitary facilities provide private cabins, baby bath, laundry facilities, dishwashing and facilities for the disabled. A large recreation room has some games and tables to sit at. Table tennis. Bread delivered daily. A few essentials are kept in reception. Snack bar/takeaway (mid May - end Sept). High season accompanied walks and entertainment programme. Motorcaravan service point. Off site: Restaurant in village.

Open: 4 May - 30 September.

Directions

Buzancy is about 22 km. east of Vouziers on RD947 towards Stenay and Montmédy. Site is just over 1.5 km. from centre of village down a small road. Well signed. GPS: N49:25.584 E04:56.406

Charges 2007

Per person	€ 3,00 - € 4,00
child (under 10 yrs)	€ 2,00 - € 3,00
pitch	€ 4,50 - € 5,50
water and waste water	€ 2,00
electricity (10A)	€ 3,50

FR10010 Camping Municipal de Troyes

1 rue de Roger Salengro, F-10150 Pont-Ste-Marie (Aube)

Tel: **03 25 81 02 64**. Email: **info@troyescamping.net**

This municipal campsite, within the Troyes city boundary and about 2 km. from the centre, has been taken over by two young enthusiastic managers who are turning it into an attractive place to stay. There are 110 level grassy pitches (6 with hardstanding), all for tourers, about equally shaded and open. All have electrical connections (5A, some need long leads), and there are plenty of water taps. Being on one of the main routes from Luxembourg to the southwest of France, and on the main route from Calais to the Mediterranean, Troyes makes a good night stop.

Facilities

Two modern toilet blocks contain British style WCs, washbasins and pre-set showers. Facilities for disabled people. Motorcaravan services. Washing machines and dryer. Shop for basics (all season). Gas supplies. Restaurant, snack bar and takeaway (15/6-15/9). TV room. Games room, free of charge. Playground. Bouncy castle. Minigolf. Table tennis. Volleyball. Boules. Bicycle hire. Off site: Bus to Troyes centre 50 m. Supermarket 100 m. Other shops, restaurants, bars, ATM 300 m. Riding 8 km.

Open: 1 April - 15 October.

Directions

From all routes follow signs for Troyes and Pont Sainte-Marie (just north of the old city centre), then signs for Camping Municipal. Site is on the Chalons road no. 77. GPS: N48:18.666 E04:05.817

Charges 2007

Per person	€ 4,40
child (2-11 yrs)	€ 3,00
pitch	€ 5,90
electricity	€ 2,70
animal	€ 1,00

FR10030 Camping du Tertre

Route de Radonvilliers, F-10500 Dienville (Aube)

Tel: **03 25 92 26 50**. Email: **campingdutertre@wanadoo.fr**

This medium sized site is situated near the lakes of the Parc l'Orient, 40 km. east of Troyes in the Champagne-Ardenne region. You will receive a warm welcome from Michel at this family owned site and some English is spoken. Of the 156 pitches, 113 are for touring units. Laid out in groups of four to six, with dividing hedges and ornamental trees providing shade, all the pitches have 10A electricity and water nearby. The small reception is part of the bar/restaurant and is modern and well kept. Adjacent to this building are the swimming pools, which are enclosed with fencing.

Facilities

Three small sanitary blocks provide basic facilities. Washing machine in each. Bar/restaurant open July/August and also during reception hours. Play area (unfenced). Heated outdoor pool and small paddling pool with large paved terrace. Off site: Walking distance to water sports centre. Bicycle hire and fishing 200 m. Golf and riding 20 km.

Open: 23 March -17 October.

Directions

From A5 exit 22, head north via Vendeuvre-sur-Barse to Dienville. Cross first roundabout at harbour for Lac Amance and site is immediately on right.

Charges 2007

Per person	€ 3,00 - € 3,80
child (4-10 yrs)	€ 2,10 - € 2,60
pitch	€ 6,40 - € 8,00
electricity	€ 2,60 - € 2,80

FR10040 Camping de la Noue des Rois

F-10100 Saint Hilaire-sous-Romilly (Aube)

Tel: 03 25 24 41 60. Email: contact@lanouedesrois.com

This is a large, family run site situated between Paris and Troyes and open all year. Primarily a site for the seasonal caravans and chalets belonging to Parisian weekenders, there are also 23 chalets to rent and just 35 pitches for touring units. The site has many attractions such as an indoor heated pool (the roof can be opened on hot days) and an outdoor swimming pool with four slides. There are three lakes for fishing (carp), the largest also good for swimming and pedaloes, a tennis court, minigolf and boules, all this at no extra charge.

Facilities

One main building and two smaller sanitary blocks. The smaller blocks are clean enough but do not look very bright and cheerful (probably since they are not used in low season). Small shop. Crêperie. Swimming pools, indoor and out, slides. Minigolf. Tennis. Boules. Fishing. Lake for swimming and pedaloes. Activities for children (high season). Off site: Supermarkets 5 km. Paris 75 minutes, Disneyland 45 minutes.

Open: All year.

Directions

From the RN19 (Paris - Troyes) in St Hilaire-sous-Romilly, turn left at site sign (in trees).

Charges 2007

Per unit incl. 2 persons	€ 17,10 - € 19,00
extra person	€ 6,00
child (under 7 yrs)	€ 3,00
electricity (16A)	€ 3,50 - € 5,50

FR52030 Kawan Village Lac de la Liez

Mobile homes ▶ page 488

Peigney, F-52200 Langres (Haute-Marne)

Tel: 03 25 90 27 79. Email: campingliez@free.fr

Managed by the enthusiastic Baude family, this newly renovated lakeside site is near the city of Langres. Only 10 minutes from the A5, Camping Lac de la Liez provides an ideal spot for an overnight stop en route to the south of France. There is also a lot on offer for a longer stay. The site provides 131 fully serviced pitches, some with panoramic views of the 200 hectare lake with its sandy beach and small harbour where boats and pedaloes may be hired. Lake access is down steps and across quite a fast road (in total 150 m). With its old ramparts and ancient city centre, Langres was elected one of the 50 most historic cities in France.

Facilities

Two toilet blocks have all facilities in cabins (only one is open in low season). Facilities for disabled people and babies. Laundry facilities. Motorcaravan services. Shop, bar and restaurant (with takeaway food). Indoor pool complex with spa and sauna. Heated outdoor pool (15/6-15/9). Games room. Playground. Extensive games area and tennis court (free in low season). Off site: Lake with beach. Boat and bicycle hire and cycle tracks around lake. Fishing 100 m. Riding 5 km. Golf 40 km.

Open: 1 April - 1 November.

Directions

From Langres take the N19 towards Vesoul. After approximately 3 km. turn right, straight after the large river bridge, then follow site signs. GPS: N47:52.440 E05:22.628

Charges 2008

Per person	€ 5,00 - € 7,00
child (2-12 yrs)	€ 3,00 - € 4,50
pitch	€ 6,00 - € 8,00
electricity	€ 3,50 - € 5,00
dog	€ 3,00

Camping Cheques accepted.

Check real time availability and at-the-gate prices...

www.alanrogers.com

FR52020 Castel Camping la Forge de Sainte-Marie

F-52230 Thonnance-les-Moulins (Haute-Marne)

Tel: **03 25 94 42 00**. Email: **info@laforgedesaintemarie.com**

This most attractive campsite, entered through an arched gateway, was created in 1995 by careful conservation of original forge buildings to create modern facilities in this secluded valley. A picturesque bridge links the upper part with a lower road to the section near the river. Another old building has been converted into gites for letting. Grass pitches, 165 for touring units, are of a very generous size on terraces amongst trees or in more open areas. Electricity (6A) and water are available and 120 pitches are fully serviced.

Facilities

Two sanitary blocks (under pressure at peak times). Additional facilities at reception or pool complex. Shop, restaurant and bar with terrace. Pizzeria in high season. Heated indoor pool and one for children (28/4-12/9). Play areas. Bicycle hire. Fishing on payment. Games room. Internet terminal. Organized games for children (high season). Programme for adults including farm visit with barbecue, music, dancing and excursions. Golfing holidays arranged. Off site: Riding 15 km. Golf 45 km.

Open: 28 April - 12 September.

Directions

Site is about 12 km. southeast of Joinville between Poissons and Germay on road D427. The site entrance may be a little tight for large units. GPS: N48:24.392 E05:16.270

Charges 2007

Per pitch incl. 2 persons	
and electricity	€ 18,00 - € 29,00
extra person	€ 3,50 - € 7,00
child (2-9 yrs)	€ 1,75 - € 3,50

Less 20% outside July/Aug.
Camping Cheques accepted.

FR52040 Camping de la Croix d'Arles

RN 74, Bourg, F-52200 Langres (Haute-Marne)

Tel: **03 25 88 24 02**. Email: **croix.arles@wanadoo.fr**

This quiet site is only 8 km. south of Langres. There are 100 pitches, of which 81 are for tourers. Most facilities are near the entrance, as is a flat grassy area mostly used by caravans and motorcaravans. There are electrical points and water taps, but no pitch markings or shade. A wooded area, where nature has been worked with rather than controlled, provides groups of numbered pitches with lots of shade (leads for electricity of up to 40 m. could be needed). Further on is an area without electricity supply. A tour operator uses the site.

Facilities

Two modern toilet blocks contain British style WCs, washbasins (some in cabins) and controllable showers. Facilities for disabled people. Baby room. Washing machines. Shop for basics. Restaurant, bar, snack bar and takeaway (1/4-31/10). Games rooms. Swimming and paddling pools, sauna & jacuzzi (15/5-15/9). Playground. Table tennis. Boules. Off site: Town 2 km. Fishing 8 km. Riding 10 km. Bicycle hire 5 km. Boat launching 8 km.

Open: 15 March - 31 October.

Directions

From north, take N74 from Langres (towards Dijon). After 8 km. site is on right. From south, turning left from N74 into site is forbidden. Go 2 km. north, take right hand slip road towards trading estate (signed to A31), turn left, pass under N74, then left to rejoin N74 going south.

Charges 2008

Per person	€ 3,00 - € 4,00
pitch incl. electricity	€ 9,50 - € 10,50

FR52050 Yelloh! en Champagne

Eclaron F-52290 (Haute-Marne)

Tel: **04 66 73 97 39**. Email: **info@yellohvillage-en-champagne.com**

Formerly known as Les Sources du Lac, this Yelloh! Village site has been recommended to us and we plan to undertake a full inspection in 2008. The site is close to the village of Eclaron and has direct access to the Lac du Der. This is a very large lake with 77km of shoreline and is home to over 270 species of birds. Part of the lake is an ornithological reserve but a wide range of water based activities are on offer in other areas. These include including fishing, windsurfing and sailing, and a separate area is reserved for motor boats. There are 55 touring pitches here and around 90 mobile homes and chalets for rent.

Facilities

Shop. Bar. Restaurant. Takeaway. Swimming pool. Paddling pool. Direct access to the lake and beach. Ornithological activities. Activity and entertainment programme. Off site: Walking and cycle trails. Fishing. The 'Champagne route'. Grange aux Abeilles (bee barn) at Giffaumont Champaubert.

Open: 26 April - 6 September.

Directions

Take southbound N44 from Chalons-en-Champagne as far as Vitry-le François and then join the eastbound N4 as far as St Dizier. From the St Dizier ring road take the D384 towards Montier-en-Der and at Eclaron-Braucourt follow signs to the site.

Charges 2008

Per unit with 2 persons	€ 14,00 - € 29,00

MAP 5

Vendée & Charente

It's not only the fine beaches that make this holiday region so appealing. Sleepy fishing harbours, historic ports and charming towns all create a great holiday atmosphere.

WE HAVE EXERCISED A LITTLE TOURISM LICENSE WITH THIS AREA TAKING ONE DÉPARTEMENT FROM THE OFFICIAL WESTERN LOIRE REGION, 85 VENDÉE, AND ONE FROM THE POITOU-CHARENTES REGION, 17 CHARENTE-MARITIME

With a sunshine record to rival the south of France, the Vendée and Charente regions are among the most popular areas in France. Running alongside the coastal area stretching down from La Rochelle past Rochefort to Royan, it boasts gently shelving sandy beaches, warm shallow waters and fragrant pine forests. Explore the coasts for traditional fishing villages or head inland for fields of sunflowers and unspoilt rural villages.

The Vendée was the centre of the counter-revolutionary movement between 1793 and 1799 and a 'son et lumière' held at Le Puy-du-Fou tells the whole story. Les Sables d'Olonne is its main resort renowned for its excellent sandy beach. The area between the Vendée and Charente, the Marais Poitevin, is one of the most unusual in France – a vast tract of marshland with a thousand or more tree-lined canals and slow moving streams. The port of La Rochelle, with massive medieval towers, buzzes with life and the island of Ré is popular with those seeking beaches and small, quiet ports.

Places of interest

Marais Poitevin: marshes known as the 'Green Venice'.

Angoulême: Hill-top town surrouded by ramparts, cathedral, Renaissance château.

La Rochelle: port, Porte de la Grosse Horloge (clock gate), Museum of the New World.

Le Puy-du-Fou: 15th-16th century castle, sound and light show involving over 700 participants.

Les Sables d'Olonne: fishing port and seaside resort.

Noirmoutier: linked to the mainland by a 3 mile bridge.

Saint Savin: 17th century abbey, mural painting.

Cuisine of the region

Fish predominates, both fresh water (eel, trout, pike), sea water (shrimps, mussels, oysters). Light fruity wines from Haut-Poitou, Deux-Sèvres and Charente, and Cognac and Pineau des Charentes – an aperitif of grape juice and Cognac.

Cagouilles: snails from Charentes.

Chaudrée: ragout of fish cooked in white wine, shallots and butter.

Mouclade: mussels cooked in wine, egg and cream, served with Pineau des Charentes.

Soupe de moules à la Rochelaise: soup of various fish, mussels, saffron, garlic, tomatoes, onions and red wine.

Sourdons: cockles from the Charentes.

FR17010 **Camping Bois Soleil**

Mobile homes ▶ page 489

2 avenue de Suzac, F-17110 Saint Georges-de-Didonne (Charente-Maritime)

Tel: **05 46 05 05 94**. Email: **camping.bois.soleil@wanadoo.fr**

Close to the sea, Bois Soleil is a fairly large site in three parts, with 165 serviced pitches for touring units and a few for tents. All touring pitches are hedged, and have electricity, with water and drainage between two. The main part, 'Les Pins', is attractive with trees and shrubs providing shade. Opposite is 'La Mer' with direct access to the beach, some areas with less shade and an area for tents. The third part, 'La Forêt', is for static holiday homes. It is best to book your preferred area and can be full mid June - late August. There are a few pitches with lockable gates. The areas are well tended with the named pitches (not numbered) cleared and raked between visitors and with an all-in charge including electricity and water. This lively site offers something for everyone, whether they like a beach-side spot or a traditional pitch, plenty of activities or the quiet life. The sandy beach here is a wide public one, sheltered from the Atlantic breakers although the sea goes out some way at low tide.

Facilities

Each area has one large sanitary block, and smaller blocks with toilets only. Heated block near reception. Cleaned twice daily, they include washbasins in cubicles, facilities for disabled people and babies. Launderette. Nursery. Supermarket, bakery (July/Aug). Beach shop. Restaurant and bar. Takeaway. Pool (heated 15/6-15-9). Steam room. Tennis. Bicycle hire. Play area. TV room and library. Internet terminal. Charcoal barbecues not permitted. Pets not accepted (24/6-2/9). Off site: Fishing, riding 500 m. Golf 20 km.

Open: 4 April - 2 November.

Directions

From Royan centre take coast road (D25) along the seafront of St Georges-de-Didonne towards Meschers. Site is signed at roundabout at end of the main beach. GPS: N45:35.130 W00:59.128

Charges 2008

Per unit incl. 2 persons, 6A electricity	€ 20,00 - € 37,00
tent incl. 2 persons	€ 15,00 - € 33,00

Less 20% outside July/Aug.
Camping Cheques accepted.

FR17050 **Camping l'Orée du Bois**

225 route de la Bouverie, La Fouasse, F-17570 Les Mathes (Charente-Maritime)

Tel: **05 46 22 42 43**. Email: **info@camping-oree-du-bois.fr**

L'Orée du Bois has 388 pitches of about 100 sq.m. in a very spacious, pinewood setting. There are 150 for touring units, mainly scattered amongst the permanent chalets and tents. They include 40 large pitches with hardstanding and individual sanitary facilities (in blocks of four with shower, toilet, washbasin and dishwashing sink). Pitches are on flat, fairly sandy ground, separated by trees, shrubs and hedges and all have electrical connections (6A). The forest pines offer some shade. Used by several tour operators. A lively site in high season which can be noisy but is tranquil in low season.

Facilities

Four main toilet blocks include some washbasins in cabins. Three have a laundry and facilities for disabled people. Shop. Excellent bar, restaurant and crêperie and takeaway service. Heated swimming pools, water slide and paddling pool (trunks, not shorts). Play areas. Tennis court, boules, volleyball, table tennis, football and basketball. Games room and TV lounge. Bicycle hire. Discos. Entertainment in July/Aug. Internet access. Barbecues in special areas only. Off site: Riding 300 m. Fishing 4 km. Golf 20 km.

Open: 26 April - 14 September.

Directions

From north follow D14 La Tremblade. At roundabout before Arvert turn on D268 (Les Mathes and La Palmyre). Site on right in Fouasse. From south, at Royan take D25 (La Palmyre). In town turn north to Les Mathes. At first roundabout in Les Mathes follow sign (Fouasse and La Tremblade). Site on left after 2 km.

Charges 2008

Per unit incl. 2 persons and electricity	€ 16,00 - € 37,00
with private sanitary facility	€ 23,00 - € 45,00
extra person	€ 7,50
child (3-10 yrs)	€ 5,50

Min. stay 7 days in high season.
Camping Cheques accepted.

Check real time availability and at-the-gate prices...

www.alanrogers.com

Bois Soleil

Camping ★★★★
Charente-Maritime

...rrounded by pine trees and a sandy beach on the ...lantic Coast, with one direct access to the beach, Bois ...leil proposes to you many attractions like tennis, ...bletennis, children playgrounds and entertainment. ...ops, take-away and snack-bar with big TV screen.

Spring and Summer 2008

2, avenue de Suzac - 17110 ST GEORGES DE DIDONNE
Tel: 0033 546 05 05 94 - Fax: 0033 546 06 27 43
www.bois-soleil.com / e-mail: camping.bois.soleil@wanadoo.fr

FR17060 Airotel Oléron

Domaine de Montravail, F-17480 Le Château-d'Oléron (Charente-Maritime)

Tel: **05 46 47 61 82**. Email: **info@camping-airotel-oleron.com**

This family run site on the outskirts of Le Château d'Oléron with very good facilities, including a superb equestrian centre, a full range of sporting activites and an attractive heated pool complex. This is a mature site with about 270 pitches of a good size, with varying degrees of shade provided by trees and shrubs. It is well laid out with 133 touring pitches and the remainder for mobile homes of which 30 are for rent. Most touring pitches have electricity (10A) and four have their own water and drainage. A full entertainment programme is provided in high season and one can enjoy the exploration of the island with its fine sandy beaches on the Atlantic coast and the miles of flat tracks for walking, cycling or horse riding. The equestrian centre offers up to a week long courses for riders ranging from novice to experienced.

Facilities

Two modern toilet blocks with facilities for disabled visitors and babies. Washing machine and dryer. Motorcaravan service point. Shop Bar, restaurant and takeaway (15/6-15/9). Heated swimming and paddling pools. Equestrian centre. Playground. Multisport court. Tennis. Minigolf. Fishing. Canoe hire. Bicycle hire. TV and games room. Internet access. WiFi. Off site: Supermarket. Local markets. Zoo. Aquarium.

Open: Easter - 30 September.

Directions

Cross the bridge onto the island and continue on D26. At second roundabout, turn right, marked Dolus and Le Château. Proceed 500 m. and take first right, marked Campings. Site is 1 km. on the right. GPS: N45:52.933 W01:12.392

Charges 2007

Per unit incl. 2 persons	€ 13,50 - € 22,00
extra person	€ 4,00 - € 6,50
electricity (8A)	€ 3,90
dog	€ 2,50

FR17020 Airotel le Puits de l'Auture

151 avenue de La Grande-Côte, F-17420 Saint Palais-sur-Mer (Charente-Maritime)

Tel: **05 46 23 20 31**. Email: **camping-lauture@wanadoo.fr**

Le Puits de l'Auture is well situated with the sea just across the road, and a long sandy beach starting 400 m. away, at the start of a pleasant coastal development down to Royan and beyond. There are 240 level touring pitches, all with electricity (10A). Some are separated by bushes with some trees giving shade and all have access to water and drainage. Mobile homes occupy the rest of the site, a few used by a tour operator.

Facilities

Well maintained toilet blocks. Most WCs are British type and all washbasins are in cabins, showers are adjustable with hot water. Facilities for disabled people and babies. Laundry and dishwashing facilities. Shop (1/5-30/9). Takeaway and bar (1/6-15/9). Swimming pool complex. Volleyball. Table tennis. Games room. Play area. Bicycle hire. Internet access. Barbecues (in a special area only). Dogs not accepted. Off site: Riding and golf 800 m. Restaurants specialising in sea food. Sea fishing.

Open: 1 May - 30 September.

Directions

Site is 2 km. from St Palais and 8 km. from Royan. From Royan take D25 past St Palais following signs for La Palmyre. At two lane junction turn back left signed Grande-Côte and St Palais. Site is 800 m. GPS: N45:38.948 W01:07.050

Charges 2007

Per unit incl. 2 persons	€ 16,00 - € 31,00
with 10A electricity	€ 23,00 - € 37,00
with water and drainage	€ 30,00 - € 43,00
extra person (over 3 yrs)	€ 5,00 - € 7,00

FR17070 Camping les Gros Joncs

Mobile homes ▶ page 489

850 route de Ponthezieres, F-17190 Saint-Georges-d'Oléron (Charente-Maritime)

Tel: 05 46 76 52 29. Email: camping.gros.joncs@wanadoo.fr

Situated on the west coast of the island of Ile d'Oléron, Les Gros Joncs is owned and run by the Cavel family who strive to keep the site up to date and of high quality. There are 50 or so touring pitches of a good size (some extra large) providing a choice between full sun and varying degrees of shade. All have water and electricity (10A) to hand. Much attention has been given to the needs of disabled visitors including chalets where space and equipment is specially adapted. The restaurant and takeaway are of a standard unusual in a campsite. The shop with its own bakery and patisserie stocks a wide range of foods, drinks and every day essentials. The site has a heated swimming pool, recently renovated and now including a water slide (1/4-15/9) with hydrotherapy and beauty treatments available. New indoor pool and fitness room. The Ile d'Oléron has much history to explore and the French are justifiably proud of the oyster and mussel production on the island – probably the best in Europe and well worth a visit (and tasting!).

Facilities

Toilet facilities are of traditional design, kept very clean and very adequate in number. Laundry facilities. Motorcaravan services. Well stocked shop with bakery (1/4-15/9). Bar with TV, restaurant and snack bar with takeaway (all 1/4-15/9). Swimming pool (1/4-15/9) with hydrotherapy and beauty treatments. Bicycle hire. Children's club (1/7-15/9). WiFi internet access. No barbecues. Off site: Beach 200 or 400 m. Bus service from Chéray. Fishing 2 km. Riding 6 km. Golf 8 km.

Open: All year.

Directions

Cross the viaduct onto the Ile d'Oléron. Take D734 (St George d'Oléron). At traffic lights in Chéray turn left. Follow signs for camping and Sable Vignier. Soon signs indicate direction of Les Gros Joncs.

Charges 2007

Per unit incl. 2 persons	€ 14,70 - € 40,10
incl. 3 persons	€ 17,20 - € 40,10
extra person	€ 5,60 - € 11,20
child (0-7 yrs)	€ 2,50 - € 6,90
electricity	€ 3,00

CAMPING LES GROS JONCS

850 Route de Ponthezieres - F-17190 St Georges-d'Oléron - France
Tél.: 05 46 76 52 29 - Fax: 05 46 76 67 74 - E-mail: camping.gros.joncs@wanadoo.fr

FR17080 Camping le Royan

10 rue des Bleuets, F-17200 Royan (Charente-Maritime)

Tel: 05 46 39 09 06. Email: camping.le.royan@wanadoo.fr

Camping Le Royan is a well established family site located close to the resort of Royan and its beaches. There are 186 good size grassy pitches, of which 80 are for touring. All but 16 have 10A electricity (Euro plugs). Some pitches may suffer from road noise from the nearby Royan bypass. The site has tarmac access roads and well maintained toilet blocks. The swimming pool is particularly attractive with a jacuzzi and a number of slides. A lively entertainment programme and children's club are organised in peak season.

Facilities

Two sanitary buildings with facilities for disabled people. Snack bar and pizzeria. Shop. Swimming pool with waterslides and other features. Paddling pool. Games room. Playground. Table tennis. Volleyball. Bicycle hire. Children's club. Entertainment. Mobile homes and chalets for rent. Gas barbecues allowed. Only small dogs accepted. Off site: Beach 2.5 km. Royan centre 2 km. La Palmyre zoo. Riding and golf 7 km.

Open: 1 April - 15 October.

Directions

Site is close to the Royan bypass to the northwest of the town heading towards La Palmyre. It is well signed. GPS: N45:38.708 W01:02.48

Charges 2007

Per pitch including 3 people and electricity	€ 21,50 - € 33,00
extra person	€ 3,50 - € 7,50
child (3-9 yrs)	€ 3,50 - € 6,50

137

FR17100 Camping Clairefontaine

6 rue du Colonel Lachaud, F-17200 Royan-Pontaillac (Charente-Maritime)

Tel: **05 46 39 08 11**. Email: **info@camping-clairefontaine.com**

Camping Clairefontaine is situated on the outskirts of Royan, 300 metres from a golden sandy beach and casino. Although it is a busy area, the site is peaceful and relaxing. There are 300 pitches, of which 282 are available for touring. Electricity is available to all pitches, but some may require long leads. The site is mostly shaded and level with easy access to pitches. American motorhomes are accepted but care is needed on the entrance road as it is not wide enough for two vehicles to pass.

Facilities

Two modern sanitay blocks. Good facilities for disabled visitors. Washing machines. Ironing room. Motorcaravan services. Shop. Bar. Restaurant with takeaway. Swimming and paddling pools. Four play areas. Tennis. Basketball. Entertainment in high season. Internet access. Off site: Beach and sailing 300 m. Bicycle hire 350 m. Fishing 2 km. Riding and golf 10 km.

Open: 24 May - 12 September.

Directions

Exit Royan on Avenue de Pontaillac towards La Palmyre. Turn right at the casino on the front, up Avenue Louise. Site is on left after 200 m. and is signed. GPS: N45:37.855 W01:03.013

Charges 2007

Per unit incl. 2 persons and electricity	€ 32,00 - € 35,00
extra person	€ 9,00 - € 9,50

FR17110 Camping Caravaning Monplaisir

26 Ave de la Palmyre, F-17570 Les Mathes-La Palmyre (Charente-Maritime)

Tel: **05 46 22 50 31**. Email: **campmonplaisir@aol.com**

Monplaisir provides a small, quiet haven in an area with some very hectic campsites. It is ideal for couples or families with young children. Quite close to the town and set back from the road, the entrance leads through an avenue of trees, past the owners home to a well kept, garden-like site. There are 114 level, marked pitches and all but a few have electrical connections (6A), long leads may be required. On 14 there are caravans for rent and there are flats and studios for rent. Visitors return year after year. Larger units would find this site difficult to navigate.

Facilities

The toilet block has some washbasins in cabins and facilities for disabled people. Laundry and dishwashing facilities. Ice pack service in reception. Bread delivered daily. TV, games room and library. Heated swimming pool and paddling pool (early May - 30/9). Small play area. Winter caravan storage. Off site: Supermarket short walk. Minigolf adjacent (owned by the site). Fishing 500 m. Riding 1 km. Golf 5 km.

Open: Easter - 1 October.

Directions

Follow D25 to La Palmyre. In town, turn north to Les Mathes. At roundabout turn right to town centre. Site on left. From north on D14 (La Tremblade) turn onto D268 (Les Mathes and La Palmyre) at roundabout just before Arvert. GPS: N45:42.924 W01:09.321

Charges 2007

Per unit incl. 2 persons	€ 17,00
electricity	€ 3,00

FR17030 Camping le Bois Roland

82 route Royan - Saujon, F-17600 Medis (Charente-Maritime)

Tel: **05 46 05 47 58**. Email: **bois.roland@wanadoo.fr**

This campsite is in an urban area on a busy N-road but, nevertheless, has some unique features. Over the past 30 years, M. Dupont, the owner, has planted a very large number of tree varieties to mark and separate the pitches and they provide some shade. The site has 88 pitches for touring units, mainly between 80-90 sq.m. All have electricity (some may need long leads) and access to water close at hand. The family run a bar and provide simple takeaway food in July and August and there is a welcoming swimming pool. The majority of the pitches are of good size and to return to them after a day in Royan may well be worth the drive. Royan, with all its noise and sophistication and well used beaches, is only 5 km. The village of Medis, with a variety of shops, is some 600 m. walk from the site.

Facilities

Two modernised toilet blocks contain a mixture of Turkish and British style toilets (no seats and no paper). Modern showers. Baby changing room. Special facilities for disabled campers. Dishwashing under cover. Laundry room with washing machines. Play area for young children. Off site: Buses pass the gate. Riding 1 km. Fishing 4 km. Bicycle hire 5 km. Golf 10 km. Supermarket with ATM 2 km. Beach 5 km.

Open: 23 April - 30 September.

Directions

Site is clearly signed on the west side of the N150, 600 m. north of the village of Medis (the N150 runs between Saujon and Royan).

Charges 2007

Per unit incl. 2 persons	€ 14,00 - € 17,50
extra person	€ 4,80
child (0-5 yrs)	€ 2,00 - € 3,50
electricity (5/10A)	€ 4,20 - € 4,90

FR17140 Castel Camping Séquoia Parc

La Josephtrie, F-17320 Saint Just-Luzac (Charente-Maritime)

Tel: **05 46 85 55 55**. Email: **info@sequoiaparc.com**

This is definitely a site not to be missed. Approached by an avenue of flowers, shrubs and trees, Séquoia Parc is a Castel site set in the grounds of La Josephtrie, a striking château with beautifully restored outbuildings and courtyard area with a bar and restaurant. Most pitches are 140 sq.m. with 6A electricity connections and separated by mature shrubs providing plenty of privacy. The site has 300 mobile homes and chalets, with 126 used by tour operators. This is a popular site with a children's club and entertainment throughout the season and reservation is necessary in high season. Member of Leading Campings Group. The site itself is designed to a high specification with reception in a large, light and airy room retaining its original beams and leading to the courtyard area where you find the bar and restaurant. The pool complex with water slides, large paddling pool and sunbathing area is impressive.

Facilities

Three spotlessly clean luxurious toilet blocks, include units with washbasin and shower and facilities for disabled visitors and children. Dishwashing sinks. New large laundry. Motorcaravan service point. Gas supplies. Large new supermarket. Restaurant/bar and takeaway. Impressive swimming pool complex with water slides and large paddling pool. Tennis, volleyball, football field. Games and TV rooms. Bicycle hire. Pony trekking. Organised entertainment all season. Off site: Fishing 5km. Golf 15km. Flying trips.

Open: 8 May - 14 September, with all services.

Directions

Site is 5 km. southeast of Marennes. From Rochefort take D733 south for 12 km. Turn west on D123 to Ile d'Oléron. Continue for 12 km. Turn southeast on D728 (Saintes). Site signed, in 1 km. on left. GPS: N45:48.699 W01:03.637

Charges 2008

Per unit incl. 2 persons	
and electricity	€ 18,00 - € 43,00
extra person	€ 7,00 - € 9,00
child (3-12 yrs)	€ 3,00 - € 5,00
dog	€ 5,00

Online bookings:
www.sequoiaparc.com
Séquoia Parc
17320 St.Just-Luzac, France
Tel: 00 33 546 85 55 55

FR17170 Domaine des Charmilles

Saint Laurent de la Prée, F-17450 Fouras (Charente-Maritime)

Tel: **08 20 20 23 27**. Email: **charmilles17@wanadoo.fr**

Les Charmilles is an impressive quality site which is maintained to a very high standard. Of the 300 large pitches, 55 are for touring. All pitches have electricity (10A) and many also have water and drainage. There is an attractive restaurant and bar and an extensive entertainment programme in high season. A plan is in place for continual improvements to the site. This is one of the very few sites in France to have all its facilities especially adapted for disabled guests, including 10 of the chalets and the swimming pools. The friendly owner wishes to ensure that all of his visitors have a great holiday.

Facilities

The modern toilet blocks are conveniently placed. Excellent facilities for babies and disabled people. Laundry facilities. Shop, bar, takeaway and restaurant (all May - Sept). Heated swimming pools (one covered), water slides, paddling pool and aqua gym (all May - Sept). Massage. Playground. Multisports court. Bicycle hire. Minibus to beach in July/Aug. No charcoal barbecues. Off site: Fishing 3 km. Golf 5 km. Sailing 10 km. Riding 15 km.

Open: 7 April - 22 September.

Directions

Leave N137 at exit for Fouras and St Laurent de la Prée, joining D937 towards Fouras. Site is on left in about 800 m. GPS: N45:59.240 W01:03.070

Charges 2007

Per pitch incl. 2 persons	
	€ 15,00 - € 30,00
extra person	€ 6,00
child (under 5 yrs)	€ 4,00
electricity	€ 4,00

FR17160 Camping le Clos Fleuri

8 impasse du Clos Fleuri, F-17600 Médis (Charente-Maritime)

Tel: **05 46 05 62 17**. Email: **clos-fleuri@wanadoo.fr**

Camping Le Clos Fleuri really does live up to its name. The profusion of different trees and the lawns and flower beds give this small site a very rural atmosphere. There is always a warm welcome from the Devais family who created this pretty site in 1974. The 125 touring pitches are mostly of generous size (a little uneven in places). They vary from being in full sun to well shaded and 110 have electrical connections. The bar/restaurant is a converted barn providing a cool haven on hot days and a very convivial venue for evening gatherings and entertainment. There is occasional noise from light aircraft. The surrounding countryside is very pleasant with crops of sunflowers, wheat and maize, while beaches of all sorts are within easy reach. All in all the Clos Fleuri combines a great deal of charm, beauty and friendliness with a location from which the attractions of the Charente-Maritime may be discovered.

Facilities

Toilet facilities are kept scrupulously clean. One block is segregated male and female, the other is unisex with each unit in its own cubicle. Facility for disabled visitors. Baby baths. Laundry facilities. Small pool and paddling pool. Sauna. Shop (1/7-15/9). Restaurant (1/7-31/8) and bar (1/7-15/9). In high season there are twice weekly 'soirées' and boules and archery competitions. Minigolf. Small football pitch. Security barrier closed at night. Off site: Médis 2 km.

Open: 1 June - 18 September.

Directions

Médis is on the N150 from Saintes, halfway between Saujon and Royan. Drive into village. Site signed to south at various points in Médis and is about 2 km. outside village. GPS: N45:37.782 W00:56.768

Charges 2007

Per pitch incl. 2 persons	€ 17,90 - € 25,50
extra person	€ 6,00 - € 7,70
child (2-7 yrs)	€ 4,00 - € 5,20
electricity (5/10A)	€ 3,00 - € 5,60
Less 25% in June and Sept.	

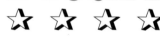
FR17210 Sunêlia Interlude

Plage de Gros Jonc, F-17580 Le Bois-Plage-en-Ré (Charente-Maritime)

Tel: **05 46 09 18 22**. Email: **infos@interlude.fr**

Camping Interlude enjoys a pleasant location with access to an excellent beach. A popular site even in low season, (may become very crowded with overstretched facilities in high season), it has 387 pitches, 136 of which are for touring units. Pitches are sand based, vary in size from 80-120 sq.m. and are mostly divided by hedges on part undulating, sandy terrain. Many are placed to the left of the site in a pine forest setting, others mingle with the tour operators and new mobile homes. Choosing a shady pitch is not a problem for there are many trees.

Facilities

Two modern, clean and well equipped sanitary blocks provide washbasins in cabins and some shower units suitable for families with twin washbasins. Baby room, child size toilets, en suite facilities for disabled visitors, laundry and dishwashing facilities. Motorcaravan service point. Newly renovated restaurant/bar and shop. Fresh bread. Swimming pools, one outdoor and one inside. Play area. Volleyball, boules. Organised events and entertainment. Games/TV room. Tennis courts. Bicycle hire. Communal barbecues. Multisport area.

Open: 5 April - 28 September.

Directions

After toll bridge to the Ile de Ré follow sign (Le Bois-Plage). Turn left at first roundabout, straight on at next two, then left at fourth roundabout. Site signed. GPS: N46:10.430 W01:22.430

Charges 2007

Per pitch incl. electricity	€ 23,00 - € 40,00
with water and waste	€ 26,00 - € 42,00
extra person	€ 5,00 - € 10,00
140 sq.m. pitch	
incl. water and drainage	€ 26,00 - € 44,00
pet	€ 8,00

FR17190 Le Logis du Breuil

F-17570 Saint Augustin-sur-Mer (Charente-Maritime)

Tel: 05 46 23 23 45. Email: camping.Logis-du-Breuil@wanadoo.fr

The first impression on arrival at this impressive campsite is space. The camping area is a 200 metre expanse of farm pasture where (on different areas) cattle graze and children play. The camping areas are set among rows of mature and shady trees giving a dappled effect to the tents, caravans and grassy pitches. The 320 pitches (250 with 3/6A electricity) are very large and have direct access to wide, unpaved alleys, which lead on to the few tarmac roads around the site. The amenities are centred around the reception area and pool complex. A 'Sites et Paysages' member.

Facilities

Four well maintained toilet blocks are spaced around the camping area. Dishwashing and laundry facilities. Swimming pools. Shop, bar and snacks and takeaway (franchised) are well run. No evening entertainment. Play area. Indoor area providing archery, pool and table tennis. Bicycle hire. Tennis and basketball. Excursions organised. WiFi. Off site: A 50 minute walk leads to the sea near St Palais-sur-Mer, another to the 'Cote Sauvage'.

Open: 1 May - 30 September.

Directions

Approaching Royan follow signs to St Palais-sur-Mer. Go straight on past first set of traffic lights and two roundabouts. At second set of lights turn right (St Augustin). Site is approx. 2 km. on left, just before village. GPS: N45:40.463 W01:05.768

Charges 2008

Per unit incl. 2 persons and electricity	€ 17,90 - € 24,30
extra person	€ 3,90 - € 6,30
child (under 7 yrs)	€ 3,35 - € 4,65
dog	€ 1,82 - € 2,30

Quiet and space — Le Logis du Breuil ★★★ CAMPING CARAVANING — 17570 SAINT-AUGUSTIN-SUR-MER Tel : (33) 05 46 23 23 45 Fax : (33) 05 46 23 43 33 — Chalet and Mobilhomes to rent — www.logis-du-breuil.com camping.logis-du-breuil@wanadoo.fr

FR17230 Kawan Village l'Océan

La Passe, la Couarde-sur-Mer, F-17670 Ile de Ré (Charente-Maritime)

Tel: 05 46 29 87 70. Email: campingdelocean@wanadoo.fr

L'Océan lies close to the centre of the Ile de Ré, just 50 m. from a sandy beach. There are 338 pitches here with 161 for touring units, the remainder occupied by mobile homes and chalets. The camping area is well shaded and pitches are of a reasonable size, all with electricity (10A). A pleasant bar and restaurant overlooks the large heated swimming pool which is surrounded by an attractive sunbathing terrace. Bicycle hire is popular here as the island offers over 100 km. of interesting, safe cycling routes.

Facilities

The new toilet blocks are modern and well maintained with facilities for disabled visitors. Motorcaravan services. Shop. Bar/restaurant and takeaway (all season). Swimming pool. Riding. Bicycle hire. Tennis court. Fishing pond adjacent. Basketball. Play area. Minigolf (free). Helicopter rides, sub-aqua diving and pony riding (high season). Entertainment in high season. No charcoal barbecues. Internet access. Off site: Beach 50 m. La Couarde 2.5 km. Golf 5 km.

Open: 5 May - 28 September.

Directions

After toll bridge, join D735 which runs along the north side of the island until you pass La Couarde. The site is 2.5 km. beyond village (in direction of Ars-en-Ré). GPS: N46:12.260 W01:28.060

Charges 2007

Per unit incl. 1-2 persons	€ 14,95 - € 38,20
extra person	€ 4,35 - € 9,65
electricity	€ 5,20
dog	€ 1,80 - € 4,55
Camping Cheques accepted.	

FR17220 Camping la Brande

Route des Huitres, F-17480 Le Château-d'Oléron (Charente-Maritime)

Tel: **05 46 47 62 37**. Email: **info@camping-labrande.com**

A quality environmentally-friendly site, run and maintained to the highest standard, La Brande offers an ideal holiday environment on the delightful Ile d'Oléron, famed for its oysters. La Brande is situated on the oyster route and close to a sandy beach. Pitches here are generous and mostly separated by hedges and trees, the greater number for touring outfits. All are on level grassy terrain and have electricity hook-ups, some are fully serviced. The many activities during the high season, plus the natural surroundings, make this an ideal choice for families. A feature of this site is the heated indoor pool (28°) open all season. The Barcat family ensures that their visitors not only enjoy quality facilities, but Gerard Barcat offers guided bicycle tours and canoe trips. This way you discover the nature, oyster farming, vineyards and history of Oléron, which is joined to the mainland by a 3 km. bridge.

Facilities

Three heated, clean sanitary blocks have spacious, well equipped showers and washbasins (mainly in cabins). Baby facilities. Excellent facilities for people with disabilities (separate large shower, washbasin and WC). Laundry rooms. Motorcaravan service point. Superb restaurant/takeaway and bar (July/Aug). Shop (July/Aug). Heated indoor swimming pool (all season). Jacuzzi. Sauna. Well equipped playground. Games room. Football field, tennis, minigolf, fishing and archery. Bicycle hire. Canoe hire. Free WiFi. New building for children Off site: Beach 300 m. Sailing 2 km. Riding 6 km. Golf 7 km.

Open: 15 March - 15 November.

Directions

After crossing bridge to L'Ile d'Oléron turn right towards Le Château d'Oléron. Continue through village and follow sign for Route des Huitres. Site is on left after 2.5 km.

Charges 2007

Per unit incl. 2 persons and electricity	€ 19,20 - € 39,00
extra person	€ 5,00 - € 8,00
dog	€ 2,50 - € 8,00

Camping Cheques accepted.

Alain BARCAT and his team welcomes you at La Brande - an open air hotel, camping and caravan site. Situated 1,5 miles outside of Château d'Oléron on la Route de Huîtres nearby the seaside, 28°C heated swimming pool opened from the 15.03 till the 15.11 (free WiFi hotspot)

ROUTE DES HUÎTRES • 17480 LE CHÂTEAU D'OLÉRON
TÉL. +33 (0)5 46 47 62 37 • FAX +33 (0)5 46 47 71 70
info@camping-labrande.com • www.camping-labrande.co.uk

FR17270 Camping l'Anse des Pins

Chemin du Râteau - Domino, F-17190 Saint-Georges-d'Oléron (Charente-Maritime)

Tel: **05 46 76 55 97**. Email: **camping-apv@wanadoo.fr**

Rock pools, sand dunes and spectacular sun sets, with sea views from many of the pitches, help to make this site attractive to those seeking an away from it all holiday in a quiet part of the island of the Ile d'Oléron. The campsite is arranged in three areas, some parts having good shade, but with a fair proportion in full sun. There are 350 pitches including 188 for touring units, the remainder used for mobile homes. Electricity connections are available (3-10A) and 22 pitches also have water and drainage. Mobile home numbers at this site increase each year.

Facilities

Two main toilet blocks (plus two small blocks for high season use) with mainly British style toilets. Showers and washbasins in cabins. Laundry facilities. Gas supplies. Bar. Shop with limited takeaway and snack bar. Swimming and paddling pools. Play area. Activities in high season (1/7-31/8). Tennis. Boules courts. Table tennis. No TV. Barbecues only permitted in a communal area. Off site: Beach 50 m. Bicycle hire 1 km. Riding 10 km. St Georges 5 km.

Open: April - September.

Directions

Cross the bridge onto Ile d'Oléron and follow D734 (St Dennis). In Chéray, turn left at traffic lights (signed Camping). Stay on this road to Domino (avoid side roads). Follow green signs to Rex and L'Anse des Pins Camping. Narrow roads. GPS: N45:58.226 W01:23.213

Charges guide

Per unit incl. 2 persons	€ 16,00 - € 28,00
extra person	€ 6,00 - € 7,00
electricity	€ 2,50 - € 4,00

FR17260 Camping le Cormoran

Route de Radia, Ars-en-Ré, F-17590 Ile de Ré (Charente-Maritime)

Tel: **05 46 29 46 04**. Email: **info@cormoran.com**

Just outside Ars-en-Ré, Le Cormoran offers a quiet rural holiday for families with young children. Pitches vary in size and are a mixture of sand and grass. All have electricity. The restaurant and bar overlook the pool. Basic provisions are stocked in the bar. There are the usual shops in Ars, which is some 800 m. away. Le Cormoran is close to the local oyster beds. The sister site, Camping La Plage, is about 3 km. away and concentrates mainly on its 142 mobile homes. There are 44 pitches for touring units but the facilities for them are a little old fashioned.

Facilities

Unisex toilet facilities are in two blocks with toilets (British and Turkish style), showers and washbasins mainly in cabins. Provision for disabled visitors. Dishwashing and laundry facilities. Motorcaravan service point. Bar, restaurant and takeaway meals. WiFi. Swimming pool (covered in low season). Fitness centre. Tennis. Volleyball. Games room. Play area. Entertainment programme in high season. Bicycle hire. Off site: Nearest beach 500 m. Ars-en-Ré 800 m. Fishing 500 m. Boat launching 1 km. Riding 3 km. Golf 10 km.

Open: 1 April - 30 September.

Directions

Cross the toll bridge from La Rochelle onto the Ile de Ré and continue on D735 to Ars-en-Ré from where site is well signed.

Charges 2007

Per unit incl. 2 persons	€ 16,80 - € 24,20
extra person	€ 5,50 - € 11,50
child (0-9 yrs)	€ 3,30 - € 11,50
electricity (10A)	€ 5,00
animal	€ 2,70 - € 5,50

FR17300 Camping Au Petit Port de l'Houmeau

F-17137 L'Houmeau (Charente-Maritime)

Tel: **05 46 50 90 82**. Email: **info@aupetitport.com**

Au Petit Port de l'Houmeau is a pretty, quiet and rural site on the edge of the small seaside village of L'Houmeau. The friendly English speaking owners ensure high standards of maintenance. Pitches (clustered in groups of four or five) are of a good size, and are all equipped with 10A electrical connections. Virtually all offer some degree of shade. Larger motorcaravans may have difficulty finding a suitable pitch. There are relatively few amenities here, but the village shops, bars and a good restaurant are very close by.

Facilities

Two well maintained toilet blocks. Washing machines and dryers. Snack bar (July/Aug). Internet point. Bicycle hire. Play area. 'Moules/frites' evenings in high season. Mobile homes and chalets for rent (all year). Off site: Beach 200 m. Hourly bus to La Rochelle from village centre. Shops, bars, restaurant.

Open: 1 April - 30 September.

Directions

From northbound N137 dual carriageway (La Rochelle bypass), leave at Lagord exit, then follow signs to L'Houmeau. On reaching L'Houmeau, site is well signed.

Charges 2008

Per unit incl. 2 persons	€ 13,00 - € 16,00
extra person	€ 3,50 - € 4,50
child (0-13 yrs)	€ 1,80 - € 2,50
electricity (5/10A)	€ 3,50 - € 4,20

FR17310 Camping le Val Vert

108 avenue Frederic Garnier, F-17640 Vaux-sur-Mer (Charente-Maritime)

Tel: **05 46 38 25 51**. Email: **camping-val-vert@wanadoo.fr**

Situated in seven acres of lush countryside (hence its name 'Green Valley'), this is a charming campsite, just 200 metres from the village of Vaux-sur-Mer, and 900 metres from the sandy beach at Nouzon. There are 95 touring pitches, all with 6/10A electricity (French connections – adaptors available). Extra long cables are required for some pitches, which are of average size (100 sq.m.) with good access, even for larger units. Some are terraced. Although entertainment is organised in high season, facilities on the site are minimal as the accent here is on peace and tranquillity.

Facilities

There are ample toilet and shower facilities. Separate facilities for people with disabilities. Laundry facilities. Shop, bar, restaurant and takeaway (all 10/6-10/9). Swimming and paddling pools (29/4-10/9; supervised in high season). Play area. Volleyball. Petanque. Off site: Village facilities including bar, supermarket and bank with ATM 200 m. Fishing 1 km. Boat launching 5 km. Golf 10 km. Riding 10 km. Beach 900 m.

Open: 8 April - 30 September.

Directions

Follow camping signs from the village of Vaux-sur-Mer. GPS: N45:38.640 W01:03:768

Charges 2007

Per unit incl. 1-3 persons	€ 17,00 - € 25,50
extra person	€ 4,00 - € 5,40
child (1-7 yrs)	€ 3,40 - € 4,40
electricity (6/10A)	€ 4,10 - € 4,70

FR17290 Camping les Peupliers

RD 735, F-17630 La Flotte-en-Ré (Charente-Maritime)

Tel: **05 46 09 62 35**. Email: **camping@les-peupliers.com**

On the Ile de Ré, you are never far from the sea and the location of this campsite is no exception. It is just 800 metres from the sea with sea views from some of the pitches. English is spoken at reception and the staff go out of their way to make your stay enjoyable. The 46 level touring pitches are in a separate area from 98 chalets for rent, in an area of light woodland. There are few water points. The trees provide some shade, but the very low hedges provide little privacy as the width and length of the pitches varies.

Facilities

Two new but traditionally designed sanitary blocks are clean and well maintained. Both have unisex facilities including showers and vanity type units in cabins. Separate facilities for people with disabilities. Laundry facilities. Shop, restaurant, takeaway and bar with TV (all 8/4-23/9). Play area. Children's club and entertainment (high season). Fridge hire. Bicycle hire. Off site: Riding 500 m. Boat launching and sailing 0.8 km. Beach 800 m. Fishing 0.8 km. Golf 20 km.

Open: 5 April - 27 September.

Directions

Over the toll bridge and turn left at second roundabout. Site is well signed. GPS: N46:10.969 W01:18.050

Charges 2007

Per unit incl. 2 persons	€ 15,00 - € 28,00
incl. electricity	€ 19,00 - € 33,00
extra person	€ 5,00 - € 8,00
child (0-5 yrs)	free - € 5,00
Camping Cheques accepted.	

FR17280 Camping la Grainetière

Mobile homes ▶ page 490

Route de Saint-Martin, F-17630 La Flotte-en-Ré (Charente-Maritime)
Tel: 05 46 09 68 86. Email: la-grainetiere@free.fr

A truly friendly welcome awaits you from the owners, Isabelle and Eric, at La Grainetière. It is a peaceful campsite set in almost three hectares of pine trees which provide some shade for the 65 touring pitches of various shapes and sizes. There are also 50 well spaced chalets for rent. Some pitches are suitable for units up to 7 metres (book in advance). There are no hedges for privacy and the pitches are sandy with some grass. Ample new water points and electricity (10A) hook-ups (Euro plugs) serve the camping area. The site is well lit.

Facilities

The unisex sanitary block is first class, with washbasins in cubicles, showers, British style WCs, facilities for children and people with disabilities. Shop (1/4-30/9). Takeaway (July/Aug). Swimming pool (heated 1/4-30/9). Bicycle hire. Fridge hire. TV room. Charcoal barbecues are not permitted. Off site: Beach and sailing 2 km. Fishing and boat launching 2 km. Riding 3 km. Golf 10 km. Bar and restaurant 2 km.

Open: 1 April - 30 September.

Directions

Follow camping signs from La Flotte, 1 km. from the village. GPS: N46:11.253 W01:20.696

Charges 2007

Per unit incl. 2 persons	€ 14,00 - € 24,00
extra person	€ 3,00 - € 7,00
child (0-7 yrs)	€ 2,00 - € 3,00
electricity (10A)	€ 4,00

Between St. Martin harbor and la Flotte. All kinds of shops at proximity. Isabelle and Eric welcome you in a wooded park. Friendly family atmosphere.

Route de Saint Martin - 17630 La Flotte - France - Tel: 0033 (0)5 46 09 68 86 - Fax: 0033 (0)5 46 09 53 13
lagrainetiere@free.fr - www.la-grainetiere.com

FR17340 Camping Port Punay

Allée Bernard Moreau, les Boucholeurs, F-17340 Châtelaillon-Plage (Charente-Maritime)
Tel: 05 46 56 01 53. Email: contact@camping-port-punay.com

Port Punay is a friendly, well run site just 200 metres from the beach and 3 km. from the centre of the resort of Châtelaillon-Plage. There are 166 touring pitches laid out on well trimmed grass, with many mature poplars and low shrubs. The site has a well stocked shop, open all season and a small bar and restaurant only open in high season. A heated swimming pool has a separate gated area for paddling. There is a good range of activities available and in high season some entertainment is arranged. This is a family run site (Famille Moreau) and the son of the family speaks excellent English, as does his Dutch wife.

Facilities

One large toilet block with good facilities including washbasins in cubicles and large shower cubicles. Facilities for disabled visitors and babies. Washing machines. Shop. Bar, restaurant and takeaway (1/7-31/8). Swimming pool. Games area. Play area. Bicycle hire. Internet access. WiFi. Off site: Châtelaillon-Plage 3 km. by road, 1.5 km. along the seafront on foot or bike. Buses to Rochefort and La Rochelle from outside site. Riding 2 km. Beach 200 m.

Open: 1 April - 30 September.

Directions

From N137 (La Rochelle - Rochefort) take exit for Châtelaillon-Plage. At the 1st roundabout follow the sign for the town centre. At the 2nd roundabout turn left. Follow signs to the site at the seaside hamlet of Les Boucholeurs. Here drive to the sea-wall then turn left through village to site. Take care, as the road has many traffic-calming measures and can be narrow in places.

Charges 2008

Per unit incl. 2 persons	€ 14,90 - € 22,00
extra person	€ 4,20 - € 5,50
child (0-3 yrs)	€ 3,20 - € 4,20
electricity (6/10A)	€ 4,00 - € 5,00

FR17490 Camping les Chirats

Route de la Platère, F-17690 Angoulins-sur-Mer (Charente-Maritime)
Tel: 05 46 56 94 16. Email: contact@campingleschirats.fr

This site is in a good position, being 8 km. south of La Rochelle and with a small sandy beach is just 100 m. from the site. The larger beaches at Aytre and Chatelaillon are 3 km. away. This is a family run site and a warm and friendly welcome awaits visitors. Of the 240 pitches, 200 are for touring units and the remainder are used for chalets which are for rent. The pitches are mainly open, level and easily accessible with some having views over the sea. Electricity supply is 10A and many have water and drainage. Leisure facilities on this site are excellent. There are attractive indoor and outdoor pools, together with a toboggan and a 'wellness' centre.There is also a large well equipped, adventure type play area which will keep the young ones happy for hours. In July and August, a varied entertainment programme is provided for all the family. Many guests return year after year to enjoy the friendly atmosphere.

Facilities

Three modern sanitary blocks all centrally placed with facilities for disabled visitors and babies. Washing machines. Bar, restaurant, snack bar and takeaway. Attractive indoor and outdoor swimming pools. Toboggan. Well equipped 'wellness' centre including sauna, jacuzzi, solarium, spa and gym. Playground. Multisport area. Fridge hire. Internet access. Entertainment (July/Aug). Off site: Fishing 100 m. Golf 5 km. Riding 4 km. Bicycle hire 500 m. Tennis 1 km. Aquarium 8 km.

Open: 1 April - 30 September.

Directions

Leave N137 at exit for Angoulins and La Jarne on to the D202. Go through Angoulins turning right on Rue de Chay. Carry on to Chemin de la Platere. Site is then well signed.

Charges 2008

Per unit incl. 2 persons	€ 12,00 - € 18,50
incl. electricity	€ 15,00 - € 21,50
extra person	€ 3,50 - € 4,00
child (under 10 yrs)	€ 2,50 - € 3,00

contact@campingleschirats.fr

Camping les Chirats***
Route de Platère
17690 Angoulins sur Mèr
Tel: 0033 546 56 94 16
Fax: 0033 546 56 65 95
www.campingleschirats.fr

FR17470 Le Domaine d'Oléron

La Jousselinière, F-17190 Saint Georges d'Oléron (Charente-Maritime)
Tel: 05 46 76 54 97. Email: chadotel@wanadoo.fr

Le Domaine d'Oleron is a member of the Chadotel group and can be found half a mile from the picturesque small town of St Georges, on the edge of the forest of Saumonards. There are 135 pitches here extending across the site's three acres. Many are occupied by mobile homes and chalets, leaving 58 grassy touring pitches, mostly with good shade. The pitches are of a good size and all have electrical connections (6A). There is an attractive swimming pool with slides and the nearest beach is 2 km. distant. There is much to see on the island and boat trips around the famous Fort Boyard are always popular.

Facilities

Toilet blocks include facilities for babies and disabled visitors. Small shop. Snack bar. Swimming pool with water slides. Children's pool. Play area. TV room. Children's club and entertainment programme in high season. Mobile homes and chalets for rent. Off site: Supermarket, shops and restaurants in St Georges and St Pierre. Nearest beach 2km. Oyster beds. Le Chassion lighthouse. Beach 2 km.

Open: 15 April - 29 September.

Directions

St Georges lies to the north of the Ile d'Oleron. From the bridge to the mainland continue north on the D26 and then the D734 to St Georges. Site is well signed from the village. GPS: N45:58.066 W01:19.116

Charges 2007

Per unit incl. 2 persons	€ 12,00 - € 23,20
incl. electricity	€ 16,70 - € 27,90
extra person	€ 5,80
child (2-13 yrs)	€ 3,80

FR17500 **Camping les Seulières**

1371 route des Seulières, F-17650 Saint Denis d'Oleron (Charente-Maritime)

Tel: **05 46 47 90 51**. Email: **campinglesseulieres@wanadoo.fr**

Situated half way between St Georges and St Denis and only 300 m. from the long golden sandy beach, this is a small site where you will receive a warm and friendly welcome for the owners. There are 135 pitches, 66 are for touring units and the remainder are for mobile homes and chalets. Pitches are level, open and easily accessible with 10A electricity. There is a comfortable bar with television and a small shop. Bread and 'viennoiserie' are delivered fresh each morning. Bicycles can be hired on site and you can go off exploring the island on one of the numerous cycle routes. Torches may be useful.

Facilities

Traditional sanitary block with facilities for disabled visitors and babies. Washing machine and dryer. Petanque. Table tennis. Games room. Bicycle hire. WiFi access. Bar with TV. Small shop. Limited entertainment in July and August. Off site: Beach 300 m. Fishing 300 m. Riding 1 km. Golf 6 km. Surf and sailing school.

Open: 1 April - 31 October.

Directions

After crossing the bridge onto the island, continue on D734 in the direction of St.Denis. Go through Cheray, turning left on Rue des Seulieres. Camping is on the right towards Plage des Huttes. GPS: N46:00.284 W01:22.986

Charges 2007

Per unit incl. 1 or 2 persons	€ 14,00
extra person	€ 4,00
electricity	€ 4,00

FR85010 **Camping le Zagarella**

Route de La Tranche, F-85560 Longeville-sur-Mer (Vendée)

Tel: **02 51 33 30 60**. Email: **contact@campingzagarella.com**

This pleasant campsite is set in a wooded, six hectare area, 900 metres walk from the beach (or 1.5 km. by road). As well as 100 chalets to rent, there are 45 small touring pitches (the site is probably unsuitable for units over 6 metres). On well drained grass and shaded, the pitches are hedged and all have water and 10A electricity (French connections). Access around the site is by tarmac roads. The site has a landscaped pool complex including slides and a covered pool. An area for sports and games including tennis is across the road via an underpass.

Facilities

Two well maintained toilet blocks of traditional design include British style WCs, washbasins in cubicles and free pre-set showers. Separate baby room and facilities for people with disabilities. Washing machines. Shop (25/5-5/9). Bar (20/5-5/9). Restaurant and takeaway (1/5-30/9). Swimming pool (1/6-30/9) and indoor pool (heated 1/4-30/9). Playground. Tennis. Bicycle hire. Gas barbecues permitted (available for rent). Off site: Beach 900 m. Riding 1 km. Golf 30 km.

Open: 1 April - 30 September.

Directions

From Longeville-sur-Mer take road to Tranche-sur-Mer and site is on the left (follow green camping signs).

Charges 2007

Per unit incl. 2 persons	€ 16,00 - € 28,00
extra person	€ 5,00 - € 6,00
child (0-7 yrs)	€ 3,50 - € 4,00
dog	€ 4,30

FR85000 Camping le Petit Rocher

1250 avenue de Docteur Mathevet, F-85560 Longeville-sur-Mer (Vendée)

Tel: 02 51 90 31 57. Email: rocher85@free.fr

A former municipal site, Le Petit Rocher is now under the same management (M. Guignard) as another local campsite, Les Brunelles. With its seaside location set in a pine forest, there is an air of peace and tranquillity. Although the area is undulating, the 150 good size touring pitches are flat and arranged in terraces throughout the wooded area. Electricity hook-ups are available (Euro style plugs) and there are adequate water points. A grassy play area for children is thoughtfully situated in a hollow, but has limited equipment. A swimming pool is planned.

Facilities

Three new, spacious sanitary blocks are clean and well maintained with showers, British style WCs. Facilities for people with disabilities. Washing machine and dryer. Tennis court. A heated pool is planned for 2008. Off site: Bars, restaurant, and small shops nearby. Riding and bicycle hire 2 km. Boat launching 11 km. Fishing 15 km. Golf 20 km. Beach 200 m.

Open: 31 May - 20 September.

Directions

From Longeville-sur-Mer follow signs for Le Rocher towards La Tranche-sur-Mer. Turn right at first roundabout, following campsite signs to site on right. GPS: N46:24.226 W01:30.431

Charges 2007

Per person	€ 3,00 - € 4,00
pitch	€ 10,00 - € 15,00
electricity	€ 13,00 - € 20,00
No credit cards.	

FR85020 Camping du Jard

123 Mal de Lattre de Tassigny, F-85360 La Tranche-sur-Mer (Vendée)

Tel: 02 51 27 43 79. Email: info@campingdujard.fr

Camping du Jard is a well maintained site between La Rochelle and Les Sables d'Olonne. First impressions are good, with a friendly welcome from M. Marton or his staff. The 242 touring pitches are level and grassy, hedged on two sides by bushes. The smallest are 100 sq.m. (the majority larger) and most are equipped with electricity, half with water and drainage. It is a comparatively new site, but the large variety of trees are beginning to provide a little shade.

Facilities

Three toilet blocks with facilities for babies and disabled people and most washbasins in cabins. Laundry facilities. Shop (1/6-10/9), restaurant and bar (25/5-10/9). Heated pool with toboggan and paddling pool, plus heated indoor pool with jacuzzi (no Bermuda-style shorts in pools). Sauna, solarium and fitness room. Tennis. Minigolf. Bicycle hire. Play area, games and TV rooms. American motorhomes are not accepted. Internet access. Pets are not accepted.

Open: 26 April - 15 September.

Directions

Site is east of La Tranche-sur-Mer on the D46. From the D747 (La Roche-sur-Yon to La Tranche) follow signs (La Faute-sur-mer) along bypass. Take exit for La Grière and then turn east to site. GPS: N46:23.280 W01:28.690

Charges 2008

Per pitch incl. 2 persons,	
electricity (10A)	€ 22,40 - € 33,90
extra person	€ 4,50 - € 5,50
child (under 5 yrs)	€ 3,00 - € 4,00

FR85040 Castel Camping Caravaning la Garangeoire

Saint Julien-des-Landes, F-85150 La Mothe-Achard (Vendée)

Tel: 02 51 46 65 39. Email: info@garangeoire.com

La Garangeoire is a stunning campsite, situated some 15 km. inland near the village of St Julien-des-Landes. Set in 200 ha. of parkland surrounding the small château of La Garangeoire of which there is an outstanding view as you approach through the gates. With a spacious, relaxed atmosphere, the main camping areas are on either side of the old road which is edged with mature trees. The 360 pitches, all named after birds, are individually hedged, some with shade. They are well spaced and are especially large (most 150-200 sq.m.), most with electricity (12A) and some with water and drainage also.

Facilities

Ample, first class sanitary facilities. All have washbasins in cabins. Facilities for babies and disabled people. Laundry facilities. Motorcaravan service point. Shop. Full restaurant, takeaway and a crêperie with bars and terrace. Pool complex with water slides, fountains and a children's pool. Play field with play equipment. Games room. Tennis courts. Bicycle hire. Table tennis, crazy golf, archery and volleyball. Riding (July/Aug). Fishing and boating. Off site: Golf 10 km. Beaches 15 km.

Open: 5 April - 24 September.

Directions

Site is signed from St Julien; entrance is to the east off the D21 road, 2.5 km. north of St Julian-des-Landes. GPS: N46:39.936 W01:42.80

Charges 2008

Per unit incl. 2 persons	€ 14,00 - € 27,50
with electricity	€ 17,00 - € 35,00
with services	€ 19,00 - € 37,50
extra person	€ 4,50 - € 7,60
child (under 10 yrs)	€ 2,50 - € 3,50
Camping Cheques accepted.	

148

FR85030 Camping la Loubine

1 route de la Mer, F-85340 Olonne-sur-Mer (Vendée)

Tel: 02 51 33 12 92. Email: camping.la.loubine@wanadoo.fr

Situated on the edge of a forest, this campsite is just 1.8 kilometres from a sandy beach and five minutes from Les Sables d'Olonne. The 60 grass touring pitches are mostly shaded, all with 6A electricity connections and adequate water points. Only a limited number of pitches is available for large units (over 7 m.) because of difficulties with manoeuvring. It is best to confirm availability and book in advance. The focal point of the site is an excellent bar and entertainment area for karaoke and discos with a patio overlooking the splendid pool complex with its water slides. There are many chalets and mobile homes on the site, both privately owned and to rent.

Facilities

Toilet blocks are clean with British style WCs, washbasins in cubicles and controllable showers. Shop. Bar and restaurant (15/5-15/9). Indoor pool (all season). Outdoor swimming pools (15/5-15/9). Tennis. Fitness room. Minigolf. Play area. Bicycle hire. A new indoor aqua park is planned. Off site: Beach 2 km. Fishing and boat launching 6 km. Golf 4 km. Riding 1 km. Boat launching 6 km. Restaurant, shop, bar within 1.5 km.

Open: 5 April - September.

Directions

Site is west of Olonne beside the D80 road. Turn towards the coast at roundabout, signed La Forêt d'Olonne and site (75 m).

Charges 2007

Per pitch incl. 2 persons	€ 15,30 - € 26,60
extra person	€ 3,20 - € 5,00
child (under 7 yrs)	free - € 2,90
electricity (6A)	€ 3,60

Camping La Loubine

Traditional-style facilities set in the grounds of an old farm only 1800 m from the beach; La Loubine is a lively site with one of the best pool complexes in the area. (2 outdoor swimming pools with 5 waterslides, 1 heated indoor pool with whirlpool bath and sauna).

Bar - Restaurant - Take Away - Shop - Tennis Court - Crazy Golf - Playground - Fitness Room - Multi Sport Pitch - Bicycle Hire - Entertainment in high season.

1, Route de la Mer - 85340 Olonne Sur mer - France
Tel.: 0033 (0)2 51 33 12 92 - Fax: 0033 (0)2 51 33 12 71

camping.la.loubine@wanadoo.fr
www.la-loubine.fr

FR85050 Le Village de Florine

La Grouinière, F-85220 Coëx (Vendée)

Tel: 02 51 60 19 51. Email: le-village-de-florine@wanadoo.fr

This is a pleasant, rural, recently developed site, under new ownership. It has 72 large, reasonably level, grassy pitches with 10A hook-ups. There is little shade at present from the recently planted small trees and shrubs but these will mature in time. Also on site are 30 privately owned mobile homes and 9 units to rent, leaving just 34 pitches for touring units. Site amenities are housed in tastefully converted farm buildings and the small modern toilet block is well equipped. Perhaps the site's greatest asset is its well fenced swimming and paddling pools.

Facilities

A single modern toilet block provides washbasins in cubicles for ladies, seated WC's and good suites for disabled people and babies. Laundry room with washing machine and ironing facilities. Bar and takeaway (1/7-31/8). Heated swimming pool (14 x 7 m.) and children's pool (May - Sept). Mini-adventure playground. Boules. Children's animation and evening entertainment in July/Aug. Off site: Town, ATM, fishing, golf and riding all 12 km. Boat launching 10 km.

Open: 1 April - 31 October.

Directions

Coëx is on the D6 between St Gilles Croix-de-Vie and Aizenay. In village take D40 south towards La Chaize-Giraud. After 2 km. turn into lane to site on right (signed). GPS: N46:41.006 W01:46.630

Charges 2007

Per unit incl. 2 persons	€ 10,00 - € 18,00
extra person	€ 4,00 - € 4,50
child (under 13 yrs)	€ 3,00 - € 3,50
electricity (10A)	€ 4,00

FR85090 Camping l'Abri des Pins

Route de Notre-Dame-de-Monts, F-85160 Saint Jean-de-Monts (Vendée)

Tel: **02 51 58 83 86**. Email: **contact@abridespins.com**

L'Abri des Pins is situated on the outskirts of St Jean-de-Monts and is separated from the sea and long sandy beach by a strip of pinewood. The site has 218 pitches, 78 of which are for touring units with 30 larger than average, with electricity, water and drainage. Electricity is also available for the other pitches which are around 100 sq.m., fully marked out with dividing hedges and shade. Many pitches are occupied by privately owned mobile homes, but there are no tour operators on the site. From the site, it is a pleasant 15 minute walk to the beach.

Facilities

The two sanitary blocks include washbasins in cabins, laundry and dishwashing sinks. Small shop (1/7-31/8) and bar/restaurant provides good value meals, both to eat in and take away. Outdoor, heated swimming pool, plus small pool for children, with decked sunbathing area (no Bermuda style shorts). Daily children's club. Aqua aerobics. Off site: Beach 700 m. Supermarket. Restaurants. Walking, cycling and fishing 1 km. Riding 2 km. Golf 5 km.

Open: 15 June - 16 September.

Directions

Site is 4 km. from town centre on St Jean-de-Monts - Notre Dame-de Monts/Noirmoutiers road (D38), on left heading north, just after Camping les Amiaux. GPS: N46:48.562 W02:06.540

Charges 2007

Per unit incl. 3 persons and electricity	€ 22,50 - € 33,70
extra person	€ 3,60 - € 6,10
child (under 5 yrs)	€ 2,55 - € 4,10

FR85110 Camping l'Océan

Rue des Gabelous, F-85470 Brem sur Mer (Vendée)

Tel: **02 51 90 59 16**. Email: **contact@campingdelocean.fr**

Set amongst grapevines and fir trees, Camping L'Océan is situated between the fishing port of St Gilles-Croix-de-Ville and Brem-sur-Mer, only 600 metres (15 minutes walk) from beautiful sandy beaches and the clear Atlantic Ocean. The campsite is family managed (Helen is English) and a very warm welcome awaits at the reception area which is well stocked with local information. The touring pitches are an average of 100 sq.m. and have 6A French style electric hook-ups (some require long leads). They are divided by hedges and centrally located with mobile homes to rent on either side.

Facilities

Three old style but very clean unisex toilet blocks have free pre-set showers, British style WCs, and washbasins in cubicles. Separate toilet and shower for people with disabilities. Shop (July/Aug). Bar and restaurant (weekends only May, June, Sept). Swimming pool (heated 15/6-30/8) with slide. Indoor pool (15/4-30/9). Fitness room. Bicycle hire. Play areas. Organised activities. Children's club. Off site: Brem-sur-Mer 15 minutes walk. Supermarket 5 minute drive. Fishing 1 km. Riding 9 km. Golf 15 km.

Open: 1 April - 15 October.

Directions

Take N160 from La Roche-sur-Yon towards Les Sables d'Olonne. Take exit for La Mothe-Achard and Bretignolles-sur-Mer. Follow D54 to Brem-sur-Mer then D38 Bretignolles-sur-Mer. Site is signed on left before Activity Centre.

Charges 2007

Per unit incl. 2 persons incl. electricity (6A)	€ 13,20 - € 19,00
	€ 15,80 - € 22,00
extra person	€ 3,50 - € 4,50
child (0-7 yrs)	€ 2,30 - € 2,90

FR85080 Hotellerie de Plein Air la Puerta del Sol

Les Borderies, chemin de Hommeaux, F-85270 Saint Hilaire-de-Riez (Vendée)

Tel: **02 51 49 10 10**. Email: **info@campinglapuertadelsol.com**

La Puerta del Sol is a good quality campsite a short distance away from the busy coast. It is suitable not only for families with teenage children to entertain, but also for those seeking a more peaceful and relaxing holiday. There are 216 pitches, of which 102 are used for touring units. Pitches are level with dividing hedges and many receive shade from the mature trees on the site. Each pitch is fully serviced with water, waste water point and electricity. There is one small French tour operator on site (20 pitches).

Facilities

Three heated toilet blocks have a mix of Turkish and British style WCs, washbasins in cabins and baby baths. Dishwashing and laundry facilities. Facilities for disabled visitors. Shop (1/5-31/8). Bar (1/5-15/9). Self-service restaurant and takeaway (1/5-31/8). Swimming pool, slide and paddling pool (1/5-30/9; no Bermuda style shorts). Play area. Tennis. Bicycle hire. Video games. American motorhomes accepted with reservation. Off site: Beach, riding, fishing and golf 5 km.

Open: 1 April - 30 September.

Directions

From Le Pissot (7 km. north of St Gilles Croix-de-Vie on D38) take D59 (Le Perrier). Site is 2 km. along this road on the right down a short side road. Site signed.

Charges 2007

Per unit incl. up to 2 persons and services	€ 19,00 - € 29,00
extra person	€ 5,00 - € 6,50
child (under 7 yrs)	€ 2,50 - € 4,50

Check real time availability and at-the-gate prices...

www.**alanrogers**.com

FR85150 Camping la Yole

 Mobile homes page 490

Chemin des Bosses, Orouet, F-85160 Saint Jean-de-Monts (Vendée)

Tel: 02 51 58 67 17. Email: contact@la-yole.com

La Yole is an attractive and well run site, 2 kilometres from a sandy beach. It offers 278 pitches, the majority of which are occupied by tour operators and mobile homes to rent. There are 100 touring pitches, most with shade and separated by bushes and trees. A newer area at the rear of the site is more open. All the pitches are of at least 100 sq.m. and have electricity (10A), water and drainage. The pool complex includes an outdoor pool, a paddling pool, slide and an indoor heated pool with jacuzzi. Entertainment is organised in high season.

Facilities

Two toilet blocks include washbasins in cabins and facilities for disabled people and babies. A third block has a baby room. Laundry facilities. Shop. Bar, restaurant and takeaway (1/5-5/9). Outdoor pool and paddling pool. Indoor heated pool with jacuzzi. Play area. Ball games. Club room. Tennis. Table tennis, pool and video games. Entertainment in high season. Gas barbecues only. Off site: Beach, bus service, bicycle hire 2 km. Riding 3 km. Fishing, golf and watersports 6 km.

Open: 5 April - 26 September.

Directions

Signed off the D38, 6 km. south of St Jean-de-Monts in the village of Orouet. GPS: N46:45.383 W02:00.466

Charges 2007

Per unit incl. 2 persons, electricity	€ 16,00 - € 29,00
extra person	€ 3,70 - € 6,00
child (2-9 yrs)	€ 2,15 - € 4,50
baby (0-2 yrs)	free - € 3,30
dog	€ 4,00 - € 5,00

Camping Cheques accepted.

Camping La Yole ★★★★

Wake up to the sound of birdsong in a wooded park of 17 acres with four star comfort. Space, security, informal atmosphere: la yole, tucked away between fields and pine trees, only 2 km from the beach.

– Chemin des Bosses - Orouet - F 85160 Saint Jean de Monts –
– Tel: 0033 251 58 67 17 - Fax: 0033 251 59 05 35 –
– contact@la-yole.com / www.la-yole.com –

 Camping Cheque

FR85130 Camping Pong

Rue du Stade, F-85220 Landevieille (Vendée)

Tel: 02 51 22 92 63. Email: info@lepong.com

A comfortable family run site, in a rural situation 12 km. southeast of St Gilles-Croix-de-Vie, and 5 km. from the coast at Brétignolles. It has 229 pitches with 187 used for touring units, the remainder for mobile homes and chalets. All have electricity connections (4/6A) and are of a good size. The bar, restaurant, function room, games room, gym and shop have all recently been rebuilt. The original part of the site around the small, lightly fenced fishing lake (there are warning signs) has mature trees, whereas, in the newer areas trees and shrubs are developing well.

Facilities

Four modern, unisex sanitary blocks provide toilets of mixed styles and some washbasins in cabins. Facilities for disabled people, baby room, dishwashing and laundry room. Shop, takeaway, bar and restaurant (15/6-15/9). Swimming pools including heated pool with jacuzzi, toboggan and paddling pool (from 15/5). Gym, TV lounge and games room. Bicycle hire. Fishing. Fenced play area and children's club. Off site: Tennis 200 m. Lac du Jaunay 2.5 km. Beach, golf, riding 5 km.

Open: 1 April - 15 September.

Directions

Site is on the edge of Landevieille and is signed from the D32 (Challans-Les Sables d'Olonne) and D12 (La Mothe Achard-St Gilles-Croix-de-Vie).

Charges 2008

Per unit incl. 2 persons and electricity	€ 15,00 - € 24,00
extra person	€ 3,20 - € 4,90
child (under 5 yrs)	€ 2,50 - € 3,70
water and drainage	€ 1,70
dog	€ 1,80 - € 2,50

FR85140 Camping Naturiste le Colombier

Le Colombier, F-85210 St Martin-Lars en Ste Hermine (Vendée)

Tel: 02 51 27 83 84. Email: lecolombier.nat@wanadoo.fr

A countryside site for naturists near La Roche sur Yon, just right for those seeking a peaceful holiday. It provides around 160 pitches in seven very natural fields on different levels linked by informal tracks. There are level, terraced areas for caravans and a feeling of spaciousness with pitches around the edges of fields, unmarked and with electricity (6/10A, some may require long leads). The bar/restaurant is in a converted barn. The site's 125 acres provide many walks throughout the attractive, wooded valley and around the lake.

Facilities

Fully equipped toilet blocks are good, providing some showers in cubicles. Dishwashing sinks. Motorcaravan service point. Grocer/baker calls daily. Bar/restaurant with á la carte and full menu (order before 1 pm), home baked bread and pizzas. Heated swimming pool. Fishing. Volleyball. Boules. Playground. Pony and trap rides and one day a week children can make their own bread. Plans for a sauna and aqua gym. Off site: Shop 1 km.

Open: 1 April - 30 October.

Directions

From N148, La Roche-sur-Yon - Niort road, at St Hermine, turn onto D8 eastward for 4 km. Turn left on D10 to St Martin-Lars. Site is signed.

Charges 2007

Per pitch, 2 persons and electricity	€ 18,50 - € 21,50
child (3-9 yrs)	€ 3,40 - € 3,50
child (10-16 yrs)	€ 4,70 - € 4,80
animal	€ 3,50

FR85890 Camping le Rouge-Gorge

F-85290 Saint-Laurent-sur-Sèvre (Vendée)

Tel: 02 51 67 86 39. Email: campinglerougegorge@wanadoo.fr

A family run site, Le Rouge-Gorge is open all year. There are 72 touring pitches, plus some units for rent and privately owned caravans and chalets. The site does accept a small number of workers' units. Slightly sloping and undulating pitches are on grass in a garden-like setting and a small wildlife pond (fenced) is in the centre of the site. It would make a suitable base from which to visit the spectacles of Puy de Fou and the steam railway which runs from Mortagne-sur-Sèvre to Les Herbiers. This is also an excellent stop-over for those heading to and from southern France and Spain, or the ski-resorts.

Facilities

Two toilet blocks, one can be heated, with washbasins in cubicles and facilities for disabled campers and babies. Laundry with washing machine and dryer. Motorcaravan service point. Bread and basic provisions stocked (1/6-30/9). Swimming pool (1/6-30/9). Some low key family entertainment in high season. Boules. Charcoal barbecues are not permitted. TV room. WiFi. Off site: Fishing 500 m. Riding 2 km. Mortagne - Les Herbiers steam railway passes close to site.

Open: All year.

Directions

Saint Laurent-sur-Sèvre is about 10 km. due south of Cholet, just south of the N149. Site is on D111 out of town towards la Verrie, entrance at top of hill on right. GPS: N46:57.486 W00:54.205

Charges 2007

Per unit incl. 2 persons	€ 14,00 - € 15,60
extra person	€ 3,60
child (under 10 rs)	€ 1,90
electricity (4-13A)	€ 2,00 - € 10,20

FR85210 Camping les Ecureuils
Route des Goffineaux, F-85520 Jard-sur-Mer (Vendée)
Tel: 02 51 33 42 74. Email: camping-ecureuils@wanadoo.fr

Mobile homes ▶ page 492

Les Ecureuils is a wooded site in a quieter part of the southern Vendée. It is undoubtedly one of the prettiest sites on this stretch of coast, with an elegant reception area, attractive vegetation and large pitches separated by low hedges with plenty of shade. Of the 261 pitches, some 128 are for touring units, each with water and drainage, as well as easy access to 10A electricity. This site is very popular with tour operators (103 pitches). Jard is rated among the most pleasant and least hectic of Vendée towns. The harbour is home to some fishing boats and rather more pleasure craft, and has a public slipway for those bringing their own boats.

Facilities

Two toilet blocks, well equipped and kept very clean, include baby baths, and laundry rooms. Small shop (bread baked on site). New snack-bar. Takeaway service (pre-order 1/6-15/9). Snacks and ice creams available from the friendly bar. Good sized L-shaped swimming pool and separate paddling pool (30/5-15/9). Indoor pool and fitness centre (all season). Two play areas for different age groups. Modern play area. Minigolf, table tennis and a pool table. Club for children (5-10 yrs) daily in July/Aug. Bicycle hire. Only gas barbecues are allowed. Dogs are not accepted. Internet access. Off site: Beach, fishing 400 m. Marina and town.

Open: 15 April - 27 September.

Directions

From Les Sables d'Olonne take the N949 towards Talmont St Hilaire. Keep right in the centre (D21 towards Jard). From la Roche sur Yon follow the D474 and the D49 towards Jard-sur-Mer. From the village follow the signs 'Autre campings' or 'Camping les Ecureuils'. Site is on the left. GPS: N46:24.683 W01:35.382

Charges 2007

Per person	€ 5,00 - € 6,70
child (0-4 yrs)	€ 1,50 - € 2,00
child (5-9 yrs)	€ 4,00 - € 4,50
per pitch with water and drainage	€ 13,00 - € 15,50
with electricity (10A)	€ 18,00 - € 22,20
Less 10% outside 30/6-1/9.	

LES ECUREUILS
85520 JARD-SUR-MER
Tel. 0033 251 33 42 74
Fax 0033 251 33 91 14
Hôtellerie de Plein Air ★★★★
SUD VENDÉE - FRANCE
WWW.CAMPING-ECUREUILS.COM

153
Check real time availability and at-the-gate prices...
www.alanrogers.com

FR85220 **Camping Acapulco**

Avenue des Epines, F-85160 Saint Jean-de-Monts (Vendée)

Tel: **02 51 59 20 64**. Email: **info@sunmarina.com**

Ideal for family beach holidays, this friendly site is situated midway between St Jean-de-Monts and St Hilaire-de-Riez, and is 600 m. from the beach. It is one of four sites on the Vendée coast owned by the Sunmarina group. Most of the pitches here are taken by mobile homes, leaving about 20 for touring. All are about 100 sq.m. on grass and divided by hedges which give some shade. The central part of the site has an excellent pool complex complete with five slides, a children's pool and a terrace for sunbathing. Adjacent to this is a spacious bar, restaurant and a safe play area.

Facilities

Two sanitary blocks are clean and include washbasins in cabins and showers. Facilities for disabled visitors. Laundry facilities. Motorcaravan service point. Shop with basic supplies. Bar, restaurant and takeaway. Large heated pool complex with five water slides and paddling pool. Play area. Entertainment in high season. Off site: Shopping centre 400 m. Sancy beach 600 m.

Open: 15 May - 15 September.

Directions

Follow the coastal road of St Jean-de-Monts south towards St Hilaire-de-Riez. Just past signs of Commune St Hilaire, turn left at first roundabout. Site is 400 m. on right (signed).

Charges 2007

Per unit incl. 3 persons and electricity	€ 31,00
extra person	€ 9,00
child (under 5 yrs)	€ 6,00

FR85230 **Camping les Ecureuils**

100 avenue de la Pège, F-85270 Saint Hilaire-de-Riez (Vendée)

Tel: **02 51 54 33 71**. Email: **info@camping-aux-ecureuils.com**

Of the seaside sites on the Vendée, Les Ecureuils has to be one of the best, run by a friendly and most helpful family. Just 300 m. from a superb beach, the site is ideally situated for exploring from Les Sables d'Olonne to Noirmoutier. Developed on what was originally a farm, there are 230 pitches (55 for touring units). On sandy grass, all have electricity (6A, Euro adaptors avalable), water and drainage. Well kept hedges and mature trees give shade and privacy, although some more open pitches are also available for sun lovers. The site is popular with British tour operators (60%).

Facilities

The two main sanitary blocks are spacious, and include some washbasins in cubicles, and facilities for babies and disabled people. Laundry and dishwashing facilities. Small shop (25/5-6/9). Restaurant. Large, airy bar with screened terrace. Pool complex including pool for small children with its own 'mini aqua park', large heated pool, and water slide with separate splash pool. New indoor pool, paddling pool and jacuzzi. Off site: Bicycle hire 200 m. Fishing 4 km. Riding 5 km. Golf 6 km.

Open: 1 May - 15 September.

Directions

Driving south D38 (St Jean-de-Monts - St Gilles), turn right at L'Oasis hotel/restaurant in Orouet (6 km. outside St Jean-de-Monts), signed Les Mouettes. After 1.5 km. at roundabout turn left (St Hilaire-de-Riez). Site is 500 m. on left. GPS: N46:44.167 W02:00.570

Charges 2007

Per unit incl. 2 persons and 3 services	€ 25,70 - € 34,35
extra person	€ 4,85 - € 5,95

FR85250 **Yelloh! Village le Littoral**

Le Porteau, F-85440 Talmont-Saint-Hilaire (Vendée)

Tel: **04 66 73 97 39**. Email: **info@yellohvillage-le-littoral.com**

Le Littoral is situated on the southern Vendée coast between the ports and beaches of Les Sables d'Olonne and Bourgenay. It has been fully modernised over recent years by the Boursin family. Although the site's 483 pitches are mainly used for mobile homes and chalets for hire, there are 67 touring pitches which are hedged and of a good size. They are interspersed with the mobile homes and all have water, electricity and drainage. The site has a heated outdoor pool complex, an indoor heated pool and the restaurant is open daily (15/5-3/9) with frequent themed evenings.

Facilities

New chalets. Four sanitary blocks have both British and Turkish style WCs, showers and washbasins in cubicles. Baby rooms. Facilities for disabled visitors. Laundry. Fridge hire. Shop. New bar (Easter-16/9). Restaurant and takeaway (15/5-3/9). Pizzeria and crêperie (high season). Indoor pool (3/4-30/9). Outdoor pool complex with slides (15/5-10/9). Bicycle hire. Multisport pitches. Tennis. Play area. Games room. Activities, entertainment and excursions. Minibus to beach. Off site: Bus. Sea fishing 200 m. Riding 500 m. Golf 1.5 km. Beach 3 km.

Open: 6 April - 16 September.

Directions

From D949 Les Sables - Talmont, take D4 south to Port Bourgenay. Turn onto D129 westward and site is on left in 300 m. GPS: N46:27.098 W01:42.121

Charges 2007

Per unit incl. 2 persons	€ 17,00 - € 34,00
extra person	€ 5,00 - € 7,00
child (0-12 yrs)	€ 3,00 - € 4,00
animal	€ 2,00 - € 3,50

Check real time availability and at-the-gate prices...

www.alanrogers.com

FR85260 Village de la Guyonnière

La Guyonnière, F-85150 Saint Julien-des-Landes (Vendée)
Tel: **02 51 46 62 59**. Email: **info@laguyonniere.com**

La Guyonnière is a spacious, rural site. It is Dutch owned but English is spoken and all visitors are made very welcome. It is a farm type site with eight different fields, each being reasonably level and seven having a toilet block. The 270 mostly large pitches have a mix of sun and shade. Some are open, others are separated by a tree and a few bushes. All have access to electricity connections and 86 are occupied by mobile homes and chalets. Bar and restaurant facilities are housed in the original farm buildings attractively converted. Entertainment is provided in the bar on high season evenings. A perfect place for families, with large play areas on sand and grass, and paddling pond with shower. Being in the country, it is a haven for cyclists and walkers, with many signed routes from the site. A pleasant 500 m. walk takes you to the Jaunay Lake where fishing is possible (permits from the village), canoeing (life jackets from reception) and pedaloes to hire. There are no tour operators and, needless to say, no road noise. It is popular for many reasons, the main one being the free and easy atmosphere.

Facilities

Modern toilet blocks. Most cubicles are quite small. Washbasins are in cubicles. Limited provision for babies and disabled visitors. Dishwashing and laundry sinks. Shop. Bar with TV and pool table (both 1/5-15/9). Restaurant (15/6-15/9). Pizzeria with takeaway (1/5-29/9). Small pool and heated pool with jacuzzi and slide. Paddling pool. Play areas, sand pit. Volleyball, tennis and football fields. Bicycle hire. Car wash. WiFi. Off site: Riding 3 km. Golf 8 km. Beaches 10 km.

Open: 28 April - 29 September.

Directions

Site is signed off the D12 road (La Mothe Achard - St Gilles-Croix-de-Vie), approx. 4 km. west of St Julien-des-Landes, down a lane about 1 km. from the main road. GPS: N46:39.152 W01:45.010

Charges 2007

Per unit incl. 2 persons	
and electricity	€ 11,00 - € 29,40
extra person	€ 4,40 - € 5,40
child (3-9 yrs)	€ 2,80 - € 3,30
animal	€ 2,90

Less 10-20% outside high season.

FR85270 Chadotel Camping l'Oceano d'Or

84 rue Georges Clémenceau, B.P. 12, F-85520 Jard-sur-Mer (Vendée)

Tel: **02 51 33 05 05**. Email: **chadotel@wanadoo.fr**

This site should appeal to families with children of all ages. It is very lively in high season but appears to be well managed, with a full programme of activities (it can therefore be noisy, sometimes late at night). The site is only 1 km. from the excellent beach. There are 430 flat, grass and sand pitches of which 40% are occupied by tour operators and mobile homes. The 260 for touring units, all with 6A electricity, are quite large (about 100 sq.m.). Some are separated by high hedges, others are more open with low bushes between them.

Facilities

Four rather dated, unisex toilet blocks include washbasins all in cabins (cleaning and maintenance is variable). Dishwashing and laundry facilities. Shop (1/6-10/9). Bar and snack bar (1/6-10/9, but limited hours outside high season). Swimming pool (heated 20/5-20/9) with slides, 2 waterfalls and children's pool. Play area. Tennis, petanque and minigolf. Electric barbecues are not allowed. Off site: Excellent beach within walking distance. Golf, riding, karting and other activities within 15 km.

Open: 7 April - 23 September.

Directions

Site is on the D21 Talmont St Hilaire - Longeville sur Mer, just east of the turning to the town centre. GPS: N46:25.264 W01:34.199

Charges 2007

Per pitch incl. 2 persons	€ 14,50 - € 24,20
with electricity	€ 19,20 - € 28,90
extra person	€ 5,80
child (under 2 yrs)	€ 3,80
animal	€ 3,00

FR85280 Camping les Places Dorées

Route de Notre-Dame-de-Monts, F-85160 Saint Jean-de-Monts (Vendée)

Tel: **02 51 59 02 93**. Email: **abridespins@aol.com**

Les Places Dorées is owned by the same family as L'Abri des Pins (FR85090) which is just across the road. It is a much newer site with maturing trees gradually beginning to offer some shade. There are 245 grassy pitches, the quietest being towards the back of the site. Each one is separated, all have electrical connections (6A) and some are also equipped with water and drainage. One small Dutch tour operator is on site (22 pitches). In low season the site is quiet but it can be noisy in high season with the bar and disco closing late.

Facilities

Three modern toilet blocks include washbasins in cubicles. Facilities for disabled visitors. Laundry and dishwashing facilities. Pool complex with slides, jacuzzi area and waterfall (no Bermuda style shorts). High season entertainment and children's club at L'Abri des Pins, also adult activities. Facilities at L'Abri des Pins may be used - shop (July/Aug), tennis, fitness room, swimming pools and a games room. Off site: Fishing 500 m. Beach 700 m. Riding 2 km. Golf 5 km.

Open: 1 June - 1 September.

Directions

Site is 4 km. north of St Jean-de-Monts on the D38 St Jean-de-Monts - Notre Dames-de-Monts road on the right hand side, almost opposite L'Abri des Pins. GPS: N46:48.690 W02:06.685

Charges 2007

Per pitch incl. 3 persons	
and electricity	€ 22,50 - € 33,70
extra person	€ 3,60 - € 6,10
child	€ 2,55 - € 4,10

FR85300 Camping la Grand Métairie

8 rue de la Vineuse en Plaine, F-85440 Saint Hilaire-la-Forêt (Vendée)

Tel: **02 51 33 32 38**. Email: **grand-metairie@wanadoo.fr**

Just five kilometres from the super sandy beach at Jard-sur-Mer, La Grand' Métairie offers many of the amenities of its seaside counterparts, but with the important advantage of being on the edge of a delightful, sleepy village, otherwise untouched by tourism. It is a busy well run site with a programme of lively entertainment in high season. The site has 180 pitches (50 touring pitches), all with electricity. Some also with water and drainage. The pitches have good shade, are all separated by mature trees and hedges and are reasonable in size.

Facilities

Two modern toilet blocks are very clean and include washbasins mainly in cabins. Units for disabled people. Washing machines and dryers. Fridge hire. Safety deposit boxes. Bar/restaurant and takeaway (all 1/5-15/9). Heated outdoor pool, indoor pool, sauna, jacuzzi and paddling pool. Gym. Tennis, minigolf. Visiting hairdressing salon. Internet access. Children's club. Off site: Village shop 100 m. Riding and fishing within 5 km.

Open: 1 April - 30 September.

Directions

From Les Sables d'Olonne take D949 (La Rochelle) towards Talmont St Hilaire and Luçon; 7 km. after Talmont turn right on D70 to St Hilaire-la-Forêt. Site is on left before village centre. GPS: N46:26.907 W01:31.580

Charges 2007

Per unit incl. 2 persons	
and electricity (6A)	€ 17,00 - € 27,00
extra person	€ 5,00 - € 8,00

FR85320 Camping Caravaning Val de Vie

Rue du Stade, F-85190 Maché (Vendée)

Tel: 02 51 60 21 02. Email: campingvaldevie@aol.com

Opened in 1999, Val de Vie is a small, good quality site run with enthusiasm and dedication by its English owners on the outskirts of a rural village back from the coast. There are 52 original pitches for touring units (42 with electricity 4, 6 or 10A) that vary in size from 80-137 sq.m. on mostly level grass with newly planted hedging. There should now also be 12 new touring pitches (including 9 'super pitches' which must be booked for high season). The ground can become very hard so steel pegs are advised.

Facilities

The toilet block provides excellent, modern facilities including some washbasins in cabins, baby bath, facilities for disabled people, dishwashing and laundry facilities. Reception also offers wine, beer, soft drinks and ice cream. Small play area. Heated swimming pool (from mid May). Bicycle hire. Off site: Tennis courts, shops, bar, tabac within walking distance. Lake d'Apremont (300 m). Vendée coast 20 km.

Open: 1 May - 30 September.

Directions

From La Roche sur Yon take D948 northwest. At end of Aizenay bypass continue for 2 km; cross River Vie and take next left (D40). Site signed in village. GPS: N46:75.268 W01:68.633

Charges 2008

Per unit incl. 2 persons	€ 19,00 - € 28,00
extra person	€ 4,50
child (under 10 yrs)	€ 3,50
electricity (4-10A)	€ 2,90 - € 3,50

FR85350 Camping Caravaning la Ningle

Chemin des Roselières 66, F-85270 Saint Hilaire-de-Riez (Vendée)

Tel: 02 51 54 07 11. Email: campingdelaningle@wanadoo.fr

At Camping La Ningle you are guaranteed to receive a warm welcome from M. et Mme. Guibert, who have established a very pleasant campsite with a friendly, family atmosphere. There are 155 pitches, 60 available for touring units. All have electricity (6A) and all are fully serviced (electricity, water and drainage). Pitches are spacious with dividing hedges and all have some shade. The beach is a 600 m. walk through a pine forest, but there are also three small heated swimming pools on site.

Facilities

Two clean toilet blocks include some washbasins in cubicles. Toilet/shower room for disabled people and large family shower room. Laundry and dishwashing facilities. Bread (July/Aug). Takeaway three evenings per week. Bar (July/Aug). Main swimming pool, larger children's pool, paddling pool and slide. Fitness course. Games field. Volleyball. Table tennis. Games room. Fishing lake. Children's activities (July/Aug), and regular petanque and tennis competitions. Off site: Small supermarket and takeaway 200 m.

Open: 20 May - 10 September.

Directions

Driving south on D38 (St Jean-de-Monts - St Gilles), turn right at L'Oasis hotel/restaurant in Orouet, signed Les Mouettes. After 1.5 km. at roundabout, turn left (St Hilaire-de-Riez). Pass two campsites, then next left, signed La Ningle. GPS: N46:44.686 W02:00.267

Charges 2007

Per pitch incl. 2 persons	
with electricity	€ 17,50 - € 28,50
extra person	€ 3,10 - € 4,50
child (under 7 yrs)	€ 1,65 - € 2,80
dog	€ 1,90

FR85770 RCN Camping la Ferme du Latois

F-85220 Coëx (Vendée)

Tel: 02 51 54 67 30. Email: info@rcn-lafermedulatois.fr

Until recently a simple 'Camping á la ferme', this site is being developed by the Dutch organisation that now owns it into an extensive and very well equipped campsite. Naturally a very high proportion of its clientele is Dutch, but the owners are keen to attract more British visitors. Located on the far side of two attractive fishing lakes, the original, very spacious pitches are attractively laid out with plenty of grass, hedges and mature trees. The new ones on the near side of the lakes are equally spacious but here the grass, bushes and trees have yet to start growing.

Facilities

Two modern sanitary blocks built in traditional style have excellent toilets, showers and washbasins in cubicles. Good facilities for disabled visitors. Tiled areas for babies and children, with special toilets, basins and showers. Laundry room ('buanderie'). Small shop. Bar counter with terrace. Play area. Bicycle hire. Fishing. Off site: Golf and riding 3 km. Beach, sailing, boat launching 12 km.

Open: 14 April - 6 October.

Directions

Coëx is 29 km. west of La Roche-sur-Yon via the D938 to Aizenay, then the D6 St Gilles-Croix-de-Vie road. Site is south of the village just off the D20 (La Chaize-Giraud - Brem-sur-Mer) and is clearly signed. GPS: N46:40.622 W01:46.131

Charges 2008

Per unit incl. 2 persons, electricity and water	€ 18,00 - € 45,50

Check real time availability and at-the-gate prices...

www.alanrogers.com

FR85360 **Camping la Forêt**

190 chemin de la Rive, F-85160 Saint Jean-de-Monts (Vendée)

Tel: **02 51 58 84 63**. Email: **camping-la-foret@wanadoo.fr**

Camping La Forêt is owned by M. and Mme. Jolivet and they work hard to provide a small, quality site. Well run and attractive, with a friendly, family atmosphere, it provides just 63 pitches with 50 for touring units. Of 100 sq.m. in size, the pitches are surrounded by mature hedges and have water and electricity. Over 50 species of trees are planted, providing shade to every pitch. There is one tour operator on site(13 pitches), but their presence is not intrusive and the site has a quiet and relaxed atmosphere, ideal for couples or families with young children.

Facilities

The central toilet block includes washbasins in cubicles. Laundry and dishwashing facilities. Baby bath. Facilities for disabled people. Motorcaravan waste tanks can be emptied on request. Basic provisions sold in reception, including fresh bread. Takeaway. Small heated swimming pool (15/5-15/9). Play area. Bicycle hire. Only gas and electric barbecues allowed, communal barbecue in centre of site. Not suitable for American motorhomes. Off site: Beach 400 m. Cycle paths.

Open: 15 May - 28 September.

Directions

Follow D38 out of St Jean-de-Monts, towards Notre Dame-de-Monts. After 5.5 km. turn left at sign for site and 'Plage de Pont d'Yeu'. Follow road and site is on left at about 100 m.

Charges 2007

Per pitch incl. 2 persons	€ 17,00 - € 26,50
extra person	€ 3,50 - € 5,00
child (under 7 yrs)	€ 3,50
electricity (6A)	€ 3,80

No credit cards.

FR85390 **Camping des Batardières**

F-85440 Saint Hilaire-la-Foret (Vendée)

Tel: **02 51 33 33 85**

Camping des Batardières is a haven of tranquillity on the edge of an unspoilt village, yet just 5 km. from the sea. It is an attractive, unsophisticated little site, lovingly maintained by its owners for more than 25 years. Many visitors return year after year. There are 75 good-sized pitches (a few up to 130 sq.m.) and all are available for touring units (there are no mobile homes and no tour operators!) All have easy access to water and electricity (6A, or 2A for tents). Otherwise there are few facilities on site.

Facilities

The sanitary block is kept very clean and visitors are encouraged to keep it that way (no shoes in the shower cubicles, for instance). Some washbasin and shower combination cubicles. Dishwashing and laundry facilities, including washing machine and dryer. TV room. Table tennis. Tennis court. Play area and field for games, kite-flying etc. Not suitable for American motorhomes or twin axle caravans. Off site: Village shop and bar 200 m. Jard-sur-Mer 5 km.

Open: 27 June - 2 September.

Directions

From Les Sables d'Olonne take D949 (la Rochelle) towards Talmont St Hilaire and Luçon. 7 km. after Talmont turn right on D70 to St Hilaire-la-Forêt. Site signed to the right approaching village. GPS: N46:26.917 W01:31.719

Charges 2007

Per unit incl. 2 persons	€ 20,00
electricity	€ 3,50
extra person	€ 3,00
child (under 5 yrs)	€ 2,00

FR85400 **Camping Bois Soleil**

Chemin des Barres, F-85340 Olonne-sur-Mer (Vendée)

Tel: **02 51 33 11 97**. Email: **camping.boissoleil@wanadoo.fr**

A traditionally laid out site with 199 marked pitches, separated by hedges, on flat or gently sloping ground. There are just two tour operators and a scattering of mobile homes and chalets, leaving some 87 pitches for tourers and tents. All have electricity (6A, French style sockets) and water points adjacent and many also have waste water pipes. The main buildings house a small reception and tourist information room as well as the bar and attached shop. There is an excellent swimming pool complex with slides and an impressive flume, plus an indoor pool.

Facilities

The two toilet blocks have hot water, mainly British style toilets, with washbasins in cubicles in new block. Locked overnight, but basic toilet facilities provided. Dishwashing and laundry facilities. Shop (July/Aug) – 'eat in'/takeaway service; bread to order. Bar (28/6-31/8). Indoor and outdoor pools. Play area. Bicycle hire. Barbecues are not permitted. Off site: Bus service in Olonne-sur-Mer. Riding 400 m. Beaches 2.5 km. Fishing and golf 3 km.

Open: 5 April - 28 September.

Directions

Site is off D80 coast road between Olonne-sur-Mer and Brem-sur-Mer, clearly signed on the inland side.

Charges guide

Per unit incl. 2 persons	€ 15,00 - € 21,50
with electricity	€ 18,00 - € 24,50
extra person	€ 2,60 - € 3,70
child (under 7 yrs)	€ 2,10 - € 2,70
animal	€ 2,60

FR85420 Camping 'Bel

Rue du Bottereau, F-85360 La Tranche-sur-Mer (Vendée)

Tel: 02 51 30 47 39. Email: campbel@wanadoo.fr

Camping Bel's owner, M. Guieau, who has a very dry sense of humour, takes an individual approach. The first priority is the contentment of the children, who receive various small gifts during their stay. A popular site with a large proportion of French clients, despite the large presence of British tour operators (115 pitches). The 85 touring pitches are on level, sandy grass and separated by hedges with mature trees giving good shade. All pitches have electrical connections (6/10A). Being just 150 m. from a sandy beach this is a good site for a family beach holiday. La Tranche-sur-Mer with all amenities is within walking distance.

Facilities

Two modern toilet blocks have washbasins in cabins, very good baby units and facilities for disabled visitors. Baker calls daily. Bar. Heated outdoor pool with jacuzzi. Plenty of entertainment for children aged 6-14 yrs (July/Aug). Table tennis. Fitness area. Tennis and badminton. Pets are not accepted. Satellite TV. Internet access. Off site: Bicycle hire 100 m. Supermarket with fuel 200 m. Fishing, watersports and aquatic centre within 150 m. Riding 5 km.

Open: 26 May - 2 September with all services.

Directions

Follow signs from roundabout on La Tranche bypass, near 'Super U' supermarket onto avenue General de Gaulle. Left after 50 m. onto Rue du Bottereau. Site on right after 100 m. GPS: N46:20.916 W01:25.913

Charges 2007

Per unit with 2 persons and water	€ 22,00
with electricity (6A)	€ 26,00
extra person	€ 6,00
child (under 5 yrs)	€ 4,00

FR85440 Camping les Brunelles

Le Bouil, F-85560 Longeville-sur-Mer (Vendée)

Tel: 02 51 33 50 75. Email: camping@les-brunelles.com

This is a well managed site with good facilities and a varied programme of high season entertainment for all the family. A busy site in high season, there are plenty of activities to keep chidren happy and occupied. In 2007 Les Brunelles was combined with an adjacent campsite to provide 600 pitches. Many of the new touring pitches have water, electricity and waste, and are in excess of 100 sq.m. to allow easier access for larger units. On the original Les Brunelles site, touring pitches are level on sandy grass and separated by hedges, away from most of the mobile homes.

Facilities

Four old, but well maintained and modernised toilet blocks have British and Turkish style toilets and washbasins, both open style and in cabins. Laundry facilities. Shop. Takeaway and large modern, airy bar. Covered pool with jacuzzi (all season). Outdoor pool with slides and paddling pools (1/5-30/9). Tennis. Bicycle hire. Off site: Golf and riding within 15 km. Good supervised sandy beach 900 m. St Vincent-sur-Jard 2 km.

Open: 5 April - 27 September.

Directions

From D21 (Talmont - Longueville), between St Vincent and Longueville, site signed south from main road towards coast. Turn left in Le Bouil (site signed). Site is 800 m. on left. GPS: N46:24.798 W01:31.388

Charges 2008

Per unit incl. 2 persons	€ 15,00 - € 23,00
with electricity	€ 19,00 - € 28,00
extra person	€ 5,00 - € 7,00
child (under 5 yrs)	free - € 5,00
Camping Cheques accepted.	

FR85450 Camping les Roses

Rue des Roses, F-85100 Les Sables d'Olonne (Vendée)

Tel: 02 51 33 05 05. Email: info@chadotel.com

Les Roses has an urban location, with the town centre and lovely beach just a short walk away. It has an informal air with the 210 pitches arranged interestingly on a knoll. Mature trees give good shade to some areas. There are 107 touring pitches of varying size, many being more suitable for tents than caravans. All pitches have access to electricity (10A) and water (long cables may be needed). In high season caravanners might find site access tricky at times due to overloaded town centre traffic systems. The site has 103 mobile homes and chalets, but no tour operators.

Facilities

Three well maintained toilet blocks have washbasins in cubicles, unit for disabled visitors, baby room, washing machines and dryers. Simple bar and takeaway (15/5-15/9). Simple shop. Heated outdoor pool (1/5-30/9). Play area. Bicycle hire. Electric barbecues are not permitted. Off site: Beach 500 m. Golf, riding, karting, watersports, zoo, sea and river fishing within 5 km.

Open: April - 31 October.

Directions

Site is signed from D949 Les Sables to La Rochelle road, north of the 'Géant Casino' roundabout. Turn south at minor junction.

Charges 2007

Per pitch incl. 2 persons	€ 14,50 - € 24,20
with electricity	€ 19,20 - € 28,90
extra person	€ 5,80
child (under 5 yrs)	€ 3,80

Check real time availability and at-the-gate prices...

www.alanrogers.com

FR85480 Camping Caravaning le Chaponnet

Mobile homes ⏵ page 492

Rue du Chaponnet N-16, F-85470 Brem sur Mer (Vendée)

Tel: 02 51 90 55 56. Email: campingchaponnet@wanadoo.fr

This well established family run site is within five minutes walk of Brem village and 1.5 km. from a sandy beach. The 80 touring pitches are level with varying amounts of grass, some with shade from mature trees. Pitches are separated by tall hedges and serviced by tarmac or gravel roads and have frequent water and electricity points (long leads may be required). Tour operators have mobile homes and tents on 70 pitches and there are 55 privately owned mobile homes and chalets. The swimming pool complex also has a jacuzzi, slides and a children's pool, together with a sauna and fitness centre.It is overlooked by the spacious bar and snack bar. Entertainment is provided for all ages by day and three or four musical evenings a week provide family fun rather than teenage activities.

Facilities

The six sanitary blocks are well maintained with washbasins in cubicles, some showers and basins have controllable water temperature. Facilities for babies and disabled people. Laundry facilities. Bar (15/5-6/9), snack bar and takeaway (1/6-30/9). No shop but bread and croissants available. Indoor (heated) and outdoor pools. Play area with space for ball games. Table tennis, tennis and bicycle hire. Indoor games room. Off site: Shops and restaurants. Beach 1.5 km. Fishing 5 km. Golf 12 km. Riding 10 km.

Open: 1 May - 15 September.

Directions

Brem is on the D38 St Gilles - Les Sables d'Olonne road. Site is clearly signed, just off the one-way system in centre of village.

Charges 2007

Per unit incl. 3 persons	€ 19,50 - € 30,00
with electricity	€ 23,80 - € 33,90
extra person	€ 4,10 - € 5,50
child (under 5 yrs)	€ 2,60 - € 3,70
dog	€ 3,00

Camping Le Chaponnet****

Near sea forest **Le Chaponnet** **** is located between Saint Gilles Croix de vie and Sables D'Olonne. We are also within 200 m of Brem village and its local shops. The ocean and beaches are within 1.3 km and we are in direct vicinity of a river.

Many facilities: fitness room, heated indoor pool. **Several types of accomodation** ranging from wooden cottage chalets to mobile homes. **Many emplacements**, all bordered by hedges, for tents and caravans.

Camping le Chaponnet • Rue du Chaponnet • F-85470 Brem sur Mer • France
Tel: [33] 2 51 90 55 56 • Fax: [33] 2 51 90 91 67 • campingchaponnet@wanadoo.fr
www.le-chaponnet.com

FR85520 Camping Domaine des Renardières

13 chemin du Chêne Vert, F-85270 Notre-Dame-de-Riez (Vendée)

Tel: 02 51 55 14 17. Email: raffin.caroline@9business.fr

Just 7 km. from the busy coastal strip, Domaine des Renardières is an oasis of calm in the traditional French manner. Converted from the family farm in 1970, the site consists of three fields with varying amounts of shade and two further open fields in full sun. Visitors are 65% French, many of whom, together with British visitors, return year after year. The 86 touring pitches are well grassed and level; torches and long cables are advisable. Mme. Raffin's benevolent authority is to be seen everywhere and the welfare of her clients is of paramount importance to her. Recycling of waste is encouraged - there are collection points for batteries and green waste and the site has a 'La Clef Verte' (green key) status.

Facilities

The new unisex toilet block has private wash cubicles, baby changing room and a bathroom for disabled visitors. Showers are closed at night except for one cold shower. Dishwashing and laundry facilities. Air-conditioned bar with TV, video games and pool (28/6-25/8). Small outdoor pool (1/5-2/9). Play area. Gas barbecues only. Motorhome service point. Not suitable for American motorhomes. Off site: Fishing 1 km. Bicycle hire 7 km. St Hilaire-de-Riez 7 km. with good sandy beach. Riding, golf 10 km.

Open: 1 April - 2 September.

Directions

Site is north east of the village of Notre-Dame-de-Riez. Turn in centre of village and cross railway. Fork right and site is on left.
GPS: N46:45.274 W01:53.940

Charges 2007

Per unit incl. 2 persons	€ 14,50
with electricity (6A)	€ 17,50
extra person	€ 3,50

Less 10-20% outside 15/7-21/8. No credit cards.

FR85510 Camping le Bois Joli

2 rue de Châteauneuf, F-85710 Bois de Céné (Vendée)

Tel: **02 51 68 20 05**. Email: **campingboisjoli@free.fr**

A warm welcome is given by the English speaking Malard family, who make every effort to make your stay enjoyable. On site is a small lake with fishing and a large sports field (with a portacabin style toilet block). The site also has a small swimming pool and paddling pool. The bar has been extended and includes a dancing area. There are 130 pitches of which 90 are for touring units. All pitches have 6A electricity, although not every pitch is serviced with water. A new, separate sanitary block with a laundry and a family room has been added. A local farmer visits the site three times a week offering local produce. This site is a hidden gem in a small village away from the hustle and bustle of the seaside resorts. Suitable for people looking for a quiet holiday, it is still within driving distance of the Vendée coast (20 km).

Facilities

Three toilet blocks – old, but with modem, bright tiles and very clean. All are unisex with some washbasins in cubicles, some controllable showers, two baby baths, two washing machines, dishwashing and laundry sinks. Bar with evening entertainment. Takeaway (1/7-31/8). Children's activities. Good play area with swings. Table tennis. Tennis court. Volleyball. Petanque. Bicycle hire. Off site: Supermarket and bus service in village (two minutes walk). Walking, cycling and canoeing. Riding 5 km. Beach 18 km.

Open: 1 April - 25 September.

Directions

From Challans take D58 direct to Bois de Céné (10 km). Turn left at first road junction and site is immediately on right.

Charges 2007

Per pitch incl. 2 persons	€ 10,30 - € 14,10
with electricity (6A)	€ 12,60 - € 16,90
extra person	€ 2,90 - € 3,90
child (under 7 yrs)	€ 1,60 - € 2,50
animal	€ 2,00 - € 3,50

CAMPING LE BOIS JOLI

2 rue de Châteauneuf - F-85710 Bois de Céné - France
Tel: +33 (0)2 51 68 20 05 - Fax: +33 (0)2 51 68 46 40 - contact@camping-leboisjoli.com

FR85620 Camping le Caravan'ile

B.P. 4, la Guérinière, F-85680 Ile de Noirmoutier (Vendée)

Tel: **02 51 39 50 29**. Email: **contact@caravanile.com**

This well appointed, family run site on the island of Noirmoutier has direct access to the dunes and an extensive sandy beach. It offers heated indoor and outdoor swimming pools with a paddling pool and flume, a sauna, steam room, jacuzzi and mini gym and a variety of entertainment in high season. Most of the 103 level touring pitches are near the beach (shielded by the dune). All have electricity (5A) and are separated by bushes and occasional maturing trees providing a little shade. The site has a very French ambience, with no tour operators, although there are 90 mobile homes for rent and many more privately-owned.

Facilities

Three very clean sanitary blocks, each with showers, some washbasins in cabins and facilities for disabled people (showers are closed overnight). Laundry. Small supermarket at entrance (1/4-15/9). Bar, snack bar and takeaway (1/4-15/9). Indoor pool (all season) and outdoor pools (15/5-15/9; heated July/Aug). Games and sports area. Games room. Off site: Restaurant, bicycle hire, boat launching and minigolf all close by. Sailing 2 km. Riding 5 km. Golf 20 km.

Open: 1 March - 15 November.

Directions

The Ile de Noirmoutier is 70 km. southwest of Nantes.Take D38 road from the mainland, cross bridge to island and continue to fourth roundabout. Take exit for La Guérinière and immediately turn left to site. GPS: N46:57.980 W02:13.046

Charges 2007

Per unit incl. 2 persons	€ 11,80 - € 18,70
incl. 5A electricity	€ 13,80 - € 22,00
extra person	€ 3,00 - € 4,60
child (2-7 yrs)	€ 2,00 - € 3,00
animal	€ 1,90 - € 2,90

161

FR85640 **Camping les Chouans**

108 avenue de la Faye, F-85270 Saint Hilaire-de-Riez (Vendée)

Tel: **02 51 54 34 90**. Email: **info@sunmarina.com**

This family run campsite is within a short drive of the Vendée beaches. A friendly greeting from Josée and Stephane is a welcome arrival before entering this well organised, smart site. Cleanliness is important here! In high season it is bustling and lively, with activities available to guests daytime and evening. The restaurant and bar area is attractive, and the pool with its slides is popular. The site mainly caters for privately owned mobile homes and touring pitches are minimal (early booking advised). Some pitches are shaded, and smaller than average but each has electricity. Water points are close by. Late night discos may be noisy in July and August. Tour operators occupy 52 pitches.

Facilities

Two sanitary blocks (one unisex) both have open, vanity style washbasins. Shower room and separate toilet for disabled campers. Baby room. Laundry facilities. Small well stocked shop. Bicycle hire. Swimming pools and slides. Sports area with tennis and basketball. Small fitness gym (charged). Entertainment programme. Weekly excursions. Off site: Beach 1.6 km. St Hillaire-de-Riez approx 3 km. Riding, golf and fishing within 6 km. St Jean-de-Monts and St Gilles-Croix-de-Vie with restaurants and shops.

Open: 15 May - 15 September.

Directions

Travel south on D38 from St Jean-de-Monts and turn right at Oruet towards Les Mouettes. At the coast join D23 southwards and follow this road to first roundabout (2.5 km). Site is signed here and is 2 km. on left.

Charges 2008

Per unit incl. 3 persons	€ 25,00 - € 32,00
extra person	€ 9,00
child under 5 yrs	€ 6,00

FR85650 **Camping le Rouge Gorge**

Route de La Verrie, F-85290 Saint Laurent sur Sèvre (Vendée)

Tel: **02 51 67 86 39**. Email: **campinglerougegorge@wanadoo.fr**

This delightful, family run site sits on a hilltop alongside a large wood above the village St Laurent. With 93 grass pitches separated by hedges and trees, the site is tranquil and comfortable. The Jorge family maintain the site to the highest standards and it offers an excellent location for long stays and those travelling from the ferry ports in Brittany or Normandy and heading further south. The excellent theme park of Puy de Fou is nearby and the Loire valley with its magnificent châteaux is within easy reach. The Vendée coast is about 90 minutes drive and Cholet is close to hand.

Facilities

Two good sanitary blocks provide WCs, showers and washbasins in cabins. Facilities for disabled campers. Washing machine. Motorcaravan service point. Bar and small shop (high season). Swimming pool. Chalets for rent. Off site: Puy de Fou.

Open: All year.

Directions

From St Laurent-sur-Sèvre climb west towards Verrie. Site is well signed and is about 2 km. from the town centre at the top of the small hill. GPS: N46:57.486 W00:54.230

Charges 2007

Per unit incl. 2 persons	€ 14,00 - € 15,60
extra person	€ 3,60
electricity	€ 2,00 - € 10,00
No credit cards. Camping Cheques accepted.	

FR85660 **Camping le Pont Rouge**

Rue Clémenceau, F-85220 Saint Révérend (Vendée)

Tel: **02 51 54 68 50**. Email: **camping.pontrouge@wanadoo.fr**

This small, tranquil site is situated down a short tree-lined lane just 600 metres from a small village. Suitable for people who prefer to be away from the nearby coastal resorts. The pitches are grassy and vary in shape and size. Most are near mature trees giving ample shade and separated by tall hedges, ensuring peace and privacy. The 17 mobile homes are situated with some touring pitches, in an open sunny aspect. All pitches have electricity but long leads may be required on some. Ample water points are close to all pitches. Not suitable for American motorhomes or twin axle caravans.

Facilities

Two toilet blocks, one in the main reception building with separate facilities for ladies and gents. The second new block has separate showers and wash cubicles with a unisex toilet section and includes facilities for babies, dishwashing and a laundry room. Sports. Small, fenced pool complex with separate children Off site: Shops, restaurant and bakery in village 600 m. Country walks, cycling. Golf and riding nearby.

Open: 1 April - 31 October.

Directions

From D6 Aizenay to St Gilles-Croix-de-Vie turn north onto D94 St Révérend about 4 km. west of Co'x. Site on left after 400 m, just before village. GPS: N46:41.790 W01:50.066

Charges 2007

Per unit incl. 2 persons	€ 14,50 - € 17,00
with electricity	€ 17,00 - € 19,50
extra person	€ 4,00 - € 4,50
child (under 8 yrs)	€ 2,50 - € 3,00

Check real time availability and at-the-gate prices...

www.alanrogers.com

FR85720 Camping Indigo Noirmoutier

23 allée des Sableaux, Bois de la Chaize, F-85330 Noirmoutier en L'Ile (Vendée)

Tel: **02 51 39 06 24**. Email: **vendelle@camping-indigo.com**

Located in woodland and on dunes along a two kilometre stretch of sandy beach just east of the attractive little town of Noirmoutier on the island of the same name, this could be paradise for those who enjoy a simple campsite in a natural setting. On land belonging to the ONF (France's forestry commission), this site is operated by Huttopia whose aim is to adapt to the environment rather than take it over. The 500 touring pitches, all with electricity, are situated among the pine trees and accessed along tracks. Those on the sand dunes have fantastic views across the Bay of Bourgneuf to Pornic and the Jade Coast. They cost a few euros extra – if you are lucky enough to get one! Cars are only allowed in these areas on arrival and departure. There are no mobile homes, just ten large, traditional, but well equipped tents for rent.

Facilities

Five sanitary blocks currently provide basic facilities including pre-set showers and some washbasins in cubicles. The central one is larger and more modern, two others have been refurbished, the others for 2008. All are kept clean and have facilities for disabled visitors. Washing machines and dryers. Motorcaravan service point. Playground and field for ball games. Bicycle hire. Off site: Riding 4 km. Golf 25 km.

Open: 28 March - 28 September.

Directions

The Ile de Noirmoutier is 70 km. southwest of Nantes. Take D38 road from the mainland, cross bridge to island and continue to Noirmoutier en l'Ile. Go through town past three sets of traffic lights and at roundabout turn right following signs to 'Campings'. GPS: N46:59.815 W02:13.200

Charges 2007

Per unit incl. 2 persons	€ 12,80 - € 17,80
incl. electricity	€ 15,70 - € 26,80
extra person	€ 3,05 - € 4,20
child (2-7 yrs)	€ 1,50 - € 2,10
Camping Cheques accepted.	

FR85680 Camping le Pin Parasol

Lac du Jaunay, F-85220 La Chapelle-Hermier (Vendée)

Tel: **02 51 34 64 72**. Email: **campingpinparasol@free.fr**

Tucked away in the Vendée countryside yet just 15 minutes drive from the beach, the site enjoys a pleasant rural setting above the Lac du Jaunay, well away from the bustle of the coast. There are 284 good-sized touring pitches, all with electricity (6/10A) and 22 with water tap and drain. The established pitches have some shade, others are in the open with hedges and tress yet to mature. The enthusiastic family owners are very hands-on and the facilities are of a high standard, most notably the pool area with its well constructed new indoor pool and fitness suite.

Facilities

Four fully equipped toilet blocks include facilities for babies and disabled visitors. Block in new area can be under some pressure at busy times. Washing machines and dryers. Shop. Restaurant and bar with terrace. Takeaway (July - Aug). Heated outdoor pool (15/6-15/9). Indoor pool. Play area. Multisports pitch. Boules. Bicycle hire. Entertainment in high season. Fishing. Tennis. Off site: Golf and riding within 5 km. Beaches 12 km.

Open: 28 April - 25 September.

Directions

La Chapelle-Hermier is 26 km. west of La Roche-sur-Yon. Site is to the south of the D42 La Chapelle-Hermier - L'Aiguillon-sur-Vie, road, 2 km. east of the junction with the D40 Coex-La Chaize - Giraud road and is well signed. GPS: N46:39.973 W01:45.317

Charges 2008

Per unit incl. 2 persons	€ 11,50 - € 25,50
extra person	€ 4,50 - € 6,00
electricity (6/10A)	€ 3,50 - € 4,00

Check real time availability and at-the-gate prices...

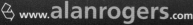

www.**alanrogers**.com

FR85810 Camping les Dauphins Bleus

16 rue du Rocher, F-85800 Givrand (Vendée)

Tel: 02 51 55 59 34. Email: **dauphins-bleus@franceloc.fr**

In a rural setting on the edge of the village and only 2 km. from the sea, this large site has 320 pitches, most taken by mobile homes and chalets for rent. There are just 12 level, grassy, touring pitches, generally small and of odd shapes, and suitable only for small units, tents and camper vans. These are scattered around the site between the rental units. The site is served by two large toilet blocks, one centrally located the other at one end of site and nearest to most of the entertainment and sports areas. The site offers an excellent pool complex and many sporting opportunities. Professional animators organise a children's club and evening entertainment in main season. The village of Givrand (walking distance) and nearby St Gilles-Croix-de-Vie between them provide supermarkets, shops and services. The region offers a number of markets including St Gilles on Monday, Thursday and Sunday.

Facilities

Two modern toilet blocks with mostly seated toilets, washbasins in cubicles, and compact showers. Facilities for babies. Units for campers with disabilities. Launderette with washing machines and dryers. Shop. Bar with TV (April - Sept) and takeaway (May - Sept). Heated outdoor pool (25 x 19m, May - Sept). Indoor pool (April - Sept). Gym. Tennis. Petanque. Multisport court. Playground. Bicycle hire. 'Pluto Club' for children, organised activities and evening entertainment July/Aug. Only gas barbecues permitted. Off site: Beach 2 km. Supermarket, ATM 2 km.

Open: 31 March - 29 September.

Directions

From D38 south of St Gilles Croix-de-Vie, turn east on D42 to Givrand where site is well signed to the left. GPS: N46:40.380 W01:53.697

Charges 2007

Per unit incl. 2 persons	€ 11,00 - € 21,00
extra person	€ 5,00 - € 6,00
child (2-7 yrs)	€ 3,50 - € 4,50
electricity (6A)	€ 3,70

FR85730 Camping les Jardins de l'Atlantique

100 rue de la Caillauderie, plage de Demoiselles, F-85164 Saint Jean-de-Monts (Vendée)

Tel: 02 51 58 05 74. Email: **info@campingjardinsatlantique.com**

This very friendly, family run site is situated on the edge of an extensive pine forest and is just over a kilometre from the attractive beaches south of St Jean-de-Monts. The main area of the site is shaded by pine trees, whilst across the (fairly minor) road are the main amenities and access to a smaller camping and mobile home area that is given plenty of shade by deciduous trees. Access to most pitches might be tricky for really large units, as the tracks wind through the trees. In total there are 90 touring pitches, all with electricity (6A), and a further 213 occupied by mobile homes.

Facilities

Three main sanitary blocks are bright and cheerful and kept very clean. Pre-set showers and washbasins in cubicles. En-suite facilities for disabled visitors. Motorcaravan service point. Shop (25/6-1/9). Bar (1/6-7/9). Restaurant, takeaway and games room (July/Aug). Swimming pool complex (20/5-10/9). Playground. Bouncy Castle. Minigolf. Multisport court. Bicycle hire. Family activities in high season. Off site: Beach 1.2 km. Fishing and riding 3 km. Sailing and golf 4 km. Boat launching 15 km.

Open: 1 April - 30 September.

Directions

Site is south of St Jean-de-Monts. From D38 (Noirmoutier - Sables d'Olonne) road at southern end of St Jean-de-Monts bypass (D38bis), turn west towards town and follow signs to site, turning left at first roundabout, crossing next one and bearing left again at roundabout onto Rue de la Chauderie. Site is on left. GPS: N46:46.225 W02:01.678

Charges 2007

Per unit incl. 2 persons	€ 13,80 - € 17,00
incl. electricity	€ 16,80 - € 21,00
extra person	€ 3,90 - € 5,20

FR85850 Flower Camping la Bretonnière

F-85150 Saint Julien-des-Landes (Vendée)

Tel: **02 51 46 62 44**. Email: **camp.la-bretonniere@wanadoo.fr**

An attractive, modern site on a family farm surrounded by beautiful peaceful countryside, this site is sure to please. With 150 pitches in an area of six hectares, there is plenty of space for everyone. There are 132 touring pitches, 8 tour operator tents and 8 alpine style chalets, spread around several fields, some quite open, others with some shade from perimeter hedges. The grassy pitches are all of a really generous size with electricity (12/16A). Two swimming pools, one covered, the other outdoor, are surrounded by a pleasant terrace, with the bar and reception close by.

Facilities

Five modern, clean and well appointed toilet blocks are spread evenly around the site, with baby rooms and facilities for disabled people at two blocks. Motorcaravan service point. Bar, snack bar and takeaway (July/Aug). Covered swimming pool (15.5 x 7 m.) and outdoor pool (11 x 5 m.) open June - Sept. WiFi around bar and reception. Games/TV room. Tennis. Boules. Fishing lake. Caravan storage. Off site: Village 2.5 km. La Mothe-Achard 7 km. Golf 12 km. Riding 2 km. Boat launching 4 km.

Open: 1 April - 15 October.

Directions

Saint Julien-des-Landes is 18 km. northeast of Les Sables d'Olonne and 5 km. northwest of La Mothe-Achard. From La Mothe-Achard take D12 west towards Bretignolles-sur-Mer, pass through St Julien and after 2 km. take first turn right (site signed). Site is 500 m. GPS: N46:38.679 W01:43.998

Charges 2007

Per unit incl. 2 persons	€ 14,00 - € 21,00
incl. electricity (6A)	€ 16,00 - € 23,50
extra person	€ 3,50 - € 4,50
child (under 10 yrs)	€ 2,50 - € 3,00

FR85740 Camping Aux Coeurs Vendéens

251 route de Notre-Dame-de-Monts, F-85160 Saint Jean-de-Monts (Vendée)

Tel: **02 51 58 84 91**. Email: **info@coeursvendeens.com**

This is a delightful little site, a real find for those wishing to enjoy the beaches and life-style of this stretch of coastline without the razzmatazz of some of the neighbouring sites. It is family run and everywhere there is attention to detail: flower tubs beside the road as you drive in, white-washed stones for the pitch numbers, engraved designs on the washbasin mirrors, even plugs for the dishwashing sinks! There are 57 touring pitches, all with electricity available (10A), and a further 60 with mobile homes and chalets, all but five available for rent.

Facilities

Two sanitary blocks are bright and cheerful and kept very clean. Controllable showers, washbasins in cubicles, two pleasant baby rooms. En-suite facilities for disabled visitors (wheel-chair users might have minor difficulties accessing this). Internet accesss. Laundry facilities. Small shop with takeaway. Swimming pools (7/5-10/9). TV and games rooms. Playgrounds. Trampoline. Minigolf. Bicycle hire. Off site: Beach, sea fishing and boat launching 700 m. Sailing, riding and golf 3 km. Fresh water fishing 7 km.

Open: 8 April - 23 September.

Directions

Site is on the D38 just over 3 km. north of St Jean-de-Monts, roughly halfway between St Jean-de-Monts and Notre Dame-de-Monts, on the western side of the road. GPS: N46:48.548 W02:06.610

Charges 2007

Per unit incl. 2 persons	€ 15,00 - € 25,50
extra person	€ 2,50 - € 4,80
child (under 5 yrs)	free - € 3,20
electricity (10A)	free - € 3,30

Check real time availability and at-the-gate prices...

www.**alanrogers**.com

FR85860 **Camping les Fosses Rouges**

8 rue des Fosses Rouges, F-85180 Le Château d'Olonne (Vendée)

Tel: **02 51 95 17 95**. Email: **info@camping-lesfossesrouge.com**

A family run site, Les Fosses Rouges was created in 1968 on the fields owned by the present owner's grandfather. Since it was built, the site has been surrounded by urban development, but never-the-less it is still a good value and well presented, if compact, site. There are 205 well hedged pitches of small to average size, most with some shade and electricity (10A). Some 45 are used for mobile homes, both private and to rent. There are also some seasonal or long stay tourers. There is a good swimming pool and a separate sports and games area. The site offers some low key entertainment in the main season. Nearby are the Zoo and sea-shell museum at Les Sables d'Olonne.

Facilities

Four colourful toilet blocks in traditional style are evenly distributed around the site. Washbasins in cubicles for ladies, push-button showers. Facilities for disabled people. Washing machine at two blocks. Bar and takeaway (1/7-31/8). Shop (15/6-30/9). Swimming pool (heated, open all season and covered when necessary). Playground. Tennis. Minigolf. Giant chess. Open air stage for animation. Internet access (July/Aug). Communal barbecue areas. Off site: ATM at supermarket 1 km. Fishing 1 km. Golf 4 km: Riding 4 km. Boat launching 5 km.

Open: 8 April - 30 September.

Directions

Site is southeast of Les Sables d'Olonne between the D949 and the sea. From large roundabout by supermarket on D949 turn towards sea on Avenue Dugay Trouin (signed La Pironnière). Continue straight on at mini-roundabout and in 150 m. turn left into Rue des Fosses Rouges to site in 500 m. GPS: N46:28.761 W01:44.501

Charges 2007

Per unit incl. 2 persons	€ 12,40 - € 15,90
incl. electricity	€ 15,90 - € 19,40
extra person	€ 2,60 - € 3,50
child (under 7 yrs)	€ 1,30 - € 1,75

FR85870 **Camping Baie d'Aunis**

10 rue du Pertuis, F-85360 La Tranche-sur-Mer (Vendée)

Tel: **02 51 27 47 36**. Email: **info@camping-baiedaunis.com**

This very popular site has direct access to a sandy beach though a pedestrian gate (with key code) and across a car park. The town centre is also only 500 m. away. Shady and level, there are 150 individual pitches, all with electricity. A good number of pitches are on a gravel base and a few are suitable only for smaller units. There are chalets and mobile homes (19) to rent. On site amenities include a heated swimming pool and a good restaurant and bar. This is a popular seaside resort with 13 km. of good quality sandy beaches. All have first aid posts, lifeguards in season and dogs are forbidden on the sands. From the pier by the Centre Nautique, just 50 m. from the site's rear pedestrian gate, you can catch ferries to the islands of Aix and Ré and to La Rochelle across the bay.

Facilities

The main centrally located sanitary unit is large, good quality and very well appointed. A smaller simpler unit is at the far end of the site. British style WCs, washbasins in cubicles, provision for babies and disabled campers. Laundry room at each block. Motorcaravan service point. Bar/restaurant and takeaway (1/5-10/9, w/ends only in low season). Outdoor pool (10m x 20 m; heated May - Sept). Playground. TV room. Dogs not accepted July/Aug. Off site: La Tranche is a sail-boarding centre. Beach 50 m.

Open: 28 April - 14 September.

Directions

From La Roche-sur-Yon take 0747 to La Tranche. At roundabout (D747 and D1046) carry straight on to next roundabout and turn right towards town centre. At next (new) roundabout continue straight on to site on left (well signed). GPS: N46:20.777 W01:25.918

Charges 2007

Per unit incl. 2 persons	€ 7,80 - € 24,70
incl. electricity (10A)	€ 11,80 - € 28,70
extra person	€ 5,00 - € 5,90

Family campsite with clearly defined pitches with an average size of 90 m² for tents, caravans and motor homes, situated 800m from the sea and 2 km from the beach.

At your disposal are sanitary facilities' with free use of hot water, heated covered swimming pool, tennis, mini golf and animation in July and August. Near shopping centre, casino and spa.

Reservations are recommended and necessary in high season.

8 Rue des Fosses Rouges - 85180 Château d'Olonne
Tel : 0033 (0)251 951 795 - Fax : 0033 (0) 251 325 421
E-mail : info@camping-lesfossesrouges.com
Internet : www.camping-lesfossesrouges.com

FR85920 Camping Loyada

Avenue de l'Atlantique, F-85440 Talmont-Saint-Hilaire (Vendée)
Tel: 02 51 21 28 10. Email: contact@camping-loyada.fr

Camping Loyada is a very new family campsite which takes its name from a beach in Djibouti. It is a spacious covering 5 hectares with 224 grassy pitches, most of which are used for accommodation to rent (144). The pitches are comfortable, modern and hedged, although these are not yet tall enough to provide shade or privacy. The enthusiastic and friendly owners are working hard to build the site and to create a family holiday atmosphere. A club is organised for small children with regular games and entertainment. A large pool complex (300 sq.m.) will delight all age groups with its outdoor and indoor heated swimming pools, water slide, jacuzzi and paddling pool. There are beaches within 3.5 km. There is much to do in the area including the very pleasant beach of 'Le Veillon' which is situated between dunes and forest.

Facilities

Two very modern toilet blocks with all the necessary facilities, including facilities for disabled visitors, a baby room and a shower and WC for children. Washing machines. Shop (July/Aug). Bar with WiFi. Snack bar. Indoor, heated swimming pool, jacuzzi, outdoor swimming pool with water slide, paddling pool. Playground. Animation in high season (karaoke, dancing). Off site: Diving, golf, riding, karting, sailing and fishing nearby. Automobile museum.

Open: 1 April - 30 September.

Directions

From the A10 take exit for Niort and follow signs for Niort then Talmont-St-Hilaire via Fontenay Le Comte and Luçon. Or in Niort take A83 towards Nantes, then exit 7 (Ste Hermine) towards Luçon and Talmont Saint Hilaire. Once in Talmont Saint Hilaire, follow signs for Port Bourgenay and site.

Charges 2008

Per unit with 2 persons and electricity	€ 16,00 - € 25,00
extra persom	€ 3,50 - € 4,50
child (1-7 yrs)	€ 1,00 - € 3,00

111, Rue de la Source - 85440 Talmont Saint Hilaire
Tel : 0033 251 21 28 10 - Fax : 0033 251 20 37 58
E-mail : contact@camping-loyada.fr
Internet : www.camping-loyada.fr

Come and discover our region, with the beautiful beaches of the Vendée and in particularly the beach of Veillon, which is situated between the dunes and the sea.
The cycle-tracks of Talmont Saint Hillaire leads you through the extensive landscapes of marches, forests and the coast.
The whole team of the Loyada is at your service and offers 224 pitches of 100 to 150 m² of high comfort.
In the water park you can enjoy several waterslides, an indoor swimming pool, a multisports area, jeux de boules.......

kawan
VILLAGES CAMPINGS

NEW

83 Quality Campsites
'At-The-Gate' Prices

A New Concept

Kawan Villages offers 83 great family campsites in France and 7 other countries.

All are graded 3 or 4 star and all can be booked direct at the campsite's own 'at-the-gate' tariff. No surcharge, no premium, no hidden costs. You simply pay what you would pay at reception. Book on 01580 214017 for convenience and courteous, reliable service – at no extra cost!

- High quality facilities, pleasant surroundings, great locations
- Fully equipped mobile homes and chalets
- Wonderful environment for children: safe, spacious, plenty to do

France
Spain
Portugal
Italy
Germany
Luxembourg
The Netherlands
Denmark
Sweden

1ᵉʳ Réseau Européen de Villages Campings

FREE BROCHURE
01580 214017

www.**kawan-villages**.co.uk

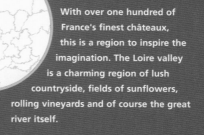

With over one hundred of France's finest châteaux, this is a region to inspire the imagination. The Loire valley is a charming region of lush countryside, fields of sunflowers, rolling vineyards and of course the great river itself.

Loire Valley

OUR TOURIST REGIONS INCLUDES ALL THE LOIRE VALLEY: 18 CHER, 28 EURE-ET-LOIR, 36 INDRE, 37 INDRE-ET-LOIRE, 41 LOIR-ET-CHER, 45 LOIRET. FROM WESTERN LOIRE: 49 MAINE-ET-LOIRE, 53 MAYENNE, 72 SARTHE. AND FROM POITOU-CHARENTES: 79 DEUX SÈVRES, 86 VIENNE

For centuries the Loire valley was frequented by French royalty and the great river winds its way past some of France's most magnificent châteaux: Amboise, Azay-le-Rideau, Chenonceau, with its famous arches that span the river and appear to 'float' on the water, and the fairytale Ussé with myriad magical turrets are just some of the highlights.

Known as the Garden of France, the Loire's mild climate and fertile landscape of soft green valleys, lush vineyards and fields of flowers makes it a favourite with the visitors. Renowned for its wines, with hundreds to choose from, all are produced from vineyards stretching along the main course of the River Loire. Imposing abbeys, troglodyte caves, tiny Romanesque churches, woodland areas such as the Sologne and sleepy, picturesque villages reward exploration. Cities like Blois and Tours are elegant with fine architecture and museums and Paris is only one hour by TGV. One of the oldest towns of Loire valley is Saumur. Its old quarter, grouped around the riverbank beneath the imposing château, is particularly pleasant to wander around.

Places of interest

Amboise: château, Leonardo da Vinci museum.

Beauregard: château with Delft tiled floors.

Blois: château with architecture from Middle Ages to Neo-Classical periods.

Chambord: Renaissance château.

Chartres: cathedral with stained glass windows.

Chinon: old town, Joan of Arc museum

Loches: old town, château and its fortifications.

Orléans: Holy Cross cathedral, house of Joan of Arc.

Tours: Renaissance and Neo-Classical mansions, cathedral of St Gatien.

Vendôme: Tour St Martin, La Trinité.

Villandry: famous renaissance gardens.

Cuisine of the region

Wild duck, pheasant, hare, deer, and quail are classics and fresh water fish such as salmon, perch and trout are favourite. Specialities include rillettes, andouillettes, tripes, mushrooms and the regional cheeses of Trappiste d'Entrammes and Cremet d'Angers, Petit Sable and Ardoises d'Angers cookies.

Bourdaines: apples stuffed with jam and baked.

Tarte a la citrouille: pumpkin tart.

Tarte Tatin: upside down tart of caramelised apples and pastry.

FR79020 Camping de Courte Vallée

F-79600 Airvault (Deux-Sèvres)

Tel: **05 49 64 70 65**. Email: **camping@caravanningfrance.com**

This small and beautifully landscaped site is family run. Set in 10 acres of parkland close to the Thouet river, it is within walking distance of Airvault (the birthplace of Voltaire). In the heart of rural France and off the main tourist tracks, the site offers tranquility and a warm and friendly atmosphere in surroundings maintained to the highest standards. There are 64 grass pitches, many with electricity, water and drainage which makes the site ideal for a long stay to explore the area. Nearby are Puy du Fou, Fontevraud Abbey, Doué la Fontaine zoo and the châteaux of Saumur and Oiron.

Facilities

A modern unisex block has spacious cubicles for showers and washbasins, and shower and WC cubicles for disabled visitors, all kept to a very high standard of cleanliness. Washing machine and dryers. Reception sells 'frites', snacks, beers and wine and ice cream. Internet access. Swimming pool. Play area. Caravan storage. Wine tasting events and barbecues. Coffee bar. Off site: Airvault is a 10-15 minute walk. Fishing 300 m. Riding 8 km.

Open: All year.

Directions

From D938 (Parthenay-Thouars) take D725 Airvault. On approaching village turn left over bridge. At T-junction turn sharp left, second exit at roundabout, left at junction to site on left. GPS: N46:49.937 W00:08.909

Charges 2008

Per person	€ 7,00 - € 8,00
pitch incl. electricity	€ 14,00 - € 16,00

No credit cards.

FR79030 Puy Rond Camping

Cornet, F-79300 Bressuire (Deux-Sèvres)

Tel: **05 49 72 43 22**. Email: **info@puyrondcamping.com**

This small site with just 21 pitches is owned and run by Mr and Mrs Robert Smith who have made major changes and improvements. It is particularly well sited for those travelling south on the non-motorway route from the Normandy ferry ports. The flat and level pitches are of a good size and all have 6A electricity. Bressuire, built in the shadow of the walls of an 11th and 13th century castle, is the second most important town in the department of Deux Sèvres. There you will find an extensive range of shops, good supermarkets and an interesting market.

Facilities

The small toilet block provides showers, washbasins and WCs, Baby bath. Facilities for disabled visitors. Motorcaravan service point. Swimming pool (unheated). Off site: Bressuire 1 km. Puy du Fou 35 km. Ideal for walking and cycling.

Open: 1 April - 15 October.

Directions

From northwest keep on N149 towards 'centre ville'. Go down hill, pass car hire outlet and after a few metres turn right on D38. Pass cattle market and turn right, keep on but turn right immediately before STOP sign. Turn left towards the site. GPS: N46:49.780 W00:10.090

Charges 2007

Per unit incl. 2 persons	€ 12,00 - € 16,50
extra person	€ 2,50 - € 3,00
electricity	€ 3,50

FR79040 Camping de la Venise Verte

178 route des Bords de Sèvre, F-79510 Coulon (Deux-Sèvres)

Tel: **05 49 35 90 36**. Email: **accueil@camping-laveniseverte.com**

This family run site on the edge of the Sevre Nortaise and the Marais Poitevin is ideal for short or long stays. With canoe and cycle hire on site you have no excuse for not exploring the local area. In the Deux-Sèvres, the 'department of discovery', so named because it has two rivers named Sevre, the Noirtaise and Nantaise, the Venise Verte provides an excellent site. The flat pitches are of a good size, some with electricity, water and drainage and with some shade. A 'Sites et Paysages' member.

Facilities

Modern, heated toilet facilities are of a high standard with free showers. Washing machine and dryer. Motorcaravan services. Restaurant/bar. Swimming pool (high season) Bicycle and canoe hire. Boules area. Off site: Coulon 1.0 km. and boat trips in the Marais. Ideal for walking, cycling or canoeing.

Open: 1 April - 30 October.

Directions

From Niort take N11 towards La Rochelle. Turn on the D3 towards Sansais and then north on D1 (Coulon). At traffic lights head towards 'centre ville' (Coulon) at mini-roundabout turn slightly right. Follow Sevre Noirtaise for 1.5 km. to site right. GPS: N46:18.888 W00:36.538

Charges 2007

Per unit incl. 2 persons and electricity	€ 16,50 - € 22,00
extra person	€ 4,00 - € 5,50
child (2-5 yrs)	€ 2,00

Check real time availability and at-the-gate prices...

www.alanrogers.com

FR79050 Kawan Village du Bois Vert

14 rue Boisseau, le Tallud, F-79200 Parthenay (Deux-Sèvres)

Tel: **05 49 64 78 43**. Email: **bois-vert@wanadoo.fr**

This former municipal site is now operated by a campsite group although so far it has changed little. There are 88 pitches of which 74 are for touring, all with electricity (10A) and 30 also with water and drainage. There are 15 mobile homes to rent. Pitches are separated by hedges and there are mature trees providing some shade. The site is on the River Thouet and although there is a secure fence, there is a steep drop to the river bank. Pleasant walkways along both sides and a footbridge close by enable you to walk into the old walled town.

Facilities

Two very traditional sanitary blocks both in need of attention. One has unisex toilets (a few British-style but seatless), showers and washbasins in cubicles. Primitive dishwashing and laundry sinks. The second is slightly better. Facilities for disabled visitors, inc. new mobile homes. Bar with snackbar and takeaway (1 May - 30 Sept). Bread can be ordered. New heated swimming pool. TV. Table tennis and boules. Small play area. Tickets available for Futuroscope and Puy du Fou. Off site: Fishing 100 m. Motorcaravan service point adjacent. Base de Loisirs nearby. Riding and golf 15 km.

Open: 1 April - 30 September.

Directions

Parthenay is 50 km. west of Poitiers (and the A10) via the N149 to Bressuire and Nantes. Site is southwest of the town at Le Tallud on the D949 La Roche sur Yon road. Take ring road and site is on right as you join D949.
GPS: N46:38.486 W00:16.035

Charges 2007

Per unit incl. 2 persons	€ 14,50 - € 17,50
extra person	€ 4,00 - € 5,00
child (2-10 yrs)	€ 2,00
Per unit incl. 2 persons and electricity	€ 16,50 - € 19,50

Camping Cheques accepted.

FR53020 Camping le Malidor

F-53250 Charchigne (Mayenne)

Tel: **02 43 03 99 88**. Email: **le-malidor@orange.fr**

A warm welcome is given by the English owners of this attractive, small, rural site, open all year. It is surrounded by farm land and it provides a real taste of the French countryside. The three private lakes provide great fishing and only a short walk away the path leads to the village. There are 20 pitches with 15 for touring, all with 10A electricity. They are terraced and divided by mature hedges. The beautiful surrounding countryside is well worth exploring and this site is a perfect place from which to do so. Large units are accepted. Fishing gear and bait are available.

Facilities

One sanitary block provides good facilities but none for campers with disabilities. Bar and restaurant. Play area, paddling pool. Boules. Darts, pool table, hall for groups up to 80. Fishing with three lakes. Minigolf. Bicycle hire. Walks and painting courses. Off site: Village with bar/restaurant and shop 500 m. Beaches 20 km.

Open: All year.

Directions

From A81 (Rennes - Le Mans) take exit 3 for Laval. Head northeast on N162 to Mayenne. Then take N12 in the same direction towards Alençon for 20 km. Just before Javron turn left on D33 to Cherghigné. Follow signs to site just before town.

Charges 2007

Per unit incl. 2 persons	€ 15,00
extra person	€ 7,50
child	€ 4,00

FR36050 Camping Municipal les Vieux Chênes

F-36310 Chaillac (Indre)

Tel: **02 54 25 61 39**

A small, delightful site on the outskirts of an attractive village, within walking distance of the centre, where there are shops, bars, cafés, restaurants, etc. The 40 grass pitches, all with electricity (16A), are very generous in size, slightly sloping, with hedging and some mature trees. The well manicured appearance and relaxed atmosphere add to the attraction of this peaceful environment. A warden lives on the site. The adjacent lake is for fishing only. There is a larger lake just 1 km. away where varied watersports can be enjoyed. The small water toboggan is free of charge.

Facilities

Heated sanitary facilities are insulated for winter use and include washbasins in private cabins. Limited facilities for disabled campers. Washing machine. Winter caravan storage. Off site: Tennis club adjacent. Fishing 25 m. Shops 200 m. Watersports 1 km.

Open: All year.

Directions

From north leave A20, south of Argenton, take D1 to St Benoit (16 km.) then west to Chaillac on D36. From south leave A20 - exit 21, take D10 to St Benoit, then D36 as before. Through village and left by the Mairie. GPS: N46:25.921 E01:17.735

Charges guide

Per person	€ 1,65
pitch incl. electricity	€ 3,80 - € 5,40
No credit cards.	

FR36110 Camping le Rochat Belle-Isle

17 avenue du Parc des Loisir, F-36000 Châteauroux (Indre)

Tel: **02 54 34 26 56**. Email: **camping.le-rochat@orange.fr**

Set amongst mature trees adjacent to a large lake on one side of the site and a gently-flowing river on two others (not fenced), this attractive municipal site is a peaceful haven tucked away from the large bustling city of Chateauroux. There are 166 numbered level pitches, mainly open but shaded by trees. The site has easy access for larger units. The Belle-Isle lake adjacent to the site offers a bar, restaurant, cycle tracks, fishing and water sports. The modern, well run reception has all the information you need to help you enjoy your stay. English is spoken.

Facilities

Two well equipped sanitary blocks with controllable showers and shower curtain divider. Washbasins in cabins. All very clean. Facilities for disabled visitors (no key required). Laundry. Small play area. Table tennis. Pétanque. Off site: All the attractions of a busy city: shops, bars, restaurants. Swimming pools close by.

Open: 1 May - 30 September.

Directions

The city of Châteauroux is accessed from junctions 12,13 or 14 from the A20 Vierzon to Limoges motorway. Head towards the city centre where site is very well signed. Signs for 'Halls Exposition' also go to this area, where site is left after municipal pool.

Charges 2007

Per unit incl. 2 persons	€ 13,60
child (7-11 yrs)	€ 1,90
electricity	€ 3,30 - € 4,50

FR37010 Camping de la Mignardière

22 avenue des Aubépines, F-37510 Ballan-Miré (Indre-et-Loire)

Tel: **02 47 73 31 00**. Email: **info@mignardiere.com**

Southwest of the city of Tours, this site is within easy reach of several of the Loire châteaux, notably Azay-le-Rideau. There are also many varied sports amenities on the site or very close by. The site has 177 numbered pitches of which 139 are for touring units, all with electricity (6/10A) and 37 with drainage and water. Pitches are of a good size on rather uneven grass with limestone gravel paths (which are rather 'sticky' when wet). The barrier gates (coded access) are closed 22.30 - 07.30 hrs. Reservation is essential for most of July/August.

Facilities

Three toilet blocks include washbasins in private cabins, a unit for disabled people, baby bath and laundry facilities. Motorcaravan service point. Shop. Takeaway. Two large, heated swimming pools (one covered). Paddling pool. Tennis court. Table tennis. Bicycle hire. Off site: Attractive lake 300 m. Family fitness run. Fishing 500 m. Riding 1 km. Golf 3 km. Tours centre 8 km.

Open: 1 April - 25 September.

Directions

From A10 autoroute take exit 24 and D751 towards Chinon. Turn right after 5 km. at Campanile Hotel following signs to site. From Tours take D751 towards Chinon.

Charges 2007

Per unit incl. 2 persons	€ 14,00 - € 21,00
with services	€ 20,00 - € 29,00
extra person	€ 4,00 - € 5,30
Camping Cheques accepted.	

FR37030 Camping le Moulin Fort

F-37150 Francueil-Chenonceaux (Indre-et-Loire)

Tel: 02 47 23 86 22. Email: **lemoulinfort@wanadoo.fr**

Camping Le Moulin Fort is a tranquil, riverside site that has been redeveloped by British owners, John and Sarah Scarratt. The 137 pitches are enhanced by trees and shrubs offering some shade and 110 pitches have electricity (6A). The swimming pool (unheated) is accessed by a timber walkway over the mill race from the snack bar terrace adjacent to the restored mill building. Although not intrusive there is some noise from the railway across the river and a few trains run at night. The site is more suitable for couples and families with young children, although the river is unfenced. All over the campsite, visitors will find little information boards about local nature (birds, fish, trees and shrubs), about the history of the mill and fascinating facts about recycling. The owners are keen to encourage recycling on the site. The picturesque Château of Chenonceaux is little more than 1 km. along the Cher riverbank and many of the Loire châteaux are within easy reach, particularly Amboise and its famous Leonardo de Vinci museum.

Facilities

Two toilet blocks with all the usual amenities of a good standard, including washbasins in cubicles and baby baths. Shop (1/4-30/9). Bar, restaurant and takeaway (all 1/4-30/9). Swimming pool (15/5-30/9). Petanque. Minigolf. Games room and TV. Library. Regular family entertainment including wine tasting, quiz evenings, activities for children and light-hearted games tournaments. Motorcaravan service point. Fishing. Bicycle and canoe hire. Petanque. Live music events. Off site: Riding 12 km. Golf 20 km.

Open: 1 April - 30 September.

Directions

Site signed from D976 Tours - Vierzon road. From D40 (Tours - Chenonceaux), go through village and after 2 km. right on D80 to cross river at Chisseaux. Site on left just after bridge. GPS: N47:19.637 E01:05.358

Charges 2008

Per unit incl. 2 persons	€ 9,00 - € 22,00
extra person	€ 3,00 - € 5,00
child (4-12 yrs)	€ 2,00 - € 4,00
electricity (6A)	€ 4,00
dog	€ 2,00 - € 3,00

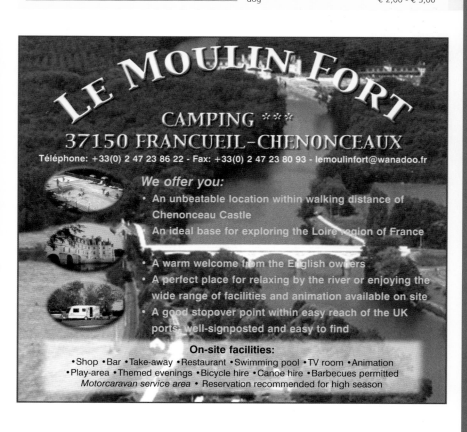

FR37060 Kawan Village l'Arada Parc

Mobile homes ▶ page 492

Rue de la Baratière, F-37360 Sonzay (Indre-et-Loire)

Tel: **02 47 24 72 69**. Email: **info@laradaparc.com**

A good, well maintained site in a quiet location, Camping L'Arada Parc is a popular base from which to visit the numerous châteaux in this beautiful part of France. The 79 grass pitches all have electricity and 35 have water and drainage. The clearly marked pitches, some slightly sloping, are separated by trees and shrubs some of which are now providing a degree of shade. An attractive, heated pool is on a pleasant terrace beside the restaurant. Entertainment, themed evenings and activities for children are organised in July/August. A new site with modern facilities and developing well.

Facilities

Two modern toilet blocks provide unisex toilets, showers and washbasins in cubicles. Baby room. Facilities for disabled visitors (wheelchair users may find the gravel access difficult). Dishwashing and laundry facilities. Shop, bar, restaurant and takeaway (24/3-31/10). Swimming pool (no Bermuda style shorts; 1/5-13/9). Play area, games area. Boules, volleyball, badminton and table tennis. TV room. Bicycle hire. Internet access. Off site: Tennis 200 m. Riding 7 km. Fishing 9 km. Golf 12 km.

Open: 22 March - 25 October.

Directions

Sonzay is northwest of Tours. From the new A28 north of Tours take the exit to Neuillé-Pont-Pierre which is on the N138 Le Mans - Tours road. Then take D766 towards Château la Vallière and turn southwest to Sonzay. Follow campsite signs. GPS: N47:31.687 E00:27.180

Charges 2008

Per unit incl. 2 persons	€ 13,50 - € 17,50
extra person	€ 3,50 - € 4,50
child (2-10 yrs)	€ 2,75 - € 3,50
electricity (10A)	€ 3,50
animal	€ 1,50

Camping Cheques accepted.

OPEN from 22th March to 26th October

Camping - Caravaning
★★★★

L'Arada Parc ★★★

At the heart of the Loire's chateau country and the vineyards of Touraine
Bar, Restaurant, Swimming pool, Activities
CHALETS AND MOBILE HOMES RENTING
Mini-golf, Tennis, Bike renting.
Accessible via the A28 exit 27, the D959 or the N138

"Golf at 10mn"

L'ARADA PARC • 37 360 Sonzay
Tél. +33 (0)2 47 24 72 69
Fax. +33 (0)2 47 24 72 70
Web : www.laradaparc.com
E-mail : info@laradaparc.com

FR37050 Kawan Village la Citadelle

Avenue Aristide Briand, F-37600 Loches en Touraine (Indre-et-Loire)

Tel: **02 47 59 05 91**. Email: **camping@lacitadelle.com**

A pleasant, well maintained site, La Citadelle is within walking distance of Loches, noted for its perfect architecture and its glorious history, at the same time offering a rural atmosphere in the site itself. Most of the 128 level, good-sized touring pitches (all with 10A electricity and 42 fully serviced) offer some shade from trees, although sun lovers can opt for a more open spot. The most recent addition is an on-site outdoor swimming pool with paddling pool (solar heated). Loches, its château and dungeons, is 500 m.

Facilities

Three sanitary blocks provide British and Turkish style WCs, washbasins (mostly in cabins) and showers. Dishwashing and laundry facilities. Motorcaravan service area. Two excellent baby units and provision for disabled people. Play equipment. Boules, volleyball and games room. Small bar and snack bar offering a variety of food and drink in a lively environment (15/6-13/9). Internet access and TV. Off site: Riding 3 km. Supermarket 3 km. Market on Wednesday and Saturday mornings. Golf 7 km.

Open: 19 March - 19 October.

Directions

From any direction take town bypass (RN143) and leave via roundabout at southern end (supermarket). Site signed towards town centre on right in 800 m. Do not enter centre. GPS: N47:07.382 E01:00.134

Charges 2007

Per pitch incl. 2 adults with electricity,	€ 13,90 - € 21,60
water and drainage	€ 18,70 - € 27,50
extra person	€ 3,90 - € 5,00
child (2-10 yrs)	€ 2,30 - € 3,50
dog	€ 1,50 - € 2,00

Camping Cheques accepted.

FR37090 Camping du Château de la Rolandière

F-37220 Trogues (Indre-et-Loire)

Tel: **02 47 58 53 71**. Email: **contact@larolandiere.com**

This is a charming site set in the grounds of a château. The owners, Sabine Toulemonde and her husband, offer a very warm welcome. There are 30 medium sized, flat pitches, some gently sloping front to rear, separated by hedges. All but four have 10A electricity and water taps nearby and parkland trees give shade. The château and adjoining buildings contain rooms to let. The site has a pleasant swimming pool (14 x 6 m.) with a sunny terrace and paddling pool, minigolf through the parkland and an area for ball games, swings and slides. A 'Sites et Paysages' member. Situated on the D760 between Ille Bouchard and St Maure-de-Touraine, the site is 5 km. west of the A10, convenient for an overnight break or for longer stays to explore the châteaux at Chinon, Loches or Azay-le-Rideau and the villages of Richelieu and Crissay-s-Manse. There are interesting excursions to gardens and grottos. In nearby Azay-le-Rideau visit the wicker craftsmen's workshops.

Facilities

The toilet block is older in style but has been refurbished to provide adequte facilities with shower, washbasin, dishwashing and laundry areas around central British style WCs. Provision for disabled visitors. Bar with terrace and snacks/takeaway. Small shop for basics (July/Aug). Swimming pool (15/5-30/9). Minigolf (no children under 12 yrs). Play area. Fitness room. Bicycle hire 25 km. Off site: Fishing 1 km. to River Vienne. Restaurant 5 km. St Maure 8 km.

Open: 15 April - 30 September.

Directions

Site is 5 km. west from exit 25 on A10 at St Maure-de-Touraine on D760 towards Chinon. Entrance is signed and marked by a model of the château. GPS: N47:06.460 E00:30.631

Charges 2007

Per person	€ 4,50 - € 6,00
child (under 10 yrs)	€ 2,50 - € 3,50
pitch	€ 6,50 - € 9,00
animal	€ 2,00 - € 3,00
electricity	€ 4,00
No credit cards.	

FR37070 Camping de l'Ile Auger

Quai Danton, F-37500 Chinon (Indre-et-Loire)

Tel: **02 47 93 08 35**

This is a well-placed site for exploring the old medieval town of Chinon and its impressive castle that was a home of England's Henry II and includes a museum to Joan of Arc. Alongside the River Vienne, it is a five minute walk over the main bridge to the town centre. The 277 pitches are numbered but not separated, with electricity (4/8/12A). A number are shaded by tall trees. A warden lives on site.

Facilities

Six toilet blocks around the site have mostly British style WCs. A very good new block is next to the office building. Washing up sinks. Barrier locked 22.00 - 07.00 hrs. Motorcaravan service point. Playground, table tennis and boules court. Off site: Tennis. Indoor and outdoor swimming pools nearby. Bicycle hire 1 km. Shop 1 km. Fishing 3 km. Riding 10 km.

Open: 15 March - 15 October.

Directions

From Chinon town cross the river and turn right at the end of the bridge. The campsite entrance is about 100 m. on the right. GPS: N47:09.827 E00:14.121

Charges guide

Per person	€ 1,85
pitch	€ 4,20
child (under 7)	€ 1,23
electricity (4-12A)	€ 1,85 - € 3,20
No credit cards.	

175

FR37120 Castel Camping Parc de Fierbois

Sainte Catherine de Fierbois, F-37800 Saint Maure-de-Touraine (Indre-et-Loire)

Tel: 02 47 65 43 35. Email: parc.fierbois@wanadoo.fr

Parc de Fierbois has an impressive entrance and a tree lined driveway and is set among 250 acres of lakes and forest in the heart of the Loire Valley. In all, there are 320 pitches including 100 for touring units, the remainder being used by tour operators and for chalets and mobile homes. There are 80 touring pitches, mostly level and separated by low hedging or small trees, with water, drainage and electricity hook-ups (2-8A). The other pitches are small or medium in size, many unmarked and some sloping and in the shade. This is a lively family holiday site with a super pool complex and a sandy beach on the shores of the lake. There is plenty here to occupy and entertain children. English is spoken in reception.

Facilities

Three toilet blocks provide British style WCs, hot showers and washbasins in cubicles. Baby room. Dishwashing and laundry facilities. Motorcaravan service point. Shop. Bar. Restaurant. Takeaway. Indoor heated pool. Water park complex (pools, slides, paddling pool, sunbathing areas). Indoor entertainment and games bar. Tennis. Volleyball. Badminton. Football. Petanque. Minigolf. Bicycle hire. Go-karts, electric cars on a circuit. TV/video room. Gym. Fishing. Pedaloes, canoeing and entertainment programme (July/Aug). Off site: Riding 10 km. Golf 30 km.

Open: 15 May - 15 September.

Directions

Travelling south on N10 from Tours, go through Montbazon and on towards St Maure and Chatellerault. Site signed 16 km. outside Montbazon near Ste Catherine. Turn off main road. Follow site signs. From A10 autoroute use St Maure exit and turn north up N10.

Charges 2007

Per unit incl. 2 persons	€ 16,00 - € 39,00
extra person	€ 6,00 - € 8,00
electricity	€ 4,20

Parc de Fierbois Camping Caravaning★★★★
Ste. Catherine de Fierbois - 37800 St. Maure de Touraine
Tel: 0033 (0)247 65 43 35 - Fax: 0033 (0)247 65 53 75
contact@fierbois.com - www.fierbois.com

FR37100 Camping la Fritillaire

Rue Basse, F-37420 Savigny-en-Véron (Indre-et-Loire)

Tel: 02 47 58 03 79. Email: lafritillaire.veron@ffcc.fr

Formerly a municipal site and now owned by the FFCC (France's Camping and Caravanning Federation), La Fritillaire is a pleasant, no-frills site offering excellent value. There are 94 touring pitches, marked by trees and bushes, on level ground and ringed by tall trees. There are 58 electric connections (10A) so for some of the shadier pitches a hook-up may not be available or you will need a long cable. The central pitches, however, all have electricity and water, and 22 also have drainage.

Facilities

A smart, modern building houses reception and the sanitary facilities which include push-button showers, washbasins in cabins, good provision for disabled visitors, dishwashing and laundry facilities. Motorcaravan service point. Play area. Boules, volleyball, table tennis and basketball. Internet access. Off site: Baker's 500 m. Shops, bar and restaurant in village. Fishing 200 m. Golf 3 km. Bicycle hire and boat launching 10 km. Riding 15 km.

Open: 1 April - 30 September.

Directions

Savigny-en-Véron is 20 km. east of Saumur via D947 to Montsoreau, then the D7 road along the south bank of the Loire. Village and campsite are both clearly signed from all approaches. GPS: N47:12.013 E00:08.366

Charges 2007

Per unit incl. 2 person	€ 7,50 - € 9,80
full services	€ 11,00 - € 13,00
extra person	€ 2,05 - € 2,50
child (under 10 yrs)	€ 1,00 - € 1,35
electricity (10A)	€ 3,05 - € 3,25

FR37140 Huttopia Rillé

Lac de Rillé, F-37340 Rillé (Indre-et-Loire)

Tel: 02 47 24 62 97. Email: rille@huttopia.com

This site in a forest by a lake has plenty of potential. It has recently been acquired by the Huttopia group which aims to provide a traffic-free environment. Cars are to be left in a carpark outside the barrier (allowed on site to unload and load). New arrivals must park outside and gain an entry code from reception. There are 146 pitches of which 32 are occupied by rental accommodation and 24 are for motorcaravans in a separate area. The touring pitches are numbered in groups amongst the trees but are not marked; they vary in size and cost.

Facilities

The central toilet block has family rooms (with showers and basins), washbasins in cubicles and facilities for disabled visitors but there are no ramps and access for wheelchairs is very difficult. Another smaller block has separate showers, washbasins and slightly better facilities for disabled visitors. Motorcaravan service point. Heated swimming pool (May - Sept). Play area. Fishing. Canoes on lake. Off site: Riding 6 km. Golf 15 km.

Open: 29 March - 2 November

Directions

Rillé is 40 km. west of Tours. From D766 Angers - Blois road at Château la Vallière take D749 southwest. From N152 Tours - Angers road go northwest at Langeais on D57. In Rillé turn west on D49. Site on right in a short distance.

Charges 2008

Per person	€ 5,00 - € 6,50
child (2-7 yrs)	€ 3,00 - € 4,30
pitch incl. electricity (6/10A)	€ 8,20 - € 24,20
Camping Cheques accepted.	

tel: +33 (0) 4 37 64 22 33 www.huttopia.com

HUTTOPIA

In the heart of the forest
around Lake Rillé
near the Châteaux of the Loire Valley...

Huttopia Rillé

Roulottes, tents
and cottages
to rent

Heated swimming-pool, Bar restaurant,
tennis courts, beach, children playground,
hiking, biking...

Lac de Rillé - 37340 Rillé
Tel. (33) 2 47 24 62 97

www.huttopia.com

FR37150 Camping les Coteaux du Lac

Base de Loisirs, F-37460 Chemillé-sur-Indrois (Indre-et-Loire)

Tel: 02 47 92 77 83. Email: lescoteauxdulac@wanadoo.fr

This former municipal site has been completely refurbished to a high standard and is being operated efficiently by a private company owned by the present enthusiastic manager, Yves Joyaut. There are 49 touring pitches, all with electricity (10A) and individual water tap; four have hard standing for motorcaravans. At present there is little shade apart from that offered by a few mature trees, but new trees and bushes have been planted and flower beds are to be added. In a few years this promises to be a delightful site; meanwhile it is smart and very well tended. The site is in pleasant countryside above a lake and next to a rapidly developing Base de Loisirs with watersports provision and a bar/restaurant. There is a good, well-equipped little swimming pool with paddling area securely separated from the main pool (open all season and heated when necessary).

Facilities

Excellent sanitary block with controllable showers, some washbasins in cabins and en-suite facilities for disabled visitors. Dishwashing and laundry facilities. Reception sells a few basic supplies and bread can be ordered. Swimming and paddling pools. Playing field. Play equipment for different ages. Chalets to rent (15) are grouped at far end of site. Off site: Fishing 100 m. Lakeside beach, sailing and other water sports 200 m. Riding 4 km. Golf 15 km.

Open: 5 April - 30 September.

Directions

Chemillé-sur-Indrois is 55 km. southeast of Tours and 14 km. east of Loches, just off the D760 from Loches to Montrésor. Site is to the north of this road and is signed just west of Montrésor. GPS: N47:09.472 E01:09.592

Charges 2007

Per pitch incl. 2 persons	€ 11,50 - € 17,20
extra person	€ 3,50 - € 4,70
child (2-9 yrs)	€ 2,00 - € 3,20
electricity	€ 3,70

Check real time availability and at-the-gate prices...

 www.alanrogers.com

FR45010 Kawan Village les Bois du Bardelet

Route de Bourges, Poilly, F-45500 Gien (Loiret)

Tel: **02 38 67 47 39**. Email: **contact@bardelet.com**

This attractive, lively family site, in a rural setting, is well situated for exploring the less well known eastern part of the Loire Valley. Two lakes (one for boating, one for fishing) and a pool complex have been attractively landscaped in 12 hectares of former farmland, blending old and new with natural wooded areas and more open field areas with rural views. Bois du Bardelet provides 260 pitches with around 130 for touring units. All are larger than 100 sq.m. and have electrical connections, with some fully serviced. The communal areas are based on attractively converted former farm buildings with a wide range of leisure facilities. A family club card can be purchased to make use of the many activities on a daily basis (some high season only). Various activities and excursions are organised, the most popular being to Paris on Wednesdays, which can be pre-booked.

Facilities

Two sanitary blocks (only one open outside 15/6-31/8) include washbasins in cabins. Facilities for disabled visitors and babies. Washing machines. Shop (1/4-30/9). Bar. Snack bar, takeaway, restaurant (all 1/4-14/9) and pizzeria (8/7-21/8). Outside pool (1/5-31/8). Indoor children's pool. Indoor pool, heated (with purchased club card). Aqua gym, fitness and jacuzzi room. Games area. Archery. Canoeing and fishing. Tennis, minigolf, boules, table tennis. Bicycle hire. Playground. Internet access. Off site: Supermarket 5 km. Riding 7 km. Golf 25 km. Walking and cycling routes.

Open: 1 April - 30 September.

Directions

From Gien take D940 (Bourges). After 5 km. turn right and right again to cross road and follow site signs. From Argent sur Sauldre take D940 (Gien). Site signed to right after 15 km. Entrance is 200 m. past what looks like the first opening to site. GPS: N47:38.497 E02:36.891

Charges 2008

Per unit incl. 2 persons and electricity	€ 18,50 - € 30,90
extra person (over 2 yrs)	€ 3,70 - € 6,20
animal	€ 4,00

Less 15-25% in low seasons (20-40% for over 60s). Camping Cheques accepted.

FR41020 Castel Camping Château de la Grenouillère Mobile homes ▶ page 493

F-41500 Suèvres (Loir-et-Cher)

Tel: **02 54 87 80 37**. Email: **la.grenouillere@wanadoo.fr**

Château de la Grenouillère is a comfortable site with good amenities. It is set in a 28 acre park and the 275 pitches (including 130 for tour operators and mobile homes) are in three distinct areas. The majority are in a wooded area, with about 60 in the old orchard and the remainder in open meadow, although all pitches are separated by hedges. There is one water point for every four pitches and all have electric hook-up (6/10A). Additionally, there are 14 'grand confort' pitches with a separate luxury sanitary block in the outbuildings of the château.

Facilities

Three sanitary blocks are modern and well appointed, including some washbasins in cabins. Laundry facilities. Shop. Bar. Pizzeria and pizza takeaway. Restaurant and Chicken Grill takeaway (1/6-5/9). Swimming complex of four pools (one covered) and slide. Tennis, table tennis, pool, baby foot and video games. Internet point. Bicycle and canoe hire (July/Aug). Off site: Suèvres 3 km. Fishing, riding, and aqua sports 5 km. Golf 10 km.

Open: 28 April - 8 September.

Directions

Site is between Suèvres and Mer on north side of N152 and is well signed.

Charges 2007

Per unit incl. 2 persons	€ 20,00 - € 33,00
with 6A electricity	€ 24,00 - € 37,00
with full services	€ 30,00 - € 45,00
extra person	€ 5,00 - € 8,00
child (under 7 yrs)	€ 3,00 - € 6,00

FR45030 Camping Touristique de Gien

Rue des Iris, Poilly lez Gien, F-45500 Gien (Loiret)

Tel: **02 38 67 12 50**. Email: **camping-gien@wanadoo.fr**

This open, attractive site lies immediately across the river from Gien on the opposite bank of the Loire with views of the château and town. It has a long river frontage, which includes a good expanse of sandy beach. There are 150 well-sized, level, grassed touring pitches. All have electricity (4/10A), 18 have water and drainage (between two). Some are shaded by mature trees. The bar and restaurant, with a large outdoor area, are open to the public and provide a sociable gathering point. Soirées with different themes are held at least weekly in July and August. The town, with its château, is within a kilometre across the bridge. The site makes an excellent base for exploring the eastern end of the Loire valley, and the town of Gien itself is of interest. The festival celebrating the heritage of this part of the Loire at Ascensiontide is well worth a visit.

Facilities

Three toilet blocks (no paper or seats in toilets, some Turkish), one heated, and one new with an en-suite unit for disabled people. Laundry. Bar and restaurant (1/4-30/9), both open to the public. Shop 20 m. outside gates (all year). Swimming pool paddling pools (15/6-15/9). Play area and grassed games area. Minigolf. Bicycle hire. Canoe hire. Fishing. Off site: Town centre less than 1 km. Hypermarket 1 km. Riding 2 km. Golf 25 km.

Open: 1 March - 9 November.

Directions

North of the river, from north (A77 and RN7) take D940 to Gien; from southeast (A77 and RN7) and from west take D952 to Gien. Follow signs to Centre Ville and turn south over bridge. At traffic lights turn west on D951 towards Pouilly-lez-Gien. Site is signed 300 m. on right. If south of the river, from D940 turn west onto D951 and site is 300 m. on right.

Charges 2008

Per unit incl. 2 persons	€ 13,00 - € 19,00
extra person	€ 6,00
child (under 12 yrs)	€ 4,00
electricity (4/10A)	€ 3,50 - € 5,00

FR41030 Yelloh! Village le Parc des Alicourts

Domaine des Alicourts, F-41300 Pierrefitte-sur-Sauldre (Loir-et-Cher)

Tel: **04 66 73 97 39**. Email: **info@yellohvillage-parc-des-alicourts.com**

A secluded holiday village set in the heart of the forest and with many sporting facilities and a super new spa centre, Parc des Alicourts is midway between Orléans and Bourges, to the east of the A71. There are 490 pitches, 150 for touring and the remainder occupied by mobile homes and chalets. All pitches have electricity connections (6A) and good provision for water, and most are 150 sq.m. (min. 100 sq.m.). Locations vary from wooded to more open areas, thus giving a choice of amount of shade. All facilities are open all season and the leisure amenities are exceptional. Member of Leading Campings Group.

Facilities

Three modern sanitary blocks include some washbasins in cabins and baby bathrooms. Laundry facilities. Facilities for disabled visitors (shallow step to reach them). Motorcaravan services. Shop. Restaurant. Takeaway in bar with terrace. Pool complex. Spa centre. 7 hectare lake (fishing, bathing, canoes, pedaloes). 9-hole golf course. Play area. Tennis. Minigolf. Boules. Roller skating/skateboarding (bring own equipment). Bicycle hire. Internet access. Walk and cycle path.

Open: 30 April - 9 September.

Directions

From A71, take Lamotte Beuvron exit (no 3) or from N20 Orléans to Vierzon turn left on to D923 towards Aubigny. After 14 km. turn right at camping sign on to D24E. Site signed in about 4 km.
GPS: N47:32.639 E02:11.516

Charges 2007

Per unit incl. 2 persons and electricity	€ 17,00 - € 41,00
extra person	€ 6,00 - € 9,00
child (1-17 yrs)	free - € 7,00

FR45040 Camping Hortus

1 route d'Orléans, D60 Sully-sur-Loire, F-45600 Saint Père-sur-Loire (Loiret)

Tel: **02 38 36 35 94**. Email: **info@camping-hortus.com**

Across the river from Sully-sur-Loire with its imposing château, this site makes a comfortable base for exploring this part of the Loire valley. The present owners acquired it from the local authority in 2005 and their drive and initiative have turned it into an attractive site with many facilities. There are 80 well-sized touring pitches, all with electricity, water and drainage, on level grass and divided into groups of four by hedges. There is also an area for tents between the main pitches and the river. Trees provide a degree of shade. New swimming pools, bar and (open air) restaurant make this an ideal site for a quiet family holiday. A 'Sites et Paysages' member.

Facilities

Two modern toilet blocks, one heated, are well equipped: some washbasins in cabins; separate suite for disabled visitors. Small shop for essentials. Bar and open-air restaurant (1/5-30/9). Heated, covered swimming pool (12 x 8 m.) and separate paddling pool (both 1/5-30/9). Fishing. Bicycle hire. Minigolf. Play areas. Off site: Town and Château 1.5 km. Two supermarkets 2 km. Golf 2 km. Riding 4 km.

Open: All year.

Directions

From Orleans take N60 then the D952 towards Gien. Turn south on D948 for Sully-sur-Loire. In St Père-sur-Loire, at roundabout just before river bridge, turn west on D60 signed St Benoit-sur-Loire. Site is 300 m. on left.

Charges 2007

Per unit incl. 2 persons and electricity	€ 12,50 - € 19,50
extra person	€ 3,65 - € 5,20
child (3-12 yrs)	free - € 3,15

FR41040 Camping Château des Marais

27 rue de Chambord, F-41500 Muides-sur-Loire (Loir-et-Cher)

Tel: **02 54 87 05 42**. Email: **chateau.des.marais@wanadoo.fr**

The Château des Marais campsite is well situated to visit the chateau at Chambord (its park is impressive) and the other châteaux in the 'Vallée des Rois'. The site, providing 133 large touring pitches, all with electricity (6/10A), water and drainage and with ample shade, is situated in the oak and hornbeam woods of its own small château. An excellent swimming complex offers pools and two flumes. English is spoken and the reception from the enthusiastic owners and the staff is very welcoming. Used by tour operators (90 pitches).

Facilities

Four modern sanitary blocks have good facilities including some large showers and washbasins en-suite. Washing machine. Motorcaravan service point. Shop and takeaway. Bar/restaurant with large terrace. Swimming complex with heated and unheated pools, slide and cover for cooler weather. TV room. Bicycle hire. Fishing pond. Excursions to Paris, an entertainment programme and canoe trips organised in high season. Internet access. Off site: Riding 5 km. Golf 12 km. Muides-sur-Loire (five minutes walk).

Open: 15 May - 15 September.

Directions

From A10 autoroute take exit 16 to Mer, cross the Loire to join D951 and follow signs. Site signed off D103 to southwest of village. 600 m. from junction with D112. GPS: N47:39.948 E01:31.726

Charges 2007

Per pitch incl. 2 persons	€ 24,00 - € 32,00
extra person	€ 6,00 - € 8,00
child (under 5 yrs)	free - € 5,00
electricity (6/10A)	€ 5,00 - € 7,00
dog	€ 5,00

Credit cards accepted for amounts over € 80.

FR41070 Kawan Village la Grande Tortue

3 route de Pontlevoy, F-41120 Candé-sur-Beuvron (Loir-et-Cher)

Tel: **02 54 44 15 20**. Email: **grandetortue@wanadoo.fr**

Mobile homes ▶ page 493

This is a pleasant, shady site that has been developed in the surroundings of an old forest. It provides 169 touring pitches the majority of which are more than 100 sq.m. 150 have 10A electricity and the remainder are fully serviced. The family owners continue to develop the site with a new multisport court already created. During July and August, they organise a programme of trips including wine/cheese tastings, canoeing and horse riding excursions. Used by tour operators. This site is well placed for visiting the châteaux of the Loire or the cities of Orléans and Tours.

Facilities

Three sanitary blocks offer British style WCs, washbasins in cabins and push button showers. Laundry facilities. Shop selling provisions. Terraced bar and restaurant with reasonably priced food and drink (15/4-15/9). Swimming pool and two shallower pools for children (1/5-30/9). Trampolines, a ball crawl with slide and climbing wall, bouncy inflatable, table tennis. New multisport court. Off site: Walking and cycling. Bicycle hire 1 km. Fishing 500 m. Golf 10 km. Riding 12 km.

Open: 9 April - 30 September.

Directions

Site is just outside Candé-sur-Beuvron on D751, between Amboise and Blois. From Amboise, turn right just before Candé, then left into campsite. GPS: N47:29.389 E01:15.515

Charges 2007

Per unit incl. 2 persons	€ 15,00 - € 26,00
incl. electricity	€ 19,50 - € 30,00
extra person	€ 5,00 - € 7,50
child (3-9 yrs)	€ 3,50 - € 5,50
animal	€ 3,70

Camping Cheques accepted.

Check real time availability and at-the-gate prices...

 www.**alanrogers**.com

FR41010 Le Parc du Val de Loire

Mobile homes ▶ page 493

Route de Fleuray, F-41150 Mesland (Loir-et-Cher)

Tel: **02 54 70 27 18**. Email: **parcduvaldeloire@wanadoo.fr**

Between Blois and Amboise, quietly situated among vineyards away from the main roads and towns, this site is nevertheless centrally placed for visits to the châteaux; Chaumont, Amboise and Blois (21 km.) are the nearest in that order. There are 210 touring pitches of reasonable size, either in light woodland marked by trees or on open meadow with separators. All the pitches have electricity (10A) and 100 of them also have water and drainage. Sports and competitions are organised in July/August with a weekly disco and dance for adults and opportunities for wine tasting are arranged weekly. There are walks and bike rides on marked paths (free maps available). Nearby there are balloon and helicopter flights over the Loire valley. New, experienced owners have recently taken over the site.

Facilities

Three original toilet blocks of varying ages are acceptable. Units for disabled visitors, babies and laundry facilities. Motorcaravan services. Shop with bakery (July/Aug). Bar. Restaurant, snack service, pizzeria and takeaway (July/Aug). TV and recreation rooms. Swimming pools, one heated all season, larger one with slide. Tennis. Playgrounds with skate board facilities. Bicycle hire. Table tennis. Minigolf. Football pitch. Volleyball, badminton and basketball. Barbecue area. Off site: Fishing 2 km. Golf 4 km. Riding 10 km.

Open: 31 March - 29 September.

Directions

From A10 exit 18 (Château-Renault, Amboise) take D31 south to Autrèche (2 km). Turn left on D55 for 3.5 km. In Darne-Marie Les Bois turn left and then right onto D43 to Mesland. Follow site signs. Or, from south, site signed from Onzain. GPS: N47:30.601 E01:06.286

Charges 2007

Per standard pitch (100 sq.m.)	
incl. 2 persons	€ 14,00 - € 24,50
large pitch (110-170 sq.m.)	
with services	€ 22,00 - € 38,50
extra person	€ 4,50 - € 7,00
child (4-10 yrs)	€ 3,50 - € 6,20
animal	€ 4,00

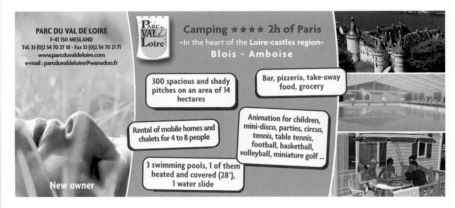

PARC DU VAL DE LOIRE
F-41 150 MESLAND
Tél. 33 (0)2 54 70 27 18 - Fax 33 (0)2 54 70 21 71
www.parcduvaldeloire.com
e-mail : parcduvaldeloire@wanadoo.fr

Camping ★★★★ 2h of Paris
«In the heart of the **Loire-castles region**»
Blois - Amboise

300 spacious and shady pitches on an area of 14 hectares

Bar, pizzeria, take-away food, grocery

Rental of mobile homes and chalets for 4 to 8 people

Animation for children, mini-disco, parties, circus, tennis, table tennis, football, basketball, volleyball, miniature golf ...

3 swimming pools, 1 of them heated and covered (28°), 1 water slide

New owner

FR49000 Camping du Lac de Maine

Avenue du Lac de Maine, F-49000 Angers (Maine-et-Loire)

Tel: **02 41 73 05 03**. Email: **camping@lacdemaine.fr**

The Lac de Maine campsite is situated in the heart of the Anjou region. Most of the 141 level touring pitches are part grass and part gravel hardstanding, with the remainder all gravel. All have water, a drain and electricity (6/10A). The main entrance has a height restriction of 3.2 m, although there is an alternative gate for higher vehicles. This is a useful site, open for a long season and only five minutes from the centre of Angers. With wide access roads, it is also suitable for American RVs.

Facilities

Two sanitary blocks, one which can be heated and includes some washbasins in cubicles. British style WCs (no seats). Facilities for babies and visitors with disabilities. Dishwashing and laundry facilities. Motorcaravan service point. Reception stocks gas. Restaurant/bar (both 15/6-15/9). Heated L-shaped swimming pool (1/6-15/9). Volleyball. Petanque. Bicycle hire. Internet point. Barrier card deposit € 20. Off site: Lake beach 500 m. Fishing 1 km. Riding 3 km. Golf 5 km.

Open: 25 March - 10 October.

Directions

Site is just west of Angers near the N23 (Angers - Nantes road). Turn south at signs for Quartier de Maine and Lac de Maine. Follow signs for Pruniers and Bouchemaine. Site on D111 and signed. GPS: N47:27.277 W00:35.777

Charges 2008

Per unit incl. 2 persons	€ 11,85 - € 17,00
extra person	€ 3,00
electricity (10A)	€ 3,40
Camping Cheques accepted.	

FR41100 Camping les Saules

D102 route de Contres, F-41700 Cheverny (Loir-et-Cher)
Tel: **02 54 79 90 01**. Email: **contact@camping-cheverny.com**

Set in the heart of the châteaux region, has recently been revitalised and re-opened by a local family. The tastefully renovated traditional reception buildings in their lakeside setting give a very pleasant welcome. There are 166 good size, level pitches with 149 available for touring units. All have shade from the many trees on the site, 150 have electrical connections (a few will require leads longer than 25 m) and there are ample water taps. Cheverny is considered to have the best interior and furnishings of all the châteaux in the Loire region, and many others are within easy reach. A 'Sites et Paysages' member.

Facilities

Two sanitary blocks with toilets, showers, washbasins in cubicles and facilities for disabled visitors. Dishwashing and laundry facilities. Motorcaravan service point. Gas supplies. Shop. Restaurant (July/Aug). Bar. Snack bar and takeaway. Swimming and paddling pools. TV/social room with toys, board games, books. Two play areas. Large grass area for ball games. Minigolf (free). Fishing. Bicycle hire. Internet and WiFi. Off site: Golf 3 km. Riding 3 km.

Open: 28 March - 30 September.

Directions

From Cheverny take D102 south towards Contres. Site is on the right after about 2 km. GPS: N47:30.000 E01:27.668

Charges 2008

Per unit incl. 2 persons	€ 15,50 - € 25,50
extra person	€ 4,50
child (4-10 yrs)	€ 2,00
electricity	€ 3,50

FR49010 Castel Camping l'Etang de la Brèche

RN152, 5 impasse de la Breche, F-49730 Varennes-sur-Loire (Maine-et-Loire)
Tel: **02 41 51 22 92**. Email: **mail@etang-breche.com**

The Saint Cast family have developed l'Etang de la Brèche with care and attention. The site provides 116 large, level touring pitches with shade from trees and bushes. Less shaded areas are used for recreation. There are electrical connections to all pitches (some long cables may be required), with water and drainage on 63 of them. The restaurant, bar and terrace, also open to the public, provides a social base and is popular with British visitors. The pool complex includes one with a removable cover, one outdoor, and one for toddlers. The site includes a small lake (used for fishing) and wooded area ensuring a quiet, relaxed and rural atmosphere and making l'Étang de la Brèche a comfortable holiday base for couples and families. A Les Castels site used by tour operators (85 pitches).

Facilities

Three toilet blocks, modernised to good standards, include facilities for babies with two units for people with disabilities. Washing up sinks and laundry. Shop and epicerie. Restaurant, pizzeria and takeaway. Heated pools. Tennis, basketball, minigolf and a field for football. Bicycle hire. General room, games and TV rooms. Internet point. Varied sporting and entertainment programme (10/7-25/8). Pony riding. Child minding is arranged in afternoons. Torch useful. Off site: Golf 7 km.

Open: 12 May - 15 September.

Directions

Site is 100 m. north off the main N152, about 4 km. northeast of Saumur on the north bank of the Loire.

Charges 2007

Per unit incl. 2 persons	€ 18,50 - € 31,00
extra person	€ 5,00 - € 7,00
child (4-10 yrs)	€ 3,00 - € 3,50
electricity (10A)	free - € 3,00
water and drainage	€ 2,50
7th night free in low season.	

FR49060 Camping Parc de Montsabert

Montsabert, F-49320 Coutures (Maine-et-Loire)

Tel: **02 41 57 91 63**. Email: **camping@parcdemontsabert.com**

Mobile homes ▶ page 494

This extensive site has recently been taken over by a friendly French couple who already have plans for improvements. It has a rural atmosphere in the shadow of Montsabert château, from where visiting peacocks happily roam in the spacious surroundings. The main features are the heated swimming pool (with cover) and the adjoining refurbished, rustic style restaurant. There are 96 large, well marked touring pitches, divided by hedges and all with water tap, drain and electricity (10A). Picnic tables are provided. Used by several small tour operators (30 pitches). Partially wooded by a variety of trees, this site offers the peace of the countryside and yet easy access to both Saumur and Angers. It is an ideal base for exploring the area, whether on foot, by bicycle or car.

Facilities

The main toilet block can be heated and has washbasins and bidets in cabins and a baby room. Laundry facilities. A second block serves the pool and another provides more WCs. Shop, bar and takeaway (31/5-31/8). Restaurant(14/6-23/8). Heated pool (no Bermuda style shorts) and paddling pool. Sports hall, minigolf, volleyball and basketball. Tennis. Play area. Bicycle hire. Entertainment (high season). Off site: Canoeing nearby. Fishing, riding 5 km. Golf 8 km.

Open: 12 April - 14 September.

Directions

Coutures is 25 km. southeast of Angers on the D751 to Saumur. From A11 take exit 14 and follow signs for Cholet/Poitiers, then Poitiers on D748. At Brissac-Quincé turn northeast on D55 and in 5 km. turn right to Coutures. Montsabert is north of village. GPS: N47:22.464 W00:20.709

Charges 2008

Per pitch incl. 2 persons	€ 16,00 - € 25,00
extra person	€ 4,00 - € 4,75
child (1-13 yrs)	€ 2,50 - € 3,20
electricity (5/10A)	€ 3,50 - € 4,20
dog	€ 3,30

PARC de MONTSABERT
www.parcdemontsabert.com
camping@parcdemontsabert.com

Spacious Pitches
25m heated Swimmingpool
Covered Pool, Childrenspool
Sportshall, Tennis, Tabletennis,
Volley, Soccer, Midget Golf, etc.
Bicycle rent, Walking- and
Cyclingroutes
Restaurant, Entertainment
English spoken
Holiday homes to let

Tel: (00 33) 2 41 57 91 63

FR49030 Camping Caroline

Route de la Bohalle, F-49800 Brain-sur-l'Authion (Maine-et-Loire)

Tel: **04 99 57 21 21**. Email: **contact@village-center.com**

Camping Caroline is an attractive former municipal site, lying on the edge of the little village of Brain-sur-l'Authion at the heart of the Anjou. This is a relaxing site with 120 large grassy pitches, mostly with reasonable shade and electricity (6A). There are several leisure amenities, notably a heated pool and snack bar. The River Authion is just 200 metres away and is popular with anglers. This is a useful base for visiting the vineyards of the Anjou which are all around. Member of the Escapades Terre Océane group.

Facilities

The two sanitary blocks are of very different designs but are clean and well maintained. Facilities for disabled visitors. Heated swimming pool and paddling pool. Snack bar. Play area. Children's club in peak season. Mobile homes for hire. Off site: Tennis. Fishing (charge applies). Boating. Multisports pitch. Walking and cycle trails. Boat trips on the Loire.

Open: 26 March - 1 October.

Directions

From Angers take the N147 towards Saumur and then the D113 to the south of the village of Brain-sur-l'Authion. Site is clearly signed from the village.

Charges 2007

pitch incl. electricity	€ 8,00 - € 12,00
Per person	€ 2,50 - € 3,00

Loire Valley

FR49040 Camping de l'Etang

Route de St Mathurin, F-49320 Brissac (Maine-et-Loire)

Tel: 02 41 91 70 61. Email: info@campingetang.com

Mobile homes ▶ page 494

At Camping de l'Etang many of the 124 level touring pitches have pleasant views across the countryside. Separated and numbered, some have a little shade and all have electricity with water and drainage nearby. 21 are fully serviced. A small bridge crosses the river Aubance which runs through the site (well fenced) and there are two lakes where fisherman can enjoy free fishing. The site has its own vineyard and the wine produced can be purchased on the campsite. Tour operators use 16 pitches. Originally the farm of the Château de Brissac (yet only 24 km. from the lovely town of Angers), this is an attractive campsite retaining much of its rural charm. The adjacent Parc de Loisirs is a paradise for young children with many activities including boating, pedaloes, pony rides, miniature train, water slide, bouncy castle and swings (free entry for campers). A 'Sites et Paysages' member.

Facilities

Three well maintained toilet blocks provide all the usual facilities. Laundry facilities. Baby room. Disabled visitors are well catered for. Motorcaravan service point. The farmhouse houses reception, small shop and takeaway snacks when bar is closed. A bar/restaurant serves crêpes, salads, etc (evenings June-August). Swimming pool (heated and covered) and paddling pool. Fishing. Play area. Bicycle hire. Wide variety of evening entertainment in high season. Off site: Golf and riding 10 km. Sailing 25 km.

Open: 1 May - 15 September.

Directions

Brissac-Quincé is 17 km. southeast of Angers on D748 towards Poitiers. Do not enter the town but turn north on D55 (site signed) in direction of St Mathurin. GPS: N47:21.560 W00:26.065

Charges 2008

Per unit incl. 2 persons	€ 15,00 - € 29,00
extra person	€ 5,00 - € 7,00
child (0-10 yrs)	free - € 4,00
electricity	free - € 3,00
dog	€ 3,00 - € 4,00

On the route of the châteaux of the Loire, 2 campsites welcome you

The same spirit of hospitality

CAMPING DE CHANTEPIE **
S'-Hilaire-S'-Florent - 49400 SAUMUR
Tél. +33 (0)2 41 67 95 34 - Fax +33 (0)2 41 67 95 85
e-mail : info@campingchantepie.com
www.campingchantepie.com

Association de
Chantepie et de l'Etang
N° 2002/DRTEFP/280

CAMPING DE L'ETANG **
Route de S'-Mathurin
49320 BRISSAC
Tél. +33 (0)2 41 91 70 61 - Fax +33 (0)2 41 91 72 65
e-mail : info@campingetang.com
www.campingetang.com

LE PACTE QUALITÉ
de vos vacances

FR49020 Camping de Chantepie

Saint Hilaire-St Florent, F-49400 Saumur (Maine-et-Loire)

Tel: 02 41 67 95 34. Email: info@campingchantepie.com

On arriving at Camping de Chantepie with its colourful, floral entrance, a friendly greeting awaits at reception, set beside a restored farmhouse. The site is owned by a charitable organisation which provides employment for local disabled people. Linked by gravel roads (which can be dusty), the 150 grass touring pitches are level and spacious, with some new larger ones (200 sq.m. at extra cost, state preference when booking). All pitches have electricity and are separated by low hedges of flowers and trees offering some shade. This is a good site for families. A 'Sites et Paysages' member.

Facilities

The toilet block is clean and facilities are good with washbasins in cubicles, new showers (men and women separately) and facilities for disabled visitors. Dishwashing and laundry facilities. Baby area. Shop. Bar, terraced café and takeaway. Covered and heated pool, outdoor pool and paddling pool. Play area with apparatus. Terraced minigolf. Volleyball, TV, video games and table tennis. Pony rides. Bicycle hire. Internet access. Off site: Fishing 500 m. Golf, riding 2 km. Sailing 7 km.

Open: 1 May - 15 September.

Directions

St Hilaire-St Florent is 2 km. west of Saumur. Take D751 (Gennes). Right at roundabout in St Hilaire-St Florent and on until Le Poitrineau and campsite sign, then turn left. Continue for 3 km. then turn right into site road.

Charges 2008

Per unit incl. 2 persons	€ 15,00 - € 29,00
extra person	€ 5,00 - € 7,00
child (3-10 yrs)	€ 3,00 - € 4,00
electricity (5/10A)	€ 3,00

185

FR49070 Camping Caravaning la Vallée des Vignes

La Croix Patron, F-49700 Concourson-sur-Layon (Maine-et-Loire)

Tel: **02 41 59 86 35**. Email: **Campingvdv@wanadoo.fr**

The enthusiasm of the English owners here comes across instantly in the warm welcome received by their guests. Bordering the Layon river, the 50 good sized touring pitches are reasonably level and fully serviced (10A electricity, water tap and drain). Five pitches have a hardstanding for cars. Attractions include an enclosed bar and restaurant, a generously sized sun terrace surrounding the pool and high season activities for children and adults. These include wine tasting, a hog roast (or similar), competitions and treasure hunts.

Facilities

The toilet block includes washbasins in cabins, and dishwashing facilities at either end. Baby room. Facilities for disabled visitors. Laundry facilities. Bar (from 15/5 or on request) serving meals, snacks and takeaway (from 15/5). Swimming and paddling pools (from 15/5). Playground, games area. Minigolf. Internet access. Fishing. Caravan storage. Off site: Grand Parc Puy du Fou.

Open: 15 April - 15 October.

Directions

Site signed off D960 Doué - Vihiers road, just west of Concourson-sur-Layon.

Charges 2007

Per unit incl. 2 persons	€ 16,50 - € 22,00
extra person	€ 4,00 - € 5,00
child (2-12 yrs)	€ 2,50 - € 3,00
electricity (10A)	€ 4,00

Special offers available.

FR49080 Kawan Village Ile d'Offard

Rue de Verden, Ile d'Offard, F-49400 Saumur (Maine-et-Loire)

Tel: **02 41 40 30 00**. Email: **iledoffard@cvtloisirs.fr**

This site is situated on an island between the banks of the Loire. The 224 touring pitches are at present on grass at the far end or hardstanding nearer the entrance. Some 34 pitches are occupied by tour operators and caravan holiday homes and these can be intrusive in some areas. Pitches have access to electricity hook-ups (10A). A new heated outdoor swimming pool has been completed together with paddling and spa pools. Within walking distance of the centre of Saumur, this site is useful as an overnight stop en-route south or as a short-term base from which to visit the numerous châteaux in the region. Fishing is possible in the Loire (permits are available from Saumur).

Facilities

Three sanitary blocks, one heated in winter, include provision for disabled visitors. Toilet facilities are unisex. Block one has a well equipped laundry. The other blocks are only open in high season. Restaurant and bar (early May - late Sept) with takeaway. Internet access. Table tennis, volleyball. Play area. Some activities with a children's club, wine tastings, etc. in high season. Off site: Thursday market 500 m. Saturday morning market 2 km. Riding 5 km.

Open: 1 March - 31 October.

Directions

From north and A85 exit 3, take N147 south (Saumur). After 2.5 km. turn left (N147 bears right). Follow old road towards river and town. Cross bridge onto island, then first left. Site ahead. GPS: N47:15.457 W00:03.660

Charges 2007

Per unit incl. 2 persons	€ 15,50 - € 24,00
extra person	€ 4,00 - € 5,00
child (2-10 yrs)	€ 2,00 - € 2,50
electricity	€ 3,50

Camping Cheques accepted.

FR49090 Kawan Village l'Isle Verte

Avenue de la Loire, F-49730 Montsoreau (Maine-et-Loire)

Tel: 02 41 51 76 60. Email: isleverte@cvtloisirs.fr

This friendly, natural site, with pitches overlooking the Loire, is just 100 m. from the centre of Montsoreau, an ideal starting point to visit the western Loire area. Most of the 90 shaded, level and good-sized tourist pitches are separated by low hedges but grass tends to be rather sparse during dry spells. All have electricity (16A). Excellent English is spoken in the reception and bar. Fishermen are particularly well catered for here, there being an area to store equipment and live bait (permits are available in Saumur). Attractions within walking distance of the campsite include the château, Troglodyte (mushroom caves and restaurant), both just 500 m, wine tasting in the cellars nearby, and a Sunday market in the town.

Facilities

A single building provides separate male and female toilets. Washbasins, some in cabins, and showers are unisex. Separate facilities for disabled campers. Baby room. Laundry and dishwashing facilities. Motorcaravan service point. Bar and snack bar (1/5-30/9). Swimming and paddling pools (15/5-30/9). Small play area. Table tennis, volleyball and boules. Bicycle hire (June - August or by special request). Fishing. Off site: Golf 6 km. Riding 15 km.

Open: 1 April - 30 September.

Directions

Take D947 from Saumur to Montsoreau and site is clearly signed on left along the road into town. GPS: N47:13.092 E00:03.159

Charges 2007

Per unit incl. 1 or 2 persons	€ 12,90 - € 17,50
extra person	€ 3,00 - € 3,50
child (2-10 yrs)	€ 2,00 - € 2,50
electricity	€ 3,00

Motorcaravan services € 6 (free if camping).
Camping Cheques accepted.

Le Camping Isle verte***

Residing on the banks of the Loire River, 100 m from centre of Montsoreau, this family campsite with 110 pitches is an excellent destination for discovering the Troglodytes (the champignonnière, wine caves within 500m) and Castles of the Loire.
Isle Verte is situated in natural settings, ideal for relaxing holidays. The site has direct access to the banks of the Loire and offers activities for all tastes and ages : excursions, fishing, walking and cycling.

Avenue de la Loire
49730 MONTSOREAU
Tél. : 0033 241 517 660
Fax : 0033 241 510 883
www.campingisleverte.com
isleverte@cvtloisirs.fr

FR49120 Centre Touristique Lac de Ribou

Allée Léon Mandin, F-49300 Cholet (Maine-et-Loire)

Tel: 02 41 49 74 30. Email: info@lacderibou.com

Situated just 58 km. southeast of Nantes and a similar distance from the River Loire at Angers and Saumur, this could be a useful place to break a journey or to spend a few days relaxing. Camping Lac de Ribou, with the adjacent 'Village Vacances', forms a holiday complex in pleasant parkland next to an extensive lake on the outskirts of the busy market town of Cholet. 162 touring pitches are on undulating land (some are sloping), divided by hedges and with mature trees proving shade on many; most have electricity (10A) and 115 also have individual water tap and drainage.

Facilities

Two sanitary blocks provide pre-set showers, washbasins in cabins and excellent dishwashing and laundry sinks. Facilities for disabled visitors. Motorcaravan service points. Large heated swimming pool plus smaller pool with slide and a paddling pool (1/6-30/9 - supervised July/Aug). Restaurant and bar with a small shop (July/Aug) and very limited takeaway. Very full programme of activities for all ages (July/Aug). Off site: Fishing and small beach (no swimming) 500 m. Sailing 1 km. Supermarket 2 km. Riding 5 km. Golf 7 km.

Open: 1 April - 30 September.

Directions

From Cholet ring road east of town, turn east on D20 towards Maulévrier/Mauléon. At roundabout by Leclerc supermarket, take first exit signed to the Centre Touristique and campsite. GPS: N47:02.182 W00:50.624

Charges 2008

Per unit incl. 2 persons	€ 16,50 - € 19,30
extra person	€ 4,10 - € 4,80
electricity (10A)	€ 3,75 - € 3,80
dog	€ 1,90 - € 2,20

No credit cards.

FR49150 Camping Le Thouet

Le Côteaux du Chalet, route Bron, F-49260 Montreuil Bellay (Maine-et-Loire)

Tel: **02 41 38 74 17**. Email: **campinglethouet@alicepro.fr**

Open all year, this countryside site occupies a grassy, tree-lined area with the River Thouet running along the far side from the reception and terrace. The site covers an area of 20 acres occupied in part by 37 good sized, unmarked pitches, 32 for touring and all with 10A electricity. Reception is part of an old farmhouse, the home of the owners who, in winter, provide a warm bathroom for the use of the campers. The owner is English and his wife is multilingual. Beside the swimming pool is an attractive sun terrace together with a bar and restaurant. There is a large hardstanding area, with electricity and water, ideal for winter visitors. This is a peaceful and quiet campsite with families and couples in separate areas. It is a good base for touring the famous châteaux of the Loire. It is a good site for birdwatching (the RSPB has recorded 90 species of birds). Booking advisable in high season.

Facilities

Two modern toilet block including facilities for campers with disabilities and baby room. Bread and much more available by request. Outdoor pool, no paddling pool (1/5-30/9) surrounded by terrace, bar/restaurant (1/4-15/10). Wine tasting. Bicycle hire. Boules. Fishing. Large play area. Boat launching, Birdwatching. Off site: Golf and canoeing 5 km. Riding 10 km. beautiful village of Montreuil Bellay, shops, restaurants etc. (5 minutes drive). Fontevraud with its interesting Abbey (15 minutes drive). Saumur, Angers, Tour (within an hours drive).

Open: All year.

Directions

From Saumur take N147 towards Poitiers. About 6 km. after Le Coudray Macouard turn left, signed Montreuil Belley Centre Ville. Immediately turn left again. Site well signed in under 2 km.

Charges 2007

Per unit incl. 2 persons and electricity (10A)	€ 20,00
extra person	€ 4,00

Camping Le Thouet
49260 Montreuil Bellay France

Tel: 0033 (0)241 387 417
Mob: 0033 (0)619563275
Fax: 0033 (0)241 509 283
E-mail: campinglethouet@alicepro.fr
www.campinglethouet.com

FR49140 Camping Au Bord de Loire

Avenue des Cadets de Saumur, F-49350 Gennes (Maine-et-Loire)

Tel: **02 41 38 04 67**. Email: **auboeddeloire@free.fr**

Au Bord de Loire is in the heart of the Loire valley, a Unesco World Heritage site. It is a very simple and inexpensive site managed by students from the adjacent Tourism and Gardening College. There are 140 good sized, mostly level, marked but unseparated, grass pitches with 135 for touring and 70 with 10A electricity. There are good views over the River Loire but only a little shade. Access is easy for large units.

Facilities

One large (access by steps) and two smaller satellite toilet blocks (high season) with no facilities for campers with disabilities. Large children's play area. Motorcaravan services. Off site: Gennes and Rosiers-sur-Loire close by with bars shops etc. Municipal swimming pool (50 m. July/Aug), Fishing 20 m. Boat ramp 500 m. Bicycle hire 1.5 km. Riding 3 km. Golf 15 km. Troglodyte villages. Mushroom museum. Sightseeing boats. Wine tasting. Châteaux of the Loire.

Open: 28 April - 30 September.

Directions

Take D952 from Angers towards Saumur. At Les Rosiers-sur-Loire cross the river, D59, towards Gennes. Site on left just after crossing river.

Charges 2007

Per unit incl. 2 persons	€ 8,00
extra person	€ 2,80
child (1-10 yrs)	€ 1,80
electricity (10A)	€ 2,70
Credit cards only accepted in July/Aug. Long stay discounts.	

FR49170 Camping de Coulvée

Route de Cholet, F-49120 Chemille (Maine-et-Loire)

Tel: **02 41 30 39 97**. Email: **camping-chemille-49@wanadoo.fr**

An exceptionally well cared for, attractive lakeside site with landscaped entrance and gardens. Each of the 53 pitches has tall mature hedges with plenty of shade and privacy; 41 pitches have their own water and electricity. The good-sized pitches are mostly level. The snack bar, indoor games room and TV room are within the modern reception building. A wonderful patio area has views across the lake, play area and lawned gardens – a magnificent place to sit on a sunny day. A number of chalets are available to rent. The staff are very helpful and we thoroughly enjoyed this very pleasant rural site.

Facilities

One central modern sanitary block, open-style basins, preset showers. Separate facilities for disabled visitors. Laundry room and dishwashing facilities. Motorcaravan service point. TV, pool table, electronic games, table football. Very good play area. Pedaloes, canoes (life jackets available from reception). Swimming in lake (lifeguard in afternoons, high season only). Miniclub every afternoon in high season. Fishing. Bicycle hire. Internet access. Off site: Shops, bars, restaurants in town 1 km. (lakeside walk). Riding 2 km.

Open: 30 April - 15 September.

Directions

From A87 Angers - Cholet motorway at junction 25, head south on the N160 for 5 km. to the town of Chemillé. Follow the signs for camping to the south side of the town.

Charges 2007

Per unit incl. 2 persons	€ 16,50
extra person	€ 3,50
child (under 7 yrs)	€ 2,00

FR72010 Camping la Route d'Or

Allée de la Providence, F-72200 La Flèche (Sarthe)

Tel: **02 43 94 55 90**. Email: **camping@ville-lafleche.fr**

This is a very busy site as La Flèche lies at the junction of the Le Mans - Angers and Laval - Saumur roads, along which Britons frequently travel. Set in quiet, park-like surroundings on the south bank of the River Loir (not to be confused with the River Loire which is further south), the site is a pleasant stroll from the town centre where there are plenty of shops and restaurants (neither on site). There are 200 pitches on flat grass, many in excess of 100 sq.m. and some with dividing hedges. Some pitches are in the open park, others are shaded by tall trees.

Facilities

Two original, older style sanitary blocks with rather cramped showers and British and Turkish style toilets. The central block has more modern equipment including second unit for disabled visitors. A separate block with facilities for disabled visitors and a laundry can be heated in cool weather (available for use by other campers in winter). Good motorcaravan service point. Tennis and playground. Swimming pool and paddling pool (indoor pool in La Flèche). Bicycle hire.

Open: 1 March - 31 October.

Directions

Site is in southwest outskirts of town just off D938 road to Saumur and is signed from a junction on the bypass.

Charges guide

Per unit incl. 1 person	€ 6,00
extra person	€ 2,00
child (under 10 yrs)	€ 1,50
electricity (10A)	€ 3,50

FR72020 Camping Municipal du Lac

Rue du Lac, F-72120 Saint Calais (Sarthe)

Tel: **02 43 35 04 81**

Camping du Lac is a pleasant, traditional municipal site with 75 marked pitches (about 60 for touring), most are separated by hedges and all with electricity (10A), water and drainage. A separate area is for tents. In high season there are themed evening walks, competitions and communal meals (campers take their own food and can join in the dancing). Reception is welcoming, the value is excellent and this would make a good night stop or a base for visiting the Le Mans 24 hour race.

Facilities

Two sanitary blocks are old but kept very clean and provide showers and some washbasins in private cabins. Washing machine. Bread and croissants (to order). Two small play areas. Fishing in lake. Off site: Swimming pool adjacent (free). Local supermarket just a short walk. Riding 10 km. Bicycle hire 15 km. Golf 40 km.

Open: 1 April - 15 October.

Directions

St Calais is 45 km. east of Le Mans. Well signed from N157, site is beside lake north of the town, near the station. Follow signs for campsite and 'Plan d'eau'.

Charges guide

Per person	€ 2,55
pitch	€ 1,05 - € 2,25
electricity (3/6A)	€ 1,70 - € 2,60
No credit cards.	

FR72030 Castel Camping le Château de Chanteloup

F-72460 Sillé-le-Philippe (Sarthe)

Tel: 02 43 27 51 07. Email: chanteloup.souffront@wanadoo.fr

An attractive and peaceful site close to Le Mans, Chanteloup is situated in the park of a 19th century château in the heart of the Sarthe countryside. There are 100 pitches all with 6A electricity although long leads will be required in some places. Some are in the woods, many are around the edges of the lawns and completely open, and a few overlook the lake, so there are differing degrees of shade throughout the site. This lack of regimentation enhances the atmosphere and feeling of spaciousness in the grounds surrounding the old château.

Facilities

All sanitary facilities are in the château outbuildings and are well maintained and kept very clean. Washbasins are in cabins. Dishwashing and laundry facilities. Small shop, takeaway and restaurant with covered outdoor seating (all 5/7-24/8). Bar (1/6-3/9). Swimming pool (fenced). Play area (parental supervision essential). Games room, tennis, volleyball, table tennis. Mountain bike hire. Organised activities (high season). WiFi. Off site: Riding 7 km. Golf 10 km. Tennis club in Le Mans.

Open: 1 June - 3 September.

Directions

Sillé-le-Philippe is 18 km. northeast of Le Mans on the D301 to Bonnétable. From autoroute take exit 23, follow signs for Le Mans and Tours, then Le Mans and Savigné l'Evèque. Site is to the east just off main road and signed on southern edge of Sillé. GPS: N48:06.281 E00:20.424

Charges 2007

Per person	€ 5,80 - € 10,00
pitch	€ 9,60 - € 15,00
electricity	€ 3,70

FR72040 Camping des Molières

Sillé-Plage, F-72140 Sillé-le-Guillaume (Sarthe)

Tel: 02 43 20 11 12. Email: campingsilleplage@wanadoo.fr

This pleasant 'no frills' site is located in forestry commission land on the edge of an attractive lake. The 120 pitches are set among the trees and many have been grassed. There is electricity (13A) available to all (long leads may be needed in places). The ground is undulating, so finding a perfectly level pitch is difficult. The great attraction of this site is its location: the lake offers fishing, swimming and many water sports, whilst the surrounding forest is a maze of marked tracks.

Facilities

Two new sanitary blocks are well maintained with push button showers, some washbasins in cubicles and good indoor dishwashing and laundry sinks. Very limited facilities for disabled visitors. No chemical disposal or motorhome service points. Small shop in reception selling a few basics; bread can be ordered. Small club room with television. Some activities organised in conjunction with sister site and the local tourist board. Off site: Golf 30 km.

Open: 1 June - 31 August.

Directions

Approaching from Mayenne, turn north 2 km. before the town on C1 towards Sillé-Plage. Cross first junction and turn left at second (campsites signed). Site on right in less than 1 km. GPS: N48:12.203 W00:07.660

Charges 2007

Per unit incl. 2 persons	€ 8,20 - € 9,00
extra person	€ 2,90 - € 3,20
electricity (10A)	€ 2,50

FR86010 Castel Camping le Petit Trianon

Saint Ustre, 1 rue du Moulin de St Ustre, F-86220 Ingrandes-sur-Vienne (Vienne)

Tel: 05 49 02 61 47. Email: chateau@petit-trianon.fr

A family owned site for many years, situated between Tours, Poitiers and Futuroscope, the approach to Le Petit Trianon is through a grand, narrow, gateway leading onto a slightly sloping meadow surrounded by trees in front of the château. There is also a large, more open field with a woodland area in between. There are 99 spacious, open but marked pitches which are arranged to leave plenty of free space. There is shade in parts from many attractive trees. All have electricity (13A). Reception is housed in the 18th century château.

Facilities

The original toilet unit includes washbasins in cabins, some washbasin and shower units, baby baths, laundry and dishwashing facilities. Smaller blocks for newer parts of site and one has facilities for disabled people. Motorcaravan service point. Shop (bread to order). Takeaway. Heated pool and paddling pools. Playground. Minigolf. Badminton, croquet and boules. TV room, books and games. Bicycle hire. Wine tastings. Organised excursions. Internet access. Caravan storage. Off site: Restaurant 50 m. Fishing 3 km. Riding 15 km.

Open: 20 May - 20 September.

Directions

Ingrandes is signed from N10 north of town (between Dangé and Châtellerault). From autoroute A10 take exit 26 for Châtellerault-Nord, at roundabout follow signs for Tours to Ingrandes where site is signed. GPS: N46:53.248 E00:35.183

Charges 2008

Per person	€ 7,00
child (3-6 yrs)	€ 3,50
pitch with electricity (5/10A)	€ 8,40 - € 8,80
dog	€ 2,10

FR86040 Kawan Village le Futuriste

F-86130 Saint Georges-les-Baillargeaux (Vienne)

Tel: **05 49 52 47 52**. Email: **camping-le-futuriste@wanadoo.fr**

Mobile homes ▶ page 494

Le Futuriste is a neat, modern site, open all year and close to Futuroscope. With a busy atmosphere, there are early departures and late arrivals. Reception is open 08.00-22.00 hrs. There are 118 individual, flat, grassy pitches divided by young trees and shrubs which are beginning to provide some shelter for this elevated and otherwise rather open site (possibly windy). 82 pitches have electricity (6A) and a further 30 have electricity, water, waste water and sewage connections. All are accessed via neat, level and firmly rolled gravel roads. On raised ground with panoramic views over the strikingly modern buildings and night-time bright lights that comprise the popular attraction of Futuroscope, this site is ideal for a short stay to visit the park which is only 1.5 km. away (tickets can be bought at the site) but it is equally good for longer stays to see the region. Details of attractions are available from the enthusiastic young couple who run the site. Note: it is best to see the first evening show at Futuroscope otherwise you will find yourself locked out of the site – the gates are closed at 23.30 hrs.

Facilities

Excellent, clean sanitary facilities in two insulated blocks (can be heated). Those in the newest block are unisex. and include some washbasins in cabins and facilities for disabled people. Laundry facilities. Shop (bread to order), bar/restaurant (all 1/5-30/9). Snack bar and takeaway (1/7-31/8). Two heated outdoor pools, one with slide and paddling pool (1/5-30/9). Games room. TV. Boules. New multisports area. Lake fishing. Youth groups not accepted. Off site: Bicycle hire 500 m. Hypermarket 600 m. Golf 5 km. Riding 10 km.

Open: All year.

Directions

From either A10 autoroute or N10, take Futuroscope exit. Site is east of both roads, off D20 (St Georges-Les-Baillargeaux). Follow signs to St Georges. Site on hill; turn by water tower and site is on left. GPS: N46:39.928 E00:23.668

Charges 2008

Per pitch incl. 1-3 persons	€ 15,00 - € 20,00
extra person	€ 2,00 - € 2,80
electricity	€ 2,80 - € 3,70
animal	€ 1,90

Camping Cheques accepted.

Check real time availability and at-the-gate prices...
www.**alanrogers**.com

FR86030 Camping le Relais du Miel

Route d'Antran, F-86100 Châtellerault (Vienne)

Tel: **05 49 02 06 27**. Email: **camping@lerelaisdumiel.com**

With very easy access from the A10 and N10 roads, in the northern outskirts of Châtellerault, this site is in the 10 acre grounds of a grand house dating from Napoleonic times. It is surrounded by majestic old trees beside the River Vienne. There is also an orchard and stone gateposts leading onto ground, previously the home farm, that now forms 80 large, flat pitches. Divided by mature trees and bushes providing plenty of shade, all the pitches have electricity (10A) and water, 15 with drainage connections. Twin barns form two sides of a courtyard behind the house, one of which has been converted very stylishly into reception, a high ceilinged function and games room, and a bar and restaurant serving good value meals. Beams taken from the original ceiling now form part of the bar top and act as arm rests. The second barn is being developed into apartments. Mobile homes and apartments to rent.

Facilities

Excellent toilet facilities include washbasins in cabins, facilities for disabled visitors, dishwashing and laundry facilities. Basic essentials and gas. Bar and restaurant. Pizzas (from local pizzeria). Takeaway. Snack bar (open in evenings 1/7-30/8). Swimming and paddling pools (15 x 7 m). Tennis courts. Volleyball, basketball. Bicycle hire. Boules. Games room with electronic games, pool and table tennis. Fishing. Observatory. Internet access. Torch useful. Off site: Supermarket 400 m. Riding 5 km. Golf 11 km. Futuroscope 16 km.

Open: 15 May - 2 September.

Directions

Châtellerault is between Tours and Poitiers. Site is north of town close to A10 autoroute. Take exit 26 (Châtellerault-Nord) and site is signed just off roundabout. From N10 follow signs for motorway (Tours - Péage) and at roundabout take exit for Antran. GPS: N46:50.307 E00:32.071

Charges 2007

Per unit incl. 2 persons, electricity	€ 20,00 - € 25,00
extra person over 5 yrs	€ 3,00 - € 4,00
extra tent	€ 3,00 - € 4,00

Less 15% for 1 week, 20% for 2 weeks.

Enjoy rest and comfort

CAMPING ★★★★
Le Relais du Miel

www.lerelaisdumiel.com
Tel: 0033 (0)549 02 06 27
Easy access : A10 Exit 26
Longitude: 0°32'5"
Latitude: 46°50'17"

FR86050 Camping le Riveau

Route de Lesigny, F-86270 La Roche-Posay (Vienne)

Tel: **05 49 86 21 23**. Email: **info@camping-le-riveau.com**

This 200 pitch site is in two parts, one new (flatter and more open), the other more mature on something of a slope but with the benefit of shade from tall trees. Each section has electrical connections (16A). The two sections are divided by a small stream with access to the river Creuse, on which boating and fishing are allowed. The town is only about 1.5 km. Le Riveau is a pleasant, well run site with a good new swimming pool. Entertainment is arranged for children in high season. With easy access to the Vienne region, the site is good for a long stay in both low and high seasons.

Facilities

Two good, fully equipped toilet blocks, one in each section, include facilities for washing, dishwashing, etc. in clean, modern surroundings. Excellent facilities for disabled visitors. Swimming pool. Play area. Barbecues are not permitted. Off site: Shops, restaurants, etc. 1 km. Golf 3 km. Riding 500 m.

Open: 1 March - 31 October.

Directions

Site is signed from the D725 town bypass, turning north at roundabout onto D5 towards Lesigny. Site is 50 m. on right. GPS: N46:48.009 E00:48.512

Charges 2007

Per person	€ 3,60 - € 4,50
child (2-10 yrs)	€ 2,00 - € 2,50
pitch	€ 4,20 - € 5,00
electricity (16A)	€ 3,60

No credit cards.

ices...

FR86080 Camping Caravaning les Peupliers

F-86700 Couhé (Vienne)

Tel: 05 49 59 21 16. Email: info@lespeupliers.fr

Family owned and run since 1968, Les Peupliers is located in a valley south of Poitiers. The site is arranged on the banks of a river (unfenced), the 160 pitches on both sides or around a fishing lake. On level grass, most are separated and all have 16A electricity, while 50 are fully serviced. There is a good pool complex that includes water slides and toboggans, a heated main pool, a paddling pool and a lagoon with two slides for younger children, jacuzzi, plus water games. There is some noise from the N10 which runs fairly close to the site.

Facilities

Three toilet blocks of varying ages are in Mediterranean style, with washbasins in cubicles and facilities for babies and disabled people. The newest is in regular use and the other two open as the season progresses. Dishwashing and laundry facilities. TV and fridge rental. Shop. Snack bar, restaurant and bar. Entertainment in peak season. Pool complex. Playgrounds. Fishing lake. Minigolf, table tennis, football, volleyball and boules. Motorcaravan service point. WiFi. Off site: Tennis 800 m. Bicycle hire 1 km. Riding 5 km.

Open: 2 May - 30 September. Chalets for hire all year.

Directions

Couhé is 30 km. south of Poitiers on N10. From north, follow signs (Couhé town centre) and campsite (a short distance from slip road on right). From south, take 2nd Couhé exit from N10. Site entrance is opposite end of slip road. GPS: N46:18.706 E00:10.670

Charges 2008

Per person	€ 7,00
pitch	€ 9,00
electricity	€ 4,00
electricity, water and drainage	€ 6,50

FR86090 Flower Camping du Lac de Saint-Cyr

F-86130 Saint-Cyr (Vienne)

Tel: 05 49 62 57 22. Email: contact@parcdesaintcyr.com

This well organised, five hectare campsite is part of a 300 hectare leisure park, based around a large lake with sailing and associated sports, and an area for swimming (supervised July/Aug). Land-based activities include tennis, two half-courts, table tennis, fishing, badminton, petanque, beach volleyball, TV room, and a well equipped fitness suite, all of which are free of charge. The campsite has around 185 tourist pitches, 10 mobile homes and 3 'yurts' (canvas and wooden tents) for rent. The marked and generally separated pitches are all fully serviced with electricity (10A), water and drainage. In high season there are extra free activities including a kids club, beach club, archery and an entertainment programme. Also in high season but charged for are sailing school, aquatic toboggan, windsurfing, canoe, kayak and water bikes. Campers can also use the 9 and 18-hole golf courses (with 20% discount for the 18-hole).

Facilities

The main toilet block is modern and supplemented for peak season by a second unit, although they do attract some use by day-trippers to the leisure facilities. They include washbasins in cubicles, dishwashing and laundry facilities, and facilities for babies and disabled persons. Shop, restaurant and takeaway (April - Sept). Playground on beach. Bicycle hire. Barrier locked 22.00-07.00 hrs (€ 10 deposit for card). Off site: Riding 200 m. Golf 800 m.

Open: 1 April - 30 September.

Directions

Saint-Cyr is approx. midway between Châtellerault and Poitiers. Site signed to east of N10 at Beaumont along D82 towards Bonneuil-Matours, and is part of the Parc de Loisirs de Saint-Cyr.

Charges 2008

Per pitch incl. 2 persons and electricity	€ 13,00 - € 29,00
extra person	€ 2,60 - € 5,50
child (2-7 yrs)	€ 1,80 - € 3,80
animal	€ 1,50

TRAVEL SERVICE SITE
TO BOOK CALL 01580 214000
Advice & low ferry-inclusive prices

TRAVEL SERVICE SITE
TO BOOK CALL 01580 214000
Advice & low ferry-inclusive prices

Check real time availability and at-the-gate prices...

www.alanrogers.com

MAP 8

Burgundy is a wonderful evocative region offering breathtaking châteaux and cathedrals, rolling hills and heady mountain views, vineyards and superlative cuisine not to mention of course, a wide variety of world renowned wines.

DÉPARTEMENTS: 21 CÔTE D'OR, 58 NIÈVRE, 71 SAÔNE-ET-LOIRE, 89 YONNE

MAJOR CITY: DIJON

In the rich heartland of France, Burgundy was once a powerful independent state and important religious centre. Its golden age is reflected in the area's magnificent art and architecture: the grand palaces and art collections of Dijon, the great pilgrimage church of Vézelay, the Cistercian Abbaye de Fontenay and the evocative abbey remains at Cluny, once the most powerful monastery in Europe.

However Burgundy is best known for its wine, including some of the world's finest, notably from the great vineyards of the Côte d'Or and Chablis, and also for its sublime cuisine.You'll also notice how driving through the country villages is like reading a wine merchant's list with plenty of opportunities for tasting and choosing your wine.

The area is criss-crossed by navigable waterways and includes the Parc Régional du Morvan; good walking country amidst lush, rolling wooded landscape.

Places of interest

Autun: 12th century St Lazare cathedral.

Beaune: medieval town; Museum of Burgundy Wine.

Cluny: Europe's largest Benedictine abbey.

Dijon: Palace of the Dukes, Fine Arts Museum, Burgundian Folklore Museum.

Fontenay: Fontenay Abbey and Cloister.

Joigny: medieval town.

Mâcon: Maison des Vins (wine centre).

Paray-le-Monial: Romanesque basilica, pilgrimage centre.

Sens: historic buildings, museum with fine Gallo-Roman collections.

Vézelay: fortified medieval hillside.

Cuisine of the region

Many dishes are wine based, including *Poulet au Meursault* and *Coq au Chambertin*. Dijon is known for its *pain d'épice* (spiced honey-cake) and spicy mustard.

Boeuf Bourguignon: braised beef simmered in a red wine-based sauce.

Garbure: heavy soup, a mixture of pork, cabbage, beans and sausages.

Gougère: cheese pastry based on Gruyère.

Jambon persillé: parsley-flavoured ham, served cold in jelly.

Matelote: fresh-water fish soup, usually based on a red wine sauce.

Meurette: red wine-based sauce with small onions, used with fish or poached egg dishes.

FR21000 Sunêlia Lac de Panthier

F-21320 Vandenesse-en-Auxois (Côte d'Or)

Tel: 03 80 49 21 94. Email: info@lac-de-panthier.com

An attractively situated lakeside site in Burgundy countryside, Camping Lac de Panthier is divided into two distinct campsites. The first, smaller section houses the reception, shop, restaurant and other similar facilities. The second, larger area is 200 m. along the lakeside road and is where the site activities and the pool can be found. The 207 pitches (157 for touring units) all have electricity connections and are mostly on level grass, although in parts there are shallow terraces. The restaurant has views over the lake which has many watersports facilities. Used by tour operators.

Facilities

Two unisex toilet blocks per site also provide for babies and disabled people. Shop, bar and restaurant. Games and TV rooms. Pool, children's pool and water-slide (15/5-15/9). Indoor pool, sauna and fitness equipment. Fishing. Riding. Bicycle and canoe hire. Watersports. Entertainment and activities organised in high season and clubs for children and teenagers. Off site: Boat excursions from Pouilly-en-Auxois (8 km). Riding and golf 10 km. Dijon, Autun and Beaune. Bus to Dijon and Poilly-en-Auxois 300 m.

Open: 8 April - 15 October.

Directions

From A6 join A38 and exit at junction 24. Take N81 towards Arnay Le Duc (back over A6), turn left on D977 for 5 km. Fork left for Vandenesse-en-Auxois. On through village on D977 for 2.5 km, left again and site is on left.

Charges 2007

Per pitch incl. 2 persons	
and electricity	€ 21,10 - € 25,00
extra person	€ 5,10 - € 6,40
child (2-7 yrs)	€ 2,80 - € 3,50
Camping Cheques accepted.	

FR21010 Camping Louis Rigoly

Esplanade St Vorles, F-21400 Châtillon-sur-Seine (Côte d'Or)

Tel: 03 80 91 03 05. Email: tourism-chatillon-sur-seine@wanadoo.fr

This well kept, small, hillside municipal site has 54 touring pitches. Mainly individual and separated, they are on fairly flat grass, all with electricity (4/6A) with mature trees providing shelter. Adjoining the site is the municipal swimming pool complex with both indoor and outdoor pools (free in July and August). There is no shop, but the town is close. The site, which has much transit trade, can become full by evening in season.

Facilities

The main toilet block at the lower end of the site is satisfactory. A smaller heated unit behind reception contains facilities for babies, a washing machine and dryer. Facilities for disabled visitors provided in a separate block. Snack bar July/Aug. Baker calls every morning (except Tuesday). Play area. Boules. Volleyball. Motorcaravan service point. Internet access. Off site: Fishing or bicycle hire 1 km. Riding 4 km.

Open: 1 April - 30 September.

Directions

On northeast outskirts of town; site is signed from centre (steep hills approaching site, narrow roads).

Charges 2007

Per person	€ 3,25
child (under 7 yrs)	€ 1,30
pitch	€ 3,15 - € 4,50
vehicle	€ 1,35
motorcycle	€ 1,00
No credit cards.	

FR21020 Camping Municipal les Cent Vignes

10 rue Auguste Dubois, F-21200 Beaune (Côte d'Or)

Tel: 03 80 22 03 91

Les Cent Vignes is a very well kept site offering 116 individual pitches of good size, separated from each other by neat beech hedges high enough to keep a fair amount of privacy. Over half of the pitches are on grass, ostensibly for tents, the remainder on hardstandings with electricity for caravans. A popular site, within walking distance of the town centre, Les Cent Vignes becomes full mid June to early Sept. but with many short-stay campers there are departures each day and reservations can be made.

Facilities

Two modern, fully equipped and well constructed, sanitary blocks, one of which can be heated, should be large enough. Nearly all washbasins are in cabins. Dishwashing and laundry sinks. Washing machines. Shop, restaurant with takeaway (all 1/4-15/10). Playground. Sports area. TV room. Barbecue area. Off site: Bicycle hire 1 km. Fishing, golf or windsurfing 4 km. Centre of Beaune 1 km.

Open: 15 March - 31 October.

Directions

From autoroute exit 24 follow signs for Beaune centre on D2 road, camping signs to site in approx. 1 km. Well signed from other routes.

Charges 2007

Per person	€ 3,55
child (under 7 yrs)	€ 1,80
pitch	€ 4,30
electricity (10A)	€ 3,60

FR21030 Camping les Premier Pres
Route de Bouilland, F-21420 Savigny-les-Beaune (Côte d'Or)

Tel: **03 80 26 15 06**. Email: **mairie.savigny-les-beaune@wanadoo.fr**

This popular site is ideally located for visiting the Burgundy vineyards, for use as a transit site or for spending time in the town of Beaune. During the high season it is full every evening, so it is best to arrive by 4 pm. The 90 level pitches are marked and numbered, with electric hook-ups and room for an awning. A former municipal site, now privately owned. Whilst the famed wine region alone attracts many visitors, Beaune, its capital, is unrivalled in its richness of art from times gone by.

Facilities

Well kept sanitary facilities are housed in a modern building behind reception. Additional WCs and water points are conveniently placed towards the middle of the site. Table tennis. Motorcaravan service point. Torch useful. Staff are pleasant and ice can be purchased. Off site: Sunday market in the village 1 km. Beaune 7 km.

Open: 29 April - 30 September.

Directions

From A6 autoroute take exit 24 signed Beaune and Savigny-les-Beaune onto D2. Turn right towards Savigny-les-Beaune (3 km) and follow signs to site.

Charges 2007

Per person	€ 2,30
child (under 7 yrs)	€ 1,20
pitch	€ 3,20
electricity	€ 3,35
No credit cards.	

FR21040 Camping de l'Etang de Fouché
Rue du 8 Mai 1945, F-21230 Arnay le Duc (Côte d'Or)

Tel: **03 80 90 02 23**. Email: **info@campingfouche.com**

Useful as a stop en route to or from the Mediterranean or indeed for longer stays. This quite large but peaceful, lakeside site with its new bar/restaurant and swimming pool complex, can be very busy during the school holidays, and is probably better visited outside the main season. There are 190 good sized pitches, on fairly level grass and all with 10A electricity (some with water). Many are hedged and offer a choice of shade or more open aspect. In July/August there are regular activities for children and adults. A 2 km. stroll around the lake is very pleasant.

Facilities

Two new toilet blocks and third one (totally refurbished) provide all the necessary modern facilities (male and female are separate). Facilities for disabled visitors. Baby room. Washing machines and dishwashing under cover. Shop, bar, restaurant, takeaway (all 15/5-15/9). TV/games room. New small heated outdoor swimming pool. Boules. Table tennis. Playground. Off site: Town centre 800 m. Lakeside beach with playground, water slides, pedaloes, canoes.

Open: 15 April - 15 October.

Directions

From A6 (exit 24) take D981, 16 km. to the town. Turn left on D906 for approx. 400 m. and site is signed to left.

Charges 2007

Per unit incl. 2 persons and electricity	€ 15,40 - € 19,00
extra person	€ 3,50 - € 4,50
child (2-10 yrs)	€ 1,80 - € 2,50
animal	€ 1,80

FR21060 Camping les Bouleaux
11 Rue Jaune, F-21200 Vignoles (Côte d'Or)

Tel: **03 80 22 26 88**

Camping Les Bouleaux is an excellent little campsite located at Vignoles, northeast of Beaune. There are just 46 pitches, all with an electrical connection (3-6A, long leads may be required on some pitches). The large flat pitches are attractively laid out and most are separated by hedges and trees giving some shade. Monsieur Rossignal takes great pride in his campsite, keeping the grounds and facilities exceptionally clean and tidy, and by planting bright flowers near the reception. The nearest shops are 3 km.

Facilities

An older unisex building provides Turkish style WCs, while the adjacent modern block houses British style WCs (no paper). Washbasins in cabins or communal; push button controllable showers, excellent facilities for visitors with disabilities. Laundry and dishwashing sinks. No shop, but wine and basic groceries can be bought at reception. Gas exchange. Off site: Beaune 3 km. Bicycle hire, fishing or golf 3 km. Riding 6 km.

Open: All year.

Directions

Leave A6 at junction 24.1 south of Beaune. Turn right at roundabout, straight on at traffic lights (centre lane), then right at next roundabout. Cross autoroute, left (Vignoles). Follow campsite signs.

Charges 2007

Per unit incl. 2 persons and electricity	€ 14,80 - € 15,70
extra person	€ 3,50
child (under 7 yrs)	€ 2,40
No credit cards.	

FR21090 Camping de l'Arquebuse

Route d'Athée, F-21130 Auxonne (Côte d'Or)

Tel: **03 80 31 06 89**. Email: **camping.arquebuse@wanadoo.fr**

This is an all year round site located in the Northern Jura with a riverside setting on the Sâone. L'Arquebuse has 100 pitches of which 30 are occupied by mobile homes and chalets. This site has been recommended by our French agent and we plan to undertake a full inspection in 2008. Auxonne is close to both the A36 and A39 motorways and this site may prove a useful overnight stop. However, the site is well equipped with a restaurant, Le Pinocchio, and the adjacent base nautique offers a good range of leisure activities, including canoeing, windsurfing, mountain biking as well as a large swimming pool. Auxonne is an attractive town, fortified by Vauban, and is renowned as the capital of the Saone valley. The town's most famous former occupant is Napoleon and he spent two years at the Auxonne military academy. Not surprisingly there are a nunber of monuments celebrating his time here!

Facilities

Restaurant/bar. Takeaway meals. Play area. TV room. Small shop. Volleyball. Chalets for rent. Off site: Swimming pool, windsurfing, canoeing. Fishing.

Open: All year.

Directions

Take exit 5 from the A39 motorway and join the N5 in the direction of Auxonne. Site is signed to the left shortly before crossing the bridge over the Saone.

Charges 2007

Per person	€ 3,60
child (under 7 yrs)	€ 2,00
pitch	€ 3,50
electricity (10A)	€ 3,50

Camping l'Arquebuse ***

- 3 star campsite
- Open all year
- Wifi
- Washing machines and dryers
- Restaurant
- At the bank of the Saône
- Pool 10 metres from the campsite

Camping l'Arquebuse - Route d'Athée - 21130 Auxonne - Tel: 0033 (0)380 31 06 89 - Fax: 0033 (0)380 31 12 62
E-mail: camping.arquebuse@wanadoo.fr - www.campingarquebuse.com

FR21080 Camping des Sources

Avenue des Sources, F-21590 Santenay (Côte d'Or)

Tel: **03 80 20 66 55**. Email: **info@campingsantenay.com**

Santenay lies in the heart of the Côte de Beaune, a region renowned for its wine and châteaux, and within easy reach of Beaune. After a day's sightseeing or 'dégustation', there is a casino and a spa to visit. It is also alongside a long distance track for cycling, roller skating and walking, from which start a number of shorter circular routes. This relatively new site is next to the village sports and leisure area, with access to the swimming pool and paddling pool (free 1/6-31/8). There are 110 comfortable level grassy touring pitches. All have electrical connections (6A) and a water tap is never far.

Facilities

The modern toilet block contains British style WCs, washbasins and pre-set showers. Facilities for disabled people. Motorcaravan services. Laundry facilities. Gas supplies. Shop. Bar, restaurant, snack bar and takeaway (15/5-15/9). Games room. WiFi. Playground. Playing field. Table tennis. Minigolf. Boules. Skittles. Off site: Tennis courts, skateboarding. Casino 300 m. Spa 400 m. Santenay 1.5 km. Bicycle hire 1.5 km. Riding 2 km. Fishing, boat launching 4 km.

Open: 15 April - 31 October.

Directions

From Beaune take N74 (Autun and Montceau-les-Mines). After 2 km. at roundabout, continue on N74. After 11 km. pass under N6 and in 3 km. turn right into Santenay. Site signed from village. GPS: N46:54.260 E04:41.060

Charges 2007

Per unit incl. 2 persons and electricity	€ 16,50 - € 20,00
extra person	€ 3,70
child (0-7 yrs)	€ 1,90
animal	€ 1,30
electricity	€ 3,50

Check real time availability and at-the-gate prices...

www.**alanrogers**.com

FR58030 Castel Camping le Manoir de Bezolle

Mobile homes ▶ page 495

F-58110 Saint Pereuse-en-Morvan (Nièvre)
Tel: **03 86 84 42 55**. Email: **info@bezolle.com**

Manoir de Bezolle, which is under new ownership, is well situated to explore the Morvan Natural Park and the Nivernais area. It has been attractively landscaped to provide a number of different areas, some giving pleasant views over the surrounding countryside. The touring pitches of good size are on level grass with shade, some with terracing and access to electricity (10A). There are two small lakes, stocked with many fish for anglers. This site is good for families, with a range of activities provided for them.

Facilities

Two main toilet blocks (opened as needed) provide washbasins in cabins, mostly British style WCs, bath, provision for disabled visitors and a baby bath. A fibreglass unit contains two tiny family WC/basin/shower suites for rent. An older block is by the pools. Laundry. Motorcaravan services. Shop. Bar and restaurant. Pizza and takeaway (main season). Internet point. Two pools (1/6-15/9). Pony rides (July-Aug). Table tennis, minigolf and boules. Mini zoo. Fishing.

Open: 15 May - 15 September.

Directions

Site is between Nevers and Autun (midway between Châtillon-en-Bazois and Château-Chinon), just north of the D978.

Charges 2008

Contact site - under new ownership

FR58010 Camping des Bains

15 avenue Jean Mermoz, F-58360 Saint Honoré-les-Bains (Nièvre)
Tel: **03 86 30 73 44**. Email: **camping-les-bains@wanadoo.fr**

You are assured of a warm welcome at this attractive family run site, in an area of rolling countryside, woods, rivers and country villages, ideal for walking or cycling. The spacious 130 level grassed pitches (all with 6A electricity) are mostly separated by hedges with mature trees offering shade. Next to the camping is the 'thermal spa' where there are opportunities to 'take the waters' for a three day session or a full blown cure of three weeks! Reception has details. There is an excellent restaurant almost opposite the campsite entrance. This site is well situated for exploring the Morvan area in the heart of Burgundy. A canal cycle route runs for 50 km. from Vandenesse (6 km).

Facilities

Two main sanitary units have mostly British style WCs, washbasins in cabins and showers (one block may be closed in low season). Dishwashing sinks, baby bath, laundry. Facilities for disabled people. Bar provides food and a takeaway. Swimming pool, slide and paddling pool (15/6-10/10). Play area. Streams for children to fish. Table tennis. Minigolf. Games room. Children's entertainment (July/Aug). TV and DVDs. Internet access. Off site: Bicycle hire or riding 500 m. Fishing 5 km.

Open: 1 April - 25 October.

Directions

From Nevers, travel east on D978; turn right onto D985 (St Honoré-les-Bains). Site is signed on entering town. Care is needed at narrow site entrance.

Charges 2008

Per unit incl. 2 persons	€ 11,00 - € 16,00
extra person	€ 4,50
child	€ 2,85 - € 3,60
electricity (6A)	€ 3,50
dog	€ 1,50

Check real time availability and at-the-gate prices...
 www.**alanrogers**.com

FR58040 Camping l'Etang de la Fougeraie

Hameau de Champs, F-58120 Saint Léger de Fougeret (Nièvre)

Tel: **03 86 85 11 85**. Email: **campingfougeraie@orange.fr**

This is a straightforward, unpretentious camping site with no 'glitz and glamour', just a small bar and restaurant serving good quality regional meals, and a well stocked shop with local produce. There are 70 pitches, 3 chalets for rent, and only 36 electric hook-ups (6A). Some of the newer pitches are more spacious and terraced, but many of the outlying pitches are more suitable for tents that do not require electricity. On a hillside deep in the countryside of the Parc Regional du Morvan, with views of pastureland and surrounding hills, you can sit back and relax.

Facilities

At top of site, a fair distance uphill from some of the pitches. Traditional buildings with modern WCs and a heated family/disabled room (although site is not ideal for wheelchair users). More recently fitted washrooms provide modern, bright facilities. Washing machine and dryer. Shop. Bar/restaurant (1/5-30/9). Lake swimming. Fishing. Playgrounds. Caravan storage. American RVs not accepted, site not really suitable for large units. Off site: Riding 2 km. Shops and services 7 km.

Open: 1 May - 30 September.

Directions

St Léger de Fougeret is about 10 km. south of Château-Chinon. From Château-Chinon take D27 south for 3 km, then fork right on D157 for 5.5 km. to St Léger. Continue through village following signs for another 2 km. to site. GPS: N47:00.394 E03:54.292

Charges 2007

Per unit incl. 2 persons	€ 12,50
child (0-16 yrs)	€ 2,30 - € 2,60
electricity	€ 3,00

FR58050 Airotel Château de Chigy

Chigy, F-58170 Tazilly (Nièvre)

Tel: **03 86 30 10 80**. Email: **reception@chateaudechigy.com.fr**

This very spacious site (20 ha. for pitches and another 50 ha. of fields, lakes and woods) lies just at the southern tip of the Morvan Regional Natural Park. The château houses the reception and apartments for rent. Most of the facilities are nearby, and behind are 54 good sized, shaded pitches, with electricity and water supply near. There is a large woodland area with paths, next to which are 100 or so more pitches, some of up to 150 sq.m. They are open and vary from level, terraced, slightly sloping and some are bumpy. All have electrical connections and there are enough water taps.

Facilities

Two toilet blocks contain British style WCs, washbasins in cubicles, and showers. A 'portacabin' has 4 cubicles, each with toilet, washbasin and shower (can be hired as private in July/August). Facilities for disabled people and babies. Laundry facilities. Shop. Bar, restaurant and takeaway (July/Aug). Two outdoor pools (15/5-30/9). Swimming in lake. Covered pool. Games and TV rooms. Playground. Minigolf. Off site: Luzy 4 km. Riding 9 km.

Open: 26 April - 30 September.

Directions

From Luzy (34 km. southwest of Autun via the N81) take the D973 towards Bourbon Lancy. After about 4 km. the site is signed to the left.

Charges 2007

Per person	€ 5,00 - € 6,00
child (6-12 yrs)	€ 4,00 - € 5,00
pitch	€ 6,00 - € 8,00
electricity	€ 4,00

FR58060 Domaine Naturiste de la Gagère

F-58170 Luzy (Nièvre)

Tel: **03 86 30 48 11**. Email: **info@la-gagere.com**

At this spacious, attractive, well equipped campsite, you will receive a really good welcome from the enthusiastic founders of Naturocamp. There are 120 good sized level grassy pitches, some shaded, some open, of which 100 are available for tourers. Many are arranged around three sides of rectangles between hedges. There is an electricity supply to 84 pitches, 6 of which are fully serviced, but some will need leads of up to 40 m. There are plenty of water points.

Facilities

Three modern unisex toilet blocks, one heated, contain British style WCs, washbasins and pre-set showers. En-suite facilities for disabled people. Baby changing. Motorcaravan services. Laundry facilities. Shop (31/5-15/9). Bar. Restaurant with snack bar and takeaway (1/5-15/9). Satellite TV. Two heated swimming pools (one all season, the other 15/5-15/9). Sauna and health suite. Playgrounds. Table tennis. Volleyball. Boules. Bicycle hire. Only gas barbecues permitted (available for hire). Off site: Fishing 5 km. Luzy 10 km. Riding 10 km.

Open: 1 April - 1 October.

Directions

Luzy is 34 km. southwest of Autun, on the N81. Travel northeast from Luzy towards Autun. After 6 km. site is signed to the right, then reached by 3 km. of winding (often narrow) road. GPS: N46:49.010 E04:03.260

Charges 2008

Per person	€ 6,00
child (0-12 yrs0	€ 3,00
pitch	€ 13,00
electricity	€ 2,50 - € 4,00
animal	€ 3,50

Check real time availability and at-the-gate prices...

www.**alanrogers**.com

FR58100 Camping de Nevers

Rue de la Jonction, F-58000 Nevers (Nièvre)

Tel: **06 84 98 69 79**. Email: **info@campingnevers.com**

On the banks of the Loire in Nevers, facing the cathedral and the Palace of the Dukes across the river, this small site has 73 grass pitches. Of these, only two are used for caravan holiday homes and 11 are only suitable for tents The 60 touring pitches all have electricity (6/10A). This site would provide a good base for a short stay to explore the region with its famous Burgundy wines of Sancerre and Pouilly Fumé. The pitches are quite tight and are not suitable for larger units, but the site is ideal for those in motorcaravans or tents because of its proximity to the town.

Facilities

One modern toilet block has unisex toilets and showers. Bright and clean, they may be under pressure in high season. Baby area. Provision for disabled visitors. Laundry. Motorcaravan service point. Very small bar (all season) with snacks in high season. Off site: All the amenities of Nevers, including swimming pool and large stores.

Open: 14 April - 14 October.

Directions

From A6 take exit 6 and follow signs for Nevers. Shortly after town sign, site is on the right. Avoid arriving between 12.00-14.00 (site closed).

Charges 2007

Per unit incl. 2 persons and electricity	€ 16,50 - € 20,30
extra person	€ 2,00 - € 3,00

Camping Cheques accepted.

FR71010 Camping Municipal Mâcon

RN 6, F-71000 Mâcon (Saône-et-Loire)

Tel: **03 85 38 16 22**

Always useful and well cared for, this site is worth considering as a stopover or for longer stays as it is close to the main route south. The 250 good sized pitches, 190 with 6A electricity and 60 with fresh and waste water points, are on mown, flat grass, accessed by tarmac roads. Gates closed 10.00-06.30 hrs. but large units note – the security barrier has a 3.8 m. height restriction so watch those top boxes! There is a generally bright and cheerful ambience. The bar/restaurant is open all year.

Facilities

Sanitary facilities in three well maintained units, are fully equipped with British and Turkish style WCs, and washbasins in cubicles. A fourth block is modern. Facilities for disabled visitors. Laundry facilities. Excellent motorcaravan service point. Shop/tabac. Bar. Takeaway and restaurant open midday and evenings. Heated swimming and paddling pools (15/5-15/9). Good TV lounge. Playground. Off site: Supermarket. Centre of Mâcon 3 km.

Open: 15 March - 31 October.

Directions

Site is on northern outskirts of Mâcon on main N6, 3 km. from the town centre (just south of A40 autoroute junction).

Charges guide

Per unit incl. 2 persons	€ 11,60
with electricity (5A)	€ 14,10
tent pitch incl. 2 persons	€ 9,90
extra person	€ 3,10
child (under 7 yrs)	€ 1,65

FR71020 Camping le Village des Meuniers

F-71520 Dompierre-les-Ormes (Saône-et-Loire)

Tel: **03 85 50 36 60**. Email: **levillagedesmeuniers@wanadoo.fr**

In a tranquil setting with panoramic views, the neat appearance of the reception building sets the tone for the rest of this attractive site. It is an excellent example of current trends in French tourism development. This is a super site, tastefully landscaped, with a high standard of cleanliness in all areas. The main part has 113 terraced, grassy pitches, some with hardstanding, are all fairly level, 86 with electricity and ample water points. Of these, 75 also have waste water outlets. A second section, used only in high season contains 16 standard pitches. All pitches enjoy stunning views.

Facilities

Sanitary facilities mainly in an unusual, purpose-built designed hexagonal block, with modern fittings, of high standard. Smaller unit in the lower area of the site, plus more toilets in the main reception building. Motorcaravan service point in car park. Café (high season). Bar, shop and takeaway. Swimming pool complex with three heated pools and toboggan run (1/6-31/8). Children's activities organised in high season. Football. Minigolf. Internet access (credit card or telephone card). Bicycle hire. Off site: Village 500 m. for all services (banks and some shops, closed Sun/Mon). Fishing 1.5 km. Riding 10 km.

Open: 1 May - 30 September.

Directions

Town is 35 km. west of Mâcon. Follow N79/E62 (Charolles, Paray, Digoin) road and turn south onto D41 to Dompierre-les-Ormes (3 km). Site is clearly signed through village.

Charges 2007

Per person	€ 4,80 - € 8,00
child (2-13 yrs)	€ 3,20 - € 4,80
pitch incl. electricity	€ 9,60 - € 14,40
dog	€ 1,50

Camping Cheques accepted.

FR71030 Camping Municipal Saint-Vital

Rue des Griottons, F-71250 Cluny (Saône-et-Loire)

Tel: 03 85 59 08 34. Email: cluny-camping@wanadoo.fr

Close to this attractive small town (300 metres walk) with its magnificent abbey (the largest in Christendom) and next to the municipal swimming pool (free for campers), this site has 174 pitches. On gently sloping grass, with some small hedges and shade in parts, electricity is available (long leads may be needed). Some rail noise is noticeable during the day but we are assured that trains do not run 23.30 - 07.00 hrs. In high season, on Friday evenings, there is a presentation of local produce in the 'salle de reunion'.

Facilities

Two sanitary buildings provide British and Turkish style WCs, some washbasins in cubicles and controllable showers. Dishwashing and laundry facilities. Chemical toilet disposal. Shop. Off site: Fishing and bicycle hire 100 m. Riding 1 km. Wine routes, châteaux, churches. Excellent traffic free cycle path from Cluny to Givry.

Open: 1 May - 30 September.

Directions

Site is east of town, by the D15 road towards Azé and Blanot.

Charges 2007

Per unit incl. 2 persons and electricity	€ 13,95
extra person	€ 6,90
child (under 7 yrs)	€ 2,25

Camping Cheques accepted.

FR71050 Kawan Village Moulin de Collonge

F-71390 Saint Boil (Saône-et-Loire)

Tel: 03 85 44 00 32. Email: millofcollonge@wanadoo.fr

This well run, family site offers an 'away from it all' situation surrounded by sloping vineyards and golden wheat fields. It has an instant appeal for those seeking a quiet, relaxing environment. There are 61 level pitches, most with electrical hook-ups although long cables may be required. Flower arrangements are in abundance and, like the shrubs and grounds, are constantly being attended. Beyond the stream that borders the site are a swimming pool, patio and a pizzeria (also open to the public all year). A new lake, 1.8 m. deep, has been created for leisure activities.

Facilities

Well kept toilet facilities housed in a converted barn. Laundry and dishwashing sinks. Washing machine and dryer. Freezer for campers' use. Bread each morning. Basic shop (1/6-3/9). Pizzeria, snack bar (1/7-31/8). Internet cafe. Swimming pool covered - some walls can be opened in good weather. Children's playgrounds. Bouncy castle. Bicycle hire. Table tennis. Fishing. Pony trekking. Off site: Riding 4 km.

Open: 1 April - 30 September.

Directions

From Chalon-sur-Saône travel 9 km. west on the N80. Turn south on D981 through Buxy (6 km). Continue south for 7 km. to Saint Boil and site is signed at south end of the village.

Charges 2008

Per person	€ 4,50 - € 5,50
child (under 7 yrs)	€ 2,50
pitch incl. electricity	€ 9,00 - € 11,50

Camping Cheques accepted.

FR71060 Camping Caravaning Château de Montrouant

F-71800 Gibles (Saône-et-Loire)

Tel: 03 85 84 51 13. Email: campingdemontrouant@wanadoo.fr

A small, pretty site beside a lake in the grounds of an imposing chateau, in a steep valley in the Charolais hills. There is shade from mature trees and the 45 pitches (12 used by Dutch tour operators) are on reasonably flat grassy terraces, separated by hedges. Some pitches overlook the lake and some are next to a field. This site is best for smaller units as the approach roads are narrow. It quickly becomes full mid-July - mid-August and access becomes difficult with extra traffic. Motorcaravan owners should always check in advance as there may not be a suitable pitch.

Facilities

The sanitary facilities, not too well designed and with variable maintenance, are housed in a part of the château. They include washbasins in cabins. Dishwashing and laundry facilities. Basic supplies available at reception. Small open-air bar/restaurant/takeaway for evening barbecues (only open certain evenings). Swimming pool with secluded sunbathing area. Half-court tennis. Fishing. Torches useful. Off site: The village of Gibles 2 km. Riding 10 km.

Open: 1 June - 4 September.

Directions

Site is to the west of Mâcon and can be reached from A6 (Jn 29) via the N79 to Charolles (50 km). Take D25 south east for 20 km. to Gibles. The last few kilometers are quite narrow and just before village, following signs, there is a very sharp turn to the left, then continue with signs.

Charges 2007

Per person	€ 5,80
pitch with electricity	€ 10,30
vehicle	€ 5,30

Camping Cheques accepted.

FR71070 Kawan Village Château de l'Epervière

Mobile homes ▶ page 495

F-71240 Gigny-sur-Saône (Saône-et-Loire)

Tel: **03 85 94 16 90**. Email: **domaine-de-leperviere@wanadoo.fr**

This site is peacefully situated in the wooded grounds of the 16th century Château, near the village of Gigny-sur-Saône, and within walking distance of the river where you can watch the river cruise boats on their way to and from Chalon-sur-Saône. There are 160 pitches in total, of which 45 are occupied by tour operators and 5 units are for rent. The 110 touring pitches, all with 10A electricity (30 fully serviced) are in two distinct areas. The original part, close to the Château and fishing lake, has semi-hedged pitches on level ground with shade from mature trees. The centre of the second area has a more open aspect, with large hedged pitches and mature trees offering shade around the periphery – birdwatchers will love this area. A partly fenced road across the lake connects the two areas. The main château's restaurant serves regional dishes. Gert-Jan and François, and their team enthusiastically organise many activities for visitors including wine-tasting in the cellars of the château. Don't forget, you are in the Maconnais and Chalonnaise wine areas and so close to the A6.

Facilities

Two well-equipped toilet blocks include washbasins in cabins, showers, baby rooms, dishwashing and laundry areas and facilities for disabled visitors. Washing machine and dryer. Basic shop (1/5-30/9). Second restaurant with basic menu and takeaway (1/4-30/9). Converted barn houses attractive bar, large TV and games room. Unheated outdoor swimming pool (1/5-30/9) partly enclosed by old stone walls. Smaller indoor heated pool, jacuzzi, sauna, paddling pool. Play area. Outdoor paddling pool. Fishing. Bicycle hire. Off site: Riding 15 km. Golf 20 km. Historic towns of Chalon and Tournus, both 20 km. The Monday market of Louhans, to see the famous Bresse chickens 26 km.

Open: 29 March - 30 September.

Directions

From the north, A6 exit Châlon-Sud, or Tournus from the south. Take N6 to Sennecey-le-Grand, turn east on D18 and follow site signs for 6.5 km.

Charges 2008

Per unit incl. 2 persons and electricity	€ 23,40 - € 32,20
extra person	€ 5,70 - € 7,70
child (under 7 yrs)	€ 3,50 - € 5,30
dog	€ 2,40 - € 3,00

Camping Cheques accepted.

FR71140 Camping du Pont de Bourgogne

Rue Julien Leneveu, Saint Marcel, F-71380 Chalon-sur-Saône (Saône-et-Loire)

Tel: **03 85 48 26 86**. Email: **campingchalon71@wanadoo.fr**

This is a well presented site, useful for an overnight stop or for a few days if exploring the local area and you want a simple site without the frills. It does get crowded in the third week of July during the Chalon street theatre festival. There are 93 fairly small pitches with 6/10A electricity, 10 with a gravel surface. The new owners of the site plan to replace or improve the facilities in the near future, but when we visited there was a bar/restaurant with an outdoor terrace and serving a good selection of simple, inexpensive meals. Although alongside the Saône river, the site is well fenced. The staff are friendly and helpful.

Facilities

Three toilet blocks, two centrally located amongst the pitches and traditional in style and fittings, the third new and modern, alongside the reception building (including facilities for disabled visitors). Dishwashing facilities but no laundry. Modern bar/restaurant. No shop but essentials kept in the bar (bread to order). Simple play area. Bicycle hire arranged. Off site: Municipal swimming pool 300 m. Golf 1 km. Riding 10 km.

Open: 1 April - 30 September.

Directions

From A6 exit 26 (Chalon-Sud) bear right to roundabout and take N80 (Dole) straight on to roundabout at St Marcel. Turn left (fourth exit) and fork right into Les Chavannes. At central traffic lights turn right and under modern river bridge to site entrance.

Charges 2007

Per person	€ 4,30 - € 5,20
child (under 7 yrs)	€ 2,10 - € 2,80
pitch	€ 4,30 - € 5,90
electricity	€ 3,20 - € 3,90

Domaine du Château de l'Epervière

Camping caravaning - Locations ★★★★

Bourgogne du Sud

FRANCE

Chalon sur Saône - Bourgogne du Sud

FR71090 Camping Intercommunal du Lac de Saint-Point

F-71520 Saint-Point (Saône-et-Loire)

Tel: **03 85 50 52 31**. Email: **camping.stpoint@wanadoo.fr**

This site is situated just below a small reservoir on the side of a valley and forms part of an amenity complex for a group of communes. It is managed by a husband and wife team. The lake offers lake swimming, fishing and pedaloes. Situated 25 km. from the A6, this could be a useful resting place if travelling north or south. The area is renowned for its wine and cheese as well as Roman churches, abbeys and châteaux. There are 39 reasonably level, serviced touring pitches, mostly separated by low hedges, and 46 tent pitches on a sloping and partly terraced field behind. There are lifeguards at the lake in July and August and the communes organise many events during the year. When we visited there was a large competition for model speed boats.

Facilities

Two sanitary blocks, provide all the usual facilities and a washing machine. Shower and toilet/washbasin in separate cabins for campers with disabilities. Bar and snacks (1/6-30/9). Play area. Volleyball, basketball and badminton. Table tennis. Games room. Boules pitch. Mountain bike hire. Off site: Nearest shop 300 m. Tennis 4 km. Organised walks on Wednesdays 4 km. Riding 5 km.

Open: 1 April - 31 October.

Directions

Leave A6 at junction 29 and take the N79 west as far as the Cluny exit (20 km). Turn left and follow signs to Saint-Point (6 km). Site is on the south side of the village on the right.

Charges 2007

Per unit incl. 2 adults, 2 children	€ 12,50
with electricity	€ 16,00 - € 19,00
extra person	€ 2,20
extra child (up to 7 yrs)	€ 1,70
dog	€ 1,70
No credit cards.	

Camping du lac de Saint-Point Lamartine ★★★

Very comfortable campsite
Near Beaujolais and Maconnais vineyards,
Cluny (romanesque abbey)
An excellent location by a lake
Quiet, shady, family atmosphere
Bathing, fishing, Mountain biking,
playground, sportsground, games room, snack-bar...
Chalets for hire
For reservations please contact Chalets Découverts: 0033 (0) 4 73 19 11 11
Open 1st April - 31st October

Le Lac - 71520 Saint-Point
Tel: 0033 385 50 52 31 - Fax: 0033 385 50 51 92
E-mail: camping.stpoint@wanadoo.fr
http://perso.wanadoo.fr/camping.stpoint

Southern Burgundy

FR71080 Camping de l'Etang Neuf

L'Etang Neuf, F-71760 Issy-l'Évêque (Saône-et-Loire)

Tel: **03 85 24 96 05**. Email: **info@camping-etang-neuf.com**

This tranquil campsite overlooking a lake, with views of a forest and the 19th century Château de Montrifaut, is a real countryside haven for relaxation. Separated by low hedges, the 61 marked, grass pitches have 6A electricity and a small hardstanding area for a car. Young trees offer a little shade. There is a separate area for tents. There is no organised entertainment but a play area, fenced swimming and paddling pools and plenty of space will keep children happily amused. Many walks and mountain bike trails start from the site with free maps available.

Facilities

Two very clean sanitary blocks includes washbasins in cabins. Dishwashing and laundry sinks. Washing machine, ironing board and baby room. Separate shower and toilet rooms for disabled people are in the lower block. Motorcaravan services. Bar/restaurant. Bread and croissants to order. Boules pitch. TV and games room. Table tennis. Volleyball. Internet access (WiFi). Off site: Minigolf just outside the site entrance. Riding 500 m. Nearest shop 1 km. in Issy-l'Évêque.

Open: 1 May - 13 September.

Directions

From D973 (Luzy - Bourbon-Lancy) turn left onto D25 (west of Luzy) and continue for about 12 km. Turn right, D42 in centre of Issy-l'Évêque, signed to campsite. The road narrows slightly, entrance on the right.

Charges 2008

Per unit incl. 2 persons	€ 16,50 - € 18,00
with electricity	€ 16,50 - € 21,00
extra person	€ 3,00 - € 4,50
child (3-8 yrs)	€ 2,00 - € 3,00
Camping Cheques accepted.	

FR71110 Camping du Lac

Le Fourneau, F-71430 Palinges (Saône-et-Loire)

Tel: 03 85 88 14 49. Email: camping.palinges@hotmail.fr

Camping du Lac is a very special campsite and it is all due to Monsieur Labille, the owner, who thinks of the campsite as his home and every visitor as his guest. The campsite has 50 pitches in total, 16 of which have 10A electricity and 20 are fully serviced. There are 6 chalets to rent. The site is adjacent to a lake with a beach and safe bathing. Set in the countryside yet within easy reach of many tourist attractions, especially Cluny, the local Château Digoin and Mont St Vincent with distant views of Mont Blanc on a clear day.

Facilities

The central sanitary block provides all necessary facilities including those for campers with disabilities. Washing machine and fridge. Bread and croissants to order. Boules. Play area. TV room. Sports field, lake beach and swimming adjacent. Bicycle and pedalo hire in July/Aug. Motorcaravan services. Off site: Bar/snack bar outside entrance (weekends only outside 1/7-31/8). Riding 200 m. Palinges is within walking distance, cycle and walking routes, museums, cruises on canals, châteaux, 'museographical' complex.

Open: 1 April - 30 October.

Directions

Palinges is midway between Montceau les Mines and Paray le Monial. From Montceau take N70, then turn left onto D92 to Palinges. Follow campsite signs. Site is also well signed from D985 Toulon-sur-Arroux to Charolles road.

Charges 2007

Per unit incl. 2 persons with electricity	€ 16,80
extra person	€ 2,20
child (under 12 yrs)	€ 1,10
caravan, 2 axle	€ 34,00

No credit cards.

FR71120 Camping la Heronnière

Lac de Laives, F-71240 Laives (Saône-et-Loire)

Tel: 03 85 44 98 85. Email: camping.laives@orange.fr

Camping la Herronière is a quiet relaxing site on the edge of a leisure lake in pleasant rolling woodland countryside. The 90 touring pitches are good sized, grassy and level. About half have shade, with electrical connections for 88 and there are plenty of water points. The site is within easy reach of Chalon-sur-Saône, Tournus and the Chalonnais vineyards and wine route. Cluny and the former industrial towns of Le Creusot and Montceau-les-Mines are each about 40 km. away.

Facilities

Well equipped modern sanitary block includes facilities for campers with disabilities. Snack bar (June - Aug). Covered area outside reception, with bread, drinks, ice cream, basic provisions and French breakfast. Heated outdoor pool. Volleyball. Table tennis. Boules. Bicycle hire. Fishing. Marquee with TV, board games. Playground. Off site: Lake swimming, grass area, beach, bar and restaurant 300 m. Exercise circuit, canoeing, windsurfing, pedaloes. Riding 10 km. Golf 15 km. Cluny, Chalon, Le Creusot and Montceau-les-Mines. Shops, etc. at Laives 4 km.

Open: 1 May - 15 September.

Directions

Leave N6 (Chalon-sur-Saône - Mâcon) at Sennecy-le-Grand (about 18 km. south of the centre of Chalon), taking D18 west to Laives (4 km). In centre of village, take right fork and continue along D18, 4 km. to the north west.

Charges 2007

Per unit incl. 2 persons	€ 15,80 - € 17,90
with electricity	€ 19,80 - € 21,90
extra person	€ 4,20

No credit cards. Camping Cheques accepted.

FR71170 Camping Le Domaine de Louvarel

F-71480 Champagnat (Saône-et-Loire)

Tel: 03 85 76 62 71. Email: contact@domainedelouvarel.com

Situated in southern Burgundy, this site nestles near the foothills of the Jura. Because of its position beside a lake in the countryside, it is really a holiday resort in its own right, although it could also serve as an en-route stop for those travelling across Europe. There are 90 level pitches, 11 of which are used for chalets and tents for hire. The touring pitches are set in a newly landscaped area overlooking the 20 hectare lake which incorporates a separate swimming lagoon. The site is well fenced from the lake but has direct access.

Facilities

A brand new toilet block built in traditional Bresse style has new, modern fittings. Baby room. Facilities for disabled visitors. Laundry with washing machine. Motorcaravan service point. Small bar/restaurant, also open to the public (1/6-30/9, weekends in May/Oct). Bicycle hire. Play area. Off site: Village of Cuiseaux 8 km. for shopping. Fishing. Riding 8 km.

Open: 1 April - 5 November.

Directions

From the A39 take exit 9 and turn left on D972 for a short distance. Take first right to site.

Charges 2007

Per unit incl. 2 persons	€ 13,00 - € 16,00
extra person	€ 3,00
child (under 7 yrs)	€ 1,50
electricity	€ 3,00

Camping Cheques accepted.

Check real time availability and at-the-gate prices...

www.alanrogers.com

FR71180 Camping de la Chevrette

Rue de la Chevrette, F-71160 Digoin (Saône-et-Loire)

Tel: **03 85 53 11 49**. Email: **info@lachevrette.com**

This pretty town site has been leased from the municipality for the last few years by an enthusiastic couple. There are 100 neat and tidy pitches which are delineated by hedges (even the pitches for tents) and flowers decorate the site. The level pitches include 75 with electricity (10A) for touring units, 23 for tents and 2 for caravan holiday homes for rent. At the far end of the site there is direct access to the Loire river and it is this aspect that attracts campers with canoes. The adjacent town swimming pool complex is free for campers.

Facilities

Four small toilet blocks, one with cold water only, each provide separate facilities for men and women and some washbasins in cabins. Washing machine and dryer in one block. Facilities for disabled visitors. Small restaurant/snack bar in high season. Club room with TV for bad weather. Off site: Supermarkets, restaurants and bars in the town. Cycle paths along the canals. Nevers and its cathedral.

Open: 1 March - 31 October.

Directions

Digion lies off the N79 and site is well signed from all directions.

Charges 2007

Per unit incl. 2 persons and electricity	€ 14,70 - € 16,70
extra person	€ 2,00
child (under 13 yrs)	€ 1,90 - € 2,20

Double axle units are charged much more (€ 42).

FR89060 Camping les Ceriselles

Route de Vincelottes, F-89290 Vincelles (Yonne)

Tel: **03 86 42 50 47**. Email: **camping@cc-payscoulangeois.fr**

A distinctive, modern site, Les Ceriselles was created in 1998 on land adjacent to the Canal du Nivernais and is owned by a group of communities. A very level site, it has 84 pitches on grass (67 for touring), all with electricity and 38 with full services. There are also 17 mobile homes. Staff live on site and the gates are locked 22.00 - 07.00 hrs. Cars are now parked on pitches which can make the site more crowded in high season. Double axle caravans are not accepted.

Facilities

Four small heated toilet blocks each provide one WC, two washbasins in cubicles and two showers per sex, with a unit for disabled visitors in block one (nearest reception). A further block has a baby room, WCs and laundry. Restaurant (all season, hours vary acc. to demand). Clubroom with TV. Playground. Bicycle hire. Fishing. Boules. Volleyball. Basketball. Archery, canoeing and kayaking on certain days in high season. Off site: Supermarket and restaurant within walking distance. Cycle path along canal for 8 km. in either direction.

Open: 1 April - 30 September.

Directions

Vincelles is about 10 km. south of Auxerre. From A6 take 'Auxerre Sud' exit and follow N65 towards Auxerre. After 4 km. turn south on N6 towards Avallon and after 10 km. turn left on D38. Site entrance is on left just before canal.

Charges 2007

Per person	€ 2,50 - € 3,50
child (3-10 yrs)	€ 1,25 - € 1,75
pitch	€ 8,00 - € 10,00
animal	€ 1,00 - € 1,50

Reductions for longer stays.

FR89070 Camping des Platanes

41 route de la Mothe, F-89120 Charny (Yonne)

Tel: **03 86 91 83 60**. Email: **campingdesplatanes@wanadoo.fr**

Peacefully situated in the village of Charny, this is a tranquil, quiet site, yet within easy reach of the A6 autoroute and only 1.5 hours from Paris. The important archaeological site of Guédelon castle is nearby, the Chablis wines of the Yonne are ready for discovery and there are delightful walks around two local lakes. There are currently 59 level, grass pitches, all with 16A electricity. With 27 used for touring units, the remainder are used for rented holiday homes and seasonal units. There are plans to enlarge the site and to increase the number of pitches to 82.

Facilities

A modern, purpose-built, heated toilet block provides separate areas for men and women. Washbasins in cabins. Facilities for disabled visitors. Laundry. Motorcaravan service point. Bicycle and barbecue hire. Play area for under fives. Off site: Fishing, riding, walking.

Open: 15 March - 31 October.

Directions

Leave A6 at exit 18 and follow D943 towards Montargis for 14 km. Turn left on D950 and site is on right at start of village.

Charges 2007

Per unit incl. 2 persons and electricity	€ 14,50 - € 16,00
extra person	€ 3,15 - € 3,50
child (4-11 yrs)	€ 2,25 - € 2,50

Camping Cheques accepted.

MAP 9

Located to the south of Alsace, the historic province of Franche Comté boasts a varied landscape ranging from flat plains to dense woodlands, rugged dramatic mountains and limestone valleys.

Franche Comté

DÉPARTEMENTS: 25 DOUBS, 39 JURA, 70 HAUTE-SAÔNE, 90 TRE. DE BELFORT

MAJOR CITY: BESANÇON

Franche Comté is really made up of two regions. The high valley of the Saône is wide, gently rolling farmland with a certain rustic simplicity, while the Jura mountains are more rugged with dense forests, sheer cliffs, craggy limestone escarpments and torrents of clear, sparkling water gushing through deep gorges. It is for this thrilling scenery that Franche Comté is best known. Nature lovers can climb, bike and hike in the mountains or explore the hills honeycombed with over 4,000 caves. The streams and lakes provide world-class fishing. The spa towns of Salins les Bains and Besançon offer relaxation and a chance to 'take the waters'.

The region has a rich architectural heritage dating from many different periods, including medieval abbeys and châteaux and a poignant chapel in memory of the war. Roman remains, fortresses perched on cliff tops and elegant spa towns can all be explored at leisure. The region's position, bordering Switzerland and close to Germany, is reflected in its culture and also the great diversity of architectural style in the many fine buildings.

Places of interest

Arbois: Pasteur Family Home and Museum, Museum of Wine and Wine Growing.

Belfort: sandstone lion sculpted by Bartholdi; Memorial and Museum of the French Resistance.

Besançon: citadel with good views over the city.

Champlitte: Museum of Folk Art.

Dole: lovely old town, Louis Pasteur's birthplace.

Gray: Baron Martin Museum.

Luxeuil-les-Bains: Tour des Echevins Museum.

Ornans: Gustave Courbet birthplace, museum.

Ronchamp: Chapel of Notre-Dame du Haut de Ronchamp designed by Le Corbusier.

Salins-les-Bains: Salt mines and tunnels.

Sochaux: Peugeot Museum.

Cuisine of the region

Freshwater fish such as trout, grayling, pike and perch are local specialities. The region has a rare wine known as *vin de paille* as well as *vin jaune* (deep yellow and very dry) and *vin du jura*, Jura wine.

Brési: water-thin slices of dried beef; many local hams.

Gougére: hot cheese pastry based on the local *Comté* cheese.

Jésus de Morteau: fat pork sausage smoked over pine and juniper.

Kirsch: cherry flavoured liqueur.

Pontarlier: aniseed liqueur.

Poulet au vin jaune: chicken, cream and *morilles* cooked in *vin jaune*.

FR25000 Castel Camping le Val de Bonnal

Bonnal, F-25680 Rougemont (Doubs)

Tel: **03 81 86 90 87**. Email: **val-de-bonnal@wanadoo.fr**

This is an impressive, generally peaceful, well managed site in a large country estate, harmoniously designed in keeping with the surrounding countryside, well away from main roads and other intrusions. The site itself is very busy, with a wide range of activities and amenities. The 350 good sized, landscaped pitches (190 for touring) with electricity (5A) are separated by a mixture of trees and bushes. A newer area has pitches of 200-250 sq.m. but are less secluded. The main attraction must be the variety of watersports on the three large lakes and nearby river.

Facilities

Four clean toilet blocks include washbasins in cabins, suites for disabled visitors and facilities for children and babies. Dishwashing and laundry facilities. Riverside restaurant, snack bar/takeaway, bar and terrace, shop (all 20/5-8/9). Swimming pool with water slides. Well equipped play areas. Sport facilities including table tennis, boules, bicycle hire, and water sports. Fishing on the river and lake. Fitness suite. Internet access. Off site: Golf 6 km. Rougemont 3.5 km. Day trips to Switzerland.

Open: 4 May - 4 September.

Directions

From Vesoul take D9 towards Villersexel. After about 20 km. turn right in Esprels signed Val de Bonnal. Continue for 3.5 km, site is on left. From autoroute A36, exit Baume-les-Dames; go north on D50, then D486 to Rougemont and follow site signs. GPS: N47:30.211 E06:21.116

Charges 2007

Per pitch with electricity,	
incl. 2 persons	€ 35,00
extra person	€ 9,00

FR25030 Camping du Bois de Reveuge

F-25680 Huanne - Montmartin (Doubs)

Tel: **03 81 84 38 60**. Email: **info@campingduboisdereveuge.com**

Bois de Reveuge has 340 pitches including 150 mobile homes located in woodland to one side of the site. The terraced pitches have good views across the surrounding countryside and lead down to two lakes which may be used for fishing and canoeing. 190 pitches available for tourers have water and electricity and some are extra large (150-180 sq.m.). There is a good solar heated swimming pool which can be covered in cool weather and another pool with four water slides and paddling pool, supervised in high season.

Facilities

Four modern sanitary blocks with all necessary facilities (only two blocks open in low season). Facilities for disabled visitors, children and babies. Dishwashing and laundry facilities. Kiosk for basics, restaurant/pizzeria (1/5-15/9). Swimming pools. Play areas. High season 'baby club'. Video screen, music and other entertainment. Bowling alley. Shooting range. Pony club. BMX track. Aqua gym. Groups may request activities such as orienteering. Package deal includes use of canoes, archery, fishing, bicycle hire and pedaloes.

Open: 23 April - 17 September.

Directions

Site is well signed from the D50. From A36 autoroute south of the site, take exit for Baume-les-Dames and head north on D50 towards Villersexel for about 7 km. to camp signs. GPS: N47:26.472 E06:20.352

Charges 2007

Per unit incl. 2 persons	
and electricity	€ 18,00 - € 36,00

FR25050 Camping Municipal de Saint Point-Lac

8 rue du Port, F-25160 Saint Point-Lac (Doubs)

Tel: **03 81 69 61 64**. Email: **camping-saintpointlac@wanadoo.fr**

A good example of a municipal campsite in which the village takes a pride, this site is on the banks of a small lake with views to the distant hills. The 84 level, numbered pitches are on grass and 60 have electricity (16A). It is worth making a detour from the Pontarlier - Vallorbe road or for a longer stay. The village shop and restaurant are an easy 200 m. walk from the site entrance. Units over 7 metres are not accepted.

Facilities

Well maintained, older style central sanitary block (partly refurbished) has British style WCs and free hot water. Suite for disabled visitors. Dishwashing and laundry facilities. Hot snacks and takeaway in high season (July/Aug). Fishing. Off site: Lakeside walk. Motorcaravan services opposite. Beach and swimming area. Pedalo hire. Bicycle hire 5 km.

Open: 1 May - 30 September.

Directions

From north, take D437 south of Pontarlier and keep on west side of the lake to the second village (Saint Point-Lac); from south exit N57 at Les Hopitaux-Neufs and turn west to lake. GPS: N46:48.709 E06:18.186

Charges 2007

Per pitch incl. 2 persons	
and electricity	€ 12,80 - € 14,50
extra person	€ 2,00 - € 2,50

Check real time availability and at-the-gate prices...

www.alanrogers.com

FR25080 Camping les Fuvettes

Mobile homes ▶ page 495

F-25160 Malbuisson (Doubs)

Tel: **03 81 69 31 50**. Email: **lesfuvettes@wanadoo.fr**

High in the Jura and close to the Swiss border, Les Fuvettes is a well-established family site with a fine, lakeside setting on Lac Saint Point. The lake is large – over 1,000 hectares and a wide range of watersports are possible from the site, including sailing, windsurfing and pedaloes. Most equipment can be hired on site. Pitches here are grassy and of a reasonable size, separated by hedges and small trees. The new swimming pool is impressive with water slides and a separate children's pool. The site's bar/snack bar is housed in an attractive, steep roofed building and offers panoramic views across the lake. Walking and mountain biking are popular pursuits and many trails are available in the surrounding countryside. The Château de Joux is a popular excursion and the nearby Mont d'Or offers fine views towards the Alps. In high season, the site runs an entertainment and excursion programme, including a children's club.

Facilities

Three toilet blocks include facilities for babies and disabled people. Shop. Bar and snack bar. Swimming pool with waterslides and jacuzzi. Paddling pool. Play area. Minigolf. Archery. Beach volleyball. Sports pitch. Fishing (permit needed). Boat hire. Games room. Children's club in peak season. Entertainment and excursions (July/Aug). Mobile homes and chalets for rent. Off site: Sailing school. Tennis. Many cycling and walking trails. Restaurants and shops in Malbuisson (walking distance).

Open: 1 April - 30 September.

Directions

From Besançon, head south on the N57 and join the D437 beyond Pontarlier signed Lac St Point and Mouthe. This road runs along the easten shores of the lake and passes through Malbuisson. Site is at the end of the village on the right.

Charges 2007

Per unit incl. 2 persons	
and electricity	€ 19,00 - € 25,00
extra person	€ 3,40 - € 4,90
child (under 7 yrs)	€ 1,70 - € 2,70

CAMPING LES FUVETTES

F-25160 Malbuisson
France

Tél.: 03 81 69 31 50
Fax: 03 81 69 70 46

les-fuvettes@wanadoo.fr

FR25070 Domaine le Chanet

9 chemin du Chanet, F-25290 Ornans (Doubs)

Tel: **03 81 62 23 44**. Email: **contact@lechanet.com**

Located in the heart of the Jura, in the Loue valley on the edge of historic Ornans, this site is on a fairly steep slope that may not appeal to everyone. The area has plenty of outdoor activities, canoeing and kayaking, mountain biking and caving, with a fishing supplies shop just inside the site entrance. With 95 pitches (70 for tourists), some terraced, there are 50 with electric hook-ups (3-16A), including 13 with multi-services and 5 with hardstanding for motorcaravans. There are also 25 mobile homes, caravans or tents to rent on the site and some gites.

Facilities

Two blocks, one at the rear of reception building, a smaller one further up the site. The main block, recently refitted and very bright and cheerful, includes a baby bath and a small children's unit with small facilities. Shop (all season). Café, bar and takeaway (1/5-15/9). Heated outdoor pool and paddling pool (1/5-15/9). Washing facility for caving suits and equipment. Internet terminal and WiFi. Games room. Play area. Boules. Fishing. Bicycle hire. Off site: Fishing adjacent. Golf 20 km. Swimming pool (400 m. free entry) in July/Aug.

Open: 29 March - 11 November.

Directions

From Besancon take D67 to Ornans. At first and second roundabouts continue straight on towards town centre. Take first right on D241 (Chassagne St Denis), cross river, follow signs and turn right by school. Continue for 500 m. and then fork right, site is on left. GPS: N47:06.033 E06:07.677

Charges 2007

Per unit incl. 2 persons	€ 12,00 - € 17,40
extra person	€ 3,70
child (3-9 yrs)	free
electricity (3-10A)	€ 3,00 - € 3,50

Check real time availability and at-the-gate prices...

 www.**alanrogers**.com

FR70020 Camping International du Lac

Avenue des Rives du Lac, F-70000 Vesoul-Vaivre (Haute-Saône)

Tel: **03 84 76 22 86**. Email: **camping-dulac@yahoo.fr**

This is one of the better examples of a town site and is part of a leisure park around a large lake. The campsite does not have direct access to the lake as it is separated by a security fence, but access is possible at the site entrance. There are 160 good sized, level, grass pitches, all with electricity (10A). Access is from hard roads and pitches are separated by shrubs and bushes. There is a large area in the centre of the site with a children's playground.

Facilities

Three good quality toilet blocks, one heated, are well spaced around the site and provide a mix of British and Turkish style WCs, washbasins and showers. Baby room. Two superb suites for disabled visitors. Washing machines and dryers. Motorcaravan service point. Baker calls daily (July/Aug); bread ordered from reception at other times. Animation (July/Aug). Bicycle hire. TV and games room. Boules. Internet access. Off site: Bar and restaurant adjacent. 9 km. velo-rail nearby. Riding 4 km.

Open: 1 March - 31 October.

Directions

On road D457 to west of Vesoul on route to Besançon, well signed around the town.
GPS: N47:37.812 E06:07.700

Charges 2007

Per person	€ 3,40
child (under 7 yrs)	€ 1,50
pitch with electricity	€ 5,25
dog	€ 1,80

FR39010 Kawan Village la Plage Blanche

3 rue de la Plage, F-39380 Ounans (Jura)

Tel: **03 84 37 69 63**. Email: **reservation@la-plage-blanche.com**

Situated in open countryside, along the banks of the River Loue, this site has 220 good sized, marked pitches on level ground, 194 of which are for touring and all have electricity (6A). Trees provide both fully shaded and semi-shaded pitches. Approximately a kilometre of riverside and beach provides the ideal setting for children to swim and play safely in the gently flowing, shallow water – inflatables are popular and there is a canoe/kayak base. The site also has a swimming pool and paddling pool.

Facilities

Modern, well kept sanitary facilities in three unusual blocks. Dishwashing facilities. Launderette. Motorcaravan service area. Bar/restaurant with terrace (1/5-30/9). Shop (15/6-30/9). Pizzeria and takeaway (all season). TV room. Library. Swimming and children's pool. Play area. River fishing. New fishing lake. Table tennis. Entertainment and activities in July and August. Internet access. Off site: Bicycle hire 200 m. Riding 700 m. Golf, paragliding and hang-gliding 10 km.

Open: 1 April - 15 October.

Directions

Ounans is 20 km. southeast of Dole. From autoroute A36, exit Dole, then D405 to Parcey, N5 to Mont-Sous-Vaudrey (8 km) then D472 towards Pontarlier. In Ounans site is signed.
GPS: N47:00.177 E05:39.823

Charges 2007

Per person	€ 5,50
pitch	€ 7,00
electricity	€ 4,00
Camping Cheques accepted.	

FR39030 Camping Domaine de Chalain

F-39130 Doucier (Jura)

Tel: **03 84 25 78 78**. Email: **chalain@chalain.com**

Doucier lies east of Lons-le-Saunier among the wooded hills of the Jura and rather away from the main routes. This large, park-like site (804 pitches with 476 for touring) is on the edge of the Lac de Chalain surrounded by woods and cliffs. Large areas are left for sports and recreation. The lake shelves gently but then becomes deep quite suddenly. The site also has an attractive, well equipped pool complex. There are 476 touring pitches, all with electrical connections (7A) but with little shade. 46 also have water and drainage. Maximum length of caravan or motorcaravan is 6.5m.

Facilities

Nine well equipped sanitary blocks with facilities for babies and disabled people. Shops (15/5-15/9). Restaurant. Bar. Takeaway, snacks (20/6-31/8), community room. Pool complex with heated indoor pool, outdoor pools with slide, sauna and spa. Children's playgrounds. Fishing. Pedalo and bicycle hire. Wide range of sports activities including rock climbing, archery, aqua gym. TV room. Disco, entertainment, organised activities. Dogs not permitted on lake beach. Off site: Signposted walk starts at edge of site. Riding 2 km. Golf 25 km.

Open: 1 May - 20 September.

Directions

Site is best approached from the east. Leave the N5 north west of Geneva at St Laurent-en-Grandvaux. Take N78 and D39 west.
GPS: N46:39.849 E05:48.848

Charges 2007

Per unit incl. 3 persons acc.	
to location and services	€ 17,00 - € 30,00
with electricity	€ 19,80 - € 32,80
dog	€ 2,70
10% discount for couples over 60 staying more than 6 nights in low season.	

FR39040 Kawan Village la Pergola

1 rue des Vernois, F-39130 Marigny (Jura)

Tel: 03 84 25 70 03. Email: contact@lapergola.com

Close to the Swiss border and overlooking the sparkling waters of Lac de Chalain, La Pergola is a neat, tidy, terraced site set amongst the rolling hills of the Jura. It is very well appointed, with 350 pitches, 127 for touring, mainly on gravel and separated by small bushes, all with electricity, water and drainage. Arranged on numerous terraces, connected by steep steps, some have shade and the higher ones have good views over the lake. The bar/restaurant terrace is beautiful and leads to a landscaped waterfall area next to the three swimming pools and entertainment area. English is spoken. It is awaiting discovery as it is not on the main tourist routes. A tall fence protects the site from the public footpath that separates the site from the lakeside but there are frequent access gates. The entrance is very attractive and the work that Mme. Gicquaire puts into the preparation of the flowerbeds is very evident. The terrace features grape vines for welcome shade and a colourful array of spectacular flowers.

Facilities

Latest sanitary block serving the lower pitches is well appointed. Slightly older blocks serve the other terraces. Facilities for disabled visitors on lower terraces. Shop (1/6-18/9). Bar. Self service restaurant. Pizzeria/takeaway. Pool complex, two pools heated. Good play areas and children's club. Archery. Boules. Pedaloes, canoes and small boats for hire. Organised programme in high season, evening entertainment with disco twice weekly. Internet access. Off site: Hang-gliding 2 km. Riding 3 km.

Open: 1 April - 15 October.

Directions

Site is 2.5 km. north of Doucier on D27 next to Lake Chalain. It is signposted from Marigny. GPS: N46:40.621 E05:46.851

Charges 2008

Per unit incl. 2 persons	
and electricity	€ 21,00 - € 36,00
extra person	€ 4,40 - € 6,50
child (2-7 yrs)	free - € 5,50
animal	€ 4,00

Various special offers available. Camping Cheques accepted.

FR39050 Yelloh! Village Fayolan

B.P. 52, F-39130 Clairvaux-les-Lacs (Jura)

Tel: 04 66 73 97 39. Email: info@yellohvillage-fayolan.com

This modern site, backed by wooded hills, is situated on the shores of Le Petit Lac about a mile from the town of Clairvaux-les-Lacs amid the lakes and forests of the Jura. The neat, tidy site is in two parts, with pitches from 80-100 sq.m. either on terraces overlooking the lake or on the flatter area near the shore. There are electrical connections (6A) and 200 pitches fully serviced. The upper part has little shade until the young trees grow but there is some on the lower section. Used by tour operators (130 pitches).

Facilities

Four modern well equipped toilet units. Baby room. Washing and drying machines. Ironing facilities. Shop. New restaurant. Bar. Snack bar/pizzeria and takeaway. Two good swimming pools (heated from mid May). Fitness centre, covered pool, sauna, massage and outdoor pool with slide. Entertainment area. Playground. Organised activities. Fishing. Entertainment. Internet access. Off site: Bicycle hire 800 m. Riding 15 km.

Open: 30 April - 6 September.

Directions

Clairvaux-les-Lacs is on the N78 between Lons-le-Saunier and Morez. In Clairvaux follow signs for 'Lacs Campings' and Fayolan. GPS: N46:33.866 E05:45.367

Charges 2008

Per unit incl. 2 persons	
and electricity	€ 17,00 - € 36,00
extra person	€ 5,00 - € 6,50
child (3-11 yrs)	€ 2,00 - € 4,00

FR39080 Kawan Village Domaine de l'Epinette

15 rue de l'Epinette, F-39130 Chatillon (Jura)

Tel: **03 84 25 71 44**. Email: **info@domaine-epinette.com**

This site is set in charming wooded countryside on land sloping down to the river Ain, which is shallow and slow moving. There are 150 grassy pitches, 126 are available for touring units, some slightly sloping. These are arranged on terraces and separated by hedges and young bushes and trees, about half being shaded. Nearly all have electricity hook-ups, although some long leads are needed. There is an attractive swimming pool, paddling pool and surrounds. An activity club for children takes place in July/August. Guided canoe trips on the river start and finish at the campsite. This quiet site has the same owners as FR39040, but is more recently established and less than half the size. Four hard standing pitches.

Facilities	Directions
Two modern toilet blocks. Unit for disabled visitors. Baby bath. Dishwashing and laundry sinks. Washing machine and dryer. Small shop for basics. Snack bar and takeaway (evenings). New reception, bar, TV room and shop. Playground. Table tennis under marquee. Boules. Direct access to river for swimming and canoeing. Off site: Riding 6 km. Golf 25 km. Shops, etc. in Doucier 6 km.	From Lons-le-Saunier take D471 eastwards towards Champagnole. After about 8 km. fork right onto D39 towards Doucier. After about 11 km. at Chatillon turn right onto D151 south towards Blye. Site is less than 2 km. on the left.

Open: 9 June - 15 September.

Charges 2007

Per unit incl. 2 persons and electricity	€ 16,00 - € 26,50
extra person	€ 3,50 - € 4,50
child (2-7 yrs)	free - € 3,00
animal	€ 2,00

Camping Cheques accepted.

Camping Domaine de L'Épinette ☆☆☆

Domaine de l'Épinette
15, rue de l'Épinette - 39130 Châtillon
Tel. : 03 84 25 71 44
E-mail : info@domaine-epinette.com
www.domaine-epinette.com

FR39060 Camping la Marjorie

640 boulevard de l'Europe, F-39000 Lons-le-Saunier (Jura)

Tel: **03 84 24 26 94**. Email: **info@camping-marjorie.com**

La Marjorie is a spacious site set on the outskirts of the spa town of Lons-le-Saunier. Bordering one area of the site are open fields and woodlands. It is a former municipal site with 200 level pitches, 185 for tourists. Mainly on hardstanding they are separated by well trimmed hedges interspersed with tall trees which gives privacy plus a little shade at some part of the day. There are 130 pitches with electricity (6/10A) and 37 are fully serviced. There is a cycle path from the site into town (2.5 km) and a mountain bike track behind the site.

Facilities	Directions
Three well maintained toilet blocks, two modern and heated, Baby baths, facilities for disabled people. Small shop (15/6-31/8). Small bar with takeaway meals (all 15/6-31/8). TV room, table tennis, small play area, boules pitch, volleyball and football field. Archery, canoeing and riding. Motorcaravan service point (charge). Off site: Swimming pool 200 m. Bus stop 400 m. Restaurants 500 m. Bicycle hire 1.5 km. Fishing 3 km. Riding 5 km. Golf 6 km. Caves and waterfalls 17 km.	Site is off N83 Lons-le-Saunier - Besancon road. From south site signed from first roundabout on the outskirts of Lons. Approaching from Bescancon on N83, follow signs for Club Nautique on outskirts of Lons. Take care entering site. GPS: N46:41.053 E05:34.096

Open: 1 April - 15 October.

Charges 2007

Per unit incl. 2 persons	€ 12,60 - € 15,40
with electricity (6A)	€ 14,40 - € 17,90
tent pitch incl. 2 persons	€ 10,00 - € 17,90

FR39120 Camping Beauregard

F-39130 Mesnois (Jura)

Tel: **03 84 48 32 51**. Email: **reception@juracampingbeauregard.com**

A hillside site on the edge of a small village with views of the rolling countryside, Beauregard has 192 pitches. A fenced oval swimming pool and a circular children's pool provide the main attraction on sunny days. Mobile homes and tents for rent leave around 155 for tourists, all with 6A electricity (long leads may be necessary). The tarmac roads are narrow in places, and many pitches are compact and could be more level. Larger outfits may have difficulty fitting everything on the pitch and with levelling, although the newer pitches on the lower level could be more suitable (but no shade). There are two adventure style playgrounds and bouncy castles for children, plus tennis and boules courts. Just across the road from the site entrance (and under the same ownership) is a good restaurant serving regional dishes, bar and takeaway.

Facilities

Three toilet blocks fairly evenly distributed around the site make a good provision, although the newest one on the lower section is only opened in peak season. Generally modern facilities, some Turkish toilets. The WCs at the block nearest the pool suffer from overuse by unsupervised children. Baby room and facilities for disabled campers. Outdoor pool (mid June - end August). Play areas. Off site: Restaurant bar and takeway (1/4-30/9) adjacent to site. Fishing 500 m. Riding 5 km. Boat launching 2 km. Other shops, bank and ATM and services in Pont de Poitte 2 km.

Open: 1 April - 30 September.

Directions

From Lons-le-Saunier (easily accessed from A39) take N78 southeast towards Clairvaux-les-Lacs. After about 17 km. in Thuron (before Pont-de-Poitte) turn left on D151 to Mesnois. Site is 1 km. on left by road junction. GPS: N46:35.980 E05:41.293

Charges 2008

Per unit incl. 2 persons	€ 17,20 - € 21,50
extra person	€ 3,28 - € 4,10
child (2-8 yrs)	€ 2,24 - € 2,80
electricity	€ 3,00

Less 20% in low season.

Camping Beauregard

2 • Grande Rue • F-39130 • France • Tél.: 03 84 48 32 51 • Fax: 03 84 48 32 51

FR39090 Camping les Bords de Loue

Chemin du val d'Amour, F-39100 Parcey (Jura)

Tel: **03 84 71 03 82**. Email: **contact@jura-camping.com**

This spacious campsite, beside the river Loue, enables canoeing, boating and fishing to be enjoyed direct from the site. It is also at the western end of the Val d'Amour, where the attractive countryside and villages make for pleasant walking and cycling. The site has 284 grass pitches, 216 are for touring. Some are undulating and/or slightly sloping, and only a few have shade. All have electricity (6A), some long leads. Some pitches at the western end of the site are some distance from the nearest water tap. In July/August there are organised events and activities, including pony rides.

Facilities

Three modern toilet blocks with all the necessary facilities, including those for disabled people. Motorcaravan services. Washing machines and dryers. Gas supplies. Bar (all season). Snack bar and takeaway (July/Aug). Satellite TV. Swimming pool and paddling pool (1/5-1/9). Playground. Tennis (free outside July/Aug). Archery. Volleyball. Boules. Off site: Parcey 1 km. with shops, bar, ATM. Golf 1.5 km. Riding 4 km. Bicycle hire 7 km.

Open: 15 April - 10 September.

Directions

Parcey is 8 km. south of Dole. From north, leave A39 exit 6 (Dole). Go southwest for 1 km. on N75/N5 (Beaune and Châlon-sur-Saône). At roundabout, turn left (southeast) (N5) to Parcey. Site well signed.

Charges 2007

Per person	€ 4,30
child (0-7 yrs)	€ 2,00
pitch	€ 4,90
electricity (6A)	€ 2,40
dog	€ 1,20

Check real time availability and at-the-gate prices...

 www.alanrogers**.com**

FR39100 Camping Trélachaume

Lac de Vouglans, F-39260 Maisod (Jura)

Tel: **03 84 42 03 26**. Email: **info@camping-trelachaume.com**

This spacious campsite is situated in an attractive part of the Jura. The site has 180 pitches of varying sizes up to large, of which 153 are for touring units. Of these, 90 have electricity (6/16A), long leads needed. There is no restaurant or bar, etc. on the site, but a good bar with snacks and a takeaway operates 20 metres from the site entrance (1/6-31/8). In high season there are organised events and activities, many of them in the municipal 'salle des fêtes' on the edge of the site.

Facilities

Renovated washblocks. Three modern toilet blocks contain British style WCs, washbasins and pre-set showers. En-suite facilities for disabled people. Baby bathing room. Washing machine, spin dryer and ironing board. Shop for basics (1/6-31/8). Gas supplies. Paddling pool (20/6-31/8). Playground. Table tennis. Charcoal barbeques are permitted. Newly planted trees to create more shaded areas. Off site: Bathing, boating, canoeing, sailing and fishing 1 km. Bus stop 2 km. Riding 3 km.

Open: 22 April - 10 September.

Directions

From the south, at the north end of the A404 motorway, continue north towards Orgelet and Lons-le-Saunier on the D31, D436, D27, and D470. Just before Charchilla go left on D301 to Maisod and follow site signs.

Charges 2007

Per unit incl. 2 persons	€ 11,90 - € 13,70
extra person (over 4 yrs)	€ 3,30
electricity	€ 2,70
dog	€ 1,50

FR39110 Camping le Moulin

Patornay, F-39130 Clairvaux-les-Lacs (Jura)

Tel: **03 84 48 31 21**. Email: **contact@camping-moulin.com**

Patornay is a pleasant village, just by the river Ain where it starts to widen on its way to the Lac de Vouglans. This well equipped 5 ha. campsite lies right on the river bank, with direct access for boating, canoeing and fishing. Of the 160 touring pitches, 120 are between well trimmed hedges and trees, with electricity (6A), and water taps very near. The other 40 are in a more natural area, where there is no electricity and water taps are a bit further apart. In July/August the site arranges activities and events for children and for all.

Facilities

Two modern heated toilet blocks. Facilities for disabled people. Baby room. Motorcaravan services. Washing machines and dryers. Basic shop. Bar, snack bar, takeaway and terrace (29/5-31/8). Satellite TV. Internet. Games room. Swimming pool with slides and flume, paddling pool (29/5-31/8). Playground. Sports field. Table tennis. Volleyball. Boules. Off site: Pont-de-Poitte 200 m. with supermarket, shops, restaurants, bars, takeaway, ATM, bus stop. Bicycle hire 1 km. Riding 4 km. Sailing 10 km.

Open: 30 April - 7 September.

Directions

From Lons-le-Saunier, take the N78 in a southeasterly direction to Pont-de-Poitte. After about 17 km. in village, cross bridge over River Ain, towards Clairvaux-les-Lacs. After 100 m., turn left at site sign and immediately fork left.

Charges 2007

Per unit incl. 2 persons	€ 16,00 - € 26,00
tent pitch	€ 13,00 - € 21,00
extra person	€ 5,00
child (2-13 yrs)	€ 2,50

FR90000 Camping l'Etang des Forges

11 rue Béthouart, F-90000 Belfort (Tre.-de-Belfort)

Tel: **03 84 22 54 92**. Email: **contact@campings-belfort.com**

Belfort (known as the City of the Lion) is a historic fortified town with much history. Although 178 pitches are marked out, this very spacious site only uses 90 of them, and you should always be able to find room here. The pitches are all on level, mostly open ground divided by bushes. A few trees around one end give a little shade to some pitches and there are electricity hook-ups (to all pitches and a good supply of water taps). The reception building also contains a small shop and café.

Facilities

A single modern sanitary building (heated in cool weather) provides washbasins in cubicles, a suite for disabled people, dishwashing and laundry sinks, a washing machine and dryer. Motorcaravan services. Outdoor swimming pool (10/6-9/9). Volleyball. Table tennis. Small playground. TV Room. Shop and café (1/7-31/8). Internet terminal. Off site: Large supermarket is on edge of town on the Mulhouse road.

Open: 7 April - 30 September.

Directions

Site is northeast of town centre towards Offemont, adjacent to the lake and sports facilities (well signed). GPS: N47:39.200 E06:51.866

Charges 2007

Per person	€ 3,50 - € 3,80
child (4-9 yrs)	€ 2,50 - € 3,10
pitch	€ 7,50 - € 8,50
electricity	€ 3,00
animal	€ 1,00 - € 1,50
Camping Cheques accepted.	

Check real time availability and at-the-gate prices...

www.**alanrogers**.com

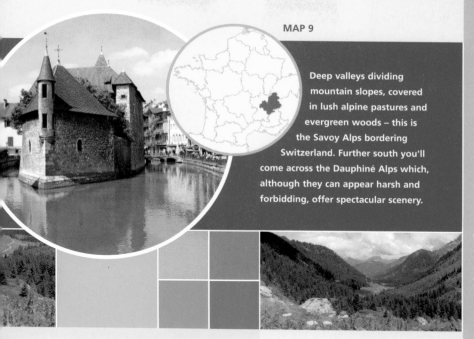

MAP 9

Deep valleys dividing mountain slopes, covered in lush alpine pastures and evergreen woods – this is the Savoy Alps bordering Switzerland. Further south you'll come across the Dauphiné Alps which, although they can appear harsh and forbidding, offer spectacular scenery.

DÉPARTEMENTS: 38 ISÈRE, 73 SAVOIE, 74 HAUTE-SAVOIE

MAJOR CITY: GRENOBLE

Lying between the Rhône Valley and the Alpine borders with Switzerland and Italy are the old provinces of Savoie and Dauphiné. This is an area of enormous granite outcrops, deeply riven by spectacular glacier hewn and river etched valleys. One of the world's leading winter playgrounds there is also a range of outdoor activities in the summer. Despite development, great care has been taken to blend the old with the new and many traditional villages still retain their charm and historical interest. For many, it is an opportunity to escape the crowds and enjoy some clean air, unusual wildlife, stunning views, hidden lakes and sometimes isolated villages in spectacular mountain settings.

From Chambéry, north to the shores of Lac Léman (Lake Geneva) are many towns and villages that, since Roman times, have attracted visitors to take the waters. Aix-les-Bains, Evian and Annecy were three major lakeside spa resorts of the Victorians; while Chamonix and Grenoble attracted the 19th century travellers who pioneered modern skiing and 'alpinism'. To the north is the region of Chartreuse famous for its monastery and liqueur!

Places of interest

Aix-les-Bains: spa resort on the Lac du Bourget, boat excursions to the Royal Abbey of Hautecombe.

Albertville: 1992 Winter Olympics, museum, now has an active night-life!

Annecy: canal-filled lakeside town, 12th century château, old quarter.

Bourg-St-Maurice: centre of Savoie café society.

Chambéry: old quarter, Dukes of Savoie château, Savoie museum.

Chamonix: site of first Winter Olympics in 1924, world capital of mountain climbing.

Evian-les-Bains: spa and casino on Lake Geneva.

Grenoble: University city, Fort de la Bastille.

Cuisine of the region

Plat gratiné applies to a wide variety of dishes; in the Alps this means cooked in breadcrumbs.

Farcement (Farçon Savoyard): potatoes baked with cream, eggs, bacon, dried pears and prunes.

Féra: a freshwater lake fish.

Fondue: hot melted cheese and white wine.

Gratin Dauphinois: potato dish with cream, cheese and garlic.

Gratin Savoyard: another potato dish with cheese and butter.

Lavaret: a freshwater lake fish, like salmon.

Longeole: a country sausage.

Lotte: a burbot, not unlike an eel.

Tartiflette: potato, bacon, onions and Reblochon cheese.

FR74010 Camping les Deux Glaciers

80 Route des Tissiéres, les Bossons, F-74400 Chamonix (Haute-Savoie)

Tel: 04 50 53 15 84. Email: glaciers@clubinternet.fr

A pleasant and well kept, naturally laid out, small mountain site for summer and winter use. Les Deux Glaciers lies at the foot of two glaciers and is close to the well known ski resort of Chamonix. The site has 135 terraced pitches, 100 for touring, with electricity (2-10A). Rock pegs are advised. It is pleasantly laid out with trees and floral displays. There are magnificent views of Mont Blanc Range and the Aiguille-de-Midi. There is significant road noise. Reservations are not taken in summer. Not ideal for large outfits and those with walking difficulties.

Facilities

Two small, heated, sanitary blocks, have dated facilities. Facilities for disabled visitors. Laundry facilities. Restaurant/takeaway. Small play area. WiFi. Off site: Shop 500 m. Fishing 600 m. Bicycle hire or riding 3 km. Golf 4 km. Chamonix, swimming, hang gliding, cable cars, ski lifts, funicular railway all within 3 km. Walks and bike rides. Bus to Chamonix and other villages. Fantastic skiing in winter.

Open: All year (excl. 15 November - 14 December).

Directions

From Geneva (N205) take second exit for Les Bossons; site shortly on right. From Chamonix turn right at sign for Les Bossons, left at T-junction and pass under the main road; site shortly on right. GPS: N45:54.123 E06:50.233

Charges 2007

Per unit incl. 2 persons	€ 14,00
extra person	€ 5,00
electricity (2-10A; higher in winter)	€ 2,30 - € 7,00

FR74030 Camping Belvédère

8 route du Semnoz, F-74000 Annecy (Haute-Savoie)

Tel: 04 50 45 48 30. Email: camping@ville-annecy.fr

This municipal site is the nearest campsite to Annecy which can be reached in 15 minutes by a quiet, but steep footpath. There are 120 good sized pitches, 106 of which are for touring and 80 have electricity (10A). Many have part hardstanding and are fully serviced and some grass pitches are reserved for tents (rock pegs essential). Space may be limited if the site is busy. Tall pines and a steep hillside to the west provide a backdrop to the site and a variety of trees provide some shade. This site is ideally placed for visiting Annecy but is not suitable for large units.

Facilities

Three modern toilet blocks, one heated in cold weather, with washroom for visitors with disabilities. Laundry facilities. Small shop, bar and takeaway (June-Aug). Games/wet weather room. Playground. Bicycle hire. Communal area for barbecues. Sporting activities. Bus to Annecy in July/Aug. Off site: Boat launching 600 m. Lakeside beach 800 m. Swimming pool 800 m. Bicycle hire 1 km. Boat trips. Lakeside cycle track.

Open: 4 April - 10 October.

Directions

Leave A41, Annecy Sud, take N508 to Annecy. After some traffic lights descend a hill looking for 'H' and 'Silence' signs. Turn right up hill, signed Le Semnoz. Fork right, then turn left, signed Camping, site shortly on right.

Charges 2007

Per unit incl. 2 persons	€ 14,20 - € 18,50
extra person	€ 4,10 - € 4,90
electricity (10A)	€ 2,60

FR74040 Camp de la Ravoire

Bout-du-Lac, route de la Ravoire, F-74210 Doussard (Haute-Savoie)

Tel: 04 50 44 37 80. Email: info@camping-la-ravoire.fr

La Ravoire is a high quality site, 800 m. from Lake Annecy, noted for its neat and tidy appearance and the quietness of its location in this popular tourist region. The 112 level pitches are on well mown grass with some shade and separated by small shrubs and some hedging. The 90 pitches for touring (21 with water and drain) have electricity (5-15A). Those looking for a campsite in this attractive region without the 'animation' programmes that many French sites feel are necessary, will find this a peaceful base.

Facilities

Very good toilet block, facilities for disabled people, laundry room, washing machines, dryers and irons. Bar, snack bar, takeaway. Shop. Outdoor pool, water slide and paddling pool. All open all season. Good play area. Sports areas. Off site: Fishing, boat launching, bicycle hire 1 km. Riding 6 km. Golf 8 km. Good restaurants on the lakeside, shops in Doussard and Annecy. Cycle track (20 km) almost to Annecy passes close by. Canyoning and hang-gliding close. Boat trips.

Open: 15 May - 15 September.

Directions

Site signed from N508 Annecy - Albertville road. Approx. 13 km. south of Annecy, at traffic lights in Brédannaz, turn right (site signed) and then immediately left. Site on left in about 1 km. GPS: N45:48.147 E06:12.579

Charges 2007

Per unit incl. 2 persons, water and electricity (5A)	€ 29,30 - € 32,60
incl. 1 child under 10 yrs	€ 30,10 - € 33,40
extra person	€ 6,00
Camping Cheques accepted	

FR74070 Camping Caravaning l'Escale

F-74450 Le Grand-Bornand (Haute-Savoie)

Tel: **04 50 02 20 69**. Email: **contact@campinglescale.com**

You are assured a good welcome from the Baur family at this beautifully maintained and picturesque site, situated at the foot of the Aravis mountain range. The 149 pitches, 122 of which are for touring, are of average size, part grass, part gravel and separated by trees and shrubs, giving a little shade. All pitches have electricity (2-10A) and 86 are fully serviced. Rock pegs are essential. The village (200 m. away) has all the facilities of a resort with activities for summer or winter holidays. In summer a variety of well signed footpaths and cycle tracks provide forest or mountain excursions. In winter the area provides superb facilities for down-hill and cross-country skiing.

Facilities

Good toilet blocks (heated in winter) have all the necessary facilities. Drying room for skis and boots. Superb complex with interconnected indoor (all season) and outdoor pools and paddling pools (10/6-31/8). Cosy bar/restaurant with local specialities (all season). Play area. Tennis. Table tennis. Torches essential. WiFi. Off site: Village (5 minutes walk), shops, bars, restaurants, archery, paragliding, hang-gliding. 150 km. of signed walks. Activities organised for children and adults. Ice skating, ice hockey in winter. Bicycle hire 200 m. Riding and golf 3 km.

Open: 15 December - 22 April, 20 May - 24 September.

Directions

From Annecy follow D16 and D909 towards La Clusaz. At St Jean-de-Sixt, turn left at roundabout D4 signed Grand Bornand. Just before village fork right signed Vallée de Bouchet and camping. Site entrance is on right at roundabout in 1.2 km. GPS: N45:56.412 E06:25.692

Charges 2007

Per unit incl. 2 persons	€ 16,00 - € 22,80
with services	€ 17,50 - € 25,80
extra person	€ 4,80 - € 5,80
electricity (2-10A)	€ 3,70 - € 8,50

Camping Cheques accepted.

Camping Caravaneige L'Escale

74450 Le Grand Bornand - France - Tel: +33 (0)4 50 02 20 69 - Fax: +33 (0)4 50 02 36 04
Email: contact@campinglescale.com - www.rentlescale.com

FR74060 Kawan Village la Colombière

Saint Julien-en-Genevois, F-74160 Neydens (Haute-Savoie)

Tel: **04 50 35 13 14**. Email: **la.colombiere@wanadoo.fr**

La Colombière, a family owned site, is on the edge of the small village of Neydens, a few minutes from the A40 autoroute and only a short drive from Geneva. It is an attractive site with only 104 pitches (82 for touring with electricity 5-15A), all reasonably level and separated by fruit trees, flowering shrubs and hedges. Neydens makes a good base for visiting Geneva and the region around the lake. It is a very pleasant, friendly site where you may drop in for a night stop – and stay for several days! The site is open all year for motorcaravans and suitable caravans. English is spoken. A 'Sites et Paysages' member.

Facilities

Good sanitary blocks (one heated) include facilities for disabled people. Motorcaravan services. Fridge hire. Gas supplies. Good bar/restaurant (all season) and terrace overlooking the pool (1/5-15/9). New heated, indoor pool, spa pool and jacuzzi (21/3-11/11). Internet (WiFi). Games room. Organised visits and activities. Bike hire. Archery. Boules. Playground. Off site: Fishing, riding 1 km. Golf 7 km. Lake beach and windsurfing 12 km. Switzerland 3 km. St Julien-en-Genevois 5 km.

Open: 20 March - 11 November
(all year for motorcaravans and suitable caravans).

Directions

From A40 south of Geneva take exit 13 and then N201 towards Annecy. After 2 km. turn left into village of Neydens and follow campsite signs to site in just over 1 km. GPS: N46:07.214 E06:10.548

Charges 2007

Per unit incl. 2 persons	€ 16,00 - € 25,50
extra person	€ 3,70 - € 5,70
child (2-12 yrs)	€ 3,50 - € 4,50
electricity (5/6A)	€ 4,70
dog	€ 2,00

Camping Cheques accepted.

FR74100 Village Camping Europa

1444 route Albertville, F-74410 Saint Jorioz (Haute-Savoie)

Tel: 04 50 68 51 01. Email: info@camping-europa.com

You will receive a friendly welcome at this quality, family run site. The flowers, shrubs and trees are lovely and everything is kept neat and tidy. There are 210 medium to large size pitches (110 for touring) on level stony grass. Rock pegs are advised. All pitches have electricity (6A) close by and 18 have water and drainage. The static units are separated from the touring section by high hedges giving the impression that you are on a small site. There may be some noise from the adjacent main road. This is a good base from which to tour the Lake Annecy area. Europa should suit those families who like to make their own entertainment although there are some activities for children and a weekly soirée (high season) and a pool complex with slides, jacuzzi, cascade and paddling pool.

Facilities

Two very good toilet blocks, recently modernised to a high standard, have all the necessary facilities including some large cubicles with both showers and washbasins. Motorcaravan service point. Good bar and restaurant (1/6-31/8). Swimming pool complex (entry bracelet € 2 each). Volleyball. Basketball. Football. Bicycle hire. Internet access. Miniclub. Some musical evenings. Off site: Fishing 300 m. Boat launching 500 m. Lakeside beach 2 km. Riding 3 km. Golf 8 km. Lakeside bike ride (40 km. long). St Joriz. Canyoning and hang-gliding nearby. Boat trips.

Open: 30 April - 13 September.

Directions

From Annecy take N508 signed Albertville. Site is well signed on the right on leaving Saint-Jorioz. GPS: N45:49.480 E06:10.550

Charges 2007

Per unit incl. 2 persons	
and electricity	€ 20,80 - € 31,80
serviced pitch	€ 22,50 - € 34,50
extra person	€ 4,70 - € 5,90
child (2-6 yrs)	€ 2,60 - € 5,10
dog	€ 3,00

Village Camping EUROPA

Charming site, 400 meters from the lake of Annecy – 1 heated swimming pool, 1 water complex (with 5 water slides, waterfalls, children's games, jacuzzi, lagoon) – Restaurant with specialities of the Savoy region Quality installations – Chalets and mobile homes to let – Bikes for hire – Situated next to a cycling track.

Village Camping EUROPA
1444, route d'Albertville 74 410 ST – JORIOZ
Tel. 33 (0) 4 50 68 51 01 Fax. 33 (0) 4 50 68 55 20
E-mail : info@camping-europa.com
www.camping-europa.com

FR74090 Camping le Plan du Fernuy

Route des Confins, F-74220 La Clusaz (Haute-Savoie)

Tel: 04 50 02 44 75. Email: info@plandufernuy.com

This neat and open site has separate summer and winter seasons. It has 80 average sized, stony, grassy, pitches, 58 for tourists with electricity and 22 fully serviced. There are good mountain views but little shade, rock pegs essential. The site's crowning glory is an excellent indoor heated pool with large windows looking out on to the mountains. This is a good site for skiing in winter (with access to a ski-tow from the campsite and a free bus to other centres). In summer it is a good base for walking and cycling with other sporting opportunities nearby.

Facilities

Very good heated sanitary provision. Baby room. Facilities for disabled visitors. Washing machine and dryer. Drying room for ski clothing and boots. Motorcaravan services. Small shop and bar, snacks, takeaway. Games, TV room. Heated indoor pool and paddling pool. Skiing from site and ski excursions organised. Off site: Shops and restaurants in village 2 km. Riding 800 m. Golf, bicycle hire and fishing 1.5 km.

Open: 4 June - 4 September and 18 December - 24 April.

Directions

From Annecy take D909 to La Clusaz and at roundabout turn towards Les Confins. Site is on right after 2 km. (well signed). It is best to avoid using D909 from Flumat particularly with caravans or motorhomes. GPS: N45:54.567 E06:27.114

Charges guide

Per pitch incl. 2 persons	
with electricity (4-13A)	€ 17,00 - € 20,50
extra person	€ 20,70 - € 27,70
	€ 5,00

Winter prices are higher and may be quoted per week only.

FR74140 Camping les Dômes de Miage

197 route des Contamines, F-74170 Saint Gervais-les-Bains (Haute-Savoie)

Tel: 04 50 93 45 96. Email: info@camping-mont-blanc.com

Saint Gervais is a pretty spa town in the picturesque Val-Monjoie valley and this site is 2 km. from its centre. It is 22 km. west of Chamonix and centrally located for discovering this marvellous mountain region. Nestled among the mountains, this sheltered, well equipped site provides 150 reasonably sized, flat grassy pitches. About half have shade and there are 100 with electricity points (3-10A). The remainder on terraced ground are used for tents. Third generation hosts, Stéphane and Sophie, will welcome you to the site and their passion for this area at the foot of Mont Blanc is infectious. There is no on-site entertainment programme, but a wealth of information about the area and activities available nearby is provided at reception where they will help you plan your itinerary. The region is good for walking and there is a bus service into Saint Gervais, from where there is a frequent shuttle bus to its spa and a tramway to the Mont Blanc range. There is also good public transport between the town and Chamonix.

Facilities

Two sanitary blocks, one heated, with a suite for disabled visitors and baby room. Washing machines, dryer. Motorcaravan services. Small basic shop. Bar/restaurant. TV room, library, ironing board. Excellent playground. Playing field with table tennis, volleyball, basketball, goal net. New motorcaravan service point. Off site: Fishing 100 m. Bicycle hire 1 km. Riding 7 km. Shops, etc. and outdoor swimming pool in St Gervais.

Open: 1 May - 21 September.

Directions

From St Gervais take D902 towards Les Contamines and site is on left after 2 km.
GPS: N45:52.423 E06:43.205

Charges 2008

Per unit incl. 1 or 2 persons	€ 16,50 - € 20,50
extra person	€ 3,00 - € 4,00
child (2-10 yrs)	€ 2,50 - € 3,50
electricity (3/6A)	€ 2,90 - € 3,90
dog	€ 2,00

Camping Cheques accepted.

FR74110 Camping le Taillefer

1530 route de Chaparon, F-74210 Doussard (Haute-Savoie)

Tel: 04 50 44 30 30. Email: info@campingletaillefer.com

This excellent, small site is family run and friendly with stunning views over the lakeside mountains. It is only 1.5 km. from Lake Annecy, yet it offers a quiet, very relaxing and beautiful environment all at a very good price. This site is terraced and abounds with flowers, shrubs and small trees. It only has 32 average sized, grassy, reasonably level and sunny pitches, 28 with electricity (6A). In high season the site is quiet as there are no organised events, although there are plenty on and around the lake close by. Explore the countryside and picturesque villages by taking to the back roads.

Facilities

Modern toilet block with facilities for disabled visitors. Small shop selling bread, drinks and ices etc. Small bar in high season. Playground. Small club/TV room. Torches needed (no site lighting). Off site: Doussard, shops, bank. Lake Annecy with beaches (2 km), restaurants, snack bars, fishing and many water sports. Cycle track 800 m. Minigolf, bicycle hire, boat launching, small nature reserve. Canyoning, hang-gliding. Boat trips. Riding 7 km. Golf 8 km. 20 km. cycle ride passes site.

Open: 1 May - 30 September.

Directions

From Annecy take N508 signed Albertville. At traffic lights in Brédannaz turn right and left. Site on left in 1.5 km. Do not turn in by reception (this is a dead end) – wait in road until directions are received. GPS: N45:48.141 E06:12.339

Charges 2007

Per unit incl. 2 persons	€ 12,00 - € 14,00
extra person	€ 3,00 - € 3,20
child (under 10 yrs)	€ 2,00 - € 2,50
electricity	€ 3,40

FR74130 Camping de la Plage

304 rue de la Garenne, F-74500 Amphion-les-Bains (Haute-Savoie)

Tel: 04 50 70 00 46. Email: info@camping-dela-plage.com

This very good, family run site is small, quiet and friendly. It has a very long season and is only a few hundred metres from Lake Geneva and the village of Amphion making it an excellent centre to relax and explore this wonderful region. The 53 fully serviced pitches (electricity 2-6A), only a few used by mobile homes, are level, medium sized and separated by trees. In addition to the very small pool on the site there is an adjacent large aqua park plus an excellent spacious playground. The site does not accept large unit or double-axle caravans.

Facilities

Excellent toilet facilities, heated off season. Washing machine, dryer, iron. Small bar and takeaway (high season). Very small heated swimming pool, covered in cool weather. Sauna. Small playground. TV room. Exercise room with play area. WiFi. Off site: Excellent aqua park with beach adjacent. Lake Geneva, beaches, restaurants, fishing, water sports. Ferry service around lake to Geneva and Lausanne. Shops, restaurants, supermarket within walking distance. Hypermarket 1 km. Golf 3 km.

Open: All year excl. 2 November - 24 December.

Directions

Site is between Thonon-les-Bains and Evian-les-Bains. Turn north off the N5 at Amphion les Bains (at roundabout with statue and fountains) and follow site signs - site is a few hundred metres on the right. GPS: N46:23.728 E06:32.079

Charges 2007

Per unit incl. 2 persons	€ 16,50 - € 22,00
extra person	€ 6,10 - € 6,50
child (under 8 yrs)	€ 3,00 - € 3,20
electricity (2-6A)	€ 2,00 - € 4,20

FR74150 Camping de la Mer de Glace

200 chemin de la Bagna, Les Praz, F-74400 Chamonix (Haute-Savoie)

Tel: 04 50 53 44 03. Email: info@chamonix-camping.com

This attractive site is convenient for Chamonix but is in a tranquil setting away from its hustle and bustle. The buildings are of typical regional timber construction, decorated with traditional painted flower designs. Set in a large level clearing, with a view of the Mont Blanc range, it has been kept as natural as possible without a pool, restaurant, bar or disco and is well suited to those looking for quiet and relaxation. The area is rich in trails for walking and mountain biking and many pass nearby. There are 150 pitches of varying sizes, most with shade and 75 have electricity connections (3-10A).

Facilities

Three sanitary blocks with facilities for disabled visitors. Washing machine, dryer. Motorcaravan services. Bread. Pizza van twice weekly in July/Aug. Meeting room, snack room. Small playground for young children. Free internet and WiFi access. Off site: Fishing and golf 500 m. Bicycle hire 1 km. Riding 5 km. Shops, etc. 700 m. in Les Praz or 1.5 km. in Chamonix. Indoor and outdoor swimming pools in Chamonix 1.5 km. Free bus/train pass in locality.

Open: 25 April - 5 October.

Directions

From Chamonix take N506 northeast towards Les Praz. After 1 km. site signed to right. NOTE: the first two signs direct you under a 2.4 m. high bridge. Continue to a small roundabout at entrance to Les Praz, turn right and follow signs.

Charges 2008

Per person	€ 5,60 - € 6,40
child (0-3 yrs)	free
pitch incl. electricity (3A)	€ 8,10 - € 9,90

FR74170 Camping Moulin Dollay

206 rue du Moulin Dollay, F-74570 Groisy (Haute-Savoie)

Tel: **04 50 68 00 31**. Email: **moulin.dollay@orange.fr**

This spacious site is a gem with only 30 pitches, all for touring. The friendly and enthusiastic owner has worked hard to develop this site to a high quality over the last few years. The large to very large, level, grass pitches are partially separated by hedging and a variety of trees provide some shade. All pitches have 6A electricity and 15 also have sole use of a tap and a drain. Rock pegs are recommended. As there are only a few activities organised for youngsters on site it is perhaps better suited to independent couples and young families. Nestling between Annecy (15 km.) and Geneva (35 km.) this site is suitable for those seeking a peaceful site in a parkland setting alongside a rushing stream. You will discover beautiful countryside with its mountains, waterfalls, woods, birds, animals and flowers. It is a good base for touring the interesting Haute-Savoie by car or bicycle, or on foot. The small adjacent river is ideal for fishing and paddling and has a picturesque track alongside suitable for walking and biking. Many marked walks and bike rides to suit all abilities. Small villages with churches, châteaux, museums and markets.

Facilities

Spacious, well appointed, heated toilet block, including facilities for disabled visitors and a baby room. Washing machine, dryer. Motorcaravan services. Bar, TV corner. Large open play and sports area, volleyball and table tennis. River fishing. Off site: Shops, restaurants, bank and supermarkets at Groisy 1 km. Interesting little town of Thorens-Glières with its 11th century château 5 km. Riding 4 km. Golf 6 km.

Open: 1 May - 30 September.

Directions

Site about 12 km. north of Annecy. Heading north on N203 Annecy - Bonneville road, turn left on D2d at Groisy le Plot. Cross river and go under road bridge and immediately turn right and then left, following site signs. GPS: N46:00.146 E06:11.450

Charges 2008

Per unit incl. 2 persons	€ 13,00 - € 16,00
extra person	€ 4,00
child (under 7 yrs)	€ 2,00
electricity	€ 3,00
No credit cards.	

Moulin Dollay
CAMPING CARAVANING
★★★★

206 rue du Moulin Dollay
74570 GROISY
Tél./Fax 04 50 68 00 31

Annecy Haute-Savoie

FR74160 Camping l'Ile des Barrats

185 chemin de l'Ile des Barrat, F-74400 Chamonix (Haute-Savoie)

Tel: **04 50 53 51 44**. Email: **campingiledesbarrats74@orange.fr**

l'Ile de Barrats is a delightful neat, tidy, small and tranquil site. It is within easy walking distance of the beautiful town of Chamonix, although there are bus and train services close by if needed. There are 53 slightly sloping, grassy pitches all for touring mostly separated by small hedges and a variety of trees offering some shade. All have electricity (5/10A) and 32 have water and a drain. This is an ideal site for those wishing to roam the mountain trails and for those seeking a peaceful and relaxing holiday in a most superb setting. No twin axle caravans.

Facilities

A modern, clean toilet block offers all necessary facilities, including those for disabled visitors. Covered picnic area with table and benches, ideal for those with small tents. Motorcaravan services. Store room for mountaineers. Mobile shop in July/Aug. No organised activities. Off site: Baker 500 m. Chamonix 800 m. level walk Hang gliding, funicular railway, cable cars and chair lifts nearby.

Open: 15 May - 1 October.

Directions

On entering Chamonix from Geneva, turn left at first roundabout after turn off for the Mont Blanc Tunnel (follow signs for Hospital). Shortly, at next roundabout, turn left and site is on right opposite hospital. GPS: N45:54.855 E06:51.689

Charges 2007

Per person	€ 6,30
pitch incl. car	€ 7,60
electricity	€ 3,30 - € 4,30

FR74180 Camping International le Lac Bleu

Route de la Plage, F-74210 Doussard (Haute-Savoie)

Tel: 04 50 44 30 18. Email: lac-bleu@nwc.fr

This lakeside site has its own beach and jetty and a short walk brings you to the lake ferry. The site has breathtaking views, a swimming pool and 220 pitches divided by privet and beech hedges. This site is perfect for walking, cycling or sailing and in low season provides a tranquil base for those just wishing to relax. In high season it will be busy and popular. The proximity of the public lakeside area which is often used as a festival venue could be either a source of noise or an exciting place to be depending on your point of view. When we visited the music stopped at 23.00. A nearby cycle track on a disused railway to Annecy gives a level 16 km. ride with mountains on the left and the lake to the right. In high season there is a children's club for the under eights. The bar has a thriving takeaway (roast whole chickens and pizza) and an 'al fresco' eating area.

Facilities

Three toilet blocks are of a high standard with free showers. Good provision for babies and disabled visitors. Bar (15/5-15/9) and integral small shop. Takeaway. Swimming pool (15/5-15/9). Bicycle hire. Boat launching (sailing lessons and boat hire nearby). Private beach. Off site: Small supermarket 100 m. Hypermarket 4 km. Village close with bars and restaurants. Fishing 100 m. Golf 4 km. Riding and bicycle hire 7 km.

Open: 1 May - 25 September.

Directions

Site is 16 km. south of Annecy on Route d'Albertville, well signed.
GPS: N45:79.042 E06:21.778

Charges 2007

Per unit incl. 2 persons	€ 16,00 - € 26,40
extra person (over 3 yrs)	€ 4,00 - € 5,80
child (0-3 yrs)	free
electricity (8A)	€ 3,80

No credit cards.

Route de la Plage - 74210 Doussard
Tel: 0033 450 44 30 18
Fax: 0033 450 44 84 35
lac-blue@nwc.fr
www.camping-lac-blue.com

Welcome to Camping Le Lac Bleu!
The whole team here will ensure that you have a great holiday on the shores of Lake Annecy on a wonderful site at the heart of the French Alps. You'll be sure to enjoy the fine beach and swimming pool, and, of course, a stunning natural setting which is the ideal place for outstanding holidays! This really is a great spot too for all watersports - waterskiing, windsurfing, sailing, pedaloes and much more.

FR74200 Camping l'Idéal

715 route de Chaparon, F-74210 Lathuile (Haute-Savoie)

Tel: 04 50 44 32 97. Email: camping-ideal@wanadoo.fr

For panoramic views of mountains and the lake, this family run site is excellent. Trim and neat, the site is well cared for and the welcome is warm. The 150 pitches are generally large and well drained, some with small hedges but mostly open and with 6A electricity. These pitches share the site with chalets which are located at the top of the site well away from the tourers. L'Idéal is far enough from the lake to avoid the noise and crowds but close enough to take advantage of the facilities there. From the site you can cycle downhill to the Annecy cycle route.

Facilities

Three very well designed toilet blocks include excellent facilities for babies and disabled visitors. A further new block is planned. Laundry facilities. Shop (June - Sept). Bar (no smoking). Restaurant, snack bar and takeaway (June - mid August). Two swimming pools. Tennis. Paragliding lessons. Bicycle hire. Play area. Children's club. Activities and excursions in high season. Off site: Lake 900 m. Golf and riding 5 km.

Open: 8 May - 5 September.

Directions

Lathuile is 18 km. southeast of Annecy and site is well signed in the village.

Charges 2007

Per unit incl. 2 persons and electricity	€ 18,70 - € 25,20
extra person	€ 3,50 - € 5,00
child (2-7) yrs	€ 2,50 - € 4,20
dog	€ 2,50

FR74220 Camping Saint Disdille

117 ave de Saint Disdille, F-74200 Thonon-les-Bains (Haute-Savoie)

Tel: **04 50 71 14 11**. Email: **camping@disdille.com**

Saint Disdille is situated close to the beautiful Lake Geneva and the famous spa town of Thonon-les-Bains, which can be reached on a bus that passes the site. There are 600 large, level pitches on stone and rough grass (rock pegs are essential). Large trees give some shade. The 300 pitches reserved for touring (200 with 6-10A electricity) are scattered amongst mobile homes and permanent weekender caravans and can be some distance from the facilities. The site is ideally situated for the large range of watersports in the area and Switzerland is easily accessible by car, bus, train or boat. This site will be lively in the high season due to the large number of long stay units and the on-site and adjacent discos finish after midnight. Although there are no problems with large units on the site, access is not easy due to the urban location. For 2009 a new bypass around Thonon will make access easier.

Facilities

Five adequate toilet blocks, 4 recently refurbished inside. Shop. Bar with TV, restaurant with takeaways (all season). Diving and rafting clubs. Play area with bouncy castle. Multisport court. Boules. Games room with pool table. WiFi (free) and internet point (fee). Twin axle vans are not accepted. Off site: Small lakeside public beach and disco 300 m. Fishing 500 m. Large open air pool 1 km. Boat ramp, windsurfing, bicycle hire 2 km. Many other water sports in the area. Golf 3 km. Thonon-les-Bains 2 km.

Open: 1 April - 30 September.

Directions

From Annemasse take N5 to Thonon-les-Bains. In Thonon follow signs for Evian to Intermarché supermarket. At next roundabout follow signs to campsite and Parc de la Chataigneraie.

Charges 2007

Per unit incl. 2 persons	€ 14,00 - € 17,00
extra person	€ 4,00
child (3-10 yrs)	€ 2,50
electricity (6/10A)	€ 3,00 - € 4,00

FR74210 Camping des Iles de Passy

245 chemin de la Cauettaz, F-74190 Passy (Haute-Savoie)

Tel: **04 99 57 21 21**. Email: **contact@village-center.com**

This Alpine site is approached by a lakeside road with mountains to the left and with unrivalled views of Mont Blanc straight ahead. Set in an area with oak trees giving shade, there are 260 very good touring pitches which are all large and divided by 1.2 m. high, well trimmed beech hedges. A small, high season takeaway is located beside the play area allowing relaxed child supervision. An electric railway may cause some noise. This is an ideal site for Alpine lovers, a perfect base for walking and cycling, while the municipal water sports area in which the site is set offers a whole range of water based activities.

Facilities

Two toilet blocks, screened by attractive hedges, are not modern but are acceptable and include hot showers and a WC/shower for disabled visitors. Laundry facilities. Basic takeaway in high season. Chalets to rent. Off site: Site is in the centre of a large municipal water sports complex. Fishing 500 m. Riding 10 km. Golf 20 km. Excellent centre for walking and cycling. Passy has shopping, restaurants and bars, 2 km.

Open: 22 May - 26 September.

Directions

Site is west of Passy. From the A40 take exit 21 (Chamonix) and drive through Passy to site (well signed).

Charges 2007

Per person	€ 4,00 - € 5,00
pitch	€ 13,00 - € 18,00

FR74230 **Camping Caravaneige le Giffre**

La Glière, F-74340 Samoëns (Haute-Savoie)

Tel: **04 50 34 41 92**. Email: **camping.samoens@wanadoo.fr**

Surrounded by magnificent mountains in this lesser known Alpine area, yet accessible to major ski resorts, Le Giffre could be the perfect spot for those seeking an active, yet relaxing holiday. There are 300 firm, level pitches on stony grass (rock pegs advised) with 270 for touring units. Most have electricity (6/10A) but long leads may be needed. They are spaced out amongst mature trees which give varying amounts of shade and some overlook the attractive lake and leisure park. The small winter/summer resort of Samoëns is only a 15 minute level stroll away. Mr Dominach loves gardening and the site is bedecked with flowers. Make sure you do not miss the small vegetable and herb garden at the entrance. There is little in the way of on site entertainment but there are many activities available in Samoëns and the surrounding area.

Facilities	Directions
Three adequate toilet blocks, heated in winter with facilities for campers with disabilities. Games room. Children's play area. Boules. Off site: Leisure park next to site with pool (entry free summer), ice skating (entry free winter), tennis (summer), archery, adventure park. Paragliding. Rafting, many walks and bike rides (summer) and ski runs (winter). Snack bar and bakers, high season 100 m. Samoens with a good range of shops, bars, restaurants 1 km. Grand Massif Express cable car 150 m.	Leave A40 autoroute at Cluses (exit 18 or 19). Go north on D902 towards Taninges. Just before Taninges turn east on D4 to Samoëns. After crossing river, at roundabout, turn left and site is immediately on the left. Park outside the entrance. GPS: N46:04.681 E06:43.117

Open: All year.

Charges 2007

Per unit incl. 2 persons	€ 11,00 - € 16,00
extra person	€ 3,50
child (4-12 yrs)	€ 2,40
electricity (5A)	€ 3,00 - € 4,50

*Camping Caravaneige Le Giffre****

Open all year, located on the edge of the Giffre and the 'Lacs aux Dames', 700m from the town and its shops and at the heart of the leisure park, our campsite has 312 level grass pitches on a well shaded site of 6.9h.

In winter, departures for cross-country skiing from the campsite and ski lifts 150m away. Access within 8 min to 265 km of downhill slopes.

Camping Caravaneige Le Giffre • La Glière • F-74340 Samoens
www.camping-samoens.com

FR38010 **Kawan Village le Coin Tranquille**

F-38490 Les Abrets (Isère)

Tel: **04 76 32 13 48**. Email: **contact@coin-tranquille.com**

Les Abrets is well placed for visits to the Savoie regions and the Alps. It is an attractive, well maintained site of 192 grass pitches (178 for tourers), all with electricity. They are separated by neat hedges of hydrangea, flowering shrubs and a range of trees to make a lovely environment doubly enhanced by the rural aspect and marvellous views across to the mountains. This is a popular, family-run site with friendly staff that makes a wonderful base for exploring the area.

Facilities	Directions
The central well appointed sanitary block is well kept, heated in low season. Facilities for children and disabled people. Two smaller blocks provide facilities in high season. Busy shop. Excellent restaurant. Swimming pool and paddling pool (15/5-30/9; no Bermuda style shorts) with sunbathing areas. Play area. TV and games in bar. Quiet reading room. Weekly entertainment for children and adults (July/Aug) including live music (not discos). Bicycle hire (limited). Off site: Les Abrets with shops and supermarket 2 km. Riding 6 km. Fishing 8 km. Golf 25 km.	Les Abrets is 70 km. south east of Lyon at junction of N6 and N75. From roundabout in town take N6 towards Chambéry, turning left in just under 2 km. (signed Restaurant and Camping). Follow signs along country lane for just over 1 km. and entrance is on right. GPS: N45:32.482 E05:36.489

Open: 1 April - 31 October.

Charges 2007

Per pitch incl. 2 persons	€ 15,00 - € 27,00
extra person	€ 4,00 - € 6,50
child (2-7 yrs)	€ 2,50 - € 4,50
pet	€ 1,00
Camping Cheques accepted.	

Check real time availability and at-the-gate prices...

www.**alanrogers**.com

FR38020 Camping Ser Sirant

Lac de Laffrey, Petichet, F-38119 Saint Théoffrey (Isère)

Tel: **04 76 83 91 97**. Email: **campingsersirant@wanadoo.fr**

This small lakeside site, a few kilometres from La Route Napoléon, has 87 touring pitches (6A reverse polarity) and 6 chalets, set on a level, partly terraced, grassed area. There is a pleasant lakeside terrace just outside the bar and reception, whilst about 70 metres up the lakeside there is a sailing school for you to improve (or start) your sailboarding skills. On site there are kayaks for hire and fishing on the lake. This is a picturesque site with the minimum of extras which will appeal especially to water lovers.

Facilities

A single toilet block is at one end of the site. Equipped to basic standards it could be under pressure at peak times. Half the WCs are Turkish style. No facilities for children. Launderette. Small bar with shop for basic supplies. Takeaway at weekends in July/Aug. Kayak hire. Fishing. Chalets to rent. Off site: Shops and restaurants within 1 km. Riding and bicycle hire 5 km.

Open: 1 May - 30 September.

Directions

Petichet is on the Route Napoléon between Grenoble and La Mure. Site is well signed and easy to find by the lake.

Charges 2008

Per unit incl. 2 persons, electricity and hot water	€ 19,50 - € 22,00
child (2-8yrs)	€ 3,50
dog	€ 2,50

No credit cards.

FR38030 Camping la Cascade

Route de l'Alpe d'Huez, F-38520 Bourg-d'Oisans (Isère)

Tel: **04 76 80 02 42**. Email: **lacascade@wanadoo.fr**

La Cascade has a long season and it is within sight and sound of the waterfall from which it takes its name. It is only 2 km. from Bourg-d'Oisans which lies in the Romanche valley 725 m. above sea level surrounded by high mountains. The area is a sun trap and gets very hot in summer. The site has 133 individual grassy pitches, 106 for touring units on mainly flat ground and of varying size. Although most are quite adequate, larger units are best near the entrance as the pitches and roads do become narrow. All have 16A electricity.

Facilities

Two heated sanitary blocks are of good quality with mainly British style toilets, washbasins in cabins and showers. Laundry and dishwashing facilities. Bar and snack bar (25/6-30/8). Good sized, heated and sheltered swimming pool and paddling pool (1/6-30/9) surrounded by large, enclosed sunbathing area. TV in bar.
Off site: Supermarket or fishing 500 m. Bicycle hire or riding 1 km. Bourg-d'Oisans 1 km. with bars, restaurants, shops and banks. Ski resorts of Alpe d'Huez 13 km. and Les Deux Alpes 25 km.

Open: 20 December - 30 September.

Directions

From Grenoble take N91 to Bourg d'Oisans, cross river bridge, after 730 m. turn left on to D211, signed Alpe d'Huez. Site is on right in 600 m. GPS: N45:03.832 E06:02.362

Charges 2007

Per unit incl. 2 persons	€ 16,90 - € 24,00
extra person (over 5 yrs)	€ 4,60 - € 6,00
electricity (16A)	€ 4,20
animal	free

FR38060 Domaine les Trois Lacs du Soleil

La Plaine, F-38460 Trept (Isère)

Tel: 04 74 92 92 06. Email: info@les3lacsdusoleil.com

Les Trois Lacs is situated on the edge of three lakes in flat, open country in the north of Dauphine. The camping area is on one side of the largest lake with tall trees on one edge and views of distant mountains. The 200 good sized pitches, with 180 for tourists, are well spaced and separated by trees and hedges. All have 6A electricity. There is plenty of activity on offer for the whole family including fishing in one lake, swimming and boating in the other two and, for the more energetic, roller blading. This is a good base to enjoy either the countryside, the historic places of the region or the programme of leisure activities provided by the site (in July/Aug). The land around the lakes has been well landscaped with grassy banks and a variety of shrubs and trees. There is plenty of space around the lake for children to play.

Facilities

Two fully equipped toilet blocks are in the centre of the camping area. Toilets for children. Baby changing and laundry room. Small shop (July/Aug). Bar/restaurant. Snack bars. Outdoor pool (all June-Sept). Lakeside beach and water slide. Discos and entertainment in high season. TV and sports hall. Roller blade hire. Walking. Fishing. Gas barbecues only. Off site: Riding 500 m. Trept 2 km. Mountain bike hire 10 km.

Open: 1 May - 10 September.

Directions

From A43 take exit 7 on to D522 north. Turn left after 7 km. on to D65 then after 5 km. turn right on to D517. Site is 2 km. east of Trept. Signs in village.

Charges 2007

Per unit incl. 2 persons and electricity	€ 15,50 - € 31,00
extra person	€ 3,00 - € 7,00
child (0-10 yrs)	free - € 3,50
animal	€ 1,50

Less 20% in low seasons.
Camping Cheques accepted.

FR38040 Camping A la Rencontre du Soleil

Route de l'Alpe d'Huez, F-38520 Bourg-d'Oisans (Isère)

Tel: 04 76 79 12 22. Email: rencontre.soleil@wanadoo.fr

The Isère is an attractive and popular region with exceptional scenery. Bourg-d'Oisans lies in the Romanche valley 725 m. above sea level surrounded by high mountains. This compact site, pleasant, friendly and family run, nestles between two impressive mountain ranges, at the base of France's largest National Park, Le Parc des Ecrins. It is only 2 km. from Bourg-d'Oisans and has 73 level, hedged pitches, most of average size, with mature trees offering good shade (43 for touring). Electricity is available (2, 6 or 10A). Rock pegs are advised. A 'Sites et Paysages' member.

Facilities

Heated toilet block provides all the usual amenities, but no facilities for disabled people. Washing machine and dryer. Motorcaravan services. Bread to order. Restaurant and takeaway (all season). Room with TV, children's play room. Small, sheltered swimming pool (all season). Play area. Activities in high season include walking, mountain biking, children's club. Off site: Supermarket 1 km. Fishing 5 km. Bicycle hire, riding 2 km. Canoeing, rafting, riding, hiking, climbing. Cable car at Alpe d'Huez.

Open: 3 May - 30 September.

Directions

Leave Bourg-d'Oisans on N91 towards Briancon. Shortly on a sharp right hand bend, turn left on D211 signed Alpe d'Huez. Site is on left just beyond Camping la Piscine. Entrance is on a sharp bend, take care. GPS: N45:03.940 E06:02.381

Charges 2008

Per unit incl. 2 persons	€ 15,00 - € 25,50
extra person	€ 5,10 - € 6,40
child (2-5 yrs)	€ 3,45 - € 4,80
electricity (2/10A)	€ 3,10 - € 4,40

Camping Cheques accepted.

Check real time availability and at-the-gate prices...

www.alanrogers.com

FR38070 Camping l'Oursière

F-38250 Villard de Lans (Isère)

Tel: 04 76 95 14 77. Email: info@camping-oursiere.fr

This friendly, family run site is ideally situated within easy walking distance of the attractive resort of Villard de Lans which provides a very wide range of activities. It is ideal for those who prefer a peaceful site in a more natural setting. The good sized grass and stone pitches are slightly uneven but have magnificent views over the surrounding mountains. There are 186 marked pitches, 155 for touring, most have electricity (6/10A). A variety of trees offer some shade. Rock pegs essential. Because the town of Villard de Lans offers so much entertainment, little is organised on site. There are good shops, bars and restaurants (all open July/August only), a bank, swimming pool complex, ice skating rink (last two open most of the year) and a gambling casino. There are many marked walks and bike rides (on and off road) around the town, several starting from the site. This is an excellent value for money base for those seeking a relaxing or active holiday, both summer and winter.

Facilities

Clean, heated toilet blocks with all necessary facilities including those for disabled campers, ski store and drying room. Motorcaravan services. Single building houses reception, bar (July/Aug), cosy lounge with open fireplace, TV room, games rooms. Snack bar (July/Aug). Internet access. Play area. Boules. Volleyball. Trout fishing. Off site: Bus to Autrans and Grenoble. Free bus to ski resorts (winter). Supermarket 1 km. Bicycle hire 1 km. Riding 2 km. Golf 5 km.

Open: All year excl. October and November.

Directions

Northwest of Grenoble, leave Autoroute A48 exit 13 or 3A. Follow N532 to Sassenage, at roundabout take D531. Entering Villard de Lans (25 km), fork left signed Villard Centre, site is shortly on left. Only route for caravans and motorcaravans. GPS: N45:4.655 E05:33.37

Charges 2007

Per unit incl. 2 persons	€ 13,60 - € 16,00
extra person	€ 4,00 - € 4,70
child (5-12 yrs)	€ 3,40 - € 4,00
electricity	€ 3,50 - € 6,00
dog	€ 0,90

Camping Caravaneige L'Oursière

Welcomes you to its exceptional, calm and relaxing surroundings

Camping Caravaneige L'Oursière
38250 Villard de Lans - France
www.camping-oursiere.fr
info@camping-oursiere.fr
Tel. +33 (0)4 76 95 14 77
Fax +33 (0)4 76 95 58 11

open from 01-12-2007 till 28-09-2008

FR38050 Camping Caravaning le Temps Libre

F-38150 Bouge-Chambalud (Isère)

Tel: 04 74 84 04 09. Email: camping.temps-libre@libertysurf.fr

You will receive a warm welcome at this spacious, family run site which is close to the A7 motorway, between Lyon and Valence. Of the 199 pitches, 90 are available for tourers. Mobile homes and seasonal pitches are in a separate area. The medium to large, partly sloping, grassy pitches are mostly separated by hedges and trees giving privacy and some shade. All have 9A electricity and water close by. Most are in cul-de-sacs, in groups of 8, and a few have tricky access. A 'Sites et Paysages' member.

Facilities

Three toilet blocks, two for tourers, providing all the necessary facilities. Motorcaravan service point. Good shop (1/5-31/8), bar/restaurant and takeaway (all 1/7-31/8). Large pool complex (15/5-30/9, no Bermuda style shorts). Playgrounds. Club/TV room. Football. Boules. Tennis. Fishing. Minigolf. Organised activities and pony cart rides (July and Aug). Internet access. Off site: Disco 3 km. Canoeing. Shops. Supermarket. Lafuma factory shop at Anneyron 8 km. Golf and riding 10 km.

Open: 1 April - 30 September.

Directions

From A7 motorway take exit 12 (Chanas) or from N7 take D510 east towards Grenoble for about 7 km. to Bougé Chambalud. Turn right in village. Site is a few hundred metres (signed).

Charges 2007

Per unit incl. 2 persons	€ 14,50 - € 20,50
extra person	€ 4,50 - € 7,00
child (2-4 yrs)	free
electricity (9A)	€ 4,50
Camping Cheques accepted.	

Check real time availability and at-the-gate prices...

 www.**alanrogers**.com

FR38080 Kawan Village Au Joyeux Réveil

Le Château, F-38880 Autrans (Isère)

Tel: **04 76 95 33 44**. Email: **camping-au-joyeux-reveil@wanadoo.fr**

The small town of Autrans is set on a plateau, 1,050 m. high, in the Vercors region. The well organised site is run by a very friendly family (English is spoken). It is on the outskirts of the town, set below a ski jump and short lift. There are 108 pitches with 78 for touring, electricity 2-10A. They are mainly on grass, in a sunny location with fantastic views over the surrounding wooded mountains with small trees giving little shade. There is a new pool area with a separate paddling pool and two other pools with river and slide. Here the days can be very hot and sunny and the nights quite chilly. It is ideally situated for any of the activities that this wonderful area has to offer – from walking, mountain biking and pot-holing in summer to downhill and cross-country skiing in winter, it is all there for you in magnificent scenery. The D531 and the D106 look a little daunting on the map and do involve a stiff climb but they are good roads and have no difficult bends.

Facilities

The new toilet block is very well appointed, with under-floor heating and all the expected facilities. Another new building houses a bar with terrace, snack bar/takeaway (July and August). New pool area with two pools, toboggan for children, sunbathing area and a separate paddling pool. Small play area. TV room. Internet point. Off site: Autrans with a few shops 500 m. Villard de Lans, supermarket, shops, restaurants, bars, ice rink and many other activities 16 km. Short ski lift is near the site and a shuttle bus runs (in winter) to the longer runs (5 km). Fishing, bicycle hire and riding 300 m. Bus to Villard de Lans and Grenoble.

Open: 1 December - 31 March, 1 May - 30 September.

Directions

Exit A48, northwest of Grenoble at exit 13 (going south) or 3A (going north). Follow N532 to Sassenage, turn west at roundabout on D531 to Lans en Vercors. At roundabout turn right on D106 signed Autrans. On entering Autrans turn right at roundabout and very shortly right again. Site is on left. This is the only route advised for caravans and motorcaravans. GPS: N45:10.515 E05:32.870

Charges 2008

Per unit incl. 1 or 2 persons	€ 18,50 - € 30,00
extra person	€ 5,00
child (under 6 yrs)	€ 3,50
electricity (2-6A)	€ 2,00 - € 8,00

Winter prices - apply to site.
Camping Cheques accepted.

CAMPING AU JOYEUX REVEIL

We take pride in providing our guests with the very best service, including sharing our love of the Vercors, one of France's most beautiful regions. Our campsite is open in both summer and winter and offers a quiet, friendly environment perfect as a base for discovering all that nature has to offer in the Vercors.

The campsite has a very nice heated pool complex, including a covered pool, modern sanitary facilities with under-floor heating in winter and the pitches with clear views of the mountains.

Located right at the heart of the Vercors natural park (history, tradition and nature) in a beautiful, restful setting, our site is located just across from the Olympic ski jump from the 1968 Games and is just 300m from the town of Autrans (1050m) which offers a full range of shops and activities.

Christine and Franck Blanc

Camping Au Joyeux Réveil • 38880 Autrans • Tel: 0033.4.76.95.33.44 • www.camping-au-joyeux-reveil.fr

FR38090 Camping Caravaning Belle Roche

F-38930 Lalley (Isère)

Tel: **04 76 34 75 33**. Email: **gildapatt@aol.com**

Belle Roche is a good, spacious, family run site. The level site is only a few years old, so is rather open at present with very little shade, but it is nonetheless neat and well maintained throughout. There are 57 large, slightly uneven and slightly sloping pitches, many part grass with a gravel hardstanding, partially delineated by shrubs and young trees. Rock pegs are necessary. All have 10A electricity (long leads may be necessary) and there are ample water points.

Facilities

Two modern, well equipped and clean toilet blocks. Facilities for disabled visitors. Laundry and dishwashing. Motorcaravan services. Bar/TV room, terrace serving simple meals (all season). Bread. Swimming pool (mid May-Sept). Very large play area. Off site: Village shop 400 m. Many marked cycling, walking and climbs to suit all capabilities. Bicycle hire 8 km. Riding 15 km.

Open: 1 April - 30 September

Directions

Follow N75 south from Grenoble (about 65 km.) turn left onto D66, signed Lalley, Mens and campsite, and then follow camping signs through the village. GPS: N44:45.295 E05:40.736

Charges 2007

Per unit incl. 2 persons	€ 11,70 - € 14,90
extra person	€ 3,50
electricity (10A)	€ 3,50

FR38140 Camping le Colporteur

Le Mas du Plan, F-38521 Bourg-d'Oisans (Isère)

Tel: **04 76 79 11 44**. Email: **info@camping-colporteur.com**

The site is within a few minutes level walk of the attractive market town making this an ideal spot for motorcaravanners. The owners have recently put in much effort to improve this site. There are 150 level grassy pitches, 130 for touring, mostly separated by hedging and a variety of mature trees that offer some shade. All pitches have 15A electricity and rock pegs are advised. Although there is no pool on the site, campers are given free entry to the adjacent municipal pool. In July and August the attractive bar/restaurant is the focal point for evening activities. At over 700 metres above sea level, Bourg-d'Oisans is in the largest national park in France. It is surrounded by high mountains making it a real suntrap and can be very hot in summer. The area is revered by serious cyclists as several mountain roads close by are regularly used by the Tour de France. This is an ideal base for exploring this scenic region with its abundance of wild flowers, old villages and rushing waterfalls; by car, on foot or by bike.

Facilities

Large well equipped, modern, airy toilet block has all the necessary facilities including washbasins in cabins, a baby room and an en-suite room for disabled campers. Games room. Boules. Table tennis. Volleyball. Small play area. Organised family activities (July/Aug). Off site: Shops, bars, restaurants in town and supermarket 500 m. Cycling, mountain biking, hiking, rafting, canoeing, climbing, riding, hang-gliding, Parc des Ecrins, cable cars (July/August) and many mountain passes. Bus services.

Open: 1 May - 30 September.

Directions

Site is in Bourg-d'Oisans. From Grenoble follow the N91 into town and shortly after the road bears left in the town centre and just beyond a petrol station, turn right (site signed). Follow signs to site, a few hundred metres. GPS: N45:03.156 E06:02.130

Charges 2007

Per unit incl. 2 persons and electricity	€ 20,50 - € 26,00
extra person	€ 5,80
child (5-10 yrs)	€ 3,50

Camping le Colporteur

chalets for rent

5 minutes walk from the town. Grassy touring pitches. Complete tranquility. Views of Alpe d'Huez.

Le Mas du Plan - F-38520 Bourg-d'Oisans - France
Tel.: +33 (0)4 76 79 11 44 - Fax: +33 (0)4 76 79 11 49
info@camping-colporteur.com - www.camping-colporteur.com

FR38100 Camping Belledonne

Rochetaillée, F-38520 Bourg-d'Oisans (Isère)

Tel: **04 76 80 07 18**. Email: **belledon@club-internet.fr**

This extremely neat and spacious site, takes its name from the nearby Belledonne mountain range. The 180 well drained, level, generous, grassy pitches, 148 for touring have electricity (3/6A). There is some road noise for a few pitches. Beech hedges and abundant mature trees provide ample privacy and shade. A bar/restaurant with terrace is next to an attractive pool complex with sunbathing space surrounded by well tended gardens and grass spaces. In July and August the site becomes quite lively with a daily programme of organised activities. A 'Sites et Paysages' member.

Facilities

Two well appointed sanitary blocks with baby room and facilities for disabled visitors. Shop. Bar/restaurant and takeaway (all open all season). TV/games room. Swimming and paddling pools. Tennis. Good play area, large meadow with fitness course. Bicycle hire (July/Aug). Off site: Allemont, shops 2 km. Bourg d'Oisans, shops, bars, restaurants, (Saturday market) 8 km. Hiking, mountain biking, white water rafting, canoeing, bungee jumping, paragliding. Cable car (high season).

Open: 14 May - 10 September.

Directions

Site is 8 km. west of Bourg-d'Oisans. From Grenoble take N85 to Vizille and then N91 towards Bourg-d'Oisans. In Rochetaillée branch left (site signed) onto D526, signed Allemont. Site is 250 m. on right. GPS: N45:06.854 E06:00.459

Charges 2008

Per pitch incl. 2 persons	€ 16,10 - € 24,20
extra person	€ 4,30 - € 6,10
electricity (3/6A)	€ 3,00 - € 4,00
Camping Cheques accepted.	

229

FR38110 Camping le Champ du Moulin

Bourg d'Arud, F-38520 Venosc (Isère)

Tel: 04 76 80 07 38. Email: info@camp-du-moulin.com

Le Champ du Moulin lies on the floor of the narrow Vénéon valley. It has generous stone and grass pitches that are part-shaded by large trees with electricity (up to 10A). Rock pegs are essential. When the mountain snows melts in late May/early June, the river beside the site changes from its winter trickle to an impressive torrent. Parents with small children need to be especially vigilant. On the edge of the Ecrins National Park with stunning mountain scenery and miles of marked cycling and walking trails, it is an ideal site for active outdoor families rather than those seeking late-night revelry. A 'Sites et Paysages' member.

Facilities

Heated, well equipped toilet block. Drying racks for clothes. Baby room. Facilities for disabled people. Motorcaravan services. Chalet restaurant/bar with home cooking. Small shop in reception with bread. Play area. TV room. Internet access. Fishing. Off site: Municipal heated outdoor pools and flume next door (open in summer). Playground, tennis, tree-top adventure park. Rafting, canoeing, paragliding, bungee jumping, hill walking and summer mountain biking available nearby. Discounted ski passes. Riding 500 m, golf 3 km. (both summer only).

Open: 15 December - 30 April, 1 June - 15 September.

Directions

From Grenoble, pass through Bourg-d'Oisans on the N91, signed Briancon. After 3 km. turn right on D530 signed Venosc. In 8 km. pass the telecabin on left. Site on right in 400 m.

Charges 2008

Per unit incl. 1 or 2 persons	€ 14,00 - € 19,40
extra person	€ 4,00 - € 4,90
child (3-7 yrs)	€ 2,40 - € 3,00
electricity (3/6/10A)	€ 3,20 - € 8,00
dog	€ 0,60 - € 1,00

FR38150 Camping Caravaning la Daxia

Route de Péage (CD4), F-38370 Saint Clair du Rhône (Isère)

Tel: 04 74 56 39 20. Email: info@campingledaxia.com

Set in the Rhône Valley, a virtually unspoilt area rich in history, this family owned site has 116 pitches and a new swimming pool. The pitches all have electricity and vary in size from 100 sq.m. to larger and are clearly marked by hedges or bushes. Many mature trees give excellent shelter and shade. Larger units should phone ahead as some of the pitches are not easily accessed, although there are some very large places available. This is a quiet country site, not in the top grade but relaxing and close to the attractions of the area.

Facilities

Two unisex toilet blocks, one new are both tiled and clean. Some Turkish style WCs. Facilities for babies and for disabled visitors. Launderette. Motorcaravan services. Good takeaway (weekends only outside July/Aug). Ice supplies. Excellent large swimming pool with slide and adjacent paddling pool. Minigolf. Barbecue area. Off site: Two small lakes. Shop 1 km.

Open: April - September.

Directions

Take the RN86 to Condrieu, then D4 to St Clair du Rhône. Site is 2 km. southeast of the village. GPS: N45:42.40 E04:78.23

Charges guide

Per person	€ 3,30 - € 3,50
child (0-7 yrs)	€ 2,30 - € 2,45
pitch	€ 6,25 - € 6,80
electricity (5/6A)	€ 2,40 - € 2,85

FR38130 Camping Belvédère de l'Obiou

Les Egats, F-38350 Saint Laurent en Beaumont (Isère)

Tel: 04 76 30 40 80. Email: info@camping-obiou.com

This very good, small Alpine site with just 45 pitches is in the centre of the Ecrins National Park. It is therefore ideal for walkers and cyclists looking to take advantage of the well marked trails. It has most things a good site should have, with its restaurant (high season), heated pool and sitting room with TV and library. The welcoming owners will even supply you with breakfast. The views from the terraced pitches are spectacular and there is a wealth of activities in the area ranging from bungee jumping to beaver watching by the Lac du Vallon. Bicycles are available to hire.

Facilities

Two modern toilet blocks, one part of the main building, the other 'Portacabin' style, are immaculate and can be heated. High standard facilities for disabled visitors. Excellent laundry. Motorcaravan services. Restaurant (high season) with Savoyard menu, high quality takeaway and breakfast. Small family run shop. Swimming pool (June - Sept). Bicycle hire. Good play area. Off site: Fishing 3 km. Walking, cycling and mountain activities.

Open: 1 April - 15 October.

Directions

From Grenoble take the RN85 to 7 km. south of Mure. Site is clearly signed on the left.

Charges 2007

Per unit incl. 2 persons	€ 13,50 - € 18,50
extra person	€ 3,60 - € 4,70
child (2-10 yrs)	€ 2,10 - € 3,10
electricity (4-10A)	€ 3,00 - € 5,00
Camping Cheques accepted.	

FR38160 Camping de Martinière

Route du Col de Porte, F-38380 Saint Pierre de Chartreuse (Isère)

Tel: 04 76 88 60 36. Email: camping-de-martiniere@orange.fr

Chamechaude, the 2,082 meter Eiger-like peak, presides benevolently over the 86 touring pitches at this beautiful, high alpine site open from May to September for the summer season. The 86 large touring pitches, with electricity available (2-10A), have some shade and are slightly sloping. The site has a heated pool in the open air so that not a moment of the views is lost. This well run, family owned enterprise, set around a Savoyard farmhouse, is a peaceful centre ideal for walking, climbing and cycling. It is in the centre of the Chartreuse National Forest. A 'Sites et Paysages' member.

Facilities

Two heated toilet blocks, one at each end of the site provide excellent, clean facilities. Facilities for babies but not for disabled visitors. Laundry facilities. Shop (1/6-15/9). Bar (1/6-15/9) with snacks (1/7-1/9). Heated swimming and paddling pools (1/6-5/9). Play area. Indoor sitting area for poor weather. Extensive paperback library (NL. IT, Fr, UK). Off site: Restaurant 50 m. from site entrance. Bicycle hire 3 km. Skiing 6 km. Walking, cycling and mountain activities.

Open: 1 May - 14 September.

Directions

From St Laurent du Pont (north from Voiron or south from Chambery), take D512 signed St Pierre de Chartreuse. Site is well signed in the village (the road south from St Pierre d'Entremont is not recommended for towing). GPS: N45:19.330 E05:47.498

Charges 2008

Per unit incl. 2 persons	€ 14,00 - € 18,00
extra person	€ 4,70 - € 5,40
electricity (2-6A)	€ 2,00 - € 3,90

FR38180 Camping Caravaning le Château

Chemin de Bouthean, Rochetaillée, F-38520 Bourg-d'Oisans (Isère)

Tel: 04 76 11 04 40. Email: jcp@camping-le-chateau.com

Set in the grounds of the small château, with spectacular views, this site has recently been upgraded to provide high quality amenities. The grounds are shared with chalets and tents to rent, with these in a separate area. There are 94 touring pitches, all with 6/10A electricity hook-ups on level areas (some large) separated by hedges and trees. The site has an excellent heated swimming pool, a fitness room, sauna, bar/restaurant and takeaway food together with a small shop with bread and basic groceries. The site is in the centre of an area ideal for walkers, cyclists and climbers.

Facilities

Three very good toilet blocks are very clean. Shower room with facilities for babies. Excellent, spacious facilities for disabled visitors. Small launderette. Freezer space. Shop, Bar, snacks, takeaway and restaurant (all 1/6-7/9). Swimming pool. Sauna, fitness room and jacuzzi. Daily activities for children (July/Aug). Guided mountain walks. Fishing. Safe hire. Barbecue area. Internet and WiFi. Off site: Mountain activities. Riding and bicycle hire 4 km.

Open: 13 May - 14 September.

Directions

Site is signed from the N91, just north of Rochetaillée. GPS: N45:06.918 E06:00.329

Charges 2008

Per unit incl. 2 persons	€ 16,50 - € 26,00
extra person	€ 4,80 - € 6,50
child (0-10 yrs)	€ 3,20 - € 4,20
electricity (6/10A)	€ 3,90 - € 4,40

FR38190 Camping le Champ Long

F-38350 La Salle en Beaumont (Isère)

Tel: 04 76 30 41 81. Email: champ.long@tiscali.fr

Set at the entrance to the Ecran National Park and overlooked by the great Obiou massif, this site has been carved from a hilly forest. It provides 97 pitches (8/10A electricity) arranged in glades between mature trees. The setting is such that it is hard to see the other units around you, yet the mountain views through trees are wonderful. The site is terraced and hilly and the winding access tracks need adequate power in reserve for towing. Very large outfits are best near the entrance as the distant pitches could be difficult to get to. There are some steep paths to the sanitary blocks.

Facilities

Two sanitary blocks, one at reception, the other high on the steep terraces provide British and Turkish style WCs, washbasins in cabins and unexceptional showers. Facilities for children and babies. Laundry facilities. Motorcaravan service point. Milk, bread and a few essentials (1/4-15/10). Bar. Good restaurant and takeaway (1/5-15/10). Heated outdoor swimming pool (1/5-31/8). Play area and games room. Barbecues to rent. Caravan storage. Off site: Riding and bicycle hire 6 km.

Open: 1 April - 15 October.

Directions

From the RN85 turn off at sign for La Roche which is close to La Salle en Beaumont. Site is signed.

Charges 2007

Per unit incl. 2 persons	€ 13,00 - € 15,00
extra person	€ 3,50 - € 3,80
child (0-7 yrs)	€ 2,50 - € 2,80

FR38200 **Camping la Ferme Noémie**

Chemin Pierre Polycarpe, Les Sables, F-38250 Le Bourg-d'Oisans (Isère)

Tel: **04 76 11 06 14**. Email: **sci.smith@libertysurf.fr**

There are many campsites at Le Bourg d'Oisans, but La Ferme Noémie offers something quite different from the rest. This is a tiny site with just 15 touring pitches which has recently been created by an English couple, Jeremy and Melanie Smith. Although there are no leisure amenities on site, the camping area is very comfortable with large, grassy pitches, all with 16A electrical connections. Given that the site is brand new, there is little shade as yet. The toilet block is bright and attractive and forms part of the main structure, a converted barn, which also houses a number of apartments.

Facilities

Well appointed toilet block with facilitiesw for disabled visitors. Play area. Mobile homes for rent. Off site: Golf 12 km. Fishing and riding 5 km. Le Bourg d'Oisans 3 km. Lake at Allemont suitable for windsurfing and sailing, many walking paths and cycle trails 5 km.

Open: 1 March - 31 October.

Directions

Head south from Grenoble initially on the N85 and then joining the N91 following signs to Le Bourg d'Oisans. Site is well signed to the right shortly after passing through the hamlet of Rochetaillée and around 3 km. before reaching Le Bourg d'Oisans.

Charges 2007

Per person	€ 4,50
child (1-7 yrs)	€ 3,20
pitch incl. electricity	€ 8,50

FR73020 **Camping Caravaneige le Versoyen**

Route des Arcs, F-73700 Bourg-St-Maurice (Savoie)

Tel: **04 79 07 03 45**. Email: **leversoyen@wanadoo.fr**

Bourg-St-Maurice is on a small, level plain at an altitude of 830 m. on the River Isère, surrounded by mountains. Le Versoyen attracts visitors all year round (except for a short time when they close). The site's 205 unseparated, flat pitches (180 for touring) are marked by numbers on the tarmac roads and all have electrical connections (4/6/10A). Most are on grass but some are on tarmac hardstanding making them ideal for use by motorcaravans or in winter. Trees give shade in some parts, although most pitches have almost none. Duckboards are provided for snow and wet weather.

Facilities

Two acceptable toilet blocks can be heated, although the provision may be hard pressed in high season. British and Turkish style WCs. Laundry. Motorcaravan service facilities. Outdoor and covered pools (July/Aug). Heated restroom with TV. Small bar with takeaway in summer. Free shuttle in high season to funicular railway. Off site: Fishing or bicycle hire 200 m. Tennis and swimming pool 500 m. Riding 1 km. Golf 15 km. Cross country ski track.

Open: All year (excl. 7/11-14/12 and 2/5-25/5).

Directions

Site is 1.5 km. east of Bourg-St-Maurice on CD119 Les Arcs road. GPS: N45:37.324 E06:47.010

Charges 2007

Per unit incl. 2 persons and electricity	€ 16,10 - € 21,00
extra person	€ 4,00 - € 4,60
child (4-13 yrs)	€ 2,50 - € 4,40
dog	€ 0,50

FR73030 **Camping les Lanchettes**

Mobile homes ▶ page 496

F-73210 Peisey-Nancroix (Savoie)

Tel: **04 79 07 93 07**. Email: **lanchettes@free.fr**

A natural, terraced site, it has 90 good size, reasonably level and well drained, grassy/stony pitches, with 80 used for touring units, 70 having electricity (3-10A). Because it is very cold in winter and quite cold on some spring and autumn evenings (warm bedding necessary) there are no outside taps. For those who love walking and biking, the wonderful scenery, flora and fauna, this is the site for you. In winter it is ideal for the serious skier being close to the famous resort of Les Arcs (via free bus service and cable car). Underpowered units not advised.

Facilities

Well appointed heated toilet block. Motorcaravan services. Restaurant, takeaway (July/Aug. and winter). Playground. Club/TV room. Large tent/marquee used in bad weather. In winter a small bus (free) runs to all the hotels, bars, ski tows. Off site: Walks in National Park. Riding next to site. Peisey-Nancroix, restaurants, bars and shops 3 km. Les Arcs winter sports centre 6 km. Outdoor swimming pool and bicycle hire 6 km. Golf and indoor pool 8 km.

Open: 15 December - 15 October.

Directions

From Albertville take N90 towards Bourg-St-Maurice, through Aime. In 9 km. turn right on D87, signed Peisey-Nancroix. Follow a winding hilly road (with hairpin bends) for 10 km. Pass through Peisey-Nancroix; site on right about 1 km. beyond Nancroix. GPS: N45:31.882 E06:46.536

Charges 2007

Per unit incl. 2 persons	€ 11,80 - € 13,50
extra person	€ 4,05 - € 4,50
electricity (3-10A)	€ 3,00 - € 8,00
Camping Cheques accepted.	

TRAVEL SERVICE SITE
TO BOOK CALL 01580 214000
Advice & low ferry-inclusive prices

FR73040 Camping Municipal le Savoy

Avenue du Parc, F-73190 Challes-les-Eaux (Savoie)

Tel: 04 79 72 97 31. Email: camping73challes-les-eaux@wanadoo.fr

This attractive municipal site is surrounded by mountains and only a few hundred metres from the centre of Challes-les-Eaux. There are 99 level pitches, mostly for touring. Some are separated by beech hedges and mature trees offer some shade. There are 12 pitches for motorcaravans, 44 part hardstanding super pitches with 10A electricity and 19 with 6A electricity. Rock pegs are advised. This site is a very good base for touring this scenic region and makes an ideal stop over for those on route to the Fréjus Tunnel and Italy.

Facilities

Two well equipped toilet blocks with all the necessary facilities. Facilities for disabled visitors. Bar with simple snacks (July/Aug). Good sized playground. Boules, table tennis and table football. Off site: Small park with lake for swimming, tennis and volleyball courts adjacent. Challes-les-Eaux, with shops, banks, bars, restaurants, small supermarket, casino and minigolf, a few hundred metres. Interesting old town of Chambery 6 km. Fréjus Tunnel 96 km. and Bardonecchia (Italy) 110 km.

Open: 1 May - 30 September.

Directions

Challes is 7 km. south east of Chambéry on the N6 to Albertville. From south on autoroute A41, join N6 north at exit 21 and head towards Challes-les-Eaux. From north on A43/A41 (Grenoble/Albertville) and join N6 at exit 18. Site is on the N6 at the northern edge of the town, next to a small park and lake. Turn east at traffic lights, site well signed. GPS: N45:33.094 E05:59.036

Charges 2007

per person	€ 3,10
pitch	€ 3,65 - € 4,10
electricity	€ 2,50

FR73050 Camping les Trois Lacs

D916a Les Chaudannes, F-73330 Belmont Tramonet (Savoie)

Tel: 04 76 37 04 03. Email: info@les3lacs.com

If you would enjoy a site surrounded by lakes with views of the distant mountains, then this is ideal for you. The site takes 100 touring units on large, well spaced pitches separated by hedges in a park with mature trees. This rural site has excellent facilities for fishing and boating and there is a hall with lots of entertainment ranging from pool to electronic games. Well away from the pitches, this hall also hosts music and discos in the evenings in high season.

Facilities

Three sanitary blocks are supplemented by small units with WCs around the site. Well equipped showers. Special new block for children. Excellent facilities for disabled visitors. Laundry facilities. Shop, bar and restaurant (full menu in high season) and takeaway (all 1/6-1/9). Small swimming pool (1/5-1/9; unheated). TV and sports hall. Entertainment in high season. Chalets and rooms to rent. Access to all three lakes at 15km.

Open: 1 May - 23 September.

Directions

From the A43 take exit 11 (St Genix-sur-Guiers) onto D916. Site is 2 km. GPS: N45:33.560 E05:40.490

Charges 2007

Per unit incl. 1 or 2 persons	€ 12,50 - € 25,00
extra person	€ 3,50 - € 6,50
child (1-7 yrs)	€ 2,50 - € 5,00
electricity (6/10A)	€ 3,50 - € 4,50
No credit cards.	

FR73060 Camping Caravaneige l'Eden

F-73210 Landry (Savoie)

Tel: 04 79 07 61 81. Email: info@camping-eden.net

L'Eden is open almost all year round (it is closed for three weeks in May). Beside the Iser river and set in beautiful woodland glades, it is perfect for winter skiing and summer walking and cycling. The site is set in a valley with the Alpine peaks as a backdrop. The 132 good, spacious pitches all have 10A electrical hook-ups and individual water supplies (available when no frost is likely). The pristine, modern sanitary blocks are heated in colder weather and include a large drying room. There is a pool for summer lounging, a bar and a welcoming communal area with bar, TV and internet access.

Facilities

Two heated toilet blocks include drying rooms, good facilities for disabled visitors and for babies. Small launderette. Communal area with bar, TV and internet. Snack bar and takeaway (July/Aug). Swimming pool (13.5 x 5 m; June - Sept). Games room. Play area. Fishing. Ski passes for sale on-site. Off site: Shops and restaurants in village. Rafting, paragliding, cycle and cross country ski tracks. Riding 10 km. Golf 15 km.

Open: All year excl. 1-23 May.

Directions

From the RN90 take D87 towards Landry. Site is on left after 250 m. and is well signed from the RN90.

Charges guide

Per unit incl. 2 persons	€ 10,70 - € 21,40
extra person	€ 2,90 - € 5,70
child (0-7 yrs)	€ 2,30 - € 4,50
electricity (10A)	€ 2,00 - € 6,00

233

FR73080 Flower Camping Lacs de Chevelu

F-73170 Saint-Jean-de-Chevelu (Savoie)

Tel: **04 79 36 72 21**. Email: **camping-des-lacs@wanadoo.fr**

This is a small, family orientated campsite which is run by a friendly family and surrounded by delightful scenery, not far from Lac du Bourget. Beside the site is a small lake which is fed by springs and has a sandy beach ideal for swimming and playing around in small boats. The site has 120 average to large size, grass pitches with 110 for touring. There are 50 with 10A electricity (long leads advised). They are numbered and marked by very small trees with a few having some shade. This site ideal for families who are happy to make their own entertainment.

Facilities

Excellent newly refurbished toilet block with all necessary facilities including those for babies and campers with disabilities. Motorcaravan services. Small kiosk and takeaway snacks at entrance. Fishing. Lake bathing (lifeguard in high season). Organised walks and bike rides. Covered games area. Family entertainment in high season. Off site: Riding, bicycle hire, canoeing, walking in trees, hang gliding 5 km. Boat ramp 7 km. Golf 10 km. Yenne with shops, bars and restaurants 5 km.

Open: 15 May - 2 September.

Directions

Leave A43 at exit 13 (Chambery) and take N504 north towards Belley. After the 'Tunnel du Chat', in Saint-Jean-de-Chevelu, turn right (site signed). Site is just over 1 km. GPS: N45:41.627 E05:49.495

Charges 2007

Per unit incl. 2 persons	€ 12,50 - € 16,00
extra person	€ 2,50 - € 3,50
child (2-7 yrs)	€ 2,00 - € 3,00
electricity (10A)	€ 1,40 - € 2,00

FR73090 Flower Camping du Lac de Carouge

Base de Loisirs, F-73250 Saint Pierre d'Albigny (Savoie)

Tel: **04 79 28 58 16**. Email: **campingdecarouge@wanadoo.fr**

Camping Lac de Carouge is a well maintained and pleasant campsite next to a very clean, gently shelving, spring fed lake. This is ideal for swimming and there are pedaloes for hire. There are many marked walks and cycle tracks in this beautiful regional park. The site provides 80 large, level, grass pitches with 67 for touring (electricity 6/10A), separated by hedges giving privacy and some shade. There are good views of the surrounding mountains. Access to the site is easy from the A41, A43 and A430 autoroutes making it ideal for a short stay but you may be tempted to stay longer.

Facilities

Two new (2007) toilet blocks with excellent facilities, including a superb family room and suite for campers with disabilities. Large tent for bar and children's room (July/Aug). Off site: Lake bathing, play area, shaded picnic and play area, pedaloes 200 m. Bar/restaurant 200 m. and 500 m. Bike rides and walks. Supermarket 1 km. St Pierre d'Albigny some shops restaurants 2 km. Albertville with large range of shops, bars, restaurants 26 km.

Open: 1 May - 30 September.

Directions

St Pierre d'Albigny is just north of the N90/N6, midway between Albertville and Chambery. Site is well signed on the outskirts of the village. GPS: N45:33.398 E06:09.970

Charges 2007

Per unit incl. 2 persons	€ 12,00 - € 15,00
extra person	€ 3,00 - € 4,00
child (2-7 yrs)	€ 2,00 - € 3,00

FR73100 Camping le Reclus

F-73700 Séez (Savoie)

Tel: **04 79 41 01 05**. Email: **contact@campinglerecus.com**

This small mountain campsite, set in the hills above Bourg St Maurice, is enthusiastically run by the Bonato sisters who have great plans to offer the unexpected. The 108 pitches, some gently sloping, are set amongst mature pine trees giving plenty of shade; 90 have electrical connections. The site borders a fast-flowing mountain stream, which is well fenced. The site is undergoing redevelopment, with many new facilities being introduced. A new TV room was just about to open on our visit. The village of Séez is a few minutes' walk away. This site is not recommended for larger units.

Facilities

Two sanitary blocks, the central one more modern, have small shower cubicles with preset hot water; and open style basins. Chemical disposal. Laundry room with washer/dryer and indoor drying area. Small play area. Bread, drinks and ice cream available. Off site: Shops and bars in the village of Séez. Access to the ski resort of Les Arcs via the funicular railway in Bourg St Maurice 2 km. Riding 1 km. Bicycle hire 2 km.

Open: All year excl. November.

Directions

From A43 Lyon - Chambéry - Grenoble motorway take A430 to Albertville and RN90 to Moutiers and Bourg St Maurice. Drive through town, at third roundabout follow signs for Tignes and Val d'Isère. Site is 2 km up the hill on the right on entering village of Séez.

Charges 2007

Per unit incl. 2 persons	€ 11,00 - € 12,20
extra person	€ 3,60 - € 4,00
electricity	€ 5,50 - € 7,50

FR73120 Camping le Sougey

Lac Rive Ouest, F-73610 Saint Alban-de-Montbel (Savoie)

Tel: **04 79 36 01 44**. Email: **info@camping-sougey.com**

In scenic surroundings, this site is only 200 m. from Lake Aiguebelette, the third largest natural lake in France. The 165 pitches (each with its own 6/10A electricity supply) are set amongst many mature trees and well-manicured hedges, giving a tropical feel and plenty of shade and privacy. Most pitches are flat, but some are on a steep hillside and therefore sloping. There are adequate water points around the site and some serviced pitches are available. This is a very peaceful quality site with good views of the surrounding countryside and mountains. The owner Philippe Kremer is very friendly and speaks excellent English. The restaurant and mini market are in a converted barn just outside the main entrance and the patio has terrific views across the lake. A traditional wood oven is used for pancakes and pizzas or there is a good choice of speciality Savoyard dishes. The lake offers many types of water sports, but to keep the purity of the water, motorboats are not allowed. The beach is free for campsite guests, and there are lifeguards present in July and August. Walks with llamas and paragliding are organised from reception.

Facilities

Two identical sanitary blocks provide excellent facilities, washbasins in cabins, controllable showers, baby bath, 2 shower units with en-suite basin. Good facilities for disabled visitors. Separate laundry. Freezer. Shop, bar, restaurant (open to public, just outside main gate). Well maintained play area. Miniclub. Volleyball, pétanque, table tennis. TV room. Off site: Lake 200 m. Bicycle hire, golf 3 km. Walks with llamas and paragliding.

Open: 1 May - 16 September.

Directions

From A43 Chambéry - Lyon motorway, take exit 12 and D921 south towards Lac d'Aiguebelette. Follow signs to Plage du Sougey. Site is on the left just before the Plage.

Charges 2007

Per unit incl. 2 persons	€ 12,40 - € 16,30
with services	€ 17,00 - € 23,60
electricity (6A)	€ 3,10
extra person (over 5 yrs)	€ 3,50

CAMPING LE SOUGEY****

Campsite du Sougey is nestled in the heart of a site naturally rich in exceptional panoramas, located at a height of 380 meters at the foot of the 'Massif de l'Epine'. You are looking for quality atmosphere and service, for a complete and diversified atmosphere of tourism then do not hesitate: **you found your place for holidays!**

Lac Rive Ouest - 73610 Saint Alban de Montbel
Tel : 0033 479 36 01 44 - Fax : 0033 479 44 19 01
E-mail : info@camping-sougey.com - Internet : www.camping-sougey.com

FR73130 Camping International l'île aux Cygnes

501 boulevard Ernest Coudurier, F-73370 Le Bourget du Lac (Savoie)

Tel: **04 79 25 01 76**. Email: **camping@bourgetdulac.com**

This is a large municipal site in a fantastic location with wonderful views on the shores of Lake Bourget, the largest natural lake in France. The surrounding mountains create a scenic backdrop. The 235 pitches are level and a few have dividing hedges. Mature trees give some shade, but the site is mostly open. Many pitches border the lake or rivers which run along two sides of the site. Caution must be taken as there are some unfenced stretches. All pitches have easy access to 10A electricity and there are adequate water points around the site. The lake offers many water sports.

Facilities

Four sanitary blocks with some basins in cubicles, preset showers, baby room, children's washbasins, en-suite facilities for disabled visitors. Washing machines and dryer. Motorcaravan service point. Well stocked shop. Bar, restaurant with terrace, takeaway and pizzas. Play area. TV room. Internet access. Fishing, swimming, canoes. Bicycle hire. Off site: Minigolf, archery, tennis, boat launching, sailing all within 500 m.

Open: 1 April - 30 September.

Directions

From motorway junction of A43 Lyon-Chambéry with A41 Annecy-Grenoble (exit 14 at Chambéry), head north on N201/N504 for 8 km. to Lac-du-Bourget. Then follow signs for 'Plage Municipal' and yacht club. Site is 300 m.

Charges 2007

Per person	€ 2,78 - € 4,08
child (2-12 yrs)	€ 1,26 - € 2,00
pitch	€ 4,89 - € 5,67
electricity (10A)	€ 3,57

MAP 10

Endless shimmering beaches, huge sand dunes, watersports aple... fragrant pine forests, the ... wines of Bordeaux, and the c... city of Biarritz: it's easy to see the allure of the Atlantic Coast.

THE COASTAL DÉPARTEMENTS OF THE OFFICIAL REGION OF AQUITAINE, STRETCHING FROM BORDEAUX IN THE NORTH TO THE PYRÉNÉES AND THE SPANISH BORDER ARE INCLUDED IN OUR 'TOURIST' REGION: 33 GIRONDE, 40 LANDES, 64 PYRÉNÉES ATLANTIQUES

The Atlantic Coast stretches north from Biarritz to Arcachon. The most notable features are the uninterrupted line of vast sandy beaches, over 100 miles long, and the endless pine woods in the hinterland - this is Europe's largest man-made forest. There are also many lakes to see, ideal for watersports activities.

The département of the Gironde covers the area from the Bassin d'Arcachon, famed for its oysters and Europe's highest sand dune, to the Gironde estuary and Bordeaux. The vineyards of Bordeaux are world famous and especially well known for their Médoc, Sauternes, and St Emilion wines.

The Pays Basque area in the southwest corner is much influenced by Spain. The most famous Basque towns are Biarritz, Bayonne and the picturesque old port of St-Jean-de-Luz. Further inland and nearer the Pyrénées is the attractive town of St-Jean-Pied-de-Port on the pilgrims' route to northern Spain and Santiago de Compostela, close to the forest of Iraty with its lakes and ski runs.

Places of interest

Bayonne: old streets and fortifications; Basque Museum.

Bordeaux: 14,000 piece Bohemian glass chandelier in foyer of the Grand Theatre, 29 acre Esplanade des Quinconces.

Pau: famous motor racing circuit on (closed) public highway; stadium for the Basque game of *pelota*.

St Emilion: visit the castle ramparts or drink premier cru St Emilion at pavement cafés.

St Jean-de-Luz: seaside resort and fishing village.

St Jean-Pied-de-Port: ancient city with citadel, bright Basque houses in steep streets.

Cuisine of the region

Seafood is popular, local specialities include carp stuffed with foie gras and mullet in red wine.

Chorizos: spicy sausages.

Chou farci: stuffed cabbage, sometimes *aux marrons* (with chestnuts).

Foie Gras: specially prepared livers of geese and ducks, seasoned and stuffed with truffles.

Gâteau Basque: shallow custard pastry with fillings.

Jambon de Bayonne: raw ham, cured in salt and sliced paper thin.

Lamproie: eel-like fish with leeks, onions and red Bordeaux wine.

FR33010 Camping de la Dune

Route de Biscarrosse, F-33115 La Pyla-sur-Mer (Gironde)

Tel: 05 56 22 72 17. Email: reception@campingdeladune.fr

La Dune is an informal, friendly site, with a range of amenities. From its situation at the foot of the enormous dune (the highest in Europe) you can reach the beach either by climbing over the dune or driving round. The 317 pitches, some sloping, some terraced but level, vary considerably in size are hedged with shade from pine trees. Nearly half are caravan pitches with electricity and water. Some of the site roads are quite narrow and sandy. English spoken. No tour operators. A busy site with good security.

Facilities

Modern, well equipped sanitary blocks. Motorcaravan services. Small supermarket. WiFi. Pleasant bar, restaurant, takeaway - (opens June, all other facilities are all season). Medium-sized swimming pool. Children's playground, miniclub. Open-air theatre, sports and tournaments organised July-end Aug. Purpose built barbecue (only gas individual ones are allowed). Fridge hire. Off site: Riding 2 km. Fishing 3 km. Golf 10 km.

Open: 1 May - 30 September.

Directions

The D259, signed from the N250 to Biscarrosse and Dune du Pilat, just before La Teste, avoids Pyla-sur-Mer. At end of new road turn left at roundabout onto D218 coast road. La Dune is second site on right. GPS: N44:34.520 W01:12.440

Charges 2007

Per pitch incl. 2 persons	€ 13,00 - € 29,00
with electricity	€ 19,00 - € 33,00
extra person	€ 5,00 - € 8,00
child (under 10 yrs)	€ 3,50 - € 5,50

FR33020 Camping Caravaning Fontaine-Vieille

4 boulevard du Colonel Wurtz, F-33510 Andernos-les-Bains (Gironde)

Tel: 05 56 82 01 67. Email: contact@fontaine-vieille.com

Fontaine-Vieille is a large, traditional site that has been operating for over 50 years. The site stretches along the eastern edge of the Bassin d'Arcachon under light woodland in the residential area of the small town of Andernos. Popular with the French, it has nearly 700 individual pitches, of which 520 are touring pitches (about 400 with electricity). On flat, grassy or sandy ground, they are marked by stones in the ground or young trees. Some pitches have excellent views of the Bassin, but a premium is charged for these.

Facilities

Seven adequate sanitary blocks with facilities for people with disabilities and children. Shop (1/6-15/9). Bar, terrace, takeaway and restaurant (15/5-15/9). Swimming pool complex. Tennis. TV room. Play areas. Adventure area. Minigolf. Boats, sailboards. Sports organised (high season). Internet access. Communal barbecue areas (only gas may be used on pitches). Off site: Grocery and bakery 1 km. Town 2.5 km. Golf 3 km. Riding 5 km.

Open: 1 April - 30 September.

Directions

From A63 at exit 22, take A660 towards Arcachon. Turn off A660 at exit 2 towards Facture then take RD3 north along edge of the Bassin. Site signed to left as you enter Andernos.

Charges guide

Per unit incl. 2 persons	€ 13,30 - € 20,40
with electricity (5A)	€ 16,30 - € 24,50
extra person	€ 3,10 - € 5,10
Camping Cheques accepted.	

FR33030 Camping Club Arcachon

5 allée Galarie, B.P. 46, F-33312 Arcachon (Gironde)

Tel: 05 56 83 24 15. Email: info@camping-arcachon.com

The Camping Club of Arcachon enjoys a situation well back from the hustle and bustle, where nights are quiet and facilities are of a high standard. Caravans, motorcaravans and tents all have their own area. The latter have pitches of varying sizes on neatly formed terraces. There are 250 pitches, with 150 for touring, electricity (6/10A). The site enjoys good security with day and night time 'guardians'. The restaurant is well thought of, and in season the outdoor pool with its slide is open all day.

Facilities

Three sanitary blocks with the usual facilities. Motorcaravan services. Washing machine, dryers. Fridge hire. Shop (15/6-15/9). Bar, restaurant, snack bar, takeaway (April - Oct). Swimming pool (1/6-30/9). Bicycle hire. Play area. Games room. Children's club (15/6-15/9). Entertainment for all age groups (15/6-15/9). Barbecues are only permitted in communal areas. Off site: Beach 1.8 km. Arcachon 2-3 km. Riding 1 km. Golf 2 km.

Open: All year (excl. 12 November - 12 December).

Directions

Approaching Arcachon on bypass (from Bordeaux) take exit for 'Hopital Jean Hameau'. Cross over bypass following signs for hospital, then signs for Abatilles. At next roundabout follow signs for 'Camping'. Take care as the route travels through suburban housing. GPS: N44:39.078 W01:10.445

Charges 2007

Per person	€ 4,00 - € 7,00
pitch	€ 3,00 - € 15,00
electricity	€ 3,00 - € 4,00

FR33040 Camping la Pinèda
Route de Cazaux, F-33260 Cazaux La Teste de Buch (Gironde)
Tel: 05 56 22 23 24. Email: info@campinglapinede.net

La Pinèda has recently undergone much reconstruction. It is a popular, family site with an attractive forest setting, close to the Dune de Pyla. The work includes a brand new swimming pool complex. In addition to mobile homes and chalets, there are 200 pitches here, mostly well shaded and with electrical connections. The site is just 3 km. from the very large Lac de Cazaux where there are many watersport activities. It also has direct access to a river with mooring opportunities.

Facilities

Sanitary buildings. Restaurant, bar and takeaway food. Shop. Swimming pool. Games room. Playground. Table tennis. Volleyball. Canoe hire. Mobile homes for rent. Off site: Hiking and cycling trails through the Landes forest. Lac de Cazaux (fishing and watersports) 3 km. Nearest beach 7 km.

Open: 1 May - 30 September.

Directions

From Arcachon head south towards Cazaux on the D112. Site is located north of the village. GPS: N44:33.300 W01:09.040

Charges 2007

Per person	€ 5,00 - € 7,00
child (1-6 yrs)	free
pitch	€ 16,00 - € 25,00
electricity	€ 3,70

FR33050 Camping les Ourmes
Avenue du Lac, F-33990 Hourtin (Gironde)
Tel: 05 56 09 12 76. Email: lesourmes@free.fr

Located only 500 metres from the largest fresh water lake in France, only 10 minutes drive from the beach and with its own pool, this is essentially a holiday site. Of the 270 pitches, 240 are for tourers, marked but in most cases not actually separated, and arranged amongst tall pines and other trees which give good shade. All have electricity connections. The site's amenities are arranged around a pleasant entrance courtyard with an evening entertainment programme in season. This site has a busy, cosmopolitan feel, with visitors of many different nationalities.

Facilities

Three refurbished toilet blocks. Washing machine, dryer. Small shop (1/7-31/8). Bar/restaurant with outdoor tables, takeaway snacks and reasonably priced meals (1/7-31/8). Medium sized swimming pool, paddling pool (1/5-15/9). Large leisure area, play area, volleyball, basketball, table tennis. TV, games rooms. Boules. Off site: Watersports and fishing possible on the lake, with bicycle hire, tennis and riding within 500 m.

Open: 1 April - 30 September.

Directions

Follow Houroin Port (Ave du Lac) from the town centre and site is signed on left. GPS: N45:10.926 W01:04.566

Charges 2007

Per unit incl. 2 persons	€ 12,00 - € 20,00
incl. electricity	€ 15,00 - € 23,00
extra person (over 2 yrs)	€ 2,00 - € 4,00
dog	€ 2,00

FR33080 Kawan Village Domaine de la Barbanne
Route de Montagne, F-33330 Saint Emilion (Gironde)
Tel: 05 57 24 75 80. Email: barbanne@wanadoo.fr

La Barbanne is a pleasant, friendly, family-owned site in the heart of the Bordeaux wine region, only 2.5 km. from the famous town of St Emilion. With 174 pitches, most for touring, the owners have created a carefully maintained, well equipped site. The large, level and grassy pitches have dividing hedges and electricity (long leads necessary). Twelve pitches for motorcaravans have tarmac surrounded by grass. The site owners run a free minibus service twice a day to St Emilion and also organise excursions in July and August to local places of interest, including Bordeaux.

Facilities

Two modern, fully equipped toilet blocks include facilities for campers with disabilities. Motorcaravan services. Well stocked shop. Bar, terrace, takeaway, restaurant (1/6-20/9). Two swimming pools, one heated with water slide (15/4-22/9). Enclosed play area with seats for parents, children's club (from 1/7). Evening entertainment (from 1/7). Tennis, boules, volleyball, table tennis, minigolf. The lake provides superb free fishing, pedaloes, canoes and lakeside walks. Bicycle hire. Off site: St Emilion and shops 2.5 km. Riding 8 km.

Open: 1 April - 22 September.

Directions

Site is 2.5 km. north of St Emilion. Caravans and motorhomes are forbidden through the village of St Emilion and they must approach the site from Libourne on D243 or from Castillon leave D936 and take D130/D243. GPS: N44:54.997 W00:08.513

Charges 2007

Per unit incl. 1 or 2 persons	€ 20,00 - € 30,00
extra person	€ 5,00 - € 8,00
child (under 7 yrs)	€ 3,50 - € 5,90
animal	free - € 3,00
Camping Cheques accepted.	

FR33090 Flower Camping le Pressoir

Petit Palais et Cornemps, F-33570 Lussac (Gironde)

Tel: 05 57 69 73 25. Email: contact@campinglepressoir.com

The 100 large pitches at Le Pressoir are arranged on either side of a gravel road leading up a slight hill. Most are shaded by attractive trees, but almost all are sloping. They are over 100 sq.m. and equipped with electricity (blue EC plugs) and interspersed with 5 mobile homes for hire. The old barn has been converted into a stylish bar and a really charming, separate restaurant. A quiet, family site, Le Pressoir provides a comfortable base for a holiday in this area famous for good food and wine. Buried in the famous wine producing countryside of the Lussac, Pomerol and St Emilion areas north of Bordeaux, Le Pressoir is surrounded by fields of vines. The manicured entrance featuring attractive trees, shrubs and flowers, together with preserved equipment from its former role as a wine farm, welcomes one to the site.

Facilities

Fully equipped toilet block with facilities for disabled visitors, and washing machine. Bar and pleasant restaurant (all season). Swimming pool (15/5-15/9, no Bermuda shorts). Playground with timber equipment. Petanque, volleyball and table tennis. Mountain bike hire. Off site: Tennis nearby. Fishing 3 km. Riding and bicycle hire 9 km.

Open: All year.

Directions

From N89 Bordeaux - Périgueux at Saint Médard de Guizières turn south towards Lussac (D21). From Castillon-la-Bataille on D936 Libourne-Bergerac road, south of site, take D17 north towards St Médard then D21 through Petit Palais. Site signed.
GPS: N44:59.824 W00:03.801

Charges 2008

Per person	€ 5,60 - € 7,50
child (2-6 yrs)	€ 3,30 - € 4,50
pitch	€ 13,00 - € 15,00
with 6A electricity	€ 13,00 - € 26,00
animal	€ 1,90 - € 2,50

CAMPING
CARAVANING
★ ★ ★ ★

Le Pressoir

Petit Palais
33570 LUSSAC
SAINT-ÉMILION

Tél. 0033 5 57 69 73 25
Fax 0033 5 57 69 77 36

www.campinglepressoir.com
contact@campinglepressoir.com

Discover a region, quiet and open, in the middle of an abundant nature with its wordwide wellknown vineyards

SPECIAL PRICE from €13,- per night based on one or two pers. Stay outside season

FR33120 Camping la Cigale

Route de Lège, F-33740 Arès (Gironde)

Tel: 05 56 60 22 59. Email: campinglacigaleares@wanadoo.fr

La Cigale is an attractive little site with charm and ambience where the owners extend a very warm welcome. Small and beautifully maintained, it is set amid pine trees and M. Pallet's floral displays. The 95 level, grassy pitches, most with electricity and of 100 sq.m. in size, are divided by hedges and flower borders. The majority have shade from the pine trees. There are two small swimming pools in a pleasant setting and under the ample shade of a large plane tree, where drinks, meals and snacks are served on the bar terrace.

Facilities

The well equipped toilet block includes a family room with two showers and facilities for disabled visitors. Washing machine and dryer. Motorcaravan services. Simple shop. Bar, terrace, meals, snacks. Pizza takeaway (all 17/6-10/9). Two small swimming pools (15/5-12/9). Small play area. Entertainers for children and adults in July/Aug. Free donkey cart rides every Sunday. Off site: Site is convenient for a wide choice of beaches. Village centre 800 m. Fishing or riding 1 km.

Open: 29 April - 2 October.

Directions

Leave Bordeaux ring road at exit 10 (D213) or exit 11 (D106) and continue direct to Arès. Turn into Arès following road to church square. Turn right following signs for Lège/Cap Ferret. Site is 800 m. on left.
GPS: N44:46.366 W01:08.537

Charges 2007

Per unit incl. 1 or 2 persons	€ 26,00 - € 46,00
extra person	€ 5,00
child (7 yrs)	€ 3,00
electricity (4/6A)	€ 5,00

FR33110 Airotel Camping de la Côte d'Argent

Mobile homes ▶ page 496

F-33990 Hourtin-Plage (Gironde)

Tel: **05 56 09 10 25**. Email: **info@camping-cote-dargent.com**

Côte d'Argent is a large, well equipped site for leisurely family holidays. It makes an ideal base for walkers and cyclists, with over 100 km. of cycle lanes. Hourtin-Plage is a pleasant invigorating resort on the Atlantic coast and a popular location for watersports enthusiasts, The site's top attraction is its pool complex with wooden bridges connecting the pools and islands, with sunbathing and play areas plus indoor heated pool. There are 550 touring pitches, not clearly defined, under trees with some on soft sand. Entertainment takes place at the bar near the entrance (until 12.30). Spread over 20 hectares of undulating sand-based terrain and in the midst of a pine forest. There are 48 hardstandings for motorcaravans outside the site, providing a cheap stop-over, but with no access to site facilities. The site is well organised and ideal for children.

Facilities

Very clean sanitary blocks include provision for disabled visitors. Washing machines. Motorcaravan service points. Large supermarket, restaurant, takeaway, pizzeria bar. Four outdoor pools with slides and flumes. Indoor pool. Massage. Astronomy once a week. Tennis. Play areas. Miniclub, organised entertainment in season. Fishing. Riding. Bicycle hire. Internet. ATM. Charcoal barbecues are not permitted. Off site: Path to beach 300 m. Golf 30 km.

Open: 17 May - 14 September.

Directions

Turn off D101 Hourtin-Soulac road 3 km. north of Hourtin. Join D101E signed Hourtin-Plage. Site is 300 m. from beach. GPS: N45:13.381 W01:09.868

Charges 2008

Per unit incl. 2 persons and electricity	€ 25,00 - € 44,00
extra person	€ 3,00 - € 7,00

Camping Cheques accepted.

FR33150 Camping Municipal les Gabarreys

Route de la Rivière, F-33250 Pauillac (Gironde)

Tel: **05 56 59 10 03**. Email: **camping.les.gabarreys@wanadoo.fr**

An attractive, small site with well tended flower beds, Les Gabarreys is surrounded by vineyards of the Médoc region. An excellent site, it has 59 pitches, 41 with hardstanding for caravans or motorcaravans (so pegging out awnings could be a problem), 14 grass pitches for tents and 6 mobile homes, all with electric hook-ups (5/10A, some may require long leads). The 'Maison du Tourisme et du Vin' should be your first port of call. The surrounding area is well supplied with wine caves, and being fairly level you could perhaps cycle to some of them.

Facilities

Two immaculate toilet blocks provide open and cubicle washbasins and excellent facilities for disabled people. Motorcaravan services. General room with satellite TV, fridge-freezer and a small library. New play area. Minigolf (free) and volleyball.

Open: 3 April - 9 October.

Directions

Pauillac lies NNW of Bordeaux. From Bordeaux take D1 to St Laurent, then D206 to Pauillac. At roundabout turn right to Pauillac Guais, then straight ahead at next roundabout and turn right before the Maison du Tourisme. GPS: N45:11.098 W00:45.524

Charges 2007

Per unit incl. 1 person	€ 8,00 - € 8,50
extra person	€ 4,00 - € 4,40

FR33160 Espace Naturiste Euronat

F-33590 Grayan-et-l'Hopital (Gironde)

Tel: **05 56 09 33 33**. Email: **info@euronat.fr**

Euronat is really a large naturist town with extensive facilities, direct access to 1.5 km. of sandy beach and a Thalassotherapy centre. The caravan and camping sites are in two areas separate from the chalets and mobile homes. A variety of good sized, fairly flat and sandy pitches, includes some suitable for large motorhomes. All pitches have 10A electricity and some also have water and drainage. The 'town centre' is superb with two supermarkets, an organic supermarket, cash-point, butcher, fish shop, bakery, restaurants including fish, brasserie, pizzeria/crêperie, and a takeaway.

Facilities

Sanitary blocks are well maintained with some heated (not all open in low season). Facilities for people with disabilities. Launderette. Motorcaravan services. Shops, restaurants. Swimming pool. Activities and workshops, archery, pony club, riding, tennis, petanque. Children's activities and day care. Multi-purpose hall for dances, film nights, music evenings, sports activities. Supervised beach.

Open: 23 March - 3 November.

Directions

From Bordeaux ring road take exit 7, then D1215 to Lesparre and Vensac, then follow (large) signed route. GPS: N45:24.976 W01:07.907

Charges 2007

Per unit incl. 2 persons	€ 15,00 - € 28,80
with electricity (10A)	€ 17,50 - € 42,00
extra person	€ 3,00 - € 6,00

Camping Cheques accepted.

Côte d'Argent

OOL COMPLEX OF 3500 M² WITH WATERSLIDES, JACUZZI AND COVERED HEATED SWIMMING POOL

Special low season offers (not in July and August)
14 = 11 and 7 = 6
campsite or accommodations

i - hotel - shops - restaurant - bar - provisions - animation (sports) - tennis - rse riding - archery - mini club - games room - sailing (4 km) - surfing (300 m)

Hourtin Plage - Aquitaine - Atlantique Sud

La Côte d'Argent is a beautiful sloping park of 20 ha in the heart of a pine tree forest. At 300 m of a long winding sandy beach at the Atlantic Ocean.
A site in the lee of dunes and the forest, this holiday village enjoys an ideal climate for enjoying relaxing nature holidays.

Sun , Life and fun

Airotel Camping Caravaning de la Côte d'Argent
33990 Hourtin Plage
Tél : 00033 (0)5.56.09.10.25
Fax : 0033 (0)5.56.09.24.96
www.camping-cote-dargent.com - www.cca33.com -
www.campingcoteouest.com

FR33140 Camping le Grand Pré

Route de Casteljaloux, F-33430 Bazas (Gironde)

Tel: **05 56 65 13 17**. Email: **legrandpre@wanadoo.fr**

In a rural position, where the owners stated philosophy of tranquillity is realised. There are only 30 grass pitches, separated by flowering shrubs and bushes. There are plans to expand and four pitches are occupied by mobile homes. All have electricity (6-16A), water and drainage. Reception facilities and a bar are in a very tastefully converted old barn, where you may have breakfast or collect bread. There is a traffic free footpath from the site to the town, which we can recommend.

Facilities

The high quality toilet block may not be adequate for demand, but we are told more units will be built. Washing machine and dryer, baby room, facilities for disabled persons. Motorcaravan services. Swimming and paddling pools. Sunbathing area. Small playground. Volleyball, boules. B&B nearby at the Château. By prior arrangement touring motorcaravans may park overnight here when the site is closed. Off site: Shops, bars, restaurants, gas supplies available in Bazas, 1.5 km.

Open: 1 April - 30 September.

Directions

Bazas is around 55 km. southeast of Bordeaux, and 15 km. south of Langon. From Bazas centre take the D655 east towards Casteljaloux, and the site entrance is about 1 km. on your right (well signed).

Charges guide

Per unit incl. 1 or 2 persons	€ 7,90 - € 18,90
incl. 3 persons	€ 9,50 - € 22,00
electricity (6-16A)	€ 3,20 - € 4,75
extra person over 10 yrs	€ 2,40 - € 3,50

FR33170 Camping les Acasias

44 route de Saint Vivien, F-33590 Vensac (Gironde)

Tel: **05 56 09 58 81**. Email: **contact@les-acacias-du-medoc.fr**

Les Acacias is a medium sized, family run site in a lovely, rural location on the edge of the pretty little village of Vensac. This attractive site has been owned by the Gomes family for 16 years, and they offer a very warm welcome in the chalet-style reception. The mixed woodland setting, with lots of flowering shrubs, makes a welcome change from the ubiquitous pines on the coast. There are 175 pitches (141 for touring) and electrical connections were being refurbished when we visited.

Facilities

Maintenance and cleaning of the attractive toilet block is of a high standard. Facilities for disabled visitors. Mother and baby room with good facilities. Washing machines and dryers. Small shop (1/7-30/8). Bar, café and takeaway (1/7-30/8). Swimming and paddling pools (unheated, 1/6-24/9). Pool table, table tennis, minigolf (all free). Play area. Mobile homes to rent. Off site: Fishing and riding 5 km. Bicycle hire in St Vivien 3 km. Nearest beach 12 km. Bus service to Lesparre and Le Verdon outside site.

Open: 1 April - 24 September.

Directions

From Bordeaux ring-road take exit 8 towards St Medard, then a quick right-left onto D1 towards Castelnau-de-Medoc. Continue on D1 as it becomes the N215, past Lesparre-Medoc. After 15 km. ignore first left turn to Vensac (despite campings sign), take second and site is on left in 200 m.

Charges guide

Per unit incl. 2 persons and electricity	€ 11,00 - € 20,00
extra person	€ 3,20

FR33330 Camping le Lilhan

8 allée Michel Montaigne, F-33780 Soulac-sur-Mer (Gironde)

Tel: **05 56 09 77 63**. Email: **contact@lelilhan.com**

A well established woodland site, popular with families, Le Lilhan was undergoing extensive renovation at the time of our visit in May 2007. There are 170 large pitches (100 with 10A electricity), 110 available for touring units, the remainder used for 50 mobile homes and chalets to rent and 10 privately owned units. Most pitches are heavily shaded and on natural woodland floor terrain. A special area is kept for younger campers away from the quieter family areas. There is an attractive and pool complex, together with a small shop for bread and basic provisions, bar and a restaurant.

Facilities

Two new unisex toilet blocks fitted to a high standard and an older refurbished unit. Family bathroom with double shower unit, facilities for babies, washbasins in cubicles, and a suite for disabled campers. Laundry facilities. Swimming pool complex, sauna and jacuzzi (15/6-15/9). Shop, bar, restaurant and pizzeria, takeaway (15/6-15/9). Entertainment and children's club (high season). Playground. Minigolf. Tennis. Archery. Riding. Bicycle hire. Internet access. American RVs or motorcaravans over 8 m. are not accepted. Off site: Town and beach 3 km.

Open: 1 April - 15 September.

Directions

Soulac-sur-Mer is on the Atlantic coast just south of the tip of the Gironde peninsula. Site is signed off the 0101 – turn east on a minor road about 3 km. south of Soulac town, and site is on the left after a short distance. GPS: N45:29.146 W01:07.074

Charges 2007

Per unit incl. 2 persons	€ 15,95 - € 19,95
extra person	€ 3,00 - € 4,50
electricity (10A)	€ 4,00 - € 4,20
No credit cards.	

FR33130 Yelloh! Village les Grands Pins

Mobile homes ▶ page 496

Plage Nord, F-33680 Lacanau-Océan (Gironde)

Tel: 04 66 73 97 39. Email: info@yellohvillage-les-grands-pins.com

This Atlantic coast holiday site with direct access to a fine sandy beach, is on undulating terrain amongst tall pine trees. A large site, with 600 pitches, 430 of varying sizes for touring units. One half of the site is a traffic free zone (except for arrival or departure day, caravans are placed on the pitch, with separate areas outside for parking). There are a good number of tent pitches, those in the centre of the site having some of the best views. This site is popular with an excellent range of facilities available for the whole season. Especially useful for tent campers are safety deposit and fridge boxes which are available for rent. Mobile homes (2 persons) are for hire. The large sandy beach is a 350 m. stroll from the gate at the back of the site.

Facilities

Four well equipped toilet blocks, one heated, including baby room and facilities for disabled people. Launderette. Motorcaravan services. Supermarket. Bar, restaurant, snack bar, takeaway. Heated swimming pool (lifeguard in July/Aug) with sunbathing surround. Jacuzzi. Free fitness activities. Games room. Fitness suite. Tennis. Two playgrounds. Adventure playground. Bicycle hire. Organised activities. WiFi in the bar (on payment). Only gas barbecues are permitted. Off site: Fishing, golf, riding and bicycle hire 5 km.

Open: 26 April - 20 September.

Directions

From Bordeaux take N125/D6 west to Lacanau-Océan. At second roundabout, take second exit: Plage Nord, follow signs to 'campings'. Les Grand Pins signed to right at the far end of road. GPS: N45:00.664 W01:11.602

Charges 2007

Per unit incl. 2 persons and electricity	€ 14,00 - € 43,00
extra person	€ 5,00 - € 9,00
child (2-12 yrs)	free - € 5,00
dog	€ 4,00

Half-board arrangements available.

FR33190 Pyla Camping

Grande Dune du Pyla, F-33115 Pyla-sur-Mer (Gironde)

Tel: **05 56 22 74 56**. Email: **info@pyla-camping.com**

Pyla Camping is set on quite steeply sloping ground in pinewood between the Biscarosse road and the 110 metre Dune de Pyla. A major attraction here is paragliding and the site has its own launch platform above the beach. The unserviced pitches closest to the beach are very popular with paragliders. In late May there is a festival which attracts flyers from all over Europe (festival music goes on well into the night). The site's 450 pitches are on terraces, 120 used for mobile homes for rent (mostly new, but a few quite old and scruffy). Of the touring pitches, 100 have 10A electricity.

Facilities	Directions
Four adequate toilet blocks (one with underfloor heating when needed). Washing machines and dryers. Very well-stocked shop. Large bar/restaurant with takeaway food (all season) and terrace. Large heated swimming pool and paddling pool. Games room. Bicycle hire. Volleyball, basketball, football (tournaments organised in July/Aug). Entertainment in high season. Off site: Golf and riding 4 km. Fishing (sea) from beach below site. **Open:** 25 April - 20 September.	From A63 (north or south) take A660 towards Arcachon. At La Teste turn off towards Dune de Pyla and at the Dune car park roundabout take left turn towards Biscarosse. Site is about 3 km. on right.

Charges 2007

Per unit incl. 2 persons and electricity	€ 16,00 - € 33,00
extra person	€ 4,00 - € 8,50
child (0-7 yrs)	€ 2,00 - € 4,00

FR33210 Sunêlia la Pointe du Medoc

Route de la Pointe de Grave, F-33123 Le Verdon-sur-Mer (Gironde)

Tel: **05 56 73 39 99**. Email: **info@camping-lapointedumedoc.com**

This site has 260 pitches, with around half for touring (6A electricity and many fully serviced). It is situated roughly equi-distant between the sandy Atlantic beach (accessed by a pleasant walk through the forest opposite the site) and that of the Gironde estuary, both around 1 km. away. Pitches are generally large. Some are in full sun but those towards the rear of the site offer much more shade. A large office has recently been converted to provide a library with internet access and a full size billiard table.

Facilities	Directions
Swimming pool, small waterfalls, paddling pool. Massage room. Beach volleyball. Minigolf. Multisport terrain. Bicycle hire. Communal barbecues. Organised entertainment and children's club (ages 4-11) all season. Small farm and children's garden. Activities for teenagers in July/Aug. Off site: Sea fishing 1 km. Riding 5 km. **Open:** 26 April - 12 September.	Site is on the RN215 just south of Le Verdon and can be accessed either from the south (Bordeaux or the Blaye ferry), or from the north using the regular Royan - Pointe de Grave car ferry.

Charges 2008

Per unit incl. 1 or 2 persons	€ 13,00 - € 20,00
with electricity	€ 16,00 - € 24,00
with water and drainage	€ 18,00 - € 26,00
extra person (over 1 yr)	€ 3,00 - € 6,00

FR33230 Camping International le Truc Vert

Route du Truc-Vert, F-33950 Lège-Cap Ferret (Gironde)

Tel: **05 56 60 89 55**. Email: **truc-vert@tiscali.fr**

Relaxing amidst the tall pines of this 10 hectare hillside site is pleasant, but if you are looking for more activity there are many cycle ways and walks to enjoy in the lovely local countryside. The site provides over 480 pitches (280 with 6A electricity) with trees giving shade. Some pitches are level but for many you will need levelling blocks. Some site roads are a little steep so care is needed and also while travelling on the local main roads through the woods (keep to speed limits) as the occasional wild boar ventures out onto the roads.

Facilities	Directions
Seven toilet blocks (not all open all season) spread well around the site offer satisfactory facilities with showers and washbasins in cubicles, facilities for disabled people (although some may find the roads on site a little steep). Motorcaravan service area. Laundry and dishwashing. Bar/brasserie (1/5-30/9). Restaurant (1/6-30/9). Internet access. Shop. Play area. Volleyball. TV/games room. Some evening entertainment in season. Off site: Riding 500 m. Fishing and beach 600 m. **Open:** 1 May - 30 September.	From Bordeaux take D106 towards Lège-Cap Ferret. Continue on D106 through town and in Les Jacquets, just before village sign for Le Petit Piquey, turn right. Follow through residential area and woods for about 4 km. Site is on left.

Charges 2007

Per unit incl. 2 persons	€ 18,50 - € 21,55
extra person	€ 4,20
electricity (6A)	€ 3,05
child (2-12 yrs)	free - € 4,20

FR33220 Sunêlia le Petit Nice

Route de Biscarosse, F-33115 Pyla-sur-Mer (Gironde)

Tel: **05 56 22 74 03**. Email: **info@petitnice.com**

Mobile homes ▶ page 497

Le Petit Nice is a traditional seaside site, just south of the great Dune de Pyla (Europe's largest sand dune, and a genuinely remarkable sight). It is a friendly, if relatively unsophisticated, site with direct (steep) access to an excellent sandy beach. The 225 pitches are for the most part terraced, descending towards the sea. Many are quite small, with larger pitches generally occupied by mobile homes. For this reason it is likely to appeal more to campers and those with smaller motorcaravans and caravans. Most pitches are shaded by pine trees but those closest to the sea are unshaded. Unusually, the site also has a private hang-gliding and paragliding take-off strip (very popular activities here).

Facilities

Two refurbished toilet blocks include washbasins in cubicles, baby rooms and facilities for disabled people. New, very smart bar/restaurant. Well stocked shop. Games room. Attractive swimming pool with small slide, children's pool and jacuzzi. Good fenced play area. Tennis. Boules court.

Open: 1 April - 30 September.

Directions

The site is on the D218 (Arcachon - Biscarosse) south of the Dune de Pyla and is the fifth site you pass after the Dune. GPS: N44:34.339 W01:13.255

Charges 2007

Per pitch incl. 2 persons	€ 14,00 - € 28,00
with electricity (6A)	€ 17,00 - € 32,00
extra person	€ 4,00 - € 7,00
child (2-12 yrs)	€ 2,00 - € 6,00

Camping Cheques accepted.

FR33240 **Camping Airotel de L'Océan**

F-33680 Lacanau-Océan (Gironde)

Tel: **05 56 03 24 45**. Email: **airotel.lacanau@wanadoo.fr**

Its location on the Atlantic coast, 600 metres from a lovely sandy beach makes this site extremely popular. Set in 10 hectares of wooded sand dunes, the site offers the total holiday experience with 550 pitches set amongst pine trees with areas for peace and quiet and areas for those who want to be on top of it all. Some pitches are quite spacious, some level and others requiring blocks. At the time of our visit everywhere was very dry and there was very little grass. There is a large swimming pool complex, a bar and soundproofed disco.

Facilities

Six toilet blocks provide spacious facilities including a room for disabled visitors in each block (although the site is quite hilly), baby rooms, washing machines. Motorcaravan services. Supermarket. Bar, restaurant, takeaway. Large leisure pool complex. Various sports facilities. Fitness gym. TV, games rooms. Internet access. Bicycle hire. Barbecue area. Off site: Beach 600 m. Shops 1 km. Many cycle routes through the woods.

Open: 9 April - 25 September.

Directions

From Bordeaux take D106 then onto D3 to Royan and through the wooded areas of the Atlantic coast. At Lacanau join D6 to Lacanau-Océan. At roundabout before village turn right and site is 800 m. on the right. GPS: N45:00.511 W01:11.544

Charges guide

Per unit incl. 2 persons	€ 12,00 - € 26,50
with electricity	€ 12,00 - € 29,50
extra person	€ 3,00 - € 7,50

FR33250 **Camping Parc du Val de l'Eyre**

8 route du Minoy, F-33770 Salles (Gironde)

Tel: **05 56 88 67 03**. Email: **levaldeleyre2@wanadoo.fr**

This comfortable, reasonably-priced site, while perhaps not having enough attractions to warrant a whole holiday, makes a good base for a few days to explore the Atlantic coast with its superb beaches. Set in 13 hectares of mature oak woodland, the 4 hectares for camping are mainly taken up by mobile homes of varying age and condition. Most of the 69 pitches for tourers (40 with 6A electricity) are set in an open, flat area in the centre of the site (therefore no natural shade here), with a few smaller pitches under the trees. Access is straightforward.

Facilities

Two smartly refurbished toilet blocks have good facilities (including seats in the shower cubicles). Shower/toilet room for disabled people (key access). Bar and restaurant (July/Aug). Unheated swimming pool. Play area and games field. Minigolf. Fridge hire. Electronic games in a marquee near the pool. Off site: Supermarket 50 m, town shops, etc. 5 minutes. Bus to Biscarosse from outside site. Riding 5 km. Bicycle hire in Salles. Beaches 12 km.

Open: 1 April - 30 September.

Directions

From A63 take exit 21 to town of Salles (2 km). Follow signs to Biscarosse in town and site is a left turn opposite the Champion supermarket. Ignore 'Camping 4 km' signs - that's a different site.

Charges 2007

Per unit incl. 2 persons	€ 14,00 - € 22,00
extra person	€ 4,00 - € 6,00
electricity (6A)	€ 3,80
No credit cards.	

FR33280 **Sunêlia la Forêt**

Route de Biscarosse, F-33115 Pyla-sur-Mer (Gironde)

Tel: **05 56 22 73 28**. Email: **camping.foret@wanadoo.fr**

Camping de la Forêt is one of a number of sites in this area that is dominated by the massive Dune de Pyla. The dune has to be negotiated in order to get to the beach (either over it or around, which is about 3 km), and the virtual wall of bright sand is all you have by way of a view to the east. This is a very well kept site with good facilities, easy access for all types of unit, and plenty of attractions for adults and children. Set on a gentle slope, mixed pine and oak trees give shade on most pitches.

Facilities

Six unisex toilet blocks (not all open in low season) have good facilities. No special facilities for babies. Facilities for disabled visitors (key from reception). Washing machines and dryers. Motorcaravan service area. Well stocked mini-market. Bar, takeaway and restaurant (1/5-30/9). Swimming and paddling pools. Two tennis courts (free except in July/Aug). Minigolf. Boules. Bicycle hire. Large play area. Children's club (with clowns) in July/Aug. Off site: Bus (infrequent service in low season) from outside site to Biscarosse and on to Bordeaux. Golf, riding and sailing all within 5 km.

Open: 7 April - 5 November.

Directions

From A63 (north or south) take A660 towards Arcachon. At La Teste turn off towards Dune de Pyla and at Dune car park roundabout take left turn towards Biscarosse. Site is about 2 km. on the right.

Charges 2007

Per unit incl. 2 persons	€ 14,00 - € 29,00
incl. electricity	€ 19,00 - € 33,00
extra person	€ 5,00 - € 8,00
child (under 7 yrs)	€ 2,50 - € 4,50

FR33320 Camping Talaris Vacances

Route de l'Océan, F-33680 Lacanau-Océan (Gironde)
Tel: 05 56 03 04 15. Email: talarisvacances@free.fr

It is located near a large lake and just 6 km. from the Atlantic coast at Lacanau-Océan, so there are opportunities for swimming in either lake or sea, for surfing, water-skiing or sailing. On site, there is plenty going on for youngsters – the many activities take place in front of the bar, restaurant and swimming pool area, so it is probably not the place for parents to relax! However, the part of the campsite allocated to the 150 tourist pitches is amongst mature trees at the far end of the site, so is surprisingly peaceful and relaxed.

Facilities

Two similar toilet blocks, but the one in the camping/caravanning area is adequate. Washing machines and dryers. Baby room and facilities for disabled people. Shop (July/Aug). Bar/restaurant and takeaway with covered terrace (1/5-13/9). Swimming pools (1/5-13/9). Off site: Lake 1 km. Riding 1 km. Golf 3 km. Sea beach 6 km.

Open: 7 April - 17 September.

Directions

From Bordeaux, take N125/D6 west to Lacanau and continue on D6 towards Lacanau-Océan. Site is on right in about 4 km. GPS: N45:00.288 W01:06.443

Charges 2007

Per unit incl. 2 persons	€ 16,50 - € 28,50
extra person	€ 3,00 - € 6,00
child (4-10 yrs)	free - € 4,00
animal	€ 3,00 - € 3,00
electricity (6A)	€ 3,50

FR33260 Camping le Braou

Route de Bordeaux, F-33980 Audenge (Gironde)
Tel: 05 56 26 90 03. Email: info@camping-audenge.com

The present owners, M. and Mme. Gharbi, were the wardens of this simple, former municipal site and now lease it from the town. They have funded several developments since they took over in 2003 including a small pool, a snack bar, play area and new electrical hook-ups. The site is flat with easy access, and the pitches are in avenues, separated by newly-planted small shrubs. There is no natural shade. The new electric hook-ups (on 116 of the 148 pitches) are 10A. Outside high season this is a pleasant, reasonably priced place to stay while exploring the Bassin d'Arcachon with its bird reserve, oyster-beds, way-marked walks and cycle tracks. As with many French sites nothing much happens here until the beginning of July. Audenge (800 m.) is a lovely little town with a good choice of shops and restaurants. The Gharbis are very proud of their site, and this shows in the welcome and the high standard of maintenance.

Facilities

The small toilet block would be stretched when the site is full, but adequate in low season. Washbasins are in cubicles on the ladies side, open for men. Showers are controllable for temperature, push button operated. Shop for basics. Bar and snack-bar (July/Aug). Small unheated swimming pool (1/6-31/8). Play area. Internet access. Motorhome service point and overnight pitches outside site. Mobile homes to rent. Off site: Town facilities 800 m. Beach and fishing 15 km. Riding 2 km. Golf 5 km.

Open: 1 April - 30 September.

Directions

From A63 take exit 22 onto A660 towards Arcachon. From A660 take exit 2 towards Facture, then D3 through Biganos to Audenge. Site is signed 'Camping Municipal' at lights in town.

Charges 2007

Per unit incl. 2 persons	€ 9,50 - € 16,50
extra person	€ 3,00 - € 5,00
child (0-13 yrs)	€ 3,00 - € 4,50
electricity	€ 3,50 - € 3,50

TO BOOK CALL 01580 214000
TRAVEL SERVICE SITE
Advice & low ferry-inclusive prices

Check real time availability and at-the-gate prices...
www.alanrogers.com

FR33290 **Camping le Tedey**

Par le Moutchic, Route de Longarisse, F-33680 Lacanau-Lac (Gironde)

Tel: **05 56 03 00 15**. Email: **camping@le-tedey.com**

With direct access to a large lake and beach, this site enjoys a beautiful tranquil position set in an area of 14 hectares amidst mature pine trees. There are 700 pitches of which 630 are for touring units with 36 mobile homes and chalets available for rent. The pitches are generally level and grassy although the site is on a slope. Dappled sunlight is available through the trees. Electricity is available to all pitches and 223 also have water and waste water drainage. The bar is close to the lake with a large indoor and outdoor seating area. The owners and staff are friendly and helpful and English is spoken. There is an open air cinema on Saturdays and Wednesdays as well as other entertainment in July and August. A children's club is also organised. The takeaway sells a variety of food and the shop next door is well stocked. This is an attractive well maintained site where you get a feeling of space and calm. There are many places of interest nearby and a short drive from Bordeaux.

Facilities

Four modern sanitary blocks with facilities for disabled visitors and babies. Laundry facilities. Bar with terrace. Creperie. Takeaway. Bicycle hire. Boating on the lake. Volleyball. Table tennis. Petanque. Playground. Gas barbecues only on pitches. Dogs accepted but not in July or August. Internet access. Off site: Surfing. Riding. Golf. Cycling. Riding.

Open: 28 April - 19 September.

Directions

From Lacanau take the D6 to Lacanau-Ocean. Take Route de Longarisse and camping is well signposted.

Charges 2007

Per unit incl. 1 or 2 persons and electricity	€ 16,00 - € 20,00
with water and drainage	€ 19,80 - € 24,00
extra person	€ 3,00 - € 5,00
child (2-10 yrs)	€ 2,50 - € 3,00

FR33300 **Domaine Residentiel Naturiste la Jenny**

F-33680 Le Porge (Gironde)

Tel: **05 56 26 56 90**. Email: **info@lajenny.fr**

Parcs Résidentiels ● page 515

Pitches at this campsite are exclusively for chalet accommodation.

FR33310 Yelloh! Village Panorama du Pyla

Grande Dune du Pyla, route de Biscarrosse, F-33260 Pyla-sur-Mer (Gironde)

Tel: **04 66 73 97 39**. Email: **info@yellohvillage-panorama.com**

Many campsites set amongst pine trees have a rather untidy look, but Panorama is different. Here the entrance is inviting with well tended flower beds and a pleasant, airy reception. There is a steep climb up to the first of the touring pitches, passing the swimming pool and play area. Some pitches are suitable for caravans and motorcaravans and others suitable for tents. The touring pitches are on terraces amongst the tall pines and most have electricity (3-10A). The sea views from almost all pitches are stunning. Access to the toilet blocks may involve a steep climb (the site is probably not suitable for people with disabilities). All potentially noisy activities – pool, play areas, shop, discos, concerts, bar and takeaway – are grouped on the entrance side of the dune, away from the pitches. A track leads down to the beach with a staircase and right next door is Europe's largest dune, the Dune de Pyla, a favourite with parascenders. The area is a maze of off road cycle tracks. There are many activities and entertainments organised in high season, even classical concerts.

Facilities

Seven toilet blocks (only two open in low season) are clean and well maintained with baby rooms and facilities for disabled people. Fridge hire. Laundry facilities. Motorcaravan services. Restaurant with panoramic view of the ocean. Three heated swimming pools and jacuzzi. Adjacent play area. Tennis. Minigolf, table tennis. Paragliding. Sub-aqua diving. Organised entertainment in high season for all ages. Library and internet access in reception. Off site: Riding and golf 10 km.

Open: 18 April - 29 September.

Directions

From N250, just before La Teste, take D259 signed Biscarrosse and Dune de Pyla. At roundabout at end of road turn left (south) on D218 coast road signed Biscarrosse and Dune de Pyla. Site is 4 km. on right. GPS: N44:34.359 W01:13.232

Charges 2007

Per unit with 2 persons and electricity	€ 17,00 - € 40,00
extra person	€ 4,00 - € 7,00
child (under 12 yrs)	€ 3,00 - € 4,00

Between the dunes and the ocean, a glimpse of what's in store

The PANORAMA is the only campsite in the region which is right by the sea and protected against the noise of motor traffic. The parking lot is patrolled by security guards at night. There is a panoramic view of the ocean, with a private staircase down to the beach. Customers have free use of the heated pool, minigolf, sauna, children's club, classical music auditorium. Tennis is free in the low season. You can find almost anything you need in the shops on the campsite. The entertainments hall and discotheque are some distance away from the camping area. There is a take-off zone for paragliding and hanggliding. The great PYLA dune can be reached directly from the campsite. Chalets and trailer homes over looking the sea, for rent.

Reductions in low season. www.camping-panorama.com

TEL: +33 (0) 556 221 044 FAX: +33 (0) 556 221 012 E-MAIL: mail@camping-panorama.com

---

FR33340 Camping les Sables d'Argent

Boulevard de l'Amélie, F-33780 Soulac-sur-Mer (Gironde)

Tel: **05 56 09 82 87**. Email: **sables@lelilhan.com**

Set amongst pine trees and undulating sand dunes, this seaside holiday site has direct access to the beach. There are 152 individual, hedged pitches on sandy grass with some terracing (some do slope). Many are under tall pines with some very large fir cones, but a few are in the open right on the shore. There are 72 pitches for touring units, the remainder being used for a mix of rented and private mobile homes and chalets. Five pitches are fully serviced and 70 have 10A electricity. Entertainment in July/August includes a children's club, themed meals, dances, karaoke and bingo.

Facilities

Two toilet blocks, both recently refitted, provide washbasins (some in cubicles), facilities for babies and disabled campers. Laundry facilities. Small shop. Bar with internet access and WiFi. Restaurant, crêperie, pizzeria and takeaway. Children's club and entertainment (July/Aug). Beachside games area. Adventure playground and communal barbecue area. Surfing and other watersports. Bicycle hire. Only gas and electric barbecues. American RVs not accepted. Off site: Boat launching 2 km. Riding 3 km. Over 100 km. of cycleways.

Open: 1 April - 30 September.

Directions

Soulac-sur-Mer is on the Atlantic coast just south of the tip of the Gironde peninsula. Site is on the long straight boulevard which runs parallel to the sea, south of town centre towards Amélie-sur-Mer (also signed from D101 along with numerous other sites (signs are small and easy to miss).

Charges 2007

Per unit incl. 2 persons	€ 15,95 - € 19,95
extra person	€ 3,00 - € 4,50
electricty (10A)	€ 4,00 - € 4,20

Camping Cheques accepted.

FR33350 Camping Chez Gendron

2 Chez Gendron, F-33820 Saint-Palais (Gironde)
Tel: **05 57 32 96 47**. Email: **info@chezgendron.com**

This useful all year site is Dutch-owned and in traditional style. In a rural setting, there are views over the Gironde estuary from the bar terrace above the small (unheated) swimming pool. The site is arranged in a number of paddocks and is part terraced, part sloping. There are 53 pitches, all on grass with electricity hook-ups (6/10A), well spaced and quite shady. Some are a fair distance from the facilities which are grouped around the reception area. It can be a steep walk up from the lowest pitches. Access to some pitches may be difficult for large or tall units especially in inclement weather.

Facilities

One small traditional toilet block, with modern fittings and underfloor heating. Facilities for babies and a suite for disabled people. Washing machine. These facilities could be stretched in peak season. Bar/restaurant and takeaway with terrace (May - Sept). Outdoor pool {May - end Sept). Playground. Games room with WiFi and internet terminal. Trampoline. Boules. Bicycle hire. Low key animation organised in season. No charcoal barbecues in summer. Off site: Fishing 8 km. Golf 15 km. Boat launching 8 km.

Open: All year.

Directions

Saint-Palais is on the D255, just west of the N137 and about 6 km. south of Mirambeau and A10 exit 37. Site lies southwest of village on minor road off the D255 and is well signed. GPS: W45:18.861 W00:36.183

Charges 2007

Per person	€ 2,25 - € 3,25
child (under 5 yrs)	free
pitch	€ 7,25 - € 10,00

Discounts of 30% April, May, June; 40% October-April.

FR33360 Camping de la Bastide

2 les Tuilleries, Pineuilh, F-33220 Sainte-Foy-la-Grande (Gironde)
Tel: **05 57 46 13 84**. Email: **contact@camping-bastide.com**

A pleasant location on the bank of the River Dordogne, this small site is about a kilometre from the town centre. Neatly presented, there are only 38 pitches, of which just 26 are available for tourists (12 mobile homes for rent). All are on grass with 10A electricity. The site roads are narrow and the pitches not large (so unsuitable for large RVs and double axle caravans) with kerbs and some low tree branches to negotiate. Some pitches are drive through style and some also have some low ranch style fence dividers. An oval swimming pool has a decking surround.

Facilities

Central refurbished toilet block is traditional in style with modern fittings. Good facility for disabled campers. Washing machine and dryer. WiFi zone around reception and pool area. Games room with TV. Playground. Boules. Fishing in the adjacent river. No charcoal barbecues allowed. Off site: Golf 5 km. Riding 5 km. Bicycle hire 1 km.

Open: 1 April - 31 October.

Directions

Sainte-Foy-la-Grande is about 20 km. west of Bergerac. Site is 1 km. east of the town centre on D130, on south bank of the river Dordogne (well signed). GPS: N44:50.648 E00:13.488

Charges 2007

Per unit incl. 1 person	€ 8,50 - € 11,00
incl. 2 persons and electricity	€ 14,50 - € 19,00
extra person	€ 2,00 - € 3,00

FR40060 Camping Club International Eurosol

Route de la Plage, F-40560 Vielle-St-Girons (Landes)
Tel: **05 58 47 90 14**. Email: **contact@camping-eurosol.com**

This attractive and well maintained site is set on undulating ground amongst mature pine trees giving good shade. The 405 pitches for touring are numbered and 209 have electricity with 120 fully serviced. Satellite reception is available in one area. A family site with multilingual entertainers, many games and tournaments are organised and a beach volleyball competition is held each evening in front of the bar. A third covered pool has recently been added to the smart, landscaped pool complex. A sandy beach 700 metres from the site has supervised bathing in high season.

Facilities

Four main toilet blocks and two smaller blocks are comfortable and clean with facilities for babies and disabled visitors. Motorcaravan services. Fridge rental. Well stocked shop and bar. Restaurant, takeaway (from 1/6). Stage for live shows arranged in July/Aug. Outdoor swimming pool complex. Tennis. Multisport court for basketball, handball and football. Bicycle hire. Charcoal barbecues are not permitted. Internet and WiFi. Off site: Riding school opposite. Fishing 700 m.

Open: 17 May - 13 September.

Directions

Turn off D652 at St-Girons on D42 towards St-Girons-Plage. Site is on left before coming to beach (4.5 km). GPS: N43:57.100 W01:21.087

Charges 2007

Per unit incl.1 or 2 persons	€ 13,00 - € 27,00
with electricity	€ 16,00 - € 31,50
with water and drainage	€ 16,00 - € 35,00
extra person (over 4 yrs)	€ 4,00
dog	€ 2,50

Check real time availability and at-the-gate prices...

www.**alanrogers**.com

FR40020 Camping les Chênes (Dax)

Bois de Boulogne, F-40100 Dax (Landes)

Tel: 05 58 90 05 53. Email: camping-chenes@wanadoo.fr

Les Chênes is a well established site, popular with the French themselves and situated on the edge of town amongst parkland (also near the river) and close to the spa for the thermal treatments. The 176 touring pitches are of two types, some large and traditional with hedges, 109 with electricity, water and drainage, and others more informal, set amongst tall pines with electricity if required. This is a reliable, well run site, with a little of something for everyone, but probably most popular for adults taking the 'treatments'. Dax is not a place that springs at once to mind as a holiday town but, as well as being a 'spa', it promotes a comprehensive programme of events and shows during the summer season.

Facilities

Two toilet blocks, one new and modern with heating, washbasins in cubicles, facilities for disabled people, babies and young children. The older block has been refurbished. Laundry and dishwashing facilities. Shop also providing takeaway food (5/4-25/10). Swimming and paddling pools (3/5-13/9). Play area. Field for ball games. Table tennis. Boules. Bicycle hire. Miniclub for children (July/Aug). Occasional special evenings for adults. Charcoal barbecues are not permitted. Off site: Restaurant opposite. Riding, fishing and golf all within 100 m. Beaches 28 km.

Open: 22 March - 1 November.

Directions

Site is west of town on south side of river, signed after main river bridge and at many junctions in town - Bois de Boulogne (1.5 km). In very wet weather the access road to the site may be flooded (but not the site). GPS: N43:42.721 W01:04.385

Charges 2007

Per pitch incl. 2 persons and electricity (5A)	€ 13,60 - € 16,30
with water and drainage	€ 16,20 - € 19,00
extra person	€ 5,00
child (0-12 yrs)	€ 3,00
animal	€ 1,00

Camping Les Chênes ★★★★

Hôtel de plein air du Bois de Boulogne
40100 DAX
Tel. 0033 558 90 05 53
Fax 0033 558 90 42 43

FR40030 Les Pins du Soleil

Route des Minieres, Quartier la Pince, F-40990 Saint Paul-lès-Dax (Landes)

Tel: 05 58 91 37 91. Email: info@pinsoleil.com

This site will appeal to families, particularly those with younger children, or those who prefer to be some way back from the coast within easy reach of shops, cultural activities, etc. and well placed for touring the area. The new young owners are keen to make improvements to what is already a very pleasant site with 145 good sized pitches. There are 76 pitches for touring units of which 59 have electricity and drainage. The site benefits from being developed in light woodland so there is a fair amount of shade from the many small trees.

Facilities

Sanitary facilities include washbasins, hot showers and provision for disabled visitors. Laundry. Motorcaravn services. Small supermarket. Bar. Takeaway. Attractive, medium sized swimming pool with café, new paddling pool and jacuzzi (all 2/6-15/9). Playground and children's miniclub in high season. Covered entertainments area. Bicycle hire. Off site: Bus to the thermal baths 1 km. Fishing 1 km. Riding 3 km.

Open: 15 March - 10 November.

Directions

From west on N124, avoid bypass, follow signs for Dax and St Paul. Almost immediately turn right at roundabout onto D459 and follow signs. Site shortly on left. It is well signed from town centre, north of river. GPS: N43:43.224 W01:05.64

Charges 2007

Per pitch incl. 2 persons with electricity,	€ 8,00 - € 18,00
water and drainage	€ 15,00 - € 24,00
extra person	€ 6,00
child (4-13 yrs)	€ 3,50
Camping Cheques accepted.	

251

FR40040 Camping Village la Paillotte

F-40140 Azur (Landes)

Tel: **05 58 48 12 12**. Email: **info@paillotte.com**

La Paillotte, in the Landes area of southwest France, is a site with a character of its own. It lies beside the Soustons Lake only 1.5 km. from Azur village, with its own sandy beach. This is suitable for young children because the lake is shallow and slopes gradually. All 310 pitches at La Paillotte are mostly shady with shrubs and trees. The 132 pitches for touring vary in price according to size, position and whether they are serviced. La Paillotte is an unusual site with its own atmosphere which appeals to many regular clients. The campsite buildings (reception, shop, restaurant, even sanitary blocks) are all Tahitian in style, circular and constructed from local woods with the typical straw roof (and layer of waterproof material underneath). Some are now being replaced but still in character. For boating the site has a small private harbour where you can keep your own non-powered boat (of shallow draught).

Facilities

Well equipped toilet blocks. Washing machines, dryers. Motorcaravan services. Shop (1/6-1/9). Good restaurant with terrace overlooking lake, bar, takeaway (all 22/4-24/9). Swimming pool complex (22/4-24/9). Sports, games and organised activities. 'Miniclub' room, with 'mini' equipment. TV room, library. Fishing. Bicycle hire. Table tennis. Sailing, rowing boats and pedaloes for hire. Torches useful. No dogs are accepted. Off site: Riding 5 km. Golf 10 km. Atlantic beaches 10 km.

Open: April - September.

Directions

Coming from the north along N10, turn west on D150 at Magescq. From south go via Soustons. In Azur turn left before church (site signed). GPS: N43:47.229 W01:18.570

Charges 2007

Per unit incl. 2 persons	
with 10A electricity	€ 15,00 - € 37,00
with electricity and water	€ 17,00 - € 39,00
pitch by the lake	€ 19,00 - € 46,00
extra person (over 4 yrs)	€ 3,00 - € 7,30

FR40050 Sunêlia le Col-Vert

Lac de Leon, F-40560 Vielle-St-Girons (Landes)

Tel: **05 58 42 94 06**. Email: **contact@colvert.com**

There are some 800 pitches in total, the 380 for touring being flat and covered by light pinewood, most with good shade and many along the lake side. They are of around 100 sq.m, only partly separated and some 120 have water and electricity points. Activities are organised in season: children's games, tournaments, etc. by day and dancing or shows in the evenings. Used by tour operators (80 pitches). The site has a supervised beach in July and August, sail-boarding courses are arranged in high season and there are some boats and boards for hire.

Facilities

Four toilet blocks, one heated. Washing machines, dryer, dishwasher, facilities for disabled people. Motorcaravan services. Shops (8/4-7/9). Bar/restaurant, takeaway. Two pools (all season, supervised), one covered and heated. New play area. TV room, table tennis. Games room. Sports areas, boules, tennis, volleyball. Fitness centre and sauna. Jogging tracks. Safety deposit boxes. Riding, bicycle hire, sauna, tennis, minigolf. Fishing. Riding. Sailing school (15/6-15/9). Communal barbecues. Off site: Walking and cycle ways in the forest. Atlantic beaches 5 km. Golf 10 km.

Open: 8 April - 21 September.

Directions

Site is off D652 Mimizan-Léon road, 4 km. south of crossroads with D42 at St-Girons. Road to lake and site is signed at Vielle. GPS: N43:54.190 W01:18.631

Charges 2007

Per unit incl. 2 persons acc.	
to season, type and location	€ 11,00 - € 46,90
extra person	€ 2,00 - € 6,30
child (3-13 yrs)	€ 1,50 - € 5,30
electricity (3/10A)	€ 4,00 - € 5,20
dog	€ 1,00 - € 4,20

FR40080 Airotel Club Marina-Landes

Rue Marina, F-40200 Mimizan (Landes)

Tel: **05 58 09 12 66**. Email: **contact@clubmarina.com**

Well maintained and clean, with helpful staff, Club Marina-Landes would be a very good choice for a family holiday. Activities include discos, play groups for children, specially trained staff to entertain teenagers and concerts for more mature campers. There are numerous sports opportunities and a superb beach nearby. A nightly curfew ensures that all have a good night's sleep. The site has 444 touring pitches (298 with 10A electricity) and 128 mobile homes and chalets for rent. The pitches are on firm grass, most with hedges and they are large (mostly 100 sq.m. or larger). If ever a campsite could be said to have two separate identities, then Club Marina-Landes is surely the one. In early and late season it is quiet, with the pace of life in low gear – come July and until 1 September, all the facilities are open and there is fun for all the family with the chance that family members will only meet together at meal times.

Facilities

Five toilet blocks (opened as required), well maintained with showers and many washbasins in cabins. Facilities for babies, children and disabled visitors. Laundry facilities. Motorcaravan services. Fridge hire. Shop (freshly baked bread). Bar and restaurant. Snack bar, pizzas and takeaway (1/7-12/9). Covered pool. Outdoor pool (1/7-27/8). Minigolf. Table tennis. Tennis. Volleyball and basketball. Bicycle hire. Play area. Internet access. Entertainment and activities (high season). Gas or electric barbecues only. Off site: Beach and fishing 500 m. Bus service 1 km. Riding 1 km. Mimizan 8 km. Golf 7 km.

Open: 27 April - 17 September.

Directions

Heading west from Mimizan centre, take D626 passing Abbey Museum. Staright on at lights (crossing D87/D67). Next lights turn left. After 2 km. at T-junction turn left. Follow signs to site.
GPS: N44:12.234 W01:17.472

Charges 2007

Per unit incl. 3 persons	€ 14,00 - € 37,00
incl. electricity	€ 17,00 - € 40,00
extra person (over 3 yrs)	€ 3,00 - € 6,00
dog	€ 2,00 - € 4,00

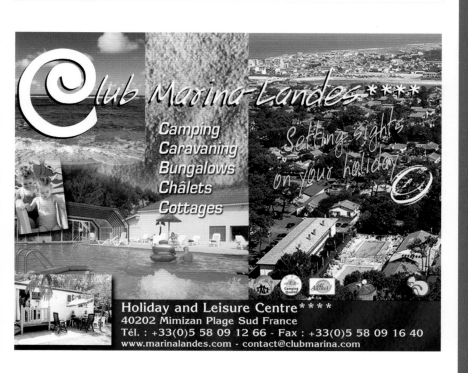

Camping
Caravaning
Bungalows
Châlets
Cottages

Setting sights on your holiday

Holiday and Leisure Centre**
40202 Mimizan Plage Sud France
Tél. : +33(0)5 58 09 12 66 - Fax : +33(0)5 58 09 16 40
www.marinalandes.com - contact@clubmarina.com

FR40100 **Camping du Domaine de la Rive**

Mobile homes ▶ page 497

Route de Bordeaux, F-40600 Biscarosse (Landes)

Tel: **05 58 78 12 33**. Email: **info@camping-de-la-rive.fr**

Surrounded by pine woods, La Rive has a superb beach-side location on Lac de Sanguinet. It provides mostly level, numbered and clearly defined pitches of 100 sq.m. all with electricity connections (6A). The swimming pool complex is wonderful with pools linked by water channels and bridges. There is also a jacuzzi, paddling pool and two large swimming pools all surrounded by sunbathing areas and decorated with palm trees. An indoor pool is heated and open all season. There may be some aircraft noise from a nearby army base. This is a friendly site with a good mix of nationalities. The latest addition is a super children's aqua park with various games. The beach is excellent, shelving gently to provide safe bathing for all ages. There are windsurfers and small craft can be launched from the site's slipway.

Facilities

Five good clean toilet blocks have washbasins in cabins and mainly British style toilets. Facilities for disabled visitors. Baby baths. Motorcaravan service point. Shop. Propane gas. Restaurant. Bar serving snacks and takeaway. Games room. Pool complex (supervised July/Aug). Play area. Tennis. Bicycle hire. Hand-ball, basketball. Table tennis, boules, archery and football. Fishing. Water skiing. Watersports equipment hire. Tournaments (June-Aug). Skateboard park. Trampolines. Miniclub for children. No charcoal barbecues on pitches. Off site: Golf 8 km.

Open: 1 April - 30 September.

Directions

Take D652 from Sanguinet to Biscarosse and site is signed on the right in about 6 km. Turn right and follow new tarmac road for 2 km. GPS: N44:27.607 W01:07.808

Charges 2008

Per pitch incl. 2 persons and electricity	€ 20,00 - € 42,00
with water and drainage	€ 23,00 - € 45,00
extra person	€ 3,40 - € 7,50
child (3-7 yrs)	€ 2,30 - € 6,00
dog	€ 2,10 - € 5,00

Camping Cheques accepted.

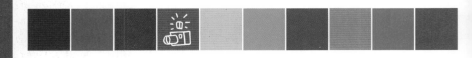

FR40070 **Yelloh! Village Lous Seurrots**

Contis Plage, F-40170 Saint Julien-en-Born (Landes)

Tel: **04 66 73 97 39**. Email: **info@yellohvillage-lous-seurrots.com**

Lous Seurrots is only a short 300 metre walk from the beach and parts of the site have views across the estuary. There are 610 pitches, mainly in pine woods on sandy undulating ground. They are numbered but only roughly marked out, most have good shade and over 80% have electrical hook-ups (adaptors required). The site's pool complex (two heated) is in a superb setting of palm trees and flower beds and the paved sunbathing areas have wonderful views out to the estuary and the sea. For all its size, Lous Seurrots is a family site with the emphasis on peace and tranquillity (no discos).

Facilities

Six well kept, modern toilet blocks, baby rooms and facilities for disabled people. Washing machines. Motorcaravan services. Large shop (15/5-15/9). Bar, restaurant (15/5-15/9). Takeaway (1/7-27/9). Swimming pool complex (2/4-30/9) and a jacuzzi with keep fit classes (July/Aug). Tennis, table tennis, archery, volleyball, minigolf. Canoeing. Bicycle hire. Fishing. Miniclub for younger children. Evening entertainment twice weekly in high season in open-air auditorium. Only gas barbecues are permitted. Internet. Off site: Riding 3 km.

Open: 5 April - 27 September.

Directions

Turn off D652 on D41 (15 km. south of Mimizan) to Contis-Plage and site is on left as you reach it. GPS: N44:05.347 W01:18.990

Charges 2007

Per unit incl. 2 persons and electricity	€ 17,00 - € 36,00
extra person	€ 4,00 - € 6,00
child (3-7 yrs)	free - € 4,00
animal	€ 3,00

Domaine de La Rive

a Paradise for Children

w.larive.fr

Pool complex and a covered heated swimming pool

Route de Bordeaux
40600 Biscarosse
él : 00 33 5 58 78 12 33
ax : 00 33 5 58 78 12 92
?@camping-de-la-rive.fr

La Clef Verte

Chalets
and mobile homes
for rent.
At the banks
of a lake,
in the heart
of the landaise
forest

F.S.F COMMUNICATION - Draguignan- Tél : 04 94 67 06 00

FR40110 Le Village Tropical Sen-Yan

Le Village Tropical, F-40170 Mézos (Landes)

Tel: 05 58 42 60 05. Email: reception@sen-yan.com

This exotic family site is about 12 km. from the Atlantic coast in the Landes forest area, just outside the village. There are 140 touring pitches set around a similar number of mobile homes. Pitches are marked with hedges and have electricity (6A). The reception, bar and pool area is almost tropical with the luxuriant greenery of its banana trees, palm trees, tropical flowers and its straw sunshades. The covered, heated pool, new water slide, gym with sauna and jacuzzi all add to the attractiveness. A new covered animation area provides entertainment and discos during high season.

Facilities

Three well maintained and clean toilet blocks with good quality fittings have showers, washbasins in cabins and British style WCs. The newest block is especially suitable for low season visitors with a special section for babies, plus excellent facilities for disabled people. Shop (from 15/6). Bar, restaurant and snacks (1/7-31/8). Outdoor swimming pools (1/7-15/9). Heated indoor pool. Archery. Practise golf. Bicycle hire. No charcoal barbecues. Off site: Fishing 500 m. Riding 6 km. Beach 12 km.

Open: 1 June - 15 September.

Directions

From N10 take exit 14 (Onesse-Laharie), then D38 Bias/Mimizan road. After 13 km. turn south to Mézos from where site is signed. GPS: N44:04.337 W01:09.380

Charges 2007

Per unit incl. 2 persons	€ 20,00 - € 30,00
with 6A electricity	€ 24,00 - € 34,00
extra person	€ 5,00 - € 6,00
child (under 7 yrs)	free - € 5,00

FR40120 Domaine Naturiste Arnaoutchot

F-40560 Vielle-St-Girons (Landes)

Tel: 05 58 49 11 11. Email: contact@arna.com

'Arna' is a large naturist site with extensive facilities and direct access to the beach. Even with 500 pitches, its layout in the form of a number of sections, each with its own character, make it quite relaxing and very natural. These sections amongst the trees and bushes of the Landes provide a variety of reasonably sized pitches, most with electricity (3/6A), although the hilly terrain means that only a limited number are flat enough for motorcaravans. The amenities are extensive and of excellent quality. There are several new mobile homes. American motorhomes not accepted.

Facilities

Heated sanitary facilities include the usual naturist site type of blocks with communal hot showers and also a number of tiny blocks. Motorcaravan services. Supermarket, other shops. Bar/restaurant, pizzeria and tapita (fish) bar. Pizza. Heated indoor swimming pool with solarium, whirlpool and slide. Outdoor pool, sunbathing area. New paddling pool. Spa, sauna, steam, whirlpool, massages. TV, games rooms. Cinema. Library. Internet point. Bicycle hire. Fishing. Torches useful. Gas and electric barbecues. Off site: Riding or golf 5 km.

Open: 1 April - 21 September.

Directions

Site is signed off the D652 road at Vielle-Saint-Girons. Follow D328 for 3-4 km. GPS: N43°54.449 W01°21.866

Charges 2007

Per unit incl. 1 person	€ 9,90 - € 34,90
extra person (over 3 yrs)	€ 2,00 - € 7,20
electricity (3/6A)	€ 3,80 - € 5,30
animal	€ 1,20 - € 3,10

Deposit on arrival for accommodation € 50.
Special offers available.
Camping Cheques accepted.

FR40160 Camping les Vignes

Route de la Plage du Cap de L'Homy, F-40170 Lit-et-Mixe (Landes)

Tel: 04 99 57 21 21. Email: contact@les-vignes.com

Les Vignes is a large holiday site close to the Atlantic coast with 450 pitches, of which 262 are occupied by a mix of mobile homes, bungalows and tents, most of which are for rent. The 188 tourist pitches are relatively level on a sandy base, all serviced with electricity (10A) and water, some with waste water drains. The site's amenities, including a supermarket, restaurant and bar, are located at the entrance to the site. The rather stylish swimming pool complex includes a six lane water slide.

Facilities

Four sanitary units with washing machines, dryers, facilities for babies and disabled people. Large supermarket (15/6-10/9). Restaurant, bar (15/6-10/9). Takeaway (July/Aug). Swimming pool complex (1/6-15/9). Tennis. Table tennis. Golf driving range. Minigolf. Volleyball, basketball. Pétanque. Kids club and playground. Bicycle hire. Internet access. Barrier closed 23.00-07.00 hrs. Off site: Golf course, canoeing, kayaking, surfing, riding. Many cycle tracks.

Open: 1 June - 15 September.

Directions

Lit-et-Mixe is on the D652 20 km. south of Mimizan. Turn west on D88 1 km. south of town towards Cap de l'Homy for 1.5 km. where site entrance is on left. GPS: N44:01.375 W01:16.787

Charges 2007

Per pitch incl. 2 persons, electricity and water	€ 16,00 - € 37,00
extra person (over 5 yrs)	€ 5,00
child (under 5 yrs)	free

FR40140 Camping Caravaning Lou P'tit Poun

Mobile homes ▶ page 497

110 avenue du Quartier Neuf, F-40390 Saint Martin-de-Seignanx (Landes)

Tel: 05 59 56 55 79. Email: contact@louptitpoun.com

The manicured grounds surrounding Lou P'tit Poun give it a well kept appearance, a theme carried out throughout this very pleasing site. It is only after arriving at the car park that you feel confident it is not a private estate. Beyond this point an abundance of shrubs and trees are revealed. Behind a central sloping flower bed lies the open plan reception area. The avenues around the site are wide and the 168 pitches (99 for touring) are spacious. All have electricity (6/10A), many also have water and drainage and some are separated by low hedges. A 'Sites et Paysages' member. The jovial owners not only make their guests welcome, but extend their enthusiasm to organising weekly entertainment for young and old during high season.

Facilities

Two unisex sanitary blocks, maintained to a high standard and kept clean, include washbasins in cabins, a baby bath and provision for disabled people. Dishwashing sinks and laundry facilities with washing machine and dryer. Motorcaravan service point. Small shop (1/7-31/8). Café (1/7-31/8). Swimming pool (1/6-15/9) Play area. Games room, TV. Half court tennis. Table tennis. Off site: Bayonne 6 km. Golf 10 km. Fishing or riding 7 km. Sandy beaches of Basque coast ten minute drive.

Open: 31 May - 15 September.

Directions

Leave A63 at exit 6 and join N117 in the direction of Pau. Site is signed at Leclerc supermarket. Continue on N117 for 3.5 km. and site is clearly signed on right. GPS: N43:31.451 W01:24.730

Charges 2008

Per pitch incl. 2 persons	
and electricity	€ 21,50 - € 32,50
extra person	€ 6,00 - € 7,00
child (under 7 yrs)	€ 4,00 - € 5,00
dog	€ 3,50 - € 4,50

Lou P'tit Poun ★★★

At 10 km from the ocean, a friendly welcome awaits you at this quality camp-site between Les Landes and the Basque country.

CAMPING LOU P'TIT POUN
40390 ST MARTIN DE SEIGNANX
Tél : 05 59 56 55 79   Fax : 05 59 56 53 71
E-mail : contact@louptitpoun.com
LANDES - AQUITAINE - FRANCE

FR40340 Village Camping Océliances

Avenue des Tucs, F-40510 Seignosse (Landes)

Tel: 05 58 43 30 30. Email: oceliances@wanadoo.fr

This is a very large campsite situated 600 m. from the beach and 600 m. from Seignosse golf course. It has been totally modernised to a very high standard with a new reception area, outdoor pool complex with extensive decking, bar, restaurant and takeaway. You can be assured of a warm welcome here. There are 542 sandy/grass pitches with tall pine trees giving some shade, 320 for touring with 121 having electricity (6A). This site will appeal to a large variety of visitors, in low season, quiet but with plenty to do in the area, and in high season, a site for families with children.

Facilities

Six refurbished toilet blocks include facilities for babies and campers with disabilities. Large laundry. Fridge hire. Large shop. Bar and restaurant (all 1/7-31/8). Pool complex (1/6-30/9). Games room. Floodlit sports court. Surf school. Play area. Children's clubs. Bicycle hire. Internet. Off site: Beach and golf 600 m. Sailing 3 km. Fishing and riding 10 km.

Open: 26 April - 28 September.

Directions

From Seigmosse Bourg take D86 west, passing golf course. Go straight on at roundabout, D86 and Ave des Tucs, to site on left. GPS: N43:41.634 W01:25.825

Charges 2007

Per unit incl. 2 persons	
and electricity	€ 16,10 - € 28,50
incl. water and drainage	€ 18,10 - € 31,00
extra person	€ 4,00 - € 6,30
child (4-17yrs)	€ 2,70 - € 4,90

257

FR40190 Le Saint Martin Airotel Camping

Mobile homes ▶ page 498

Avenue de l'Océan, F-40660 Moliets-Plage (Landes)

Tel: 05 58 48 52 30. Email: contact@camping-saint-martin.fr

A family site aimed mainly at couples and young families, Airotel St Martin is a welcome change to most of the sites in this area in that it has only a small number of chalets (85) compared to the number of touring pitches (575). First impressions are of a neat, tidy, well cared for site and the direct access to the beach is an added bonus. The pitches are mainly typically French in style with low hedges separating them plus some shade. Electric hook ups are 10-15A and a number of pitches also have water and drainage. Entertainment in high season is low key (with the emphasis on quiet nights) – daytime competitions and a miniclub, plus the occasional evening entertainment, well away from the pitches and with no discos or karaoke. With pleasant chalets and mobile homes to rent, and an 18-hole golf course 700 m. away (special rates negotiated), this would be an ideal destination for a golfing weekend or longer stay.

Facilities

Seven toilet blocks of a high standard and very well maintained, have washbasins in cabins, large showers, baby rooms and facilities for disabled visitors. Motorcaravan service point. Washing machines and dryers. Fridge rental. Supermarket. Bars, restaurants and takeaways. Indoor pool (22/3-1/11), jacuzzi and sauna (charged July/Aug). Outdoor pool area with jacuzzi and paddling pool (15/6-15/9). Multisport pitch. Play area. Internet access. Electric barbecues only. Off site: Excellent area for cycling, bicycle hire 500 m. Golf and tennis 700 m. Riding 8 km.

Open: 22 March - 1 November.

Directions

From the N10 take D142 to Lèon, then D652 to Moliets-et-Mar. Follow signs to Moliets-Plage, site is well signed. GPS: N43:51.145 W01:23.239

Charges 2008

Per unit incl. 2 adults, 1 child	€ 17,50 - € 39,00
with electricity	€ 21,00 - € 43,20
services	€ 24,00 - € 48,50
extra person	€ 6,00
dog	€ 3,50

Prices are for reserved pitches.

★ ★ ★ ★

Le Saint Martin

Airotel Camping
Caravaning

Avenue de l'Océan
40660 Moliets-Plage

Tél : (33) 05.58.48.52.30
Fax : (33) 05.58.48.50.73

www.camping-saint-martin.fr
contact @camping-saint-martin.fr

FR40220 Camping les Acacias

Route d'Azur, quartier Delest, F-40660 Messanges (Landes)

Tel: 05 58 48 01 78. Email: lesacacias@lesacacias.com

Close to the Atlantic beaches of Les Landes, this small family run site is quiet and peaceful. There are 79 large, generally flat touring pitches separated by trees and shrubs, with chalets and mobile homes arranged unobtrusively on two sides of the site. There are also some seasonal caravans. All the touring pitches have electricity (5/10A), 8 have water, which is also available at the toilet block. Pitches are easily accessed by tarmac internal roads. M. and Mme. Dourthe are constantly improving the site and the facilities and services show the care taken in design.

Facilities

One modern, clean and well designed toilet block with facilities for disabled people. Washing machines, dryer and ironing board. Motorcaravan services. Fridge hire. Shop (15/6-15/9). Takeaway (high season). Games room. Small play area. Football. Volleyball. Table tennis. Boules. Bicycle hire. Off site: Bus service 1 km. Beach 2 km. Fishing 3 km. Riding 1.5 km. Golf 4 km. Supermarket 2 km.

Open: 19 March - 19 October.

Directions

Site is signed off the D652, turning inland (east) 2 km. north of Vieux-Boucau; 3 km. south of Messanges.

Charges 2007

Per unit incl. 1 or 2 persons	€ 8,90 - € 13,50
extra person	€ 2,60 - € 3,40
child (0-7 yrs)	€ 1,80 - € 2,30
electricity	€ 2,70 - € 4,00
animal	€ 10,80 - € 1,60

FR40180 Camping le Vieux Port

Plage sud, F-40660 Messanges (Landes)

Tel: 01 72 03 91 60. Email: contact@levieuxport.com

Mobile homes ▶ page 498

A well established destination appealing particularly to families with teenage children, this lively site has 1,406 pitches of mixed size, most with electricity (6A) and some fully serviced. The camping area is well shaded by pines and pitches are generally of a good size, attractively grouped around the toilet blocks. There are many tour operators here and well over a third of the site is taken up with mobile homes and another 400 pitches are used for tents. The heated pool complex is exceptional boasting five outdoor pools and three large water slides. There is also a heated indoor pool. The area to the north of Bayonne is heavily forested and a number of very large campsites are attractively located close to the superb Atlantic beaches. Le Vieux Port is probably the largest and certainly one of the most impressive of these. At the back of the site a path leads across the dunes to a good beach (500 m). A little train also trundles to the beach on a fairly regular basis in high season (small charge). All in all, this is a lively site with a great deal to offer an active family.

Facilities

Nine well appointed, recently renovated toilet blocks with facilities for disabled people. Motorcaravan services. Good supermarket and various smaller shops in high season. Several restaurants, takeaway and three bars (all open all season). Large pool complex (no Bermuda shorts) including new covered pool and Polynesian themed bar. Tennis, football, multisport pitch, minigolf. Bicycle hire. Riding centre. Organised activities in high season including frequent discos and karaoke evenings. Only communal barbecues are allowed. Off site: Fishing 1 km. Golf 8 km.

Open: 1 April - 30 September.

Directions

Leave RN10 at Magescq exit heading for Soustons. Pass through Soustons following signs for Vieux-Boucau. Bypass this town and site is clearly signed to the left at second roundabout. GPS: N43:47.863 W01:23.959

Charges 2008

Per unit incl. 2 persons	€ 12,00 - € 39,00
extra person	€ 3,50 - € 7,00
child (under 10 yrs)	€ 2,50 - € 5,00
electricity (6/8A)	€ 4,00 - € 7,00
animal	€ 2,00 - € 4,50

Camping Cheques accepted.

TRAVEL SERVICE SITE
TO BOOK CALL 01580 214000
Advice & low ferry-inclusive prices

Check real time availability and at-the-gate prices...
www.alanrogers.com

FR40250 Camping les Grands Pins

1039 avenue de Losa, F-40460 Sanguinet (Landes)

Tel: **05 58 78 61 74**. Email: **info@campinglesgrandspins.com**

Approached by a road alongside the lake, this site is set amongst tall pine trees. The gravel pitches are of average size, mostly level and shaded. Hedges divide those available for tourers and these are set amongst the many mobile homes. Large units may find manoeuvring difficult. There may be some aircraft noise at times from a nearby army base. A central pool complex includes a covered heated indoor pool, an outdoor pool, water slide and flume. In early and late season this is a very quiet site with very few facilities open. However, there are plenty of walks, cycle rides and the lake to enjoy. The poolside bar, restaurant and shops are only open in July/August. In July and August the site becomes busy, offering watersports, minigolf, a children's club, boat trips and organised activities. All four sanitary blocks are open for July and August. Fishing is also available. The charming small village of Sanguinet is 2 km. away with shops, bars, restaurants and an archaeological museum.

Facilities

Four toilet blocks include washbasins in cabins, showers and British style toilets (not all open in low seasons). Baby bath and provision for disabled visitors. Laundry facilities. Motorcaravan service point. Shop, bar, restaurant and takeaway (1/7-31/8). Indoor pool (all seson). Outdoor pool complex (1/7-31/8). Play area. Games room and TV in bar. Tennis. Bicycle hire (July/Aug). Pets are not accepted in July/Aug. Barbecues are not allowed (dedicated area provided). Off site: Beach 30 m. Fishing 2 km. Golf and riding 15 km. Boat launching 1 km.

Open: 1 April - 31 October.

Directions

Enter Sanguinet from the north on the D46. At one way system turn right. Do not continue on one way system but go straight ahead toward lake (signed) on Rue de Lac. Site is 2 km. on left. GPS: N44:29.038 W01:05.383

Charges 2007

Per unit incl. 2 persons and electricity	€ 14,00 - € 34,50
extra person	€ 3,50 - € 6,00
child (3-10 yrs)	€ 3,00 - € 4,50

FR40240 Camping Mayotte Vacances

368 chemin des Roseaux, F-40600 Biscarrosse (Landes)

Tel: **05 58 78 00 00**. Email: **mayotte@yellohvillage.com**

This appealing site is set amongst pine trees on the edge of Lac de Biscarrosse. Drive down a tree and flower lined avenue and proceed toward the lake to shady, good sized pitches which blend well with the many tidy mobile homes that share the area. Divided by hedges, all the pitches have electricity (10A) and water taps. There may be some aircraft noise at times from a nearby army base. The pool complex is impressive, with various pools, slides, chutes, jacuzzi and sauna, all surrounded by paved sunbathing areas. The excellent lakeside beach provides safe bathing for all ages with plenty of watersports available.

Facilities

Four good quality, clean toilet blocks (one open early season). Good facilities for visitors with disabilities. Unusual baby/toddler bathroom. Motorcaravan services. Laundry. Supermarket. Boutique. Comprehensive rental shop (July/Aug). Restaurant. Swimming pools (one heated; supervised July/Aug. and weekends). Play area. Further children's area (extra cost) with trampolines, inflatables and a small train. Bicycle hire. Fishing. Watersports. Organised activities and entertainment (July/Aug). Clubs for toddlers and teenagers (July/Aug). Charcoal barbecues not permitted. Hairdressers (seasonal). ATM. Internet access. Off site: Golf 4 km. Riding 100 m. Beach 10 km. Town 2 km. with restaurants, shops and bars.

Open: 30 April - 24 September.

Directions

From the north on D652 turn right on D333 (Chemin de Goubern). Pass through Goubern and Mayotte Village. Take next right (signed to site) into Chemin des Roseaux. GPS: N44:26.097 W01:09.303

Charges 2007

Per unit incl. 2 persons	€ 17,00 - € 39,00
extra person	€ 3,50 - € 7,50
child (3-7 yrs)	free - € 3,50
dog	€ 3,00 - € 5,00

Check real time availability and at-the-gate prices...

www.alanrogers.com

Les Grands Pins

CAMPING CARAVANING ★★★★

Sanguinet

www.campinglesgrandspins.com

Lac de Biscarosse

Lake, Pool complex;
many activities under the landaise sun

Chalets and mobile
homes for rent

Avenue de Losa (route du lac) 40460 SANGUINET
Tél : 00 33 5 58 78 61 74 - Fax : 00 33 5 58 78 69 15
info@campinglesgrandspins.com

LANDES

FR40200 Yelloh! Village le Sylvamar

Mobile homes ▶ page 498

Avenue de l'Océan, F-40530 Labenne-Océan (Landes)

Tel: **04 66 73 97 39**. Email: **info@yellohvillage-sylvamar.com**

Less than a kilometre from a long sandy beach, this campsite has a good mix of tidy, well maintained chalets, mobile homes and touring pitches. The 562 pitches (216 for touring) are level, numbered and mostly separated by low hedges. Most have electricity (10A), many also have water and drainage and there is welcoming shade. The swimming pool complex is superbly set in a sunny location. The pools are of various sizes (one heated, one not) with a large one for paddling. With four toboggans and a fast flowing channel for sailing down in the inflatable rubber rings provided, this is a haven for children. All are surrounded by ample sunbathing terraces and overlooked by the bar/restaurant.

Facilities

Four modern toilet blocks (one recently refurbished) have washbasins in cabins, and facilities for babies and disabled visitors. Washing machines. Shop. Bar/restaurant and takeaway. Internet access. Play area. Games room. Cinema and video room. TV room. Miniclub (July/Aug). Fitness centre. Tennis. Bicycle hire. Library. Extensive entertainment programme for all ages, incl. evening shows in the outdoor amphitheatre. Fridge hire. No charcoal barbecues. Internet access. Off site: Beach 900 m. Fishing, riding 1 km. Golf 7 km.

Open: 26 April - 17 September.

Directions

Labenne is on the N10. In Labenne, head west on D126 signed Labenne-Océan and site is on right in 4 km. GPS: N43:35.742 W01:27.383

Charges 2007

Per unit incl. 2 persons, electricity	€ 17,00 - € 38,00
extra person (over 7 yrs)	€ 3,00 - € 7,00
extra person (3-7 yrs)	free - € 5,00
dog	free - € 5,00

Le Sylvamar Avenue de l'Océan F-40530 - Labenne Océan - France
T [33] 05 59 45 75 16 - F [33] 05 59 45 75 16 - sylvamar@wanadoo.fr

Nestled in a 37-acre (15 hectares) pine forest, this village is paradise for nature lovers, beachgoers and marine activities. Located on the southern coast of France's Landes region, Sylvamar is right next to Basque country and Spain, between Biarritz and Hossegor. It's up to you to choose wether you'd like an active or relaxing vacation, with plenty of clean, fresh air to make the best of it.

A DREAM COME TRUE - THE AQUATIC AREA IS AT YOUR DISPOSAL:
Blue lagoon, quiet green, luxurious vegetation, natural surroundings. For aquatic fun, there are 2 heated pools, a play river and triple waterslide. For relaxation, use deck chairs to soak up sun, stroll about on bridges and whatever you feel like. It's all designed around games, having fun and taking it easy. Smiling children and parents and all in complete safety, with on-duty lifeguards.

FR40260 Camping les Chevreuils

Route de Vieux-Boucau á Hossegor, F-40510 Seignosse (Landes)

Tel: **05 58 43 32 80**. Email: **contact@chevreuils.cegeteldsl.com**

Set in a mature pine and oak forest, 1.2 km. from the beach, this campsite has randomly spaced, well shaded pitches of a variety of sizes. Sandy ground and tree roots can make for uneven ground. Little evening entertainment is organised, as the emphasis here is on peace and quiet. This site is ideal for couples and families with small children who wish to stay in natural surroundings reflecting the traditional style of camping. The site is not recommended for people with disabilities due to the uneven, sandy ground. Two swimming pools are set in a sunny area with plenty of space for sunbathing.

Facilities

Three clean toilet blocks are traditional in style. Facilities for disabled visitors (but see above). Motorcaravan service point. Laundry facilities. Fridge box hire. Shop (15/6-2/9). Bar (1/6-15/9). Restaurant (1/6-15/9). Children's club (5-12 yrs) in July/Aug. Barbecues are not allowed (communal area supplied). Off site: Disco 800 m. Fishing 3 km. Golf 5 km. Riding 7 km. Beach 1.2 km. Sailing 3 km. Bus service to Bayonne, Leon and Dax.

Open: 1 June - 15 September.

Directions

From N10 take exit 11 and D116 to Soustons. Head west on D652 towards Vieux-Boucau. Turn left on D79 heading south and site is 6 km. on the left.

Charges 2007

Per unit incl. 2 persons	€ 15,40 - € 22,00
extra person	€ 4,20 - € 6,00
child (4-12 yrs)	€ 3,50 - € 5,00
electricity	€ 4,00 - € 5,00

FR40270 Parc Saint-James Eurolac

Promenade de l'Etang, F-40200 Aureilhan (Landes)

Tel: 05 58 09 02 87. Email: eurolac@camping-parcsaintjames.com

This well shaded and wooded site is located on the banks of Lac de l'Aureillan (with a road in between), just 8 km. from the Atlantic beaches. The natural surroundings of the lake shore provide many bicycle and walking tracks, together with a sandy beach. Consisting mainly of pitches for mobile homes (most privately owned), there are only 11 small pitches available for tourers, each with an electrical hook-up (6A). They are really only suitable for small units and tents as negotiating the sometimes low lying branches and trees along the roadways may prove difficult.

Facilities

Four traditional toilet blocks provide washbasins in cabins, showers and British style toilets. Ramped facilities for disabled visitors. (key provided). Laundry. Heated swimming pool (May - Sept) Games room. Minigolf. Bicycle Hire. Fishing (licence from Mimizan). Sandy play area with good equipment for young children. Mini club (4-12 yrs) and evening entertainment (July/Aug). Barbecues not permitted (communal area provided). Off site: Fishing 20 m. (permit). Boat launching. Riding 1 km. Golf 5 km. Sea and beach 8 km.

Open: 8 April - 30 September.

Directions

Heading east from the centre of Mimizan take the D626. After 2 km. take next left signed Aureilhan. Continue to 'stop' sign and turn left. Go through the village to the lake and turn right down the promenade to site on the right.
GPS: N44:13.347 W01:12.207

Charges guide

Per unit incl. 1 person	
and electricity	€ 8,50 - € 22,00
extra person	€ 1,50 - € 4,50
child (4-10 yrs)	€ 1,50 - € 2,50
dog	€ 5,00

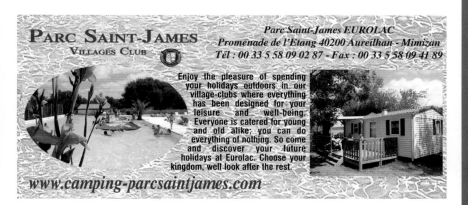

PARC SAINT-JAMES
VILLAGES CLUB

Parc Saint-James EUROLAC
Promenade de l'Etang 40200 Aureilhan - Mimizan
Tél : 00 33 5 58 09 02 87 - Fax : 00 33 5 58 09 41 89

Enjoy the pleasure of spending your holidays outdoors in our village-clubs where everything has been designed for your leisure and well-being. Everyone is catered for young and old alike; you can do everything of nothing. So come and discover your future holidays at Eurolac. Choose your kingdom, well look after the rest.

www.camping-parcsaintjames.com

FR40280 Airotel Lou Puntaou

Au bord du Lac, F-40550 Léon (Landes)

Tel: 05 58 48 74 20. Email: reception@loupuntaou.com

Set between Lac de Léon and the nature reserve park of Huchet, this site offers plenty for young families. The level pitches are mainly grass, hedged and have electricity (15A). Trees offer reasonable shade. In July and August only, there may be some noise from the lake car park and activities. The lake is 200 metres away with watersports, fishing, restaurants and bars, plus plenty of cycle rides. In July and August a full range of activities is organised on the site with sports and clubs for children and activities and evening entertainment for adults. A number of tour operators use the site.

Facilities

Three traditional style toilet blocks include facilities for disabled visitors and children. Laundry facilities. Motorcaravan service point. Simple shop at site entrance. Bar, restaurant and takeaway (all season). TV and games rooms. Tennis. ATM. Internet. Only electric barbecues are permitted (communal area available). Off site: Village 500 m. with shops restaurants and bars. Bus to village (July/Aug). Lake 200 m. Beach 7 km. Riding 10 km. Golf 7 km.

Open: 1 April - 30 September.

Directions

From N10 take exit 12 towards Castets. Take D142 to Léon and at island take first exit 'Centre Ville'. At T- junction turn left on D652. After 300 m. turn left at sign for site and lake. After 500 m. site is on left.

Charges 2007

Per person	€ 3,00 - € 6,00
child (2-13 yrs)	free - € 4,00
pitch incl. electricity	€ 9,00 - € 27,00
dog	free - € 2,00

FR64020 Camping Barétous-Pyrénées

Quartier Ripaude, F-64570 Aramits (Pyrénées-Atlantiques)

Tel: 05 59 34 12 21. Email: atso64@hotmail.com

Located on the edge of the Pyrénées, this quiet site is well away from the tourist bustle, particularly in early or late season. It has a rural location, yet is close to the town. This is a wonderful location for exploring the region and offers a peaceful haven for those wishing to stay in quiet surroundings. The shady, grass pitches are attractive and of a good size with hedges. They offer both water and electricity (10A). The welcoming reception (English spoken) sells local produce and organic food. The heated swimming and paddling pool area is overlooked by a small sun terrace with a café/bar.

Facilities

Two sanitary blocks, one old, one modern, offer clean facilities with unisex toilets and showers. Facilities for disabled visitors. Café/bar with hot and cold meals (July/Aug). Heated swimming and paddling pools (May - Sept). Communal room with TV, games, library and drinks. Small shop selling organic food. Boules. Play area with sandpit. Off site: Town with supermarket 250 m. Fishing 50 m. Riding 3 km. Snow skiing 25 km.

Open: 1 Feburary - 15 October.

Directions

From Oloron Sainte Marie, head southwest on D919 to Aramits. Through village bear right on D918. Cross river and immediately turn right at campsite sign. GPS: N43:07.284 W00:43.939

Charges 2007

Per unit incl. 2 persons	€ 13,00 - € 19,00
extra person	€ 3,50 - € 5,00
electricity	€ 3,50

No credit cards.

FR64030 Camping Ametza

Boulevard de l'Empereur, B.P. 19, F-64700 Hendaye (Pyrénées-Atlantiques)

Tel: 05 59 20 07 05. Email: ametza@meuf.fr

With a beautiful long sandy beach and the town of Hendaye only 900 metres away (a 20 minute walk) this well cared for, family run campsite, offers plenty for everyone. Attractively laid out, the grass pitches are flat and shady, most having electricity (6A). We found the railway line running nearby was not intrusive. There is a pleasant bar and restaurant together with an excellent pool area (comfortable and with good sunbeds and umbrellas). The beach at Hendaye is popular for surfing, particularly for beginners. Having shallow water, it offers safe bathing and many other watersports.

Facilities

Two clean and bright sanitary blocks have good facilities with a new (2006) laundry and en-suite facility for disabled people. Excellent bathroom for babies and children. Laundry facilities. Fridge hire. Shop (w/ends only in early season). Bar and restaurant. Swimming pool (from May). TV room. Playground. Entertainment and activities (July/Aug). Electric barbecues are not permitted. Internet access. Shuttle bus to beach (July/Aug). Off site: Beach and town 900 m. Bicycle hire 1 km. Boat launching 2 km. Fishing 5 km. Golf and riding 10 km.

Open: 8 April - 31 October.

Directions

From the A63 exit 2 (St Jean-de-Luz Sud) take D913 signed Hendaye. At roundabout turn left on coast road D912. In 6 km. turn left on D358 (San Sebastian) Cross railway bridge and site is on left. GPS: N43:22.379 W01:45.351

Charges 2007

Per unit incl. 2 persons	€ 16,80 - € 21,50
extra person	€ 4,20 - € 4,90
child (2-10 yrs)	€ 2,10 - € 3,50
electricty	€ 3,90

FR40290 Yelloh! Village Punta Lago

Avenue du Lac, F-40550 Léon (Landes)

Tel: 04 66 73 97 39. Email: info@yellohvillage-punta-lago.com

Five hundred metres from the charming village of Léon, this site offers above average size, level, grass pitches (some sandy). Most have electricity, water and drainage and they are separated by hedges. Shade is welcome from the tall oak trees. Whilst the pitches would be considered typical for the region, the buildings are a mix of old and new, the old being the sanitary block, in good order, clean and with all the usual facilities including a new children's bathroom and facilities for disabled visitors. The new encompasses an indoor heated pool, a recreation room/gym and a TV room.

Facilities

The single toilet block is old, but kept clean and well maintained. Facilities for children and disabled visitors. Laundry facilities. Large shop. Restaurant and takeaway. Bar. Heated indoor and outdoor pools. Bicycle hire. Play area. Entertainment and activities (July/Aug). Barbecues are not permitted. Off site: Lake 300 m. with sailing, windsurfing, swimming and fishing. Léon 500 m. with market (June/Sept). Beach 7 km. Golf 8 km. Riding 5 km.

Open: 18 April - 27 September.

Directions

From N10 take exit 12 towards Castets. Take D142 to Léon and at island take first exit to 'Centre Ville'. At T-junction turn left on D652 and after 300 m. turn left at sign for site and lake. After 500 m. site is on the left.

Charges 2007

Per unit incl. 2 persons and electricity	€ 17,00 - € 38,00
extra person (over 3 yrs)	free - € 5,50

Check real time availability and at-the-gate prices...

www.alanrogers.com

FR64060 Camping le Pavillon Royal

Avenue du Prince de Galles, F-64210 Bidart (Pyrénées-Atlantiques)

Tel: **05 59 23 00 54**. Email: **info@pavillon-royal.com**

Le Pavillon Royal has an excellent situation on raised ground overlooking the sea, with good views along the coast to the south and to the north coast of Spain beyond. There is a large swimming pool and sunbathing area on site. The site is divided up into 303 marked, level pitches, many of a good size. About 50 are reserved for tents and are only accessible on foot. The remainder are connected by asphalt roads. All have electricity and most are fully serviced. Much of the campsite is in full sun, although the area for tents is shaded. Beneath the site – and only a very short walk down – stretches a wide sandy beach where the Atlantic rollers provide ideal conditions for surfing. A central, marked-out section of the beach is supervised by lifeguards (from mid June). There is also a section with rocks and pools. Reservation in high season is advisable.

Facilities

Good quality toilet blocks with baby baths and unit for disabled people. Washing facilities are closed at night except for two single night units. Washing machines, dryers. Motorcaravan services. Shop (including gas). Restaurant and takeaway (from 1/6). Bar (all season). Swimming and paddling pools. Sauna. Playground. General room, TV room, games room with table tennis, films. Fishing. Surf school. Dogs are not accepted. Barrier card with deposit (€ 20). Off site: Golf 0.5 km. Bicycle hire 2 km. Riding 3 km. Sailing 5 km.

Open: 15 May - 25 September.

Directions

From A63 exit 4, take the N10 south towards Bidart. At roundabout after the 'Intermarché' supermarket turn right (signed for Biarritz). After 600 m. turn left at campsite sign. GPS: N43:27.275 W01:34.562

Charges 2008

Per unit incl. 2 persons, electricity and water	€ 27,00 - € 45,00
tent pitch incl. 1 or 2 persons	€ 20,00 - € 33,00
extra person (over 4 yrs)	€ 6,50 - € 9,00

Le Pavillon Royal
camping caravaning **** NN

64210 BIDART
Tél: 05.59.23.00.54
Website: www.pavillon-royal.com
E-mail: info@pavillon-royal.com

1 Right by a sandy beach with direct access

1 On the outskirts of Biarritz

1 Very peaceful situation

1 Sanitary installations of really exceptional quality

FR64040 Camping des Gaves

Quanitien Pon, F-64440 Laruns (Pyrénées-Atlantiques)

Tel: **05 59 05 32 37**. Email: **campingdesgaves@wanadoo.fr**

Set in a secluded valley, Camping Des Gaves is a clean, small and well managed site, open all year, with very friendly owners and staff. It is set high in Pyrennean walking country on one of the routes to Spain and is only 30 km. from the Spanish border. There are 99 pitches including 50 level grassed touring pitches of which 38 are fully serviced, numbered and separated (the remainder are used for seasonal units). Mature trees provide plenty of shade.

Facilities

The very clean toilet block can be heated in cool weather and has modern fittings. Washbasins for ladies in curtained cubicles and one shower in ladies' suitable for showering children. Dishwashing and laundry sinks. Laundry room. No shop but baker calls daily (July/Aug). Small bar with large screen TV, pool and video games (July/Aug). Larger bar with table tennis. Small play area. Boules. Volleyball. Fishing. Card operated barrier (€ 20 deposit). Off site: Bicycle hire 800 m. Shops, restaurant and bars 1 km.

Open: All year.

Directions

Take N134 from Pau towards Olorons and branch left on D934 at Gan. Follow to Laruns and just after town, turn left following signs to site. GPS: N42:58.929 W00:25.057

Charges 2007

Per person	€ 2,90 - € 3,70
child (under 10 yrs)	€ 1,90 - € 2,40
pitch	€ 4,50 - € 9,60
electricity (3-10A)	€ 2,50 - € 4,00

265

FR64050 Camping Itsas Mendi

Acotz, F-64500 Saint Jean-de-Luz (Pyrénées-Atlantiques)

Tel: **05 59 26 56 50**. Email: **itsas@wanadoo.fr**

This large campsite is ideal for families. Set close to the beach (400 metres), it boasts two swimming areas. Both fenced, one is overlooked by a terrace and has a jacuzzi and the other is made for children with a paddling pool, whirlpool, water slides and plenty of grassed sunbathing area. During July and August entertainment, activities and excursions are organised. Together with surfing, scuba and children's clubs, rafting and mountain bike trails, there is something for all ages. All pitches are of medium size, shaded with electricity (10A). May be difficult for large vehicles to manoeuvre and have full choice of pitches.

Facilities

Five sanitary blocks (not all open early season) are clean and one has facilities for disabled visitors. Laundry facilities. Motorcaravan service point. Fridge hire. Bar and restaurant (1/6-15/9). Tennis. Football field. TV room. Internet access. Off site: Large supermarket 1 km. Bus (50 m.) runs every hour to St Jean-de-Luz. Fishing 1 km. Golf, riding and bicycle hire 4 km.

Open: 1 April - 30 September.

Directions

From the A63 take exit 3, then the N10 toward Bayonne. Turn second left signed 'Acotz Campings Plages'. At T-junction turn right and site is on left. GPS: N43:24.822 W01:37.007

Charges 2007

Per unit incl. 2 persons	€ 16,20 - € 32,50
extra person	€ 3,70 - € 6,00
child (2-10 yrs)	€ 2,20 - € 3,70

FR64070 Castel Camping le Ruisseau des Pyrénées

Route d'Arbonne, F-64210 Bidart (Pyrénées-Atlantiques)

Tel: **05 59 41 94 50**. Email: **francoise.dumont3@wanadoo.fr**

This busy site, with a large play area filled with equipment is ideal for young families. It is about 2 km. from Bidart and 2.5 km. from a sandy beach. There are two swimming pools with slides on the main site and across the road, an indoor heated pool and new spa complex (charged July/Aug) with outdoor fitness equipment. Pitches on the main campsite are individual, marked and of a good size, either on flat terraces or around the lake. The terrain is wooded so the majority of them have some shade. Electrical connections are available throughout. The site has some steep hills to negotiate.

Facilities

Two main blocks and some extra smaller units. Washing machines. Motorcaravan service point. Shop. Large self-service restaurant with takeaway and bar with terraces, and TV (all 15/5-12/9). Outdoor swimming pools, indoor pool and spa complex (15/5-12/9). Sauna. Large play area. Two tennis courts (free outside July/Aug). Fitness track. TV and games rooms. Minigolf. Bicycle hire. Fishing. Internet access. Off site: Riding and golf 2 km.

Open: 28 April - 16 September.

Directions

Site is east of Bidart on a minor road towards Arbonne. From A63 autoroute take Biarritz exit (4), turn towards St Jean-de-Luz and Bidart on N10. After Intermarche turn left at roundabout and follow signs to site. GPS: N43:26.207 W01:34.068

Charges 2007

Per unit incl. 2 persons	€ 15,00 - € 30,00
extra person	€ 5,00 - € 6,50
electricity	€ 3,00 - € 5,00

FR64080 Camping les Tamaris Plage

Quartier Acotz, F-64500 Saint Jean-de-Luz (Pyrénées-Atlantiques)

Tel: **05 59 26 55 90**. Email: **tamaris1@wanadoo.fr**

This is a popular, small and pleasant site which is well kept. It is situated outside the town and just across the road from a sandy beach. The 35 touring pitches, all with 7/10A electricity, are of good size and separated by hedges, on slightly sloping ground with some shade. The site becomes full for July and August with families on long stays, so reservation then is essential. There is no shop, but bread is available daily across the road. Mobile homes for rent occupy 40 pitches. Opposite, a popular surf school offers instruction to new and experienced surfers.

Facilities

The single toilet block of good quality and unusual design should be ample provision for the site with facilities for disabled people. Washing machine. TV room for adults and children's room with TV and games. Playground. Outdoor jacuzzi. Off site: Fishing, surfing 30 m. Bicycle hire or golf 4 km. Riding 7 km.

Open: 1 April - 30 September.

Directions

Proceed south on N10 and 1.5 km. after Guethary take first road on right (before access to the motorway and Carrefour centre commercial) and follow camp signs. GPS: N43:25.077 W01:37.429

Charges 2007

Per unit (100 sq.m. pitch) incl. 2 persons and electricity (5A)	€ 21,00 - € 30,00
tent pitch (80 sq.m.) incl. 2 persons	€ 16,00 - € 27,00
extra person (over 2 yrs)	€ 4,00 - € 6,00

FR64110 Sunêlia Col d'Ibardin

F-64122 Urrugne (Pyrénées-Atlantiques)

Tel: 05 59 54 31 21. Email: info@col-ibardin.com

Mobile homes ▶ page 499

This family owned site at the foot of the Basque Pyrénées is highly recommended and deserves praise. It is well run with emphasis on personal attention, the friendly family and their staff ensuring that all are made welcome and is attractively set in the middle of an oak wood. Behind the forecourt, with its brightly coloured shrubs and modern reception area, various roadways lead to the 191 pitches. These are individual, spacious and enjoy the benefit of the shade (if preferred a more open aspect can be found). There are electricity hook-ups (4/10A) and adequate water points. From this site you can enjoy the mountain scenery, be on the beach in 7-10 km. or cross the border into Spain in approximately 14 km.

Facilities

Two toilet blocks, one rebuilt to a high specification, are kept very clean. WC for disabled people. Dishwashing and laundry facilities. Motorcaravan service point. Shop for basics and bread orders (15/6-15/9). Catering, takeaway service and bar (15/6-15/9). Heated swimming pool. New paddling pool. Playground and club (adult supervision). Tennis courts, boules, table tennis, video games. Bicycle hire. New multi-purpose sports area. Not suitable for American motorhomes. Off site: Supermarket and shopping centre 5 km. Fishing and golf 7 km. Riding 20 km.

Open: 21 March - 30 September.

Directions

Leave A63 autoroute at St Jean-de-Luz sud, exit no. 2 and join RN10 in direction of Urrugne. Turn left at roundabout (Col d'Ibardin) on D4. Site on right after 5 km. Do not turn off to the Col itself, carry on towards Ascain. GPS: N43:20.035 W01:41.077

Charges 2008

Per unit incl. 2 persons	
and electricity	€ 16,50 - € 34,00
extra person	€ 3,00 - € 6,00
child (2-7 yrs)	€ 2,00 - € 3,50
animal	€ 2,50

267

FR64120 Camping Beau Rivage

Allée des Maronniers, F-64190 Navarrenx (Pyrénées-Atlantiques)

Tel: **05 59 66 10 00**. Email: **beaucamping@free.fr**

Cross the picturesque river and follow the old town walls to discover this well cared for family owned campsite (English). The site is tiered and the large, well maintained grass pitches are surrounded by mature hedges offering a peaceful and relaxed setting. Currently torches may be needed. The attention to well cared for detail is carried into the two sanitary blocks. Recent projects include a heated swimming pool, low key entertainment area (wine tasting, barbecues, etc), additional chalets, hardstandings and a baby room, adding to an already impressive campsite. The welcoming owners are using their experience to enhance roadway lighting, redesign facilities for disabled visitors, improve laundry facilities, add serviced pitches, a motorcaravan drainage point and more electrical points. With plenty of walks, cycling, kayaking and sightseeing, this site offers plenty for everyone. A walk through the fortified town and along its walls, rewards with superb views across the countryside.

Facilities

Two very clean sanitary blocks with good separate facilities for ladies and men include provision for disabled visitors. Laundry facilities in top block. Playground for small children (rubber matting). Play field for games. Off site: Shop at end of road. Town is five minutes walk for further shops, bars, restaurants, ATM and bicycle hire. Fishing 200 m. Riding 15 km.

Open: 15 March - 15 October.

Directions

From the north take D936 to Navarrenx. Turn left at first roundabout on D115 into Navarrenx. Turn left at T-junction, go over bridge and follow walls of town all the way around. At next island turn right on D947 and site is signed from here.

Charges 2007

Per unit incl. 2 persons	€ 12,00 - € 17,00
incl. electricity	€ 15,50 - € 20,50
extra person	€ 3,50 - € 4,50
child (0-7 yrs)	€ 2,00 - € 3,00

CAMPING BEAU RIVAGE

Enjoy the long season in the southwest, where spring comes early and summer lasts into October.

The fortified town of Navarrenx has everything close at hand – shops, bars, restaurants, beautiful views over the river, walking, cycling, rafting, ballooning...

Take the car and you can be in Biarritz, Spain - or on top of the Pyrenees - within an hour.

For a relaxing stay on a small, friendly campsite with spotless facilities, swimming pool and serviced pitches.

Camping Beau Rivage - 64190 Navarrenx - Tél.: +33 559 66 1000
Email: beaucamping@free.fr - www.beaucamping.com

FR64100 Camping Etche Zahar

Allée de Mesplès, F-64240 Urt (Pyrénées-Atlantiques)

Tel: **05 59 56 27 36**. Email: **info@etche-zahar.fr**

Although this attractive site is small, the hardcore roads give access to remarkably large grass pitches separated by small hedges. The larger pitches have little shade but at the far end an area of trees offers smaller shaded pitches for tents.There are also 9 immaculate mobile homes and 9 chalets. Electricty (10A) is available for 14 pitches. The site is 'Tourisme & Handicap' approved and offers two chalet and facilities specifically for disabled visitors. The English speaking owner is justly proud and offers a warm welcome to her eco-friendly site. Quietly positioned, it is ideal for those who wish to enjoy relaxed rural pursuits.

Facilities

The single sanitary block was very clean when we visited. Laundry facilities. Meals (July/Aug).Swimming pool (June - Oct). Small Library. Motorcaravan grey water point (hose required). Some play equipment. Bicycle hire. Internet facilities. WiFi. Pets not accepted 1-20 Aug. Off site: Town with supermarket, shops, restaurants and bars 10 minute walk. Fishing 1 km. Boat launching 1 km. Sailing 10 km. Golf 20 km. Beach 22 km.

Open: 20 March - 3 November.

Directions

From Bayonne go east on D1 and join the A64. Take exit 4 turning right on D936. Turn left on D123 to Urt. Follow 'Toute Directions' to D257. Turn right at fire station to site on the left. GPS: N43:29.494 W01:17.792

Charges 2008

Per person	€ 3,70
child (0-10 yrs)	€ 2,50
pitch incl. electricity	€ 11,60 - € 14,20

FR64150 Airotel Résidence des Pins

Mobile homes ▶ page 499

Avenue de Biarritz, F-64210 Bidart (Pyrénées-Atlantiques)

Tel: 05 59 23 00 29. Email: lespins@free.fr

This is a very pleasant, reasonably priced site which will appeal greatly to couples and young families. Set on a fairly gentle hillside, the top level has reception and bar. Slightly lower are the paddling and swimming pools in a sunny location with sunbeds. Next comes the well stocked shop, tennis courts and the rest of the pitches. Some pitches are behind reception and others, lower down, some slightly sloping, are under trees and separated by hydrangea hedges. Some have electricity (10A, long leads required). There is a varied entertainment programme in July and Aug. The site is not suitable for American motorhomes. It is used by tour operators and there are mobile homes around the outer edges of the site. Buses pass the gate. There is a little day-time road noise but not intrusive.

Facilities

The two toilet blocks have some washbasins and showers together. Washing machines, dryers, ironing boards and facilities for disabled people. Motorcaravan services. Shop and bar open all season, restaurant (1/6-10/9) and takeaway (1/7-31/8). Pool open all season. Games room. Table tennis. Tennis (charged in July/Aug). Play area (3-8 yrs). Bicycle hire. Off site: Lake 600 m. with fishing (no licence required). Golf 1 km. Riding 1 km. Beach with lifeguard 600 m.

Open: 8 May - 20 September.

Directions

Heading south on the A63 towards Spain, take exit J4 onto the N10 towards Bidart. At the roundabout straight after Intermarche turn right towards Biarritz. The site is on the right after 1 km.
GPS: N43:27.185 W01:34.425

Charges 2007

Per unit with 2 persons	€ 15,90 - € 24,50
extra person (over 2 yrs)	€ 3,30 - € 5,80
electricity	€ 3,30 - € 5,10
dog	free - € 2,50

Camping Cheques accepted.

FR64140 Sunêlia Berrua

Rue Berrua, F-64210 Bidart (Pyrénées-Atlantiques)

Tel: 05 59 54 96 66. Email: contact@berrua.com

Berrua, 1 km. from the sea, is an ideal location for visiting the beaches in southwest France. A neat and tidy site, it has 270 level pitches (120 for touring units) set amongst trees. Most have electricity (6A) and some are fully serviced. The focal point of the site is an excellent swimming pool complex with several pools, slides and paddling pools which is surrounded by sun beds for sunbathing. Organised activities and entertainment for both adults and children in high season, guided walks, dances, sporting competitions, bingo and karaoke. A member of the Sunêlia group.

Facilities

Toilet facilities are good (unisex) consisting of two blocks with washbasins in cabins, baby rooms, facilities for disabled visitors, washing machines and dishwashing sinks (cold water only). Motorcaravan services. Shop (July/Aug). Bar/restaurant and takeaway (15/4-15/9). New pool complex. Games room. Play area (3-10 yrs only). Bicycle hire. Archery. Boules. Off site: Fishing 1 km. Golf and riding 3 km. Beach 1 km.

Open: 6 April - 5 October.

Directions

From A63 exit 4, take N10 south towards Bidart. At roundabout after the 'Intermarché' supermarket, turn left. Bear right then take next right (site signed). GPS: N43:26.293 W01:34.942

Charges 2007

Per unit incl. 2 persons	€ 16,10 - € 30,20
extra person	€ 3,20 - € 6,15
child (2-9 yrs)	€ 2,30 - € 3,80
electricity (6A)	€ 2,90 - € 4,90
animal	€ 1,00 - € 3,40

Camping Cheques accepted.

FR64250 Camping Atlantica

Quartier Acotz, F-64500 Saint Jean-de-Luz (Pyrénées-Atlantiques)

Tel: **05 59 47 72 44**. Email: **info@campingatlantica.com**

Atlantica is a family site located 3 km. north of St Jean-de-Luz and just 500 m. from the Plage de Sénix. This site has been recommended by our French agent and we plan to undertake a full inspection in 2008. There are 201 pitches, of which around half are occupied by mobile homes and chalets. The touring pitches are grassy and well shaded and all have electrical connections (6A). Although the beach is a major attraction, the site also has a swimming pool with a separate children's pool, as well as a spa and sauna. St Jean-de-Luz is an important resort with an excellent range of shops, restaurants and a vibrant nightlife. The beaches here are justly famous and the close proximity of the Pyrénées and Spanish border provides great opportunities for day trips.

Facilities

Swimming pool. Children's pool. Sauna and spa. Bar, snack bar, takeaway meals. TV room. All weather sports pitch. Children's play area. Small shop. Minigolf. Entertainment in high season. Mobile homes and chalets for rent. Off site: Nearest beach 500 m. St Jean-de-Luz centre 3 km. Golf 8 km. Walking and mountain biking in the Pyrénées.

Open: 1 April - 30 September.

Directions

From the A63, take exit for St Jean-de-Luz Nord and join the N10 towards Biarritz. After 1 km, turn left towards Quartier Acotz. Site is well signed from here. GPS: N43:24.919 W01:37.013

Charges 2007

Per unit incl. 2 persons	€ 14,50 - € 26,00
exytra person	€ 3,00 - € 6,00
child (under 7 yrs)	€ 2,00 - € 3,50
electricity (6A)	€ 3,00 - € 4,20

CAMPING ATLANTICA***

Quartier Acotz - 64500 Saint-Jean-de-Luz
Tel: 0033 559 47 72 44 - Fax: 0033 559 54 72 27
info@campingatlantica.com - www.campingatlantica.com

On 500 m distance from the beach in a green and floral environment for a quiet and pleasant stay in a pleasant family ambiance. Water park, relaxing area with spa and sauna, mini golf, sports terrain. All facilities present for pleasant stay. Mobile homes for rent. Dogs not allowed in accommodation.

Campsite open from 1st April till 30th September.

FR64160 Camping Merko-Lacarra

Plage d'Acotz, F-64500 Saint Jean-de-Luz (Pyrénées-Atlantiques)

Tel: **05 59 26 56 76**. Email: **contact@merkolacarra.com**

Positioned 50 metres from the beach, scattered with pretty Tamaris trees and enjoying views of the surrrounding coutryside, this beautifully cared for campsite offers everything for a relaxing stay. The proud owners maintain the campsite to a high standard with a light, clean toilet block and well kept, tidy garden areas. The site is sloping but the pitches are predominately level and are all of grass. All have electricity (16A via French connectors; adaptors not available). There is little shade. Tidy mobile homes are on the boundaries of the site. There may be some railway noise but we did not find this intrusive. An excellent children's play area (fenced and immaculate), a small shop and a snack bar complete the amenities at this small landscaped campsite.

Facilities

The single toilet block is well kept and clean. Facilities for disabled visitors. Baby room. Laundry facilities. Motorcaravan service point (charged). New mobile home and washblock. Small shop and snack bar (15/6-15/9). Excellent play area. Electric barbecues are not permitted. Off site: Limited public transport July/Aug. Beach and fishing (sea) 50 m. Golf 5 km. Bicycle hire 5 km. Riding 12 km. Mountains (8 km) for walking and cycling.

Open: 1 April - 30 October.

Directions

From the A63 take exit 3, then the N10 toward Bayonne. Turn second left signed 'Acotz Campings Plages'. At T-junction turn right and follow signs for site. However this right turn leads to a low bridge – height restriction 3.5 m. To avoid the bridge, turn left at T-junction and continue along road until reaching the site on the right. GPS: N43:25.116 W01:37.389

Charges 2007

Per person	€ 4,20 - € 6,00
pitch incl. electricity	€ 18,50 - € 30,00

FR64230 Camping Municipal de Mosqueros

F-64270 Salies de Béarn (Pyrénées-Atlantiques)

Tel: **05 59 38 12 94**

In scenic surroundings convenient for the A64, this 3 star municipal site is worthy of its grading and is attractively located in a parkland situation 1 km. from the pretty little town of Salies de Béarn. It has an immaculate appearance, welcoming wardens and very clean facilities. Tarmac roads lead from the entrance barrier (locked at night), past reception to spacious, numbered pitches. Most have electricity (10A), some have water taps and drainage and all are separated by tall shrubs and hedges giving privacy. Salies de Béarn, with its old houses overhanging the river and its thermal baths, is only minutes away. Large units should take care when negotiating narrow roadways and trees.

Facilities	Directions
The two fully equipped toilet blocks are maintained to a high standard. Dishwashing and laundry area with sinks, washing machine, dryer and iron. TV and recreation room. Off site: Swimming pool (special rates for campers) and tennis court adjacent. Golf and riding 2 km. Fishing 7 km.	Site is well signed in the town and is on the D17 Bayonne road, west of the town. GPS: N43:28.51 W00:56.282

Open: 15 March - 31 October.

Charges 2007

Per person	€ 2,60
child (1-7 yrs)	€ 1,60
pitch	€ 2,70 - € 5,30
electricity	€ 2,55

FR64240 Camping Uhaitza le Saison

Route de Libarrenx, F-64130 Mauleon-Licharre (Pyrénées-Atlantiques)

Tel: **05 59 28 18 79**. Email: **camping.uhaitza@wanadoo.fr**

Like its sisters in the Campings de Charme group, this campsite is small and attractive with 50 good sized grass, shady pitches. There are 43 for touring, all with electricity (4-10A) and 37 with water and waste. The clear waters of the river cascade directly behind the site and offer fishing and swimming from the man-made rock formations. This quiet location offers peace and relaxation but also for the adventurous, unlimited mountain walks are only 30 minutes drive away. The charming medieval town of Mauleon is within a 1.5 km. level walk.

Facilities	Directions
One traditional style sanitary block (plus one small unit opened in high season) is clean and comfortable. Facilities for babies and campers with disabilities. Motorcaravan services. Laundry. Gas. Small play area. Bread to order. Small bar, snacks (1/6-30/9). American RVs and twin-axle caravans are not accepted. Off site: Town 1.5 km. with banks, shops, restaurants and bicycle hire. Riding 4 km.	From north, take D23 to Mauleon Licharre. In town, follow bypass. At large roundabout take second exit, D611. At T-junction turn right. Campsite is on right in 0.8 km. and is well signed from the town. GPS: N43:12.476 W00:53.800

Open: 1 March - 15 November.

Charges 2007

Per unit incl. 2 persons	€ 12,80 - € 15,90
extra person	€ 3,40 - € 4,30
child (under 10 yrs)	€ 2,25 - € 2,75
electricity (4/10A)	€ 2,50 - € 4,70

FR64280 Camping Ur-Onea

Rue de la Chapelle, F-64210 Bidart (Pyrénées-Atlantiques)

Tel: **05 59 26 53 61**. Email: **uronea@wanadoo.fr**

Situated on the outskirts of Bidart and 600 m. away from a fine sandy beach, this large, attractively terraced site has 132 grass pitches with electricity (10A) and 10 with the addition of water and drainage. There are some hardstandings for motorcaravans. Three well maintained and clean sanitary blocks are of good size with large showers (all also have washbasins) and wall mounted hairdryers. A separate area is reserved for washing surf boards, barbecues and there is even a shower for washing dogs. With local transport available all year (600 m.) this campsite is ideal for exploring the surrounding areas.

Facilities	Directions
Three excellent sanitary blocks. Facilities for babies and disabled visitors. Laundry. Shop (5/4-13/9). Bar and restaurant (14/6-6/9). Swimming pool (May-Sept). Two excellent play areas for younger children. Off site: Golf 700 m. Riding 2 km. Beach 600 m. Bars, restaurants and shops 600 m.	Take N10 north from St Jean-de-Luz. Continue through Guethary and site sign is on the right. Turn right and site is on the left in 800 m. GPS: N43:26.028 W01:35.433

Open: 5 April - 13 September.

Charges 2007

Per unit incl 2 persons	€ 13,00 - € 23,50
incl. electricity (10A)	€ 18,50 - € 28,50
extra person	€ 3,20 - € 5,00
child (under 10 yrs)	€ 2,00 - € 4,00

(271)

MAP 11

The Dordogne is an histo
region of great beauty, f
of pretty golden-stoned
villages and ancient castle
Home to delicacies such as f
gras, truffles and walnuts, plus
Roquefort cheese and Cognac, it is o
of the gastronomic centres of France

TO FORM 'THE DORDOGNE' WE HAVE USED
DÉPARTEMENTS FROM THESE OFFICIAL REGIONS:
FROM AQUITAINE: 24 DORDOGNE AND 47 LOT-ET-
GARONNE, FROM MIDI-PYRÉNÉES: 12 AVEYRON,
46 LOT, FROM POITOU-CHARENTES: 16 CHARENTE

The Dordogne's history goes back many
thousands of years when man lived in the
caves of Périgord and left cave paintings
at sites such as Les Eyzies and Lascaux.
Aquitaine was ruled by the English for
300 years following the marriage of
Eleanor of Aquitaine to Henry Plantagenet,
who became King of England in 1154.

The villages and castles of the area bear
evidence of the resulting conflict between
the French and English, and today add
charm and character to the countryside.
Monpazier is the best example of the
'bastides' (fortified towns) and is set in a
diverse region of mountains, vineyards, and
fertile river valleys. The rolling grasslands
and dense forests include the beautiful
valleys of the Dordogne and Vézère.

South of the cultivated fields and cliff-side
villages beside the river Lot lie the higher,
stony lands of the Quercy Causse and the
rocky gorges of the Rivers Aveyron and
Tarn. Centred around Millau, there are
tortuous gorges and valleys, spectacular
rivers, underground caves and grottes,
and thickly forested mountains.

Places of interest

Agen: rich agricultural area, famous for
its prunes.

Angoulême: Hill-top town surrounded by
ramparts, cathedral, Renaissance château.

Cognac: the most celebrated *eau de vie* in
the world, cellars, Valois Castle.

Cordes: medieval walled hilltop village.

Monflanquin: well preserved fortified village.

Rocamadour: cliffside medieval pilgrimage
site.

Saint Cirq-La Popie: medieval village perched
on a cliff.

Sarlat: Saturday market.

Cuisine of the region

Local specialities include the fish dishes: carp
stuffed with foie gras, mullet in red wine
and *besugo* (sea bream), plus *cagouilles*
(snails from Charentes).

Cassoulet: a hearty stew of duck, sausages
and beans.

Cèpes: fine, delicate mushrooms; sometimes
dried.

Chou farci: stuffed cabbage, sometimes
aux marrons (with chestnuts).

Confit de Canard (d'oie): preserved duck
meat.

Foie Gras: specially prepared livers of
geese and ducks, seasoned and stuffed
with truffles.

Magret de canard: duck breast fillets.

Mouclade: mussels cooked in wine, egg
yolks and cream, served with Pineau des
Charentes.

FR12000 Flower Camping Caravaning de Peyrelade

Route des Gorges du Tarn, F-12640 Rivière-sur-Tarn (Aveyron)

Tel: 05 65 62 62 54. Email: campingpeyrelade@wanadoo.fr

The 130 touring pitches (100-150 sq.m.) are terraced, level and shady with 6A electricity hook-ups (long leads may be required for the riverside pitches). There are also 43 mobile homes. The site is ideally placed for visiting the Tarn, Jonte and Dourbie gorges, and centres for rafting and canoeing are a short drive up the river. Other nearby attractions include the Caves of Aven Armand, the Chaos de Montpellier, Roquefort (of cheese fame) and the pleasant town of Millau. Many of the roads along and between the Gorges are breathtaking for passengers, but worrying for drivers who won't like looking down! Situated at the foot of the Tarn gorges on the banks of the river, this attractive site is dominated by the ruins of the Château de Peyrelade. Bathing from the pebble beach is safe and the water is clean.

Facilities

Two well equipped toilet blocks. Young children are catered for, also people with disabilities. Washing machines, dryer. Bar, restaurant, pizzeria, takeaway (all from 1/6). Paddling pool, attractive heated swimming pool (proper swimming trunks, no shorts). Good playground. Games room, miniclub. Fishing. Off site: Bicycle hire 100 m. Riding 3 km. Nearby leisure centre can be booked at reception at reduced charges. Millau, hypermarket, shops, night markets but note road to/from Millau can be jammed at peak hours.

Open: 15 May - 6 September.

Directions

Take autoroute A75 to exit 44-1 Aguessac then onto D907 (follow Gorges du Tarn signs). Site is 2 km. past Rivière sur Tarn, on the right – the access road is quite steep. GPS: N44:11.428 E03:09.383

Charges 2008

Per unit incl. 2 persons and electricity	€ 18,00 - € 29,00
extra person	€ 3,50 - € 6,00
child (under 7 yrs)	€ 2,00 - € 4,00
dog	€ 2,00

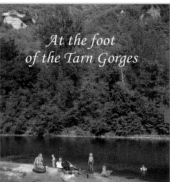
FR12010 Camping le Val de Cantobre

F-12230 Nant-d'Aveyron (Aveyron)

Tel: 05 65 58 43 00. Email: info@rcn-valdecantobre.fr

This very pleasant terraced site has been imaginatively and tastefully developed by the Dupond family over the past 30 years. Most of the 200 touring pitches (all with electricity and water) are peaceful, generous in size and blessed with views of the valley. A unique activity programme at Val de Cantobre is supervised by qualified instructors in July and August, some arranged by the owners and some at a fair distance from the site. The terrace design provides some peace and privacy, especially on the upper levels and a warm welcome awaits. Rock pegs are advised.

Facilities

Fully equipped toilet block is beautifully appointed. Fridge hire. Small shop with wide variety of provisions; including many regional specialities. Attractive bar, restaurant, pizzeria, takeaway (some fairly steep up and down walking from furthest pitches to some facilities). Three swimming pools. Minigolf. Table tennis. Play area. River rafting, white water canoeing, rock climbing, paragliding. All weather sports pitch. Torch useful. There are some fairly steep climbs between the levels on the site. Off site: Fishing 4 km. Riding 15 km. Bicycle hire 25 km.

Open: 14 April - 6 October, with all facilities.

Directions

Site is 4 km. north of Nant, on D991 road to Millau. From Millau direction take D991 signed Gorge du Dourbie. Site is on left, just past turn to Cantobre.

Charges 2008

Per unit incl. 2 persons, electricity and water	€ 18,00 - € 45,50
Camping Cheques accepted.	

273

FR12020 Camping Caravaning les Rivages

Avenue de l'Aigoual, route de Nant, F-12100 Millau (Aveyron)

Tel: **05 65 61 01 07**. Email: **campinglesrivages@wanadoo.fr**

Les Rivages is a large, well established site on the outskirts of the town. It is well situated, being close to the high limestone Causses and the dramatic gorges of the Tarn and Dourbie. Smaller pitches, used for small units, abut a pleasant riverside space suitable for sunbathing, fishing or picnics. Most of the 314 pitches are large, and well shaded. A newer part of the site has less shade but larger pitches. All pitches have electricity (6A), and 282 have water and drainage. The site offers a very wide range of sporting activities close to 30 in all (see facilities). Don't miss the night markets, but don't eat before you get there; there are thousands of things to taste, many of them grilled or spit roasted. Millau is a bustling and pleasant town with easy access via a footpath from the site. The gates are shut 23.00 - 08.00, with a night-watchman on duty.

Facilities

Four well kept modern toilet blocks have all necessary facilities. Special block for children. Small shop (1/6-15/9). Terrace, restaurant and bar overlooking swimming pool, children's pool (from 10/5). Play area. Entertainment, largely for children, child-minding, miniclub. Impressive sports centre with tennis (indoor and outdoor), squash and badminton. Table tennis. Boules. River activities, walking, bird watching, fishing. Off site: Rafting and canoeing arranged. Bicycle hire 1 km. Riding 10 km. Hypermarket in Millau.

Open: 1 April - 15 October.

Directions

From Millau, cross the Tarn bridge and take D991 road east towards Nant. Site is about 400 m. from the roundabout on the right, on the banks of the Dourbie river.

Charges 2008

Per pitch incl. 2 persons and electricity	€ 18,60 - € 26,60
with water and drainage	€ 20,60 - € 28,60
extra person (over 3 yrs)	€ 3,30 - € 4,80
pet	€ 1,50 - € 3,50

Open from 1ˢᵗ April till 15ᵗʰ October

Airotel ✱✱✱✱
Les Rivages
camping • caravaning mobil-home • tentes

www.campinglesrivages.com
e-mail : campinglesrivages@wanadoo.fr

GORGES DU TARN • MILLAU • AVEYRON
Avenue de l'Aigoual - 12100 MILLAU - France
Tél. 00 33 (0)5 65 61 01 07 • Fax 00 33 (0)5 65 59 03 56

FR12040 Camping les Tours

F-12460 Saint Amans-des-Cots (Aveyron)

Tel: **04 99 57 21 21**. Email: **contact@village-center.com**

This impressive campsite is set in beautiful countryside close to the Truyère Gorges, Upper Lot valley and the Aubrac Plateau. Efficiently run, it is situated on the shores of the Lac de la Selves. There are 275 average sized pitches with 6A electricity, some bordering the lake, the rest terraced and hedged with views of the lake. About 100 pitches also have water points. The site has a spacious feel, enhanced by the thoughtfully planned terraced layout and it is well kept and very clean. There is some up and down walking to the facilities, especially from the upper terraces. Used by tour operators (70 pitches).

Facilities

Four very well equipped toilet blocks. Attractive central complex housing the amenities. Restaurant, bar. Swimming pools. Shop (with gas), Takeaway. Play area. Volleyball, tennis, football and table tennis. Varied programme of daytime and evening activities, with mini-club, archery and tree climbing (all supervised). Lake activities include canoeing, pedaloes, windsurfing, water skiing and provision for launching small boats. Internet terminal. Off site: Riding and golf 8 km.

Open: 20 May - 9 September.

Directions

Take D34 from Entraygues-sur-Truyère to St Amans-des-Cots (14 km). In St Amans take D97 to Colombez and then D599 to Lac de la Selves (site signed, 5 km. from St Amans).

Charges 2007

Per unit incl. 2 persons	€ 17,00 - € 37,00
extra person	€ 5,00
Camping Cheques accepted.	

FR12050 Flower Camping les Terrasses du Lac

Route du Vibal, F-12290 Pont-de-Salars (Aveyron)

Tel: 05 65 46 88 18. Email: campinglesterrasses@wanadoo.fr

A terraced site, it provides 180 good sized, level pitches, 112 for touring, with or without shade, all with electricity. Some pitches have good views over the lake which has direct access from the site at two places-; one for pedestrians and swimmers, the other for cars and trailers for launching small boats. This site is well placed for excursions into the Gorges du Tarn, Caves du Roquefort and nearby historic towns and villages. Although there are good facilities for disabled visitors, the terracing on the site may prove difficult. At an altitude of some 700 m. on the plateau of Le Lévézou, this outlying site enjoys attractive views over Lac de Pont-de-Salars. The site seems largely undiscovered by the British, perhaps as it is only open for a short season.

Facilities

Four toilet blocks with adequate facilities. Fridge hire. Shop. Bar/restaurant with a lively French ambience serving full meals (high season) snacks (other times), takeaway (all 1/7-31/8). Heated swimming pool, children's pool (1/6-30/9). Solarium. Playground. Volleyball, petanque, table tennis, billiards. Games, TV rooms. Activities high season. Barbecue area. Off site: Tennis 3 km. Riding 5 km. Golf 20 km.

Open: 1 April - 30 September.

Directions

Using D911 Millau - Rodez road, turn north at Pont-de-Salars towards lake on D523. Follow camp signs. Ignore first site and continue, following lake until Les Terraces (about 5 km).

Charges 2008

Per pitch incl. 2 persons	€ 10,50 - € 21,50
extra person	€ 3,95 - € 4,95
child (2-7 yrs)	€ 3,30 - € 3,95
electricity (6A)	€ 3,95
dog	€ 1,65

FR12060 Camping Beau Rivage

Lac de Pareloup, route de Vernhes, F-12410 Salles-Curan (Aveyron)

Tel: 05 65 46 33 32. Email: camping-beau-rivage@wanadoo.fr

This family run, immaculate site has a wonderful position alongside the beautiful Lac de Paraloup. There are 80 level, grassy pitches (60 for touring) attractively arranged on terraces, separated by neat hedges and a variety of small trees offering little shade. All have electricity (10A). A range of watersports is available on the lake (mostly July and August) and many activities are organised both in high season. On arrival at the site, park outside and go to reception. The site entrance is narrow and quite steep and tractor assistance is available. Once on site access to pitches is easy.

Facilities

Two well equipped and clean toilets blocks provide all the necessary facilities, including those for disabled visitors. Washing machines. Bar, snacks, terrace, takeaway (July/Aug). Small shop (July/Aug). Swimming pool. Games rooms. TV room. Pool table, table tennis. Volleyball. Play area. Fishing, boating, lake bathing. Off site: Salles-Curan (4 km), shops, bars, restaurants. Boat ramp 200 m. Watercraft for hire (July/Aug). Bicycle hire 2 km. Tennis 3 km. Riding 12 km. Golf 35 km. Canoeing, rafting, paragliding, caving, windsurfing.

Open: 1 May - 30 September.

Directions

From D911 Rodez - Millau road turn south on the D993 signed Salles-Curan. In 7 km, just after bridge over the lake, turn right on D243 (site signed). Entrance is on right in just over 1 km. Park outside gate. GPS: N44:12.550 E02:46.376

Charges 2007

Per unit incl. 2 persons	€ 11,50 - € 26,00
extra person	€ 3,00 - € 6,00
child (2-7 yrs)	free - € 4,00
electricity (6A)	€ 13,50 - € 29,00
animal	€ 2,00 - € 3,50

FR12070 Flower Camping la Grange de Monteillac

F-12310 Sévérac-l'Eglise (Aveyron)

Tel: **05 65 70 21 00**. Email: **info@la-grange-de-monteillac.com**

La Grange de Monteillac is a modern, well equipped site in the beautiful, well preserved small village of Sévérac-l'Église. A spacious site, it provides 105 individual pitches, 70 for touring, on gently sloping grass, separated by flowering shrubs and mostly young trees offering little shade. All pitches have electricity (6A, long leads may be required), and 24 have water and waste water connections. There are 35 chalets, mobile homes and tents for rent in separate areas.

Facilities

Modern toilet block with facilities for babies and disabled people. Washing machine, dryer. Shop (1/7-31/8). Poolside restaurant/snack bar serving pizzas, grills etc, takeaway (1/7-31/8). Music or groups feature in the bar (July-Aug). Two swimming pools (1/6-15/9). Spacious, well equipped playground. Organised activities include children's club, bicycle hire, archery. Floodlit boules court. Off site: Fishing 1 km. Shops in village 3 km. Riding 9 km. Golf 25 km. Many marked walks and bicycle rides, canoeing, rafting, canyoning, rock climbing and hang-gliding.

Open: 1 May - 15 September.

Directions

Site is on the edge of Sévérac-l'Église village, just off N88 Rodez - Sévérac Le Château road. From A75 use exit 42. At Sévérac-l'Église turn south onto D28, site is signed. Site entrance is very shortly on left. GPS: N44:21.911 E02:51.086

Charges 2007

Per unit incl. 2 persons and electricity	€ 21,50 - € 23,50
extra person	€ 4,20
child (under 7 yrs)	€ 3,00
dog	€ 1,50

FR12080 Camping Club les Genêts

Lac de Pareloup, F-12410 Salles-Curan (Aveyron)

Tel: **05 65 46 35 34**. Email: **contact@camping-les-genets.fr**

The 162 pitches include 80 grassy, mostly individual pitches for touring units. These are in two areas, one on each side of the entrance lane, and are divided by hedges, shrubs and trees. Most have electricity (6A) and many also have water and waste water drain. The site slopes gently down to the beach and lake with facilities for all watersports including water skiing. A full animation and activities programme is organised in high season, and there is much to see and do in this very attractive corner of Aveyron. The site is not suitable for American style motorhomes.

Facilities

Two sanitary units with a suite for disabled people. The older unit has been refurbished. Baby room. Laundry. Well stocked shop. Bar, restaurant, snacks (main season). Swimming pool, spa pool (from 1/6; unsupervised). Playground. Minigolf, volleyball, boules. Bicycle hire. Pedaloes, windsurfers, kayaks. Fishing licences available. WiFi in bar.

Open: 31 May - 11 September.

Directions

From Salles-Curan take D577 for about 4 km. and turn right into a narrow lane immediately after a sharp right hand bend. Site is signed at junction.

Charges 2007

Per unit incl. 1 or 2 persons and electricity (6A)	€ 11,00 - € 29,00
lakeside pitch	€ 11,00 - € 36,00
extra person	€ 4,00 - € 7,00

FR12120 Camping du Rouergue

Avenue de Fondiès, F-12200 Villefranche-de-Rouergue (Aveyron)

Tel: **05 65 45 16 24**. Email: **campingrouergue@wanadoo.fr**

A spacious and well appointed site in the Vallée de l'Aveyron, Camping du Rouergue is adjacent to the municipal sports facilities. Now under new ownership, you will receive a helpful and friendly welcome. The site has 85 grassy individual touring pitches of varying sizes, served by tarmac roads, and all serviced with electricity (16A), water and drain. Some pitches are shady. A further 13 pitches are for mobile homes or tents for rental. There are reduced rates for campers at the municipal swimming pool and shops and restaurants are within walking distance along the riverside foot and cycle path. A smaller pool is also available on site.

Facilities

The modern spacious sanitary unit includes washbasins in cubicles. Facilities for babies and disabled persons. Dishwashing and laundry sinks. Washing machine. With two identical sections to the block, only one is open during low season. Motorcaravan service point outside campsite entrance. Shop. Small bar, restaurant and takeaway (June - Aug). TV room. Swimming pool. Well equipped playground. Bicycle hire. Off site: Fishing 1 km. Riding 5 km.

Open: 15 April - 30 September.

Directions

Villefranche-de-Rouergue is about midway between Cahors and Rodez. Site is 1 km. southwest of town on D47 towards Monteils, follow signs from D911 to campsite and 'Stade'.

Charges 2007

Per pitch incl. 2 persons	€ 11,00 - € 14,00
extra person (over 10 yrs)	€ 2,50
child (4-10 yrs)	€ 1,50
electricity	€ 3,00

FR12150 Kawan Village Marmotel

F-12130 Saint Geniez-d'Olt (Aveyron)

Tel: **05 65 70 46 51**. Email: **info@marmotel.com**

The road into Marmotel passes various industrial buildings and is a little off-putting – persevere, as they are soon left behind. The campsite itself is a mixture of old and new. The old part provides many pitches with lots of shade and separated by hedges. The new area is sunny until the trees grow. These pitches each have a private sanitary unit (shower, WC, washbasin and dishwashing). New and very well designed, they are reasonably priced for such luxury. All pitches have electricity (10A). A lovely restaurant has a wide terrace with views of the hills and overlooking the heated swimming and paddling pools. These have fountains, a toboggan and sun beds either on grass or the tiled surrounds. The Lot river runs alongside the site where you can fish or canoe.

Facilities

Good sanitary facilities include baby baths and facilities for disabled visitors. Washing machines. Bar/restaurant, takeaway (all season). Swimming pools. Small play area. Multi-sports area (tennis, volleyball, basketball). Entertainment July/Aug. including disco below bar, cinema, karaoke, dances, miniclub for 4-12 yr olds. Bicycle hire. Fishing. Canoeing. Off site: Riding 10 km. Large supermarket 500 m. Bicycle tours and canoe trips on the Lot and rafting on the Tarn are organised.

Open: 1 July - 31 August.

Directions

Heading south on autoroute 75 (free) take exit 41 and follow signs for St Geniez d'Olt. Site is at western end of village. Site is signed onto D19 to Prades d'Aubrac, then 500 m. on left.

Charges 2007

Per unit incl. 1 or 2 persons, 10A electricity	€ 17,50 - € 26,20
extra person	€ 2,10 - € 5,00
child under 4 yrs	€ 1,00 - € 2,60

Camping Cheques accepted.

FR12160 Kawan Village les Peupliers

Route des Gorges du Tarn, F-12640 Rivière-sur-Tarn (Aveyron)

Tel: **05 65 59 85 17**. Email: **lespeupliers12640@wanadoo.fr**

Les Peupliers is a friendly, family site on the banks of the Tarn river. Most of the good-sized pitches have shade, all have electricity, water and a waste water point and are divided by low hedges. It is possible to swim in the river and there is a landing place for canoes. The site has its own canoes (to rent). In a lovely, sunny situation on the site is a swimming pool with a paddling pool, sun beds and a new slide, all protected by a beautifully clipped hedge and with a super view to the surrounding hills and the Château du Peyrelade perched above the village.

Facilities

Large, light and airy toilet facilities, baby facilities with baths, showers and WCs, facilities for disabled visitors. Washing machines. Shop (1/6-30/9). Bar, TV. Internet. Snack bar, takeaway (1/5-30/9). Swimming pool (from 1/5). Games, competitions July/Aug. Fishing. Volleyball. Football. Badminton. Play area. Weekly dances July/Aug. Canoe hire. Refundable deposit for barrier card € 50. Off site: Village with shops and restaurant 300 m. Riding 500 m. Bicycle hire 2 km. Golf 25 km. Rock climbing, canyoning, cycling and walking.

Open: 1 April - 30 September.

Directions

Heading south from Clermont Ferrand to Millau on the A75 autoroute take exit 44-1 signed Aguessac/Gorges du Tarn. In Aguessac turn left and follow signs to Riviere-sur-Tarn (5 km.) and site is clearly indicated down a short road to the right. GPS: N44:11.061 E03:07.402

Charges 2007

Per unit incl. 2 persons	€ 20,00 - € 28,00
extra person	€ 5,00 - € 7,00
child (under 7 yrs)	€ 2,00 - € 4,00
electricity (6A)	€ 4,00
dog	€ 2,50

Camping Cheques accepted.

FR12170 Castel Camping le Caussanel

Lac de Pareloup, F-12290 Canet-de-Salars (Aveyron)

Tel: **05 65 46 85 19**. Email: **info@lecaussanel.com**

The site has 235 large, fairly level, grassy pitches, 135 for touring. Most have 6-10A electricity but very long leads may be necessary, and 33 are fully serviced. The pitches are defined by a tree or boulder in each corner and offer little privacy but many have wonderful views over the lake. Most pitches have little shade, a few having good shade. The site has swimming pools with toboggan and slides and a large paddling pool for children with small slides. The adjacent lake offers a large area, 1 km. long, for swimming and all the usual watersports. This large, extremely spacious site on the banks of Lac de Pareloup is greatly improved. It is ideal, in low season, for those seeking a tranquil holiday in a beautiful region of France or in high season, for those seeking an active holiday. One tour operator takes 20 pitches.

Facilities

Modern toilet blocks have all the necessary facilities. Motorcaravan services. Shop. Bar. Restaurant, takeaway (07/06-06/09). Swimming pool complex from June. Large play area. Boules. Tennis. Football. Volleyball. Table tennis. TV room, clubhouse. Organised activities (July/Aug). Fishing. Bicycle hire (July/Aug). Motor boat launching. Water sports (July/Aug), swimming in lake. Internet access. Off site: Paths around lake (24 km). Other marked walks and cycle rides. Shops, banks, restaurants 8 km. Riding 10 km. Golf 30 km. Canoeing, rafting, paragliding caving, windsurfing.

Open: 26 April - 13 September.

Directions

From D911 Rodez - Millau road, just east of Pont de Salars, turn south on D993 signed Salles-Curan. In 6 km. at crossroads turn right on D538 signed Le Caussanel. Very shortly turn left and continue to site. GPS: N44:12.877 E02:45.995

Charges 2008

Per unit incl. 2 persons	€ 13,20 - € 26,90
extra person	€ 3,50 - € 6,90
child (2-7 yrs)	€ 2,60 - € 4,80
incl. electricity	€ 16,30 - € 31,10
incl. electricity, water and drain	€ 18,70 - € 34,70

Camping Cheques accepted.

FR12300 Camping Le Muret

F-12200 Saint Salvadou (Aveyron)

Tel: **05 65 81 80 69**. Email: **info@lemuret.com**

The new owners (Alain and Annette Larroque) bought this forty year old campsite in 2006 and are already making improvements, such as a new restaurant and appointing their own chef. A very peaceful site, the loudest noise you are likely to hear is the sound of croaking frogs and the birds singing. There are 43 pitches (40 for touring), 3 chalets and equipped tents for rent. They are large (120-200 sq.m.) and all on grass, with dividing hedges and ample shade given by mature trees. You can be assured of a relaxing time here in the heart of the countryside.

Facilities

Single sex toilet block with both Turkish and British style toilets. Facilities for disabled visitors. Washing machine. Small shop for basics. New bar and restaurant (all season). Lake for swimming and fishing. Play area on grass. Barbecue area. Activities for children in high season. Musicians weekly in high season. Torches useful. Off site: Riding 1 km. Golf and bicycle hire 16 km.

Open: 1 April – 31 October.

Directions

From Figeac take N140 east to Decazeville, then north on D963 to Flagnac. Take D508 for 5 km. when site is on left side of road.

Charges 2007

Per person	€ 2,40 - € 3,00
child	€ 1,60 - € 3,00
pitch	€ 7,00 - € 8,50
electricity	€ 4,50

FR12240 Camping Saint Pal

Route du Gorges du Tarn, F-12720 Mostuéjouls (Aveyron)

Tel: 05 65 62 64 46. Email: saintpal@wanadoo.fr

Saint Pal is ideally situated on the approach road to the Gorges du Tarn, so access to the site is easy. This small, very neat site is run by a very friendly family and is aimed at those who prefer peace and quiet and less in the way of organised activity. Beside the Tarn river, the site is arranged in the open valley and is fairly flat. There are 74 large, level, grassy pitches, with 64 for touring. Separated by hedging, most are shaded by mature trees and 6A electricity is available. Some pitches are alongside the attractive river. This is a wonderful area for touring, cycling, mountain biking, flowers and birds of prey. Activities such as canoeing, rafting, caving, walking in the trees, rock climbing and bungee jumping are possible. There is a lot to see and do in this area including the new Millau viaduct, designed by Norman Foster and the Observatory for Vultures at Gorges de la Jonte.

Facilities

One very clean, modern toilet block with good facilities includes a room for babies and campers with disabilities. Motorcaravan service point. Small shop (1/6-15/9). Bar/restaurant and takeaway (1/7-31/8). Small swimming pool (all season). Play area, TV/games room. River bathing, boating and fishing. Organised walks and low key entertainment in July/Aug but no musical events. Off site: Bicycle hire 500 m. Riding 5 km. Le Rozier 1 km. Millau 20 km.

Open: 19 May - 15 September.

Directions

Leave A75 at exit 44, north of Millau. Take N9 south for 14 km. to Aquessac. Turn left on D907 and site is on right in 14 km. just before village of Le Rosier. GPS: N44:11.751 E03:11.983

Charges 2007

Per unit incl. 2 persons and electricity	€ 14,60 - € 23,20
extra person	€ 3,30 - € 4,80
child (under 5 yrs)	€ 23,00 - € 3,50
dog	€ 1,20 - € 2,00

Camping Saint Pal ★★★

Welcome in a picturesque landscape, at the confluence of the Gorges du Tarn and the Gorges de la Jonte, at the gate of the Grands Causses and the Cévennes. Be sure to find here all you need to have a good stay: tranquillity, friendly atmosphere and entertainment: swimming pool, private beach along Tarn river, modern toilet facilities.

Rates and availibilities at:
www.campingsaintpal.com

Camping Saint Pal - 12720 Mostuéjouls - France
Tel: 0033 (0) 565 626 446 - Fax: 0033 (0) 565 587 982
saintpal@wanadoo.fr
www.campingsaintpal.com

FR12210 Flower Camping la Source

Presqu'île de Laussac, F-12600 Therondels (Aveyron)

Tel: 05 65 66 27 10. Email: info@camping-la-source.com

This extremely spacious, steeply terraced site borders the long and narrow Lac de Sarrans with its steep wooded sides. The site is run by a very friendly family and is better suited for the younger family. All the facilities are first class, although the layout of the site means that pitches may be some distance and a steep climb away. The owners prefer to provide tractor assistance for caravans. There are 110 medium to large, slightly sloping, grassy pitches with 64 for touring, all with electricity, water and a drain. They are separated by trees offering some shade and have views over the lake. Rock pegs are essential. The site is not suitable for very large units and those with walking difficulties.

Facilities

Two large, well appointed and clean toilet blocks with all the necessary facilities including those for babies and campers with disabilities. Shop (28/6-29/8). Bar with TV (17/5-7/9). Restaurant and takeaway (28/6-29/8). Swimming pool with toboggan and paddling pool (17/5-7/9, heated 17/5-7/9). Play area. TV room. Activities in high season for all the family. Lake fishing. Off site: Boat ramp 500 m. Golf 6 km. Riding and bicycle hire 15 km.

Open: 17 May - 7 September.

Directions

Leave the A75 at exit 28 or 29 (St Flour). Go through town and take D921 towards Rodez. After 12 km. turn right on D990 to Pierrefort and 3 km. after village turn left on D34, signed Laussac. Follow narrow twisting lanes down to site (about 9 km). GPS: N44:51.223 E02:46.263

Charges 2008

Per unit incl. 2 persons	€ 15,50 - € 25,90
extra person	€ 3,00 - € 4,70
electricity (6/10A)	€ 2,00

Camping Cheques accepted.

Check real time availability and at-the-gate prices...

 www.alanrogers.com

FR12280 Camping du Viaduc

121 avenue de Millau Plage, F-12100 Millau (Aveyron)

Tel: **05 65 60 15 75**. Email: **info@camping-du-viaduc.com**

Run by a young French couple, this site is situated on the banks of the Tam, across the river from Millau. Of medium size, the site has 237 pitches of which about 200 are for touring units and the rest for chalets. Being close to the town it has access to its services but there is also easy access for discovering the beauty and nature of the gorges. The pitches are flat, of average size, shaded under tall trees and have adequate water and electric points. The site is on the banks of the shallow Tam, where a sandy beach has been created. The site has a rectangular pool with a paved sunbathing terrace close to the reception, a well stocked shop and a bar/restaurant and takeaway. The bar opens out onto a terrace where there is a small stage for animation in high season. Millau was infamous for its tortuous route across the Tam valley, but is now famous for the spectacular viaduct which carries the A75 over the Tam valley, designed by British architect Norman Rogers. Natural sites in the area include the regional park of the grand causes, the Tarn, Dourbie and Jonte gorges.

Facilities

One large, centrally situated sanitary block with the usual facilities and covered dishwashing areas. Bar with restaurant and takeaway. Swimming pool and children's pool. Shop (01/06-31/08). Laundry area. Entertainment in July and August. Free children's club in high season. Play area. Fishing and river bathing. Off site: Bicycle and canoe hire 200 m. Hypermarket in Millau and all services of a large town.

Open: 25 April - 29 September.

Directions

Follow signs for 'campings' from Millau centre across the Tam to the east side. At roundabout take last exit signed Paulhe (D187) to second campsite on the left in a short distance. GPS: N44:06.199 E03:05.402

Charges 2007

Per unit incl. 2 persons	€ 13,00 - € 22,00
extra person	€ 3,00 - € 5,00
child (under 5 yrs)	free - € 3,50
electricity (6A)	€ 3,00

FR12250 Flower Camping du Lac de Bonnefon

L'Etang de Bonnefon, F-12800 Naucelle (Aveyron)

Tel: **05 65 69 33 20**. Email: **email-camping-du-lac-de-bonnefon@wanadoo.fr**

This small family-run site, popular with French campers, lies in a picturesque region waiting to be discovered, with rolling hills, deep river valleys, lakes and many old fortified villages. This site is more suitable for those seeking a quieter holiday with less in the way of entertainment. There are 112 good sized, grassy, slightly sloping pitches with 74 for touring (50 with 10A electricity). Some are separated by hedging with others more open and maturing trees give a little shade. The new keen and friendly owners have recently extended the site and refurbished the facilities to a high standard.

Facilities

Two toilet blocks include some washbasins in cabins and good facilities for disabled visitors. No shop but bread to order. Bar with TV (all season). Snack bar (July/Aug, other times on demand). Swimming and paddling pools (1/6-30/9). Playground. Archery. Good lake fishing but no bathing. Activities for all the family in July/Aug. Off site: Riding 500 m. Small village of Naucelle with a few shops and large heated pool complex (1 km).

Open: 1 April - 31 October.

Directions

Site is just off the N88 about halfway between Rodez and Albi. From Naucelle Gare take D997 towards Naucelle. In just over 1 km. turn left on D58 and follow signs to site in just under 1 km. GPS: N44:11.283 E02:20.896

Charges 2007

Per unit incl. 2 persons and electricity	€ 13,50 - € 22,00
extra person	€ 4,00 - € 5,00

Camping Cheques accepted.

FR12350 Camping Côté Sud

Avenue de l'Aigoual, F-12100 Millau (Aveyron)

Tel: 05 65 61 18 83. Email: camping-cotesud@orange.fr

Le Côté Sud can be found just 500 m. from the centre of the lively town of Millau.This site has been recommended to us and we plan to undertake a full inspection in 2008. There are 160 pitches here, most of which are available to tourers. Around 14, however, are occupied by mobile homes. Pitches are of a good size and grassy, all with electrical connections (6A). Given its proximity to Millau and the A75 autoroute, this site may appeal as an en route stop. However, it does have a good range of amenities including a swimming pool, snack bar and a lively entertainment and activity programme. The surrounding area, of course, has a great deal to offer. The gorges of the Tarn, Dourbie and Jonte are all close at hand and the Grands Causses (massive limestone plateaux) are best explored on foot or by mountain bike.

Facilities

Swimming pool. River swimming. Sauna. Snack bar. TV room. Play area. Activity and entertainment programme. Off site: Millau centre 500 m. Walking and cycling in the Grands Causses park. Roquefort cheese cellars. Caves (Aven Armand and Dargilan).

Open: April - September.

Directions

Leave the A75 motorway at exit 45 (Millau) before crossing the viaduct. Follow signs to the town and, at each roundabout, follow signs for 'Campings'. All the town's campsites are grouped in the same area and are well signed.

Charges 2008

Per unit with 2 persons and electricity	€ 10,00 - € 24,00
extra person	€ 3,00 - € 4,50
child (5-11 yrs)	€ 2,00 - € 3,50
dog	free - € 1,50

Camping Coté Sud

Avenue de l'Aigoual
12100 MILLAU

Tel: 0033 565 61 18 83
Fax: 0033 565 61 18 83

camping-cotesud@orange.fr
www.camping-cotesud.fr

FR12310 Camping de la Cascade

Route de Pont, F-12490 Saint Rome-de-Tarn (Aveyron)

Tel: 05 65 62 56 59. Email: campingdelacascade@wanadoo.fr

De la Cascade is situated on a terraced hillside, beside the Tarn river. One may have an action packed holiday or enjoy peace and tranquillity relaxing by the river. There are 99 pitches, 50 for touring with electricity (6A) with plenty of shade and manicured hedges. This is an ideal starting point for walkers to explore the surrounding hills and gorges as the owner will organise transport. Canoes, pedaloes are available for hire to explore the gorge. A restaurant and bar overlook the swimming pool. There are some steep paths that make this site unsuitable for visitors with disabilities and large units.

Facilities

Good toilet block with showers and washbasins in cubicles. Toilet facilities are dotted around the site. No facilities for disabled visitors. Washing machine, dryer, ironing board. Shop, bar, restaurant (July/Aug). Swimming and paddling pools with slide (15/6-15/9). River beach. Activity clubs and entertainment in high season. Play area on grass, well away from the river. Tennis. Fishing. Off site: Riding 15 km. Shops, restaurants within 2 km.

Open: All year.

Directions

From the north on A75 take exit 46, D999 signed St Rome-de-Carmon, then D31, then D933 to Rome-de-Tarn. Site is on right through village. From the south, take exit 47, follow directions as above.

Charges 2007

Per unit incl. 2 persons and electricity	€ 17,00 - € 25,00
extra person	€ 6,50
child (2-10 yrs)	€ 4,00

FR12340 Résidence les Clédelles le Colombier

Parcs Residentiels ▶ page 514

F-12130 Saint Geniez d'Olt (Aveyron)

Tel: **05 65 47 45 72**. Email: **cledelles.reservations@wanadoo.fr**

Pitches at this campsite are exclusively for chalet accommodation.

FR16030 Camping le Champion

F-16230 Mansle (Charente)

Tel: **05 45 20 31 41**. Email: **ot.pays-manslois@wanadoo.fr**

Le Champion is a convenient stop-over from the N10 or a good base to explore the northern Charente area. Beside the Charente river, the site has a cool, relaxing atmosphere created by its attractive location and the 'hippodrome' provides open grassy space on the other side. The site, with 116 average sized and separated touring pitches, is mostly open with little shade. All pitches have electricity (10A) and 15 have water points. Groups are welcome and there is a dedicated area with a second toilet block at the back of the site for groups of more than ten caravans.

Facilities

Modern, well appointed sanitary block is well maintained and provides facilities for disabled people. Washing machine. An additional smaller, older block is in the tenting area at the rear of the site. Motorcaravan service point at entrance. Minigolf. Volleyball. Basketball. Petanque. English spoken. Off site: Restaurant and snacks outside site. Town with its Roman bridge. Tourist office 500 m. Swimming pool in town (discount for campers), recreation area next to the site.

Open: 15 May - 15 September.

Directions

From N10, 30 km. north of Angoulême, take exit for Mansle. From the south, follow signs for Centre Ville, continue past town centre and church, and site is on right, immediately after crossing river. Site is well signed. GPS: N45:52.692 E00:10.891

Charges guide

Per person	€ 2,20
child (under 7 yrs)	€ 1,20
pitch incl. car	€ 2,80
electricity	€ 2,80

FR16040 Camping Devezeau

F-16230 Saint Angeau (Charente)

Tel: **05 45 39 21 29**. Email: **bookings@campingdevezeau.com**

Camping Devezeau is open all year and provides a pleasant stopping place on the way to and from the south. It is also within easy reach of Cognac. The site has British owners who are working hard to upgrade what is already an attractive site. There are just 39 pitches (34 for touring units) mainly on grass and separated by immature shrubs, although there are four hardstandings for motorcaravans. Most have electricity. The swimming pool is an added attraction for such a small site. It is particularly suited to families looking for a quiet holiday.

Facilities

The toilet block in a converted barn provides single sex facilities, facilities for disabled people, laundry and dishwashing sinks, and a washing machine. Gas supplies. Swimming pool (12 x 12 m; 1/5-30/9). Play area. Off site: Shop and bar in village 1.5 km. Fishing 2 km.

Open: All year.

Directions

From north, N10 exit for Mansle. Turn left (east) at lights onto D6 for St Angeau. After 9 km, at junction with D15, turn south onto D15, signed for Tourriers. Take first left, after 300 m, site signed, site is 150 m.

Charges 2007

Per unit incl. 2 persons	€ 10,00 - € 18,00
extra person	€ 4,00 - € 5,00
child	€ 1,00 - € 2,00
electricity	€ 2,00 - € 5,00
No credit cards.	

FR16020 Castel Camping les Gorges du Chambon

Eymouthiers, F-16220 Montbron (Charente)

Tel: 05 45 70 71 70. Email: gorges.chambon@wanadoo.fr

A welcoming and friendly, family site in pretty, rolling Périgord Vert countryside, Gorges du Chambon is arranged around a restored Charente farmhouse and its outbuildings. It provides an attractive, spacious setting with 140 large, marked pitches of which 90 are for touring units. All have electrical connections (6A) and 4 have water and drainage. On gently sloping grass and enjoying extensive views over the countryside, the pitches are arranged in two circular groups with a sanitary block at the centre of each. The pitches for mobile homes and tour operator tents are not obtrusive.

Facilities

Traditional style blocks include facilities for disabled people. Washing machine, dryer. Basic shop. Bar, restaurant (all season). Takeaway (all season). Swimming pool, children's pool. Children's play area. Games room, TV, table tennis. Tennis, archery, minigolf. Bicycle and canoe hire. Organised activities July/Aug, children's club, youth disco, teenagers' corner. No pets. Off site: Private fishing (free) 6 km; with licence 200 m. Golf 6 km. Riding 6 km. Sailing 20 km. Visits are organised to local producers and day trips (low season).

Open: 19 April - 20 September (camping).

Directions

From N141 Angoulême - Limoges road at Rochefoucauld take D6 to Montbron village. Follow D6 in direction of Piegut-Pluviers and site is signed to the north on D163 just as you enter Tricherie. GPS: N45:39.588 E00:33.460

Charges 2007

Per person	€ 3,85 - € 6,80
child (1-7 yrs)	€ 1,55 - € 3,40
pitch	€ 5,45 - € 8,30
car	€ 1,55 - € 2,20
electricity (6A)	€ 3,25 - € 3,35

Camping Cheques accepted.

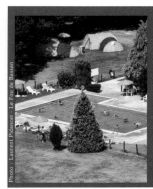
FR16050 Camping de Cognac

Boulevard de Châtenay, route de Sainte-Sévère, F-16100 Cognac (Charente)

Tel: 05 45 32 13 32. Email: info@campingdecognac.com

This area is a must for lovers of brandy, with abundant vineyards and little roadside chalets offering tastings of Pineau (a Cognac based aperitif) and a vast range of cognacs. This site by the Charente river is convenient as a night stop or longer stay to visit the area, and for sleeping off the effects of the 'tastings' – you probably won't even notice the slight noise from the nearby road! The 168 large touring pitches, all with electricity (5/6A), are neatly laid out and separated by shrubs and trees. A few mobile homes are discreetly positioned along one boundary.

Facilities

Two well equipped, fairly modern toilet blocks (access by steps) include children's toilets and a washing machine. Separate ground level facilities for disabled visitors. Motorcaravan services. Small swimming pool on site (municipal pool nearby). Shop, snack bar, takeaway and entertainment (15/6-15/9). Fishing. Volleyball. Table tennis. Play area on grass. Off site: Bicycle hire 2 km. Riverside walks. Restaurants, bars and shops in the town (2.3 km). Golf 5 km. Riding 6 km.

Open: 1 May - 15 October.

Directions

Site is signed from N141 Saintes - Angoulême road following signs for town centre. It is to the north of the town beside the river on the D24 to Boutiers and Ste-Sévère. GPS: N45:42.544 W00:18.759

Charges 2007

Per unit incl. 2 persons	€ 7,20 - € 9,30
extra person	€ 3,50 - € 3,80
child (0-2 yrs)	free
animal	€ 1,50

Less for stays over 3 days.

FR24130 Camping les Grottes de Roffy

Mobile homes ▶ page 500

Sainte Nathalène, F-24200 Sarlat-la-Canéda (Dordogne)

Tel: **05 53 59 15 61**. Email: **roffy@perigord.com**

A pleasantly laid out site, about 5 km. east of Sarlat, Les Grottes de Roffy has 162 clearly marked pitches, some very large. Set on very well kept grass terraces, they have easy access and good views across an attractive valley. Some have plentiful shade, although others are more open, and all have electricity (6A). The reception, bar, restaurant and shop are located within converted farm buildings surrounding a semi-courtyard. The campsite shop is well stocked with a variety of goods and a tempting charcuterie section (prepared on site) with plenty of ideas for the barbecue. Various entertainments and excursions are organised during high season. Conveniently located for Sarlat and all other Dordogne attractions, this is a good site for families. Used by tour operators (64 pitches).

Facilities

Two toilet blocks with modern facilities are more than adequate. Well stocked shop. Bar and restaurant with imaginative and sensibly priced menu. Takeaway (all amenities from 6/5). Good swimming pool complex comprising two deep pools (one heated), a fountain, children's pool and heated jacuzzi. Tennis, volleyball and badminton courts. Games room. Play area. Off site: Fishing 2 km. Bicycle hire 7 km. Riding 10 km. Golf 15 km.

Open: 26 April - 21 September.

Directions

Take D47 east from Sarlat to Ste Nathalène. Just before Ste Nathalène the site is signed on the right hand side of the road. Turn here, and the site is about 800 m. along the lane. GPS: N44:54.230 E01:16.920

Charges 2008

Per pitch with 2 persons and electricity	€ 20,80 - € 27,50
extra person	€ 5,50 - € 7,20
child (2-7 yrs)	€ 4,00 - € 5,80
dog	€ 2,00

les **Grottes** de **Roffy**
camping
caravaning

★ ★ ★ ★

Sainte-Nathalèle • 24200 Sarlat • France

E-mail roffy@perigord.com   Tél. +33 (0)5 53 59 15 61 • Fax +33 (0)5 53 31 09 11

FR24040 Castel Camping le Moulin du Roch

Route des Eyzies - Le Roch, D47, F-24200 Sarlat-la-Canéda (Dordogne)

Tel: **05 53 59 20 27**. Email: **moulin.du.roch@wanadoo.fr**

The site has 195 pitches, of which 124 are for touring units. Pitches are mostly flat (some slope slightly) and grassy and all have electricity (6A). Pitches on the upper levels have plenty of shade, whilst those on the lower level near the amenities and the fishing lake are more open. Entertainment and activities are organised from June to September, with something for everyone from craft workshops and sports tournaments to canoeing and caving for the more adventurous. An excellent multi-lingual children's club runs in July and August. Walking and mountain biking lead from the site through surrounding woodland.

Facilities

Modern, well maintained, clean toilet blocks. Washing machines, dryers. Good shop (all season). Bar with WiFi and terrace (12/5-9/9). Takeaway (5/5-15/9). Superb restaurant (12/5-9/9). Attractive swimming pool, paddling pool, sun terrace (all season). Fishing lake, tennis, table tennis, boules, volleyball, playground, discos twice weekly in high season. Pets are not accepted. Off site: Supermarkets, banks, etc. at Sarlat 10 km. Bicycle hire and riding 10 km. Golf 15 km.

Open: 28 April - 15 September.

Directions

Site is 10 km. west of Sarlat la Canéda, on south side of D47 Sarlat - Les Eyzies road. GPS: N44:54.516 E01:06.883

Charges 2007

Per pitch incl. 2 persons	€ 15,00 - € 27,00
with electricity	€ 19,00 - € 31,00
with full services	€ 23,00 - € 35,00
extra person	€ 4,00 - € 7,80
child (4-9 yrs)	free - € 3,00

Camping Cheques accepted.

FR24050 Camping les Hauts de Ratebout

Saint Foy de Belvès, F-24170 Belvès (Dordogne)

Tel: **05 53 29 02 10**. Email: **camping@hauts-ratebout.fr**

Situated southwest of Sarlat, there are some stunning views of the surrounding countryside from many of the 200 pitches at this pretty hilltop campsite. The terraced pitches vary in size (80-130 sq.m), some flat and some sloping. All have electricity (6A) and water. Housed in an older building, the restaurant/bar has plenty of atmosphere and is interestingly furnished. The swimming pool complex includes a 200 sq.m. unheated pool with slide, a shallow 100 sq.m. pool which is covered and heated as necessary, a fun pool with another slide and a small paddling pool. The site is used by tour operators (57 pitches). The walled town of Belvès is worth a visit.

Facilities

Four high standard toilet blocks offer the usual amenities including private washbasins and facilities for people with disabilities. Washing machines and dryers. Small shop (with gas) and takeaway service. Restaurant/bar and second bar and terrace. Swimming pool complex (proper trunks). Adventure playground on gravel. General room with pool and football tables and TV. Volleyball, table tennis. Tennis. Organised activities in season. Nightly videos and sporting events. Off site: Fishing and bicycle hire 6 km. Riding 7 km. Golf 8 km.

Open: 13 May - 10 September.

Directions

From Belvès, take D710 southwards for 2 km. then turn east on D54. After 2 km. turn left, and after a further 500 m. left again (following campsite signs all the way). Site is 1.5 km. along on the right.

Charges guide

Per unit incl. 2 persons, water and electricity	€ 20,00 - € 32,00
with drainage	€ 20,00 - € 33,00
extra person	€ 5,00 - € 7,00
child (3-7 yrs)	€ 3,00 - € 5,50

Camping Cheques accepted.

FR24070 Camping Lestaubière

Pont Saint Mamet, F-24140 Douville (Dordogne)

Tel: **05 53 82 98 15**. Email: **lestaubiere@cs.com**

The site is just off the main N21 road near Pont St Mamet, mid-way between Bergerac and Perigueux. There are 104 large pitches, most are flat, shaded and wooded, some on more sloping open meadow with views across the valley and others on flat ground beside the lake. Pitches are marked and all have electricity (6/10A), some requiring long leads. The swimming pool and small lake with diving platform and beach encourage longer stays. A pleasant, shaded patio terrace under vines and maples leads to a general room with a bar and a separate room for young people with amusement machines (July/Aug).

Facilities

Three toilet blocks include baby baths, large family room and facilities for disabled visitors. Ample dishwashing and laundry sinks. Washing machine and dryers. Small shop. Bar. Library. Swimming pool (unsupervised) and paddling pool. Excellent adventure style play area. Volleyball. Boules. Fishing. Children's club and organised activities in July/Aug. Off site: Tennis 500 m.

Open: 1 May - 1 October.

Directions

Site is 19 km. north east of Bergerac. From N21 Bergerac - Perigueux road take exit for Pont St Mamet. Site is 500 m. north of the village, on the eastern side of the road, and is well signed.

Charges 2008

Per person	€ 6,90
child (under 7)	€ 3,90
pitch	€ 10,00
electricity (6A)	€ 3,50
animal	€ 2,00

FR24010 **Kawan Village le Châteaux de Verdoyer**

Champs Romain, F-24470 Saint Pardoux (Dordogne)

Tel: 05 53 56 94 64. Email: **chateau@verdoyer.fr**

Mobile homes ▶ page 499

The 26 hectare estate has three lakes, two for fishing and one with a sandy beach and safe swimming area. There are 135 good sized touring pitches, level, terraced and hedged. With a choice of wooded area or open field, all have electricity (5/10A) and most share a water supply between four pitches. There is a swimming pool complex and in high season activities are organised for children (5-13 yrs) but there is no disco. This site is well adapted for those with disabilities, with two fully adapted chalets, wheelchair access to all facilities and even a lift into the pool. Le Verdoyer has been developed in the park of a restored château and is owned by a Dutch family. We particularly like this site for its beautiful buildings and lovely surroundings. It is situated in the lesser known area of the Dordogne sometimes referred to as the Périgord Vert, with its green forests and small lakes. The courtyard area between reception and the bar is home to evening activities, and provides a pleasant place to enjoy drinks and relax. The château itself has rooms to let and its excellent lakeside restaurant is also open to the public.

Facilities

Well appointed toilet blocks include facilities for disabled people and baby baths. Serviced launderette. Motorcaravan services. Fridge rental. Shop with gas. Bar, snacks, takeaway and restaurant, both open all season. Bistro (July/Aug). Two pools the smaller covered in low season, slide, paddling pool. Play areas. Tennis. Volleyball, basketball, badminton, table tennis, minigolf. Bicycle hire. Small library. Off site: Riding 5 km.

Open: 26 April - 6 October.

Directions

Site is 2 km. from Limoges (N21) - Chalus (D6bis-D85) - Nontron road, 20 km. south of Chalus and is well signed from main road. Site on D96 about 4 km. north of village of Champs Romain. GPS: N45:33.083 E00:47.683

Charges 2008

Per unit incl. 2 persons	
and electricity	€ 18,00 - € 29,00
full services	€ 18,00 - € 33,50
extra person	€ 5,00 - € 6,50
child (under 3-7 yrs)	€ 3,00 - € 4,50
dog	free - € 4,00

Between 9/7-20/8 stay 14 nights, pay for twelve. Camping Cheques accepted.

Château ★★★★ Le Verdoyer

Dordogne Périgord vert

Accommodation
Restaurant
Camping
★★★★
F 24470
Champs
Romain

Camping Cheque

Tél.+ 33 5 53 56 94 64
Fax.+ 33 5 53 56 38 70
E mail :
chateau@verdoyer.fr

www.verdoyer.fr

FR24020 Camping Caravaning les Granges

Mobile homes ▶ page 500

F-24250 Groléjac-en-Perigord (Dordogne)

Tel: **05 53 28 11 15**. Email: **contact@lesgranges-fr.com**

Situated only 500 metres from the village of Groléjac, Les Granges is a lively and well maintained campsite set on sloping ground in woodland. There are 188 pitches, of which 100 are available for touring units. The pitches are marked and numbered on level terraces, and most receive good shade from mature trees and shrubs. All pitches have electricity (6A) and water either on the pitch or close by. The site has a good sized swimming pool and a large shallow pool for children. A bridge connects these to a fun pool with water slides. Regular entertainment is organised in high season, along with a children's club every weekday morning. Around 88 pitches are used by tour operators.

Facilities

The toilet blocks are of a very high standard with good facilities for disabled visitors. Bar/restaurant and snack bar also providing takeaway food (15/05-15/09). No shop, but bread and milk can be ordered. Play area. Table tennis, volleyball, basketball, minigolf, climbing wall. Canoe and bicycle hire. Off site: Shops in the nearby village of Groléjac and hypermarkets of Sarlat or Gourdon are not far away. Golf and riding 6 km.

Open: 2 May - 15 September.

Directions

In centre of village of Groléjac on main D704 road. Site signed through a gravel parking area on west side of road. Drive through this area and follow road around to T-junction. Turn right, under railway bridge, and immediately left (site signed). Site is just along this road on left. GPS: N44:48.950 E01:17.470

Charges 2007

Per unit incl. 2 persons	€ 15,00 - € 27,00
extra person (over 5 yrs)	€ 6,40 - € 720,00
electricity (6A)	€ 3,50
dog	free - € 3,00

CAMPING LES GRANGES 4 ★★★★
24250 GROLEJAC
Tél :+ 33.(0)5.53.28.11.15. - Fax : + 33. (0)5.53.28.57.13.
www.lesgranges-fr.com
Email : contact@lesgranges-fr.com

In pure Perigord-style buildings, les Granges welcomes you in lush vegetation and offers all the modern conforts of 4 star campsite. You will find spacious terraced emplacements 100 m², bordered by hedges in bloom and more 3 Pools including 1 heated, 2 water chutes. At 500m The Dordogne with canoë hire and Cycle paths, mountain bike hire, washing machin, dryer, iron, fridge...

All the services are open from the 1st june : restaurant, take away, pizza, bar.
From 01/07 till 31/07 : Animations, childrens Club
Hire mobil homes and chalets open from 27/04 till 15/09.

Acces A20 from Paris to Toulouse, exit at Souillac. D704 between Sarlat 10 km and Gourdon 12 km.

FR24080 Camping Caravaning le Moulin de David

Gaugeac, F-24540 Monpazier (Dordogne)

Tel: **08 25 00 20 30**. Email: **contact@village-center.com**

Set in a 14 hectare wooded valley, it has 160 pitches split into two sections,102 are available for touring vans – 33 below the central reception complex in a shaded situation, and 69 above on partly terraced ground with varying degrees of shade. All pitches have electricity (3/6/10A). Spacing is good and there is no crowding. The site has been attractively planted with a pleasing variety of shrubs and trees and combined with the small stream that runs through the centre of the site they create a beautiful and tranquil setting.

Facilities

Three good toilet blocks, including facilities for disabled visitors and babies. New mobile home. Laundry room. Good shop. Bar/restaurant with shaded patio, takeaway. Swimming pool and children's paddling pool, freshwater pool with waterslide. Play area. Boules, half-court tennis, table tennis, volleyball, basketball, trampoline, football. Library. Bicycle hire. Events, games and canoe trips. Off site: Small supermarket and cash point in Monpazier 2.5 km.

Open: 17 May - 13 September.

Directions

From Monpazier take the D2 Villeréal road. Take third turning left (after about 2 km), signed to Moulin de David and 'Gaugeac Mairie'. Site is about 500 m. along this road on the left.

Charges 2007

Per person (over 5 yrs)	€ 5,00
pitch incl. water and drainage	€ 16,00 - € 27,00
large pitch incl. water and drainage	€ 19,00 - € 32,00

FR24030 Camping les Périères

Rue Jean Gabin, F-24203 Sarlat-la-Canéda (Dordogne)

Tel: **05 53 59 05 84**. Email: **les-perieres@wanadoo.fr**

Les Périères is a good quality small site set on an attractive hillside within walking distance of the beautiful medieval town of Sarlat. The 100 pitches are arranged on wide terraces around the semi-circle of a fairly steep valley, overlooking a central leisure area that includes indoor and outdoor swimming pools and two tennis courts. The pitches are of a very good size, all equipped with electricity (6A), individual water and drainage points and many have dappled shade from the numerous walnut trees on the site (the walnuts can be bought in the campsite shop). Reservations are advised for high season, when the site becomes busy. The site has a refreshingly spacious and open feel, quite free from overcrowding, even at busy times.

Facilities

Good toilet blocks with facilities for disabled visitors, baby bathroom, washing machines, dryers. Motorcaravan services. Small shop. Pleasant bar. Small snack bar/takeaway (July/August). Outdoor swimming pool (no shorts), paddling pool, indoor spa pool and sauna (all season). Tennis, football, fitness track. Stone cottages to rent. Electric barbecues not allowed. Off site: Bicycle hire 1 km. Fishing 5 km. Riding and golf 7 km.

Open: Easter - 30 September.

Directions

Site is on the east side of Sarlat, on the D47 to Ste Nathalene (negotiating Sarlat town centre is best done outside peak hours). GPS: N44:53.61 E01:13.66

Charges 2007

Per unit incl. 2 persons	€ 19,40 - € 30,50
with electricity	€ 23,20 - € 34,40
extra person	€ 6,30
child (under 7 yrs)	€ 4,30

Credit cards accepted with 2% fee.

FR24100 Kawan Village le Moulinal

F-24540 Biron (Dordogne)

Tel: **05 53 40 84 60**. Email: **lemoulinal@perigord.com**

A rural, lakeside site in woodland, Le Moulinal offers activities for everyone of all ages. Of the 280 grassy pitches, only around 62 are available for touring units and these are spread amongst the site's own mobile homes, chalets and a small number of British tour operator tents. All pitches are flat, grassy and have electricity (6A), but vary considerably in size from 75-100 sq.m. The five-acre lake has a sandy beach and is suitable for boating (canoe hire available), swimming and fishing. Ambitious, well organised animation is run all season including craft activities, children's club.

Facilities

Toilet facilities, built to harmonise with the surroundings, include facilities for disabled people and babies. Washing machines, dryers. Motorcaravan services. Excellent restaurant. Bar. Snack bar/takeaway. Large, heated swimming pool with jacuzzi and children's pool. Rustic play area. Multisport court, table tennis, boules, volleyball, tennis, football, basketball, archery, roller skating. Mountain bike hire. All facilities open all season. Off site: Riding and climbing 5 km. Potholing 10 km. Bastide towns of Monpazier, Villeréal and Monflanquin 15 km.

Open: 1 April - 16 September.

Directions

Site is 53 km. southeast of Bergerac. From D104 Villeréal - Monpazier road take the D53/D150 south. Just before Lacapelle Biron turn right onto D255 towards Dévillac, (site signed), site is 1.5 km. along on the left. GPS: N44:35.988 E00:52.249

Charges 2007

Per pitch incl. 2 persons and electricity	€ 20,00 - € 43,00

Camping Cheques accepted.

FR24090 Domaine de Soleil Plage

Mobile homes ► page 500

Caudon par Montfort, Vitrac, F-24200 Sarlat-la-Canéda (Dordogne)

Tel: 05 53 28 33 33. Email: info@soleilplage.fr

This site is in one of the most attractive sections of the Dordogne valley, with a riverside location. The site has 199 pitches, in three sections, around 104 are for touring units. The smallest section surrounds the main reception and other facilities. There are 59 mobile homes, 20 chalets and 17 bungalow tents. The site offers river bathing from a sizeable pebble or sand bank. All pitches are bounded by hedges and are of adequate size. Most pitches have some shade and have electricity and many have water and a drain. Various activities are organised during high season including walks and sports tournaments, and daily canoe hire is available from the site. Once a week in July and August there is a 'soirée' (charged for) usually involving a barbecue or paella, with band and lots of free wine – worth catching! The site is busy and reservation is advisable. Used by UK tour operators (42 pitches). English is spoken. The site is quite expensive in high season and you also pay more for a riverside pitch, but if you like a holiday with lots going on, you will like this one.

Facilities

Toilet facilities are in three modern unisex blocks (only two open). You will need to hire a plug (5 euro) for the baby bath. Washing machines and dryer (charged for). Motorcaravan service point. Pleasant bar with TV. Restaurant. Well stocked shop. Very impressive main pool, paddling pool, spa pool and two water slides. Tennis court and minigolf, (both charged for in high season), table tennis, volleyball, football pitches. Playground. Fishing. Canoe and kayak hire. Bicycle hire. Currency exchange. Small library. Off site: Golf 1 km. Riding 5 km.

Open: 1 April - 30 September.

Directions

Site is 8 km. south of Sarlat. From A20 take exit 55 (Souillac) towards Sarlat. Follow the D703 to Carsac and on to Montfort. At Montfort castle turn left for 2 km. down to the river.
GPS: N44:49.510 E01:17.470

Charges 2007

Per person	€ 4,50 - € 7,00
child (2-9 yrs)	€ 2,50 - € 4,50
pitch with electricity	€ 9,00 - € 15,50
with full services	€ 12,00 - € 23,00

Awards in 2007:
Alan Rogers Welcome Award
ANWB Camping of the Year

Take advantage of our prices in low season to enjoy our heated pool & the beautiful scenery from your chalet or your pitch along the river

Right on the Dordogne riverside
(Sand beach, swimming, fishing, canoeing)
An exceptional site, 6 km from Sarlat
mediaeval town. In the heart of Périgord
beautiful landscapes & castles

Many quality facilities for couples, families or groups:
Mini-mart (fresh bread & croissants), restaurant périgourdin, pizzeria, take-away, bar, meeting room.
Numerous activities: heated pool complex with slides, fitness, tennis, mini-golf, multi-sport pitch, hiking, cycling, golf (1 km), riding (5 km), numerous visits (caves, castles, vines, farms...)

English fluently spoken

Domaine de Soleil Plage****
Caudon par Montfort, VITRAC, 24200 SARLAT
Tel: +33 5 53 28 33 33 - Fax: +33 5 53 28 30 24
www.soleilplage.fr

FR24060 Camping le Paradis

Saint Léon-sur-Vézère, F-24290 Montignac (Dordogne)

Tel: 05 53 50 72 64. Email: le-paradis@perigord.com

Le Paradis is a well maintained riverside site, halfway between Les Eyzies and Montignac. Well situated for exploring places of interest in the Dordogne region, the site is very well kept and laid out with mature shrubs and bushes of different types. It has 200 individual pitches of good size on flat grass, divided by trees and shrubs (148 for touring units). All have electricity, water and drainage, and there are some special pitches for motorcaravans. At the far end of the site, steps down to the Vézère river give access for canoe launching and swimming. The site welcomes a good quota of Dutch and British visitors, many through a tour operator. Organised games, competitions and evening events are aimed at maintaining a true French flavour. English is spoken. This is a site of real quality, which we thoroughly recommend.

Facilities

High quality, well equipped, heated toilet blocks (unisex), baby baths and toilets. Well stocked shop (with gas). Good restaurant, takeaway. Good pool complex heated in low season, paddling pool. Tennis, football, BMX track, volleyball, table tennis and pool activities. Multisport court. Canoe hire. Fishing. Bicycle hire. Quad bike and horse riding excursions. Playground. Off site: Riding 3 km. Various trips organised to surrounding area.

Open: 22 March - 25 October.

Directions

Site is 12 km. north of Les Eyzies and 3 km. south of St Léon-sur-Vézère, on the east side of the D706. GPS: N45:00.100 E01:04.260

Charges 2007

Per unit incl. 2 persons	€ 17,50 - € 26,00
extra person	€ 5,20 - € 7,20
child (3-12 yrs)	€ 4,20 - € 6,20
electricity (10A)	€ 3,50

Low season reductions.
10% discount for pensioners in low season.
Camping Cheques accepted.

Camping Le Paradis - 24290 St. Leon sur Vézère
tel.: 05 53 50 72 64 - fax: 05 53 50 75 90 - le-paradis@perigord.com - www.le-paradis.com

FR24150 Camping les Deux Vallées

F-24220 Vézac (Dordogne)

Tel: 05 53 29 53 55. Email: les2v@perigord.com

This site is enviably situated almost under the shadow of Beynac castle in the heart of the Dordogne. There are 96 flat marked touring pitches, most of a good size, some large and with electricity (6/10A). There is plenty of shade and the general feel is of unspoilt but well managed woodland. There is a small fishing lake on site and it is only a short distance to the Dordogne river for bathing or canoeing. The site is being steadily upgraded by its Dutch owners who provide a warm and friendly welcome. English is spoken.

Facilities

The modern unisex, clean toilet blocks (one heated) have facilities for disabled visitors. Shop, bar/restaurant (both 1/6-30/9) meals to take away, eat inside or on the terrace. Good sized pool, children's pool (from mid May). Bicycle hire. Volleyball, basketball, minigolf, boules, table tennis, table football. Quiz nights and barbecues are a regular feature in the main season. Facilities may open earlier than stated if demand is sufficient. Off site: Riding 2 km. Golf 8 km.

Open: All year.

Directions

Site is on the northwest side of the D57 Beynac-et-Cazenac - Sarlat road, about 2 km. from Beynac. From Beynac follow D57, under railway bridge, second left and then first left over bridge. Turn immediately left to site.

Charges 2007

Per person	€ 3,20 - € 5,20
child (3-7 yrs)	€ 2,20 - € 3,20
pitch	€ 4,00 - € 6,75
electricity (6A)	€ 3,50
animal	€ 1,00 - € 1,50

FR24140 Camping Bel Ombrage

F-24250 Saint Cybranet (Dordogne)

Tel: 05 53 28 34 14. Email: belombrage@wanadoo.fr

Bel Ombrage is a quiet, well maintained site located in a pretty location by the little River Céou, with a pebble beach that is safe and clean for bathing. The site has a good pool complex, but otherwise there are few on site facilities. The 180 well shaded, good sized and flat grass pitches are marked by trees and bushes and all with electricity. The quiet and tranquil setting makes the site particularly popular with couples. Bel Ombrage is very close to Domme and Castelnaud and would make an ideal and inexpensive base for visiting the southern Dordogne area. It is a short walk to the village of St Cybranet, with bar, restaurant and a small well stocked supermarket, and a short drive takes you to the beautifully restored village of Daglan.

Facilities

Two modern toilet blocks are kept spotlessly clean, with facilities for disabled visitors and babies. Laundry facilities. Bread van. Large swimming pool with sun terrace, children's pool. Paddling pool. Play area. Games room. Fishing. Excursions can be booked at reception. Off site: Pizzeria next door. Tennis and canoeing close. Riding and bicycle hire 3 km. Golf 6 km. More shops at Cénac.

Open: 1 June - 5 September.

Directions

Site is about 14 km. south of Sarlat, on the east side of the D57 Castelnaud-la-Chapelle - St Cybranet road, about 1 km. north of the junction with the D50. GPS: N44:47.442 E01:09.740

Charges 2007

Per person	€ 5,30
child (under 7 yrs)	€ 3,30
pitch	€ 7,00
electricity (10A)	€ 3,80

No credit cards.

Bel Ombrage camping-caravaning
24250 St. Cybranet
Tel: 0033 (0)553 28 34 14 - Fax: 0033 (0)553 59 64 64
E-mail: belombrage@wanadoo.fr
www.belombrage.com

FR24110 Camping Caravaning Aqua Viva

Route Sarlac-Souillac, Carsac-Aillac, F-24200 Sarlat-la-Canéda (Dordogne)

Tel: 05 53 31 46 00. Email: contact@village-center.com

This shaded woodland site is ideally situated for visits to Rocamadour and Padirac, as well as exploring the Dordogne region, including the medieval town of Sarlat, only 7 km. away. The site is divided into two sections, separated by a small access road. Pitches are flat, mainly on grass, divided by shrubs and they vary from average to large size. Many have shade from the numerous trees. All have electricity (6/10A). A wide range of organised activities, children's clubs and entertainments run throughout the season, making this site popular with families, especially those with pre-teen and younger teenage children. English is spoken. One small tour operator, but the site attracts a good mixture of nationalities, resulting in a very 'international' ambience.

Facilities

Each part of the site has a modern toilet block, with facilities for disabled people and babies. Bar, restaurant/takeaway with terrace. Good shop. Heated swimming pool, children's pool. Small fishing lake. Minigolf. Half tennis, table tennis, volleyball, badminton. Good under 7's play park. Floodlit boules pitch and multisports court. Bicycle hire. Mobile homes and chalets to rent. Off site: Aerial woodland assault course 500 m. Riding and golf 5 km.

Open: 24 April - 16 September.

Directions

Site is 7 km. from Sarlat south of the D704A road from Sarlat to Souillac. From Souillac, the access road to the site is just around a left hand bend, not easy to see.

Charges 2007

Per person	€ 5,00
child (0-7 yrs)	€ 4,00
pitch incl. electricity (6/10A)	€ 16,00 - € 30,00
animal	€ 3,00

FR24170 Camping le Port de Limeuil

F-24480 Allés-sur-Dordogne (Dordogne)

Tel: 05 53 63 29 76. Email: didierbonvallet@aol.com

At the confluence of Dordogne and Vézère rivers, opposite the picturesque village of Limieul, this delightful family site exudes a peaceful and relaxed ambience. There are 65 marked touring pitches on grass, some spacious and all with electricity (5A). The buildings are in traditional Périgourdine style and surrounded by flowers and shrubs. A sports area on a large open grassy space between the river bank and the main camping area adds to the feeling of space and provides an additional recreation and picnic area (there are additional unmarked pitches along the bank here).

Facilities

Two clean, modern toilet blocks provide excellent facilities. Bar/restaurant with snacks and takeaway (all 20/5-5/9). Small shop. Swimming pool with jacuzzi, paddling pool and children's slide (1/5-30/9). Badminton, football, boules and volleyball. Mountain bike hire. Canoe hire - launched from the site's own pebble beach. WiFi in bar area. Off site: The pretty medieval village of Limeuil 200 m. Riding 1 km. Golf 10 km.

Open: 1 May - 30 September.

Directions

Site is 7 km. south of Le Bugue. From D51/D31E Le Buisson to Le Bugue road turn west towards Limeuil. Just before bridge into Limeuil, turn left (site signed), across another bridge. Site shortly on the right. GPS: N44:52.878 E00:53.444

Charges 2008

Per pitch incl. 2 persons	€ 14,00 - € 24,90
extra person	€ 4,50 - € 6,50
electricity (5A)	€ 2,50 - € 3,50

FR24180 Camping Caravaning Saint-Avit Loisirs

Le Bugue, F-24260 Saint Avit-de-Vialard (Dordogne)

Tel: 05 53 02 64 00. Email: contact@saint-avit-loisirs.com

Although Saint Avit Loisirs is set in the middle of rolling countryside, far from the hustle and bustle of the main tourist areas of the Dordogne the facilities are first class, providing virtually everything you could possibly want without the need to leave the site. This makes it ideal for families with children of all ages. The site is in two sections. One part is dedicated to chalets and mobile homes, whilst the main section of the site contains 199 flat and mainly grassy, good sized pitches, 99 for touring, with electricity (6A), arranged in cul-de-sacs off a main access road.

Facilities

Three modern unisex toilet blocks provide high quality facilities, but could become overstretched in high season. Shop, bar, restaurant, cafeteria. Outdoor swimming pool, children's pool, water slide, 'crazy river', heated indoor pool with jacuzzi, fitness room. Sound-proofed disco. Tennis. Play area. Canoe trips and other sporting activities. Off site: Sarlat and Périgeux (markets and hypermarkets).

Open: 1 April - 27 September.

Directions

Site is 6 km. north of Le Bugue. From D710 Le Bugue - Périgueux road, turn west on narrow and bumpy C201 towards St Avit de Vialard. Follow road through St Avit, bearing right to site in 1.5 km. GPS: N44:57.082 E00:50.825

Charges 2007

Per person	€ 4,00 - € 9,70
child (under 4 yrs)	free
pitch incl. electricity	€ 10,10 - € 19,30

FR24190 Centre Naturiste le Couderc

Le Couderc, F-24440 Naussannes (Dordogne)

Tel: 05 53 22 40 40. Email: le.couderc@perigord.com

Le Couderc is a friendly, welcoming naturist site based on an old coaching inn. It's name comes from the 12th century Occitan meaning 'gathering place' and it is set at a crossroads on the route of the Bastide (fortified) towns of the Dordogne. The stables have been sensitively converted to provide a bar and clubroom complete with a large, open fire for cooler evenings. There is a covered terrace, a small museum and an art display. The 180 large pitches are around the edges of three gently sloping valleys radiating from the old inn.

Facilities

Good quality, fully equipped, recently extended, unisex sanitary blocks are kept very clean. Facilities for disabled people in some blocks. Washing facilities. Small shop. Bar and snack bar. Restaurant (closes Wed). Solar heated pool. Sauna (free). Small lake with sandy beach. Bicycle hire. Play areas and paddling pool. Children's club. Adult painting and sculpture classes. Small library. Internet access. Torches necessary. Off site: Fishing 5 km. Riding 4 km. Golf 15 km. Issigeac with its Sunday market is 8 km. Beaumont 7 km.

Open: 1 April - 30 September.

Directions

10 km. east of Bergerac on D660 Sarlat road, turn into Mouleydier and take D21 to St Aubin-de-Lanquais. In that village turn left on D19 to Faux and in Faux follow directions to Naussannes. Pass Micalie and 300 m. after second crossing to Monsac, turn left at sign and follow track for 1 km. to site.

Charges guide

Per person	€ 5,00
child (under 14 yrs)	€ 3,50
pitch incl. electricity	€ 13,25
dog	€ 3,50

FR24160 Camping le Grand Dague

Mobile homes ▶ page 501

Atur, F-24750 Périgueux (Dordogne)

Tel: 05 53 04 21 01. Email: info@legranddague.fr

Le Grand Dague is close to Périgueux, in a rural and tranquil setting. Built on a hillside, the site is clean, attractive and very spacious and 68 of the 93 pitches are for touring units. The pitches are only slightly sloping and are divided by tall, mature hedging (electricity 6A). There is a large field suitable for large motorhomes. Those with disabilities might find the roads quite steep. Several large, open grassy areas provide space for youngsters to play. Good range of equipment in the play area makes this an ideal site for young families.

Facilities

Excellent, part heated sanitary facilities include a baby room and facilities for people with disabilities. Small shop (15/6-15/9). Bar, attractive restaurant with appetising menu and takeaway (both from June). Swimming pool, water slide and paddling pool (from early May). Football, volleyball, badminton, petanque, minigolf and table tennis. Play area. Fishing. Off site: Paintball outside gate. Riding 5 km. Bicycle hire 8 km. Golf 10 km.

Open: 28 April - 15 September.

Directions

From the Bordeaux - Brive inner ring road in Périgueux take D2 south, signed Atur. Campsite signed. Turn east at roundabout just before entering Atur. Site is in 3 km. GPS: N45:08.880 E00:46.657

Charges 2007

Per person	€ 4,25 - € 6,50
child (0-7 yrs)	€ 2,75 - € 4,25
pitch with electricity	€ 8,45 - € 11,75
animal	€ 1,75

LE GRAND DAGUE ★ ★ ★ ★

In one of the most beautiful and quiet parts of the Dordogne region lies the campsite 'Le Grand Dague'. Set in 22 hectares of open and peaceful countryside, its high altitude gives wonderful views of the forests, hills and valleys that make up this region. The entire area is accessible to all guests, making it perfect for long walks and all manner of sports including jogging. The campsite is also very well situated for trips in the whole of the Dordogne region. The spacious pitches have water and electricity. There's a large swimming pool with a waterslide, a restaurant and a shop.

24750 Atur/Périgueux • T (+33) 5-53042101 • F (+33) 5-53042201 • Web: www.legranddague.fr

FR24220 Camping Domaine des Chênes Verts

Route de Sarlat, F-24370 Calviac en Périgord (Dordogne)

Tel: 05 53 59 21 07. Email: chenes-verts@wanadoo.fr

This peaceful countryside family campsite is set in a beautiful area of the Dordogne valley, and is complemented by the renovated Périgourdine farm buildings which house the amenities at the centre of the site. The spacious grounds which contain many trees provide 143 pitches on either side of the main buildings, of which 63 are for touring units. Most of the good sized, grassy pitches are shaded and all are separated by hedging. There is electricity (6A) to all pitches and water points nearby. The majority of pitches are large and level but some are gently sloping.

Facilities

Two fully equipped unisex toilet blocks include washbasins in cabins, dishwashing and laundry areas. Washing machine. Small shop (fresh bread daily), bar, snack bar and takeaway. Motorcaravan service point. Fridge hire. Gas supplies. Medium sized swimming pool with large sunbathing area (15/6-15/9), covered, heated pool (1/4-20/9) and a paddling pool. Play area. Multisport court. Animation for children. TV and games room. Charcoal barbecues provided. Off site: Forest walks and cycle tracks lead from the site.

Open: 1 May - 28 September.

Directions

From D704 Sarlat - Gourdon road turn east on D704A towards Souillac and Calviac (this turning is about 3.5 km. from Sarlat). Site is about 5 km. along this road on the left. GPS: N44:51.794 E01:17.824

Charges 2007

Per person	€ 3,75 - € 4,70
child (under 7 yrs)	€ 2,15 - € 2,70
pitch incl. electricity	€ 11,70 - € 13,90
dog	€ 1,75 - € 2,20

FR24230 Camping le Moulin de Paulhiac

F-24520 Daglan (Dordogne)

Tel: 05 53 28 20 88. Email: Francis.Armagnac@wanadoo.fr

You will be guaranteed a friendly welcome from the Armagnac family, who are justifiably proud of their well-kept and attractive site, built in the grounds surrounding an old mill. The 150 shady pitches (98 for touring) are separated by hedges and shrubs, all fully serviced. Many pitches are next to a stream that runs through the site and joins the River Ceou along the far edge. A tent field slopes gently down to the river, which is quite shallow and used for bathing. This site will appeal especially to families with younger children. Used by a tour operator (44 pitches).

Facilities

Two clean toilet blocks provide modern facilities, including those for disabled visitors. Good shop, restaurant, takeaway. Main pool, heated and covered by a sliding roof in low season, children's pool, a further small pool and two slides. Volleyball, table tennis, badminton, boules. Bicycle hire. Canoe trips organised on the Dordogne. Organised evening activities. Children's club in high season.

Open: 15 May - 15 September.

Directions

Site is about 17 km. south of Sarlat, and is on the east side of the D57, about 5 km. north of the village of Daglan.

Charges 2007

Per person	€ 6,75
child (2-10 yrs)	€ 4,95
pitch with electricity	€ 20,50 - € 24,00
dog	€ 1,80
Special offers in low season.	

FR24240 Camping les Bo-Bains

F-24150 Badefols-sur-Dordogne (Dordogne)

Tel: 05 53 73 52 52. Email: info@bo-bains.com

Offering a limited number of touring pitches, but with a good range of facilities and activities, Les Bo-Bains is a well kept site in an attractive location alongside the Dordogne river. The flat, grassy and good sized pitches are all set along the river bank, with beautiful views across the Dordogne. Pitches are divided by hedges, shrubs and bushes of different varieties and they have plenty of shade. All pitches have electricity, with water taps and drainaway points between each pair. Canoeing can be arranged from reception and there are places to launch one's own small craft.

Facilities

Good quality toilet blocks with baby rooms and laundry facilities. Small shop. Bar (all season), restaurant, takeaway (15/5-15/9). Swimming pool, another shallower one, three slides. Small play areas. TV room. Multi-gym, football, minigolf, archery, tennis, basketball. Organised events in high season. Quad bike and bicycle hire. Riding. Canoeing excursions. Off site: The small village of Badefols is within easy walking distance.

Open: 15 April - 30 September.

Directions

Site is on D29 Bergerac - Sarlat road, about 4 km. east of Lalinde, on the north side of the road.

Charges 2007

Per pitch incl. 2 persons and electricity (5A)	€ 13,00 - € 31,00
extra person over 7 yrs	€ 3,00 - € 8,00
child (0-7)	free - € 8,00
animal	free - € 3,00

FR24280 Camping de Barnabé

Rue des Bains, F-24750 Périgueux (Dordogne)

Tel: 05 53 53 41 45. Email: contact@barnabe-perigord.com

A 1936 Art Deco style building houses the reception, bar, restaurant and games room, complete with terrace overlooking the River L'Isle. This site has 42 touring pitches, hedged and shaded by mature trees, all with electricity (4/6A) and 12 are fully serviced. The entrance and access roads are narrow (larger units take great care). The ground may be rather firm for tent pegs and it occasionally floods in winter.

Facilities

Six sanitary buildings around the site (one on the far side of the river). Not modern, but functional, simple and clean with spacious shower cubicles. Unisex facilities, with both British and Turkish style toilets. One heated block is open in winter. Bar (1/5-31/10). Fishing. Off site: Périgueux town centre 2 km. Golf 7 km. Riding 10 km.

Open: 1 March - 3 October.

Directions

Approaching from the east of Pèrigueux on the N221, at roundabout with N2089, take exit for Pèrigueux 'centre ville'. After about 3 km. turn right at traffic lights at town boundary. Site well signed. GPS: N45:11.207 E00:44.515

Charges 2007

Per person	€ 4,00
child (under 7 yrs)	€ 2,60
pitch	€ 3,30 - € 5,50
electricity (4/6A)	€ 2,80 - € 3,20
Less 10-15% for longer stays in low season.	

FR24320 Camping les Peneyrals

Mobile homes ▶ page 501

Le Poujol, F-24590 Saint Crépin-Carlucet (Dordogne)

Tel: 05 53 28 85 71. Email: camping.peneyrals@wanadoo.fr

Within easy reach of all the attractions of the Périgord region, M. and Mme. Havel have created an attractive and friendly family campsite at Les Peneyrals. There are 199 pitches, 80 of which are for touring. The pitches at the bottom of the hill tend to be quieter as they are further from the main facilities, but are all level and grassy (some on terraces), with electricity (5/10A), and most have some shade. An attractive bar and restaurant with terrace overlook the excellent pool complex and at the bottom of the site is a small fishing lake. The site is set on a wooded hillside, with flowers in abundance (thanks to the dedication of Mme. Havel's mother). Activities are organised over a long season, including archery, various sports tournaments, aquagym, discos and a children's club. It is used fairly unobtrusively by a UK tour operator (70 pitches).

Facilities

Two modern, unisex toilet blocks provide good quality facilities, including provision for babies and disabled visitors. Motorcaravan services. Good value shop, excellent restaurant and takeaway. Pool complex with two large pools (one heated), paddling pool and four slides with splash pool. Indoor heated pool. Bicycle hire. Minigolf, tennis court (charged). Badminton. Play area. Games room, TV room and small library. Off site: Supermarkets, banks, etc. in Sarlat (11 km).

Open: 15 May - 15 September.

Directions

Site is 11 km. north of Sarlat. From D704 Sarlat - Montignac road turn east on D60 towards Salignac-Eyvigues. After 4 km. turn south on D56 towards St Crépin-Carlucet. Site is about 500 m. along this road on the right. GPS: N44:57.46 E01:16.37

Charges 2007

Per person	€ 4,60 - € 7,60
child (under 7 yrs)	free - € 5,40
pitch	€ 6,70 - € 10,70
electricity (5/10A)	€ 2,00 - € 3,70

FR24290 Camping le Moulin du Bleufond

Avenue Aristide Briand, F-24290 Montignac (Dordogne)

Tel: 05 53 51 83 95. Email: le.moulin.du.bleufond@wanadoo.fr

Built on flat ground around a 17th century mill, this former municipal site has its own pool and nearby town sporting facilities. The 83 pitches (66 for touring units) are marked and divided by mature hedges, all have electricity and most have some shade. Pitches vary considerably in size. The small town of Montignac is only 5 minutes walk, with shops, restaurants and bars. The site is separated from the river by a reasonably quiet road; there is a sizeable bank for fishing. This is an ideal base from which to visit a fascinating and beautiful part of the Perigord.

Facilities

Modern, clean, heated sanitary facilities are well cared for. Bread and a few essentials available at reception. Bar, snack bar, terrace restaurant (all season). Heated swimming pool, paddling pool. Sauna. Games room with table football, pool, table tennis and giant TV. Canoe trips and bicycle hire. Musical evenings weekly in high season. WiFi. Off site: Shops, supermarkets, bars and a range of interesting restaurants in the town only 5 minutes walk away.

Open: 1 April - 15 October.

Directions

Site is just south of Montignac, on D65 to Sergeac. Just after crossing stone bridge on one way system in centre of town turn sharp right (allow for a wide sweep!) The site is 750 m. on left.

Charges 2008

Per person	€ 3,98 - € 5,30
child (1-7 yrs)	€ 2,40 - € 3,20
pitch	€ 4,72 - € 6,30
electricity (10A)	€ 3,20
animal	€ 1,27 - € 1,70

TRAVEL SERVICE SITE
TO BOOK CALL 01580 214000
Advice & low ferry-inclusive prices

FR24340 Camping le Val de la Marquise

D35, F-24260 Campagne (Dordogne)

Tel: **05 53 54 74 10**. Email: **val-marquise@wanadoo.fr**

This well kept little campsite, between Le Bugue and Les Eyzies, is an ideal base to explore the châteaux and prehistoric sites of the Perigord region. The 104 pitches (82 for touring) are flat, grassy and all of a good size. The pitches are divided by shrubs and some have shade from mature trees, whilst others are more open. Most have electricity (15A). Reception stocks a range of basic groceries including bread and croissants made freshly on site every morning. Weekly entertainment and excursions are organised in high season. The site retains a relaxed peaceful air and is an ideal retreat after a busy day of sightseeing in the area.

Facilities

Clean toilet block provides first-rate facilities, baby bath. Smaller block near reception houses good facilities for disabled visitors. Washing and drying machines. Good bar (1/6-30/9), snack bar/takeaway (1/7-30/8), terrace. Swimming pool, sun terrace, paddling pool. Small fishing lake. Off site: Bars and restaurants in the village of Campagne 500 m. Supermarket in Le Bugue 5 km.

Open: 1 April - 15 October.

Directions

Site is 5 km. southeast of Le Bugue. Take the D703/D706 Le Bugue - Les Eyzies road. At Campagne take D35 south east towards St Cyprien (there is a peculiar 'Y' junction with 3 roads). Site is about 500 m. on right. GPS: N44:54.210 E00:58.270

Charges 2008

Per person	€ 3,10 - € 4,70
child (2-10 yrs)	€ 2,10 - € 3,50
pitch	€ 4,90 - € 7,50
electricity (15A)	€ 4,00
animal	€ 1,20 - € 1,80

FR24300 Camping la Rivière Fleurie

Saint Aulaye de Breuilh, F-24230 Saint Antoine de Breuilh (Dordogne)

Tel: **05 53 24 82 80**. Email: **info@la-riviere-fleurie.com**

This quiet and pleasant campsite is close to the vineyards of Pomerol and St Emilion, and not far from the extensive shopping of St Foy la Grande and Bergerac. The 60 pitches are all spacious, divided by shrubs and maturing trees are beginning to provide shade. All pitches have electricity (4/10A) There are no tour operators, but 14 pitches are used for site owned mobile home, and there are also studio apartments to let throughout the year. The site has a tranquil and peaceful ambience, suitable for anyone looking for a quiet and relaxing holiday.

Facilities

Sanitary facilities are plentiful and modern (no toilet paper). Bar and terrace restaurant serving a range of basic meals. Swimming pool (100 sq.m.) and toddlers' pool. Football, volleyball, table tennis, table football and TV room. Weekly 'soirées' where the owners host an evening of French food and entertainment. Canoe trips arranged. Off site: Municipal tennis court adjacent (free to campers). Fishing 100 m. Riding 4 km. Bicycle hire 8 km.

Open: 1 April - 30 September.

Directions

Site is in St Aulaye, about 3 km. south of D936 Bordeaux - Bergerac road. 6 km. east of Lamothe-Montravel turn south on local roads and follow signs to site 150 m. from river. GPS: N44:49.743 E00:07.343

Charges 2007

Per unit incl. 2 persons	€ 14,50 - € 18,00
extra person	€ 4,50 - € 5,50
child (under 7 yrs)	€ 2,80 - € 3,50
electricity	€ 3,10 - € 4,50
animal	€ 1,80 - € 2,00

FR24310 Camping Caravaning la Bouquerie

F-24590 Saint Geniès-en-Périgord (Dordogne)

Tel: 05 53 28 98 22. Email: labouquerie@wanadoo.fr

La Bouquerie is a well maintained site, situated within easy reach of the main road network in the Dordogne, but without any associated traffic noise. The main complex is based around some beautifully restored traditional Périgordin buildings. It includes a shop and a bar and restaurant overlooking the pool complex, with a large outdoor terrace for fine weather. The excellent restaurant menu is varied and reasonably priced. Of the 180 pitches, 91 are used for touring units and these are of varying size (80-120 sq.m.), flat and grassy, some with shade, and all with electrical connections (10A).

Facilities

Three well maintained toilet blocks with facilities for disabled visitors and baby rooms. Washing machines and covered drying lines. Small shop (15/05-15/09), takeaway food. Bar, restaurant (both 15/05-15/09). Paddling pool, large shallow pool (heated), large deep pool, sunbathing areas with loungers. Carp fishing in lake on site. Bicycle hire. Riding. Off site: Shops and restaurants, etc. in the nearby village of St Geniès.

Open: 19 April - 19 September.

Directions

Site is signed on east side D704 Sarlat - Montignac, about 500 m. north of junction with D64 St Geniès road. Turn off D704 at campsite sign and take first left turn signed La Bouquerie - site is straight ahead.

Charges 2008

Per pitch with 2 persons	
and electricity	€ 19,00 - € 25,50
extra person	€ 4,60 - € 6,50
child (under 7 yrs)	€ 3,20 - € 4,50

FR24330 Camping de l'Etang Bleu

F-24340 Vieux-Mareuil (Dordogne)

Tel: 05 53 60 92 70. Email: marc@letangbleu.com

There are 169 pitches, 151 for touring, with the remainder taken up by site owned mobile homes for rent. The pitches are a good size, flat and grassy, with mature hedging and trees providing privacy and plenty of shade. All pitches have water and 90 have electricity (10/16A). At the bottom of the site is a fishing lake stocked with carp (permit required) and various woodland walks start from the campsite grounds. The bright and cheerful 'bistro bar' provides good value food and drinks, and becomes a focal point for evening socialising on site.

Facilities

Modern well maintained toilet block provides facilities for babies and disabled people. Laundry. Small playground, paddling pool. Swimming pool, sun terrace. Bar with terrace (all season), restaurant (1/6-30/9), poolside bar. Takeaway (1/6-30/9). Small shop. Table tennis, boules, volleyball, badminton. Canoe and bicycle hire. Entertainments, sporting activities, excursions in high season. Off site: Restaurant 'Auberge de L'Etang Bleu' adjacent to campsite, small supermarket, post office etc. in Mareuil (7 km).

Open: Easter/1 April -18 October.

Directions

Site is between Angoulême and Périgueux. Leave D939 in Vieux Mareuil, take D93, and follow narrow road. Just after leaving village site signed on right, just past Auberge de L'Etang Bleu. Turn right, follow signs to site.

Charges guide

Per person	€ 3,75 - € 5,50
child (2-7 yrs)	€ 1,25 - € 2,00
pitch and car	€ 5,75 - € 7,25
with electricity	€ 7,75 - € 11,50

FR24350 RCN le Moulin de la Pique

F-24170 Belvès (Dordogne)

Tel: 05 53 29 01 15. Email: info@rcn-lemoulindelapique.fr

Set in the grounds of a converted former mill and iron foundry, this impressive and well managed site offers something for every member of the family. The 135 touring pitches are flat, grassy and extremely spacious (most well over 100 sq.m.) and most have electricity (6A), water and drainage. Some pitches border the lake which can be used for both fishing and boating. The 11th century fortified town of Belvès is only 2 km. away and the campsite is well located for access to the many other attractions of the Dordogne valley.

Facilities

Modern good quailty toilet blocks provide facilities for disabled visitors. Washing facilities. Bar, restaurant, snack bar, shop (open all season), Swimming pool (heated), paddling pool, water slides, 'lazy river'. Playing field. Volleyball. Tennis. Minigolf. Play areas. TV, games room. Toddler's playroom. Library. Internet. Off site: Bars, restaurants and shops in the village of Belvès 2 km.

Open: 12 April - 11 October.

Directions

Site is 35 km. southwest of Sarlat on the east side of the D710, about 7 km. south of Siorac-en-Périgord.

Charges 2008

Per pitch incl. 2 persons,	
electricity and water	€ 18,00 - € 45,50

See advertisement on the inside front cover.

297

FR24380 Camping BleuSoleil

Domaine Touvent, F-24580 Rouffignac-Saint Cernin (Dordogne)

Tel: **05 53 05 48 30**. Email: **infos@camping-bleusoleil.com**

Camping BleuSoleil is delightfully and quietly located in the countryside and has magnificent views from all areas of the site. It comprises 70 acres and, at present, has 110 pitches, 95 for touring and 15 used for wooden chalets. Electricity is avaliable on every pitch. Set in an open, woody, and hilly area, some of the pitches have partial shade from well sited trees and hedges. There is some terracing. You will receive a warm welcome at BleuSoleil and a comfortable stay. The village of Rouffignac-St Cernin-de-Reilhac, is 1 km. away and is within walking distance.

Facilities

Three modern unisex sanitary blocks are clean, well maintained and adequate for the number of pitches. En-suite toilet for disabled visitors. Baby room with bath. Enclosed laundry area with two washing machines and dryer. Shop, small bar with TV, and restaurant (high season) Large 200 sq.m. swimming pool and paddling pool. New multisports area. Boules. Small play area . Off site: Village facilities 1 km. Fishing 2 km. Riding 4 km.

Open: 3 April - 30 September.

Directions

From Périgueux take N89 east for 17 km. to Thenon, then D31 south signed Balou. Continue from Balou for 3 km. to the outskirts of Rouffignac-St Cernin-de-Reilhac and look for site sign on the left. Turn off main road to site (less than 1 km). GPS: N45:03.30 E00:59.22

Charges 2007

Per person	€ 3,20 - € 4,60
pitch incl. electricity (10A)	€ 9,10 - € 13,80

FR24360 Camping le Mondou

F-24370 Saint Julien de Lampon (Dordogne)

Tel: **05 53 29 70 37**. Email: **lemondou@camping-dordogne.info**

This quiet and peaceful site mid-way between Sarlat and Souillac is ideally situated for exploring the Dordogne and Lot departments. It is set amongst countryside at the edge of the small village of St Julien and only 2 km. from the Dordogne river. The 62 grassy pitches are of medium to large size, divided by shrubs and with some shade from a wide variety of trees. All have electricity (6A). The friendly and helpful owners, John and Lia, organise regular evening entertainment during high season and they work hard to ensure that everyone enjoys their stay at Le Mondou.

Facilities

Two sanitary blocks provide basic facilities, including facilities for disabled visitors, baby baths, washing machine, ironing board and iron. Terrace bar and snack bar with reasonably priced menu. Large swimming pool with sun terrace and paddling pool. Rustic style play area and large playing field. WiFi. Boules pitch. Off site: Bar, restaurant and small shop in the village of St Julien-de-Lampon about 1 km. away.

Open: 1 April - 15 October.

Directions

Site about 12 km. southwest of Souillac. From D807, at Rouffillac, turn south across the river Dordogne (D61 signed St Julien-de-Lampon). Entering village turn left (D50, signed to Mareuil). Site in 500 m. beyond village. GPS: N44:51.783 E01:22.433

Charges 2007

Per person	€ 4,50
child (under 7 yrs)	€ 2,00
pitch incl. electricity	€ 4,50 - € 8,00

FR24410 Camping Caravaning Le Bois du Coderc

Route des Gaunies, F-24420 Antonne et Trigonant (Dordogne)

Tel: **05 53 05 99 83**. Email: **coderc-camping@wanadoo.fr**

Located in the scenic Perigord region, 10 km. from Périgueux, Les Bois du Coderc is a calm, picturesque, part wooded, riverside site, ideally situated for visiting many interesting places. The touring pitches (there are no individual markedout pitches) and a mobile home are spaced out over a field and woodland, with electricity hook-ups (10A) and water points. This campsite has a calm, relaxing atmosphere. However, it is well placed near the historical town of Périgueux which is rich in history and culture and full of charm and character, with cobbled streets.

Facilities

One male and female sanitary block with pre-set showers (no charge) clean and well maintained (only one toilet and a shower are open in winter). Baby changing area. Dishwashing area. Laundry facilities, small shop. Snacks and takeaway. Bar/games room. Small play area. The river Isle runs through the campsite and is suitable for paddling. WiFi.

Open: All year.

Directions

Heading north on the N21 Limoges - Périgueux road, 2.5 km. north of Antonne et Trigonant turn right at Routier Restaurant (near km. marker 49). Continue along this country road following signs. Travelling south from Limoges direction turn is on left 3 km. south of Sarliac sur L'Isle. GPS: N45:31.166 E00:51.816

Charges 2007

Per person	€ 2,50 - € 3,00
pitch incl. electricity	€ 7,50 - € 10,00

FR24420 Camping les Valades

D703, F-24220 Coux-et-Bigaroque (Dordogne)

Tel: 05 53 29 14 27. Email: camping.valades@wanadoo.fr

Sometimes we come across small but beautifully kept campsites which seem to have been a well kept secret, and Les Valades certainly fits the bill. Set on a hillside overlooking countryside between the Dordogne and Vezère rivers each of the 49 touring pitches is surrounded by variety of flowers, shrubs and trees. Pitches are flat and grassy, mostly on terraces, all with electricity (10A) and most with individual water and drainage as well. At the bottom of the hill, away from the main area, is the swimming pool, a good sized lake for carp fishing, swimming or canoeing (free canoes). From the moment you arrive you can see that the owners, M. and Mme. Berger, take enormous pride in the appearance of their campsite, with an abundance of well tended flowers and shrubs everywhere you look. There are also a few well shaded 'woodland' camping pitches.

Facilities

The clean modern toilet block includes facilties for disabled people. Washing machine. Main reception building houses bar, snack bar (both July/Aug), enlarged terrace overlooking valley. Swimming pool, sun terrace, paddling pool (all season). New play area near the lake and pool. Off site: Small shop, bar, restaurant in Coux-et-Bigaroque 5 km. Supermarket at Le Bugue 10 km. Riding and bicycle hire 5 km. Golf 6 km.

Open: 1 May - 15 October.

Directions

Site is signed down a turning on west side of D703 Le Bugue - Siorac-en-Perigord road, about 3.5 km. north of village of Coux-et-Bigaroque. Turn off D703 and site is 1.5 km. along on right. GPS: N44:51.620 E00:57.880

Charges 2008

Per unit incl. 2 persons and electricity	€ 28,00
extra person	€ 5,20
child (0-7 yrs)	€ 3,70
dog	€ 2,70

No credit cards.

24220 Coux et Bigaroque
FRANCE

www.lesvalades.com

FR24440 Camping les Acacias

Bourg de la Canéda, F-24200 Sarlat-la-Canéda (Dordogne)

Tel: 05 53 31 08 50. Email: camping-acacias@wanadoo.fr

Only 2.5 kilometres from the historic medieval town centre of Sarlat, and yet surrounded by peaceful countryside, this campsite is suited to those seeking a relaxing and peaceful site within easy reach of the major attractions of the Dordogne. The 122 grassy pitches are mostly flat, divided by hedges or trees, with plenty of shade, and all have electricity (6A). The small but welcoming bar and terrace are the focal point for daily events and entertainment during high season, with activities for both adults and children. A bus service 50 m. from the site entrance runs six times daily into Sarlat centre.

Facilities

Two toilet blocks provide clean and comfortable showers, washbasins in cabins, British style toilets, facilities for disabled people, baby bath and children's shower, toilet and washbasin. Laundry facilities. Bar serving snacks and takeaway food (May - Sept). Bread to order from reception (no shop, but large supermarket only 1.5 km). Swimming pool and paddling pool (10/5-20/9), with sun loungers and parasols. Volleyball. Football. Table tennis. Play area. Bicycle hire. Canoe excursions arranged from site. Off site: Supermarket, bar/restaurant, pizza takeaway all 1.5 km. River fishing 3 km.

Open: 1 April - 30 September.

Directions

From Sarlat follow directions for Souillac and Cahors. Pass under an impressive stone railway viaduct, then take the second turn right, signed La Canéda. Follow this road until a small sports field and stadium on your left, and bear right here into the village of La Canéda. Site is signed about 500 m. along on the right.

Charges 2007

Per unit incl. 2 persons	€ 10,40 - € 15,90
extra person	€ 3,50 - € 5,00
child (0-7 yrs)	€ 1,60 - € 2,00
electricity	€ 2,80

299

FR24450 Camping Maisonneuve

Vallée du Céou, F-24250 Castelnaud la Chapelle (Dordogne)

Tel: 05 53 29 51 29. Email: contact@campingmaisonneuve.com

This family run site is beautifully situated in the Céau Valley, in the Perigord. There are 140 spacious touring pitches, all with 6/10A electricity. Some are well separated whilst others are on an open field. Most pitches have shade. The site's facilities are grouped around the old farmhouse. Swimming, diving, fishing and canoeing are all possible in the Céou river which borders the site and can be accessed directly. There are also swimming and paddling pools on site and some entertainment is organised several evenings each week in high season.

Facilities

Three sanitary blocks are kept clean and tidy. Facilities for babies and disabled visitors. Laundry. Shop with bread. Snack bar. Bar. Swimming and paddling pools. Minigolf. Play areas. TV room. Games room. Dance evenings. Karaoke. Sport tournaments.

Open: 22 March - 4 October.

Directions

From A20 take exit 55 on the D703 towards Sarlat and Beynac. Follow signs for D57 (Castelnaud la Chappelle). Site is well signed. GPS: N44:48.220 E01:09.320

Charges 2007

Per person	€ 3,70 - € 5,30
child (0-5 yrs)	€ 2,50 - € 3,60
pitch	€ 5,00 - € 7,20
electrity (6/10A)	€ 2,50 - € 4,20

FR24460 Flower Camping le Temps de Vivre

F-24590 Salignac-Eyvigues (Dordogne)

Tel: 05 53 28 93 21. Email: contact@temps-de-vivre.com

Le Temps de Vivre is situated in the centre of the Périgord Noir, in the countryside and lies about 250 m. above sea level. The area of the campsite covers about 4.5 acres in total, with 1.5 acres in use at present. It is a small, friendly, family run site with 50 pitches, 30 of which are for touring and 20 for mobile homes. The pitches are wide and terraces separate some of them. All have electricity connections available (10A) and you will find a variety of trees and bushes often as a natural separation. This is a delightful and peaceful rural site.

Facilities

One modern unisex sanitary block, very clean, well maintained, serviced, and adequate for the number of pitches. En-suite toilet for disabled visitors. Baby room with bath. Covered laundry area. Small shop all season in the reception area. Small bar, restaurant and takeaway (July/Aug). Two swimming pools (one for children). Boules. Play area. Off site: Shops and restaurants, etc. within walking distance in the nearby village of Salignac- Eyvigues.

Open: 1 April - 1 November.

Directions

From Brive-La-Gaillarde heading south on the A20 continue for 30 km. to exit 55 signed Souillac. Take D62/D15 northwest for 12 km. until Salignac-Eyvigues. As you drive through the town centre look for blue sign for site. Follow the sign off the main road for about 2 km.

Charges 2007

Per unit incl. 1 person	€ 11,00 - € 18,50
extra person	€ 2,50 - € 4,50
child (2-7 yrs)	€ 2,00 - € 3,00

FR24470 Flower Camping les Nauves

Le Bos Rouge, F-24170 Belvès (Dordogne)

Tel: 05 53 29 12 64. Email: campinglesnauves@hotmail.com

Les Nauves is a pretty and well maintained site, 4 km. from the beautiful medieval village of Belvès in the Périgord Noir region of the Dordogne. The site consists of 100 pitches, 60 for touring and 40 dedicated to mobile homes, chalets and bungalow tents. There are some pitches that are separated and shaded by mature trees, while others are open with good views of the surrounding countryside. The ground on most of the pitches is soft, sandy soil and may cause some difficulty for large vehicles in wet weather. The owners are very dedicated to providing a quality site.

Facilities

The single sanitary block is clean and well maintained. Facilities for disabled visitors. Baby room (with adult shower). Laundry area with one washing machine. Good shop. Bar/restaurant with patio, and takeaway on request. Swimming pool and children's paddling pool. Good play area. Boules. Library (French and Dutch books). Games room. Riding. Off site: Fishing 2 km. Golf 10 km. Bicycle hire 4 km.

Open: 29 April - 23 September.

Directions

From Belvès take D53 southwest towards Monpazier. Site is 4 km. from Belvès on the left hand side. Follow signs and site is 800 m. off the main road.

Charges 2007

Per person	€ 2,50 - € 4,50
child (0-7 yrs)	€ 2,00 - € 3,00
pitch	€ 10,50 - € 16,70
electricity (6A)	€ 3,20

FR24510 Camping les Trois Caupain

Le Port, F-24260 Le Bugue (Dordogne)

Tel: 05 53 07 24 60. Email: info@camping-bugue.com

A superb, mature, ex-municipal site, Les 3 Caupain is less than 1 km. from Le Bugue, which has a range of supermarkets and tourist attractions. The site carefully blends mobile homes and camping pitches and fruiting plum trees abound on the site. The well marked pitches are neat, level and mostly shaded, with water and electricity hook ups close by. The current owners, the three Caupain family members, will do all they can to make your stay a pleasant one. The campsite is less than 50 m. away from the river. Popular with tourists, Le Bugue is a delightful town where you can get a coffee, beer, quality meal, or just stroll around looking at the sights, including the lovely river La Vézerè. Sarlat-la-Canéda is less than 10 km.

Facilities

Two clean and well maintained sanitary blocks include toilet and shower for disabled people. Excellent dishwashing and laundry room. Baby room with bath. Motorcaravan service point. Small shop selling local produce all season. Bar with pool table and TV. Restaurant with terrace (high season). Swimming pool and paddling pool. Play area. Boules. Fishing. Animation and twice weekly entertainment in high season. Off site: Riding 3 km. Golf 8 km. Supermarkets in Le Bugue.

Open: 1 April - 30 October.

Directions

From Le Bugue, take D703 heading southeast and site is less than 1 km. from the town centre, well signed. Turn right off the main road and site is less than 800 m. along this road on the left.

Charges 2008

Per unit incl. 2 persons	€ 12,40 - € 16,50
extra person	€ 3,50 - € 4,50
child (2-12 yrs)	€ 1,90 - € 3,20

Camping Les Trois Caupain

Le Port
24260 · LE BUGUE
France

tél: 05 53 07 24 60
fax: 05 53 08 72 66

e-mail: info@camping-buque.com

FR24480 Camping les Tailladis

Marcillac St Quentin, F-24200 Sarlat (Dordogne)

Tel: 05 53 59 10 95. Email: indo@taillabis.com

Les Tailladis is a well situated, mature campsite of some 17 hectares of woodland, owned by the same Dutch and French family for over 42 years. It is about 12 km. from Sarlat, Eyzies and Montignac-Lascauax, and 35 km. from Souillac. Four hectares of the total provides medium to large pitches which are grassy, terraced and partially shaded, with electricity (6A), and water points close by. The hosts are welcoming and you will be greeted with a drink and warm, friendly service. You will find greater emphasis placed on serving the customer and friendliness than you will find on well managed, tidy pitches.

Facilities

One heated sanitary block is well sited for all pitches. En-suite toilet for disabled visitors. Baby bath and changing area. Laundry room. Motorcaravan service point. Large shop (fresh bread and milk can be ordered). Restaurant, bar. Library. Swimming pool and paddling pool. Play area with trampoline. Activities organised during high season. Internet access (charged for). Off site: Riding 3 km. Bicycle hire 12 km. Golf 25 km. Boat launching 25 km.

Open: All year.

Directions

From Sarlat-la-Canéda, take D704 heading north. After 10 km, look for signs on the left for Marcillac St Quentin. Take this road heading northwest, and site is less than 3 km. after Marcillac St Quentin on the left hand side. Access and site roads are narrow for large units.

Charges 2008

Per person	€ 5,20
child (3-8 yrs)	€ 3,70
pitch	€ 6,75
electricity (6A)	€ 3,40

301

FR24640 Camping de Nontron

Saint Martial de Valette, F-24300 Nontron (Dordogne)

Tel: 05 53 56 02 04. Email: camping-de-nontron@orange.fr

Open all year, this site is ideally situated in the Perigord Vert either as a first stop en-route south, or for a much longer stay. This is a neat and well presented site against a background of tall trees. There are 70 pitches of which 60 are for touring units, two are for mobile homes and eight are studios which are all available to rent. All are level with easy access and separated by hedges. This year a new sports complex opens next to the site which will include a swimming pool, toboggan, jacuzzi, sauna, solarium and tennis court. Buses pass outside the site on weekdays but not on Sundays.

Facilities

Well equipped sanitary block with facilities for disabled visitors and babies. Laundry with washing machines and ironing boards. Motorcaravan service point. Shop (all year). Takeaway in July and August. TV and games room. Table tennis. Boules. Volleyball. Play area. Gas and electric barbecues only on pitches, special areas for charcoal. Off site: New sports complex next to camping. Riding, karting 10 km. Bicycle hire 20 km. Golf.

Open: All year.

Directions

From Angoulême take D939 to Périgueux. Branch left to Nontron on D4, then carry onto D75. After Nontron take D675 towards Brantome and campsite is 200 m. on the left after entering St Martial de Valette.

Charges 2007

Per person	€ 2,50
child (under 10 yrs)	€ 1,50
electricity (6A)	€ 3,50

FR24520 Camping le Perpetuum

F-24250 Domme (Dordogne)

Tel: 05 53 28 35 18. Email: luc.parsy@wanadoo.fr

Located alongside the Dordogne river, this is a small and friendly, family run site. Attractive and mature, the site is in an ideal location where you can make the most of the river and the Périgord region. The French owners are dedicated to providing a comfortable site and are warm and welcoming, particularly to families with young children. The river has two bathing areas, pebble and sand, and there are canoes to hire.

Facilities

Three well maintained sanitary blocks. En-suite toilet for disabled visitors. Newly renovated washblock. Toilet, shower, washbasins for children. Baby room. Laundry room. Motorcaravan service point. Well stocked shop available high season with fresh bread and milk. Bar and snack bar with TV (high season). Swimming pool and paddling pool. Two play areas. Covered games area. Canoeing on the river. WiFi internet access. Animation and entertainment most days (high season). Off site: Sarlat 3 km. Golf 2 km. Tennis 2 km. Riding 3 km.

Open: 1 May - 10 October.

Directions

Take D703 to Vitrac. At Vitrac, head south for several hundred metres and take the bridge over the river, onto the D46e. Follow for 1.5 km. until crossroads at the end. Turn right following signs to site. It is less than 1 km. from the crossroads on the right hand side.

Charges 2007

Per person	€ 4,00 - € 5,30
pitch	€ 4,00 - € 6,00
electricity (10A)	€ 3,00 - € 3,50
No credit cards.	

FR24530 Camping Port Vieux

1 rue de la Paix, F-24700 Montpon-Ménestérol (Dordogne)

Tel: 04 99 57 21 21. Email: contact@village-center.com

Port Vieux was originally a municipal site established over 25 years ago, but for the last two years, it has been managed by the Terre Océane group. There are 120 pitches, of which 115 are used for touring pitches, most with partial shade and separated by well established hedges. Three mobile homes and two bungalow tents are available to rent. The beautiful river Isle runs through the site, which is within walking distance of the town of Montpon-Ménestérol with its many amenities. Within walking distance there is a large, tree lined recreational park with a man-made river beach for swimming and paddling.

Facilities

Two sanitary blocks are clean, well maintained and adequate for the number of pitches. En-suite toilet for disabled visitors. Laundry facilities. Bread ordering service, ice-cream and cold drinks vending machine. Bar open in the evening with TV. Small play area. Boules. Fishing. Canoe hire. Off site: Boat hire 500 m. Bicycle hire 500 m. Lake beach and large play area 500 m. Good supermarkets less than 1 km. Riding 10 km. Golf 20 km.

Open: 15 May - 16 September.

Directions

From N89 (Périgueux - Bordeaux) exit 12, head north to Montpon-Ménestérol on the D708. Look for signs to site, which is just over the river bridge. Entrance to site is on a sharp steep bend to the right.

Charges guide

Per unit incl. 2 persons	€ 5,00 - € 9,00
extra person	€ 2,10 - € 3,00
child (2-12 yrs)	€ 1,70 - € 2,50
electricity	€ 3,00

FR24570 Camping la Palombière

Sainte Nathalène, F-24200 Sarlat (Dordogne)

Tel: 05 53 59 42 34. Email: la.palombiere@wanadoo.fr

This is a spacious site, set in a peaceful valley east of the town of Sarlat, with a quiet and tranquil atmosphere. It has 177 well shaded woodland pitches, some fully serviced, delineated by trees and bushes. A large recreation area provides high quality sports facilities and a range of amenities are arranged on a various terraced levels. This is an ideal site for families where children are at an age where they need a wide range of activities, but it nevertheless preserves a relaxed ambience and general tranquility.

Facilities

Two very clean modern toilet blocks include facilities for babies and disabled people. Laundry. Well stocked shop Bar and restaurant complex, with good range of meals. Good sized, heated swimming pool and children. Off site: Fishing 3 km. Riding 3 km. Golf 10 km.

Open: 26 April - 14 September.

Directions

Take D47 east from Sarlat to Ste Nathalène. Site is signed from village and is reached by taking a left turn just beyond it. GPS: N44:54.730 E01:26.450

Charges 2008

Per person	€ 4,80 - € 7,30
child (1-7 yrs)	free - € 5,00
simple pitch	€ 7,00 - € 10,40
with services	€ 11,50 - € 15,10
with electricity	€ 9,70 - € 13,40

Camping-Résidences-Loisirs

LA PALOMBIERE

Ste. Nathalène - 24200 SARLAT

Tel: 0033 553 59 42 34

Fax: 0033 553 28 45 40

- A free kids club (from 4 to 12 years old)
- Heated swimming pool
- Tennis, mini-golf, volley...
- Grocery shop, bar, snack, restaurant and cooked dishes

E-mail: la.palombiere@wanadoo.fr   Internet: www.lapalombiere.fr

FR24660 Camping Brin d'Amour

St Cirq, F-24260 Le Bugue (Dordogne)

Tel: **05 53 07 23 73**. Email: **campingbrindamour@orange.fr**

This really is one of the most beautiful sites in the Dordogne. Situated in the Perigord Noir with wonderful views across the undulating hills and the Vézère valley. Here there is a feeling of tranquility, spaciousness and calm. The site changed owners in 2006 and the new owners offer a welcome and outstanding customer service. Of the 80 pitches, 60 are for touring units and the remaining 20 are for chalets and mobile homes which are all available to rent. All are level, easily accessible and mostly shaded. This is a small site where you can relax in a family atmosphere.The main building is of fine traditional Perigordine quality and houses a very attractive restaurant and bar. There is also a pool at the far end of the site. This is an ideal place from which you can explore the countryside by foot or by bicycle, visit the caves or canoe down the river. The site has romantic history as the name translated means 'a piece of love'. Definitely a site not to be missed.

Facilities

Modern sanitary block with facilities for disabled visitors and babies. Shop, bar restaurant and takeaway all open (1/6-15/9). Swimming pool, toddler's pool. Tennis court. Fishing. Table tennis. Petanque. Play area. Children's club July and August. Bicycle hire. Electric and charcoal barbecues only. Fridge hire. Washing machine. WiFi access. Off site: Riding 2 km. Canoeing 5 km. Sailing, golf 10 km. Prehistoric Park. Caves.

Open: 1 April - 30 October.

Directions

Take D710 from Perigueux to Le Bugue. 500 m. after you pass the name entry sign for Le Bugue, turn sharp left on D32e to St Cirq. Camping is signed from here. GPS: N44:56.41 E00:57.36

Charges 2007

Per unit incl. 2 persons	€ 12,00 - € 18,00
extra person	€ 3,50 - € 5,00
child (1-10 yrs)	€ 2,50 - € 4,00
electricity	€ 3,00

Camping Brin d'Amour* - 24260 Saint Cirq/Le Bugue
Tél/Fax: 0033 553 07 23 73
campingbrindamour@orange.fr
www.brindamourcamping.com

FR24540 Camping le Peyrelevade

Avenue André Maurois, F-24310 Brantôme (Dordogne)

Tel: **04 99 57 21 21**. Email: **contact@village-center.com**

Le Peyrelevade is a quiet and peaceful site in the Périgord Vert region. Of a very good standard, it comprises 165 spacious and well kept touring pitches and 5 mobile homes. The site is set in an area that is part open, part wooded and most pitches have partial shade from well sited trees and hedges. The beautiful village of Brantôme on an island surrounded by a river, is close by and there you will find small bars, restaurants and other amenities. You can also relax on a river boat trip. This same river runs through the rear of the site and this adds to its charm. There is a 3.5 tonne weight restriction on the main road through the village.

Facilities

Two modern unisex sanitary blocks are clean, well maintained and adequate for the number of pitches. En-suite toilet for disabled visitors. Baby changing area with bath. Laundry area with washing machine. Bread ordering service, icecream and cold drinks vending machine. Open air swimming pool. Small play area (3-10 yrs). River is suitable for paddling. Fishing. Bicycle hire. Off site: Boat trips.

Open: 1 May - 16 September.

Directions

Take D939 south from Angoulême, or north from Périgueux. Brantôme is around 35 km. north of Périgueux. Drive through town and look for sign for site which is about 1.5 km. north outside Brantôme. There is a 3.5 tonne weight restriction on the main road through the village.

Charges guide

Per unit incl. 2 persons	€ 5,00 - € 13,00
extra person	€ 1,90 - € 4,00
electricity	€ 3,00

FR24670 Camping les Terrasses du Périgord

Pech-d'Orance, F-24200 Sarlat-la-Canéda (Dordogne)

Tel: 05 53 59 02 25. Email: terrasses-du-perigord@wanadoo.fr

Set on a hill top on the edge of Sarlat, this site has panoramic views across the Perigord. There are 105 pitches, of which 90 are for touring units, with the remaining 15 being for chalets and mobile homes for rent. The site is sloping on different levels but the pitches are generally level. All are shady, marked and separated by trees. Electricity is 6, 10 or 16A. For those with larger units, it is essential to phone in advance for pitch availability, as not all are suitable. A warm and friendly welcome is given by the French owners. An old, fully restored farmhouse fitted out as a bar and a wine cave offers you tasting together with a bistro. A well stocked shop is next to the games room which doubles up for evening entertainment. This includes Perigordine dancing and shows. The swimming pool and children's pool have only recently been added and a large playground has a cable slide. There are many places to visit in the surrounding area. Sarlat is 2 km. away.

Facilities

One modern sanitary block divided into two provides all facilities including those for disabled visitors and babies. Washing machine and dryer. Motorcaravan services. Shop. Bar with snack bar and takeaway. Wine tastings. Swimming pool and toddlers pool. Play area with cable slide. Minigolf. Bicycle hire. Gas and electric barbecues only. Evening entertainment. Off site: Caves. Chateaux. Riding. 8 km. Fishing 2 km. Canoeing 2 km.

Open: 27 April - 8 September.

Directions

From Sarlat, take D47 to Proissans. Continue on the D56 to Proissans and site is 500 m. on the left. In Sarlat, follow the signs for hospital as it is nearby. GPS: N44:54.372 E01:14.201

Charges 2007

Per person	€ 3,80 - € 4,90
child (under 7 yrs)	€ 2,20 - € 2,90
pitch	€ 4,90 - € 6,50
electricity	€ 2,90 - € 4,10
No credit cards.	

Camping Les Terrasses du Périgord* **

2 km from the medieval city of Sarlat.

Arranged in a former wine field of 6ha bordered with a truffle field on the top of a hill, the panorama is exeptional. Very quiet, the seperated and flowering pitches are shaded, grassy and level with electricity and fountain. Wine tasting in wine cellar.

3229 Les Terrasses du Périgord - 24200 SARLAT - France - Tel: (33) 05 53 59 02 25
Fax: (33) 05 53 59 16 48 - terrasses-du-perigord@wanadoo.fr - www.terrasses-du-perigord.com

FR24560 Domaine le Cro Magnon

Le Raisse, Allas-les-Mines, F-24220 Saint Cyprien (Dordogne)

Tel: 05 53 29 13 70. Email: contact@domaine-cro-magnon.com

Le Cro Magnon is pleasantly situated in the heart of the Dordogne valley in the Périgord Noir. The 160 spacious, mostly shady pitches are divided in two different types: tent pitches without electricity and serviced pitches (6A electricity hook up, water and waste water drain). The site also offers various accommodation for rent. The swimming complex includes two pools (one outdoor, one indoor), one heated, water slides, a jacuzzi and a sauna. Near the entrance of the site are a snack bar, pizzeria, bar, a well stocked shop and reception. From a viewpoint on the site are incredible views over the Dordogne valley. The site is ideally situated for exploring the countryside by bike, foot or car.

Facilities

Two toilet blocks provide the usual facilities including facilities for disabled visitors. Washing machines. Motorcaravan services. Shop. Bar with TV. Snack bar and takeaway. Swimming pools with slides, jacuzzi and sauna. Multisport court. Boules. Play area. Off site: Canoeing, walking and cycling. Fishing.

Open: 11 May - 30 September.

Directions

From the A20 (Limoges - Brive) take exit 55 for Souillac and Sarlat. In Sarlat take D57 to Vézac, then D703 to St Cyprien. In St Cyprien follow D703, then D50 (left) to Berbiguières and follow signs for site.

Charges 2007

Per person (over 4 yrs)	€ 3,40 - € 7,00
child (0-4 yrs)	free
pitch	€ 5,00 - € 10,40
incl. services	€ 8,10 - € 17,10

305

FR46040 **Camping Moulin de Laborde**

F-46700 Montcabrier (Lot)

Tel: **05 65 24 62 06**. Email: **moulindelaborde@wanadoo.fr**

Based around a converted 17th century watermill, Moulin de Laborde has been created by the Van Bommel family to provide a tranquil and uncommercialised campsite for the whole family to enjoy. Bordered by woods, hills and a small river, there are 90 flat and grassy pitches, all of at least 100 sq.m. with electricity (6A). A variety of pretty shrubs and trees divide the pitches and provide a moderate amount of shade. A gate at the back of the site leads walkers onto a 'Grand Randonée' footpath which passes through the village of Montcabrier, 1 km. away. A small lake with rafts and rowing boats and an adventure-type play area with rope bridges and 'death slide' will keep children amused, whilst parents can relax in the charming courtyard area which houses the bar and restaurant.

Facilities

Well designed, clean toilet block, unit for disabled people. Washing machine, dryer. Basic shop (all season). Small bar, restaurant, takeaway. Swimming pool, sunbathing area, paddling pool (all season). Play area. Small lake, free rafts and rowing boats. Fishing. Volleyball. Badminton. Boules. Covered recreation area. Table tennis. Mountain bike hire. Rock climbing. Archery. No dogs. Off site: Riding 5 km. Golf 8 km. Tennis nearby and canoeing on the Lot. The Château of Bonaquil 6 km. Fumel 12 km.

Open: 25 April - 8 September.

Directions

Site is on the north side of the D673 Fumel - Gourdon road about 1 km. northeast of the turn to village of Montcabrier.

Charges 2007

Per person	€ 6,20
child (under 7 yrs)	€ 3,30
pitch	€ 8,40
electricity (6A)	€ 2,60

Less 20% outside July/August. No credit cards.

Moulin de Laborde

F-46700 Montcabrier - France - Tél: 0033 05 65 24 62 06 - Fax: 0033 05 65 36 51 33
moulindelaborde@wanadoo.fr - www.moulindelaborde.com

FR46030 **Flower Camping les Pins**

F-46350 Payrac-en-Quercy (Lot)

Tel: **05 65 37 96 32**. Email: **info@les-pins-camping.com**

Set amongst four hectares of beautiful pine forest, Camping Les Pins is well situated for exploring the historical and natural splendours of the Dordogne region, as well as being a convenient overnight stop when heading north or south. There are 125 clearly marked, level pitches (100 sq.m), of which 55 are for touring units. The pitches are well marked and separated by small shrubs or hedges. Many have shade from the abundant pine trees and all have 10A electricity connections. There is a bar and a good value restaurant with a terrace overlooking the pool area.

Facilities

Three toilet blocks (heated April and May), well maintained and include washbasins in cabins and good baby bath facilites. Dishwashing and laundry sinks, washing machines and dryer (with plenty of drying lines). Motorcaravan service point. Shop with limited range of basics (1/6-14/9). Bar with T.V. Restaurant and takeaway. Heated Swimming pool (1/5-14/9). Three water slides and smaller paddling pool (1/5-14/9). Tennis. Small library. Some entertainment in season, including weekly family discos. Walking routes starting from site. English and Dutch are spoken. Off site: Fishing 7 km. Riding 10 km.

Open: 4 April - 14 September.

Directions

Site entrance is 16 km. from Souflas on western side of the N20 just south of the village of Payrac-en-Quercy.

Charges 2007

Per unit incl. 2 persons	€ 13,60 - € 28,40
incl. electricity	€ 3,60 - € 4,70
extra person	€ 3,80 - € 6,30
child (under 7 yrs)	€ 1,50 - € 4,20
dog	€ 2,00 - € 2,50

Special low season family price.

Check real time availability and at-the-gate prices...

www.**alanrogers**.com

FR46010 Castel Camping le Domaine de la Paille Basse

F-46200 Souillac-sur-Dordogne (Lot)

Tel: 05 65 37 85 48. Email: paille.basse@wanadoo.fr

Mobile homes ▶ page 501

Set in a rural location some 8 km. from Souillac, this family owned site is easily accessible from the N20 and well placed to take advantage of excursions into the Dordogne. It is part of a large domain of 80 hectares, all available to campers for walks and recreation. The site is quite high up and there are excellent views over the surrounding countryside. The 262 pitches are in two main areas – one is level in cleared woodland with good shade, and the other on grass without shade. Numbered and marked, the pitches are a minimum 100 sq.m. and often considerably more. All have electricity (3/6A) with about 80 fully serviced. The site is well placed to take advantage of excursions into the Dordogne. A wide range of activities and entertainment are organised in high season. The site can get very busy in high season and is popular with three tour operators. If you like a livelier type of site, you will enjoy La Paille Basse.

Facilities

Three main toilet blocks all have modern equipment and are kept very clean. Laundry. Small shop. Restaurant, bar, terrace, takeaway. Crêperie. Main swimming pool, a smaller one, paddling pool (unheated), water slides. Sun terrace. Sound-proofed disco (three times weekly in season). TV (with satellite). Cinema below the pool area. Tennis (charged), football, volleyball, table tennis. Play area. Library. Massage. Off site: Golf 4 km.

Open: 15 May - 15 September.

Directions

From Souillac take D15 and then D62 roads leading northwest towards Salignac-Eyvignes and after 6 km. turn right at camp sign and follow steep and narrow approach road for 2 km.
GPS: N44:56.730 E01:26.450

Charges 2007

Per person	€ 5,40 - € 7,00
child (under 7 yrs)	€ 3,80 - € 5,00
pitch	€ 7,80 - € 10,80
incl. water and drainage	€ 9,80 - € 13,00
dog	€ 4,00

Less 20% outside 15/6-1/9.
Camping Cheques accepted.

FR46050 Camping le Rêve
F-46300 Le Vigan (Lot)

Tel: **05 65 41 25 20**. Email: **info@campinglereve.com**

Le Rêve is a peaceful site situated in the heart of rolling countryside where the Perigord runs into Quercy. You are assured of a warm reception from the Van Iersels, a Dutch couple who have been providing a friendly and hospitable welcome to their clients for the past 20 years. The 56 flat and grassy touring pitches are all of good size, with access to electricity (6A) and divided by shrubs and trees. A few of the pitches are situated at the edge of the forest and provide plenty of shade.

Facilities

The toilet block includes an enclosed area for cooler weather. Washbasins in cabins, special cubicles for disabled people and a baby room. New dishwashing and laundry section. Small shop for basics (bread, milk etc.), pleasant bar, restaurant and takeaway (all open all season). Small, clean, solar heated swimming pool and large paddling pool with 'mushroom' fountain. Play area. Boules. Table tennis and volleyball. Off site: Riding 2 km. Fishing 5 km. Golf 20 km.

Open: 25 April - 21 September.

Directions

From D820 Souillac - Cahors road turn west onto D673 3 km. south of Payrac. After 2 km. site signed down lane on west side of road. Turn here, follow signs, site in 2.5 km.

Charges 2007

Per person	€ 4,60
child (under 7 yrs)	€ 2,60
pitch	€ 6,25
electricity (6A)	€ 2,60

Less 20-30% outside July/Aug. No credit cards.

FR46070 Camping de la Plage
F-46330 Saint Cirq-Lapopie (Lot)

Tel: **05 65 30 29 51**. Email: **camping-laplage@wanadoo.fr**

The site is situated next to the River Lot and is a good base for those who want an active holiday, with many sporting activities available either on site or in the immediate area. It does attract organised groups of young people and can be quite lively at times. The site is a rental base for canoeing and kayaking (lifejackets and all equipment included in hire charge). The campsite has 120 pitches including 109 for touring pitches, all with electricity, a few fully serviced and some hardstandings. Most are on a very slight slope and have good shade from mature trees and bushes.

Facilities

Two practical sanitary blocks, clean and well maintained, both have dishwashing and laundry sinks. Facilites for disabled people. Two washing machines and dryer (charged for). Motorcaravan service point (usual services and toilet block, charged for) outside at the rear of site on the river bank. Bar/café at entrance with internet terminal. Play area. Large children's room for animation. Canoeing, kayaking and swimming from beach at the rear of the site (lifeguard July/Aug). Off site: Riding, rock climbing, caving and canyoning all near by. Bicycle hire 5 km. Riding 9 km.

Open: All year.

Directions

From Cahors take D653 east to Vers, then take D662 for 17 km. to Tour de Faure. Cross river on narrow bridge and site entrance is on right by bar/restaurant. Do not approach via Saint Cirq-Lapopie.

Charges guide

Per person	€ 5,00
child (under 7 yrs)	€ 3,00
pitch	€ 4,00 - € 6,00
electricity (6/10A)	€ 3,00 - € 4,00

FR46110 Camping du Port
F-46600 Creysse (Lot)

Tel: **05 65 32 20 82**. Email: **contact@campingduport.com**

Set off the beaten track this small, unassuming riverside campsite provides an unusual combination of peace and tranquillity alongside a range of sporting activities to occupy even the most adventurous of people. Pitches are mostly flat and of a large size, with plenty of shade from the abundant trees, but no dividing hedges or fences. Of the 92 touring pitches, 70 have electricity (4/6A). The campsite owner runs daily activities including canoeing, caving, climbing, canyoning, cycling, walking and woodland assault course through the trees, all under qualified supervision.

Facilities

Basic, well cleaned toilet block with washbasins (cold water only) both open and in cubicles. Washing machine. Small shop (15/6-15/9). Open air bar, terrace (15/6-15/9), small snack bar/takeaway (July-Aug). Attractive swimming pool, terrace (no paddling pool). Off site: Bar/restaurant in the pretty medieval village of Creysse, about 500 yds away, providing a varied menu.

Open: 1 May - 30 September.

Directions

Site is about 15 km. east of Souillac. From the village of Martel on the D703 take the D23 south to Creysse. The site is signed on the left just before you enter the village.

Charges guide

Per person	€ 4,00
child (under 7 yrs)	€ 3,00
pitch with electricity	€ 7,00
animal	€ 0,50

FR46140 Club de Vacances Duravel

Port de Vire, F-46700 Duravel (Lot)

Tel: **05 65 24 65 06**. Email: **clubduravel@wanadoo.fr**

This quality site is beautifully situated on the banks of the Lot River, only 35 km. from the historic town of Cahors. The site has 300 clearly defined, large pitches all with electricity. Some of these are fully serviced with water and drainage, and private sanitary facilities. The reception, bar, restaurant, snack bar and the shop are all located beside the river and from the terrace you can enjoy lovely views over the water. The pool complex offers two large pools (one is heated) with water slides and a children's pool. Duravel is a holiday destination which would suit all ages. Bridge and petanque contests are organised in low season. During high season an animation team provides plenty of activities to suit all tastes and ages, including 'anything can happen' evenings when you will be surprised with a special theme night. The region also offers many possibilities for exploring, canoeing on the river, visiting wine cellars or strolling around local markets.

Facilities

Two clean toilet blocks include facilities for disabled people, baby rooms, laundry facilities and chemical disposal points. Serviced pitch facility provides a toilet, shower and sink (with hot water; cleaning charge € 13,50 per stay). Well stocked shop. Restaurant. Bar. Pizzeria and takeaway. Two tennis courts. Multisports area. Play area. Fishing. Boat ramp. WiFi.

Open: 28 April - end September.

Directions

From Paris A10 towards Orleans and A71 towards Vierzon. Follow A20 and take exit 57 to Villeneuve sur Lot. Take the D811 to Cahors, Puy l'Evêque and the D58 to Duravel. Site is well signed.

Charges 2007

Per person	€ 4,30 - € 6,35
pitch	€ 6,85 - € 10,00
with individual sanitary facilitiy	€ 14,75 - € 18,00
electricity	€ 3,50

FR46150 Camping la Truffière

F-46330 Saint Cirq-Lapopie (Lot)

Tel: 05 65 30 20 22. Email: contact@camping-truffiere.com

Set in 4 hectares of mature oak woodland, only 2.5 km. from the cliff top village of St Cirq-Lapopie, La Truffière is well suited to those seeking a peaceful countryside holiday amongst the stunning natural scenery of the 'Parc naturel régional des Causses de Quercy'. The 90 terraced touring pitches are of varying sizes and on a mixture of grass and gravel (larger units should reserve pitches in advance). All pitches have electricity (6A) and most have shade from the abundant trees. There are various walks and mountain bike trails in the area and you can hire bikes on site.

Facilities

Two well appointed, clean, modern toilet blocks (one heated) include facilities for disabled visitors. Motorcaravan services. Fridge hire. Bar/restaurant (1/6-31/8), terrace overlooking pool and playing field. Snack bar (1/6-31/8). Swimming pool, paddling pool, sun terrace (May - Sept). Small shop (open all season). Playing field, volleyball, basketball, football. Adventure style play area. Table tennis. Trampolines. Boules. English spoken. Off site: Small shop in village, hypermarkets 36 km. in Cahors. Riding 3 km. Fishing (in the River Lot) 3 km.

Open: 1 April - 30 September.

Directions

From D911 Cahors - Rodez road, turn north on D42 at Concots (signed St Cirq-Lapopie). Site about 5 km. on right. Approaching from north on D42 via St Cirq-Lapopie not recommended due to extremely tight left turn in village.

Charges 2007

Per person	€ 5,00
pitch	€ 5,50
electricity	€ 3,50

Less 10% outside July/Aug.
Camping Cheques accepted.

FR46180 Camping le Ventoulou

Ventoulou, F-46500 Thégra (Lot)

Tel: 05 65 33 67 01. Email: contact@leventoulou.com

Le Ventoulou is a small, well kept and peaceful site on the Périgord 'walnut' route, at the heart of the Quercy Causses natural park. The site is based around an ancient farmhouse located between the quaint villages of Padirac and Thégra. Of just over half a hectare, the site is compact, yet because of careful spacing of pitches does not seem crowded. You will receive a warm welcome from the French owners. The Padirac Aquapark is just 3 km. away. There is a weekly soirée during the high season.

Facilities

One very well equipped sanitary block is clean and well maintained. Good facilities for disabled visitors. Baby room with bath. Laundry facilities. Shop. Bar with TV. Restaurant and takeaway. Swimming pool and paddling pool. Bicycle hire. Boules. Play area with two trampolines. Games room and library. Off site: Riding 2 Km. Fishing 10 km. Golf 15 km.

Open: 4 April - 28 September.

Directions

From A20 south exit 54 follow the N140 southeast to Gramat. Take the D807 northeast to Lavergne, then the D11 to Thégra and look for signs to the site which is less than 2 km.

Charges 2008

Per unit incl. 2 persons	€ 11,50 - € 19,50
extra person	€ 3,50 - € 6,00
electricity (10A)	€ 4,20 - € 4,20

FR46190 Kawan Village Domaine de la Faurie

F-46240 Séniergues (Lot)

Tel: 05 65 21 14 36. Email: contact@camping-lafaurie.com

A stunning array of tended shrubs and thoughtful flower plantings is spread throughout this very pretty site which is located on a hilltop with wide open views of the surrounding hills and valleys. Although hidden away, it is an excellent base for exploring the Lot and Dordogne regions. The site is separated into two distinct areas, an open, lightly shaded front section and a much more densely shaded area with tall pine trees all around the pitches. The pitches are large and most are at least 100 sq.m. The friendly French owners will tell you that they consider the three hectacre site their personal garden.

Facilities

The single sanitary block is clean and well maintained. Facilities for disabled visitors. Washing machine. Motorcaravan service point. Excellent gift shop selling regional wines, pâtés, specialist tinned meats, and local produce (bread available). Bar, restaurant and takeaway. Swimming pool and paddling pool. TV and games rooms. Bicycle hire. Play area. Library. Weekly soirées in high season. Off site: Fishing 3 km. Golf 8 km. Riding 15 km.

Open: 7 April - 30 September.

Directions

A20 exit N56, turn right, in the direction of St Germain du Bel Air, continue 5km. The campsite is on the right.

Charges 2007

Per person	€ 5,00
child (1-7 yrs)	€ 3,50
pitch	€ 6,50
electricity (6A)	€ 3,50

Camping Cheques accepted.

FR46170 Campéole les Reflets du Quercy

Mas de Bastide, F-46150 Crayssac (Lot)

Tel: **05 65 30 00 27**. Email: **cplquercy@atciat.com**

Set in the west of the Lot department, about 16 km. from the large town of Cahors, this site is owned by the Campéole group and is classed as a holiday village. Located on a hill with good views of the surrounding countryside, the pitches are hilly and terraced. Most are partially shaded with Quercy oak trees and some are set apart by small Crayssac stone walls. Almost half of the touring pitches are located on good, level hardstanding. At the rear of the site is a large independent mobile home area and residents here also have access to the campsite facilities. The site has a good 25 m. swimming pool overlooked by the terrace of the bar and snack bar. The site is managed by a very friendly French couple and a welcoming Campéole team.

Facilities

Three clean and well maintained sanitary blocks (not all open outside high season). Facilities for disabled visitors. Baby room with bath. Laundry facilities. Motorcaravan service point. Shop (July/Aug). Bar and snacks (July/Aug). Swimming and paddling pool (July/Aug). TV and games room. Boules. Tennis court. Play area with large bouncy castle. Animation in high season. Off site: Fishing and riding 7 km. Bicycle hire 15 km. Good shops 16 km.

Open: 5 April - 28 September.

Directions

From Cahors on the RN20, follow D911 northwest towards Puy-l'évêque, Mercuès and Prayssac. Several kilometres after Labarthe, take D23, on the left near Crayssac. Site is well signed from Crayssac.

Charges guide

Per unit incl. 2 persons	€ 13,00 - € 18,90
extra person	€ 4,00 - € 6,10
child (2-5 yrs)	free - € 3,90
electricity (10A)	€ 3,90

Campéole Les Reflets du Quercy

Mas de Bastide - 46510 - Crayssac (Lot)
Tél.: 05 65 30 00 27
Fax: 05 65 30 01 43
www.camping-lot.info

FR46200 Camping les Chênes

F-46500 Padirac (Lot)

Tel: **05 65 33 65 54**. Email: **les_chenes@hotmail.com**

Les Chênes is situated in the heart of the Quercy Causses natural regional park and on the route de Gouffre. With a total area of 4.5 hectares, the hilly site is terraced and well shaded with trees and hedges. The 120 touring pitches are of medium size and not all are well levelled. Some larger vehicles may have trouble negotiating the site due to narrow paths and closely planted trees. During the months of July and August, campers have free access to the Padirac Aquapark, just 500 m. from the campsite and under the same ownership.

Facilities

The three sanitary blocks are clean and well maintained. Facilities for disabled people. Baby room with bath. Two washing machines and dryer. Shop. Bar with TV. Restaurant and takeaway. Swimming pool. Boules. Minigolf. Play area. Games room with electronic games. Animation in high season. Off site: Aquatic park 500 m. Fishing 4 km. Riding 10 km.

Open: 15 April - 30 September.

Directions

From A20 exit 54, take N140 southeast to Gramat. Turn onto D807 northeast to Lavergne, then the D11 to Thégra and follow signs for Padirac. Follow D90 northwest for 2 km. and the site is well signed on the left hand side.

Charges 2007

Per person	€ 3,80 - € 6,50
child (under 8 yrs)	€ 2,60 - € 4,80
pitch	€ 4,50 - € 9,00
electricity (6A)	€ 3,00

FR46220 Camping les 3 Sources

Peyratel, F-46190 Calviac-Sousceyrac (Lot)

Tel: 05 65 33 03 01. Email: info@les-trois-sources.com

This rural site is beautifully situated in the hilly surroundings of the Lot region, only 20 km. from the Dordogne river. The site offers 120 well maintained pitches in an attractive, wooded area. There are also 16 chalets and 20 mobile homes for rent. The pitches are numbered and have 6/10A electricity connections and water points within easy reach. Following a fire in 2005 when the site's facilities burned down, and at the time of our visit, the reception and snack bar were housed in chalets on what was the terrace of the restaurant. A new restaurant, shop and reception are promised.

Facilities

Two toilet blocks provide good facilities including washbasins in cabins. Facilities for babies and disabled visitors. Laundry facilities including ironing. Snack bar (to be replaced by new bar and restaurant). Swimming and paddling pools. Games room. Trim trail on island in the lake. Fishing. Play area. Activities and entertainment including children's club. Off site: Riding 15 km. Lake beach 17 km.

Open: 29 April - 17 September.

Directions

From A20 (Chateauroux, Limoges, Brive) follow D8/D20 towards Vayrac and Bretenoux. Do not go through Martel. Follow signs for St Cère and Sousceyrac (D673) and turn left to Calviac after 6 km. (towards Lamativie). After 2 km. site is on right hand side.

Charges 2008

Per unit incl. 2 persons and electricity	€ 6,35 - € 10,35
extra person	€ 2,15 - € 4,50

FR46230 Camping des Arcades

Moulin de Saint Martial, F-46800 Saint Pantaléon (Lot)

Tel: 05 65 22 92 27. Email: info@des-arcades.com

Recently taken over by an enthusiastic, young Dutch couple, Camping des Arcades is situated in the hilly surroundings of the Lot Valley. There are 80 level, grass pitches with 6A electricity hook ups. The heated swimming pool is small but provides plenty of fun during hot summer days. Those who enjoy fishing can enjoy lazy afternoons on the banks of the site's lake (the lake is unfenced). The site's facilities such as the reception, the bar and the restaurant are housed in a 13th century watermill. Entertainment and excursions are organised all season. The D653 road runs beside the site, which may cause some nuisance.

Facilities

Two toilet blocks provide good facilities with facilities for disabled visitors in one block. Laundry facilities. Shop for basics in high season (bread available all season). Bar, restaurant and takeaway. Swimming pool. Fishing. Activities and entertainment. Off site: Canoeing, walking, cycling and riding nearby.

Open: 28 April - 30 September.

Directions

From the A20 take the N20 to Cahors. Continue until roundabout (Atrium wine), then take D653 towards Agen and Montcuq. Site is on left after 10 km.

Charges guide

Per person (over 4 yrs)	€ 5,00
pitch	€ 7,00 - € 10,00
electricity	€ 3,00

FR47030 Camping le Château de Fonrives

Rives, F-47210 Villeréal (Lot-et-Garonne)

Tel: 05 53 36 63 38. Email: chateau.de.fonrives@wanadoo.fr

Le Château de Fonrives is situated in Lot-en-Garonne. The site is set in pretty part-farmed, part-wooded countryside. It is a mixture of hazelnut woodland with lake and château (mostly 16th century). An attractive avenue leads to the barns adjacent to the château which have been converted. There are 200 pitches, 96 of which are for touring units, with electricity. Pitches near the woodland receive moderate shade, but elsewhere there is light shade from hedges and young trees. Former barns have been converted to provide a restaurant with covered terrace and bar with an open terrace overlooking the outdoor pool.

Facilities

One sanitary block. Shop. Restaurant, snacks and takeaway. Bar with disco area and terrace. Covered swimming pool (April - Oct), outdoor pool, water slides, paddling pool. Small play area. Small field for volleyball and football. Library. Minigolf, tennis, bicycle hire (all charged). Activities organised for children and adults in season, including excursions and walks. Caravan storage. Off site: Riding 8 km.

Open: 4 May - 14 September.

Directions

Site is about 2 km. northwest of Villeréal, on west side of the D14/D207 Bergerac - Villaréal road.

Charges 2007

Per unit incl. 2 persons	€ 16,00 - € 24,50
extra person	€ 4,00 - € 4,30
child (under 6 yrs)	€ 2,00 - € 2,30
electricity (6A)	€ 2,50 - € 4,50

FR47010 **Kawan Village Moulin du Périé**
F-47500 Sauveterre-la-Lemance (Lot-et-Garonne)
Tel: 05 53 40 67 26. Email: **moulinduperie@wanadoo.fr**

Mobile homes ▶ page 502

Set in a quiet area and surrounded by woodlands this peaceful little site is well away from much of the tourist bustle. It has 125 reasonably sized, grassy pitches, all with 6A electricity, divided by mixed trees and bushes with most having good shade. All are extremely well kept, as indeed is the entire site. The attractive front courtyard is complemented by an equally pleasant terrace at the rear. Two small, clean swimming pools overlook a shallow, spring water lake, ideal for inflatable boats and paddling and bordering the lake, a large grass field is popular for games. The picturesque old mill buildings, adorned with flowers and creepers, now house the bar and restaurant where the food is to be recommended, as is the owner's extensive knowledge of wine that he is pleased to share with visitors. A quiet, friendly site with regular visitors – reservation is advised for July/Aug. Bergerac Airport is an hour away so would suit those choosing a mobile home or bungalow tent and wanting to travel light.

Facilities

Two clean, modern and well maintained toilet blocks include facilities for disabled visitors. Motorcaravan services. Fridge, barbecue, chemical toilet hire (book in advance). Basic shop. Bar/reception, restaurant, takeaway. Two small swimming pools (no Bermuda-style shorts). Boules, table tennis, outdoor chess. Playground. Trampoline. Small, indoor play area. Bicycle hire. Organised activities in high season; including canoeing, riding, wine tasting visits, sight seeing trips, barbecues, gastronomic meals. Winter caravan storage. Off site: Fishing 1 km. Small supermarket in village and larger stores in Fumel.

Open: 12 May - 21 September.

Directions

From D710, Fumel - Périgueux, turn southeast into Sauveterre-le-Lemance. Turn left (northeast) at far end on C201 signed campsite, Château Sauveterre and Loubejec. Site is 3 km. on right.

Charges 2007

Per unit incl. 2 persons	€ 13,05 - € 21,85
with electricity	€ 16,95 - € 25,75
extra person	€ 4,20 - € 6,50
child (under 7 yrs)	€ 1,80 - € 3,45
animal	€ 2,15 - € 4,10
Camping Cheques accepted.	

FR47110 Camping le Cabri

Route de Savignac, F-47120 Duras (Lot-et-Garonne)

Tel: 05 53 83 81 03. Email: holidays@lecabri.eu.com

Le Cabri is delightfully situated in the heart of Lot-et-Garonne. This pleasantly wooded, terraced site with a pond is recently been acquired by Englishman James Cook and is currently undergoing development and expansion. There are currently 20 pitches which include 11 wooden chalets, 3 mobile homes and 6 touring pitches. One chalet is reserved disabled visitors with an en-suite shower and toilet. Previously known for its excellent chalet accommodation and fine restaurant, the expansion plans include a further 50 pitches with electricity and water and a much larger (160 sq.m.) swimming pool. The site is less than fifteen minutes walk from the château town of Duras with its many amenities, where you can shop, visit the weekly market, as well as hire bikes and canoes. You will receive a warm welcome and enjoy a comfortable stay.

Facilities

One sanitary block, with pre-set hot showers. Toilet for disabled visitors. Washing machine and dryer. Bar and restaurant with TV. Swimming pool. Minigolf. Boules. Play area and covered games area with range of children's toys. Off site: Riding 2 km. Golf (international course) 15 km. Tennis 1 km. Water sports 7 km. Canoeing 8 km. Aquatic park 45 minutes drive.

Open: All year.

Directions

From N113 southeast or northwest to Marmande, head through Marmande north on D708 to Duras for about 24 km. Look for the D203 through Duras and follow sign for site. It is less than 1 km. away.

Charges 2007

Per person	€ 4,00
child (under 7 yrs)	€ 2,00
pitch	€ 5,00
electricity (10A)	€ 4,00

Le Cabri Holiday Village

Route de Savignac - 47120 Duras

Tel-fax: 0033 (0) 553 838 103

Mobile: 0033 (0) 685 449 711

E-mail: holidays@lecabri.eu.com - www.lecabri.eu.com

FR47050 Camping Moulin de Campech

F-47160 Villefranche-de-Queyran (Lot-et-Garonne)

Tel: 05 53 88 72 43. Email: campech@wanadoo.fr

This well shaded, pretty site is run by Sue and George Thomas along with Sue's parents, Dot and Bob Dunn. At the entrance to the site, a trout lake with graceful weeping willows feeds under the restored mill house which is home to the owners as well as housing the bar and restaurant. Children will need supervision around the lake and at the pool which is on an elevated area above the mill house. The 60 large-sized pitches are mostly divided by hedges, with electricity (6A, long leads may be necessary in places, but can be borrowed free of charge).

Facilities

The single, rather ordinary toilet block has modern fittings. Washing machine and tumble dryer. Bar, restaurant. Terraced swimming pool. Open grassy games area. Board games and English library. Boules. Barbecue, gourmet nights in high season. Fishing (discounted rate for campers - no permit required). Torch useful. Off site: Watersports, bicycle hire, golf or riding 10 km. Markets every day in villages and towns around the region. Numerous wine caves and armagnac products.

Open: 1 April - 22 October.

Directions

Take A10 south to Bordeaux. Join A62 for Toulouse and take exit 6 for Damazan. Follow D8 to Mont de Marsan, at Cap du Bosc turn right onto D11 for Casteljaloux. Site is signed, 5 km. on right.

Charges 2008

Per person	€ 3,85 - € 5,60
child (under 7 yrs)	€ 2,85 - € 3,80
pitch	€ 7,50 - € 10,40
electricity (2/6A)	€ 3,80
dog	€ 2,40

FR47150 Domaine de Guillalmes

Condat, F-47500 Fumel (Lot-et-Garonne)

Tel: **05 53 71 01 99**. Email: **info@guillalmes.com**

Mobile homes ▶ page 502

Domaine de Guillalmes is a very attractive site and was until recently exclusively for chalets but the British owners have now added a 10 pitch touring caravan area. These pitches are all on hardstanding, divided by small hedges and with some shade from small trees. The pitches are very large and are ideal for very large outfits and American motorhomes. Each pitch has electricity (up to 16A) and there is a central motorcaravan service point. All facilities at this three hectare site are available to the touring units, including the magnificent pool and bar terrace. The site is on the banks of the river Lot and in the summer the river provides opportunities for water sports. The site is an ideal stopover for even the largest units and because of the facilities it is well worth staying longer.

Facilities

A shower and toilet are available 24 hours a day (more showers planned), plus dishwashing facilities. Other facilities including separate toilets, washbasins and facilities for disabled people are located in the restaurant area and are open 08.00 - 22.00. Large laundry room. Restaurant. Bar terrace and takeaway. Swimming pool (June - Oct) with jacuzzi. Play area. Tennis. Football. Volleyball. Boules. Canoeing. Table tennis. Badminton. Fishing. Boat slipway. Off site: Cycling and walking routes. Vineyards 2 km. Fummel, Rocamadour and Cahors.

Open: All year.

Directions

From Fumel, take D911 following signs to Cahors, then signs to Domaine de Guillalmes. The site is situated between Fumel and Soturac, 150 m. before Soturac (D911). GPS: N44:28.983 E01:00.562

Charges 2008

Per unit incl. 2 persons	€ 18,00 - € 22,00
extra person	€ 3,50 - € 5,50
child (under 7 yrs)	€ 2,50 - € 4,50
electricity (4/6A)	€ 5,00 - € 6,00

Owned and run by an English family, Domaine de Guillalmes is a perfect site whether you are looking for comfortable accomodation in a relaxing environment or large pleasant camping pitches.

Domaine de Guillalmes - Condat - 47500 Fumel - France - Tel: 0033 (0)553 71 01 99
Fax: 0033 (0)553 71 02 57 - info@guillalmes.com - www.guillalmes.com

FR47100 Camping Municipal Le Robinson

RN 113 Robinson, F-47400 Tonneins (Lot-et-Garonne)

Tel: **05 53 79 02 28**

Close to the River Garonne, this small site has a rather formal charm with neat flower beds, well mown lawns and an extremely well cared for appearance. With a small reception, the Gardien based on site and a security barrier, it only has 32 pitches plus a meadow for additional camping. All with electricity (15A), the pitches are of a reasonable size, separated by small trees which provide a little shade. There is some road and rail noise at times. This is a good stopping off point or base from which to explore the local area.

Facilities

Sanitary facilities are roomy but of fairly old design, they are adequate rather than luxurious. Washing machine. No proper chemical disposal point. Ice and cold drinks available. Under cover area with fridge, freezer, tables and chairs. Small play area, sandpit, table tennis. Torch useful. Off site: 1.5 km. to Tonneins town centre, with a full range of supermarkets, bars and restaurants.

Open: 1 June - 30 September.

Directions

Take either exit 5 from autoroute to Marmande then the N113 south or exit 6 to Aiguillon (avoid town) and follow N113 north. Site on west side of the N113, just south of Tonneins.

Charges guide

Per pitch incl. 1 person	€ 5,50
incl. 2 persons	€ 8,00
extra person	€ 3,00
electricity	€ 3,50
No credit cards.	

Check real time availability and at-the-gate prices...

www.**alanrogers**.com

FR47130 Camping des Bastides

Terre Rouge, F-47150 Salles (Lot-et-Garonne)

Tel: 05 53 40 83 09. Email: info@campingdesbastides.com

Attractive and well maintained, this 6.5 hectares is hilly and terraced with good views from the top of the site. Although the terrain is hilly, most of the 90 medium sized touring pitches are fairly level and moderately shaded. The friendly Dutch owners of 11 years are warm and welcoming. Tight turns with narrow gravel paths and overhanging trees may cause some difficulties for larger units. Reception keeps information on a variety of local walking and cycling routes. Weekly trips are arranged to one of the wine growing châteaux in the region.

Facilities

Two modern, clean and well maintained sanitary blocks can be heated. Facilities for the disabled. Excellent children's facilities with baby bath and child-size facilities. Private en-suite facilities for hire. Shop for essentials (with gas). Bar/reception and snack restaurant (including takeaway). Swimming pool complex,. Boules. Play area. Small indoor play area with TV and small library. WiFi access. Animation (high season) including excursions and weekly barbecues. Off site: Fumel 8 km. Fishing 1 km. Riding and bicycle hire 10 km. Golf 25 km.

Open: 1 May - 15 September.

Directions

From Fumel, take D710 north towards Cuzorn. Before reaching Cuzorn, turn northwest on D162 and site is 6 km. on the right hand side (well signed). GPS: N44:33.090 E00:52.530

Charges 2007

Per unit incl. 2 persons and electricity (6A)	€ 15,00 - € 24,00
extra person	€ 4,00 - € 5,50
child (under 7 yrs)	€ 2,25 - € 2,75

FR47120 Camping la Vallée de Gardeleau

F-47410 Sérignac-Péboudou (Lot-et-Garonne)

Tel: 05 53 36 96 96. Email: valleegardeleau@Wanadoo.fr

Camping La Vallée is a delightful, small, family run site established over 12 years ago. It is well hidden and private, some 9 km. from civilization and deep in the countryside of Lot-et-Garonne, very close to the border of the Dordogne and 150 km. from the Atlantic coast. It has a total of 33 pitches, 26 for touring, 7 mobile homes, and 4 bungalow tents. The medium sized pitches are well laid out, all with hedges and some shade, some with views. The owners, Pierre and Marie-Madeleine Pécheux, are very conscientious and work extremely hard to keep the site clean and well maintained.

Facilities

Two sanitary blocks are well sited and clean. Facilities for disabled visitors. Baby room. Washing machine. Shop with daily deliveries of fresh bread. Bar with snack bar and TV. Restaurant (high season). Swimming pool. Large boules area (need to bring own boules). Small play area. Communal stone barbecue. Library. Animation for children (high season). Off site: Fishing and riding 2 km. Bicycle hire 9 km. Golf 20 km. Atlantic coast 150 km.

Open: 1 April - 31 October.

Directions

From Castillones on the N21 find the D254 to Sérignac-Péboudou and follow this. Some 10 km. along this road, look for signs to site which is on the left hand side.

Charges 2008

Per person	€ 2,50 - € 3,90
child (under 7 yrs)	€ 1,50 - € 2,35
pitch	€ 3,80 - € 6,00

FR47140 Camping Naturiste Domaine Laborde

Paulhiac, F-47150 Monflanquin (Lot-et-Garonne)

Tel: 05 53 36 08 16. Email: fontaine.du.roc@wanadoo.fr

Ideally situated on the border of Lot-et-Garonne and Dordogne, Domain Laborde is a naturist site of outstanding quality, with sweeping views from many of the higher pitches. This hilly and terraced site has 120 well maintained touring pitches, many shaded, some partially and all surrounded by woodland. Electricity (3/6/10A) is available, although some need long leads. There are 25 chalets for rent. This site has something for everyone and even in low season it is very popular. If you are new to naturist sites, then this is a must. The ambience is good and you will make new friends.

Facilities

New washblock and three sanitary blocks are well sited and clean. Washing facilities. Shop with daily deliveries of fresh bread and milk. Bar with TV. Snack bar serving pizzas. Restaurant. Large swimming pool, whirlpool, children's pool and indoor heated pool. Play areas. Giant chess board. Communal barbecue. Animation for children (high season). Various excursions and organised activities for adults and children. Off site: Riding 2 km. Golf 30 km.

Open: 1 April - 1 October.

Directions

From Monflanquin take D272 towards Monpazier. About 10 km. along the road look for the signs to site. It is very well signed at regular intervals and will read 'Laborde FFN'. GPS: N44:36.450 E00:50.230

Charges 2007

Per person	€ 4,50 - € 5,50
child (under 6 yrs)	€ 3,50 - € 4,00
pitch	€ 9,00 - € 12,00
electricity (6A)	€ 3,50 - € 4,50

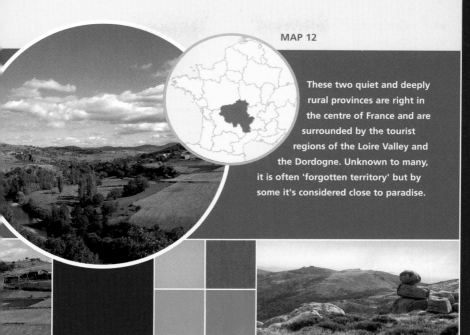

MAP 12

These two quiet and deeply rural provinces are right in the centre of France and are surrounded by the tourist regions of the Loire Valley and the Dordogne. Unknown to many, it is often 'forgotten territory' but by some it's considered close to paradise.

Limousin & Auvergne

WE HAVE COMBINED TWO OFFICIAL REGIONS: LIMOUSIN WITH DÉPARTEMENTS 19 CORRÈZE, 23 CREUSE, 87 HAUTE-VIENNE; AND AUVERGNE, 03 ALLIER, 15 CANTAL 43 HAUTE-LOIRE, 63 PUY-DE-DÔME. ALSO INCLUDED IS 48 LOZÈRE, PART OF THE OFFICAL REGION OF LANGUEDOC-ROUSSILLON

This is the home of Limoges porcelain and Aubosson tapestry, of exceptional Romanesque and Gothic churches and fairytale Renaissance châteaux. Limousin is an unspoilt, thinly populated region on the western side of the Massif Central. With hills and gorges and lush green meadows, numerous ancient village churches dot the landscape as well as more imposing abbey churches and fortresses. The many lakes and rivers of the Limousin provide endless possibilities for canoeing, sailing, wind-surfing and other watersports. To the south, fortified cities cling to mountain sides, home to many religious events and legends.

The Auvergne, set in the heart of the Massif Central, was formed by a series of volcanic eruptions and is a dramatic region of awe-inspiring non-active volcanoes, lakes, sparkling rivers, green valleys and forests. There are also numerous underground streams that have carved out extensive and fantastic cave systems, for which the region is famous. It is a wonderful destination for nature lovers, those who enjoy active outdoor pursuits or for people who want to relax at spa resorts.

Places of interest

Aubusson: long tradition of tapestry making, Hotel de Ville tapestry collections.

Clermont-Ferrand: old city centre, 11th and 12th century Notre Dame du Port Basilica, 13th century cathedral; known as *ville noire* for its houses built in local black volcanic rock.

Limoges: porcelain, enamel and faience work, château, church of St Michel-de-Lions, cathedral of St Etienne.

Vichy: spa, natural spring park.

Cuisine of the region

Limousin is known for a thick soup called *bréjaude* and its beef, which is extremely tender and full of flavour. Local specialties in the Auvergne include ham and andouille sausages, stuffed cabbage, and bacon with lentil and *cèpes* (mushrooms). Le Puy is famed for its lentils and *Vereine du Velay* – yellow and green liqueurs made from over 30 mountain plants.

Aligot: purée of potatoes with Tomme de Cantal cheese, cream, garlic and butter.

Friand Sanflorin: pork meat and herbs in pastry.

Jambon d'Auvergne: a tasty mountain ham.

Perdrix à l'Auvergnate: partridge stewed in white wine.

Potée Auvergnate: a stew of vegetables, cabbage, pork and sausage.

FR03010 **Camping de la Filature**

Ile de Nieres, F-03450 Ebreuil (Allier)

Tel: **04 70 90 72 01**. Email: **camping.filature@libertysurf.fr**

Near the spa town of Vichy and beside a fine fly fishing river, this traditional touring and camping site makes a good base to explore the Auvergne including the nearby river gorges, châteaux, mountains and lakes. There are 80 spacious, grassy pitches, most with shade from mature trees and many directly by the river. The river is clean, shallow and pleasant to play in with a deeper swimming area 500 m. away. Most pitches have electricity (3/6A). You will receive a warm welcome from the English owners (the takeaways are good value and very popular). The quiet country roads are ideal for walking and cycling, especially mountain biking and touring by car. Bird watching and rare wild flowers are additional attractions.

Facilities

Very clean sanitary facilities are in individual cubicles. Fully equipped, they include mostly British type toilets, a bathroom and a room for disabled visitors. Laundry facilities. Small shop for essentials (1/5-30/9). Baker calls. Bar (1/6-30/9). Excellent takeaway (1/6-30/9). Barbecues and pizza nights organised in high season. River bathing and fishing. Play area. Bicycle hire. Minigolf. Off site: Riding, canoeing and tennis nearby. Ébreuil with shops and restaurants 1 km.

Open: 31 March - 1 October.

Directions

Site is well signed from exit 12 of A71 autoroute to Clermont Ferrand in the direction of Ébreuil. It is about 6 km. from the A71 and 1 km. west of Ébreuil beside the river on the D915 towards the Chouvigny gorges. GPS: N46:06.526 E03:04.403

Charges 2007

Per unit incl. 2 persons	€ 16,00
extra person	€ 5,00
child (under 16 yrs)	€ 2,50
electricity (3/6A)	€ 3,00
Discounts in low season.	

Don't wait to die to go to heaven, come to: ★★★★
CAMPING DE LA FILATURE DE LA SIOULE
03450 EBREUIL, FRANCE
See us on website www.campingfilature.com

- Very clean facilities and a bathroom
- Really hot water • Excellent take away with pizza and barbecue evenings in high season • Bar and terrace
- Low season bargains for long stays
- Children up to 16 charged child rate
- Near to exit 12 of A71 for stopover or long stay

Tel: 0033 (0)4 70 90 72 01 Fax: 0033 (0)4 70 90 79 48
E-mail: camping.filature@libertysurf.fr

FR03020 **Camping Château de Chazeuil**

F-03150 Varennes-sur-Allier (Allier)

Tel: **04 70 45 83 26**. Email: **camping-dechazeuil@hetnet.nl**

This spacious, peaceful site is set in the attractive parkland surrounding the château. Here you will be surrounded by beautiful plants, flowers and bird song (if you are lucky, you will hear the nightingale). The 60 large, marked pitches are laid out on well maintained lawns and all have electricity (6/10A, although long leads may be necessary). Mature trees provide some pitches with shade. Although the entrance is adjacent to the main N7, traffic noise is no problem as the site is set up a long drive. A one-way road system operates to ensure a safe exit from the site.

Facilities

The modern sanitary block provides washbasins and showers in cabins, a washing machine and dishwashing and laundry sinks. It is maintained to a satisfactory level. Very pleasant unheated swimming pool (May to Sept) and sunbathing area. Play area. Table tennis. Reading/information room. Off site: Shops, restaurants, etc. in Varennes 2 km. Fishing and canoeing in River Allier 2 km. Bicycle hire 2 km. Marked walks and cycle rides.

Open: 1 April - 15 October.

Directions

Site is 25 km. south of Moulins and just north of Varennes. In Chazeuil leave N7, turn east (site signed) onto D268, signed Montoldre and immediately enter site through gateway on juction. Note: D46 has been realigned with new roundabout.

Charges 2007

per person	€ 4,95
child (under 7 yrs)	€ 3,00
pitch incl. electricity (6A)	€ 10,75
animal	€ 1,00
Credit cards are not accepted.	

FR03030 Camping Beau Rivage

Rue Claude Decloître, les Berges de l'Allier, F-03700 Bellerive-sur-Allier (Allier)

Tel: 04 70 32 26 85. Email: camping-beaurivage@wanadoo.fr

This well maintained, compact, urban site beside the River Allier is on the outskirts of the famous spa town near of Vichy. It has recently been completely refurbished by the enthusiastic new owners (good English and Dutch spoken). Some of the 80 medium sized, reasonably level pitches have delightful views across the river to the beautiful Parc Napoléon beyond. They are separated by flowering shrubs and hedging, and mature trees offer some shade; 10A electricity is available and 12 are fully serviced. Almost 50% of the pitches are occupied by mobile homes and chalets to rent. There are swimming and paddling pools and a separate toboggan. Family entertainment including discos and karaoke finishes at 23.00. Vichy offers a wealth of attractions, spas, theatre, cinema, a racecourse, many sports opportunities and numerous shops, bars and restaurants. There is an overspill site adjacent.

Facilities

Very clean, modern airy sanitary facilities in individual cubicles in pleasantly decorated buildings. Fully equipped, they include mostly British type toilets and a baby room. Washing machine and ironing facilities. Motorcaravan service point. Small bar with snacks (March - Oct). River fishing. Play area. Bicycles and pedaloes. Minigolf. Archery. Internet including WiFi. Off site: Riding, canoeing and tennis nearby. Very close to the site are several bars and restaurants. Hypermarket complex within 1 km. Vichy 2 km.

Open: 22 March - 30 October.

Directions

Well signed in Bellerive on the west bank of the River Allier. Leave A71 at exit 12 (Vichy). After about 15 km. turn right at large roundabout with fountains and follow signs, Berges des Allier, Campings and Beaurivage.

Charges 2008

Per person	€ 3,80 - € 4,90
child (0-7 yrs)	€ 2,90 - € 3,80
pitch	€ 3,80 - € 6,00
electricity (10A)	€ 3,00
Camping Cheques accepted.	

BEAU RIVAGE

CAMPING****

In the AUVERGNE where you can find volcano's, at 3mn distance from the city centre.

Pitches, chalets and mobil homes "RIVIERA" for rent situated along the water site.

Great view over the parks of VICHY. Beautiful and peaceful park with lots of shade. Activities all for free: pedalo, canoeing, swimming-pool, aqua-toboggan.   03700 BELLERIVE

Web site: www.camping-beaurivage.com   Tel: 0033 (0)470 32 26 85

FR03040 Camping Champ de la Chapelle

F-03360 Braize (Allier)

Tel: 04 70 06 15 45. Email: info@champdelachapelle@wanadoo.fr

Champ de la Chapelle is a 6 hectare site in the Forest of Troncais. It is ideal for families who want to get away from it all. The 72 touring pitches are slightly sloping, up to 250 sq.m. and there is plenty of shade and open space. Electricity (16A) and water is available to 64 of the pitches. It is the policy of the owner to keep the site quiet and unsophisticated (no discos here) and the reward is the wealth of wild life. The area is a paradise for nature lovers, cyclists and walkers.

Facilities

Modern sanitary block includes washbasins in cabins. Low toilets for children. Dishwashing and laundry facilities. Small snack kiosk with bread to order. Very small pool (from 15/5). Play area. Courts for volleyball, flip-ball and petanque. Off site: Supermarket and restaurant at St Bonnet 5 km. Lake 5 km. offers fishing, bathing, pedaloes, canoes, sail-boarding, minigolf, volleyball, tennis. Riding 11 km. The museum at nearby St Armand-Montrond traces 100,000 years of local history and at Ainay-le-Viel you can visit 'Little Carcassone'.

Open: 6 April - 30 October.

Directions

From N144 Bourges-Montlucon road, 14 km. south of St Amand Montrond, take D978A east, signed Clermont Ferrand. At roundabout take D28 north, signed Braize. After 3 km. turn right, signed church and campsite (easy to miss). Follow site signs for approx. 3 km. (narrow lane).
GPS: N46:38.562 E02:39.325

Charges 2007

Per unit incl. 1 or 2 persons	€ 9,75 - € 15,50
extra person	€ 2,75
electricity (16A)	€ 2,50

FR03050 **Camping Caravaning la Petite Valette**

Sazeret, F-03390 Montmarault (Allier)

Tel: **04 70 07 64 57**. Email: **la.petite.valette@wanadoo.fr**

Originally a working farm, La Petite Valette has been transformed by its hard working Dutch and German owners into a very attractive and peaceful, secluded campsite. There are 55 level grassy pitches of good size, many with rural views, each with an electricity point (6A). They are separated by flowering bushes and trees giving some shade and privacy and many have pleasant, rural views. A small lake in one of the lower fields is stocked with fish for anglers. The countryside is ideal for cycling and there are many interesting old villages nearby.

Facilities

Good clean toilet facilities in outbuildings. Unit for disabled people, families and babies. Laundry. Bread. Meals, snacks (to order). Takeaway. Small swimming, paddling pools, sunbathing areas. Play area with seating. Table tennis, mountain bike hire, organised activities in July/Aug. Off site: Tennis, riding and sailing in the area. Small town of Montmarault 6 km. for shopping needs.

Open: 1 April - 30 October.

Directions

Leave A71 exit 11. First roundabout take D46 signed St Pourcain. Shortly at roundabout take D945 signed Deux-Chaises and La Valette. After 3 km. take third left, site sign, follow narrow lanes to site (just under 2 km). GPS: N46:32.568 E02:59.581

Charges 2007

Per person	€ 3,95 - € 4,95
pitch with electricity	€ 9,20 - € 10,90

FR03170 **Camping Municipal Dompierre-sur-Besbre**

F-03290 Dompierre-sur-Besbre (Allier)

Tel: **04 70 34 55 57**

This immaculate, attractive and excellent value for money site has 68 level, partly shaded, individually hedged, grassy pitches, all with easy access. There are a few long stay units, leaving about 65 for tourists, all with electricity (10A) and most being fully serviced. It is located next to the municipal sports fields and is ideal for motorcaravans being within easy walking distance of the town centre and supermarket (700 m). The warden is very proud of his efficiently run site and its award-winning floral displays. Twin axle caravans are not accepted.

Facilities

Modernised, heated toilet blocks, very clean with all necessary facilities including provision for disabled visitors. Some washbasins in curtained cubicles for ladies. Washing machine. Excellent Motorcaravan services. Off site: The small town has shops, restaurants, Saturday market. Vallée de la Besbre has a wealth of activities, several rivers and small lakes nearby for fishing. Cycle tracks, footpaths. Le Pal theme park and zoo 8 km.

Open: 15 May - 15 September.

Directions

Dompierre is 35 km. east of Moulins. Leave N79 at eastern end of Dompierre bypass, turn southwest on N2079 towards town. Entrance to sports complex and campsite is on left beyond D55 before the river bridge and town centre. GPS: N46:31.052 E03:41.24

Charges 2007

Per person	€ 2,10
pitch	€ 1,70 - € 2,00
electricity	€ 2,00

FR19020 **Camping les Aubazines**

F-19110 Bort-les-Orgues (Corrèze)

Tel: **05 55 96 08 38**. Email: **email.lesaubaz@aol.com**

Owned by a group of several communes, this very spacious site is set out on wide terraces over looking a lake on the River Dordogne, although a short distance from it. Wide but steep site roads give good access to the 113 pitches. Slightly sloping, the grassy pitches (77 for touring) are mostly separated by flowering shrubs and hedging with some shade provided by trees. Most pitches have 10A electricity and a few have drains. Not suitable for those with walking difficulties as access to the facilities often involve a long, steep climb. The owners want to keep this a quiet and relaxing site.

Facilities

Three clean modern toilet blocks have all the necessary facilities but access to them is not easy (see above). Bread (July/Aug). Large bar/restaurant (all season) near entrance and lakeside beach. Games/TV room. Play area. Tennis. Boules. Family activities and excursions (July/Aug). Off site: Lakeside beach adjacent to site with large play area and pedaloes and canoes for hire (July/Aug). Boat ramp. Bort-les-Orgues with a good range of shops, bars, restaurants, large swimming pool and magnificent rock formations 4 km.

Open: 17 June - 10 September.

Directions

Bort-les-Orgues is 80 km. southwest of Clermont Ferrand. Leave A89 at exit 23, signed Ussel West. Take D979 signed Bort-les-Orgues for 25 km. Site is on the left 4 km. before the town. GPS: N45:24.964 E02:28.818

Charges 2007

Per unit incl. 2 persons	€ 7,00 - € 13,50
extra person	€ 2,80
child (2-10 yrs)	free - € 1,50
electricity (10A)	€ 2,60

FR15030 Camping Caravaning le Val Saint-Jean

F-15200 Mauriac (Cantal)

Tel: 04 71 67 31 13. Email: contact@revea-vacances.com

Le Val Saint-Jean is set beside a lake in the heart of the département of Cantal. The campsite has 100 generously sized, slightly sloping, touring pitches (with 10A electricity), many with good views. It is organised for the maximum of privacy and you are never far from a sanitary block. Most of the activities are situated by the lake where you can use all the facilities of the leisure club (high season) including cycling, canoeing, kayaking and pedaloes. This less well known region is well worth exploring and the local gastronomy can be experienced in the village of Mauriac with its attractive architecture typical of the area. Salers, one of the most beautiful French towns is 20 km.

Facilities

The two toilet blocks are well equipped with hot water throughout, providing some washbasins in cabins, dishwashing sinks and a laundry room. Facilities for people with disabilities. Limited shop. Bar, snack bar and restaurant (all May - Sept). Play area, playing field and table tennis. Activities organised for children in July/Aug. Off site: Sandy beach. Lake fishing and swimming. Swimming pool (1/6-15/9). Golf course. Guided walks. Mauriac village 1.6 km. Riding 3 km.

Open: 26 April - 28 September.

Directions

Mauriac is around 120 km. south west of Clermont-Ferrand. Leave A89 autoroute at junction 23 (Ussel West), take D979 (Bort-les-Orgues) for 5 km. Turn right onto D982 (Mauriac) for 40 km. Follow site signs in town.
GPS: N45:13.120 E02:18.953

Charges 2008

Per unit incl. 2 persons	€ 13,50 - € 19,50
extra person	€ 4,40 - € 5,40
child (2-7 yrs)	free - € 3,30
dog	€ 1,50
electricity (10A)	€ 3,60

FR19030 Camping la Plage

La Plage, F-19260 Treignac (Corrèze)

Tel: 05 55 98 08 54. Email: camping.;a.plage@wanadoo.fr

Carved out of the wooded hillside, Camping La Plage sits alongside Lac Variousses and the D940 road (some traffic noise). Mature trees provide a filigree of sunlight and shade on the four terraces which overlook the lake. The 127 grassy pitches, some sloping, are numbered and separated, all with electricity (6A). An underpass leads to the attractive sandy beach beside the lake where bathing is safe (lifeguard in high season) with permitted areas well marked. Pedaloes, canoes, etc. may be hired. The owners have planned 17 walks and 15 cycle rides from the site and copies of these are available from reception.

Facilities

Two toilet blocks can be heated and afford very satisfactory facilities including washbasins in cabins. Dishwashing and laundryfacilities. Motorcaravan services. Small shop, combined with reception area, provides essentials.Bread is only available in July/Aug. Library of English and French books with TV/games room adjacent. Play area and children's club organised (4-10 yrs). Snack bar and entertainment area on beach. Off site: Riding 5 km. Bicycle hire 3 km. Sailing in lake or on Vézère river. Discover the Haute Corrèze and the Monédières hills.

Open: 1 April - 30 September.

Directions

From A20 take exit 43 or 44 for Amerce and Treignac. Site is 3 km. north of Treignac on D940 beside Lac Vamousses.
GPS: N45:33.581 E01:48.806

Charges guide

Per person	€ 3,40 - € 4,80
child (4-10 yrs)	free - € 2,30
pitch	€ 3,70 - € 4,10
electricity (6A)	€ 2,50
dog	€ 1,00

FR19060 **Camping Domaine le Mialaret**

Route d'Egletons, F-19160 Neuvic (Corrèze)

Tel: **05 55 46 02 50**. Email: **info@lemialaret.com**

Mialaret is 4 km. from the village of Neuvic and only 6 km. from the Gorges of the Dordogne. It is set in the grounds of a 19th century château, now a hotel and restaurant with a good reputation. Most pitches are set in a gently sloping parkland situation where 80 trees and many bushes have been planted. Some pitches are level and separated by small bushes, most have some shade and 10A electricity. Entertainment and activities are organised in high season including Djembe drum workshops, a circus school, fishing lessons and evening concerts. In low season there are cooking courses with the chefs of the hotel, also at that time of the year the owner has time to take customers on a conducted tour of the estate in his 4x4 vehicle. Ten pitches are used by a tour operator.

Facilities

Refurbished sanitary blocks give an adequate provision, one heated, facilities for disabled people, washing machines. Motorcaravan services. Shop with bread. Bar, snacks, takeaway. Dinner at hotel. Swimming pool with shallow area. Play areas. Tennis. Table tennis. Fishing. Volleyball, football. Off site: Village with shops and lake 4 km. Golf 4 km. Canoeing, cycling and riding trips organised.

Open: 1 April - 31 October.

Directions

From Clermont-Ferrand or Brives on the A89, take exit 23 for and follow signs for Neuvic (20 km). In Neuvic follow signs for La Mialaret (take first right after Ecomarché). Site is 4 km. GPS: N45:22.945 E02:13.746

Charges 2007

Per person	€ 5,00 - € 7,50
child (2-8 yrs)	free - € 5,00
pitch incl. electricity	€ 8,50 - € 12,50
dog	free
Camping Cheques accepted.	

Domaine de Mialaret

a 45 hectare nature- and castle park, near the Gorges de la Dordogne with a ****campsite, chalets and tents for rent. Swimming pool, tennis, 2 fishing lakes, 2 playgrounds, miniclub, circus school, djembe workshops.

Route d'Egletons, 19160 Neuvic
Tel.: +33 (0)555 46 02 50
www.lemialaret.com - info@lemialaret.com

FR19050 **Camping la Rivière**

Route du Camping Louis Madrias, F-19270 Donzenac (Corrèze)

Tel: **05 55 85 63 95**. Email: **info@campingdonzenac.com**

The Corrèze is less well known than the Dordogne to the immediate south, but it is a beautiful area deserving more attention. Donzenac is an attractive small town with a variety of shops, restaurants, etc. This former municipal site is situated on the outskirts, just under a mile from the centre (an uphill walk). The site is small and neat with 68 fairly large pitches on level grass, the majority with electricity (8A). A variety of trees and shrubs give some shade. The site is next door to the town tennis courts and swimming pool (July/Aug, free to campers).

Facilities

Modernised sanitary facilities are very good and include a laundry room with washing machine and microwave. Baker calls at site in July/Aug. Table tennis, boules and minigolf. Fishing. WiFi in bar area. Double axle caravans are not accepted. Off site: Riding 4 km. Golf 15 km.

Open: 1 April - 30 September.

Directions

At roundabout at southern end of Donzenac (D920) turn southwest onto D170 signed Ussac and La Rivière. Entrance to site is shortly on the right. GPS: N45:13.126 E01:31.122

Charges 2007

Per unit incl. 2 persons	€ 13,50 - € 14,30
extra person	€ 4,30 - € 4,70
child (4-12 yrs)	€ 2,30 - € 2,70
electricity	€ 2,80
dog	€ 1,00
No credit cards.	

FR19090 Camping le Vaurette

Monceaux-sur-Dordogne, F-19400 Argentat (Corrèze)

Tel: 05 55 28 09 67. Email: info@vaurette.com

You are assured of a warm welcome at this immaculate site, beautifully situated beside the shallow river Dordogne and just a few kilometres from Argentat. There are 120 large, gently sloping grass pitches, 118 for touring. Separated by a large variety of beautiful trees and shrubs offering varying amounts of shade, all have 6A electricity and many have good views over the river Dordogne as the pitches nearest the river are slightly terraced. The owners run an active campsite for all the family whilst maintaining an air of tranquillity (no radios). Excellent English and Dutch is spoken. The ancient barn at the far end of the site houses the bar and a large TV room (large screen) and the terrace overlooks the good sized and attractive, but unheated, swimming and paddling pools (all season).

Facilities

Two very clean traditional toilet blocks offer all the expected facilities, including facilities for disabled people. Further facilities are near the bar and heated pool. Motorcaravan service point. Shop and takeaway (July/Aug). Football. Gym. Volleyball. Badminton. Boules. Table tennis. Tennis. Fishing. River bathing. Accompanied canoe trips, walks and mountain bike rides. Organised activities for all the family (July and Aug) but no late night discos etc. Off site: Argentat (9 km) with shops and watersports centre. Riding 15 km.

Open: 1 May - 21 September.

Directions

A20 or A89 - Tulle exit - then N120 to Argentat, onto D12 towards Beanliem. Site is on the left. GPS: N45:02.739 E01:53.058

Charges 2007

Per unit incl. 2 persons	€ 14,50 - € 21,20
extra person (over 2 yrs)	€ 3,30 - € 5,00
electricity (6A)	€ 3,20
dog	€ 2,00 - € 3,50

Camping ★★★★ Le Vaurette

Vallée de la Dordogne
19400 Argentat
Tél. +33 5 55 28 09 67   Fax +33 5 55 28 81 14   www.vaurette.com

FR19070 Camping Château de Gibanel

Saint Martial Entrayguis, F-19400 Argentat (Corrèze)

Tel: 05 55 28 10 11. Email: contact@camping-gibanel.com

This slightly terraced campsite is located in a beautiful estate, dominated by the 16th century château, on the banks of a very clean lake in this lesser known part of the Dordogne valley. The very friendly family ensures that everything is of a very high standard. Nearly all of the 250 grassy pitches are used for touring units. All have electricity (6A) and are separated by a variety of mature trees giving varying amounts of shade. Many of the trees have low branches making access to most pitches rather difficult for large motorcaravans.

Facilities

Four modern, spacious and very clean toilet blocks include many large cubicles with a shower and washbasin. Good provision for disabled visitors. Washing machine and dryer. Good shop for basics. Bar, snack and takeaway (July/Aug). Swimming and paddling pools. Range of family activities in July/Aug, including dance evenings, folklore events, watersports, walking and cycling. Bicycle hire (July/Aug). TV room. Table tennis. Boules. Volleyball. Off site: Argentat 5 km.

Open: 1 June - 6 September.

Directions

Site is 5 km. northeast of Argentat. Take D18, signed Eggletons, and after 4 km, alongside the lake, fork right at site sign. Follow lane down to site. GPS: N45:06.650 E01:57.536

Charges 2007

Per person	€ 4,30 - € 5,35
child (2-7 yrs)	€ 2,00 - € 2,70
pitch	€ 5,20 - € 6,50
electricity	€ 3,20
dog	free - € 1,50

FR19100 Sunêlia Au Soleil d'Oc

Monceaux-sur-Dordogne, F-19400 Argentat (Corrèze)

Tel: **05 55 28 84 84**. Email: **info@dordogne-soleil.com**

You will be assured of a very warm welcome, throughout the long season, at this attractive family run site set amongst a variety of tall trees on the banks of the river Dordogne. The 120 large, level, grass pitches, 80 for tourists, all with 6A electricity, are mostly separated by neatly trimmed shrubs and hedges. They are set out on two levels; the lower level nearer the river, with fewer static pitches, being some distance from the toilet facilities and sports area. The shop, bar, restaurant and swimming pools are near the entrance and just across the little road is the large sports area. This site should appeal to lovers of water and other sports, particularly in July and August when there are many activities for all the family. This region is famous for its prehistoric caves, castles and ancient villages and their markets.

Facilities

Two unisex toilet blocks offer all the facilities one would expect. Baby facilities. Shop. Bar. Restaurant and takeaway (1/6-30/9). Outdoor pool (1/5-15/10). New indoor pool planned. Motorcaravan service point. Bathing in the river Dordogne. Canoe hire and organised trips. Volleyball, football, table tennis, pool table and electronic games. Archery. Minigolf. Fishing. Bicycle hire. Guided walks and bike rides. Entertainment programme (July/Aug). WiFi. Off site: River Dordogne. Argentat 4 km. Riding 15 km.

Open: 20 March - 16 November.

Directions

Leave Argentat on D12 heading southwest (Beaulieu). In 3.5 km. (village of Laygue) turn left across a single track bridge spanning the river Dordogne. Immediately turn left and site is a few hundred metres on left.
GPS: N45:04.514 E01:55.025

Charges 2008

Per unit incl. 2 persons	€ 14,50 - € 20,70
extra person	€ 3,80 - € 5,80
child (2-13 yrs)	free - € 3,90
dog	free - € 3,00

Camping Cheques accepted.

FR19080 Camping le Vianon

F-19160 Palisse (Corrèze)

Tel: **05 55 95 87 22**. Email: **camping.vianon@wanadoo.fr**

You will receive a very warm welcome from the Dutch owners of this spacious and peaceful site and they speak excellent English. The site is tucked away in the lesser known, very beautiful Corrèze region yet it is only a few kilometres from the river Dordogne. This region is reputed to have the purest air in France. The grassy, slightly sloping pitches are of a good size in a natural woodland setting with tall trees offering shade and all have 16A electricity. The bar, restaurant and terrace overlook the swimming pool and sunbathing area and are open all season.

Facilities

Modern toilet blocks with all the necessary facilities. Unit for disabled visitors. Bar. Restaurant, takeaway. Shop. Boules. Table tennis. Volleyball. Spacious play area, Bicycle hire. Lake fishing. Off site: Small town Neuvic (9 km.) with shops, restaurants. Large lake with water sports, swimming. Canoeing in the Dordogne (30 minutes). Riding and golf course at Neuvic. Marked walks and cycle rides.

Open: All year (please ring site in October).

Directions

Leave A89 southwest of Ussel and take N89 towards Egletons. In about 7 km, just before Combressol, turn left on D47 signed Palisse and Camping le Vianon. Site entrance is on the left in 7 km.
GPS: N45:25.607 E02:12.350

Charges 2007

Per person	€ 4,75 - € 6,10
child (3-9 yrs)	€ 2,90 - € 3,90
pitch incl. electricity	€ 8,75 - € 11,00
dog	€ 1,50 - € 2,00

FR19140 Camping le Coiroux

Centre Touristique du Coiroux, F-19190 Aubazine (Corrèze)

Tel: 05 55 27 21 96. Email: cplcoiroux@atciat.com

Le Coiroux, part of the Campeole group, is set in a picturesque location in the heart of a forest on the edge of a large leisure park and lake. There are 174 large pitches, 62 for touring all with 10A electricity. They are flat and grassy with small dividing hedges and trees giving shade. The large number of mobile homes and chalets on site are separate from the camping area and not intrusive. There is everything one needs for a family holiday at this site which caters for adults and children of all ages.

Facilities

One large modern very well equipped sanitary block with all necessary facilities including those for campers with disabilities and baby room. Washing machines and tumble dryers. Motorcaravan service point. Large heated swimming pool (16/6-16/9). Poolside bar and snack bar and large shop selling groceries, fruit and vegetables (14/6-14/9). Boules, tennis and table tennis. Organised activities for children, teenagers and adults throughout the day (July/Aug). Off site: Leisure park (reduced fees charged). Excellent 27-hole golf complex 800 m. Lake fishing 300 m. Tree walking adventure course. Paintball. Rocamadour and many other tourist destinations are within 1 hours drive.

Open: 5 April - 28 September.

Directions

Leave A20 exit 50 Brive centre, take N28 towards Tulle. At the village of Gare d'Aubazine turn right to Aubazine. Continue for 6 km, through village, take road to Chastang and follow signs to Parc Touristique du Coiroux about 4 km.
GPS: N45:11.163 E01:42.462

Charges 2007

Per unit incl. 2 persons	€ 13,00 - € 19,80
extra person	€ 4,00 - € 6,40
child (2-5 yrs)	€ 3,40 - € 4,10
electricity	€ 4,00

Le Coiroux ★★★
www.camping-coiroux.com

Mobile Home rental, bungalow and pitches rental.

Campéole

CAMPINGS ET LOCATIONS

Nearby the Dordogne valley
Parc Touristique du Coiroux
19190 Aubazine
Phone : 00 33 5 55 27 21 96
Fax : 00 33 5 55 27 19 16
Mail : cplcoiroux@atciat.com
Entertainment for
the whole family.

Open from 29/03 to 29/09/2008

Heated swimmingpool from 17/05 to 28/09/2008

FR23030 Creuse Naturisme

Route de Bétête - D15, F-23600 Boussac (Creuse)

Tel: 05 55 65 18 01. Email: creuse.nature@wanadoo.fr

This is a very spacious and well maintained naturist site set in the beautiful Limousin region in the centre of France. The 100 large grassy pitches, some slightly sloping, are laid out in an open wooded parkland setting. The 80 touring pitches all have electricity (10A) and are mainly positioned around the perimeter of the site or the small fishing lake. A central feature is the swimming pool, bar and restaurant complex. Various activities are organised for all the family and there are many footpaths to enjoy around the borders of the site.

Facilities

Four modern, very clean toilet blocks with the usual facilities (open-plan, so little privacy). Facilities for disabled visitors. Dishwashing and laundry facilities. Small shop (baker calls). Indoor (heated) and outdoor pools. Paddling pool. Sauna. Bar (all season). Restaurant (July/Aug). Archery (high season). Volleyball. Boules. Bicycle hire. Lake fishing. Internet access. Gas barbecues only on pitches. Off site: Small market town of Boussac 5 km. Other towns, villages and châteaux.

Open: 1 April - 31 October.

Directions

Boussac lies 35 km. west of Montluçon, midway between the A20 and A71 autoroutes. In Boussac, site is well signed. Take D15 west for about 3 km. Site is on right.

Charges 2007

Per person	€ 3,50 - € 6,00
child (under 3 yrs)	free - € 2,00
child (3-12 yrs)	€ 2,50 - € 3,50
pitch	€ 9,00 - € 11,00
electricity (10A)	€ 3,50

Check real time availability and at-the-gate prices...
www.alanrogers.com

FR23010 Castel Camping le Château de Poinsouze

Mobile homes ▶ page 503

Route de la Châtre, B.P. 12, F-23600 Boussac-Bourg (Creuse)

Tel: 05 55 65 02 21. Email: **info.camping-de-poinsouze@wanadoo.fr**

Le Château de Poinsouze is a well established site with pitches arranged on the open, gently sloping, grassy park to one side of the Château's main drive – a beautiful plane tree avenue. It is a well designed, high quality site. The 145 touring pitches, some with lake frontage, all have electricity (6-25A), water, drain and 66 have sewage connections. The site has a friendly family atmosphere, there are organised activities in main season including dances, children's games and crafts, family triathlons and there are marked walks around the park and woods. All facilities are open all season. This is a top class site with a formula which should ensure a stress-free, enjoyable family holiday. Boussac (2.5 km.) has a market every Thursday. The massive 12/15th century fortress, Château de Boussac, is open daily all year. The Château (not open to the public) lies across the lake from the site. Exceptionally well restored outbuildings on the opposite side of the drive house a new restaurant serving superb cuisine, other facilities and the pool area.

Facilities

High quality, sanitary unit, washing machines, dryer, ironing, suites for disabled people. Motorcaravan services. Well stocked shop. Takeaway. Bar, internet, two satellite TVs, library. Restaurant with new mini-bar for low season. Heated swimming pool, slide, children's pool. Fenced playground. Table tennis, petanque, pool table, table football. Bicycle hire. Free fishing in the lake, boats and lifejackets can be hired. Football, volleyball, basketball, badminton and other games. No dogs (7/7-21/8).

Open: 10 May - 14 September.

Directions

Site entrance is 2.5 km. north of Boussac on D917 (towards La Châtre). GPS: N46:22.356 E02:12.157

Charges 2007

Per unit incl. 2 persons with electricity (6A), water, waste water	€ 13,00 - € 22,00
with electricity (10A), water, waste water, sewage connection	€ 19,00 - € 28,00
	€ 24,00 - € 29,00
extra person	€ 3,00 - € 6,00

Camping Cheques accepted.

Centre of France
Château de Poinsouze
★★★★

Family Campsite. Calm & Nature. Exceptional fully enclosed sanitary facilities.
Heated swimming pool. Animation 4-12 years, Chalets & mobil-homes for hire. Gites all year long.
Route de la Châtre 23600 Boussac-Bourg - Tel: 0033 555 65 02 21 - Fax: 0033 555 65 86 49
info.camping-de-poinsouze@orange.fr / www.camping-de-poinsouze.com

FR43030 Kawan Village de Vaubarlet

Vaubarlet, F-43600 Sainte-Sigolène (Haute-Loire)

Tel: 04 71 66 64 95. Email: camping@vaubarlet.com

This peacefully located, spacious riverside family site has 131 marked, level, grassy, open pitches, with those around the perimeter having shade, all having electricity (6A). With 102 pitches for tourists, the remainder are occupied by site owned tents or mobile homes. Those who really like to get away from it all can use a small 'wild camping' area on the opposite side of the river with its own very basic facilities. This area is reached either by footbridge or a separate road access. The main site is separated from the river (unfenced) by a large field used for sports activities.

Facilities

Good, clean toilet blocks, baby room, washing machine, dryer. Two family bathrooms are also suitable for disabled people. WiFi. Small shop, bread. Takeaway. Bar. Attractive swimming pool, children's pool. Bicycle hire. Boules, volleyball and large games area. New childrens playground. Activities in season include camp fire, music evenings, children's canoe lessons. Trout fishing. Birdwatching, walking. Off site: Shops in Ste-Sigolène 6 km. Riding 15 km. Walks and cycle tracks from site.

Open: 1 May - 30 September.

Directions

Site is 6 km. southwest of Ste-Sigolène on the D43 signed Grazac. Keep left by river bridge, site signed. Site shortly on right.
GPS: N45:12.936 E04:12.766

Charges 2008

Per unit incl. 2 persons	€ 18,00
extra person	€ 4,00
child (2-7 yrs)	€ 2,00
electricity	€ 3,00

Camping Cheques accepted.

FR87020 Castel Camping le Château de Leychoisier

Domaine de Leychoisier, 1 route de Leychoisier, F-87270 Bonnac-la-Côte (Haute-Vienne)

Tel: 05 55 39 93 43. Email: contact@leychoisier.com

You will receive a warm welcome at this beautiful, family run 15th century château site. It offers peace and quiet in superb surroundings. It is ideally situated for short or long stays being only 2 km. from the A20/N20 and 10 km. north of Limoges. The large, slightly sloping and grassy pitches are in a parkland setting with many magnificent mature trees offering a fair amount of shade. Of the 90 pitches, 85 are for touring, 80 have 10A electricity and many have a tap, although long leads and hoses may be necessary. Explore the grounds and walk down to the four hectare lake. The lake provides free fishing, boating, canoeing and a marked off area for swimming.

Facilities

The toilet block is very clean, but perhaps cramped at busy times. Some washbasins in cabins with good provision for disabled visitors. Washing machine. Basic food provisions. Restaurant (from 10/5). Bar, TV room and snack bar. Small swimming pool with sunbathing area (proper trunks, no shorts). Lake. Play area. Bicycle hire. Tennis and boules courts (in need of repair when we visited), volleyball and bar billiards. Torch useful. Off site: Shop 2 km. Supermarket 5 km. Riding 7 km. Golf 20 km.

Open: 15 April - 20 September.

Directions

From A20, north of Limoges, take exit 27 (west) signed Bonnac-La-Côte. In village turn left and follow signs to site. GPS: N45:55.958 E01:17.404

Charges 2008

Per person	€ 6,00 - € 7,00
child (under 7 yrs)	€ 4,00 - € 5,00
pitch	€ 9,00
electricity	€ 5,00
dog	€ 1,00

No credit cards.

Château de Leychoisier
Camping & caravaning ★ ★ ★ ★

1 Route de Leychoisier
F-87270 Bonnac-la-Côte
Tél./fax: +33 (0)55 53 99 343
E-mail: contact@leychoisier.com
www.leychoisier.com

LES CASTELS ★★★★

FR87030 Camping de Beaufort

F-87400 Saint Léonard-de-Noblat (Haute-Vienne)

Tel: 05 55 56 02 79. Email: **info@campingdebeaufort.com**

Camping de Beaufort is a riverside site located around 20 km. east of Limoges. This site has been recommended by our French agent and we hope to undertake a full inspection in 2008. There are 86 large grassy pitches (all with electricity 15A) and a further 12 pitches occupied by mobile homes and chalets. A number of activities are possible on the River Vienne including canoeing and fishing. The site has a small bar and shop, with a good selection of other shops and restaurants in nearby St Léonard de Noblat, 1.5 km. distant and accessible by a footpath. St Léonard is an interesting market town, perched above the River Vienne, with two or three museums and an 11th century church. Further afield, the Haute Vallee de la Vienne and le Plateau des Millevaches both offer some excellent opportunites for walking and cycling.

Facilities

Small shop. Bar. Play area. Paddling pool. Games room. TV room. Motorcaravan services. Entertainment and activities in peak season. Off site: St Léonard de Noblat 1.5 km. Fishing. Riding. Golf. Walking and cycle trails. Limoges 20 km.

Open: 7 April - 30 September.

Directions

Take the N141 from Limoges as far as St Léonard de Noblat. Then take the southbound D39 until you reach the campsite.

Charges 2007

Per unit incl. 2 persons	€ 10,00 - € 13,00
extra person	€ 2,50 - € 3,00
child (under 7 yrs)	€ 2,00 - € 2,20
electricity (15A)	€ 3,00 - € 4,00

Camping de Beaufort * * *

Beaufort 87400 St Léonard de Noblat Tél : 05.55.56.02.79
www.campingdebeaufort.com

FR48000 Camping Caravaning le Champ d'Ayres

Route de la Brèze, F-48150 Meyrueis (Lozère)

Tel: 04 66 45 60 51. Email: **campinglechampdayres@wanadoo.fr**

This is a traditional family run site, set in the heart of the Cevennes Champ d'Ayres. Neat, tidy and well kept, it is run with young families in mind (teenagers might be bored). The site is slightly sloping with 85 grass pitches, 68 for touring, the majority hedged with well trimmed bushes and most with some shade. All have electricity (6/10A) but some may require long leads. The area is surrounded by mountains and gorges and some of the roads are not for the faint-hearted or those with large and under-powered units.

Facilities

The excellent toilet block is kept very clean and has all the necessary facilities. Baby room. Facilities for disabled visitors. Laundry and dishwashing facilities. Small bar (15/5-15/9). Shop (15/5-15/9). Takeaway (20/5-15/9). New swimming and paddling pool (20/5-15/9). Play area. Games room. Table tennis, basketball and boules. In July/Aug activities are arranged. Off site: The small, pretty town of Meyrueis (500 m.) has many good shops and restaurants. Fishing 100 m. Bicycle hire 500 m. Riding 3 km.

Open: 12 April - 21 September.

Directions

From N9 at Aquessac (5 km. north of Millau) take D907 (Gorge du Tarn). At Rozier turn right on D996 (Meyrueis and Gorges de la Jonte). In Meyrueis follow signs for Château d'Ayres and site signs. Site is 500 m. east of town. GPS: N44:10.860 E03:26.135

Charges 2008

Per unit incl. 2 persons	€ 12,00 - € 20,00
extra person	€ 2,50 - € 4,00
child (under 7 yrs)	€ 1,60 - € 2,50
electricity (6A)	€ 3,00

FR48020 Kawan Village de Capelan

F-48150 Meyrueis (Lozère)

Tel: **04 66 45 60 50**. Email: **camping.le.capelan@wanadoo.fr**

The Lozère is one of France's least populated regions but offers some truly spectacular, rugged scenery, wonderful flora and fauna and old towns and villages. Le Capelan has 119 grassy pitches in total, 79 are for touring and are strung out alongside the river, most with some shade and all with electrical connections. Around 40 pitches are used for mobile homes. There is river access from the site and fishing is popular. Although there are facilities, the site is not ideal for disabled visitors.

Facilities

Well maintained toilet blocks, facilities for disabled visitors (but not ideal). Three bathrooms for rent. Small shop. Bar (both from 1/6). Takeaway (from 1/7). Swimming, paddling pools, sunbathing terrace (from 1/6), access via 60 steps. Multi-sports terrain. Satellite TV. Play area. Leisure activities include supervised rock climbing. Fishing. Internet. Communal barbecue area (gas and electric only) Off site: Town centre with shops 1 km. Bicycle hire 1 km. Riding 3 km. Canoeing. Cévennes national park. Caves. Vulture visitor centre.

Open: 5 May - 15 September.

Directions

From Clermont Ferrand on the A75 take exit 44-1 Aguessac-le Rozier towards Meyrueis. The site is 1 km. west of Meyruels on the D996, the road to La Jonte. It is well signed from the centre of the town. GPS: N44:11.150 E03:25.193

Charges 2007

Per unit incl. 2 persons	€ 13,00 - € 19,00
with electricity	€ 16,00 - € 22,00
extra person	€ 3,00 - € 4,10
child (under 7 yrs)	€ 1,80 - € 2,80

Camping Cheques accepted.

FR48040 Camping la Cascade

Salvinsac, F-48150 Meyrueis (Lozère)

Tel: **04 66 45 45 45**. Email: **contact@camping-la-cascade.com**

A delightful small site run by a friendly family, La Cascade is located in the Lozère, one of France's least populated regions. There is some truly spectacular, rugged scenery, wonderful flora and fauna and old towns and villages. This site has only 50 good sized, grassy pitches, separated by trees giving varying amounts of shade. There are 37 for touring and 24 with 10A elecricity. It is not recommended for large outfits due to the narrow access road. This is an ideal site for unwinding and exploring this wonderful region on foot, on bike or by car.

Facilities

Two small toilet blocks with good facilities including baby bath. Washing machine. Bread to order, cold drinks and local specialities. Family room. Play area. Trout fishing. Communal barbecue. Bicycle hire. Guided walks. Off site: Meyrueis, shops, bars, restaurant, banks 3 km. Riding 3 km. Canoeing. Cévennes National Park. Caves. Vulture visitor centre.

Open: 1 April - 30 September.

Directions

From Clermont Ferrand on the A75 take exit 44-1, Aguessac-le Rozier, towards Meyrueis. Pass though Meyruels on to the D996 (signed Florac). In 3 km turn right down ramp onto narrow road to site. GPS: N44:11.800 E03:27.383

Charges 2007

Per unit incl 2 persons	€ 9,72 - € 13,50
extra person	€ 2,56 - € 3,55
electricity (10A)	€ 3,20 - € 3,31

FR48060 Camping les Terrasses du Lac de Naussac

Lac de Naussac, F-48300 Langogne (Lozère)

Tel: **04 66 69 29 62**. Email: **info@naussac.com**

With friendly, family owners, this very spacious campsite and hotel complex is on the side of a steep hill at nearly 1,000 m. altitude (nights can be cold). There are 180 good size, grassy, sloping pitches, often with part hardstanding (165 for touring). All have 6/10A electricity and many have panoramic views over the lake and surrounding hills. There are small trees on site offering a little shade. The lake offers a wide range of water based activities, notably sailing and fishing.

Facilities

Three modern, well maintained, newly refurbished toilet blocks. Motorcaravan service point. Small shop (1/5-30/9). Restaurant/takeaway in hotel. Small swimming pool (1/6-30/9). Lively 'animation' programme in peak season including children's club but no discos. Play area. Communal barbecue area. Gas and electric barbecues only. Internet point and WiFi. Off site: Disco 300 m. Many water sports on lake. Cycle ride around lake of 30 km. Langogne (shops, restaurants, Stevenson trail etc.) 2 km. Golf 3 km. Riding and bicycle hire 3 km.

Open: 15 April - 30 September.

Directions

Leave N88 (Le Puy - Mende) just southwest of Langogne. Turn north on D26 towards Lac de Naussac and follow signs to site (2.5 km). Park beside lake and just before hotel. Reception inside hotel. GPS: N44:44.083 E03:50.116

Charges 2007

Per pitch incl. 2 persons	€ 12,50 - € 13,50
extra person	€ 3,50
child (2-6 yrs)	€ 1,50
electricity	€ 2,50

Camping Cheques accepted.

329

FR48070 Camping le Tivoli

F-48000 Mende (Lozère)

Tel: **04 66 65 00 38**. Email: **tivoli.camping@libertysurf.fr**

Le Tivoli is a small family run site, located close to the Lot river on the outskirts of Mende. It has the advantage of being open all year. Of the 100 good sized and level grass pitches, 82 are for touring, all with 6A electricity. They are separated by mature trees which give varying amounts of shade. The site has been developed from farmland and has been owned by the same family for forty years. It offers simple, but adequate, facilities making it ideal for a short stay.

Facilities

Two toilet blocks with adequate facilities including for disabled visitors. Washbasins are open and in cabins and showers are preset. Laundry sinks and washing machine. Motorcaravan Services. Bar (July/Aug). Swimming pool (June-Aug). Play area. Room with table games (July/Aug). Communal barbecue area. Fishing. Off site: Supermarket 500 m. Interesting old town of Mende with shops, bars and restaurants. Riding 3 km. Gorges du Tarn.

Open: All year.

Directions

On entering Mende on N88, from south, turn left at first roundabout. Continue past supermarket to site in 800 m. GPS: N44:30.85 E03:28.45

Charges 2007

Per unit incl. 2 persons and electricity (6A)	€ 14,95
extra person	€ 4,50
child (under 7 yrs)	€ 2,90
dog	€ 1,00

No credit cards.

FR63020 Camping Municipal Saint-Eloy

F-63630 Saint-Germain-l'Herm (Puy-de-Dôme)

Tel: **04 73 72 05 13**. Email: **contact@revea-vacances.com**

This spacious and attractive municipal site is set on two terraces overlooking the nearby village of Saint Germain. There are 63 good sized, slightly sloping, grassy pitches, 53 for touring. Set away from 10 privately owned mobile homes, the touring pitches are separated by some neat conifer hedging and maturing trees offering limited shade. All have water and electricity (6-10A) close by. Barbecues not allowed but there are three communal areas. In July and August a few activities are organised.

Facilities

Two well maintained and clean toilet blocks offering all the necessary facilities plus some further limited facilities next to a large games/TV room. A few snacks are available to order. Good play area. Off site: Village 500 m, with mini-market, restaurant, bank, bicycle hire, riding and tennis. Lake fishing 1 km. Many marked footpaths.

Open: 3 May - 14 September.

Directions

Saint-Germain-l'Herm is 60 km. southeast of Clermont Ferrand. Leave A75 at exit 13 (Issoire) and take D996 east for 3 km. Turn right on D999 signed Saint-Germain-l'Herm for 29 km. From village continue on D999 for just under 1 km. to site on right. GPS: N45:27.412 E03:32.884

Charges 2008

Per person	€ 2,50 - € 3,00
child (2-7 yrs)	free - € 1,70
pitch	€ 8,50 - € 11,10
electricity (8A)	€ 3,00

No credit cards.

FR63000 Les Chalets du Hameau du Lac

Parcs Residentiels ▶ page 516

Lieu dit le Pré Bad, Le Lac Chambon, F-63790 Chambon sur Lac (Puy-de-Dôme)

Pitches at this campsite are exclusively for chalet accommodation.

Check real time availability and at-the-gate prices...

www.**alanrogers**.com

FR63050 Sunêlia la Ribeyre

Jassat, F-63790 Murol (Puy-de-Dôme)

Tel: **04 73 88 64 29**. Email: **laribeyre@free.fr**

The friendly Pommier family have put much personal care into the construction of this site. There are 400 level, grassy pitches, of which 310 are for tourers and 200 of these have electricity (6/10A). Electricity, water and drainage is available for 51 pitches. A superb large indoor/outdoor water park includes slides, toboggan and lazy river and a small man-made lake at one end provides facilities for water sports. It is a great base for touring being only 1 km. from Murol, dominated by its ancient Château, 6 km. from St Nectaire and about 20 km. from le Mont Dore and Puy de Sancy, the highest peak in the area. There is a picturesque reception area with a fountain and prize-winning floral decorations. Many young trees have been planted to add to those already established and there are fantastic views over the wooded mountains. The surrounding area has some superb scenery, from mountains rising to over 6,000 ft, to steep valleys, lakes and caverns. This site is a wonderful area for walking and cycling.

Facilities

Six excellent, very clean modern toilet blocks with facilities for disabled persons. Washing machines, dryers. Snack bar in peak season (1/6-31/8). Large indoor/outdoor water park (heated). TV, games room. Tennis, volleyball, fishing. Lake swimming and canoeing. Many organised activities in high season. Off site: Riding 300 m. Shops and restaurants and a large Wednesday market (high season) in Murol 1.5 km. Bicycle hire 1 km. Fishing and watersports at Lac Chambon 3 km.

Open: 1 May - 15 September.

Directions

From A75 Autoroute, exit 6 signed St Nectaire. Continue to Murol, D978 then D996, several sites signed in town. Turn left up hill, D5, shortly turn right opposite car park, D618, site signed. Site is second on left. GPS: N45:33.770 E02:56.377

Charges 2008

Per unit incl. 2 persons and electricity	€ 18,25 - € 30,40
extra person	€ 3,70 - € 5,50
child (under 1-5 yrs)	€ 3,65 - € 4,95

Camping Cheques accepted.

SUNÊLIA LA RIBEYRE

Covered heated swimming-pool complex with 4 slides, river splash and indoor pool

To Rent on-site: 70 Mobile Homes, 10 Chalets.

460 pitches with 64 Grand Confort on 11 ha.

JASSAT 63790 MUROL - Tel: 0033 473 88 64 29 - Fax: 0033 473 88 68 41
Mail: laribeyre@free.fr - www.camping-laribeyre.com

FR63030 Camping Caravaning de l'Europe

Route de Jassat, F-63790 Murol (Puy-de-Dôme)

Tel: **04 73 39 76 66**. Email: **europe.camping@wanadoo.fr**

L'Europe is, in high season, a lively site, dominated by its mobile homes, on the edge of the little town of Murol. The site is 800 m. from the Lac de Chambon which boasts a sandy beach and range of water sports. There are 219 level grassy pitches, 59 for touring, of good size and offer reasonable shade. It has a busy animation programme including evening entertainment. The bar/restaurant overlooks the pool complex and is the site's focal point and entertainment centre. The surrounding area offers many walking and cycling opportunites, and the site organises a number of popular excursions.

Facilities

Sanitary facilities include washbasins in cabins and showers and provision for disabled visitors. Laundry facilities. Bar, restaurant and takeaway (30/6-31/8). Swimming pool and paddling pool. Tennis. Archery. Football. Aquagym. Water polo. Play area and sports area. Internet access and WiFi. Off site: Fishing and bicycle hire 300 m. Riding 5 km. Golf 20 km. Murol 1.5 km. Lac Chambon 2 km. St Nectaire 6 km. Le Mont Dore 20 km.

Open: 31 May - 31 August.

Directions

Site is approx. 40 km. south west of Clermont Ferrand. Leave A75 autoroute at exit 6 (St Nectaire). Take D978 to Murol (34 km). At far end of village turn left onto D5. In 300 m. turn right onto D618 (Jassat). Site on left in 300 m.

Charges 2007

Per unit incl. 1 person	€ 7,00 - € 16,00
extra person (over 5 yrs)	€ 2,30 - € 5,30
electricity	€ 4,70 - € 5,50

Check real time availability and at-the-gate prices...

www.**alanrogers**.com

FR63040 Château Camping la Grange Fort

Les Pradeaux, F-63500 Issoire (Puy-de-Dôme)

Tel: **04 73 71 02 43**. Email: **chateau@lagrangefort.com**

This site has good, modern facilities, yet is oozing with character. It is very popular with the Dutch. The new reception is well stocked with tourist information and an internet access point. The cosy bar still has the old stable stalls and hay racks. The 120 pitches (90 for touring units) are of average size, mostly on grass but with some crushed stone hardstandings, and they are connected by rather narrow roads with limited play space for children. Some of the smaller pitches are in sunny fields around the castle, others in bays with hedges and trees. All have 6A electricity.

Facilities

Refurbished sanitary blocks have facilities for disabled visitors and a 'hydra shower'. Laundry room. Bread. Restaurant (1/5-15/9), bar (15/6-15/9), takeaway (1/5-15/9). Small indoor pool, sauna, massage table (15/4-15/10). Two outdoor pools (15/6-1/10), grass sunbathing areas. Play area, games room. Internet. Tennis. Organised activities in season. Torches useful. Off site: Fishing 250 m. Riding 8 km.

Open: 10 April - 15 October.

Directions

From A75 autoroute take exit 13 onto D996 east towards Parentignat. At first roundabout take first exit on D999 new road (St Remy, La Vernet). At next roundabout take first exit (D34) and follow campsite signs.

Charges 2007

Per person	€ 4,50 - € 5,95
child (under 7 yrs)	€ 3,50 - € 3,70
pitch with electricity	€ 12,45 - € 15,65

FR63060 Camping le Clos Auroy

Rue de la Narse, F-63670 Orcet (Puy-de-Dôme)

Tel: **04 73 84 26 97**. Email: **info@campingclub.info**

A friendly welcome guaranteed at Le Clos Auroy. It is a very well maintained and popular site, 300 m. from Orcet, a typical Auvergne village just south of Clermont Ferrand. Being close (3 km) to the A75, and open all year, it makes an excellent stopping off point on the journey north and south but you may be tempted to stay longer. The 90 good size pitches are on level grass, separated by very high, neatly trimmed conifer hedges, offering lots of privacy but not much shade. All have electricity (5/10A) and 25 are fully serviced. In winter only 20 pitches are available. Access is easy for large units.

Facilities

High quality, very clean toilet blocks. Washing facilities. Motorcaravan services. Small shop, takeaway (1/7-15/9). Heated pool, jacuzzi, large pool for children (15/5-30/9), terrace near bar (15/5-30/9). Playground. Coffee mornings. Tennis. Children's activities. Off site: Large playground nearby and riverside walk just outside. Village shops and three wine 'caves' 300 m. Fishing and canoeing 500 m. .

Open: All year.

Directions

From A75 take exit 4 or 5 towards Orcet and follow campsite signs. It is just before the village. GPS: N45:42.030 E03:10.154

Charges 2008

Per unit incl. 2 persons	€ 14,50
extra person	€ 4,50
child (1-7 yrs)	€ 3,05
electricity (5/10A)	€ 3,25 - € 4,75
No credit cards.	

FR63070 Camping le Pré Bas

Lac Chambon, F-63790 Murol (Puy-de-Dôme)

Tel: **04 73 88 63 04**. Email: **prebas@campingauvergne.com**

Le Pré Bas is especially suitable for families and those seeking the watersports opportunities that the lake provides. Level, grassy pitches are divided up by mature hedging and trees and, with 63 mobile homes for rent, around 120 pitches are available for tourists, all with electricity (6A). A gate leads to the lakeside, where in high season there is windsurfing, pedaloes, canoes and fishing, and 50 m. away is a beach with supervised bathing and a snack bar. The site has a new pool complex with heated swimming pools (one covered), a large slide and a paddling pool.

Facilities

Refurbished toilet building with facilities for disabled guests plus four smaller units. Laundry facilities, baby room. Motorcaravan services. Snack bar (10/6-10/9 and some weekends in low season). Three pools of different depths (20/5-10/9, lifeguard in July/Aug). Watersports, fishing in lake. Games room, table tennis, table football, pool, TV, library. Adventure style playground, football, basketball. Organised activities. Off site: Lakeside bars, restaurants, shops. Murol 4 km.

Open: 1 May - 30 September.

Directions

Leave A75 autoroute at exit 6 and take D978 signed St Nectaire and Murol, then D996. Site is located on left, 3 km, west of Murol towards Mont Dore, at the far end of Lac Chambon. GPS: N45:34.513 E02:54.854

Charges 2007

Per pitch incl. 2 persons	€ 9,40 - € 15,10
extra person	€ 4,00 - € 5,40
child (5-10 yrs)	€ 2,60 - € 5,40
electricity (6A)	€ 4,20 - € 4,50

FR63080 Camping le Moulin de Serre

D73 vallée de la Burande, F-63690 Singles (Puy-de-Dôme)

Tel: **04 73 21 16 06**. Email: **moulin-de-serre@wanadoo.fr**

Off the beaten track, this spacious and well maintained site is set in a wooded valley beside a river where one can pan for gold. It offers a good base for those seeking quiet relaxation in this lesser known area of the Auvergne. The 90 large pitches (55 for touring) are separated by a variety of trees and hedges giving good shade. Some pitches have hardstanding and all have electricity (3-10A), long leads may be necessary. Access around the site is easy but the narrow lanes leading to it are twisting which might prove difficult for larger units.

Facilities

Well appointed. clean toilet blocks, one heated having excellent facilities for disabled people and babies. New communal BBQ's. Heated swimming pool, terrace (8/6-28/9). Takeaway (July/August), bar/restaurant (July/Aug). Bread ((19/5-16/9). Washing machine, dryer. Motorcaravan services. Large play area. Tennis. Canoe hire in high season. Organised activities (July/Aug). Off site: Lake for fishing 2 km. Château de Val 20 km. Spa town of La Bourboule 25 km. Barrage de Bort les Orgues offers watersports. Many marked walks and cycle tracks. Riding.

Open: 12 April - 14 September.

Directions

Site is about 25 km. southwest of La Bourboule. Turn west off the D922 just south of Tauves at site sign. Follow site signs along the D29 and then the D73 for about 10 km.

Charges 2007

Per unit incl. 2 persons	€ 9,95 - € 16,60
extra adult	€ 2,90 - € 4,10
child (under 10 yrs)	€ 1,95 - € 2,85
electricity (3-10A)	€ 3,00 - € 4,60

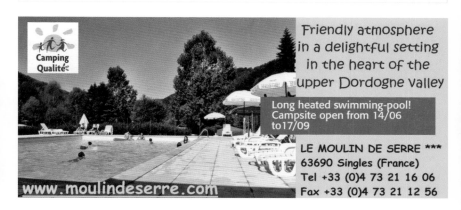

FR63090 Camping les Domes

Les Quatre Routes de Nébouzat, F-63210 Nébouzat (Puy-de-Dôme)

Tel: **04 73 87 14 06**. Email: **camping.les-domes@wanadoo.fr**

A popular site, it is ideally situated for exploring the beautiful region around the Puy de Dôme. The site has 65 small to medium sized pitches, most for touring, 50 with 10/15A electricity, separated by trees and hedges. Some pitches have a level, paved area ideal for caravans and motorcaravans. Rock pegs are advised. The attractive reception area comprising the office, a small shop for essentials (high season only) and a meeting room has lots of local information and interesting artefacts. An added small attraction is a heated, covered swimming pool, which can be opened in good weather.

Facilities

Well appointed, clean toilet block, no special facilities for disabled visitors. Basic shop (baker calls). Breakfast, snacks. Boules, pool table, table football, table tennis, giant chess, drafts. Small play area. TV and games room. Off site: Fishing 100 m. Restaurant 200 m. Nebouzat 1.3 km. (shops etc). Riding 6 km. Hang-gliding and parascending 8 km. (Puy de Dôme). New Vulcania exhibition 15 minutes drive. Watersports 9 km. Golf 10 km. Clermond Ferrand with its interesting old town and hypermarkets (18 km). Many marked walks and cycle routes.

Open: 1 May - 15 September.

Directions

Site is 18 km. southwest of Clermont Ferrand and is well signed from the roundabout at the junction of the D2089 and the D941A. It is a few hundred metres from the roundabout along the D216 towards Orcival. GPS: N45:43.537 E02:53.403

Charges 2008

Per unit incl. 2 persons	€ 9,50
extra person	€ 6,00
child (under 5 yrs)	€ 3,00
electricity (10A)	€ 5,00
No Credit Cards.	

FR63130 Camping le Repos du Baladin

Groire, F-63790 Murol (Puy-de-Dôme)

Tel: **04 73 88 61 93**. Email: **reposbaladin@free.fr**

Recommended by a reader, this is a lovely small and friendly campsite that offers an alternative to the larger sites in this area. The owners are aiming for a quiet, relaxing site, attracting nature lovers who want to spend time walking, cycling or touring in this beautiful region rather than creating a holiday park with everything on site. Attractively and well laid out, there are 62 good sized pitches, 49 for touring (5A electricity), and many with good privacy. They are separated by neat conifer hedges with mature trees offer varying amounts of shade. Murol with its ancient castle is 1.5 km.

Facilities

One excellent, very clean and central toilet block provides all the necessary facilities. TV/games room in same block. Small shop (15/6-15/9). Bar with TV (1/6-15/9). Restaurant with snacks and takeaway (1/6-15/9). Heated swimming pool and sunbathing area (1/6-15/9). Large play area. Boules. Off site: Murol 1.5 km. Fishing, bicycle hire and boat launching at Lac Chambon, 2 km.

Open: 1 May - 15 September.

Directions

Site is 40 km. southwest of Clermont Ferrand. Leave A75 at exit 6 (St Nectaire) and take D978 beyond St Nectaire to Murol (34 km). At far end of the village turn left up hill on D5. In 800 m. turn right on D146, signed Groire and site. Entrance on right in 900 m. GPS: N45:34.437 E02:59.449

Charges 2007

Per unit incl. 2 persons	€ 12,20 - € 16,90
extra person	€ 3,20 - € 3,90
electricity (5A)	€ 4,00

FR63140 Camping les Loges

F-63340 Nonette (Puy-de-Dôme)

Tel: **04 73 71 65 82**. Email: **les.loges.nonette@wanadoo.fr**

A pleasant, spacious, rural site bordering the River Allier and close to the A75 Autoroute. There are 126 good sized, level, grassy pitches offering plenty of shade, 100 for touring and all with 6A electricity. A site to suit those seeking a quieter holiday without too many organised activities. The river is good for bathing and canoeing and there are many walks and bike rides in the area. It is also well placed to explore the beautiful Auvergne countryside.

Facilities

Modern toilet blocks contain all the usual facilities. Small shop (July/Aug). Bar, restaurant, takeaway (mid June-mid September). TV room. Heated swimming pool with toboggan, paddling pool (June-Sept). Sauna, spa room (July/Aug). Volleyball. Table tennis. Play areas, play room. River fishing, bathing. Sunday evening dances in high season. Canoe trips. Off site: Walking and cycling routes. Riding 5 km. Small village of Nonette 3 km. Saint Germain 5 km. Issoire 13 km. Parc des Volcans,

Open: Easter - 13 October.

Directions

From A75 exit 17 (south of Issoire), turn left (D214) signed Le Breuil. Bypass Le Breuil, turn left (D123) signed Nonette. Cross river, turn left then immediately very sharp left just after roundabout, take care (site signed). Entrance is 1 km.

Charges 2007

Per unit incl. 2 persons	€ 12,00 - € 16,20
extra person	€ 3,60 - € 4,60
child (2-7 yrs)	€ 2,40 - € 3,20
electricity (6A)	€ 3,50

FR63160 Camping Bel-Air

F-63230 Saint Ours (Puy-de-Dôme)

Tel: **04 73 88 72 14**. Email: **camping.belair@free.fr**

This is an attractive, family run site. In traditional style, but with modern facilities, it has a rural location lying within the Parc des Volcans. There are 60 level grass pitches, 25 with 6/10A electricity, including three with hardstanding for larger motorcaravans and three chalets. The pitches are spaced around a wooded clearing, most with varying degrees of shade. This site is ideal for those seeking a peaceful holiday in a wonderful area yearning for exploration – there are no organised activities here. Its position only 6 km. from the A89 autoroute makes it ideal for both short and long stays. Double axle caravans are not accepted.

Facilities

Modern well equipped toilet block with baby room and facilities for disabled visitors. Washing machine and dryer. Motorcaravan service point. Small shop (bread to order). Minigolf and boules. Gas and electric barbecues only (communal barbecue provided). Play area. WiFi in reception. Off site: Pontgibaud with shops, restaurants 3 km. Puy de Dôme 18 km. Excellent area for touring on foot, bike or by car.

Open: 1 May - 30 September.

Directions

Leave A89 west of Clermont Ferrand at exit 26. Take D941 bypassing Pontgibaud. At roundabout turn left, D941 St Ours. Site shortly on left. GPS: N45:50.65 E02:52.60

Charges 2007

Per person	€ 4,50
child (0-10 yrs)	€ 2,60
pitch incl. electricity (6A)	€ 7,20
No credit cards.	

FR63120 Camping Indigo Royat

Route de Gravenoire, F-63130 Royat (Puy-de-Dôme)

Tel: **04 73 35 97 05**. Email: **royat@camping-indigo.com**

This is a spacious and attractive site sitting high on a hillside on the outskirts of Clermont Ferrand, but close to the beautiful Auvergne countryside. It has nearly 200 terraced pitches on part hardstanding. There are 142 available for touring units, all with 6/10A electricity (long leads may be needed). The pitches are informally arranged in groups, with each group widely separated by attractive trees and shrubs. The bar and terrace overlooks the irregularly shaped swimming pool, paddling pool, sunbathing area, tennis courts and play areas. Although very peaceful off season, it could be lively in July and August. This site would be ideal for those who would like a taste of both the town and the countryside.

Facilities

Five well appointed toilet blocks, some heated. They have all the usual amenities but it could be a long walk from some pitches. Small shop. Bar, takeaway. Internet. Attractive swimming pools. Tennis. Boules. Bicycle hire. Two grassy play areas. Organised entertainment in high season. Internet. Off site: Royat 20 minutes walk. Clermont Ferrand, Puy de Dôme, Parc des Volcans.

Open: 6 April - 28 October.

Directions

From A75 exit 2 (Clermont Ferrand) follow signs for Bordeaux (D799). At third roundabout exit left signed Bordeaux. Shortly take exit right then turn right, signed Ceyrat. Leaving Ceyrat, at traffic lights take D941C signed Royat and Puy de Dôme. At top of hill turn left (D5) site signed. Entrance 800 m. GPS: N45:45.526 E03:03.308

Charges 2007

Per person	€ 4,20 - € 5,00
child (2-7 yrs)	€ 2,50 - € 3,20
pitch incl. electricity (6/10A)	€ 9,50 - € 18,20

Camping Cheques accepted.

tel: +33 (0) 4 37 64 22 33 www.camping-indigo.com

CamPING INdigo Royat★★★★

Mobile-homes, tents and chalets to rent

Heated swimming-pool, Bar restaurant, tennis, sporting activities...

Route de Gravenoire - 63130 Royat
Tel : (33) 4 73 35 97 05

At the gateway to the Park of the vulcanoes of Auvergne
At the foot of the Puy de Dôme...

w w w . c a m p i n g - i n d i g o . c o m

FR63180 Camping la Vallée Verte

Route des Granges, F-63710 Saint Nectaire (Puy-de-Dôme)

Tel: **04 73 88 52 68**. Email: **lavalleeverte@libertysurf.fr**

Vallée Verte is a very well tended, peaceful, good value campsite. Set in the heart of the beautiful Parc des Volcans d'Auvergne, it is only a short walk from the small spa town of Saint Nectaire and close to Lac Chambon with its sandy beach and some water sports. There are many other interesting towns and villages waiting to be explored. The site has 90 level grass pitches (5/8A electricity) with 74 for touring units. Separated by wooden rails or a variety of hedging, a mixture of trees gives shade to some of the pitches. Twin axle caravans are not accepted.

Facilities

Excellent new toilet block with all necessary facilities including a superb room for families and campers with disabilities. Motorcaravan services. Shop, bar and restaurant with takeaway (all season). Play areas. Boules. Organised meals and walks in high season. Off site: St Nectaire with shops, bars, restaurants. Casino. Caves. Petrified fountains 500 m. Lac Chambon 6 km. Vulcania Exhibition. Puy de Dôme, Puy de Sancy.

Open: 15 April - 15 September.

Directions

Leave autoroute A75 at exit 6 south of Clermont Ferrand. Take D978 then D996 to St Nectaire. On entering St Nectaire turn left, D642 (site signed). Entrance is a few hundred metres. GPS: N45:34.519 E02:59.972

Charges 2007

Per unit incl. 2 persons	€ 9,00 - € 13,00
extra person	€ 2,50 - € 4,00
electricity (5/8A)	€ 2,70 - € 3,00

Check real time availability and at-the-gate prices...

www.**alanrogers**.com

MAP 13

With such a rich and var
landscape, the Rhône Va
offers a spectacular regio
of craggy gorges and scent
hills, ideal for life at a leisurely
pace - easy to do when there are so
many stunning views to take in.

DÉPARTEMENTS: 01 AIN, 07 ARDÈCHE,
26 DRÔME, 42 LOIRE, 69 RHÔNE

MAJOR CITY: LYON

The region's 2,000 year history as a cultural crossroads has blessed the area with a rich blend of customs, architecture and sights of interest. The city of Lyon was developed by the Romans as a trading centre, and was once the capital. It is now the second largest city of France. The Place de la Terreur in the centre of the city is where the guillotine was placed during the French revolution – until it wore out through over-use. Not far from Lyon lies the Dombes, the land of a thousand lakes, and the medieval village of Pérouges and Roman ruins of Vienne.

The Rhône valley holds areas of great interest and natural beauty. From the sun-baked Drôme, with its ever-changing landscapes and the isolated mountains of the Vercors to the deep gorges and high plateaux of the Ardèche, studded with prehistoric caves and lush valleys filled with orchards; and encompassing the vineyards of the Beaujolais and the Rhône Valley. For the energetic there are cycling, horse riding and even white water rafting opportunities, while for the more leisurely inclined, the remote areas are a haven for bird watching and walking.

Places of interest

Beaujolais: vineyards and golden-stone villages.

Bourg-en-Bresse: church of Notre-Dame, craft shops, museum of Ain.

Dombes: lakes, ornithological park.

Lyon: Gallo-Roman artifacts, Renaissance quarter, historical Fabric Museum, silk museum.

Pérouges: medieval village, Galette de Pérouges.

St Etienne: museum of Modern Art.

Vallon-Pont d'Arc: base from which to visit Gorges de l'Ardèche; canoe and rafting centre.

Vienne: Gothic style cathedral, 6th century church St Pierre.

Cuisine of the region

The poultry, cheese, freshwater fish and mushrooms are superb. Local wines include Beaujolais, Côte Rotie, St Julien, Condrieu, Tain-Hermitage, Chiroubles and Julienas.

Bresse (Poulet, Poularde, Volaille de): the best French poultry, fed on corn and when killed bathed in milk; flesh is white and delicate.

Gras-double: ox tripe, served with onions.

Poulet au vinaigre: chicken, shallots, tomatoes, white wine, wine vinegar and a cream sauce.

Poulet demi-deuil (half-mourning): called this because of thin slices of truffle placed under the chicken breast.

Rosette: a large pork sausage.

Sabodet: Lyonnais sausage of pig's head, pork and beef, served hot.

FR01040 Camping Lac du Lit du Roi

La Tuillière, F-01300 Massignieu-de-Rives (Ain)

Tel: 04 79 42 12 03. Email: acamp@wanadoo.fr

This attractive and well cared for, family run site is ideal for those seeking an active holiday in a peaceful setting. This superb, picturesque area offers wonderful opportunities for exploration by foot, bicycle, car and boat. Take time to sample the wines and other local produce on offer. Of the 120 pitches (electricity 10A), 90 are available for touring, all being close to the lake and many having wonderful views over the lake and the wooded hills beyond. The slightly sloping, grassy pitches are set on low terraces and are partly separated by hedging and a variety of trees give some shade. It has a commanding position beside a beautiful lake which forms part of the River Rhône waterway giving direct access to the much larger Lac du Bourget. In July and August a few social events are organised, suitable for all the family, but this site is best suited for those not requiring a programme of organised activities.

Facilities

Two modern toilet blocks offer all necessary facilities with provision for disabled visitors. Washing machines. Motorcaravan services. Bar, snack bar, terrace. Bread. Small heated swimming pool (all season). Tennis. Volleyball. Table tennis. Play area beside lake. Grassy beach, pedaloes, canoes, surf bikes for hire. Bicycle hire. Lake fishing. Winter caravan storage. Off site: Shops at Belley 8 km. Lac du Bourget (watersports, boat hire). Nature reserve. Cycle tracks and walks (maps available). Marina, boat ramp nearby. Golf 8 km. Riding 15 km.

Open: 14 April - 30 September.

Directions

Site is about 8 km. east of Belley. Turn east off N504 at roundabout (Champion supermarket) on D992 signed Culoz and Seyssel. After 4 km. turn right over bridge, D37 signed Massignieu. Follow signs to campsite (2 km). GPS: N45:46.122 E05:46.92

Charges 2007

Per unit incl. 2 persons	
and electricity	€ 17,00 - € 23,00
extra person	€ 5,00 - € 6,50
child (0-7 yrs)	€ 3,00 - € 5,00
animal	€ 4,00 - € 5,00
Camping Cheques accepted.	

SITUATED AT THE LAKESIDE IN THE SAVOIE

★★★★ CAMPING DU

Lac du Lit du Roi

SHADED PITCHES
MOBILES-HOMES RENTAL,
SWIMMING-POOL...

01300 Massignieu-de-rives - Tél : 33(0)4 79 42 12 03 - Fax : 33(0)4 79 42 19 94
Email : info@camping-savoie.com - www.camping-savoie.com - www.via-camp.com

FR01010 Camping la Plaine Tonique

Base de Plein Air, F-01340 Montrevel-en-Bresse (Ain)

Tel: 04 74 30 80 52. Email: plaine.tonique@wanadoo.fr

This excellent site, ideal for active families, belongs to a syndicate of several local villages. It is a very well maintained, large site with 560 marked and numbered pitches, all with 10A electricity. The majority are of a good size, hedged and on flat grass, with reasonable shade in most parts. The site is very spacious and broken up into sections by trees and hedges. It is on the edge of an attractive, 320 acre lake with its own beach and adjacent public beach.

Facilities

Very clean sanitary facilities are in eleven blocks and include some washbasins in cabins, baby rooms and washing machines. Motorcaravan service point. Restaurant, bar and shop (July/Aug) next to site. 'Aquatonic' centre with five pools (reduced charge for campers, no Bermuda shorts). Watersports and fishing. Minigolf. Tennis. Adventure play area. Games and TV rooms. Archery, bicycle hire and roller skating. Fitness trail. Off site: Montrevel town 300 m. walk. Riding 2 km.

Open: 14 April - 22 September.

Directions

Montrevel is 20 km. north of Bourg-en-Bresse and 25 km. east of Macon. The site is on the D28 500 m. east of town towards Etrez and is well signed. GPS: N46:20.249 E05:08.188

Charges 2007

Per pitch incl. electricity	
and 2 persons	€ 13,70 - € 22,60
extra person	€ 3,20 - € 5,30
child (3-7 yrs)	€ 2,00 - € 3,00

337

FR01100 Camping le Vaugrais

F-01510 Artemare (Ain)

Tel: **04 79 87 37 34**

This unpretentious, quiet site is located near a small village peacefully nestled between low mountains, near the Séran river. In addition to some new mobile homes, there are 60 grass pitches divided by hedges and all with electricity (6A). This area would suit couples or families with young children looking for a quiet site and the opportunity for activities such as walking and cycling. The site is a good starting point for walks in summer and is well located to reach ski slopes in winter

Facilities

One traditional style sanitary block behind the reception with few showers (with hot water) and toilets. Washing machine. Snack bar at reception. Swimming pool should be complete for 2008. Play area. Fishing. Bicycle hire. Off site: Riding, donkey trekking, canyoning, walking. Supermarkets 50 m.

Open: All year.

Directions

From Annecy, take A41 (Genève) to exit 14 towards Aix-les-Bains. Go through Grésy and Aix. Near Viviers-du-Lac, turn onto N211 and N504 for 35 km. Near Pugieu, take D904 towards Virieu-le-Grand and follow then signs to Artemare.

Charges 2007

Per unit incl. 2 persons	
and electricity	€ 12,50 - € 15,50
extra person	€ 2,00

FR01030 Camping les Ripettes

Chavannes-sur-Reyssouze, F-01190 Pont de Vaux (Ain)

Tel: **03 85 30 66 58**. Email: **info@camping-les-ripettes.com**

A friendly welcome is assured from the owners of this spacious site situated in quiet, flat countryside near the pleasant small town of Pont-de-Vaux. The 2.5 hectare site has 54 large (100-400 sq.m.) level grassy pitches, 51 of which are available to tourists. Nearly all are separated by hedges and about half are shaded by the many trees on the site. All but two have electrical connections (10A), and there are ample water points. It is a useful stop on the way to or from the south of France.

Facilities

Two well appointed, small sanitary blocks contain a suite for disabled visitors. Washing machine and dryer. Limited range of food stocked and wine, ice cream, meat for barbecues at reception. Two swimming pools. Small play area, sandpit. Areas for ball games, volleyball, badminton, table tennis, boules. Board games, books. Bicycle hire. WiFi. Communal Sunday barbecues are popular. Off site: Restaurant 1 km. Riding 2 km. Shops, etc., in Pont-de-Vaux 4 km. Fishing 4 km. Golf 15 km.

Open: 1 April - 30 September.

Directions

Leave N6 at Fleurville (14 km. south of Tournus). Go east on D933A to Pont-de-Vaux (5 km) where site is signed. Take D2 east towards St Trivier-de-Courtes. After 3 km. turn left after water tower, left again at next junction (100 m). Site is 300 m. GPS: N46:26.620 E04:58.841

Charges 2007

Per person	€ 3,50
pitch incl. car	€ 2,50 - € 6,50
electricity (10A)	€ 2,50

FR01050 Camping des Gorges de l'Oignin

Rue du Lac, F-01580 Matafelon-Granges (Ain)

Tel: **04 74 76 80 97**. Email: **camping.lesgorgesdeloignin@wanadoo.fr**

This family run, terraced site (English spoken) offers lovely views across the lake to the hills beyond. There are 132 good sized pitches, 70 for touring, separated by young trees and flowering shrubs and with a choice of grass or hardstanding. About half have their own water point and all have 10A electricity. Twin axle caravans are not accepted. The reception, bar/restaurant and the pool complex are at the top of the site with a steep road down to the terraces and the rest of the campsite. At the bottom of the site is a large grassy area next to the lake.

Facilities

Two modern, well equipped and clean toilet blocks with all the usual facilities excepting facilities for disabled people. Bar/restaurant, takeaway and TV room (July/Aug). Swimming pool, paddling pool and new Lazy River (1/6-30/9). Playground and sports area. Swimming, fishing and boating on lake (no motorboats). Off site: Golf 2 km. Riding 2 km. Matafelon 800 m. Thoirette 6 km. Oyonnax with range of shops, market, bar/restaurants 10 km.

Open: 1 April - 30 September.

Directions

Matafelon is 40 km. east of Bourg-en-Bresse. Leave autoroute A404 at Oyonnax, exit 11 and head west on D13 to Matafelon (10 km). On entering village and opposite the Mairie turn left, signed camping, and descend to site (800 m).

Charges 2007

Per unit incl. 2 persons	
and electricity	€ 14,50 - € 20,20
extra person	€ 3,00 - € 4,60
child (3-10 yrs)	€ 2,00 - € 3,20
dog	€ 1,00 - € 2,00

FR01080 Camping Etang du Moulin

F-01240 Saint Paul de Varax (Ain)

Tel: 04 74 42 53 30. Email: moulin@campingendombes.fr

This extremely spacious and well run campsite, which is owned by several villages, lies within a larger leisure complex which will be very busy at weekends. The major attraction here is one of the largest swimming pools in Europe – 5,500 sq.m. It is irregularly shaped, has shallow areas all around, two large toboggans and eight lifeguards always on duty – ideal for all the family and free for campers. The 165 very large, level grassy pitches include 156 for touring, with 4 hardstandings for motorcaravans. All have 6A electricity and are separated by hedges, with shade provided by a variety of trees. The reception, bar, restaurant and entertainment centre is at the entrance well away from the pitches. There is an extensive programme of entertainment in high season. There is also a 13 hectare, well stocked fishing lake, large spaces set aside for sporting activities and a new adventure trail in the forest. This site would be ideal for those active families seeking a campsite based holiday. No animals are accepted.

Facilities	Directions
Two very clean and well maintained toilet blocks, functional rather than luxurious, have all the necessary facilities including those for disabled visitors. Motorcaravan service point. All facilities open all season. Bar, TV room, restaurant and takeaway. Large swimming pool with toboggans and pebble sunbathing beach. Marquee for entertainment. Bicycle hire. Large area for games. New adventure trail. Paintball. Off site: In adjacent leisure complex – fishing, tennis, minigolf. Bourg-en-Bresse (20 km.) has a wide range of shops, bars and restaurants, plus a market.	Site is 20 km. southwest of Bourg-en-Bresse. Leave the N83 at St Paul de Varax and turn southeast on the D17. In 3 km. turn right down the bumpy lane, signed Base de Loisirs. Site is 1 km. GPS: N46:05.206 E05:09.122

Open: 2 June - 2 September.

Charges 2007

Per person	€ 3,70
child (3-12 yrs)	€ 2,20
pitch incl. 6A electricity	€ 7,50
vehicle	€ 2,20

**** Campsite   Play Areas
Restaurant   Animation
Adventure Trail
Paint Ball

-5% discount on all online reservations

In the hart of la Dombes region, between Bourg en Bresse and Lyon
Discover one of the largest swimming pools in Europe
Giant waterslide

CAMPING **** ETANG DU MOULIN

Camping**** Etang du Moulin - 01240 Saint Paul de Varax - ☎ +33 (0)4 74 42 53 30
Swimming trunks only - Animals not permitted - www.camping-etang-du-moulin.fr

FR01060 Flower Camping Ile de la Comtesse

Route des Abrets, F-01300 Murs-et-Géligneux (Ain)

Tel: **04 79 87 23 33**. Email: **camping.comtesse@wanadoo.fr**

A very pleasant, family run, lakeside site, there are 100 medium to large, level grassy pitches here. With 69 for touring, many are separated by low hedges and tall poplar trees offer some shade. All have 6A electricity (but very long leads may be necessary) and most have views over the lake and craggy hills beyond. High season activities are aimed mainly at younger children and the family. Fishing, sailing, canoeing and bathing are possible on the lake that borders the site. There is plenty of space around the lake for leisure activities, including marked walks and cycle trails.

Facilities	Directions
Traditionally styled, modern and well appointed toilet block with all the necessary facilities. Facilities for disabled visitors. Motorcaravan service point. Small bar/restaurant with takeaway and small shop. Large marquee used for TV and organized activities. Swimming and paddling pools. Daily programme of activities for the family in high season. Bicycle hire. Off site: Restaurant adjacent. Aost with shops, etc. 5 km. Riding 10 km. Golf 20 km. **Open:** 16 May - 1 September.	From the A43 (Lyon - Chambery) autoroute, take exit 10 and go north on D592 for about 10 km. After crossing the lake turn right on the D992 and site is shortly on the right. GPS: N45:38.407 E05:38.948

Charges 2008

Per unit incl. 2 persons and electricity	€ 14,50 - € 29,90
extra person	€ 4,90 - € 7,50
child (2-7yrs)	€ 2,90 - € 5,40

FR01090 Camping La Pierre Thorion

Base de Loisirs, Les Luizants, F-01290 Cormoranche-sur-Saône (Ain)

Tel: **03 85 23 97 10**. Email: **contact@lac-cormoranche.com**

Situated in a region famous for its wines, gastronomy and picturesque old villages, this site is part of the 42 hectare landscaped recreation park that surrounds a tree lined lake. The 117 generous pitches are level, grassed and enclosed by hedges, all with electricity and drainage. A small dam divides the lake into two areas, one for swimming, the other, larger part for fishing (also permitted at night) and boating. To the far side of the park is a TGV railway track. During the day the trains are fairly frequent, but there are no night services and the daytime noise is a moderate rumble.

Facilities	Directions
Modern sanitary building provide free preset showers and (a little small), washbasins in cabins. Facilities for disabled people. Laundry room with washing machine. Motorcaravan service point. Small shop (order bread for following morning). Bar and restaurant with takeaway, overlooking lake. Lake swinning with a separate area for small children. Off site: Macon, Bourg-en Bresse and the village of Perouges. **Open:** 1 April - 30 September.	Site is 5 km. south-southwest of Macon on the eastern site of the Saône. It is well signed from all directions 'Base de Loisirs'. If approaching from the west via Creches, there is a 2.6 m. height restriction.

Charges 2007

Per person	€ 4,10 - € 5,00
child (2-12 yrs)	€ 1,60 - € 2,50
pitch	€ 5,00 - € 7,00
incl. electricity	€ 5,80 - € 8,50

FR07020 Camping Caravaning l'Ardéchois

Le Chambon, Gluiras, F-07190 Saint Sauveur-de-Montagut (Ardèche)

Tel: **04 75 66 61 87**. Email: **ardechois.camping@wanadoo.fr**

This attractive site is quite a way off the beaten track and the approach road is winding and narrow in places. However, it is worth the effort, to find it in such a spectacular setting. This site has 106 pitches (83 for touring with 10A electricity) laid out on steep terraces and many separated by trees and plants. Some are alongside the small, fast-flowing stream, while the rest (60%) are on higher, sloping ground nearer the restaurant/bar and pool. The main site access roads are tarmac but are quite steep and larger units may find access to some terraces difficult.

Facilities	Directions
Two very good sanitary blocks include facilities for families and people with disabilities. Dishwashing and laundry facilities. Motorcaravan services. Shop. Cosy restaurant. Swimming and paddling pools (heated), adjacent bar, snack bar, terrace (all open all season). TV. Table tennis. Volleyball. Bicycle hire, archery, fishing. Comprehensive entertainment programme. Only gas/electric barbecues. Off site: Canyoning, climbing, river walking and canoeing trips organised. **Open:** 27 April - 30 September.	From Valence take N86 south for 12 km. At La Voulte-sur-Rhône turn right onto D120 to St Sauveur de Montagut (site well signed), in centre turn left onto D102 towards Mézilhac for 8 km. to site.

Charges 2007

Per unit incl. 2 persons and electricity	€ 28,30 - € 47,50
extra person	€ 5,50 - € 8,50
child (2-13 yrs)	€ 4,00 - € 6,70
Camping Cheques accepted.	

FR07090 Camping le Domaine des Plantas

F-07360 Les Ollières-sur-Eyrieux (Ardèche)

Tel: 04 75 66 21 53. Email: plantas.ardeche@wanadoo.fr

Under new ownership, this is a good quality site in a spectacular setting on the steep banks of the Eyrieux river. Old, original buildings house the reception, restaurant and bar. The terrace provides a stunning viewpoint. The 169 pitches (100 for touring) are steeply terraced and shaded with electricity (10A, long leads may be needed). Much up and down walking is required making this site unsuitable for those with walking difficulties There is a sandy beach beside the quite fast-flowing, but fairly shallow river (used for bathing). The 3 km. approach road is a twisting, single track and may present a problem to those with larger outfits. Domaine des Plantas offers an attractive alternative to those in the more popular southern parts of the Ardèche. The Eyrieux valley is less well known, but arguably just as attractive as those further south and a good deal less crowded, particularly in the main season.

Facilities

Two excellent well equipped toilet blocks (one heated). There are some facilities which will certainly please the very young. Washing machine. Motorcaravan services. Small shop, bar, restaurant, disco. Heated, covered and outdoor swimming pools, paddling pool and toboggans. Adventure play area. High season children's activities, discos for 14-18 year olds held in cellar (strictly no alcohol). Many activities and excursions. Only gas and electric barbecues. Off site: Riding 15 km. Mountain biking, canoeing, canyoning, riding and walking. A wonderful area for touring.

Open: 21 April - 5 October.

Directions

Leave A7 exit 15 (Valence Sud). Turn right to Valence centre, follow signs to Montélimar via N7 for 7 km. Turn right towards Charmes sur Rhône to Beauchastel. Take D120 to Ollières sur Eyrieux. Cross river, turn left and follow site signs (3 km.) along narrow track. GPS: N44:48.520 E04:38.125

Charges 2007

Per unit incl. 2 persons	
and electricity	€ 19,00 - € 31,00
extra person over 4 yrs	€ 4,00 - € 7,50
child (2-4 yrs)	€ 2,00 - € 3,00
animal	free - € 3,00
Camping Cheques accepted.	

FR07030 Yelloh! Village Soleil Vivarais

Soleil Vivarais, F-07120 Sampzon (Ardèche)

Tel: 04 66 73 97 39. Email: info@yellohvillage-soleil-vivarais.com

A large, lively, high quality site bordering the River Ardèche, complete with beach, Soleil Vivarais offers much to visitors, particularly families with children. Of the 350 pitches, 110 generously sized, shady and level pitches are for tourers, all with 10A electricity. Rock pegs are advised. During the day the proximity of the swimming pools to the terraces of the bar and restaurant make it a pleasantly social area. A new section beyond the beach has a very attractive new pool complex.

Facilities

Modern, clean, well equipped toilet blocks, disabled facilities. Washing facilities. Motorcaravan services. Small supermarket. Bar/restaurant, takeaways and pizzas (cooked in a wood burning oven). Heated pool, paddling pool. Water polo. Aquarobics. Fishing. Archery. Bicycle hire. River bathing. Extensive animation programme in June, July and August. Off site: Riding 800 m. Mountain biking, walking, canoeing, rafting, climbing, caving.

Open: 5 April - 14 September.

Directions

On D579, 2 km. south of Ruoms, turn left at roundabout, signed Vallon-Pont-d'Arc. Shortly turn right over river bridge, site on right.

Charges 2008

Per unit incl. 2 persons	
and electricity	€ 19,00 - € 43,00
extra person	€ 5,00 - € 7,00
dog	free - € 4,50

FR07050 Sunêlia le Ranc Davaine

Saint Alban-Auriolles, F-07120 Ruoms (Ardèche)

Tel: 04 75 39 60 55. Email: camping.ranc.davaine@wanadoo.fr

Le Ranc Davaine is a large, busy, family oriented site with direct access to the River Chassezac. There are 435 pitches with 113 for touring, all with electricity (6/10A) for which very long leads are required (some may cross roads). Most pitches are scattered between static caravan and tour operator pitches on fairly flat, stony ground under a variety of trees, some of which are quite low giving much needed shade. Rock pegs are advised. A lively entertainment programme (July/Aug) is aimed at young children and teenagers with an enclosed disco four nights a week until 3am.

Facilities

Fully equipped, very clean and modern toilet blocks include facilities for disabled visitors. Washing machines, dryers. Large shop. Cash point. Internet. Bar/restaurant, pizzeria, takeaway. Swimming pools, covered pool (heated). Large play area. Tennis. Archery. Minigolf. Fishing. Extensive activity and sports programme. Discos. Off site: Canoe hire nearby. Rafting. Canyoning. Bicycle and quadbike hire 2 km. Riding 6 km. Karting.

Open: 23 March - 14 September.

Directions

From Ruoms go south on the D111. Just before Grospierres turn right onto D246, cross the river bridge (2.5 m. width restriction) and then left on D208 towards site. GPS: N44:24.848 E04:16.374

Charges 2007

Per unit incl. 2 persons	€ 20,60 - € 36,00
with electricity	€ 25,75 - € 40,20
child (2-13 yrs)	€ 3,75 - € 9,60

Camping Cheques accepted.

FR07070 Kawan Village les Ranchisses

Route de Rocher, F-07110 Largentière (Ardèche)

Tel: 04 75 88 31 97. Email: reception@lesranchisses.fr

This is a very well equipped, modern campsite in a lesser known area of the Ardèche. There are 165 good-sized, level, grassy pitches, 88 for tourists with electricity (10A) including 44 which are fully serviced. There are two distinct areas, one which is well shaded and the lower part with less shade. There is traffic noise in some areas. A small river pool provides opportunities for bathing, fishing or canoeing. Well run and with the emphasis on personal attention, this is a highly recommended site.

Facilities

Comprehensive toilet buildings include facilities for babies and disabled persons. Laundry. Motorcaravan services. Mini market. Restaurant (regional specialities), bar, takeaway/pizzeria and terrace. Two large pools, paddling pool (heated). New indoor pool complex is planned. Adventure style playground. Organised amusements for children (from 1/6). Skate park. Tennis. Minigolf. Canoeing. Internet access. Off site: Canoe, kayaking arranged (mid-June - end Aug). Largentière (1.5 km.) with Tuesday market. Riding 8 km. Bicycle hire 10 km. Take to the back roads to see the real Ardèche.

Open: 7 April - 16 September.

Directions

Largentière is southwest of Aubenas best approached using D104. Just beyond Uzer, 16 km. From Aubenas, turn northwest on D5. After 5 km. at far end of Largentière, fork left downhill signed Rocher and Valgorge. Site on left in about 1.8 km. just beyond rocky gorge. The approach from Valgorge is not recommended.

Charges 2007

Per unit incl. 2 persons and electricity	€ 24,00 - € 35,00
extra person (over 1 yr)	€ 4,50 - € 7,50

Camping Cheques accepted.

FR07080 RCN la Bastide en Ardèche

RD 111, route d'Alès, Sampzon, F-07120 Ruoms (Ardèche)

Tel: 04 75 39 64 72. Email: info@rcn-labastideenardeche.fr

You are assured of a good welcome at this recently upgraded site. There are 300 good sized, level, grassy pitches marked out by trees which give plenty of shade. All have electricity 3/5A, and 86 are fully serviced. On driving down to your pitch, it seems that there are many mobile homes, actually there are only 46 with 25 small chalets plus another 16 pitches used by a tour operator. Canoe trips are arranged down the Gorge d'Ardèche.

Facilities

Two well equipped toilet blocks, one new and one due to be refurbished, with baby room and facilities for the disabled. Shop. Attractive restaurant, pizzeria and bar. Heated swimming pool and sunbathing area. Play area. Volleyball, football, basketball, tennis. Fishing. Organised activities. Recreation room in cellar. Only gas barbecues. Off site: Riding, bicycle hire 3 km. Watersports on River Ardèche. Ruoms 4 km. Vallon-Pont-d'Arc 7 km. Medieval villages of Balazuc, Labaume and Largentière.

Open: 15 March - 15 October.

Directions

Going south from Ruoms on the D579, after 2.5 km. at roundabout, turn right on D111 signed Alès. After 1 km. cross river bridge and site is 200 m. on the left. GPS: N44:25.375 E04:19.297

Charges 2008

Per unit incl. 2 persons, electricity and water	€ 18,00 - € 45,50

Many discounts offered in low season.

FR07110 Domaine le Pommier

RN102, F-07170 Villeneuve-de-Berg (Ardèche)
Tel: 04 75 94 82 81. Email: info@campinglepommier.com

Domaine Le Pommier is an extremely spacious Dutch owned site of 10 hectares in 32 hectares of wooded grounds. The site is steeply terraced (a tractor is available for assistance) and has wonderful views over the Ardèche mountains and beyond. There are 400 pitches with 275 for tourists. They are grassy/stony, of good size and well spaced. Separated by young trees and hedges, some have little or no shade. All have access to electricity and water is close by. The site is not recommended for large units. Recent developments include a mini-farm, including llamas, goats and ponies, and an unusual pancake restaurant. This serves an excellent range of pancakes of various flavours. The site has first class facilities, including the most up-to-date toilet blocks, a very good bar/restaurant and one of the best swimming and paddling pool complexes we have seen – ideal for all the family.

Facilities

Four excellent toilet blocks, one with under-floor heating, provide all the necessary facilities. Comprehensive shop. Bar/restaurant. Swimming pool complex with slides, paddling pools, etc. Everything opens from the end of April. Boules. Minigolf. Activities including games in the woods, archery, water polo and tug of war. Bridge and water colour classes. Tennis. Sound proof disco. Very extensive programme of events on and off site. Off season excursions. Off site: Villeneuve de Berg 1.5 km. River Ardèche 12 km. Potholing, rock climbing, canoeing, canyoning, mountain biking, walking or riding.

Open: 1 May - 30 September.

Directions

Site is west of Montélimar on the N102. The entrance is adjacent to the roundabout at the eastern end of the Villeneuve-de-Berg bypass. GPS: N44:34.350 E04:30.669

Charges 2007

Per unit incl. 2 persons	€ 14,00 - € 29,50
extra person over 4 yrs	€ 4,00 - € 6,50
electricity	€ 4,00
dog	free - € 4,00

Max. 6 persons per pitch.
Special offers for longer stays in low season.

FR07100 Camping la Garenne

Chemin de la Garenne, F-07800 Saint Laurent-du-Pape (Ardèche)

Tel: 04 75 62 24 62. Email: info@lagarenne.org

This spacious, family orientated site has a long season and is within easy reach of the A7/N7 south of Valence. It is only a short stroll from the village which has a range of small shops. Guests are predominantly Dutch but all are made welcome and English is widely spoken. The 120 hard pitches (rock pegs advised), some terraced and some sloping, have varying degrees of shade. Some are separated by hedges and all have electricity, but only 4A (some need long leads). Visitors' pursuits have been carefully considered resulting in a variety of family activities from mid-May to mid-September. People with diverse interests are therefore attracted throughout the season, for example, bridge evenings are organised during May, June and September. Accompanied walks are organized throughout the season, as well as a lively activity and entertainment in peak season.

Facilities

Excellent and very clean, modern toilet blocks provide all necessary facilities including those for children and disabled visitors. Small shop for basics, bar, restaurant and takeaway (all 15/5-15/9). Swimming pool and sunbathing terrace (20/5-30/9). Paddling pool. Boules. Games room. Volleyball. Barbecues are not permitted. Off site: The village is close by. Fishing 1 km. Riding 2 km. Bicycle hire 3 km. Walking, biking, canoeing, canyoning and exploring the Ardèche region. Some off site activities run from site.

Open: 1 March - 1 November.

Directions

Leave the N86 south of Valence at Beauchastel. Turn west on D21 to St Laurent du Pape, cross the river and turn left. Shortly, just before La Poste, turn right (site signed but not clearly), the campsite is shortly on the left. GPS: N44:49.574 E04:45.732

Charges 2008

Per unit incl. 2 persons and electricity	€ 18,50 - € 30,50
extra person	€ 5,50
child (under 4 yrs)	free

Reductions in low season for over 55s.

FR07130 Camping les Coudoulets

Pradons, F-07120 Ruoms (Ardèche)

Tel: 04 75 93 94 95. Email: camping@coudoulets.com

For those who prefer a more intimate, peaceful campsite beside the river Ardèche, only a short distance away from the main centre, then this very well cared for site, run by a very friendly family, could be for you. There are 125 good sized, grassy and well shaded pitches, separated by trees and shrubs. There are 109 for touring, all with 6A electricity. Organised family activities take place in July/August such as barbecues and musical evenings (no discos). There is an area for bathing in the river and it is an ideal spot for canoeists. The family have a small vineyard and their wine is on sale in the bar; we fully recommend it.

Facilities

Good, clean, recently refurbished block has all the necessary facilities including excellent facilities for disabled people. Motorcaravan services. Bar, TV, terrace (May - Sept) bread, ices, drinks. Snacks (July/Aug). Butcher calls in high season. Small heated swimming pool, paddling pool. Superb new aquatic play area and pool for children (May - Sept). Fishing, football, volleyball, table tennis. WiFi. Off site: Shop 300 m. Ruoms with

Open: 1 May - 10 September.

Directions

Leave Montélimar westwards on N102 towards Aubenas. After passing Villeneuve de Berg turn left on D103 towards Vogüé for 5 km. Turn left on D579 towards Ruoms, site on right on entering Pradons (approx 10 km). GPS: N44:28.598 E04:21.514

Charges 2007

Per unit incl. 2 persons	€ 13,00 - € 22,50
extra person	€ 4,00 - € 5,50
child (under 7 yrs)	€ 3,50 - € 4,50
electricity (6A)	€ 3,70

FR07120 Camping Nature Parc l'Ardéchois

Mobile homes ▶ page 503

Route touristique des Gorges, F-07150 Vallon-Pont-d'Arc (Ardèche)

Tel: **04 75 88 06 63**. Email: **ardecamp@bigfoot.com**

This very high quality, family run site is within walking distance of Vallon-Pont-d'Arc. It borders the River Ardèche and canoe trips are run, professionally, direct from the site. This campsite is ideal for families with younger children seeking an active holiday. The facilities are comprehensive and of an extremely high standard, particularly the central toilet block. Of the 244 pitches, there are 225 for tourers, separated by trees and individual shrubs. All have electrical connections (6/10A) and 125 have full services. Forming a focal point is the bar and restaurant (good menus), with a terrace and stage overlooking the attractive heated pool. Member of Leading Campings Group.There is also a large paddling pool and sunbathing terrace. For children, there is a well thought out play area plus plenty of other space for youngsters to play, both on the site and along the river. Activities are organised throughout the season; these are family based – no discos. Patrols at night ensure a good night's sleep. Access to the site is easy and suitable for large outfits.

Facilities

Two well equipped toilet blocks, one superb with 'everything' working automatically. Facilities are of the highest standard, very clean and include good facilities for babies, those with disabilities, washing up and laundry. Four private bathrooms to hire. Washing machines. Well stocked shop. Swimming pool and paddling pool (no Bermuda shorts). Football, volleyball, tennis and table tennis. Very good play area. Internet access point. Organised activities, canoe trips. Only gas barbecues are permitted. Communal barbecue area. Off site: Canoeing, rafting, walking, riding, mountain biking, golf, rock climbing, bowling, wine tasting and dining. Vallon-Pont-d'Arc 800 m. Explore the real Ardèche on the minor roads and visit Labaume, Bazakuc and Largentière (market Tuesday).

Open: Easter - 30 September.

Directions

From Vallon-Pont-d'Arc (western end of the Ardèche Gorge) at a roundabout go east on the D290. Site entrance is shortly on the right.
GPS: N44:23.873 E04:23.929

Charges 2008

Per pitch incl. 2 persons and electricity	€ 42,00

Check real time availability and at-the-gate prices...
www.**alanrogers**.com

FR07150 Camping Domaine de Gil

Mobile homes ▶ page 503

Route de Vals-les-Bains, Ucel, F-07200 Aubenas (Ardèche)

Tel: 04 75 94 63 63. Email: info@domaine-de-gil.com

Under new ownership, this very attractive and well organised, smaller site in a less busy part of the Ardèche should appeal to couples and families with younger children. The 80, good sized, level pitches, 43 for touring, are surrounded by a variety of trees offering plenty of shade. All have 10A electricity. The focal point of the site is formed by the very attractive swimming pool, paddling pool and large sunbathing area, with the bar, restaurant and well appointed children's play areas all adjacent. A spacious sports area and shady picnic/play area are alongside the river Ardèche – an ideal spot to cool off on a hot day.

Facilities

Modern well appointed toilet block, washing machine and iron. Motorcaravan services. Basic shop. Bar/restaurant, takeaway (from June). Heated swimming pool, paddling pool. Two play areas. Volleyball, boules, minigolf, football, tennis. Canoeing, boating, fishing. Organised activities in high season. Only gas and electric barbecues. Off site: Shops at Vals-les-Bain 1.5 km. Interesting old town of Aubenas with larger range of shops, restaurants, bars 3 km. Organised canoe trips, canyoning on river Ardèche. Bicycle hire, riding 4 km.

Open: 14 April - 23 September.

Directions

Site north of Aubenas. From southeast (N102), after tunnel, turn right, roundabout (signed Ucel), cross river into Pont d'Ucel (3.5 tonne limit). Bear right and at roundabout, last exit (signed Ucel). Shortly turn left (signed Ucel D218), then right (Ucel D578B). Site is 2 km. GPS: N44:38.558 E04:22.775

Charges 2007

Per unit incl. 2 persons	€ 14,00 - € 29,00
extra person	€ 3,50 - € 5,75
child (under 10 yrs)	free - € 4,25
electricity	€ 4,00
animal	€ 2,00 - € 3,00

07200 Ucel-Aubenas - Ardèche
Tel. +33 4 75 94 63 63 (english spoken)
www.domaine-de-gil.com
e-mail: info@domaine-de-gil.com

On the banks of the river Ardèche
Heated Swimmingpool
Rent of Mobilhomes

FR07170 Ludocamping

F-07170 Lussas (Ardèche)

Tel: 04 75 94 21 22. Email: info@ludocamping.com

This is a quiet family campsite offering a really wide range of activities. From mid-July - early August, only families with children under 14 yrs are accepted which allows the activities to be focussed on this age group. The 160 grassy pitches, all for touring, 5-10A electricity, are in two areas. The upper area has large super pitches with wonderful views but little shade. The lower area, closer to the small river, has pitches set naturally amongst the trees and they have good shade. There is an attractive swimming pool (heated all season), good sized paddling pool and large sunbathing area.

Facilities

Clean, good quality toilet blocks offering all necessary facilities. Bar (all season), takeaway (from 1/5), terrace overlooking the valley. Play area. Volleyball. Table tennis. Recreational area next to river. Fishing. Bicycle hire. Club for over 6/7 yr olds offering a very wide range of activities. Off season club for older children. Seniors excursions in campsite coach. Only gas and electric barbecues. Off site: Lussas (few shops, restaurant, bar) 600 m. Riding 6 km. Gliding, hang-gliding, canoeing, speed boating.

Open: 1 April - 15 October.

Directions

From Montélimar take N102 west towards Aubenas, pass around Villeneuve, at traffic lights in Lavilledieu turn right onto D224 towards Lussas. Site entrance is on right just before village (about 4 km. from N102).

Charges 2007

Per unit incl. 2 persons	€ 11,00 - € 25,00
extra person	€ 2,00 - € 6,00
child (under 6 yrs)	€ 2,00 - € 3,00
electricity (6A)	€ 3,00
dog	€ 1,00 - € 1,50

Special long stay, low season offers. No credit cards.

Check real time availability and at-the-gate prices...

www.alanrogers.com

FR07190 Camping le Chambourlas

F-07360 Les Ollières-sur-Eyrieux (Ardèche)

Tel: **04 75 66 24 31**. Email: info@chambourlas.com

Tucked away in a beautiful setting, in the hills above Privas, this is a small, neat and tidy family owned site (Dutch and English spoken). The 78 grassy, sloping pitches (72 for touring, electricity 10A) are set on low terraces, separated by an interesting variety of trees with excellent views over the wooded hills. The attractive reception, restaurant and shop are in one building close to all the facilities. Although there are special facilities, this is not an ideal site for those with walking difficulties. It is not ideal for very large units due to the steep and narrow local roads. There is a wide range of family orientated activities, especially in July and August, but these do not extend late into the night.

Facilities

One modern very clean toilet block with all the necessary facilities including those for disabled visitors. Bar, restaurant and takeaway (all 15/5-28/8). Small shop (mid May - Oct). Swimming pool, paddling pool and sunbathing area (1/5-30/9). Play area. Volleyball. Table tennis. Boules. Good range of activities, some in low season, no discos. River fishing. Only gas barbecues. Off site: Many walks and bike rides. Excursions. Village of les Ollières-sur-Eyrieux 6 km. Riding 15 km. Privas 19 km. Cévennes Regional Mountain Park.

Open: 1 May - 1 October.

Directions

At traffic lights in Privas take D2 north, signed Le Cheylard. Follow road over two river bridges. Site entrance is on right (about 11 km. after traffic lights). Take care – this is a fairly tortuous climb. GPS: N44:46.870 E04:37.016

Charges 2007

Per unit incl. 2 persons and electricity	€ 15,00 - € 29,00
extra person	€ 4,90 - € 5,90
child (2-12 yrs)	€ 4,60 - € 5,60
dog	free - € 2,50

Camping Cheques accepted.

FR07180 Kawan Village Ardèche

Boulevard de Paste, F-07000 Privas (Ardèche)

Tel: **04 75 64 05 80**. Email: jcray@wanadoo.fr

This spacious, family run site is on the southern outskirts of Privas and would be a good base for exploring the lesser known parts of the Ardèche. Bus and coach trips are available to explore these areas. The site has 166 large, grass, reasonably level pitches, of which 153 are for tourers. A wide variety of trees provide reasonable shade and electricity (6/10A) should now be available on most pitches. Two tour operators use the site. Recent additions are new heated swimming and paddling pools. There is a play area for children and a miniclub, but (deliberately) no provision for teenagers.

Facilities

Two toilet blocks, only one open in low season. Facilities for disabled people. Motorcaravan service point. Bar and restaurant (1/5-30/9). Volleyball. Boules. Table tennis. Play area. Miniclub. Entertainment (high season). Only gas barbecues are permitted. Tents (4) for rent. Off site: Swimming pool and tennis courts adjacent. Supermarket 100 m. Bicycle hire 2 km. Riding 5 km.

Open: 1 April - 30 September.

Directions

At traffic lights in the centre of town take D2, signed Montélimar. Descend the winding road for about 1 km. then at roundabout (near Intermarché) turn right and then shortly left, signed Espace Ouvéze. The entrance is straight on. GPS: N44:43.569 E04:35.898

Charges 2007

Per unit incl. 2 persons	€ 14,50 - € 19,00
extra person	€ 3,50 - € 5,00
child (3-6 yrs)	€ 2,50 - € 3,00
electricity (6A)	€ 3,50

Camping Cheques accepted.

FR07290 **La Domaine d'Imbours**

F-07220 Larnas (Ardèche)

Tel: **04 75 54 39 50**. Email: **info@domaine-imbours.com**

This large site is part of a holiday complex with many mobile homes (99), chalets (41), hotel and 200 camping pitches. These are on scrub grass, not marked, with some shade from mature trees and 6A electricity (long leads may be helpful). For those looking for more or less everything organised for them in high season, this complex may suit. Out of season it is different, with not much happening. The complex is dominated by the hotel which is about 1 km. from the camping area along a descending site road. Around the hotel is a large and well designed pool complex. In high season there are evening shows and dancing, again at the hotel. Here too one can play tennis on one of four courts. To use the laundry one needs to transport washing to the hotel complex, where there are machines. There are quad bikes for hire which seem to be driven round the camping area with some speed As the complex of 270 hectare is rather remote, there is a well stocked, small supermarket and even a cash machine on site. For those who wish to visit towing a caravan – please do use the recommended route – other roads are not suitable.

Facilities

Good sanitary blocks with well designed showers and hot and cold water for washing (in cubicles) Facilities for children and disabled visitors. Laundry. Small but well stocked supermarket (the site is quite remote). ATM. Bar and restaurant. Takeaway (1/6-31/8). Swimming pool complex (outdoor pools heated 1/430/9, indoor pool all season). Play area on sand. Tennis. Volleyball. Bicycle and quad bike hire. Archery. Riding. Activity clubs for all ages and entertainment (high season). Barbecues are not permitted.

Open: 24 March - 6 October.

Directions

From the N86 Bagnols - Aubanas road, exit onto the D4 at Bourg St Andeo to Remeze (a good road). Turn right at entrance to village on the D362 towards Larnas and site is on the right in Imbours. Do not attempt other routes with a caravan.

Charges 2007

Per person	€ 4,20 - € 7,00
child (0-7 yrs)	€ 2,30 - € 4,20
pitch (low season)	€ 4,20
incl. 3 persons (high season)	€ 26,00 - € 29,00

Camping Cheques accepted.

Domaine d'Imbours

Le Domaine d'Imbours offers a large choice of facilities: pool complex with heated indoor pool, outdoor pools, paddling pools and many activities.

Le Domaine d'Imbours
07220 Larnas
Tél. 0033(0)4 75 54 39 50
Fax. 0033(0)4 75 54 39 20
www.campings-franceloc.com

Ardèche

FR07250 **Yelloh! Village la Plaine**

F-07120 Ruoms (Ardèche)

Tel: **04 66 73 97 39**. Email: **info@yellohvillage-la-plaine.com**

One of the 'all singing, all dancing' type of campsite, La Plaine is quiet in low season, but in high season with all-day and evening activities for both teenagers and adults, and a mini-club each day, there is no reason to feel bored! There are 212 pitches of moderate size (52 used for their air conditioned mobile homes), of which 160 have electricity. They are protected from the sun and marked by many trees. A stage and sound equipment are in use most nights and might cause some noise problems. This is a young family site for people with lots of energy.

Facilities

Three sanitary blocks, clean and modern provide all facilities under cover. Young children's toilet facilities. Good facilities for disabled visitors. Laundry room. Shop, restaurant, bar and takeaway. Heated swimming pool complex. Gym. Fitness room. Activity and entertainment programme day and evening. Miniclub. Fishing. River beach. Off site: Town 3 km. Bicycle hire and riding 2 km.

Open: 5 April - 14 September.

Directions

Exit Ruoms south on the D579 and at junction 2 km, south, take D111 signed St Ambroix. Site is on the left. GPS: N44:25.624 E04:20.137

Charges 2007

Per unit incl. 2 persons and electricity (6A)	€ 17,00 - € 38,00
extra person	€ 4,00 - € 6,00
child (0-7 yrs)	free - € 5,00

FR07310 Camping la Roubine

Route de Ruoms, F-07150 Vallon-Pont d'Arc (Ardèche)

Tel: **04 75 88 04 56**. Email: **roubine.ardeche@wanadoo.fr**

This site on the bank of the Ardèche has been in the same family ownership for some 30 years. During this time there has been constant upgrading and it must now be considered one of the best sites in the area. There are 114 touring pitches, all with electricity (10A) and quite spacious. Well tended grass, trimmed hedging and mature trees and smart tarmac roads create a calm and well kept atmosphere. Much attention is given to cleanliness – the toilet blocks are cleaned three times a day. A variety of sporting facilities are available on the site. The pool complex is heated when necessary throughout the season. There is a bar and restaurant of most modern design which, together with a mini-market, are open throughout the season. The campsite also caters for their young visitors with children's club in high season complete with an adventure playground and even an amphitheatre. There is an internet room for visitors. The proprietors, M. Moulin and Mme. Van Eck like to welcome guests and are available to help during the day – they are rightly proud of their well run campsite.

Facilities

Several small sanitary blocks include washbasins in cubicles. The main toilet block has showers, washbasins in vanity units, a baby bathroom and facilities for disabled visitors. Laundry. 4 Swimming pool, inc. a paddling pool and seperate childrens pool. Tennis. Boules. Fishing. Barbecues only permitted on three communal sites. River beach. Off site: Bicycle hire and riding 1 km. Footpath to town (700 m). Supermarket in town.

Open: 21 April - 14 September.

Directions

From Vallon take the D579 towards Ruoms. Site is well signed on left about 400 m. from town. From west (Ruoms) site signed on right near Vallon town sign. New roundabout on the west of Vallon. From Vallon - turn left at roundabout (signed).

Charges 2007

Per unit incl. 2 persons	€ 19,00 - € 33,00
extra person	€ 3,40 - € 7,00
child (0-13 yrs)	free - € 7,00
electricity	€ 4,20

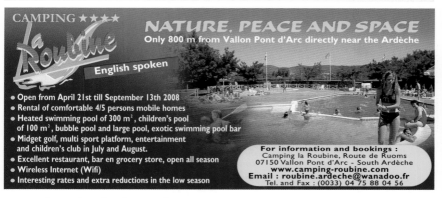

FR07140 Camping les Lavandes

Le Village, F-07170 Darbres (Ardèche)

Tel: **04 75 94 20 65**. Email: **sarl.leslavandes@online.fr**

Situated to the northeast of Aubenas, in a quieter part of this region, Les Lavandes is surrounded by magnificent countryside, vineyards and orchards. The enthusiastic French owners, who speak good English, run a site that appeals to all nationalities. The 70 pitches (58 for touring) are arranged on low terraces separated by a variety of trees and shrubs that give welcome shade in summer. Electricity 6/10A is available to all. At the end of May the campsite trees are laden with luscious cherries. Organised activities include wine tasting, shows, musical evenings and children's games. A ride along the panoramic road to Mirabel is a must.

Facilities

Comprehensive and well maintained facilities, baby room, excellent facilities for disabled people. Washing machine. Small shop (1/7-31/8). Bar, terrace (1/6-31/8). Restaurant (5/6-31/8). Takeaway (15/4-31/8). Swimming and paddling pools, sunbathing areas, with super views. Play areas for younger children. Table games. Billiard room. Open air chess. No electric barbecues. Off site: Fishing 1 km. Riding 3 km. Tennis 5 km. Bicycle hire 15 km. Canoeing, carting. Caves, historical villages. Wonderful area for birds.

Open: 15 April - 30 September.

Directions

Site best approached from south. From Montélimar take N102 towards Aubenas. After Villeneuve, in Lavilledieu, turn right at traffic lights on D224 to Darbres (10 km). In Darbres turn sharp left by post office (care needed) and follow site signs.

Charges 2007

Per unit incl. 2 persons	€ 11,50 - € 17,00
extra person	€ 2,80 - € 3,50
electricity	€ 3,50

FR07320 Camping des Gorges

Chemin de Sauze, F-07700 Saint Martin d'Ardèche (Ardèche)

Tel: 04 75 04 61 09. Email: info@camping-des-gorges.com

Situated just outside the extremely attractive village of Saint Martin d'Ardèche, this site is on the north bank of the river, right at the end of the gorge. From here one can explore this unique river and indeed the attractive, small villages on the banks. With a total of 145 pitches (119 for tourists), nearly every pitch has some shade, which is helpful in this region of hot summers. The pitches are of average size on grass, all with 5A electricity (French plugs) and 8 with full services. This family run site is associated with Camping La Roubine at Vallon-Pont d'Arc. Although the village is a ten minute walk, there is a surprisingly large and well stocked shop on the site. The site does cater for children – there is an underground games room, pony rides and games, and activities are organised. The modern swimming pool has a section for young children. Teenagers are asked to enjoy themselves at a disco in the village, not on the site! Boules are played regularly. There is a barrier at night.

Facilities

The sanitary blocks are modern and very clean with washbasins in cabins. Facilities for disabled people. Laundry room. Good shop. Bar, restaurant and takeaway. Swimming pool and large sunbathing area. Organised activities. Games room. Pony rides. Boules. Barbecues are not permitted. Off site: Fishing 200 m. Riding 4 km. Bicycle hire 8 km. Cash point and internet access in village.

Open: 1 April - 15 September.

Directions

From the N86 Aubenas - Bagnols road take road signed St Martin d'Ardèche at the roundabout at St Just. Site is signed on the Sauze road out of the village, about 800 m. on the left.

Charges 2007

Per unit incl. 2 persons	€ 14,00 - € 25,00
extra person	€ 3,00 - € 6,00
child (0-13 yrs)	free - € 6,00
electricity	€ 4,00

* Swimming pool of 200 m2
* Rental of mobile homes
* Bar restaurant
* Grocery store
* Canoe and kayak rental
* Mini club and entertainment in the high season
* Children's playground
* Special rates in the low season

FOR INFORMATION AND BOOKINGS
Camping des Gorges ★★★
07700 St. Martin d'Ardèche
Tel/Fax : 00 33 4 75 04 61 09
Email: info@camping-des-gorges.com
Internet: www.camping-des-gorges.com

FR07550 Camping du Lion

Chemin du Chenevier, F-07700 Bourg-Saint-Andeol (Ardèche)

Tel: 04 75 54 53 20. Email: contact@campingdulion.com

Du Lion is a large site bordering the River Rhône, attractively landscaped and thoughtfully laid out. Access to and around the campsite is very easy and a large parking area at the entrance makes arrival and departure easy. The site offers 140 pitches, some formally arranged around internal roadways and two more informal camping areas. Pitch sizes range from 100-250 sq.m. but some pitches may require very long electricity leads. The site has three outdoor heated swimming pools. The sports and entertainment facilities are carefully arranged to ensure that the camping area remains tranquil even in high season. English is spoken.

Facilities

Three dated but clean toilet blocks. Laundry room. Bar and snack bar. Bread ordering service. Three outdoor heated swimming pools. Pentanque. Play area including trampoline. TV and games room. Free WiFi. Fishing. Entertainment and activity programme for adults and children (July/Aug). Torches required. Off site: Supermarket 500 m. Town 800 m. Crocodile Farm 4 km.

Open: 1 April - 15 September.

Directions

From N7, exit west on D59 towards Bourg-Saint-Andeol. Cross river and at roundabout before entering Bourg-Saint-Andeol, take first exit. At T-Junction, turn right on D86 and first right onto Chemin du Chenevier. Continue under bridge (4 m. height restriction). Site entrance is immediately on right. Site is well signed from Bourg-Saint-Andeol.

Charges 2007

Per unit incl. 2 persons	€ 15,00 - € 18,00
extra person	€ 4,00 - € 5,50
electricity (6A)	€ 3,00

FR07360 **Camping le Petit Bois**

87 rue du Petit Bois, F-07120 Ruoms (Ardèche)

Tel: **04 75 39 60 72**. Email: **vacances@campinglepetitbois.fr**

Situated only 800 metres from the ancient town centre of Ruoms, and yet within an area of trees and rocky outcrops, this site offers a centre for those wishing to explore this part of the Ardèche valley. The 118 pitches are of irregular shape and size and are a mix of stone and grass (76 are used for mobile homes). There is some shade. The site is now thirty years old and is needing some restoration, which is now underway. Some standpipes have coils of tubing attached. Perhaps these should not be used for domestic water purposes. There are three toilet blocks, although only one is open in low season including facilities for disabled people (however there may be some difficulty with some of the stone paths). Shortly after our inspection a new multi-sport facility was due to be installed. A 'Sites et Paysages' member.

Facilities

Three toilet blocks (only one open in low season) were in need of some maintenance when we visited. Cleaning appeared somewhat erratic. Bar. Restaurant and takeaway (1/7-31/8). Modern swimming pool, covered outside July/Aug. Playground. Games and TV rooms in season. Fishing. Entertainment organised in high season. Off site: Town with shops, etc. 300 m. Riding and bicycle hire 1 km.

Open: 1 April - 30 September.

Directions

Approaching Ruoms on the D579 from Vallon-Pont-d'Arc go straight on at second and second roundabouts. At third roundabout turn left (southwest) signed Largentier (site is signed). GPS: N44:27.638 E04:20.240

Charges 2007

Per unit incl. 2 persons	€ 14,00 - € 21,00
extra person	€ 3,80 - € 5,80
child (1-6 yrs)	€ 2,50 - € 3,80
electricity	€ 4,00

CAMPING ★★★
Le Petit Bois
ESPACE AQUATIQUE CHAUFFÉ ET COUVERT
TOBOGGAN - PATAUGEOIRE LUDIQUE
RIVIÈRE - LOCATIONS
ANIMATIONS
07120 RUOMS
TÉL : 04 75 39 60 72 - Fax : 04 75 93 95 50
Internet : www.campinglepetitbois.fr - Courriel : vacances@campinglepetitbois.fr

FR07340 **Domaine du Cros d'Auzon**

Saint Maurice d'Ardèche, F-07200 Vogüé Gare (Ardèche)

Tel: **04 75 37 75 86**. Email: **camping.auzon@wanadoo.fr**

This site can be described with the word 'immaculate'. The 55 pitches on well cut grass, are all of a very generous size and all have water, drainage and electricity. On the banks of the Ardèche, the site is part of a holiday complex which includes a hotel and conference centre, separated by a 300 m. driveway. Out of season it is very quiet, but in July and August a newly built bar, takeaway and restaurant together with an 'animations' building, become the focal point of the evenings. There are 55 mobile homes for hire (some tour operators). The hotel complex has an outdoor pool of a modern design which is available to camping customers at no cost, as are minigolf and tennis.

Facilities

Two excellent, modern toilet blocks of an unusual design are kept very clean. Well equipped laundry room. Fridge hire. Bar, takeaway, restaurant and shop (July/Aug). At the hotel: swimming pool (1/5-15/9), minigolf and tennis. Children's playground of generous size. Charcoal barbecues are not permitted. Bicycle hire. Internet access. Off site: Golf nearby. Riding 10 km.

Open: 1 April - 15 September.

Directions

The D579 between Ruoms and Aubenas passes through the village of Vogue. At the only roundabout take road to the southwest. Site is signed from the roundabout (about 800 m).

Charges 2007

Per unit incl. 2 persons and electricity	€ 17,50 - € 27,50
extra person	€ 4,00 - € 6,70

FR07380 Camping le Provençal

Route des Gorges, F-07150 Vallon-Pont-d'Arc (Ardèche)

Tel: **04 75 88 00 48**. Email: **camping.le.provencal@wanadoo.fr**

Le Provençal is a large, well laid out and well equipped campsite on the banks of the Ardèche. We were impressed with the size and quality of the 178 hedged, grass touring pitches (8A electricity available). There are also 22 pitches used for mobile homes to rent. The excellent fittings and cleanliness in the three modern toilet blocks demonstrate that this is a well cared for site. The bars, takeaways and restaurant are clean and attractive and the pool layout is well planned. Altogether, this site should appeal to those who enjoy the Ardèche area and all that it has to offer.

Facilities

Sanitary facilities are excellent and clean, with heating in low season. Facilities for children and visitors with disabilities. Laundry facilities. Good shop (all season) Bar, restaurant and takeaway. Good swimming pools, heated when necessary. Play area. Tennis. Volleyball. Fishing. Canoe hire. Charcoal barbecues are not permitted. Off site: Riding and bicycle hire 1 km. Golf 10 km.

Open: 10 April - 20 September.

Directions

From Vallon Pont d''Arc take the Route Gorges d'Ardèche (D290). Site is about 1 km. on right. GPS: N44:23.880 E04:23.992

Charges 2007

Per unit incl. 2 persons	
and electricity	€ 24,90 - € 34,90
extra person	€ 5,00 - € 7,00
child (under 4 yrs)	€ 3,50 - € 5,00

FR07420 Camping du Pont

Route de Chauzon, F-07120 Pradons (Ardèche)

Tel: **04 75 93 93 98**. Email: **campingdupont07@wanadoo.fr**

This is a gem of a small campsite, run by a friendly outgoing family who have recently moved here. Beside the Ardèche river, the site has a small sandy beach and a deep river pool for swimming. There are 65 average sized, grassy pitches with 52 for touring (6/10A electricity), all separated by hedges and trees giving good shade. The welcoming bar, takeaway, small shop and pool are open all season. Family activities are organised in July and August. The site is ideal for those seeking a less commercialised site close to the Ardèche Gorges.

Facilities

The good toilet block provides separate facilities for men and ladies, an excellent room for children and facilities for disabled visitors. Small shop. Bar and takeaway. Heated swimming and paddling pools (all season). Games/TV room. Play areas. Small sandy river beach. Deep pool for swimming. Fishing. Canoe trips. Organised walks from site. WiFi. Charcoal barbecues are not allowed. Off site: Supermarket 200 m. Vallon Pont d'Arc 12 km. Canyoning, rafting etc on the river Ardèche. Rock climbing. Tennis. Bicycle hire 3 km. Riding 4 km.

Open: 15 May - 30 September.

Directions

Leave Montélimar westwards on N102 towards Aubenas. Passing Villeneuve de Berg, turn left on D103 towards Vogüé for 5 km. Turn left on D579 towards Ruoms. In Pradons turn right D308, signed Chauzon. Site shortly on left before river bridge. GPS: N44:24.43 E04:21.20

Charges 2007

Per unit incl. 2 persons	
extra person	€ 13,50 - € 25,00
extra person	€ 3,30 - € 4,90
child (under 7 yrs)	€ 2,00 - € 3,90
electricity	€ 3,60

FR07400 Flower Camping Le Riviera

F-07120 Sampzon (Ardèche)

Tel: **04 75 39 67 57**. Email: **leriviera@wanadoo.fr**

This large, well organised, family run site is situated beside the River Ardèche not far from Vallon-Pont-d'Arc. There are 180 pitches in total with 144 of average size on grass and stone for touring (rock pegs are advised). Separated by hedges and trees, pitches have varying degrees of shade and 10A electricity connections are available. In July and August daily and evening activities are organised for all the family. The site's facilities are of a high standard and disabled visitors are well provided for. Access to some of the pitches is not ideal in some parts and may prove to be difficult for larger units.

Facilities

Two toilet blocks, one new and excellent, providing cubicles with washbasins, showers, baby room and excellent facilities for disabled visitors. Washing machines and dryer. Swimming and paddling pools (May-Sept). Bar, restaurant (6/8-8/9 and weekends). Shop (July/Aug). Bicycle and canoe hire (July/Aug). Stony river beach. Disco or karaoke every evening until midnight. Off site: Riding 1 km. Bicycle hire 3 km.

Open: 1 April - 30 September.

Directions

On D579 2 km. south of Ruoms, turn left at roundabout signed Vallon Pont d'Arc. Shortly turn right over river bridge. Site on left. GPS: N44:25.77 E04:21.37

Charges 2007

Per unit incl. 2 persons	
and electricity (10A)	€ 16,00 - € 39,00
extra person	€ 4,50 - € 7,00
child (under 7 yrs)	free - € 6,50

FR07440 Camping Mas de Champel

Quartier Champel, F-07360 Les Ollières-sur-Eyrieux (Ardèche)

Tel: 04 75 66 23 23. Email: masdechampel@wanadoo.fr

This is a simple campsite with easy access and within walking distance of a small village. It has a lively entertainment programme plus many organised activities in the high season. There are 95 unmarked, level grassy pitches, 51 for touring (electricity 6A, may need long leads) with almost no shade. A small sandy beach alongside the Eyrieux river offers lots of space for children to play in the shallow water. The bar and restaurant offer arrange of meals including breakfast and entertainment is provided in the area adjacent.

Facilities

Two small old, adequate toilet blocks with all necessary facilities. Bar, restaurant/takeaway (all open all season). Swimming pool, heated paddling pool and sunbathing area. Games/TV room. Small, simple play area. Fishing. Bicycle hire. Motorcaravan services. Only gas barbecues permitted. Many organised family activities in July/Aug. Off site: Ollières-sur-Eyrieux, small shops, bar, restaurant 500 m. Riding 7 km.

Open: 20 April - 22 September.

Directions

Leave N86 south of Valence at Beauchastel. Turn west, D120, to Ollières sur Eyrieux (about 20 km). Site is on right at entrance to village and is signed. GPS: N44:48.356 E04:36.916

Charges 2008

Per unit incl. 2 persons and electricity	€ 17,90 - € 28,80
extra person	€ 3,90 - € 6,90
child (2-7 yrs)	free - € 4,90

FR07570 Domaine de la Plage

Neyrac-les-Bains, F-07380 Aubenas (Ardèche)

Tel: 04 75 36 40 59. Email: contact@lecampingdelaplage.com

A great deal of care and attention to detail has gone into developing this compact site and its superb facilities. However, of its 45 pitches, only 8 are available for camping. The site is beautifully landscaped with flora and fauna and the facilities are sympathetically incorporated into a former textile factory. It has a very attractive solar heated pool and sunbathing terrace, bar and snack service, On-site shop, games room and library. The river can be directly accessed from the site and the owners have constructed a delightful bridge walkway crossing a waterfall and into a small picnic area. Advance booking is essential. A 'Sites et Paysages' member.

Facilities

Modern sanitary facilities include superb facilities for disabled visitors although access around the site is quite steep. Comprehensive laundry room. Fridge hire. Microwave and oven facilities. Gas. Bar. Snack service. Shop, Solar heated swimming pool and poolside bar. Large games room, library and TV room. Play area. Entertainment and children's animation programmes. Fishing. Canoeing excursions with site pickup. Off site: Thermal baths 700 m. Tennis 3 km. Golf 8 km, Bicycle hire 2 km. Boat launching and sailing 35 km.

Open: 30 March - 26 October.

Directions

From A7 exit 17 take N7 (Montelimar) for 20 km. Turn west on N102 to Aubenas. Continue on N102 for 30 km. towards Neyrac-les-Bains. Cross river at Pont-de-Labeaume and site is 2 km, on left just before entering village.

Charges 2007

Per unit incl. 2 persons	€ 14,00 - € 22,00
extra person	€ 4,00 - € 5,00
child (under 7 yrs)	€ 2,50 - € 3,50
electricity (4-10A)	€ 3,00 - € 4,00

FR26040 Kawan Village le Couspeau

F-26460 Le Poët Célard (Drôme)

Tel: **04 75 53 30 14**. Email: **info@couspeau.com**

As one approaches this site, a magnificent landscape of mountains and valleys unfolds. The site has 127 pitches with 83 for touring (6A electricity). Access to the older section of the site is reasonably easy and mature trees here provide some shade. The 30 fully serviced pitches on the lower section are large and separated by small hedges with little shade. Access is via a steep road but tractor assistance is available. Rock pegs are advised. The most direct approach to the site is via a steep road and with several hairpin bends to negotiate, care is required.

Facilities

Three sanitary blocks. Washing machines, dryer. Facilities for disabled campers (the site is not ideal with steep roads and steps). Shop (15/4-14/9). Bar (20/6-14/9). Restaurant and takeaway (25/6-25/8). Pool (1/6-30/8) and small, heated, covered, toddler's pool (14/4-14/9). Play area, organised activities. Tennis. Bicycle hire. Rafting, canoe trips (on River Drôme), riding, paragliding. Off site: Riding, fishing 5 km.

Open: 15 April - 14 September.

Directions

From A7, exit 16, take D104 towards Crest. At traffic lights on Crest bypass, turn right, D538 towards Bourdeaux. Before Bourdeaux turn right over bridge, D328B. Climb for 1.5 km. to T-junction, turn right. D328. Before Le Poët Célard turn left, D328A to site. GPS: N44:35.744 E05:06.680

Charges 2007

Per unit incl. 2 persons	€ 14,00 - € 28,00
child (under 12 yrs)	free - € 4,00
electricity (6A)	€ 3,00
Camping Cheques accepted.	

FR26030 Le Grand Lierne

B.P. 8, F-26120 Chabeuil (Drôme)

Tel: **04 75 59 83 14**. Email: **contact@grandlierne.com**

In addition to its obvious attraction as an overnight stop, fairly convenient for the A7 autoroute, this site provides a pleasant base to explore this little known area between the Ardèche and the Vercors mountains and the Côtes du Rhône wine area. It has 198 marked, stony pitches, 90 for touring units (6/10A electricity), separated by hedges and oak trees which offer varying amounts of shade. A more open area exists for those who prefer less shade and a view of the mountains, but this area contains many mobile homes. The site has an attractive pool complex with several pools and surrounded by terraces with loungers for sunbathing. One pool is covered in poor weather. There are very good sporting facilities with many organised activities making this a lively site in July and August. English and Dutch are spoken. The site is used by tour operators (30%).

Facilities

Two old sanitary blocks with modern facilities including those for disabled people. Washing machines, dryers. Motorcaravan services. Shop/restaurant, terrace (1/7-31/8). Bar/takeaway (1/5-8/9). Fridge rental. Three pools 1/5-30/9, one very small, covered and heated. Paddling pool, water slide, toboggans and lazy river. Playgrounds. Library. Extensive entertainment programme. Only gas and electric barbecues. WiFi. No pets (8/7-18/8). Off site: Golf 3 km. Bicycle hire 4.5 km. Fishing 5 km. Riding 7 km. Chabeuil 5 km. Valence 11 km.

Open: 28 April - 30 September, with all services.

Directions

Site signed from Chabeuil about 11 km. east of Valence. Best approached from south side of Valence via Valence ring road. D68 to Chabeuil. Site is off D125 to Charpey, 5 km. from Chabeuil, well signed. GPS: N44:54.951 E05:03.907

Charges 2007

Per unit incl. 2 persons	€ 16,90 - € 30,20
extra person	€ 7,90 - € 8,50
child (2-7 yrs)	€ 4,80 - € 6,20
electricity (6/10A)	€ 4,30 - € 5,70
Camping Cheques accepted.	

Check real time availability and at-the-gate prices...

www.alanrogers.com

FR26100 Camping Le Sagittaire

Pont de Mirabel, F-26110 Vinsobres (Drôme)
Tel: 04 75 27 00 00. Email: camping.sagittaire@wanadoo.fr

Le Sagittaire is beautifully situated in this picturesque region with its Côtes du Rhône vineyards, lavender fields and medieval hilltop villages. It is only 2.5 km. from Vinsobres and 6 km from Nyons, well known for its olives and its Provencal market. There are 270 level grassy pitches with 124 for touring, all with electricity (6/10A). Most are separated by hedges and there are mature trees offering some shade. The hub of the site is a water park with indoor and outdoor pools, slides and toboggans. A one hectare lake surrounded by a sandy beach is ideal for children. Leisure activities for all ages are organised in July and August, with sports during the day and barbecues, discos, karaoke and live shows in the evening, making this a lively site. This is a good base for a family holiday in a wonderful region which can be explored on foot, bike or by car.

Facilities

Three excellent modern toilet blocks. Facilities for disabled campers and families. Motorcaravan services. Shop Bar with TVs. Restaurant, takeaway, games room (1/4-30/9). Outdoor swimming pool, toboggan, slides, lazy river, cascades (1/5-30/8). Heated covered pool, paddling pool, jacuzzi (1/4-30/9). Small lake with sandy beach, picnic area. Excellent range sporting facilities, play areas. Fitness room. Extensive programme family activities in July/Aug. Fishing. Bicycle hire. Minigolf. Charcoal barbecues not allowed. Cycling is forbidden. Off site: Riding nearby. Nyons, Vaison la Romaine, Chateaux at Grignan and Suze la Rousse. Mont Ventoux for keen cyclists. Mediterranean beaches 1.5 hours away.

Open: All year.

Directions

Leave A7 at exit 19 (Bollène) and follow signs for Nyons (D94). Site is well signed on right just beyond Vinsobres (about 30 km). GPS: N44:19.664 E05:04.743

Charges 2007

Per unit incl. 2 persons	€ 17,50 - € 31,00
extra person	€ 3,60 - € 7,50
child (under 7 yrs)	€ 2,10 - € 4,50
electricity (3/6A)	€ 3,70 - € 4,80

Long stay off season discounts.

FR26140 Flower Camping la Chataigneraie

Route de Mantaille, F-26140 Anneyron (Drôme)

Tel: **04 75 31 43 33**. Email: **contact@chataigneraie.com**

Small and neat, La Chataigneraie is a family run, terraced site (English spoken) tucked away in the countryside and will suit those seeking a quieter, relaxing family orientated site. It is not ideal for those with walking difficulties. There are 71 medium sized, slightly sloping, grassy pitches, 30 for touring away from the static units. They are separated by a variety of hedges and young trees provide varying degrees of shade and all have 6/10A electricity. The Drôme is a beautiful area to explore with many old towns and villages with their markets and museums. Enjoy the local produce and the wines of the Rhône valley.

Facilities

The single toilet block at the top of the site is a good, modern building kept very clean. Bar and small shop. Good restaurant/takeaway with full menu at weekends and high season, otherwise a 'menu de jour'. Swimming and paddling pools (15/5-15/9). Short tennis. Two small play areas, TV and games room. Bicycle hire. Farmer's market twice a week. Entertainment for children and adults (July/Aug). WiFi internet access near bar. Only electric barbecues can be used. Off site: Marked walks and cycle tracks in the hills around. Fishing and golf 3 km. Riding 8 km.

Open: 1 April - 30 September.

Directions

Leave A7 south of Lyons at exit 12 and go south on the N7 for 7 km. Turn left on D1 to Anneyron. In the village turn right on D161 signed Mantaille and in 3 km. turn right on D301, signed Albon. Site is shortly on the right, is well signed. GPS: N45:15.282 E04:54.191

Charges 2008

Per unit incl. 2 persons and electricity	€ 14,90 - € 23,50
extra person	€ 4,00 - € 5,00
child (3-14 yrs)	€ 2,00 - € 3,80
dog	€ 2,00 - € 2,20

CAMPING LA CHATAIGNERAIE***

Route de Mantaille - 26140 Anneyron - Tel: 0033 475 31 43 33 - Fax: 0033 475 03 84 67
E-mail: contact@chataigneraie.com - Internet: www.chataigneraie.com

FR26110 Les 4 Saisons Camping de Grâne

Route de Roche-sur-Grâne, F-26400 Grâne (Drôme)

Tel: **04 75 62 64 17**. Email: **camping4saisons@wanadoo.fr**

This small, terraced site, open all year, nestles in the hillsides of the lower Drôme valley close to the Vercors Mountains. With its 80 pitches (73 for touring units), it provides mainly overnight accommodation but it is worth a longer stay. The pitches are level and stony, of variable size, cut out of the hillside and reached by a one-way system on tarmac roads. All pitches have electricity (6-10A), some with water and drain. The modern main building houses reception on the top floor, with other facilities below, and provides commanding views across the valley towards Crest and the Vercors.

Facilities

Good sanitary facilities, heated in low season, include, baby room, en-suite facilities for disabled visitors (but site is very sloping and not suitable for wheelchairs). Washing machine. Bar (15/4-15/10. TV room. Small swimming pool (15/4-15/9). Play area. Bicycle hire. Off site: Village nearby with shops catering for most needs. Fishing 1 km. Riding 3 km. Crest.

Open: All year.

Directions

From A7 exit 17, or the N7 at Loriol, take the D104 towards Crest. After 8 km. in Grâne take D113 south. Site is on left about 600 m. beyond the village. GPS: N44:43.661 E04:55.592

Charges 2007

Per unit incl. 2 persons	€ 13,00 - € 16,00
extra person	€ 3,00 - € 5,00
child (under 13 yrs)	€ 2,00 - € 4,00
electricity	€ 4,00
dog	€ 3,00

FR26150 Flower Camping Lac Bleu

Quarter la Touche, F-26410 Chatillon-en-Diois (Drôme)

Tel: **04 75 21 85 30**. Email: **info@lacbleu-diois.com**

This spacious and peaceful site is run by a very friendly family who have made many improvements to the site with many more in the pipeline. It lies in a beautiful valley surrounded by mountains, south of the Vercors National Park. The 90 pitches (78 for touring) are large, level, with rough grass, slightly bumpy and separated by a variety of trees offering some shade (rock pegs advised). All have electricity (6-10A). At the centre of the site is a lake of 2.5 hectares with warm clean water fed by springs making it ideal for swimming and fishing. A good bar, restaurant and terrace overlook the lake and there is plenty of space for children to play. An evening stroll around the lake is recommended. The site is near the very small River Bez and not far from the interesting and ancient small town of Die, the home of the famous Clairette de Die – a sparkling wine mentioned in dispatches by the Romans around 40 AD. It is a very good site for exploring this picturesque part of France, to completely unwind and enjoy the views, the sunset over the mountains and the clean air.

Facilities

Two clean toilet blocks one new, the other refurbished for 2007, with all the necessary facilities including baby room and facilities for disabled campers. Motorcaravan service point. Small shop. Bar/restaurant. Takeaway. TV and games room. Play area bordering the lake. Large sports/play area. Bicycle hire. Footpaths around lake. Lake bathing and fishing. Pedaloes. Internet point. Only gas and electric barbecues allowed. Off site: Medieval villages (Châtillon 2 km). Canoeing, canyoning, grottos.

Open: 1 April - 30 September.

Directions

Head southeast from Die on the D93, signed Gap. After about 5 km. turn left on D539 signed Châtillon-en-Diois. After 4.5 km. bear right onto D140, site signed. Follow signs to site, shortly on left. GPS: N44:40.947 E05:26.799

Charges 2007

Per unit incl. 2 persons	€ 9,90 - € 23,00

Quartier la Touche - 26410 Châtillon en Diois - France
Tel.: 0033 (0)4 75 21 85 30 - Fax: 0033 (0)4 75 21 82 05
E-mail: info@lacbleu-diois.com - www.lacbleu-diois.com

Camping Qualité

flower camping

FR26130 Kawan Village l'Hirondelle

Bois de St Ferreol, F-26410 Menglon (Drôme)

Tel: **04 75 21 82 08**. Email: **contact@campinghirondelle.com**

This natural, spacious and peaceful site is run by a very friendly family and you are assured a good welcome. It lies in a beautiful valley, south of the Vercors mountains and the Vercors National Park, beside the River Bez, a tributary of the River Drôme which is also close by. In natural openings in woodland, the 100 large to very large pitches all have electricity (3/6A) and are stony and slightly bumpy (rock pegs advised). There are 58 for touring units. The large pitches are separated from others by a wide variety of trees with the 1.5 km. of river bank on one side.

Facilities

Two large toilet blocks offer all the necessary facilities. Good bar/restaurant with menus and takeaway. Small range of supplies, including bread, on sale from the bar. Excellent pool complex with small slide, paddling pool and jacuzzi (1/5 -17/9). Room to play and paddle in the river. Playground. Club/TV room. Internet. Fishing. Football, boules, archery. Multisport court. Organised events. Occasional evening events. Off site: Riding and bicycle hire 3 km. Canoeing, kayaking, climbing, rambling, mountain biking and cycling over the steep local passes.

Open: 28 April - 17 September.

Directions

From Die follow D93 southwards and after 5 km, at Pont de Quart, turn left on D539 signed Châtillon. After approx. 4 km. turn right on D140, signed Menglon. Site is shortly on right just after crossing a small river. GPS: N44:40.885 E05:26.846

Charges 2007

Per pitch incl. 2 persons	€ 16,20 - € 25,00
extra person	€ 4,85 - € 7,00
electricity (3/6A)	€ 3,15 - € 4,20
Camping Cheques accepted.	

Check real time availability and at-the-gate prices...

www.alanrogers.com

FR26210 Camping les Bois du Chatelas

Mobile homes ▶ page 504

Route de Dieulefit, F-26460 Bourdeaux (Drôme)

Tel: **04 75 00 60 80**. Email: **contact@chatelas.com**

Located at the heart of the the Drôme Provencale, Les Bois du Chatelas is a smart, family run site which has undergone many recent improvements. The site is just 1 km. from the delightful village of Bourdeaux which offers a good range of shops, cafés, etc. There are 120 pitches here of which 69 are occupied by mobile homes. Although situated on a hillside, the pitches are level and of a good size. They all offer electricity, water and drainage. Les Bois du Chatelas is a particularly good choice for those seeking an active holiday. Member of Sites et Paysages de France. The long distance GR9 footpath passes through the site and there are very many walking and cycle routes close at hand. A popular aqua-gym is organised in the large outdoor pool in peak season. In the high season, a lively entertainment programme is organized as well as a number of cycling and walking excursions.

Facilities

Two heated toilet blocks (on upper and lower levels) with facilities for babies and disabled people (note: the site is hilly and may be unsuitable). Restaurant/pizzeria. Shop. Bar. Indoor swimming pool. Outdoor pool with water slide, waterfall and jacuzzi. Sports pitch. Archery. Play area. Bicycle hire. Entertainment and excursion programme (July/Aug). Mobile homes for rent. Off site: Rafting and canoe trips. Riding 5 km. Fishing 1 km. Very extensive walking and cycle (mountain bike) opportunities. Vercors mountain range. Mediaeval villages.

Open: 7 April - 30 September.

Directions

From the north, leave A7 at exit 16 and join the eastbound D104 to Crest. Upon reaching Crest take D538 south to Bourdeaux and continue towards Dieulefit. Site is on the left 1 km. beyond Bourdeaux and is well signed.

Charges 2008

Per unit incl. 2 persons	€ 14,00 - € 24,00
extra person	€ 4,20 - € 5,00
child (1-7 yrs)	€ 2,70 - € 2,90
electricity (10A)	€ 4,30 - € 4,50

Camping Les Bois du Chatelas

Route de Dieulefit - F-26460 Bordeaux - Tl.: (33) 4 75 00 60 80 - Fax (33) 4 75 00 60 81
E-mail: contact@chatelas.com - www.chatelas.com

FR26090 Camping les Truffières

Lieu-dit Nachony, F-26230 Grignan (Drôme)

Tel: **04 75 46 93 62**. Email: **info@lestruffieres.com**

This is a delightful small site in a rural setting within walking distance of the picturesque ancient village of Grignan with wonderful views and providing peace and tranquillity. The 85 good sized pitches are level and fairly stony with 79 for touring units, all with 10A electricity. They are shaded by oak trees and separated by rosemary or laurel hedging. The Croze family is most welcoming and achieves high standards of cleanliness and order while maintaining a friendly and relaxed atmosphere. The Drôme is one of the most beautiful regions of France; vineyards, olive orchards, lavender, sunflowers, wild flowers and fruit orchards abound.

Facilities

Good toilet block provides all necessary facilities. Bar (all season), snack bar, takeaway (mid June - end Aug). Swimming pool, smaller pool for children. Volleyball, table tennis, boules. Little in the way of on site entertainment but many off site activities can be booked. No dogs. Only communal barbecues. Off site: Riding 200 m. Fishing 2 km. Bicycle hire 5 km. Golf 6 km. Grignan with its château. Nyons with excellent market (Thurs) 26 km. Vaison la Romaine with Roman ruins 33 km.

Open: 20 April - 20 September.

Directions

From N7 (or A7 autoroute exit 18) south of Montélimar, take D133 (changes to D541) signed Grignan. After 9 km, just before entering Grignan, take D71 towards Charamet and site is shortly on the left. GPS: N44:24.714 E04:53.433

Charges 2007

Per unit incl. 2 persons	€ 13,50 - € 16,50
extra person	€ 4,70
electricity (10A)	€ 4,20

No credit cards.

FR26260 Camping les Acacias

F-26340 Vercheny (Drôme)

Tel: 04 75 21 72 51. Email: info@campinglesacacias.com

Midway between Crest and Die, les Acacias is a comfortable riverside site. There are 90 pitches here with 6 or 10A electricity to most. The pitches are of a good size and generally well shaded. They are separated by trees and hedges and some are available along the riverside. The site slopes down to the banks of the Drôme river and some up and down walking will probably be required. A small canoe base has been established here and canoe excursions to the Gorges de Saillans are justifiably popular. The site's bar and snack bar is housed below reception and have a small terrace. Given the proximity of the D93 and railway line, there may be some background road and rail noise. Walking and mountain biking are popular pursuits and many trails are available in the surrounding countryside. Nearby mountains such as Archiane and Les Trois Becs are popular excursions. In high season, the site runs an entertainment and excursion programme, including a club for children.

Facilities

Three toilet blocks with facilities for babies and disabled visitors. Bar and snack bar. Small shop. Play areas. Canoe hire. Fishing (permit needed). TV room. Entertainment and children's club (peak season). Entertainment and excursion programme (July/Aug). Mobile homes and chalets for rent. Off site: Cycling and walking trails. Restaurants, cafés and shops in Saillans and Vercheny.

Open: 1 April - 30 September.

Directions

Head east from Crest on the D93. Site is located on the right, midway between Saillans and Vercheny.

Charges 2007

Per pitch incl. 2 persons	€ 12,00 - € 14,50
extra person	€ 3,20 - € 3,90
child (under 4 years)	free
electricity (6A)	€ 3,10

Situated between the Vercors and Provence, nestled at the foot of the mountain 'Les Trois Becs' at the riverside of the Drôme with crystal blue water. Les Acacias is the right place to be for relaxing and activities. Flat and wooded terrain amidst nature. We offer canoes for rent for a discovery tour through the Drôme.

26340 Vercheny - France
Tél. 04 75 21 72 51 - Fax 04 75 21 73 98
E-mail info@campinglesacacias.com

www.campinglesacacias.com

FR42030 Camping Bel' Epoque du Pilat

Route De Malleval, F-42410 Pélussin (Loire)

Tel: 04 74 87 66 60. Email: camping_belepoque@orange.fr

This is a peaceful, family run site located within the relatively little known Pilat Regional Park and close to the pretty town of Pélussin. There are fine views over the Rhône Valley and the distant mountains from many of the site's 70 pitches. These are generally level and of a good size with reasonable shade, the majority with electrical connections (6A); 20 pitches are occupied by mobile homes. The site is well maintained with an attractive pool and small bar and snack bar (only open in July and August). The surrounding area offers very many superb walking and cycling opportunites, with over 700 km. of marked trails. A 'Sites et Paysages' member.

Facilities

Well appointed toilet block with facilities for disabled visitors. Small shop in reception. Bar, snack bar, and takeaway meals. Swimming pool (May - Sept). Tennis. Play area, Limited entertainment in peak season. Mobile homes for rent. Off site: Golf 12 km. Fishing and riding 5 km. Vienne (Roman town). Safari park at Peaugres. Excursions to Côtes du Rhone vineyards. Lyon (50 km. to the north). Many walking paths and cycle trails through the Regional park.

Open: 1 April - 30 September.

Directions

From the north, leave A7 autoroute at exit 10 and join southbound N86. Continue through Condrieu to Chavanay and then take the westbound D7 sign Pélussin. Shortly before reaching the village centre bear left to follow 'camping' signs. Site is 1.5 km. further on the right.

Charges 2007

Per unit incl. 2 persons and electricity	€ 16,00 - € 20,00
extra person	€ 4,50

359

Check real time availability and at-the-gate prices...

www.alanrogers.com

FR26270 Camping Champ la Chèvre
F-26220 Lus la Croix Haute (Drôme)

Tel: 04 92 58 50 14. Email: info@campingchamplachevre.com

This is a pleasant, unpretentious site with some really magnificent views across towards the western Alps. Formerly a farm (hence its name!) and now under new management, Champ la Chèvre is undergoing a steady process of refurbishment and is attractively located just 200 m. from the village and 500 m. from the N75. There are 100 pitches, for the most part sunny and quite spacious, and many with fine mountain views. Some pitches are sloping and most pitches have 6A electrical connections. Although there is no swimming pool on site, the large municipal pool adjacent is free for all campers. This is a good base for exploring the mountains and the owners have many ideas for excursions in the area, including downhill mountain biking, swimming in local rivers and hundreds of kilometres of walking trails. The nearby village of Lus La Croix Haute is pretty and has a good range of shops and a small railway station.

Facilities

Centrally located toilet block with facilities for disabled visitors. Motorcaravan services. Play area. Minigolf. Mobile homes and chalets for rent. Off site: Heated swimming pool adjacent (free to campers). Village of Lus La Croix Haute 200 m. Railway station 300 m. Tennis. Many walking and cycle trails.

Open: 28 April - 30 September.

Directions

From the north, head south from Grenoble initially on the A480 and then the A51 towards Sisteron. Then join the southbound N75 for around 35 km to Lus La Croix Haute. Drive through the village and site is well signed.

Charges 2007

Per person	€ 3,60
child (under 10 yrs)	€ 2,60
pitch	€ 5,30
electricity (6A)	€ 3,40

Camping** Champ la Chèvre

Mobile Homes, chalets and cabins for rent
Bar, restaurant, take-away and pizza during high season
New sanitary facilities, table tennis, soccer, volleyball, jeu de boules and evening entertainment

Please make reservations for high season

D505 - 26620 Lus La Croix Haute - Tel.: 0033 (0)4 92 58 50 14
E-mail: info@campingchamplachevre.com - www.campingchamplachevre.com

Summerseason from 26/4 to 28/9
Winterseason from 28/9 to 26/4

FR69020 Camping Municipal la Grappe Fleurie
La Lie, F-69820 Fleurie (Rhône)

Tel: 04 74 69 80 07. Email: camping@fleurie.org

With easy access from both the A6 autoroute and the N6, this site is ideally situated for night stops or indeed for longer stays to explore the vineyards and historic attractions of the Beaujolais region. Virtually surrounded by vineyards, but within walking distance (less than 1 km.) of the pretty village of Fleurie, this is an immaculate small site, with 85 separated touring pitches. All are grassed and fairly level with the benefit of individual access to water, drainage and electrical connections (10A). Baker calls 07.30 hrs - 08.30 hrs. Wine tasting twice per week in high season. Only gas or electric barbecues are allowed. Restaurant and shopping facilities are available in the village.

Facilities

Sanitary facilities in two blocks have British and Turkish style toilets and very satisfactory shower and washing facilities (showers closed 22.00-07.00 hrs). Facilities for disabled visitors. Two cold showers are provided for those wishing to cool down in summer. Washing machine and tumble dryer. Outdoor swimming pool (15m by 7m). Small playground. Table tennis, tennis and volleyball. Off site: Fishing 10 km. Fleurie 600 m.

Open: End of March - End of October.

Directions

From N6 at Le Maison Blanche/Romanech-Thorins, take D32 to village of Fleurie from where site is signed. GPS: N46:11.258 E04:41.955

Charges 2007

Per unit incl. 2 persons and electricity	€ 13,50 - € 15,00
tent pitch incl. 2 persons and electricity	€ 11,50 - € 13,00
extra person	€ 4,20 - € 5,20
child (5-10 yrs)	€ 2,90 - € 3,40

Check real time availability and at-the-gate prices...
www.alanrogers.com

FR69010 Camping Indigo Lyon

Lyon, F-69570 Dardilly (Rhône)

Tel: **04 78 35 64 55**. Email: **lyon@camping-indigo.com**

Camping International is a modern overnight site just off the A6 autoroute. Kept busy with overnight trade, reception and the café (in main season) open until quite late. There are 180 separate numbered plots. Many have electricity (10A), water and waste water drainage. Those for caravans are mostly on hardstandings on a slight slope, with another small grassy part, while those for tents are on a flatter area of grass. A very large commercial centre has been developed just outside the site, with eight hotels, restaurants, a supermarket, petrol station, etc. There is some road noise. Lyon is a very attractive city, especially noted for the excellence of its food, and well worth a visit. A bus stop for the centre (8 km.) is nearby (timetables in reception).

Facilities

Three heated sanitary blocks have free hot water (solar heated) and washbasins in cabins. Baby facilities and washing machines. Motorcaravan services. Unheated swimmed pool (1/6-15/9, supervised). Playground. TV room. Games room. Picnic and barbecue area.

Open: All year.

Directions

Travelling south, do not take A46 motorway around Lyon, continue on A6, take exit Limonest, Dardilly, Porte de Lyon. About 8 km. north of Lyon tunnel; turn left for Porte de Lyon (well signed).

Charges 2007

Per person	€ 3,10 - € 3,72
child (7-15 yrs)	€ 2,40 - € 2,88
pitch with electricity	€ 12,20 - € 17,40

Camping Cheques accepted.

FR69030 Camping les Portes du Beaujolais

Avenue Jean Vacher, F-69480 Anse (Rhône)

Tel: **04 74 67 12 87**. Email: **campingbeaujolais@wanadoo.fr**

Being just off the main motorway south to the Mediterranean, this campsite would make a good overnight stop. Also the good public transport from Anse means that it could be used as a base for visiting Lyon. However, despite some noise from the motorway and the main line railway, there is much more to it than that. The well run site has good facilities and modern buildings of traditional design and materials. Its 150 formal pitches are shady, level, numbered and marked, with neatly trimmed grass and hedges, and electrical connections (6A). There are 20 fully serviced pitches.

Facilities

New reception area, chalets and mobile homes. Modern toilet blocks, facilities for disabled people. Baby changing room. Motorcaravan services. Washing machines. Shop (all season). Gas supplies. Bar, restaurant, takeaway (1/6-15/9). Games room. Internet. Swimming pool, paddling pool (1/5-30/9) Playground. Playing field. Tennis. Minigolf. Boules. Free loan of barbecues. Off site: Anse 1 km. with supermarket, shops, restaurants, bars, takeaway, ATM, bus stop. Narrow gauge railway at exit. Fishing 200 m. Boat launching 500 m. Bicycle hire 1 km. Riding 1.5 km. Sailing 1.5 km. Golf 2 km.

Open: 1 March - 31 October.

Directions

Anse is on N6, 6 km. south of Villefranche-sur-Saône, 21 km. north of Lyon. Site signed from northern and southern ends of village. There are height limits on all approaches (3 or 3.2 m). GPS: N45:56.418 E04:43.596

Charges 2007

Per unit incl. 2 persons, electricity	€ 17,00 - € 18,70
incl. services	€ 18,00 - € 21,00
extra person	€ 4,40 - € 4,80
child (2-7 yrs)	€ 3,40 - € 3,60
animal	€ 3,00

MAP 14

This is a corner of France that evokes dreamy ima of lazy afternoons among sleepy village squares, sunr vineyards and beautiful lavend fields basking under the dazzling b of the sky.

ONLY THE DÉPARTEMENTS FROM THE MOUNTAINOUS REGION OF PROVENCE HAVE BEEN INCLUDED IN THIS SECTION: 04 ALPES-DE-HAUTE-PROVENCE, 05 HAUTES-ALPES, 84 VAUCLUSE

Provence is a region of magical light, bleached landscapes, olive groves, herb-scented garrigue, vineyards and Roman and medieval antiquities. The river valleys provide natural routes through the mountain barrier. Roman monuments can be seen at Orange, and Vaison-la-Romaine, where a 2,000 year old bridge is still in use. Avignon was the site of the papal court and the Palais des Papes at Avignon is a spectacular construction.

The Hautes-Alpes will reward with stunning vistas, peace and quiet. Briançon is the highest town in Europe and many of the high passes are not for the faint-hearted. The Vaucluse, where in the late spring the southern slopes of the Montagne du Luberon are a mass of colour with wild flowers. The extinct volcanic cone of Mont Ventoux provides dramatic views. The scents, the colours and an amazing intensity of light have encouraged artists and writers to settle amidst the sleepy villages, with narrow streets and ancient dwellings topped with sun-baked terracotta tiles, where the air is fragrant with the perfume of wild herbs and lavender.

Places of interest

Avignon: ramparts, old city, Papal Palace, old palace, Calvet museum.

Mont Ventoux: near Carpentras, one of the best known stages of the classic Tour de France annual cycle race.

Orange: Roman city, gateway to the Midi, Colline St Europe.

St Vaison la Romaine: Roman city, the French Pompei.

Cuisine of the region

Influenced by the Savoie area to the north and the Côte d'Azur to the south, with emphasis on herbs and garlic, and fish. The wine region is mainly known for its dry, fruity rosé wines: Bandol, Bellet, Palette, Cassis. Red wines include Côtes du Rhône and Châteauneuf-du-Pape.

Aigo Bouido: garlic and sage soup with bread (or eggs and cheese).

Farcement (Farçon Savoyard): potatoes baked with cream, eggs, bacon, dried pears and prunes.

Pissaladière: Provencal bread dough with onions, anchovies, olives.

Ratatouille: aubergines, courgettes, onions, garlic, red peppers and tomatoes in olive oil.

Tartiflette: potato, bacon, onions and Reblochon cheese.

FR04010 Sunêlia Hippocampe

Mobile homes ▶ page 504

Route de Napoléon, F-04290 Volonne (Alpes-de-Haute-Provence)

Tel: 04 92 33 50 00. Email: camping@l-hippocampe.com

Hippocampe is a friendly family run, 'all action' lakeside site, with families in mind, situated in a beautiful area of France. The perfumes of thyme, lavender and wild herbs are everywhere and the higher hills of Haute Provence are not too far away. There are 447 level, numbered pitches (221 for touring units), medium to very large (130 sq.m.) in size. All have electricity (10A) and 243 have water and drainage, most are separated by bushes and cherry trees. Some of the best pitches border the lake. The restaurant, bar, takeaway and shop have all been completely renewed. Games, aerobics, competitions, entertainment and shows, plus a daily club for younger family members are organised in July/August. A soundproof underground disco is set well away from the pitches and is very popular with teenage customers. Staff tour the site at night ensuring a good night's sleep. The site is, however, much quieter in low season and, with its good discounts, is the time for those who do not want or need entertaining. The Gorges du Verdon is a sight not to be missed and rafting, paragliding or canoe trips can be booked from the site's own tourist information office. Being on the lower slopes of the hills of Haute-Provence, the surrounding area is good for both walking and mountain biking. All in all, this is a very good site for an active or restful holiday and is suitable for outfits of all sizes. Used by tour operators (20 pitches). English is spoken.

Facilities

Toilet blocks vary from old to modern, all with good clean facilities that include washbasins in cabins. Washing machines. Motorcaravan service point. Bread available (from 26/4). Shop, bar, restaurant and pizzeria (26/4-7/9). Large, pool complex (open from 5/4, heated in early and late seasons). Tennis. Fishing. Canoeing. Boules. Several sports facilities (some with free instruction). Charcoal barbecues are not permitted. Off site: Village of Volonne 600 m. Bicycle hire 2 km. Riding 12 km. Various sporting opportunities.

Open: 22 March - 30 September.

Directions

Approaching from the north turn off N85 across river bridge to Volonne, then right to site. From the south right on D4, 1 km. before Château Arnoux. GPS: N44:06.366 E06:00.933

Charges 2008

Per unit with 2 persons	
simple pitch:	€ 13,00 - € 27,00
with electricity	€ 16,00 - € 32,00
with water/drainage 100 sq.m.	€ 16,00 - € 34,00
with water/drainage 140 sq.m.	€ 20,00 - € 39,00
extra person (over 4 yrs)	€ 3,00 - € 6,50

Special low season offers.
Camping Cheques accepted.

363

FR04020 Castel Camping le Camp du Verdon

Mobile homes  page 504

Domaine du Verdon, F-04120 Castellane (Alpes-de-Haute-Provence)

Tel: 04 92 83 61 29. Email: contact@camp-du-verdon.com

Close to the 'Route des Alpes' and the Gorges du Verdon. Two heated swimming pools and numerous on-site activities during high season help to keep non-canoeists here. Du Verdon is a large level site, part meadow, part wooded, with 500 partly shaded, rather stony pitches (390 for tourists). Numbered and separated by bushes, they vary in size, have 6A electricity, and 125 also have water and waste water. They are mostly separate from the mobile homes (60) and pitches used by tour operators (110). Some overlook the unfenced river Verdon, so watch the children. This is a very popular holiday area, the gorge, canoeing and rafting being the main attractions, ideal for active families. One can walk to Castellane without using the main road. Dances and discos in July and August suit all age groups – the latest finishing time is around 23.00 (after that time patrols make sure that the site is quiet). The site is popular and very busy in July and August.

Facilities

Refurbished toilet blocks include facilities for disabled visitors. Washing machines. Motorcaravan services. Restaurant, terrace, log fire for cooler evenings. New supermarket. Pizzeria/crêperie. Takeaway. Heated swimming pools, paddling pool with 'mushroom' fountain (all open all season). Organised entertainments (July and August). Playgrounds. Minigolf, table tennis, archery, basketball, volleyball. Organised walks. Bicycle hire. Riding. Small fishing lake. ATM. Room for games and TV. Internet access and WiFi. Off site: Castellane and the Verdon Gorge 1 km. Riding 2 km. Boat launching 4.5 km. Golf 20 km. Water sports.

Open: 15 May - 15 September.

Directions

From Castellane take D952 westwards towards Gorges du Verdon and Moustiers. Site is 1 km. on left.

Charges 2008

Per unit with 2 or 3 persons	€ 18,00 - € 32,00
incl. 6A electricity	€ 24,00 - € 38,00
extra person (over 3 yrs)	€ 7,00 - € 12,00
dog	€ 2,50

Camping Cheques accepted.

FR04100 Kawan Village International

Mobile homes  page 504

Route Napoleon, F-04120 Castellane (Alpes-de-Haute-Provence)

Tel: 04 92 83 66 67. Email: info@camping-international.fr

Camping International has very friendly, English speaking owners and is a reasonably priced, less commercialised site situated in some of the most dramatic scenery in France with good views. The 274 pitches, 130 good sized ones for touring, are clearly marked, separated by trees and small hedges, and all have electricity and water. The bar/restaurant overlooks the swimming pool with its sunbathing area set in a sunny location, and all have fantastic views. In high season English speaking young people entertain children (3-8 years) and teenagers. Access is good for larger units. On some evenings the teenagers are taken to the woods for campfire 'sing-alongs' which can go on till the early hours without disturbing the rest of the site. There are guided walks into the surrounding hills in the nearby Gorges du Verdon – a very popular excursion, particularly in high season. The weather in the hills here is very pleasant without the excessive heat of the coast.

Facilities

Small toilet blocks are of an older design. One newer block has modern facilities, including those for disabled visitors. Washing machines and dryer. Motorcaravan services. Fridge hire. Shop. Restaurant/takeaway (May-Sept). Swimming pool (1/5-30/9). Club/TV room. Children's animation, occasional evening entertainment (July/Aug). Play area. Boules. Internet access. WiFi free whole site. Off site: Riding 800 m. Castellane (1.5 km), with river, canyon and rapids, ideal for canoeing, rafting and canyoning etc. Walking, biking. Boat launching 5 km.

Open: 31 March - 1 October.

Directions

Site is 1 km. north of Castellane on the N85 'Route Napoleon'. GPS: N43:50.500 E06:30.420

Charges 2007

Per unit incl. 2 persons	€ 14,00 - € 19,00
extra person	€ 3,00 - € 4,00
electricity (6A)	€ 3,00 - € 4,00
dog	€ 2,00

Camping Cheques accepted.

Camping International
Route Napoléon
04120 Castellane
Tél : +33 492 836 667
Fax : +33 492 837 767
mail : info@campinginternational.fr
www.campinginternational.fr

Castel Camping Caravaning
Domaine du Verdon
04120 Castellane
Tél : +33 492 836 129
Fax : +33 492 836 937
E-mail : contact@camp-du-verdon.com
www.camp-du-verdon.com

Provence
Castellane
Canyon du Verdon

3 SEASONS ELITE

Camping Cheque

FR04040 RCN les Collines de Castellane

Route de Grasse, F-04120 Castellane (Alpes-de Haute-Provence)

Tel: **04 92 83 68 96**. Email: **info@rcn-lescollinesdecastellane.fr**

RCN, a Dutch company, runs a chain of good campsites in the Netherlands. They now operate five sites in France, all with Dutch managers who speak good French and English. Les Collines de Castellane is pleasantly situated in the mountainous landscape of the Alpes-de Haute-Provence. There are 160 touring pitches spread over a series of flat terraces under umbrella pines with electric tricycles provided for transport up and down the quite steep pathways. At the top of the site, near the entrance, is a combined reception and small restaurant area. The adjoining swimming pool is quite large and offers a water slide and a paddling pool for small children.

Facilities

Tiled, modern toilet facilities include individual cabins and facilities for disabled visitors and babies. Laundry facilities. Shop. Library. Small restaurant (including takeaway) with terrace. Heated swimming pool with slides and paddling pool. Tennis court. Football and volleyball pitch. Boules. Three play areas. Organised activities (May - Sept). Off site: Golf 10 km.

Open: 22 April - 22 September.

Directions

Directions: Take the N85 (Route Napoleon) from Digné-les-Bains towards Castellane and Grasse. Site is 6 km. south of Castellane, on the right hand side of the road.

Charges 2007

Per unit incl. 2 persons,	
electricity and water	€ 18,00 - € 45,50
incl. up to 6 persons	€ 23,40 - € 46,00

FR04060 Camping Caravaning le Haut-Verdon

RD 908, F-04370 Villars-Colmars (Alpes-de-Haute-Provence)

Tel: **04 92 83 40 09**. Email: **campinglehautverdon@wanadoo.fr**

For those seeking a quiet, family site set in most spectacular scenery, Camping Le Haut-Verdon is ideal. It is on the banks of the Verdon, an excellent trout river, which flows through the spectacular gorge. Surrounded by the majestic peaks of the Alpes-de-Haute-Provence, it is on the doorstep of the Mercantour National Park. Set amongst the pines, the 87 pitches are mostly on the large size but are rather stony. With 73 for touring units, all have electricity (6/10A) but some require long leads. There is a small village near, and the town of St André is 23 km.

Facilities

Refurbished, heated toilet block. Washing machines. Freezer for ice packs, room for tenters for inclement weather. Motorcaravan services. Small shop. Bar/restaurant, takeaway. Barbecue areas (portable ones banned). Heated swimming, paddling pools (from 1 June). Small play area. Boules. Skittle alley. Table tennis. Tennis. TV room. Organised games, competitions. Fishing. Off site: Bicycle hire and riding 10 km.

Open: 5 May - 16 September.

Directions

Follow D955 north from St André les Alpes towards Colmar. After 11 km. road number changes to D908. Site on right at southern edge of Villars-Colmars. Caravans not advised to use the D908 from Annot or Col d'Allos from Barcelonnette.

Charges 2007

Per person	€ 3,00 - € 5,00
child (2-7 yrs)	€ 2,00 - € 4,00
pitch incl. electricity	€ 10,00 - € 19,00

FR04080 Yelloh! Village l'Etoile des Neiges

F-04140 Montclar (Alpes-de-Haute-Provence)

Tel: **04 66 73 97 39**. Email: **info@yellohvillage-etoile-des-neiges.com**

This attractive, family run site near the mountain village and ski resort of St Jean Montclar is open most of the year. Being at an altitude of 1,300 m. the nights can get quite cold in summer. The 130 shady terraced pitches, with 70 for touring, are separated by small shrubs and alpine trees. All pitches are close to electricity and water points. An attractive bar and restaurant overlooks the two swimming pools, with the shallow pool having a water slide ideal for children. The site has no shop but local shops are only a few minutes walk away. A 'Sites et Paysages' member.

Facilities

Central toilet block (heated in winter) and facilities for disabled visitors. Two washing machines. Motorcaravan services. Bar/restaurant. Swimming pool (all amenities open 15/5-9/9). Tennis, table tennis, boules. Two play areas. Rafting, walking (July/Aug). Off site: Shops in village a few minutes walk. Bicycle hire and riding in village. Fishing 1.5 km. Watersports and beach at Lac Serre Ponçon 7 km.

Open: 30 April - 25 March.

Directions

Site is 35 km. south of Gap via D900B. Beyond Serre Ponçon, turn right, D900 signed Selonnet. Entering St Jean Montclar turn right, shops fork right to campsite. Approach roads are steep and icy in winter.

Charges 2007

Per unit incl. 2 persons	€ 14,00 - € 31,00
extra person	€ 4,00 - € 5,00
child (2-5 yrs)	free - € 4,00
Camping Cheques accepted.	

Check real time availability and at-the-gate prices...

www.**alanrogers**.com

FR04030 Kawan Village Moulin de Ventre

Niozelles, F-04300 Forcalquier (Alpes-de-Haute-Provence)

Tel: **04 92 78 63 31**. Email: **moulindeventre@aol.com**

This is a friendly, family run site in the heart of Haute-Provence, near Forcalquier, a bustling small French market town. Attractively located beside a small lake and 28 acres of wooded, hilly land, which is available for walking. Herbs of Provence can be found growing wild and flowers, birds and butterflies abound – a nature lovers delight. The 124 level, grassy pitches for tourists are separated by a variety of trees and small shrubs, 114 of them having electricity (6A; long leads may be necessary). Some pitches are particularly attractive, bordering a small stream. English is spoken. A 'Sites et Paysages' member. The site is well situated to visit Mont Ventoux, the Luberon National Park, the Gorges du Verdon and a wide range of ancient hill villages with their markets and museums etc.

Facilities

Refurbished toilet block. Facilities for disabled people. Baby bath. Washing, drying machines. Fridge hire. Bread. Bar/restaurant, takeaway (all season), themed evenings (high season). Pizzeria. Swimming pools (15/5-15/9). New playground. Bouncy castle. Fishing, boules. Some activities organised in high season. No discos. Only electric or gas barbecues. Internet access. Off site: Shops, local market, doctor, tennis 2 km. Supermarket, chemist, riding, bicycle hire 5 km. Golf 20 km. Walking, cycling.

Open: 5 April - 30 September.

Directions

From A51 motorway take exit 19 (Brillanne). Turn right on N96 then turn left on N100 westwards (signed Forcalquier) for about 3 km. Site is signed on left, just after a bridge 3 km. southeast of Niozelles. GPS: N43:56.100 E05:52.520

Charges 2008

Per unit incl. 2 persons	
and electricity	€ 17,20 - € 26,70
extra person (over 4 yrs)	€ 3,50 - € 5,50
child (2-4 yrs)	€ 2,00 - € 3,00
dog	€ 1,50 - € 3,00

No credit cards.
Camping Cheques accepted.

Haute-Provence
**Camping
Moulin de Ventre**
04300 Niozelles
**Tel: 0033 492 78 63 31
Fax: 0033 492 79 86 92**
www.moulin-de-ventre.com
Situated between Verdon and Luberon

FR04120 Camping Indigo Forcalquier

Route de Sigonce, F-04300 Forcalquier (Alpes-de-Haute-Provence)

Tel: **04 92 75 27 94**. Email: **forcalquier@camping-indigo.com**

Although Camping Indigo is an urban site, there are extensive views over the surrounding countryside where there are some excellent walks. The pitches are on grass and are of good size, all with electricity, 6 fully serviced. The site is secure, with an electronic barrier (card deposit required) and there is no entry between 22.30 and 07.00. Local guides lead tours of the historic town and areas. This is an excellent base for visiting Forcalquier, a 15th century fortified hill town and the Monday market (the best in Haute Provence). Since this site has acquired new owners, an extensive modernisation programme has been put into effect.

Facilities

Two refurbished toilet blocks with washbasins in cubicles and excellent facilities for disabled visitors. They are cleaned twice daily. Bar. Snack bar and takeaway (15/6-1/9). Play area. Heated swimming and paddling pools. Off site: All shops, banks etc. available in town centre, 200 m.

Open: 28 March - 19 October.

Directions

From town centre, follow 'Digne - Sisteron' for 400 m, turning sharp left onto Sigonce road after Esso petrol station, then first right and site is 200 m. on the right. Well signed from town. GPS: N43:57.660 E05:47.226

Charges 2007

Per person	€ 4,70 - € 5,50
child (2-7 yrs)	€ 3,10 - € 3,70
pitch	€ 3,90 - € 8,50
electricity (6A)	€ 4,20

FR04110 Yelloh! Village Verdon Parc

Domaine de la Paludette, F-04800 Gréoux Les Bains (Alpes-de-Haute-Provence)

Tel: **04 66 73 97 39**. Email: **info@yellohvillage-verdon-parc.com**

Friendly and family run, this very spacious site borders the River Ardèche and is close to the attractive spa town of Gréoux les Bains. The 280 medium to very large, stony or gravel pitches (159 for tourists) are in two sections. The main part of the campsite has large pitches laid out in rows separated by poplar trees. Along the river bank the larger, more natural pitches are scattered amongst the trees and are of irregular shape and size. These have very pleasant views across the river to the town beyond. Electrical connections (10A) and water taps are reasonably close to most pitches. Unfortunately river swimming is forbidden but there is a large swimming pool on site.

Facilities

Several toilet blocks (one heated in low season) are clean and to a high standard, with all the necessary facilities including those for disabled visitors. Laundry room. Motorcaravan service point. Small shop. Bar and courtyard terrace. Restaurant and takeaway (May-Sept). TV. Internet point. Table tennis. Large play area. Miniclub for younger children (high season). Organised sports. Evening entertainment. Dogs are not accepted in high season. Gas and electric barbeques only. Off site: Gréoux les Bains 1 km. Riding and bicycle hire 1 km. Small lakeside beach 8 km.

Open: 21 March - 29 October.

Directions

Leave A51 autoroute at Manosque and take D907 southeast towards Gréoux les Bains. Turn right on D4, then left on D82 to Gréoux les Bains. Follow main road downhill through town to roundabout with fountain. Take second right, signed D8 St Pierre and descend for about 1km. Cross river and immediately turn left. Campsite shortly on the left.

Charges 2007

Per unit incl. 2 persons	€ 13,00 - € 27,00
extra person	€ 3,00 - € 5,00
child (under 13 yrs)	€ 2,00 - € 4,00
animal (not accepted 6/7-18/8)	€ 2,00 - € 3,00

FR04140 Camping les Prairies

Haute-Greyere, F-04140 Seyne les Alpes (Alpes-de-Haute-Provence)

Tel: 04 92 35 10 21. Email: **info@campinglesprairies.com**

Les Prairies lies in a beautiful part of the French Alps, at the foot of the Grand Puy (1,800 m), at the entrance to the once fortified town of Seyne. This quiet site is run by a brother and sister team who grew up on a campsite on the French Riviera. With lovely views of the mountains and the river running beside the site, there are 91 good grass pitches (with 10A electricity) and 17 mobile homes. There is a pleasant swimming pool and a bar forming part of the reception area. A few picnic tables have been provided for travellers with tents. Although only small, Seyne is the main centre of the region. Walking through this historical jewel alone is worth a stay at Les Prairies. The surrounding region offers numerous possibilities for walking, mountain biking and climbing. The nearby airfield provides opportunities for glider flying and there is paragliding from the slopes of the Grand Puy.

Facilities

The two toilet blocks near the pool are immaculate and regularly kept that way. Preset showers are quite small. Facilities for disabled visitors and babies. Laundry room. Bar and snack bar (15/6-20/8). Heated swimming pool (1/6-15/9). Petanque. Occasional entertainment in high season. Fishing. Off site: Riding adjacent. Bicycle hire 5 km.

Open: 15 April - 13 September.

Directions

Site is southeast of Gap and north of Digne-les-Bains. From Gap take D900B and turn right at T-junction where it joins the D900. Cross Col de St Jean and go through Seyne to small airfield on the left. Turn right, following signs to site (do not take an earlier sign as road is very narrow). Coming from Digne, turn left at the airfield.

Charges 2007

Per unit incl. 2 persons	€ 13,00 - € 18,00
extra person	€ 5,00
child (2-6 yrs)	€ 3,00
electricity (10A)	€ 3,50

Camping Caravaning - Les Prairies ★★★

Les Prairies provides you with PEACE, COMFORT and RELAXATION with Quality services and a friendly atmosphere.

Camping caravaning - Les Prairies ★★★
Haute-Gréyère 04140 Seyne les Alpes

Phone : +33 (0)4 92 35 10 21
Fax : +33 (0)4 92 35 26 96
Mail : info@campinglesprairies.com

FR04170 Camping les Matherons

F-04700 Puimichel (Alpes-de-Haute-Provence)

Tel: 04 92 79 60 10. Email: **lesmatherons@wanadoo.fr**

Small, but perfectly formed, Les Matherons is attractively laid out amongst a variety of trees and wild flower meadows. Surrounded by olive trees and herb gardens it Is secluded, but not remote, and offers a calming experience of gentle living. It is owned and run by a Dutch couple and offers just 23 large, terraced, grassy and well separated pitches, within a natural setting of 23 hectares. Many pitches have good views and all have 3A electricity (rock pegs advised). Campers with caravans and tents are asked to keep their vehicles in a car park. Tractor assistance is available.

Facilities

Modern well appointed toilet block with facilities for campers with disabilities. Daily free coffee hour. Snacks. Twice weekly meals (all season). Boules, table tennis, giant chess, sand pit. Play area. Organised walks. Children's activities (high season). Rafting organised from site. Only gas barbecues permitted. Off site: Fishing 2 km. Bicycle hire 9 km. Riding 13 km. Village of Puimichel 2.5 km. Oraison with lake swimming 10 km.

Open: 20 April - 1 October.

Directions

From A51 junction 19 take road through Oraison past square and church and then take second left, D12 signed Castellet, towards Puimichel. Site is well signed 2 km before Puimichel.

Charges 2007

Per person	€ 3,75
child (under 9 ys)	€ 2,75
pitch	€ 7,50
electricity (3A)	€ 2,50

FR04160 **Camping les Relarguiers**

Route de Colmar, F-04370 Beauvezer (Alpes-de-Haute-Provence)

Tel: **04 92 83 47 73**. Email: **contact@relarguiers.com**

With a very long season, Les Relarguiers is situated at an attitude of 1,150 m. beside the river in the valley of the Haut Verdon. It is ideal for summer and winter holidays, although the nights may be chilly. The new enthusiastic owners are undertaking a complete renovation of this site and the bar/restaurant is already complete. This mountainous area is a haven for nature lovers, hikers and mountain bikers. There are 172 good sized, level, stony, grass pitches shaded by mature trees with 75 for touring all with 10A electricity though long leads may be needed.

Facilities

Two toilet blocks with facilities for campers with disabilities (plans for renovation). Shop. Bar, restaurant and takeaway. Heated pool (15/6-15/9). Boules. Play area. Organised activities in high season. WiFi. Only gas and electric barbecues are permitted. Off site: Bicycle hire 1 km. Riding 5 km. Skiing 15 km. Picturesque mountain villages and scenery.

Open: All year excl. 1 November - 14 December.

Directions

Follow D955 north from St André les Alpes towards Beauvezer. After 11 km. the road number changes to D908. Site on right in village. This is the only recommended route to the site for caravans. GPS: N44:08.816 E06:35.472

Charges 2007

Per unit incl. 2 persons	€ 11,00 - € 28,00
extra person	€ 3,00 - € 4,00
electricity (10A)	€ 2,50 - € 3,60

FR04150 **Camping Rose de Provence**

F-04500 Riez la Romaine (Alpes-de-Haute-Provence)

Tel: **04 92 77 75 45**. Email: **info@rose-de-provence.com**

This site in the heart of the Verdon Regional Nature Park, originally a municipal site, is a good example of what can be achieved by dedication and imagination. On the lowest reaches of a hill 81 attractive, small pitches are delineated by shrubs and small trees offering good shade, 54 with 6A electricity. The two toilet blocks are tiled and decorated in imaginative style. Riez is a charming Provençal village with markets, all the usual facilities and shops; including bike hire, allowing one to explore this ancient and historical area. No large outfits and twin axle caravans.

Facilities

Two attractive, well appointed toilet blocks including facilities for campers with disabilities. Small play area. Table football, table tennis. Gas and electric barbecues only. Off site: Village shops, bicycle hire 500 m. Riding 3 km. Lake beach, fishing, sailing 10 km.

Open: 1 April - 6 October.

Directions

Riez is situated between Gréoux and Moustiers on the D952. Sie is 500 m. south east of Riez. Follow signs for site and municpal tennis courts. GPS: N43:48.783 E06:05.955

Charges 2007

Per unit incl. 2 persons	€ 10,80 - € 13,20
extra person	€ 2,80 - € 3,60
child (under 7 yrs)	€ 2,00 - € 2,40
electricity (6A)	€ 2,95

Credit cards accepted for reservations only.

FR05000 Camping des Princes d'Orange

F-05700 Orpierre (Hautes-Alpes)

Tel: 04 92 66 22 53. Email: campingorpierre@wanadoo.fr

This attractive, terraced site, set on a hillside above the village has been thoughtfully developed. The genuine, friendly welcome means many families return year upon year, bringing in turn new generations. Divided into five terraces, each with its own toilet block, all its 100 generously sized pitches (96 for tourists) enjoy good shade from trees and wicker canopies and have electricity connections (4/6/10A). In high season one terrace is reserved as a 1-star camping area for young people. Orpierre also has an enchanting maze of medieval streets and houses, almost like a trip back through the centuries. Whether you choose to drive, climb, walk or cycle there is plenty of wonderful scenery to discover in the immediate vicinity, whilst not far away, some exhilarating hang-gliding and parascending can be enjoyed. For those seeking to 'get away from it all' in an area of outstanding natural beauty, there can be few more tranquil sites. There can be no doubt that you will be made most welcome and will enjoy the quiet splendours the region has to offer. Renowned as a serious rock climbing venue.

Facilities

Six well equipped toilet blocks. Baby bath. Laundry facilities. Bread. Bar, takeaway (1/4-25/10). Heated swimming pool, paddling pool (15/6-15/9). Play area with small trampoline with safety net. Table tennis. Boules. Games room. Fridge hire. Only gas barbecues are permitted. Off site: Orpierre with a few shops and bicycle hire 500 m. Fishing 7 km. Nearest shopping centre Laragne 12 km. Riding 19 km. Hang-gliding, parascending. Gorges de Guil.

Open: 1 April - 25 October.

Directions

Turn off N75 road at Eyguians onto D30 - site is signed on left at crossroads in centre Orpierre village. GPS: N44:18.675 E05:41.801

Charges 2007

Per person incl. 2 persons	€ 20,00
incl. 3 persons	€ 21,50
extra person	€ 4,10
child (under 7 yrs)	€ 3,10
electricity	€ 3,10

Less 25% in low season. No credit cards.

Camping des Princes d Orange

05700 Orpierre
Tel: 0033 492 662 253
Fax: 0033 492 663 108
campingorpierre@wanadoo.fr
www.camping-orpierre.com

FR05060 Camping la Pause

F-05260 Saint Léger-les-Mélèzes (Hautes-Alpes)

Tel: 04 92 50 44 92. Email: valerie-portier@wanadoo.fr

Camping La Pause is situated amongst some of the most impressive scenery in France with breathtaking views and friendly and helpful owners. There are 80 spacious grassy pitches, with 44 for touring, including some good sized ones for larger units. They are clearly marked and separated by trees and small hedges, some with electricity and water. Access is good for larger units. The weather in these mountains is very pleasant without the excessive heat of the coast. There are guided walks into the surrounding mountains – a very popular excursion, particularly in high season.

Facilities

The heated toilet block in the main building is quite basic with preset showers. Baby room. Washing machines, dryer and irons. Motorcaravan service point. Restaurant and takeaway. Swimming pool during summer. Sauna and gym. Club/TV room. Children's animation and evening entertainment in July/Aug and during the ski season. Play area. Free internet access. Off site: Riding 100 m. Ideal area for canoeing, rafting and canyoning etc.

Open: All year.

Directions

From the A51 (Aix-en-Provence - Gap) take exit 24 and continue north via N185. After Gap and Col de Bayard, turn right on D944 to Layer and Le Cros. From here via D14 to Forrest-St Julien and on via D13 to St Leger-les- Mélèzes. Site is signed at the entrance to the village.

Charges 2008

Per unit with 2 persons	€ 16,00 - € 18,00
electricity per amp	€ 1,00

FR05070 Camping Les Cariamas

Fontmolines, F-05380 Châteauroux-Les-Alpes (Hautes-Alpes)

Tel: **04 92 43 22 63**. Email: **p.tim@free.fr**

Set 1,000 metres up in the stunning scenery of the Alps, Les Cariamas is at the gateway to Ecrin National Park and within easy reach of the Serre-Ponçon lake and the Rabioux-Durance river. The 150 pitches, which all have electrical connections, are pleasantly shaded and many offer beautiful views of the surrounding countryside. There are some mobile homes and chalets to rent. There is an outdoor heated pool on site.

Facilities

Small shop. Takeaway. Laundry. Communal barbecue. Swimming pool. Play area. Mountain bike hire. Volleyball. Tourist information point. Off site: Golf. Riding. Canoeing. Climbing. Fishing. Hiking. Mountain biking. Rafting. Tennis courts.

Open: 1 April - 31 October.

Directions

From Gap follow signs to Embrun Briançon. Take turning for Châteauroux-les- Alpes at first roundabout after Embrun. Shortly (800 m.) before the village turn right and follow signs to site.

Charges 2008

Per person	€ 4,75
child (under 7 yrs)	€ 2,10
pitch	€ 5,50
electricity	€ 3,25

Camping, hôtel de plein air Les Cariamas

Les Cariamas

Fontmolines

05380 Châteauroux-les-Alpes

t. 00 33 (0)4 92 43 22 63

f. 00 33 (0)6 30 11 30 57

e. p.tim@free.fr

http://les.cariamas.free.fr

FR05080 Camping Solaire

F-05400 Veynes (Hautes-Alpes)

Tel: **04 92 58 12 34**. Email: **info@camping-solaire.com**

An attractive, well kept site surrounded by mountains and scenes of pastural beauty, the owners have developed Le Solaire to offer a wide range of facilities including a large jacuzzi heated to 30ºC. The swimming pools for adults and youngsters are supervised by a lifeguard, who also gives swimming lessons. The owners are particularly proud of their grasslands and of the167 large pitches. There are 73 for touring in a separate area, many with good shade and all with 6A electricity and with water close by. The site is well placed to explore the area around Gap and the surrounding countryside. The village of Veynes is ancient and attractive and has a range of shops and facilities.

Facilities

Modern, clean and heated toilet blocks with facilities for campers with disabilities. Bar (1/6-30/9). Shop, snacks, takeaway (1/7-30/9). Swimming pools (1/6-30/9). Jacuzzi (1/7-30/9). Large games room/TV. Bicycle hire. Off site: Fishing 100 m. Lake, beach, swimming, boating, 300 m. Rafting, hang gliding, Rock climbing, many bike rides and hiking tracks. Veynes with range of shops and facilities 2 km. Old market towns with museums and ancient house.

Open: All year.

Directions

From Grenoble on N75, in town of Aspres-sur-Buëch, take D994a to join D994 travelling northeast towards Veynes. Site is signed on right 1 km. before village. After 300 m. take next right, entrance on right within 50 m.

Charges 2007

Per unit incl. 2 persons	€ 8,10 - € 16,20
extra person	€ 3,25 - € 6,50
child (2-9 yrs)	€ 1,75 - € 3,50
electricity (5A)	€ 3,00

FR05100 Camping la Vieille Ferme

La Clapière, F-05200 Embrun (Hautes-Alpes)

Tel: 04 92 43 04 08. Email: info@campingembrun.com

This is a quiet, urban site in the Hautes-Alpes region. Surrounded by imposing mountains and with a rural ambience, the 100 large, spacious pitches are all for touring. There is good shade and all the pitches have water, 6A electricity, drainage and sewage disposal. The Dutch owners have created a unique mix of activities. In high season one can explore the grandeur of the area and enjoy activities on site including musical evenings, trad jazz groups and community barbecues. The pretty Roman historical town of Embrun with its 12th century cathedral is well worth a visit.

Facilities

Modern, spotless, well equipped toilet block with family rooms, facilities for campers with disabilities. Bar, restaurant. Takeaway (1/6-30/8). Play area. Family activities (July/Aug). Off site: Embrun, range of shops and facilities. Bicycle hire 300 m. Lakeside sports complex 400 m. Golf 1 km. Riding 1.5 km. Boat ramp 2 km. Gap 10 km. Rafting, canoeing. Mountain bike rides, hiking.

Open: 1 May - 1 October.

Directions

Site is clearly signed at the western end of Embrun on the N94. It is about 200 m. south of the main road. GPS: N44:33.244 E06:29.186

Charges 2007

Per unit incl. 2 persons	€ 14,00 - € 23,00
extra person	€ 6,00
electricity (6/10A)	€ 3,00 - € 5,00

No credit cards.

FR05110 Camping la Rochette

F-05600 Guillestre (Hautes-Alpes)

Tel: 04 92 45 02 15. Email: guillestre@aol.com

At a height of 800 metres, this municipal site looks fresh and well kept. Located in a beautiful mountainous region, it is run under contract by a very welcoming young couple who are fully responsible for the day to day running of the site. English and Dutch are spoken. There are 190 grassy pitches separated by trees that give welcome shade with 185 for touring and 150 with 4-10A electricity. Although there are few amenities on site, most can be found in the town only 10 minutes walk away. The Monday market is well worth a visit.

Facilities

Three well appointed toilet blocks are clean and modern. Facilities for disabled visitors. Small shop (July/Aug). Internet access. Play area. Table tennis. Boules. Only gas and electric barbecues are permitted. Off site: Municpal heated swimming pool and tennis courts adjacent. Guillestre, restaurant, bars, shops, supermarket, etc. 800 m. Bicycle hire 1 km. Riding 3 km. Lake, river 3 km. Walking, biking, climbing, rafting, canoeing, canyoning. Many ancient villages and magnificent scenery to explore.

Open: 15 May - 22 September.

Directions

Between Briançon and Gap on the RN94, at roundabout signed Guillestre, turn towards the village. Site is signed with the entrance in 900 m. GPS: N44:39.513 E06:38.290

Charges 2007

Per unit incl. 2 persons	€ 10,90 - € 13,40
extra person	€ 2,90 - € 3,60
child (under 10 yrs)	€ 1,80 - € 2,30
electricity (4-10A)	€ 2,30 - € 3,30

FR84020 Domaine Naturiste de Bélézy

F-84410 Bédoin (Vaucluse)

Tel: 04 90 65 60 18. Email: info@belezy.com

Mobile homes ▶ page 505

At the foot of Mt Ventoux, surrounded by beautiful scenery, Bélézy is an excellent naturist site with many amenities and activities and the ambience is relaxed and comfortable. The 238 marked pitches are set amongst many varieties of trees and shrubs. Electricity points (12A) are plentiful but long leads are necessary. So far as naturism is concerned, the emphasis is on personal choice, the only stipulation being the requirement for complete nudity in the pools and pool area. An area of natural parkland with an orchard, fishpond and woodland, has a good range of sports. facilities.

Facilities

Sanitary blocks differ – newer ones are excellent, with showers and washbasins in cubicles, others have hot showers in the open air, screened by stone dividers. One block has a superb children's section. Shop (22/3-21/9). Excellent restaurant and takeaway. Two swimming pools. Sauna. Tennis. Adventure play area. Activities in low season. Archery. Guided walks. Children's club. Hydrotherapy centre (1/4-30/9). Barbecues are prohibited. Pets are not accepted. Off site: Bédoin 1.5 km.

Open: 15 March - 5 October.

Directions

From A7 autoroute or RN7 at Orange, take D950 southeast to Carpentras, then northeast via D974 to Bédoin. Site is signed in Bédoin, being about 1.5 km. northeast of the village. GPS: N44:08.011 E05:11.247

Charges 2008

Per unit incl. 2 persons	€ 22,00 - € 36,50
extra person	€ 5,00 - € 8,50
child (3-8 yrs)	€ 5,50 - € 8,80
electricity (12A)	€ 4,50

Camping Cheques accepted.

FR84040 Domaine le Jantou
535 Chemin des Coudeliéres, F-84250 Le Thor (Vaucluse)
Tel: **04 90 33 90 07**. Email: **accueil@lejantou.com**

Le Jantou has been expanded over the years from an 18th century farm and farmhouse. It is bordered by a small river said to be good for trout fishing. The 160 level, small to medium sized, fairly stony pitches (rock pegs advised) are in small groups separated by tall hedges and mature trees giving heavy shade to many. All have electricity (3-10A). About half of them are used for touring with most of them in a separate section. There is a large pool, children's pool and paddling pool surrounded by paved and grass sunbathing areas.

Facilities

Two central toilet blocks partially refurbished with all the necessary facilities, include washbasins in cabins, a baby room and facilities for disabled visitors. Washing machine and dryer. Motorcaravan service point. Small bar/restaurant with takeaway (July/Aug). Small shop with basics. Swimming pools. Play area. Large sports area. Fishing. Bicycle hire. Small games room with TV and internet access. Barbecues are not allowed (four central barbecues). Off site: Supermarket 1 km. Riding 5 km. Canoeing. Thor, shops, bars, restaurants, 2 km.

Open: 1 April - 31 October.

Directions

Site is just west of Le Thor. Leave A7 autoroute at Avignon north (exit 23) onto D942 signed Carpentras. Shortly turn south on D6 and in 8 km. turn east on N100, signed Le Thor. Just before bridge turn left on D1 and shortly left again to site entrance. GPS: N43:55.764 E04:58.989

Charges 2007

Per unit incl. 2 persons	€ 19,00 - € 22,00
extra person	€ 4,60 - € 6,50
child (2-12 yrs)	€ 2,50 - € 4,00
electricity	€ 3,00 - € 4,70

FR84050 Camping Caravaning la Sorguette
Route d'Apt, F-84800 L'Isle sur la Sorgue (Vaucluse)
Tel: **04 90 38 05 71**. Email: **sorguette@wanadoo.fr**

This popular, well organised site is well placed, 1.5 km. from Isle sur la Sorgue. Arranged in groups of four, the 164 medium sized level pitches (124 for touring) all have electricity (4-10A). Each group is separated by tall hedges and most have a little shade during the day. In high season a few competitions are organised (boules or volleyball), plus some children's entertainment, but this is quite low key. Running alongside the site, the river Sorgue is only 6 km. from its source in the mountains. It is still very clear and used for canoeing, swimming or fishing.

Facilities

Well maintained toilet blocks, washing machines. Units for disabled people. Baby room. Motorcaravan services. Fridge hire. Shop, bar, snacks (1/7-25/8). Entertainment in July/Aug. Play area, volleyball, half-court tennis, basketball. Canoe, bicycle hire. Internet. Indian tipis; yurts; Mongolian circular tents and Inuit style tents with kitchens. Off site: Fishing and riding 5 km. Canoeing.

Open: 15 March - 15 October.

Directions

Site is 1.5 km. east of L'Isle sur la Sorgue on the N100 towards Apt. It is well signed from the town. GPS: N43:54.893 E05:04.655

Charges 2008

Per unit incl. 2 persons	€ 11,00 - € 14,00
extra person (over 7 yrs)	€ 5,50 - € 7,00
child (1-6 yrs)	€ 2,70 - € 3,50
electricity (4/10A)	€ 3,70 - € 5,20

FR84080 Camping Caravaning la Simioune
F-84500 Bollène (Vaucluse)
Tel: **04 90 30 44 62**. Email: **la-simioune@wanadoo.fr**

This unsophisticated, rural site is a peaceful and inexpensive base, especially for those who love horses and it is open all year. Off the beaten track it is amongst tall pines on sandy, undulating ground, bordered, by a vineyard. This is a riding school, campers can hire horses by the hour. The favourite is the day-long guided trek with a river crossing and picnic lunch. The 80 unmarked and uneven pitches, many used for long stay caravans, are of varying size and shape, most with electricity (6A). Long leads and rock pegs are needed. The site is not recommended for large units.

Facilities

Basic toilet block, quite old but clean with room for disabled people although the site is difficult for wheelchairs and those with walking difficulties. Washing machine. Small bar, simple meals mid June to mid Sept. Takeaway all year. Small unheated swimming pool (June - Sept). Central barbecue area (individual ones not permitted). Chalets for rent. Off site: Tennis, fishing, walking and canoeing nearby. Bollène 5 km.

Open: All year.

Directions

From A7 exit 19 (Bollène). At first roundabout, third exit signed Suze la Rousse. After traffic lights, before river, turn left, site signed (Rue Alphonse Daudet), follow signs for 5 km. (windy, narrow lane). GPS: N44:17.811 E04:47.245

Charges 2007

Per person	€ 3,50
pitch incl. electricity (6A)	€ 5,50 - € 6,00
No credit cards.	

FR84070 Camping Club International Carpe Diem

Route de St Marcellin, B.P. 68, F-84110 Vaison-la-Romaine (Vaucluse)

Tel: 04 90 36 02 02. Email: contact@camping-carpe-diem.com

Carpe Diem is a new site, attractively themed with Greek statues and an amphitheatre surround to its main pool. This is a good site for active families seeking all day entertainment and the situation is quite impressive with magnificent views over one of the most beautiful parts of France, yet only 800 m. from the fascinating town of Vaison-la-Romaine. There are 232 pitches with 119 small to medium sized, grass touring pitches all with electricity and many with some degree of shade. A new terraced area has mobile homes, chalets and unshaded touring pitches. The main pool is impressive with its tiered seating, plants, etc. It is used as a theatre for evening entertainment. A simple square pool with grass surrounds is near the play area. Organised activities off the site include canoeing, riding, climbing, walking and mountain biking.

Facilities

Central toilet block with fountain and super children's facilities. Washing machine. Motorcaravan services. Reception, small shop (25/3-1/11). Bar (3/6-2/9), pizzeria (14/4-30/9). TV. Swimming pools including slides and flumes, one new, covered and heated. Play area. Minigolf, archery, volleyball, football, basketball. Mountain bike hire. Miniclub. Extensive entertainment programme. Barbecues for hire. Off site: Fishing 1 km. Riding 2 km. Golf 20 km. Organised canoeing, riding, climbing, walking, mountain biking. Vaison-la-Romaine (800 m), magnificent Roman ruins, shops, restaurants, market.

Open: 25 March - 1 November.

Directions

Leave Vaison-la-Romaine on D938 heading south towards Carpentras. 1 km. beyond the 'Super U' roundabout turn left on D151, signed St Marcellin. Site entrance is on the left immediately after the junction. GPS: N44:14.064 E05:05.381

Charges 2007

Per pitch incl. 2 persons	€ 16,00 - € 29,00
extra person	€ 4,60 - € 7,00
child (under 10 yrs)	€ 2,50 - € 4,20
electricity (6/10A)	€ 3,70 - € 4,70

Camping Cheques accepted.

FR84090 Camping du Pont d'Avignon

10 chemin de la Barthelasse, Ile de la Barthelasse, F-84000 Avignon (Vaucluse)

Tel: 04 90 80 63 50. Email: info@camping-avignon.com

This is a city site, yet it is in a quiet location and only a short walk or ferry ride from the town. There are 300 level pitches, some on grass and some with hardstanding. 118 with electricity (10A). All have some shade but those with electricity are well shaded. A good play area, tennis courts and volleyball pitch are in the centre of the site separating the tent pitches on one side and the electric pitches on the other. Many pitches are separated by hedges. The restaurant, bar and terrace overlook the attractive pool.

Facilities

Well maintained and clean toilet blocks, facilities for disabled visitors. Washing machines, dryer. Motorcaravan services. Well stocked shop (1/4-30/9). Bar/restaurant, takeaway (1/4-30/9). Swimming pool, paddling pool (15/5-15/9). Play area with new climbing frame. Tennis (free). Volleyball. Bicycle hire (July/Aug). Internet. Off site: Avignon with famous bridge and Pope's Palace. Ferry to town centre.

Open: 19 March - 27 October.

Directions

Site is on an island in River Rhône. Well signed from roads into Avignon, ring road has complex junctions. Accessed from Pont Daladier towards Villeneuve les Avignon. Just after crossing first section of river fork right, site signed, site about 1 km. GPS: N43:57.092 E04:48.116

Charges 2007

Per unit incl. 2 persons	€ 10,20 - € 33,90
extra person	€ 2,90 - € 4,30
electricity	€ 2,60 - € 3,10

Camping Cheques accepted.

FR84130 Camping les Chênes Blancs

Route de Gargas, Saint Saturnin-les-Apt F-84490 (Vaucluse)

Tel: **04 90 74 09 20**. Email: **robert@les-chenes-blancs.com**

Les Chênes Blancs lies in the Pays d'Apt, between the mountains of the Luberon and the Vaucluse. This region has a wealth of history and natural beauty including the medieval hill top villages of Gordes and Roussillon and the yellow ochre mines. It has something for everyone, for those seeking to unwind as well as for the young and old who prefer a more active break. There are 192 irregular shaped shady pitches of varying size scattered amongst the trees. Some of the 172 touring pitches can accommodate large outfits and all have 6A electricity.

Facilities

Two clean toilet blocks, the newer one centrally located with older one on the perimeter of the site. Facilities for campers with disabilities. Motorcaravan services. Small shop, bar (15/3-31/10). Restaurant, takeaway, outside terrace (1/5-30/9). Unheated swimming pool, two paddling pools (1/5-30/9). Playground. Boules. Table tennis. Multisport court. Electric barbecues only (1200W). Off site: Rock climbing at Buoux and the Dentelles de Montmirail. Canoeing and kayaking on the Sorgue and Durance. Fishing 5 km. Riding, bicycle hire 10 km. Hiking trails at all levels, for all ages. Provençal markets. Isle sur la Sorgue, famous for its antiques.

Open: 15 March - 31 October.

Directions

Exit A7, junction 24 Avignon Sud, take D22 and then N100 towards Apt. Through le Chêne to the end of the town, turn left, D4 for 3 km, then turn right, follow signs to site (3 km). GPS: N43:55.267 E05:20.150

Charges 2007

Per unit incl. car and 2 persons	€ 12,00 - € 16,40
extra person (over 7 yrs)	€ 3,60 - € 5,20
extra person (0-7 yrs)	€ 2,40 - € 3,60
electricity (6A)	€ 4,60 - € 5,40

Camping Cheques accepted.

Camping Les Chênes Blancs*

Route de Gargas - 84490 St. Saturnin Les Apt
Tel: 0033 490 74 09 20 - Fax: 0033 490 74 26 98
E-mail: robert@les-chenes-blancs.com - Internet: www.les-chenes-blancs.com

FR84100 Camping le Soleil de Provence

Route de Nyons, F-84110 Saint Romain-en-Viennois (Vaucluse)

Tel: **04 90 46 46 00**. Email: **info@camping-soleil-de-provence.fr**

The site has been developed to a high standard. The 162 average sized pitches, 150 for touring are separated by hedges and a variety of young trees offering only a little shade (10A electricity). The excellent pool, surrounded by a sunbathing terrace, and overlooked by the bar, is an unusual shape with an island in the centre. Although there is no paddling pool one end of the pool is very shallow. There is some organised entertainment in July and August but the emphasis is on a quiet and peaceful environment and is an ideal site for relaxing and unwinding.

Facilities

Modern well appointed, heated toilet blocks, facilities for disabled visitors, baby room. Washing machine, dryer. Motorcaravan services. Small shop for bread, open on demand. Bar, snack bar, all season. New aqua-park with waterslides and paddling pool. Small play area. Volleyball, table tennis, boules. Off site: Tennis 1 km. Vaison-la-Romaine 4 km. Rafting, hiking, cycling, mountain biking 4 km. (Mont Ventoux is a real challenge). Bicycle hire 5 km. Fishing 15 km. Medieval villages, market towns. vineyards, wine tasting.

Open: 15 March - 31 October.

Directions

Site is 4 km. north of Vaison-la-Romaine on the D938 road to Nyons. Turn right, signed St Romain-en-Viennois (site signed) and take first left to site. GPS: N44:16.141 E05:06.358

Charges 2007

Per person	€ 3,50 - € 5,50
child (0-7 yrs)	€ 2,50 - € 3,00
pitch	€ 3,00 - € 5,00
car	€ 3,00 - € 4,00
electricity (10A)	€ 3,50

No credit cards.

FR84140 Camping Beauregard

Route d'Uchaux, F-84550 Mornas (Vaucluse)

Tel: 04 90 37 02 08. Email: **beauregard@wanadoo.fr**

Just a kilometre off the D7 and near an A7 exit, this site may appeal to those needing a night stop when travelling to or from the Mediterranean coast. Although there are many mobile homes, there are 89 pitches available for tourists. The pitches are under large pine trees and are rather sandy. Firm pegging might be difficult. They are of various shapes and sizes, mainly about 90 sq.m. Efforts are being made to upgrade what was an old fashioned campsite. There is a new and attractive pool complex including a covered pool (heated from April) – the pools are used by some local people. Entertainment is organised for high season evenings. A good sized shop sells the essentials.

Facilities

Two toilet blocks, one of which is heated when necessary, with washbasins in cabins. Facilities for disabled visitors (access by key). Laundry facilities. Shop (April - Oct). Bar, restaurant and takeaway (April - Sept). Swimming pools, one covered. Volleyball. Tennis. Play area. Boules. Quad bike hire. Fitness trail. Entertainment (high season). Barbecues are not permitted. Off site: Fishing and riding 5 km. Golf 12 km.

Open: 25 March - 4 November.

Directions

From the A7 take exit for Bollene, then the N7 towards Orange. At north end of Mornas village, turn left on D74-signed Uchaux. Site is on left after 1.7 km.

Charges 2007

Per unit incl. 2 persons	€ 21,00 - € 24,00
extra person	€ 4,60 - € 7,00
child (under 7 yrs)	€ 2,50 - € 4,20
electricity	€ 4,70

FR84150 Camping Flory

Route d'Entraigues, F-84270 Vedéne (Vaucluse)

Tel: 04 90 31 00 51. Email: **campingflory@wanadoo.fr**

Camping Flory is a traditional, country site in the heart of Provence and only ten minutes drive from the historic Papal town of Avignon. The area dedicated to camping is somewhat sloping, with shade provided by mature pine trees. There are 100 touring pitches, all with electricity (10A). Mobile homes occupy a separate area. Vedène lies in a low area not far from the confluence of the Rhône and Durance rivers, but the site is on a hillside and the danger of flooding is minimal with excellent precautions in place. An award-winning warm welcome is offered by owners, Ernest and Jeannine Guindos.

Facilities

Three toilet blocks, two of the buildings are old but have been refurbished to a good standard, with some washbasins in cabins and pre-set showers. Very basic facilities for disabled visitors. Motorcaravan services. Small restaurant (1/7-30/8) with simple menu and takeaway. Shop providing basic supplies. Swimming pool (no shorts) with paddling pool. Play area. Boules. Table tennis. Some organised activities in high season. Off site: Golf 2 km. Riding 3 km. Bicycle hire and fishing 10 km. Wine tasting locally. Walking and cycling in area, including Mont Ventoux and the Nesque Gorge. Towns of Avignon, Orange, Carpentras.

Open: 15 March - 30 September.

Directions

From A7 Autoroute du Soleil, take exit 23 (Avignon Nord) and follow D942 towards Carpentras for 3 km then turn right at the second sign for Vedène. GPS: N43:59.260 E04:54.470

Charges 2007

Per unit incl. 2 persons	€ 15,00 - € 18,00
wztra person	€ 4,00
child (under 7 yrs)	€ 2,50 - € 3,00
electricity (10A)	€ 4,50 - € 5,50

MAP 15

Rolling fields of yellow sunflowers, the Armagn vineyards and crumblin ancient stone buildings amidst the sleepy villages make this colourful region popu with those who enjoy good food, good wine and a taste of the good

DÉPARTEMENTS: 09 ARIÈGE, 31 HAUTE-GARONNE, 32 GERS, 65 HAUTES-PYRÉNÉES, 81 TARN, 82 TARN-ET GARONNE. WE HAVE LEFT OUT THE DÉPARTEMENTS OF AVEYRON (12) AND LOT (46), WHICH ARE IN OUR DORDOGNE/AVEYRON REGION

Still a relatively unknown region, the Midi-Pyrénées is the largest region of France, extending from the Dordogne in the north to the Spanish border. It is blessed by radiant sunshine and a fascinating range of scenery. High chalk plateaux, majestic peaks, tiny hidden valleys and small fortified sleepy villages, which seem to have changed little since the Middle Ages, contrast with the high-tech, industrial and vibrant university city of Toulouse.

Lourdes is one of the most visited pilgrimage sites in the world. Toulouse-Lautrec, the artist, was born at Albi, the capital of the département of Tarn. Much of the town is built of pink brick which seems to glow when seen from a distance. In the east, the little town of Foix, with its maze of steep, winding streets, is a convenient centre from which to explore the prehistoric caves at Niaux and the Aladdin's Cave of duty-free gift shops in the independent state of Andorra. The Canal du Midi that links Bordeaux to the Mediterranean was commissioned by Louis XIV in 1666 and is still in working order.

Places of interest

Albi: birthplace and Museum of Toulouse-Lautrec, imposing Ste Cécile cathedral with 15th century fresco of 'The Last Judgement'.

Auch: capital of ancient Gascony, boasts a fine statue of d'Artágnan.

Collonges-la-Rouge: picturesque village of Medieval and Renaissance style mansions and manors.

Conques: 11th century Ste Foy Romanesque church.

Cordes: medieval walled hilltop village.

Foix: 11th/12th century towers on rocky peak above town; 14th century cathedral.

Lourdes: famous pilgrimage site where Ste Bernadette is said to have spoken to the Virgin Mary in a grotto and known for the miracles said to have been performed there.

Cuisine of the region

Food is rich and strongly seasoned, making generous use of garlic and goose fat, and there are some excellent regional wines. Seafood such as oysters, salt-water fish, or piballes from the Adour river are popular.

Cassoulet: stew of duck, sausages and beans.

Confit de Canard (d'oie): preserved duck meat.

Grattons (Graisserons): a mélange of small pieces of rendered down duck, goose and pork fat.

Magret de canard: duck breast fillets

Poule au pot: chicken simmered with vegetables.

Ouillat (Ouliat): Pyrénées soup: onions, tomatoes, goose fat and garlic.

Tourtière Landaise: a sweet of Agen prunes, apples and Armagnac.

FR09060 Kawan Village le Pré Lombard

F-09400 Tarascon-sur-Ariege (Ariège)

Tel: 05 61 05 61 94. Email: leprelombard@wanadoo.fr

This busy, good value site is located beside the attractive river Ariège near the town. There are 180 level, grassy, pitches with shade provided by a variety of trees (electricity 10A). At the rear of the site are 69 site-owned chalets and mobile homes. A gate in the fence provides access to the river bank for fishing. Open for a long season, it is an excellent choice for early or late breaks, or as a stop-over en-route to the winter sun destinations in Spain. This region of Ariège is in the foothills of the Pyrénées and 85 km. from Andorra. Didier Mioni, the manager here follows the town motto, 'S'y passos, y demoros' – 'if you wish to come here, you will stay here' in his aim to ensure your satisfaction on his site. At Tarascon itself you can visit the Parc Pyrénéen de l'Art Préhistorique to view rock paintings, or the really adventurous can take to the air for paragliding or hang-gliding.

Facilities

Five toilet blocks of varying age, facilities for disabled people. Laundry. Motorcaravan services. Bar and takeaway. Shop. Restaurant, entertainment, dancing (1/5-30/9). Heated swimming pool (1/5-30/9). Playgrounds for toddlers and older children. Video games machines, table tennis, table football, boules. Multicourt sports. Fishing. Internet. Satellite TV. Entertainment (high season), nightclub, children's club, sports tournaments. Activity programmes for small groups. Off site: Supermarket 300 m. Town 600 m. Archery, kayaking and fishing nearby. Riding 5 km. Golf 30 km. Skiing 20 km.

Open: 22 March - 11 November.

Directions

Site is 600 m. south of town, adjacent to the river. From north, turn off main N20 into the town, site well signed. From south (Andorra) site signed at roundabout on town approach. GPS: N42:50.391 E01:36.720

Charges 2008

Per unit incl. 2 persons and 10A electricity	€ 15,00 - € 29,50
extra person	€ 4,00 - € 8,50
child (2-7 yrs)	free - € 6,50
dog	free - € 2,00

Camping Cheques accepted.

FR09020 Camping l'Arize

Mobile homes ▶ page 505

Lieu-dit Bourtol, F-09240 La Bastide-de-Sérou (Ariège)

Tel: 05 61 65 81 51. Email: camparize@aol.com

The site sits in a delightful, tranquil valley among the foothills of the Pyrénées and is just east of the interesting village of La Bastide-de-Sérou beside the River Arize (good trout fishing). The river is fenced for the safety of children on the site, but may be accessed just outside the gate. The 70 large pitches are neatly laid out on level grass within the spacious site. All have 3/6A electricity and are separated into bays by hedges and young trees. An extension to the site gives 24 large, fully serviced pitches and a small toilet block.

Facilities

Toilet block includes facilities for babies and disabled people. Laundry room, dryer. Motorcaravan services. Small swimming pool, sunbathing area. Entertainment, high season, weekly barbecues and welcome drinks on Sundays. Fishing, riding and bicycle hire on site. Off site: Golf 5 km. Several restaurants and shops within a few minute's drive.

Open: 7 March - 12 November.

Directions

Site is southeast of the village La Bastide-de-Sérou. Take the D15 towards Nescus and site is on right after about 1 km. GPS: N43:00.109 E01:26.723

Charges 2008

Per pitch incl. 2 persons and electricity	€ 16,40 - € 31,60
extra person	€ 4,00 - € 5,40
child (0-7 yrs)	€ 3,00 - € 3,60

Discounts for longer stays in mid and low season.

FR09050 Camping Municipal la Prade

F-09110 Sorgeat (Ariège)

Tel: 05 61 64 36 34. Email: sorgeat.mainie@wanadoo.fr

Superbly situated high on the mountainside overlooking a valley, this site has magnificent views, with a river 300 m. and a lake 2 km. A small site, it provides just 40 pitches on terraces, some of which are occupied by long stay units, (electricity 5-10A). Well supervised, with the warden present at varying times, the site is kept very clean. A small stream tinkles through the edge of the site and the attractive hills towering above it reverberate with the sound of goat bells. A separate area has permanent brick barbecues for use by campers. A most reasonably priced campsite.

Facilities

The original, rather small sanitary block has only two showers and two WCs in each half. However, a second block has now been added and standards are very high. Hot water is provided for dishwashing. Facilities for the disabled are also very good with special washbasin and a very large shower suite. Chemical disposal and waste water point. Washing machine. Small play area. Shop and cafe in village. Off site: Fishing 500 m. Riding and bicycle hire 5 km.

Open: All year.

Directions

From Ax-les-Thermes take D613 towards Quillan for 4 km. Turn onto D52 and continue for 1 km. Follow site signs. Bear left at first junction up through Sorgeat village to site. Mountain roads may be difficult for large units. GPS: N42:43.974 E01:51.234

Charges 2007

Per person	€ 3,00
pitch	€ 1,70 - € 1,90
electricity (5/10A)	€ 2,80 - € 5,40

No credit cards.

FR09080 Camping du Lac

RN 20, F-09000 Foix (Ariège)

Tel: 05 61 65 11 58. Email: camping-du-lac@wanadoo.fr

Du Lac is a traditional, urban lakeside site just 3 km. north of the very pretty town of Foix. There is road and rail noise (the site is alongside the old N20). There is space to manoeuvre at the entrance. The site is informally divided into four areas, one for mobile homes. The other areas are generally flat or slightly sloping with some shade under mature trees. There are 135 pitches, most with electricity (8-13A). Access to the lake is through a gate which is locked at night and the fence is secure. Children will need supervision in this area.

Facilities

Adequate but cramped, toilet blocks of varying ages, facilities for disabled campers, baby room. Cleanliness variable. Washing machine. Reception sells basic goods. Snack bar, bar/drinks stall close to pool. Small swimming pool. Play areas. Watersports, fishing, canoe instruction. TV room. Tennis. Some organised activities, high season. Torches are necessary. Off site: Cycling and walking tours, riding, golf or even white water rafting.

Open: All year.

Directions

From the north leave the N20 at exit 10 and take the old road towards the town. Site is well signed on the left, 3 km. north of the town centre (avoid new bypass and tunnel). GPS: N42:59.366 E01:36.942

Charges 2007

Per unit incl. 2 persons and electricity	€ 13,50 - € 35,00
extra person	€ 3,00 - € 9,00

Camping Cheques accepted.

FR09090 Naturiste Camping Millfleurs

Le Tuilier Gudas, F-09120 Varilhes (Ariège)

Tel: 05 61 60 77 56. Email: ag.kos@wanadoo.fr

Millfleurs is a quiet site in a secluded location for naturists. It is peaceful with some 70 acres of woods and meadows providing guided naturist walks in total privacy. The site has 40 large, flat, mostly terraced pitches (26 with 4/6/8A electricity), long leads if pitching off the terraces. There are also very secluded pitches in wooded areas with shade, or you can pitch a tent in the meadows if you prefer. There are few of the normal camping leisure facilities here and the site is definitely aimed at the more mature naturist camper.

Facilities

An excellent toilet block, facilities for disabled campers. Bread available to order in high season. Guests dine together in the 'salle de reunion' within the farmhouse two nights a week or just meet friends for a drink. Refrigerator with drinks. Petanque, guide book for walks and cycle rides. Torches essential. Pick ups from airports and stations arranged. Off site: The coast is about 1.5 hours.

Open: 15 April - 30 September.

Directions

From Varilhes, 8 km. south of Pamiers on D624 (parallel to N20). Take D13 for Dalou and Gudas cross railway and N20. The site is 2 km. past Gudas, on right. GPS: N42:59.566 E01:40.731

Charges 2007

Per person (all ages)	€ 4,60 - € 5,40
pitch	€ 4,60 - € 5,40
electricity	€ 2,60

No credit cards.

FR09100 Parc d'Audinac les Bains

Montjoie - Audinac, F-09200 Saint Girons (Ariège)

Tel: 05 61 66 44 50. Email: accueil@audinac.com

Remnants of an old thermal springs can be found on the site at Parc d'Audinac les Bains, a tranquil haven with wonderful views of the surrounding mountains. Owned by a charming French couple, Olivia and Jérôme Barbry, you are guaranteed a friendly welcome on this site which has 90 touring pitches and 25 chalets for rent. The terraced touring pitches are mostly level, although some do have a slight slope. They are on well drained grass and each has 10A electricity supplied (the older part of the site via French sockets). Water supplies are conveniently located.

Facilities	Directions
Two small bright and modern toilet blocks (one unisex) with hot and cold water to showers and washbasins. British and Turkish style WC's. Washing machines. Motorcaravan service point. Good sized outdoor swimming pool and paddling pool and a small shop for drinks and ice creams (July/Aug) in the old thermal spring building adjacent to the pool. Children's club (July/Aug). Tennis. Boules. Sports area. New chalets. Off site: Shops, bars, restaurants and supermarket at St Girons 3 km.	From St Girons take D117 towards Foix. Turn left on D627 signed St Croix and Merigon. Site is on the right just after Audinac-les-Bains.

Directions

From St Girons take D117 towards Foix. Turn left on D627 signed St Croix and Merigon. Site is on the right just after Audinac-les-Bains.

Charges 2007

Per unit incl. 2 persons	€ 11,50 - € 16,00
extra person	€ 4,00 - € 6,00
child (0-6 yrs)	€ 3,00 - € 5,00
electricity (10A)	€ 3,50

Open: 1 May - 30 September.

FR09110 Camping le Pas de l'Ours

F-09310 Aston (Ariège)

Tel: 05 61 64 90 33. Email: contact@lepasdelours.fr

In the small town of Aston, which is located in the heart of the scenic Vallées d'Ax in the Haute-Ariège region, you will find the secluded campsite of Le Pas de l'Ours. With panoramic views of the mountains, this charming site has a total of 57 pitches, although only 30 of these are for tourers, as the rest are taken up by chalets to rent. Six of the smaller touring pitches are reserved for tents and have no electricity, but the other 24 grassy and mainly level pitches are well kept and attractively laid out, separated by shrubs and bushes and have 6A electricity. A 'Sites et Paysages' member.

Facilities	Directions
Two modern sanitary blocks are well equipped and include preset showers. Large en-suite room for disabled visitors. Motorcaravan service point. Bakers van calls every morning in July/Aug. Communal covered purpose built barbecue area with picnic tables. Small play area. Tennis courts. Off site: Heated outdoor swimming pool in village adjacent to site. Skiing 16 km. Golf 30 km. Riding 20 km. Shops, restaurant and bars 4 km.	From N20 between Ax-Les-Thermes and Tarascon take exit to Les Cabannes on D522a signed Verdun and Aston. After 1.8 km. turn left on D520 to Château Verdun and Aston. Site is well signed. GPS: N42:46.337 E01:40.293

Charges 2007

Per unit incl. 2 persons	€ 13,00 - € 16,00
extra person	€ 3,00 - € 4,00
electricity (6A)	€ 3,00

Open: 1 June - 15 September (chalets all year).

FR09120 Camping Ascou la Forge

F-09110 Ascou (Ariège)

Tel: 05 61 64 60 03. Email: mountain.sports@wanadoo.fr

The Dutch owners of Ascou La Forge will give you a warm, friendly welcome at their oasis in the mountains of the Pyrenees, close to the borders of Andorra and Spain. The site is 3,500 feet above sea level but is easily accessible for motorhomes and caravans. Lying alongside the Lauze river, there are 50 pitches. In low season 44 mainly level, grass touring pitches with electricity are available, but this number reduces to 20 in July and August to allow more room for the large influx of campers with tents. There are also 2 chalets available to rent.

Facilities	Directions
Modern, bright, sanitary block is fully equipped including facilities for disabled visitors which double as a family shower room with a baby bath. Shop. Bar with large screen for major sports events and films about the local flora/fauna. Play area. Maps and walking routes are available from reception. Free WiFi internet access. Off site: Restaurant next door to site (all year). Restaurants, bars and shops in Ax-les-Thermes 7 km.	From Ax-Les-Thermes take D613 signed Quérigat, Quillan and Ascou-Pailhéres. After 3.6 km. turn right on D25 to site on right after 3.4 km.

Charges 2007

Per unit with 2 persons and electricity	€ 15,00 - € 20,50
extra person	€ 3,50 - € 4,00
child (0-7 yrs)	€ 2,50 - € 3,00
dog	€ 1,00 - € 1,50

Open: 1 May - 16 October.

FR09130 Camping du Lac

F-09400 Mercus-Garrabet (Ariège)

Tel: **05 61 05 90 61**. Email: **info@campinglac.com**

Situated in the small town of Mercus just one kilometre from the N20 between Foix and Andorra, this is a lovely campsite on the shores of a lake, devotedly run by Jacky and Martine Podvin. The site has 70 pitches (38 for touring and 20 chalets and mobile homes to rent). The grassy pitches are attractively laid out, level and partially shaded by mature trees. Each has electricity (6/10A; Europlug) adjacent and all are reasonably close to the modern sanitary blocks. There is some background road noise and also several trains run alongside the site throughout the day between 06.00-22.00.

Facilities

Two modern sanitary blocks are well equipped. One also has facilities for disabled visitors and a family shower room with a baby bath. Motorcaravan service point. Cold drinks and ice cream available in reception building in July/Aug. Bread, sandwiches (hot and cold) and pizzas (July/Aug). Good sized heated swimming pool. Small play area. Off site: Shops, restaurant and bar 1 km. Watersports (July/Aug) 1 km. Riding 5 km. Golf 7 km. Buses to Toulouse and Tarrascon.

Open: 8 April - 10 October.

Directions

From the N20 between Foix and Andorra take exit 14 to Mercus which is only 1 km. Site is signed in Mercus and is on the right 300 m. after the town centre. GPS: N42:52.283 E01:37.350

Charges 2007

Per unit incl. 2 persons	
and electricity	€ 17,00 - € 27,50
extra person	€ 3,50 - € 6,00
child (0-7 yrs)	€ 2,50 - € 5,00

No credit cards.

FR32020 Camping du Lac

F-32230 Marciac (Gers)

Tel: **05 62 08 21 19**. Email: **camping.marciac@wanadoo.fr**

Set in the rolling countryside of the beautiful Gers region, Camping du Lac is on the edge of the ancient fortified town of Marciac. Rob and Louise Robinson, the English owners since 2002, offer a friendly welcome and a quiet, relaxing stay. The well shaded site has 95 pitches, including 15 used for having mobile homes and chalets for rent. There are 60 touring pitches with electricity connections (6/10A, Europlug) on the lower, reasonably level area of the site, including five with hardstanding for motorcaravans.

Facilities

The centrally situated sanitary block uses solar energy to help to heat water. Washbasins in cubicles. Facilites for disabled visitors. Washing machine. Motorcaravan service point. Bar. Bread delivered daily. Pool. Library and reading room. Play area. Internet access. Off site: Shops, restaurant and bars 1 km. Major international jazz festival in Marciac (first 2 weeks in August) 1 km. Fishing, watersports, sailing and riding 300 m. Golf 7 km. Walking (maps at reception).

Open: 16 March - 30 October.

Directions

From Auch take the D943 west towards Bassoues and Marciac. Just before Marciac turn left opposite the floating restaurant on the lake (site is signed). Site is 200 m. on the left.

Charges 2007

Per unit incl. 2 persons	
and electricity (6A)	€ 11,00 - € 20,00
extra person	€ 2,50 - € 5,00
child (4-16 yrs)	€ 1,50 - € 3,50

FR32030 Camping la Plage de Verduzan

Rue du Lac, F-32410 Castera Verduzan (Gers)

Tel: **05 62 68 12 23**. Email: **contact@camping-verduzan.com**

On the edge of the town of Castera Verduzan, this site enjoys a quiet, rural location next to a lake that is managed by the town council. Very attractive, it is well laid out and well cared for with neat hedges and grass pitches. There are views over the surrounding hills, the site enjoying an open aspect yet with plenty of shade from trees and shrubs. There are 100 pitches, with 70 used for touring units and 30 for mobile homes. Electricity (10A) is available throughout.

Facilities

Two toilet blocks, one recently refurbished with modern fittings, will be more than adequate. Facilities for disabled people. Washing machine. Motorcaravan service point. Small snack bar (July/Aug). Low key entertainment, games and competitions (July/Aug). WiFi. Simple play area. Off site: Lake amenities including swimming and fishing. Town with shops, restaurants, etc. 500 m. Riding 5 km.

Open: 23 March - 31 October.

Directions

Site is 20 km. north of Auch. Use the D930 to reach Castera Verduzan. From the south, site is signed on entering the town. From the north pass through town and site is signed left (sharp turn). GPS: N43:48.485 E00:25.848

Charges 2007

Per unit incl. 2 persons	
electricity (6A)	€ 11,00 - € 15,50
	€ 2,00 - € 3,00

FR32010 Kawan Village le Camp de Florence

Mobile homes ▶ page 506

Route Astaffort, F-32480 La Romieu (Gers)
Tel: **05 62 28 15 58**. Email: **info@lecampdeflorence.com**

Camp de Florence is an attractive site on the edge of an historic village in pleasantly undulating Gers countryside. The 183 large, part terraced pitches (95 for tourers) all have electricity, 10 with hardstanding and 25 fully serviced. They are arranged around a large field (full of sunflowers when we visited) with rural views, giving a feeling of spaciousness. The 13th century village of La Romieu is on the Santiago de Compostela pilgrim route. The Pyrénées are a two hour drive, the Atlantic coast a similar distance. There are 20 tour operator pitches. It is run by the Mynsbergen family who are Dutch (although Susan is English) and they have sympathetically converted the old farmhouse buildings to provide facilities for the site. The collegiate church, visible from the site, is well worth a visit (the views are magnificent from the top of the tower), as is the local arboretum, the biggest collection of trees in the Midi-Pyrénées.

Facilities

Two toilet blocks. Washing machine, dryer. Motorcaravan services. Air-conditioned restaurant (open to the public) 1/5-30/9, barbecue. Takeaway. Bread. Swimming pool area with water slide. Jacuzzi, protected children's pool (open to public in afternoons). Adventure playground, games and pets areas. Games room, tennis, table tennis, volleyball, petanque. Bicycle hire. Video shows, discos, picnics, musical evenings. Excursions. Internet and WiFi. Off site: Shop 500 m. in village. Fishing 5 km. Riding 10 km. Walking tours, excursions and wine tasting.

Open: 1 April - 8 October.

Directions

Site signed from D931 Agen - Condom road. Small units turn left at Ligardes (signed), follow D36 for 1 km, turn right turn La Romieu (signed). Otherwise continue until outskirts of Condom and take D41 left to La Romieu, through village to site. GPS: N43:58.975 E00:30.091

Charges 2007

Per unit incl. 2 persons and electricity	€ 16,00 - € 30,90
extra person	€ 3,50 - € 6,90
child (4-9 yrs)	€ 2,60 - € 4,80

Camping Cheques accepted.

FR32060 Yelloh! Village le Lac des Trois Vallées

F-32700 Lectoure (Gers)
Tel: **04 66 73 97 39**. Email: **info@yellohvillage-lac-des-3-vallees.com**

This is a large 140 hectare site with many facilities. It is a large holiday complex and good for families with young children or teenagers. The large lake provides the opportunity for canoeing, swimming, diving and there are four water slides. There is a large safe paddling area and a separate fishing lake. The impressive heated pool complex complete with gymnasium and jacuzzi also has paved areas for sunbathing and a large paddling pool. Of the 500 pitches, over 200 are well situated for touring on shaded or open ground, all with electricity (10A). Used by tour operators (100 pitches).

Facilities

Eight modern sanitary blocks each with baby bathing facilities. Provision for disabled visitors. Laundry facilities. Motorcaravan services. Mini-market. Restaurants and bars. Lakeside snack bar. Heated swimming pool complex. Lake complex. Multisports pitch. BMX/skateboard area. Fishing. Tennis. Minigolf. Disco. Cinema. Children's club. Off site: Golf 10 km. Riding 20 km.

Open: 24 May - 7 September with all facilities.

Directions

Take N21 south from Lectoure for 2 km. Site is well signed and is a further 2 km. after turning left off the N21.

Charges 2008

Per unit incl. 2 persons and electricity	€ 17,00 - € 42,00
with electricity and water	€ 18,00 - € 43,00
extra person	€ 5,00 - € 8,00

FR32080 Kawan Village le Talouch

F-32810 Roquelaure (Gers)

Tel: 05 62 65 52 43. Email: info@camping-talouch.com

Although enjoying a quiet, rural location, this neat and tidy site is only a short drive from the town of Auch with its famous legendary son, d'Artagnan. The entrance is fronted by a parking area with reception to the right and the bar and restaurant facing. Beyond this point lies the top half of the touring area with generous pitches of at least 120 sq.m. located between mature trees and divided by hedges, some with chalets. There are 100 pitches for touring, with electricity (4A). The rear half of the site has unshaded pitches in a more open aspect, and chalets have been built on the hillside to one side of the site. This is a family run site, which takes its name from the small Talouch river.

Facilities

Two toilet blocks with open style washbasins and controllable showers. Baby unit. One toilet for disabled visitors. Washing machine. Shop (1/4-30/9). Bar, restaurant and takeaway. Two excellent pools. Bicycle hire. GPS hire with pre-programmed walking routes. Play areas. Tennis and hard surface sports area. Organised entertainment, high season. Library. Internet and WiFi in reception. Off site: Walking routes. Fishing and riding within 8 km.

Open: 1 April - 30 September.

Directions

Situated some 11 km. north of Auch on the D149, and 64 km. east of Toulouse the site is well signed. From the north approach via the A62 motorway, leaving at Layrac and heading towards Auch on the N21.

Charges 2007

Per unit incl. 2 persons	€ 22,95 - € 26,15
with electricity	€ 30,60
Camping Cheques accepted.	

FR32090 Camping le Pardaillan

27 rue Pardaillan, F-32330 Gondrin (Gers)

Tel: 05 62 29 16 69. Email: camplepardaillan@wanadoo.fr

In the heart of the Armagnac region of the Gers between Condom and Eauze make a stop at the village of Gondrin and stay at the attractive, family run campsite of Le Pardaillan. Neatly manicured and well laid out, the site has 115 pitches arranged on four separate terraced areas; 51 of these are for tourers, the remainder used for chalets (to rent all year). Level and grassy, the touring pitches are small to average in size, separated by tidy hedges and partially shaded by mature trees. Each has 6/10A electricity and 30 also have water and waste water points.

Facilities

Three toilet blocks include WCs, hot showers and washbasins in cubicles. Facilities for disabled visitors. Heated family shower room. Laundry facilities. Bar, restaurant/takeaway (mid June - mid Sept). WiFi internet access. Play area. Children's club (July/Aug). Fishing lake. Off site: Shops, restaurant and bars 500 m. Leisure centre 200 m. Golf 6 km. Riding 15 km.

Open: Easter - mid October.

Directions

From the A62 exit at Agen and take the D931 west towards Eauze. Site is in village of Gondrin (between Condom and Eauze) and is signed.

Charges 2007

per unit incl. 2 persons and electricity (6A)	€ 9,00 - € 23,50
extra person (over 4 yrs)	€ 3,00 - € 5,50
10A electricity	€ 1,60 - € 2,00

FR32110 Camping du Lac de l'Uby

Barbothan-les-Thermes, F-32150 Gaubazon (Gers)

Tel: 05 62 09 53 91. Email: balia-vacances@wanadoo.fr

Camping du Lac de l'Uby is a large, mature site set alongside a lake and close to the thermal spa town of Barbotan-Les-Thermes in the Gers Gascogne region. The site is well shaded by mature trees in most areas and has 280 pitches with 240 available for tourers, the remainder taken up with mobile homes and chalets to rent. The mixture of large and average sized pitches are on level grass and gravel, all having 5/10A electricity (French sockets). Children are well catered for with a good play area and organised activities in July and August, including a circus school two days each week.

Facilities

Five well distributed sanitary blocks include facilities for disabled visitors and a separate baby bathroom. Two blocks are recently refurbished and the others will be done next year. Separate laundry room. Motorcaravan service point. Shop, restaurant and bar, (1/6-30/9). Play area and covered entertainment area. Fishing. Bicycle hire. Off site: Leisure centre with pool, beach and large play area 500 m. Golf 20 km. Lakeside path outside entrance.

Open: 15 March - 30 November.

Directions

From Condom take D931 to Eauze then head west on N524 to Cazaubon. From Cazaubon continue on the N524 towards Barbotan-Les-Thermes, sight is signed on right after 2 km.

Charges 2007

Per person	€ 3,50 - € 5,50
child (3-12 yrs)	€ 2,00 - € 4,00
pitch	€ 6,50 - € 13,00
electricity (6A)	€ 2,50 - € 5,50
No credit cards.	

FR32100 Camping les Lacs de Courtés

F-32240 Estang (Gers)

Tel: 05 62 09 61 98. Email: contact@lacs-de-courtes.com

This small site has been owned and managed by a friendly French couple for the last 24 years. It is situated on a hillside overlooking a lake and has 114 pitches neatly arranged on terraces. There are 50 level touring pitches each with adjacent 6A electricity supply (French sockets), the remaining pitches being used for 64 mobile homes and chalets of which 29 are to rent. The touring pitches are mainly grassed and are well separated by hedges and mature trees which provide shade. Some are situated alongside a private lake that is used for fishing and canoeing. There is a full programme of organised sports competitions and entertainment for children and adults in July and August, including dancing, karaoke, fancy dress and social evenings with local speciality meals. There is also a mini-market each week in July and August when local producers of wine, foie gras etc. bring their products to site for tasting and sale.

Facilities

Centrally situated toilet block with showers, WCs, washbasins and covered dishwashing and laundry sinks. Separate facilities for disabled people at entrance to site. Laundry room. Motorcaravan service point Bar and small restaurant (1/7-31/8) with covered entertainment area. Two outdoor pools and paddling pool. Play area. Private lake for fishing and canoeing. New for 2007, jacuzzi. Off site: Shops, restaurant and bars in Estang 200 m. Golf 18 km. Riding 12 km. Barbotan-Les-Thermes thermal spa 11 km.

Open: Easter - 30 September.

Directions

From Condom take D931 to Eauze then N524 west to Cazaubon. After 4 km. take D30 to Estang. Site is on left as you enter the village of Estang.

Charges 2007

Per unit incl. 2 persons	€ 7,80 - € 13,00
extra person	€ 3,00 - € 5,00
child	€ 1,50 - € 2,50
electricity (6A)	€ 3,00

Les Lacs de Courtes***

Gers en Gascogne
32240 Estang
Tél: +33 (0)5 62 09 61 98
Fax: +33 (0)5 62 09 63 13
Email: contact@lacs-de-courtes.com
www.lacs-de-courtes.com

- Green setting, quiet shady site
- Spacious pitches clearly defined
- Permanent access to high-standing accomodations
- Swimming pool, snack-bar, private lake for fishing activities all year long

---

FR32120 Camping de l'Arros

Allée des Ormeaux, F-32160 Plaisance du Gers (Gers)

Tel: 05 62 69 30 28. Email: infos@plaisance-evasion.com

The village of Plaisance is in the Gascogne region of the Gers and the small and friendly Camping De L'Arros is just on the edge of the village, alongside the river. The site is well shaded and has 82 pitches, with 50 available for touring units, all with 6A electricity. The remainder are taken up with mobile homes and chalets for rent. The large pitches are level, grassy and well separated by hedges and mature trees which provide good shade. Traffic noise is noticeable on some areas of the site. There is a large municipal swimming pool just 100 m. away from the site.

Facilities

Two sanitary blocks with WCs, hot showers and washbasins in cubicles. Washing machines, dryers, iron and ironing board. Shop with local produce. Bar, restaurant and takeaway (July/Aug). Free WiFi internet access. Play area. Children's club (July/Aug). Canoeing. Communal evening meal. Off site: Shops, restaurant and bars 500 m. Outdoor pool 100 m. Minigolf 50 m. Golf 20 km. Riding and tennis 500 m. Major international jazz festival in Marciac (first 2 weeks in August) 14 km.

Open: 1 April - 30 September.

Directions

From Auch take N21 towards Tarbes then after village of Miélan turn right on D3 towards Marciac and Plaisance. At Plaisance turn left on D946, site is signed on left.

Charges 2007

Per person	€ 3,00 - € 5,00
child (3-10 yrs)	€ 2,50 - € 3,70
pitch	€ 2,40 - € 6,00
electricity (6A)	€ 2,00

385

FR31000 Camping le Moulin

F-31220 Martres-Tolosane (Haute-Garonne)

Tel: **05 61 98 86 40**. Email: **info@campinglemoulin.com**

Set in a 12 hectare estate of woods and fields, Camping Le Moulin is a family run campsite in the foothills of the Pyrénées, close to the interesting medieval village of Martres-Tolosane and situated on the site of an old mill on the bank of the River Garonne. There are 99 pitches (60 available for tourers) all of which have electrical connections. Most pitches are level and grassy, of a good size and with shade from mature trees. Some very large (150-200 sq.m.) 'super' pitches are also available and there are 34 chalets/mobile homes for rent.

Facilities

Large modern sanitary block with separate ladies and gents WC's. Communal area with showers and washbasins in cubicles. Heated area for disabled visitors with shower, WC and basin. Baby bath. Motorhome services. Outdoor bar with WiFi. Snackbar and takeaway (July/August). Daily bakers van (except Monday). Heated swimming and paddling pools (July/August). Tennis. Canoeing. Archery. BMX track. Playground. Entertainment and children's club (high season). Off site: Martres-Tolosane 1.5 km. Walking trails and cycle routes.

Open: 22 March - 30 September.

Directions

From the A64 motorway (Toulouse-Tarbes) take exit 21 (Boussens) or exit 22 (Martres-Tolosane) and follow signs to Martres-Tolosane. Site is well signed from village.

Charges 2007

Per person	€ 4,20 - € 6,00
child (2-7 ys)	€ 2,10 - € 3,00
pitch	€ 5,95 - € 13,00
electricity (6/10A)	€ 2,45 - € 5,00

Less 20% outside July and August.

FR65010 Domaine Naturiste l'Eglantière

Aries-Espenan, F-65230 Castelnau-Magnoac (Hautes-Pyrénées)

Tel: **05 62 39 88 00**. Email: **info@leglantiere.com**

Alongside a small, fast flowing river, in woods it comprises 12 hectares for camping and caravanning, with a further 32 for walking and relaxing. The river is suitable for swimming and canoeing, with fishing nearby. The 83 traditional, varying size, grassy, level pitches have 10A electricity (long leads). The older secluded ones are separated by a variety of tall trees and bushes, the newer ones more open. There is a tenting area across the river. The site has a medium sized swimming pool with sunbathing areas and a children's pool, overlooked by the clubhouse and terrace.

Facilities

Two toilet blocks in typically naturist style, providing under cover, open plan, facilities. Small block has individual cubicles. Shop (July-Aug). Clubhouse, bar (all season), small restaurant (June-Sept), pizzeria, takeaway (July-Aug), internet. Soundproofed activities/disco area, play room for younger children. Pool. Play area, children's entertainment in season. River activities. Canoe, mountain bike hire. No barbecues. Torches useful.

Open: Easter - October.

Directions

From Auch take D929 south towards Lannemezan. After Castelnau-Magnoac continue past aerodrome and turn onto the D9 towards Monleon-Magnoac. Take the first left towards Ariès-Espénan and follow site signs. GPS: N43:15.829 E00:31.252

Charges 2007

Per unit incl. 2 persons	€ 9,50 - € 32,90
electricity (10A)	€ 4,90

Camping Cheques accepted.

FR65020 Sunêlia les Trois Vallées

Avenue des Pyrénées, F-65400 Argelès-Gazost (Hautes-Pyrénées)

Tel: **05 62 90 35 47**. Email: **3-vallees@wanadoo.fr**

This is a large, ever-expanding site on the road from Lourdes into the Pyrénées. It has a rather unprepossessing entrance and pitches near the road suffer from noise, but at the back, open fields allow views of surrounding mountains on all sides. Amenities include an indoor pool, two jacuzzis and an enormous play area that seems to have everything! The site has 483 flat, grassy pitches of reasonable size, 200 are for tourers, all with 3 or 6A electricity, some fully serviced. The site is popular with young people and could be quite lively at times.

Facilities

The toilet blocks are a little dated, facilities for disabled people. Cleaning can be variable and facilities could be under pressure at peak times. Bread. Bar/disco. Café, takeaway. Swimming pool complex (from 15/5), paddling pool, spa bath, large jacuzzi and two slides. TV room. Good playground. Entertainment in high season. Off site: Bicycle hire 50 m. Fishing 500 m. Riding 3 km.

Open: 4 April - 12 November.

Directions

Argelès-Gazost is 13 km. south of Lourdes. From Lourdes take the new N21 (Voie rapide) south and leave at the third exit. Site entrance is directly off the next roundabout. GPS: N43:00.733 W00:05.833

Charges 2008

Per pitch incl. 2 persons	€ 11,00 - € 26,00
with electricity	€ 12,50 - € 32,00
extra person	€ 5,00 - € 9,00

FR65030 Airotel Pyrénées

46 avenue du Barége, F-65120 Esquieze-Sere (Hautes-Pyrénées)

Tel: **05 62 92 89 18**. Email: **airotel.pyrenees@wanadoo.fr**

It is located on the main road into the mountains, south from Argelès-Gazost and surrounded by the high peaks (some pitches will have daytime road noise). There are 163 level pitches, with 85 for touring units, all with electricity and 90 fully serviced. They are on terraced ground and separated by bushes. Lighting runs through the site and across some pitches. The layout of the pitches with the mobile homes can give a rather crowded feel. In high season a programme of activities and tournaments is arranged, from walking and mountain bike trips to rafting.

Facilities

Fairly modern, well appointed, toilet blocks (one heated), facilities for disabled people also doubling as a baby room. Bottled water is advised for drinking and cooking. Motorcaravan services. Small shop (1/7-31/8), bread (15/5-15/90. Outdoor pool (15/6-15/9). Indoor pool, balneotherapy pool, sauna, fitness room (1/12-30/9). Water slides. Practice climbing wall, half court tennis, table tennis. Small playground. Off site: Skiing 10 km.

Open: All year, excl. 1 October - 30 November.

Directions

Take N21 (Voie rapide) south from Lourdes past Argelès-Gazost towards Luz-St-Sauveur. The site is on left at Esquièze-Sere, just before Luz-St-Sauveur. Site is on left immediately after Camping International. GPS: N42:52.749 W00:00.610

Charges 2007

Per unit incl. 2 persons	€ 15,50 - € 24,00
extra person	€ 5,00
electricity (3/10A)	€ 3,50 - € 6,50

FR65040 Camping International

F-65120 Luz-Saint-Sauveur (Hautes-Pyrénées)

Tel: **05 62 92 82 02**. Email: **reception@international-camping.fr**

Located in the foothills of the Pyrénées, Camping International is an attractive, family run site with 180 pitches, most are on the fairly level lower section. There are 146 grassy pitches for tourists all with electricity (2/6A), many divided by hedges and some with a little shade. Around 40 pitches (more for tents) are on terraces on the mountainside at back of the site, all accessed by tarmac roads and with stunning views. However some fairly steep up and down walking will be necessary. Most of the amenities are grouped around the reception area along the front of the site.

Facilities

Well equipped toilet blocks (one heated), facilities for babies and disabled campers. Shop. Snack bar, takeaway. Heated swimming pool and jacuzzi, all open (1/6-30/9). Playground. Organised activities, main season. Off site: Climbing, rafting, walking, winter skiing. Fishing 500 m. Bicycle hire 1 km. Riding 7 km. Golf 30 km.

Open: 1 June - 30 September.

Directions

From Lourdes take N21 (Voie rapide) south, pass Argelès-Gazost continuing towards Luz-St-Sauveur on D921. Site is on left at Esquièze-Sere (just before Luz). GPS: N42:52.961 W00:00.806

Charges 2007

Per unit incl. 1 or 2 persons	€ 19,50
extra person	€ 4,10 - € 4,90
electricity	€ 1,90 - € 5,00

FR65060 Castel Camping Pyrénées Natura

Route du Lac, F-65400 Estaing (Hautes-Pyrénées)

Tel: **05 62 97 45 44**. Email: **info@camping-pyrenees-natura.com**

Pyrénées Natura, at an altitude of 1,000 metres, on the edge of the National Park is the perfect site for lovers of nature. The 60 pitches (46 for tourists), all with electricity, are in a large, level, open and sunny field. Around 75 varieties of trees and shrubs have been planted – but they do not spoil the fantastic views. The reception and bar are in a traditional style stone building with an open staircase. The small shop in the old water mill stocks a variety of produce, it is left unmanned and open all day and you pay at reception.

Facilities

First class toilet blocks include facilities for disabled visitors and babies. Washing machine and airers (no lines allowed). Motorcaravan services. Small shop, takeaway (15/5-15/9). Small bar (15/5-15/9), lounge area. Lounge, library, TV (mainly used for videos of the National Park). Sauna, solarium (free between 12.00-17.00). Music room. Play area for the very young. Small 'beach' beside river. Giant chess. Weekly evening meal in May, June and Sept. Internet. Off site: Village has two restaurants.

Open: 1 May - 20 September.

Directions

From Lourdes take N21 towards Argelès-Gazost. Exit 2, N2021/D21, into Argelès. Approaching town turn onto D918 towards Aucun. After 8 km. turn left, D13 to Bun, cross river, right on D103 to site (5.5 km). Narrow road, few passing places. GPS: N42:56.451 W00:10.631

Charges 2008

Per unit incl. 2 persons and electricity (3A)	€ 15,50 - € 24,50
extra person	€ 5,25
Less in low season.	

387

FR65080 **Kawan Village du Lavedan**

Lau-Balagnas, F-65400 Argelès-Gazost (Hautes-Pyrénées)

Tel: **05 62 97 18 84**. Email: **contact@lavedan.com**

Camping du Lavedan is an old established and very French site set in the Argelès-Gazost valley south of the Lourdes. It is beside the main road so there is some daytime road noise. The 105 touring pitches are set very close together on grass with some shade and all have electricity (2-10A). The area is fine for walking, biking, rafting and of course, in winter, skiing. There is a swimming pool which can be covered and a twice weekly event is organised in July/Aug, weekly in June.

Facilities

Acceptable toilet block. Baby room. Facilities for disabled visitors. Washing machines and dryer in separate block heated in winter. Restaurant with takeaway and terrace (1/5-15/9). Bar, TV (all year). No shop, bread delivery (1/5-15/9). Swimming pool (with cover), paddling pool. Excellent play area. Internet (July/Aug). Boules, table tennis. Off site: Fishing or bicycle hire 1 km. Supermarket or rafting 2 km. Riding 5 km. Golf 15 km. Nearby is 'La Voie Verte' - a 17 km. traffic-free cycle path from Lourdes south to Soulom.

Open: All year.

Directions

Lau-Balagnas, 15 km. south of Lourdes. From Lourdes take the N21 (Voie rapide) south, exit 3 (Argelès-Gazost). Take N2021, D921 or D21 towards Luz-St-Sauveur for 2 km. to Lau-Balagnas. Site on right, southern edge of town. GPS: N42:59.293 W00:05.340

Charges 2008

Per unit incl. 2 persons	€ 15,00 - € 23,00
electricity (10A max)	€ 1,00
extra person	€ 4,50 - € 6,50

Camping Chèques accepted.

FR65090 **Camping Soleil du Pibeste**

16 avenue du Lavedan, F-65400 Agos Vidalos (Hautes-Pyrénées)

Tel: **05 62 97 53 23**. Email: **info@campingpibeste.com**

Soleil du Pibeste is a quiet, rural site with well tended grass and flower beds. It has 67 pitches for touring, all having electricity (3-15A) with some shade. The Dusserm family welcomes all arrivals with a drink and they are determined to ensure that you have a good stay. There is no shop but the supermarket is only 5 km. and ordered bread is delivered to your door daily. The swimming pool is on a terrace above the pitches, with sun beds, a paddling pool and waterfall and has the most magnificent view of the mountains.

Facilities

Two heated toilet blocks. Baby room. Facilities for disabled visitors (key). Cleaning can be variable. Washing machine, dryer. Motorcaravan services. Bar, snacks, piano, internet. Room for playing cards or reading. Swimming, paddling pools. Small play area. Boules, archery, basketball, volleyball. Table tennis. Bicycle hire.Off site: Fishing 800 m. Golf 10 km. Rafting 2 km. Skiing 2 km.

Open: 1 May - 30 September.

Directions

Agos Vidalos is on the N21, 5 km. south of Lourdes. Leave express-way at second exit, signed Agos Vidalos and continue to site, a short distance on the right. GPS: N43:02.134 W00:04.256

Charges 2007

Per unit incl. 2 persons and 3A electricity	€ 12,00 - € 24,00
extra person	€ 3,00 - € 5,00

FR65100 **Camping le Moulin du Monge**

Avenue Jean Moulin, F-65100 Lourdes (Hautes-Pyrénées)

Tel: **05 62 94 28 15**. Email: **camping.moulin.monge@wanadoo.fr**

A well organised, family run site with a friendly welcome, Moulin du Monge has a convenient location for visiting Lourdes, only 3 kilometres away. There will be some traffic noise from the nearby N21 and railway line. This attractive garden-like site has 57 grassy pitches in several different areas and on different levels. Some are in a level orchard area and are closest to the main road. A few pitches are on a little woodland knoll behind reception, with the remainder on a higher level at the back of the site. All have electricity hook-ups (2-6A).

Facilities

The heated toilet blocks have all necessary facilities, including washing machine, dryer, sauna. Facilities for disabled campers. Baby room. Motorcaravan services. Well stocked shop. Heated swimming pool, sliding cover (1/5-20/9), paddling pool. Games/TV room. Barbecue, terrace. Table tennis. Sauna. Boules. Playground, trampolines. Off site: Good transport links to the city centre with its famous grotto and all shops and services. Fishing 3 km. Golf 4 km. Bicycle hire 500 m.

Open: 1 April - 10 October.

Directions

Site is just off the N21 on northern outskirts of Lourdes. From north, on N21 (2 km. south of Adé) be prepared to take slip lane in centre of road. Turn left into Ave. Jean Moulin. Site shortly on left. GPS: N43:06.931 W00:01.895

Charges 2007

Per unit incl. 2 persons	€ 13,80
incl. electricity (2-6A)	€ 15,80 - € 17,80
extra person	€ 4,60
child (0-7 yrs)	€ 2,90

FR65110 Camping Cabaliros

Pont de Secours, F-65110 Cauterets (Hautes-Pyrénées)

Tel: 05 62 92 55 36. Email: info@camping-cabaliros.com

After driving up a steady incline through a sheer sided, tree lined valley, the terrain opens up just before you reach the town of Cauterets. Here you will find the delightful Camping Cabaliros where you will receive a warm and friendly welcome. With wonderful views, the site is owned by Jean and Chantal Boyrie and has been in the family since it was opened in 1959. There are 4 chalets for rent, 36 pitches without electricity (mainly for tents) and 60 pitches with 6A electricity (French sockets) for tourers. All of the touring pitches are on well manicured grass and those around the perimeter of the site are reasonably level with some shade provided by mature trees.

Facilities

Sanitary block near to site entrance with WCs, hot showers and washbasins in cubicles. Dishwashing and laundry sinks with cold water only. Washing machine and dryer. Motorcaravan service point. Large library (mainly French). Play area for over 7s. Fishing. Off site: Restaurant (July/Aug) 50 m. Supermarket 1 km. Shops, restaurants and bars 2 km. Riding 10 km. Indoor and outdoor pools 2 km. Walking. Pont d'Espagne 9 km.

Open: 1 June - 30 September.

Directions

From Lourdes head south on the N21 to Argelès-Gazost then take D921 followed by the D920 to Cauterets. Site is on right 1 km. after 'SHOPI' supermarket just before Cauterets.
GPS: N42:54.100 W00:06.250

Charges 2008

Per unit incl. 2 persons	€ 11,80 - € 13,20
incl. electricity (2-10A)	€ 14,80 - € 16,50
extra person	€ 4,15 - € 4,60

FR65130 Camping Pyrenevasion

Route de Luz-Ardiden, Sazos, F-65120 Luz-Saint-Sauveur (Hautes-Pyrénées)

Tel: 05 62 92 91 54. Email: camping-pyrenevasion@wanadoo.fr

In the heart of the Pyrénées, Camping Pyrenevasion is at a height of 830 metres on a picturesque hillside with panoramic views of the mountains and the town of Luz-St-Sauveur in the valley below. This family run site, where you will receive a warm and friendly welcome, has 60 well laid out, tidy touring pitches. On level, grassy terraces on the hillside which are partially shaded by young trees, each pitch has electricity (French socket) adjacent and all are reasonably close to the modern heated sanitary block. There are 12 modern, comfortable chalets for rent (all year).

Facilities

Heated sanitary block with showers, WCs, washbasins (cubicles and open area). Facilities for disabled visitors. Baby bath. Washing machine and dryer. Motorcaravan services. Bread to order. Bar (all year). Takeaway (1/6-1/10). Heated swimming and paddling pools (15/5-1/10). Small play area (up to 6 yrs). Sports area. Off site: Shops, restaurant and bar 2 km. Fishing 200 m. Riding 10 km. Golf 30 km. Skiing 10 km.

Open: All year.

Directions

From Lourdes take N21 south to Pierrefit-Nestalas then the D921 to Luz-St-Sauveur. Follow signs from Luz-St-Sauveur to Luz-Ardiden (D12). Site is on right as you enter the village of Sazos.

Charges 2007

Per unit incl. 2 persons	€ 10,00 - € 16,00
extra person	€ 5,00
electricity (3-10A)	€ 3,50 - € 11,50
No credit cards.	

FR65160 Camping le Monlôo

RD8 chemin du Monlou, F-65200 Bagnères-de-Bigorre (Hautes-Pyrénées)

Tel: 05 62 95 19 65. Email: campingmonloo@yahoo.com

A relatively small site of 120 touring pitches, Le Monlôo is set in a wide valley in the Pyrénées. The immediate surroundings of farmland, with crops growing and cows at pasture, give way to some magnificent views of the mountains towering away from the front of the site, whilst the back is right at the foot of some smaller foothills. This area is a paradise for walkers and cyclists. The friendly family take their job seriously and will even show you a selection of available pitches from the comfort of their electric car.

Facilities

Ample toilet facilities are provided in three blocks. Facilities for disabled visitors. Washing machines. Motorcaravan services. Bread to order. Open air heated pool with slide. Simple play area. Gas or electric barbecues are permitted. Off site: Spa town of Bagnères-de-Bigorre 2 km.

Open: All year.

Directions

From the A64 take exit 14 signed Bagnères-de-Bigorre. Enter town and take D8 road to the right for Ordizan. Site is just a few hundred metres along this road, well signed.

Charges 2007

Per unit incl. 2 persons	€ 11,00 - € 16,50
extra person	€ 3,50 - € 4,00
electricity (2-6A)	€ 2,00 - € 5,50

389

FR65170 Aire Naturelle de Camping l'Arrayade

Arrayade, F-65100 Ger (Hautes-Pyrénées)

Tel: 05 59 56 10 60

This unique little campsite, situated quite high up in the Pyrénées with some amazing views down the valley, could well be near perfect for anyone seeking a relaxing, informal and friendly atmosphere. On a very small site of just 15 pitches, Mme. Pique is a gracious host who will do her utmost to ensure your stay is as pleasant as possible. She has prepared plenty of information on the local area, the best walks to go on and the cycle pathway that runs past the site that takes you into Lourdes centre in just 3 km. You can taste the freshness of the air up here and outdoor lovers will feel really at one with nature.

Facilities

One very modern toilet block situated in the reception area. Provision is adequate. All fittings are very new and the arrangement makes this area feel almost like a private bathroom. Washing machine and dryer. Small bar for breakfast and evening meals. Peaceful lounge. Sauna, jacuzzi and small gym. Internet access. Off site: Monsieur Pique, a qualified pilot, offers flights over the Pyrénées for the ultimate sightseeing experience.

Open: 15 May - 15 September.

Directions

From Lourdes head south on the D921 signed Lugagnan. After 3 km. bear right on D13 for Ger. As you approach a few houses on your left the site entrance is on the right, set back a little in a lay-by.

Charges 2007

Per unit incl. 2 persons	€ 10,00
extra person	€ 2,50
child (under 7 yrs)	€ 1,50
electricity	€ 2,50 - € 5,00

FR81030 Camping de Gourjade

Route de Roquecourbe, F-81100 Castres (Tarn)

Tel: 05 63 59 33 51. Email: contact@campingdegourjade.com

Camping de Gourjade is a family run site set in a country park which belongs to the town of Castres. It has the river running along one side and the country park on the other. There are 100 level pitches (88 for tourers), all with electricity (6/10A) and separated by well trimmed hedges, and some with shade. Those nearest the river are sloping and can be soft. There is a barrier at the entrance and a night watchman for security. A play area caters for children of 3-12 yrs and there is a small swimming pool on site.

Facilities

The two well appointed toilet blocks have facilities for disabled visitors and baby room. Maintenance and cleaning are variable. Washing machine, dryer. Motorcaravan services. Small shop, bread. Attractive restaurant (all season). Small swimming pool. Bicycles kept at reception for the free use of campers. Barrier card deposit €15 (main season). Off site: Country park adjacent. Supermarket 1 km.

Open: 1 April - 3 October.

Directions

Castres is 42 km. south of Albi. Site is on D89 in Parc de Gourjade north of city. Follow signs to Roquecourbe until roundabout with supermarket, then signs to 'Rive droite', camping. After 1 km. turn left at T-junction, site is 300 m.
GPS: N43:37.240 E02:15.247

Charges 2008

Per person	€ 3,00 - € 4,00
pitch and vehicle	€ 9,00 - € 14,50
electricity	€ 2,50 - € 3,50

FR81060 Camping les Clots

F-81190 Mirandol-Bourgnounac (Tarn)

Tel: 05 63 76 92 78. Email: campclots@wanadoo.fr

Les Clots is a very rural, simple site in the heart of the countryside with 62 touring pitches and 12 used for canvas tents, chalets and caravans for rent. The 2.5 km. road from the nearest village of Mirandol is quite narrow. The site has been carved out of a steep hillside giving variously sized terraces taking from 1 to 10 units. Nearly all pitches have electricity (6A). A few pitches, mainly for tents, are set well away from the others giving lots of seclusion. Being amongst the trees there is enough shade.

Facilities

Toilet blocks are kept very clean. Baby bath. Facilities for disabled visitors. Washing machines. Bar (July/Aug). Shop with basic provisions incl. bread (July/Aug). Simple swimming and paddling pools (1/7-30/9) with grass sunbathing area. Table tennis. Minigolf. In July/Aug a local comes twice weekly to prepare an evening meal (to order). Fishing. Site is not suitable for American style motorhomes. Off site: Riding 15 km.

Open: 1 May - 1 October.

Directions

Heading south on N88 from Rodez, just before reaching Carmaux turn right onto the D905 towards Mirandol. The site is 5.5 km. north of Mirandol.

Charges 2007

per unit incl. 3 persons	€ 22,00 - € 26,00
extra person	€ 4,60
child (under 8 yrs)	€ 2,80
electricity (6A)	€ 2,80
Low season reductions.	

FR81070 Camping Indigo Rieu Montagné

Lac du Laouzas, F-81320 Nages (Tarn)

Tel: 05 63 37 24 71. Email: rieumontagne@camping-indigo.com

Rieu Montagné is a delightful site in the heart of the Haut Languedoc Regional park and at the corner of the départements of the Tarn, Aveyron and Hérault. There are 127 touring pitches, mostly on broad terraces with reasonable shade, all with electrical connections (6/10A) and 56 fully serviced. A heated swimming pool overlooks the lake and is used for occasional aquagym. In high season there is a varied entertainment programme, and a number of guided walks. Most leisure facilities are available at the lakeside complex. Lakeside facilities include tennis, a play area, sailing and other water activities. This site is on a fairly steep slope. The site is a member of the Indigo group and lies close to the Lac du Laouzas where a wide range of sporting activities can be enjoyed.

Facilities

The two toilet blocks, comprehensively refitted in 2005, provide mostly British style toilets, washbasins in cubicles and facilities for disabled people and babies. Laundry. Shop with basic provisions (July/Aug). Bar and snack bar with takeaway. Swimming pool (14/6-14/9). Entertainment programme (high season). Chalets, tents and mobile homes to let (53). Off site: Lakeside leisure complex.

Open: 14 June - 14 September.

Directions

Nages about 80 km. southeast of Albi. From Albi, D999 east towards St Affrique. 11 km. after Albon right, D607, to Lacaune. At T-junction left, D622, for 6.5 km. Right, D62, 2 km. South of town left over bridge, D162. First left uphill to site. GPS: N43:38.877 E02:46.888

Charges 2007

Per person	€ 4,80 - € 5,50
child (2-7 yrs)	€ 3,00 - € 3,50
pitch	€ 4,20 - € 18,00
electricity (6/10A)	€ 4,00 - € 6,00

Camping Cheques accepted.

FR81100 Camping de la Rigole

Route de Barrage, F-81540 Les Cammazes (Tarn)

Tel: 05 63 73 28 99. Email: mary@campingdlr.com

A pleasant, traditional site with 64 pitches in a countryside location, La Rigole is partly wooded, and gives a friendly reception. A slightly sloping site, most of the 43 touring pitches are on small terraces and many have quite deep shade. All have electricity (4-13A). There is a small bar and a snack bar. One evening each week in main season a regional meal is organised. Small children are well catered for with play areas for tiny tots and under 7s, and a delightful children's farm with animals. The site is totally unsuitable for American RVs.

Facilities

Fairly modern toilet block. Baby room. Facilities for disabled campers (althought the slopes might be difficult). Washing machines, dryer. Small shop. Bar. Takeaway. Swimming pool. All open 15/4-15/10. Table tennis. Badminton. Volleyball. Boules. Small animal farm. Off site: Lac des Cammazes with its dam 400 m. Lac de St Ferréol 5 km., with large sandy beach. Fishing 0.4 km. Riding 1.5 km.

Open: 15 April - 15 October.

Directions

Les Cammazes is 25 km. northeast of Castelnaudary, 10 km. southeast of Revel. From Revel take D629 to Cammazes, continue on D629 through village, after 1 km. turn left towards Barrage, site entrance is 200 m. on right. GPS: N43:24.472 E02:05.196

Charges 2008

Per unit incl. 2 persons and electricity	€ 18,50
extra person	€ 4,50
child (0-7 yrs)	€ 2,70

FR81110 Camping Saint-Martin
F-81540 Sorèze (Tarn)

Tel: 05 63 50 20 19. Email: mary@campingsaintmartin.com

There are 48 individual tourist pitches with 10A electricity and six wooden chalets for rent. The pitches are all on grass, some divided by newly planted hedging and there are some mature trees for shade. Six pitches are reserved for motorcaravans, although these are rather compact. A small swimming pool is well fenced and gated. Reception has a small bar and snack bar and can also provide basic supplies including drinks, sweets, speciality foods and snacks. However, you are only 100 metres from the town centre shops.

Facilities
Sanitary unit is well built, Facilities for disabled visitors. Covered dishwashing and laundry sinks plus a washing machine. Small shop. Bar with TV. Snack bar. Swimming pool. All amenities open 15/6-15/9. Table tennis. Boules. Volleyball. Communal barbecue. Small playground. Entertainment in high season. No pets. Off site: Municipal leisure and sports facilities including tennis courts adjacent.

Open: 15 June - 15 September.

Directions
Sorèze is on the D85 about 25 km. southwest of Castres, 5 km. east of Revel. The site is well signed within the town. GPS: N43:27.271 E02:04.175

Charges 2008
Per unit incl. 2 persons and electricity	€ 17,10
extra person	€ 4,50
child (0-7 yrs)	€ 2,70

FR81120 Camping le Rouquié
Lac de la Raviège, F-81260 Lamontélarié (Tarn)

Tel: 05 63 70 98 06. Email: contact@campingrouquie.com

Le Rouquié, a family run campsite, is on the edge of Le Lac de Raviège, deep in the heart of the 'parc naturel régional Haut-Languedoc'. The 97 level pitches (79 for tourers) are of varying sizes between 80 and 130 sq.m. They are grassed and arranged on terraces which slope quite steeply to the edge of the lake. All the pitches have superb views over the lake, They are separated by small trees and are partially shaded, with electricity (6A; Europlug) available near each one. A separate section of the site has 12 wooden chalets to rent.

Facilities
Separate ladies and gents sanitary facilities provide hot and cold water to showers and washbasins. Washing machines. Small shop (July/Aug). Bar and snack bar with takeaway (1/6-31/10). Play area. Fishing. Limited English spoken. Off site: Nearest supermarket 8 km. Watersports. Riding 8 km. Golf 30 km.

Open: 1 April - 31 October.

Directions
From Castres take N112 towards Bezier. At Lacabarède turn north on D52 to Anglès. Continue on D52 towards Lac de Raviège and cross bridge at the dam. Keep on the D52 for another 1.5 km. then turn right on D62 toward Salvetat-sur-Agout. Site is on right after another 1.4 km. GPS: N43:35.815 E02:36.434

Charges 2007
Per unit incl. 2 persons	€ 11,20 - € 11,80
extra person	€ 3,90
electricity (6A)	€ 4,00

FR81130 Camping l'Amitié
Vallée du Tarn, F-81340 Trébas (Tarn)

Tel: 05 63 55 84 07. Email: amitie@trebas.net

A winding road with wonderful views of the surrounding countryside leads down to the small unspoilt village of Trébas in the Vallée du Tarn, and there on the banks of the Tarn river lies the small friendly site of Camping L'Amitié. There are 60 level, well drained and manicured grass pitches, 49 of which are available for tourers. A few wooden chalets are also available to rent. All with electricity (French sockets), the pitches are on terraces which slope gently towards the riverbank and most have partial shading although some are in the open area close to the river.

Facilities
The toilet block is near the site entrance with Turkish and British style toilets, hot showers and washbasins in cubicles (cold water only). No shop. Bar/restaurant (1/5-15/9). Swimming pool (1/6-31/8). Play area. Some activities and entertainment in high season. Off site: Site is in small village with mini-supermarket, pharmacy, baker and butcher. Bar/restaurant 250 m. (July/Aug. only).

Open: 1 April - 15 September.

Directions
From Albi take D999 east (signed Millau). At Alban take D53 north to St Andre and Trébas. Cross river at Villeneuve sur Tarn to Trébas, the site is in the village and signed. GPS: N43:56.521 E02:28.902

Charges 2007
Per unit incl. 2 persons	€ 8,30 - € 11,80
extra person	€ 2,80 - € 3,90
child (2-7 yrs)	€ 1,80 - € 2,60

FR81090 Camping le Manoir de Boutaric

Route de Lacabarède, Angles F-81260 (Tarn)

Tel: 05 63 70 96 06. Email: manoir.boutaric@accesinter.com

Le Manoir de Boutaric is a 19th century château hidden deep in the Haut Languedoc countryside. The château lies in a attractive park and offers 110 touring pitches as well as a number of mobile homes and chalets. Pitches are spacious, well shaded and all have electrical connections (5A), as well as a water and drainage point. Leisure facilities include a swimming pool and paddling pool and the site also has an attractive restaurant. In high season, entertainment includes discos and film screenings in the château cellars. The village of Anglès-du-Tarn is just 100 m. from the site and has a good range of shops.

Facilities

Restaurant and bar. Takeaway. Swimming pool, paddling pool. Mountain bike hire. Entertainment in high season. Children's club (high season). Mobile homes and chalets for rent. Off site: Off site: Fishing, lake with private beach 6 km. Tennis, riding, golf nearby.

Open: 15 April - 30 October.

Directions

From Toulouse, take the westbound N126 to Castres and then the D622 to Brassac. From Brassac head southeast on the D68 to Angles. Site is well signed from the village.

Charges 2007

Per unit incl. 2 persons and electricity	€ 13,00 - € 26,00
extra person	€ 3,10 - € 5,50

FR82010 Camping les Trois Cantons

F-82140 Saint Antonin-Noble-Val (Tarn-et-Garonne)

Tel: 05 63 31 98 57. Email: info@3cantons.fr

Les Trois Cantons is a well established and very friendly family run with 100 pitches (85 for tourers) set among mature trees that give dappled shade. The pitches are of average size, reasonably level and all have electricity connections. The swimming pool is covered and heated in early and late season, with activities organised there in July and August. There are also walks, archery and boules, clay modelling plus wine tastings and a weekly dance. When the trees are bare early in the season, there could be a little road noise when the wind is in a certain direction.

Facilities

The two sanitary blocks include British and Turkish style WCs, showers, washbasins (some in cubicles) and facilities for disabled visitors, which have recently been refurbished. Laundry and dishwashing facilities. Very limited shop (bread daily). Bar serving snacks and takeaways. Swimming pool (heated from 15/5-30/9) and paddling pool. Games/TV room. Play area. Small farm area. Tennis. Volleyball. Boules. English spoken. Off site: Riding 1 km. Fishing 7 km. Many pretty medieval villages to visit.

Open: 15 April - 30 September.

Directions

From A20 or N20 at Caussade, take D926 signed Caylus and Septfonds. Site is signed to right 5 km. after Septfonds. Do not take the D5 towards St Antonin as it involves 5 km. of narrow road.

Charges 2008

Per pitch and 2 people	€ 14,50 - € 21,00
extra person	€ 4,55 - € 6,40
child (2-9 yrs)	€ 2,70 - € 4,20
electricity (2-10A)	€ 2,70 - € 6,80
Camping Cheques accepted.	

FR82040 Flower Camping les Gorges de l'Aveyron

Marsac bas, F-82140 Saint Antonin-Noble-Val (Tarn-et-Garonne)

Tel: 05 63 30 69 76. Email: info@camping-gorges-aveyron.com

This is a friendly, family site which is undergoing a process of renovation by its new owners, Marie-Therese and Dominique Defoort. The site has an attractive wooded location, sloping down to the River Aveyron and facing the Roc d'Anglars. Reception and the two toilet blocks are housed in traditional, converted farm buildings. There are 80 pitches of which 65 are available for tourers, and these all have electrical connections (3/5A). The pitches are grassy and well shaded and may become very soft in times of poor weather. Some pitches are available close to the river but we would suggest that these are unsuitable for younger children as the river is unfenced.

Facilities

Two toilet blocks with washing machines and dryers. Small shop. Bar. Snack bar and takeaway food. Direct access to river. Fishing. Canoeing. Play area. Entertainment and activities in high season. Mobile homes for rent. Off site: St Antonin-Noble-Val with a wide choice of shops, restaurants and bars 1.5 km.

Open: 1 February - 30 November.

Directions

From the north, take exit 59 from the A20 autoroute joining the D926 and follow signs to St Antonin. Site is on the D115, 1.5 km. east of the town.

Charges 2007

Per pitch incl. 2 persons and electricity	€ 11,90 - € 20,50
extra person	€ 2,80 - € 5,00

Languedoc and Roussillon form part of the Massif Central. With its huge sandy beaches the mountainous Languedoc region is renowned for its long sunshine records, and the pretty coastal villages of Roussillon are at their most beautiful at sunset erupting in a riot of colour.

THIS SECTION COVERS THE SOUTH WEST COASTAL REGION OF THE MEDITERRANEAN, DÉPARTEMENTS: 11 AUDE, 30 GARD, 34 HÉRAULT, 66 PYRÉNÉES-ORIENTALES.

Once an independent duchy, the ancient land of Languedoc combines two distinct regions: the vineyards of the Corbières and Minervois and the coastal plain stretching from the Rhône to the Spanish border. Much of the region is rugged and unspoilt, offering opportunities for walking and climbing.

There is ample evidence of the dramatic past. Ruins of the former Cathar castles can be seen throughout the region. The walled city of Carcassonne with its towers, dungeons, moats and drawbridges is one of the most impressive examples of medieval France.

Today, Languedoc and Roussillon are wine and agricultural regions. Languedoc, with considerable success, is now a producer of much of the nation's better value wines. But above all, vast hot sandy beaches and long hours of sunshine make this a paradise for beach enthusiasts. La Grande Motte, Cap d'Agde and Canet, are all being promoted as an alternative to the more famous Mediterranean stretches of the Côte d'Azur.

Places of interest

Aigues-Mortes: medieval city.

Béziers: wine capital of the region, St Nazaire cathedral, Canal du Midi.

Carcassonne: largest medieval walled city in Europe.

Limoux: medieval town, Notre Dame de Marseilla Basilica, St Martin church.

Montpellier: universities, Roman sites; Gothic cathedral.

Nîmes: Roman remains, Pont du Gard.

Perpignan: Kings Palace; Catalan characteristics, old fortress.

Pézenas: Molière's home.

Villeneuve-lés-Avignon: Royal City and residence of popes in 14th century.

Cuisine of the region

Cooking is Provençal, characterised by garlic and olive oil with sausages and smoked hams. Fish is popular along the coast. Wines include Corbières, Minervois, Banyuls and Muscat.

Aïgo Bouido: garlic soup.

Boles de picoulat: small balls of chopped-up beef and pork, garlic and eggs.

Bouillinade: a type of *bouillabaisse* with potatoes, oil, garlic and onions.

Boutifare: a sausage-shaped pudding of bacon and herbs.

Cargolade: snails, stewed in wine.

Ouillade: heavy soup of *boutifare* leeks, carrots, and potatoes..

Touron: a pastry of almonds, pistachio nuts and fruit.

FR11040 Camping le Martinet Rouge Birdie

F-11390 Brousses et Villaret (Aude)

Tel: **04 68 26 51 98**. Email: **campinglemartinetrouge@orange.fr**

Le Martinet Rouge provides a peaceful retreat in the Aude countryside to the north of Carcassonne. It is a small site where the owners have been working hard to improve the facilities. The most striking features of the site are the massive granite boulders (outcrops of smooth rock from the last ice age). The site offers 50 pitches for touring units, all with electricity (3/6A), in two contrasting areas – one is well secluded with irregularly shaped, fairly level, large pitches amongst a variety of trees and shrubs, while the other is on a landscaped gentle hill with mature trees.

Facilities

Four sanitary blocks of various ages, including facilities for disabled visitors, baby bathroom, laundry facilities. Swimming pool (15/6-15/9). Small shop (no others locally). Bar, terrace, TV (1/7-15/9). Snack bar (1/7-31/8). Barbecue area. Fitness room. Croquet, volleyball, half court tennis, table tennis, small play area. Internet access. Off site: Visit the paper mill in the village. Tennis, riding and fishing quite close.

Open: 1 April - 15 October.

Directions

Site is south of Brousses-et-Villaret, 20 km. northwest of Carcassonne. Best approached via D118, Carcassonne - Mazamet road. Turn onto D103 15 km. north of Carcassonne to Brousses-et-Villaret. Western outskirts of village turn south to site (signed) in 50 m. GPS: N43:20.350 E02:15.127

Charges 2007

Per unit incl. 2 persons	€ 12,50 - € 15,50
with electricity	€ 15,00 - € 18,00
extra person	€ 4,50 - € 5,50
No credit cards.	

FR11050 Camping Rives des Corbières

Avenue du Languedoc, F-11370 Port Leucate (Aude)

Tel: **04 68 40 90 31**. Email: **rivescamping@wanadoo.fr**

Port Leucate is part of the major Languedoc development which took place during the sixties and seventies and it is now a thriving resort. The campsite is situated on the old coast road into Port Leucate between the Etang de Salas and the beach, 800 m. from the centre of the town and port and only 150 m. from the beach. A mixture of tall poplars and pine trees provide reasonable shade for the 305 pitches. On good-sized sandy plots, all have 6A electricity connections. About 90 are used for mobile homes. With no tour operators this is a good value site, essentially French.

Facilities

Four toilet blocks opened as required. Two have mainly Turkish toilets. Facilities for disabled people. Laundry room. Small supermarket, bar and takeaway (July/Aug). Swimming pools. Play area. Daytime games and tournaments and in the evening, live music, karaoke and dancing. Off site: Beach 150 m. (lifeguards July/Aug). Port 800 m.

Open: 1 April - 30 September.

Directions

From the A9 take exit 40 and follow signs for Port Leucate on D627 (passing Leucate village) for 14 km. Exit the D627 which is like a bypass into Port Leucate village. Go right into Avenue du Languedoc and site is 800 m. GPS: N42:50.009 E03:02.004

Charges 2007

Per unit incl. 2 persons and electricity	€ 16,30 - € 20,40

FR11060 Yelloh! Village Domaine d'Arnauteille

F-11250 Montclar (Aude)

Tel: **04 68 26 84 53**. Email: **info@yellohvillage-domaine-arnauteille.com**

Enjoying some beautiful and varied views, this site is ideal exploring the little known Aude Département and for visiting the walled city of Carcassonne. The site is set in farmland on hilly ground with the original pitches on gently sloping, lightly wooded land. Newer ones are on open ground, of good size, with water, drainage and electricity (5/10A), semi-terraced and partly hedged. Of the 198 pitches, 140 are for touring. The facilities are quite spread out with the swimming pool complex, in the style of a Roman amphitheatre, set in a hollow basin surrounded by fine views.

Facilities

Toilet blocks, one with a Roman theme. Laundry, facilities for disabled people and a baby bath. Motorcaravan services. Small shop (15/5-30/9). Restaurant in converted stable block, takeaway (15/5-30/9). Swimming pool (25 m), paddling pool. Play area. Riding (1/7-31/8). Day trips. Library, internet, games room, TV. Off site: Fishing 3 km. Bicycle hire 8 km. Golf 10 km. Rafting and canoeing near, plus many walks with marked paths.

Open: 20 March - 3 October.

Directions

D118 from Carcassonne, pass Rouffiac d'Aude. Before the end of dual-carriageway, turn right to Montclar up narrow road (passing places) for 2.5 km. Site signed very sharp left up hill before village. GPS: N43:07.636 E02:15.571

Charges 2007

Per pitch incl. 2 persons	€ 14,00 - € 29,00
with electricity (6A)	€ 17,00 - € 33,00
extra person	€ 5,00 - € 7,70
Camping Cheques accepted.	

FR11020 Camping Aux Hamacs

Route des Cabanes, F-11560 Fleury (Aude)

Tel: **04 68 33 22 22**. Email: **administration@campingauxhamacs.com**

If you are looking for sun, sea and sand, Aux Hamacs is a good venue. It is situated adjacent to the Aude river with the attractive village of Fleury nearby and a good beach less than 2 km. away. It is also well located for exploring Cathar country with its amazing hill top castles and attractions such as the Canal du Midi. The site is well away from the frenzy associated with some of the resorts in this region but near enough to visit for an evening out. With 253 large pitches, there are 122 for touring with 6A electricity and some fully serviced (10A electricity plus water and waste water). The remaining pitches are used for a range of chalets and mobile homes to rent. This is a peaceful site but without much shade, although there is a relaxing pool and an interesting range of activities, and a new water park has been added.

Facilities

One fully equipped new toilet block is opened for the main season. A small older one which can be heated is open all season (with plans to rebuild). All facilities are unisex. Baby room and facilities for disabled visitors (key). Washing machine. Shop, bar, restaurant and takeaway (all fully operational 27/6-15/9). Swimming pool (27/6-15/9). Play areas. Activities and entertainment (high season). Off site: Riding 5 km.

Open: 25 April - 15 September.

Directions

From A9 autoroute take exit 36 Beziers Ouest. Follow directions for Vendres Plage on the D64. At the 4th roundabout turn left to the river Aude and over the bridge, just a little up river from Grau de Venfres.

Charges 2008

Per unit incl. 2 persons, electricity	€ 16,70 - € 28,60
extra person	€ 3,50 - € 6,30
child (2-7 yrs)	free - € 3,70

FR11030 Camping Municipal la Pinède

Avenue Gaston Bonheur, F-11200 Lézignan-Corbières (Aude)

Tel: **04 68 27 05 08**. Email: **reception@campinglapinede.fr**

Within walking distance of the town and only 35 km. from Narbonne Plage, La Pinède is set on terraces on a hillside, with good internal access on made-up roads. The 90 individual, level pitches vary in size and are divided up mainly by various trees and shrubs with 6A electricity (17 mobile homes). The guardian organises weekly local wine tasting and local walks to show visitors what is growing in the garden and how plants can be used as natural remedies. Outside the gates are a municipal swimming pool (July/Aug), a disco, a restaurant and tennis courts. Generally better than many municipal sites in season, it is uncomplicated and peaceful.

Facilities

Three fully equipped sanitary blocks. Not all blocks are opened outside high season. Washing machine. Motorhome service point. Gas. Pleasant bar providing decently priced hot food (July/Aug). Fresh vegetables can be sampled from the garden (small charge). Communal barbecue (private barbecues are not permitted). Torches necessary. Caravan storage. Off site: Bicycle hire 1 km. Riding 3 km. Fishing 4 km.

Open: 1 March - 30 October.

Directions

Access is directly off the main N113 on west side of Lézignan-Corbières. From A61 (to avoid low bridge) exit at Carcassonne or Narbonne onto N113 and follow to site.

Charges 2007

Per person	€ 3,30 - € 4,40
child (under 10 yrs)	€ 2,10 - € 3,30
pitch	€ 5,90 - € 7,60
animal	€ 1,50

FR11080 Camping la Nautique

Mobile homes ▶ page 506

La Nautique, F-11100 Narbonne (Aude)

Tel: **04 68 90 48 19**. Email: **info@campinglanautique.com**

Owned and run by a very welcoming Dutch family, this well established site has pitches each with individual sanitary units. It is an extremely spacious site situated on the Etang de Bages, where flat water combined with strong winds make it one of the best windsurfing areas in France. La Nautique has 390 huge, level pitches, 270 for touring, all with 10A electricity and water. Six or seven overnight pitches with electricity are in a separate area. The flowering shrubs and trees give a pleasant feel. Each pitch is separated by hedges making some quite private and providing shade. Entertainments are organised for adults and children from Easter to September (increasing in high season), plus a sports club for supervised surfing, sailing, rafting, walking and canoeing (some activities are charged for). The unspoilt surrounding countryside is excellent for walking or cycling and locally there is horse riding and fishing. English is spoken in reception by the very welcoming Schutjes family. This site caters for families with children including teenagers and is fenced off from the water for the protection of children. Windsurfers can have a key for the gate (with deposit) that leads to launching points on the lake.

Facilities

Each pitch has its own fully equipped sanitary unit. Specially equipped facilities for disabled visitors. Laundry, dishwashing sinks. Shop. Bar/restaurant, terrace, TV. Takeaway. All 1/5-30/9. Snack bar (1/7-31/8). Swimming pools, water slide, paddling pool, slide. Play areas, children Off site: Large sandy beaches at Gruissan 12 km and Narbonne Plage 20 km. Narbonne is only 4 km. Walking and cycling. Canoeing, sailing and windsurfing on the Etang.

Open: 15 February - 15 November.

Directions

From A9 take exit 38 (Narbonne Sud). Go round roundabout to last exit and follow signs for La Nautique and site, then further site signs to site on right in 2.5 km. GPS: N43:08.500 E03:00.140

Charges 2008

Per person	€ 5,00 - € 7,50
child (1-7 yrs)	€ 3,00 - € 5,50
pitch incl. electricity, water and sanitary unit	€ 9,50 - € 22,00
dog	€ 1,50 - € 3,50

Camping La Nautique Narbonne France

www.campinglanautique.com

Private Sanitary facilities on every pitch.
Open from 15/02 till 15/11

✆ **(+33) 04 68 90 48 19**

FR11110 Camping Val d'Aleth

F-11580 Alet-les-Bains (Aude)

Tel: **04 68 69 90 40**. Email: **camping@valdaleth.com**

In the gateway to the upper Aude valley, open all year round, this popular small site is run by Christopher and Christine Cranmer who offer a warm welcome. The mellow medieval walls of Alet les Bains form one boundary of the site, while on the other and popular with anglers, is the River Aude (fenced for safety). Beyond this is the D118 and a railway which produces noise at times. The 37 mainly small, numbered pitches, around half of which are on hardstandings, all have electricity hook-ups (4-10A) and are separated by hedges and mature trees which give shade.

Facilities

New bright toilet blocks, fully equipped and heated in winter. Facilities for disabled people. Washing facilites. New reception with small shop, drinks, wine, beer, use of freezer. Small play area. Mountain bike hire. Internet. Off site: White water sports nearby. Bus and train services to Carcassonne and Quillan. Shops and restaurants in town, full range at Limoux (10 km. north).

Open: All year.

Directions

From Carcassonne take D118 south for 32 km. Ignore first sign to Alet (to avoid narrow stone bridge) and after crossing the river, turn into town. Site is 800 m. on the left (signed). GPS: N42:59.682 E02:15.333

Charges 2007

Per unit incl. 2 persons and electricity	€ 16,00 - € 18,00
extra person	€ 3,50

FR11070 Kawan Village les Mimosas

Mobile homes ▶ page 506

Chaussée de Mandirac, F-11100 Narbonne (Aude)

Tel: 04 68 49 03 72. Email: info@lesmimosas.com

Six kilometres inland from the beaches of Narbonne and Gruissan, this site benefits from a less hectic situation than others by the sea. The site is lively with plenty to amuse and entertain the younger generation whilst offering facilities for the whole family. A free club card is available in July/Aug. to use the children's club, gym, sauna, tennis, minigolf, billiards etc. There are 250 pitches, 150 for touring, many in a circular layout of very good size, most with electricity (6A). There are a few 'grand comfort', with reasonable shade, mostly from 2 m. high hedges. There are also a number of mobile homes and chalets to rent. This could be a very useful site offering many possibilities to meet a variety of needs, on-site entertainment (including an evening on Cathar history), and easy access to popular beaches. Nearby Gruissan is a fascinating village with its wooden houses on stilts, beaches, ruined castle, port and salt beds. Narbonne has Roman remains and inland Cathar castles are to be found perched on rugged hill tops.

Facilities

Refurbished to a high standard sanitary buildings. Washing machines. Shop and 'Auberge' restaurant (open all season). Takeaway. Bar. Small lounge, amusements (July and Aug). Landscaped heated pool with slides and islands (open 1/5), plus the original pool and children's pool (high season). Play area. Minigolf. Mountain bike hire. Tennis. Volleyball. Sauna, gym. Children's activities, sports, entertainment (high season). Bicycle hire. Multisports ground. Off site: Riding. Windsurfing/sailing school 300 m. Gruissan's beach 10 minutes. Lagoon, boating fishing via footpath (200 m).

Open: 24 March - 31 October.

Directions

From A9 exit 38 (Narbonne Sud) take last exit on roundabout, back over the autoroute (site signed from here). Follow signs La Nautique and then Mandirac and site (6 km. from autoroute). Also signed from Narbonne centre.

Charges 2007

Per basic pitch incl. 1 or 2 persons	€ 13,50 - € 21,00
pitch with electricity	€ 17,00 - € 27,00
with electricity, water and waste water	€ 21,20 - € 31,00
extra person	€ 4,00 - € 5,90

Camping Cheques accepted.

Check real time availability and at-the-gate prices...

www.alanrogers.com

FR11090 Camping Naturiste le Clapotis

F-11480 Lapalme (Aude)

Tel: **04 68 48 15 40**. Email: **info@leclapotis.com**

Le Clapotis is a small and tranquil naturist site, situated between Narbonne and Perpignan in a secluded pine wood beside the Etang de Lapalme (a large sea lagoon). With direct access to the lagoon, it is popular with those in pursuit of the ideal conditions provided for windsurfing. The site comprises 173 touring pitches, all with electricity (4A) and of a good size on stony or sandy ground. Pitches in the older part have excellent shade from the pine trees and in the newer area, shade will come as the hedges grow. There is a relaxed feeling of harmony and freedom about the site.

Facilities

Two large and one small sanitary block, a little basic but fully equipped. Showers are both open and in cabins. Facilities for babies and disabled campers. Washing machines. Well stocked shop (end May - mid Sept). Bar and restaurant (from 15/6) and takeaway. Swimming pool (15/6-15/9). Two half tennis court. Windsurfing. Fishing. Torches useful. Off site: Sandy beach 4 km. Riding 4 km. Bicycle hire 9 km. Golf 10 km.

Open: 1 April - 31 October.

Directions

Exit the N9 junction 40 in direction of Port Leucate. At roundabout take N9 north for 3 km. to next roundabout. Turn right (Port-la-Nouvelle). Site sign in 500 m. on right. Follow narrow, poorly made up road for 2 km. bearing left up hill to site.

Charges 2007

Per pitch incl. 2 persons	€ 17,40 - € 21,50
with electricity (4A)	€ 21,50 - € 25,10
extra person (over 4 yrs)	€ 3,45 - € 3,65

FR11190 Domaine Naturiste La Grande Cosse

Saint Pierre la Mer, F-11560 Fleury (Aude)

Tel: **04 68 33 61 87**. Email: **contact@grandecosse.com**

Any slight difficulty in finding this secluded naturist site is compensated for immediately when you arrive. The abundance of flowers, shrubs and the generally peaceful ambience makes this a delightful place for a relaxing naturist holiday, and the extensive facilities mean you only need to leave the site for sightseeing rather than for necessities. Naturism here is pretty relaxed – the only area where clothing is not permitted is in the swimming pools, of which there are three, two for adults and a smaller one for children (there are no noisy slides or toboggans).

Facilities

Five sanitary blocks, opened progressively throughout the season. Fully equipped modern facilities, including a choice of private or communal showers, and some washbasins in cabins. Laundry facilities. Motorcaravan services. Gas. Shop. (8/4-30/9). Bar (15/5-30/9). Restaurant (1/6-30/9). Takeaway (30/6-30/9). Swimming pools (5/5-30/9). Play area. Tennis. Archery. Internet access. Communal barbecues. Off site: Riding 10 km.

Open: 30 March - 6 October.

Directions

From the A9 take exit 36 to Vendres. Pass through town, continue to Lespignan, then Fleury. At roundabout turn left signed Cabanes de Fleury. Follow for 4 km. to pick up site sign to left. Continue for 2 km. and site signed to right.

Charges 2007

per unit incl. 2 persons	€ 15,50 - € 31,00
extra person	€ 5,20 - € 6,90
electricity (8A)	€ 3,90

FR11210 Camping le Moulin de Sainte-Anne

Chemin De Sainte Anne, F-11600 Villegly-en-Minervois (Aude)

Tel: **04 68 72 20 80**. Email: **campingstanne@wanadoo.fr**

Just a few years ago Le Moulin Sainte-Anne was a vineyard but, with much hard work by Antoine and Magali Laclive and the backing of the Mairie, there is now a flourishing campsite on the edge of the town. There are 45 level grass pitches of a good size and hedged. All have water and electricity and are terraced where necessary and landscaped with growing trees and shrubs. The facilities are modern, well kept and in keeping with the area. They include a heated pool and a very attractive entertainment area. A 'Sites et Paysages' member.

Facilities

A very well equipped modern toilet block. Shared facilities for the disabled people and babies. Washing machine. Motorcaravan service point planned. Snack bar (15/6-25/8) with takeaway. Heated swimming and paddling pools (1/5-30/9). Play area. Communal barbecue (no barbecues on pitches). Chalets to rent (15). Off site: Village amenities: multi-sports pitch, tennis (free), fishing, (licence from garage). Shops. Bus stop by bridge. Carcassonne 12 km.

Open: 1 March - 15 November.

Directions

Driving north from Carcassonne on D118 turn on D620 signed Villalier and Villegly for 7 km. Site is at entrance to village. Turn right over bridge just before the cemetery.

Charges 2007

Per person	€ 2,90 - € 4,20
child (under 13 yrs)	€ 1,85 - € 3,10
pitch incl. electricity	€ 6,00 - € 9,65

FR11230 Yelloh! Village le Bout du Monde

Ferme de Rhodes, Verdun en Lauragais, F-11400 Castelnaudary (Aude)

Tel: 04 66 73 97 39. Email: info@yellohvillage-leboutdumonde.com

Le Bout du Monde can be found at the heart of the Montagne Noire, on the edge of the Haut Languedoc regional park. This small site is a member of the Yelloh! Village group and has 53 touring pitches with a further 27 pitches used for mobile homes. Le Bout du Monde has been recommended to us and we plan to undertake a full inspection in 2008. This is a very remote rural setting (hence the site's name!) with large, grassy pitches , a fishing lake and a stream rushing through the site. There is also a children's farm and riding stable. Farm produce is available for purchase.

Facilities

Shop. Restaurant (specialising in local cuisine). Takeaway meals. Swimming pool. Fishing lake. Archery. Sports field. Children's farm. Bicycle hire. Riding. Entertainment and activity programme. Mobile homes for rent. Off site: Multisports pitch. GR7 long distance footpath. Haut Languedoc Regional Park. Sailing. Canoeing. 'Accrobranche' aerial assault course.

Open: 20 June - 14 September.

Directions

From the A61 take Castenaudary exit and proceed to Castelnaudary. Here, take the D103 towards Saissac. After passing through St Papoul, turn left to join the D803 to Verdun en Lauragais. Join the northbound D903 and site is well signed.

Charges 2008

Per unit with 2 persons and electricity	€ 17,00 - € 27,00
extra person (over 1 yr)	€ 4,00 - € 5,00

FR30000 Kawan Village Domaine de Gaujac

Boisset-et-Gaujac, F-30140 Anduze (Gard)

Tel: 04 66 61 67 57. Email: gravieres@club-internet.fr

The 293 level, well shaded pitches include 175 for touring with electricity (4-10A) with 22 fully serviced. Access to some areas can be difficult for larger units due to narrow, winding access roads, trees and hedges. Larger units should ask for lower numbered pitches (1-148) where access is a little easier. In high season this region is dry and hot, thus grass quickly wears off many pitches leaving just a sandy base. There are 12 special hardstanding pitches for motorcaravans near the entrance. The site has a new covered animation area and courtyard terrace.

Facilities

Heated toilet blocks include facilities for disabled visitors. Washing machines, dryer. Motorcaravan services. Good shop (2/6-27/8). Newsagent. Takeaway/crêperie (15/4-15/9). Bar, restaurant (15/4-15/9). New heated swimming, paddling pool (all season with lifeguard 5/7-15/8) and jacuzzi. Playground, sports field. Tennis. Minigolf. Only gas and electric barbecues. Off site: Fishing 100 m. Bicycle hire 5 km. Riding, golf 8 km. River beach 70 km.

Open: 1 April - 30 September.

Directions

From Alès take N110 towards Montpellier. At St Christol-les-Alès fork right on D910 towards Anduze and in Bagard, at roundabout, turn left on D246 to Boisset et Gaujac. Follow signs to site in 5 km. GPS: N44:02.148 E04:01.455

Charges 2007

Per unit incl. 2 persons	€ 15,00 - € 23,00
extra person	€ 4,50 - € 5,20
electricity (4-10A)	€ 3,00 - € 5,00
Camping Cheques accepted.	

FR30020 Yelloh! Village la Petite Camargue

B.P. 21, F-30220 Aigues-Mortes (Gard)

Tel: 04 66 73 97 39. Email: info@yellohvillage-petite-camargue.com

This is a large, impressive site (553 pitches) with a huge swimming pool complex and other amenities to match, conveniently situated beside one of the main routes across the famous Camargue. The busy road is an advantage for access but could perhaps be a drawback in terms of traffic, although when we stayed overnight in season it was virtually silent. It offers a variety of good sized pitches, regularly laid out and with varying amounts of shade. There are 70 touring pitches (with 6/10A electricity) interspersed amongst more than 300 mobile homes and 145 tour operator pitches.

Facilities

Three toilet blocks provide modern facilities including many combined showers and washbasins. Laundry facilities. Motorcaravan service point. Range of shops, bar/restaurant with pizzeria and takeaway. Hairdresser and beauty centre. Pool complex with jacuzzi. Play area, and children's club. Riding. Bicycle hire. Quad bikes. Disco. Diving school. Off site: Fishing 3 km. Nearest beach 3.5 km. with free bus service July/Aug. Golf 8 km.

Open: 26 April - 19 September (with all services).

Directions

From A9, exit 26 (Gallargues), towards Le Grau-du-Roi, site 18 km. Continue past Aigues-Mortes on D62, site 2 km. on the right, just before large roundabout for La Grand-Motte and Le Grau-du-Roi junction. GPS: N43:33.766 E04:09.583

Charges 2007

Per unit incl. 1 or 2 persons and electricity	€ 17,00 - € 43,00
extra person	€ 3,00 - € 7,50

FR30060 Camping Domaine des Fumades

Les Fumades, F-30500 Allègre (Gard)

Tel: **04 66 24 80 78**. Email: **domaine.des.fumades@wanadoo.fr**

Domaine des Fumades is a pleasant, busy site with a friendly atmosphere near the thermal springs at Allègre. The entrance as a whole has a very tropical feel with its banana plants and palm trees. The 230 pitches, 80 for touring, are large and level, all with 4A electricity. A variety of trees add privacy and welcome shade. Three pleasantly landscaped swimming pools have ample sunbathing space, bridges and new jacuzzis. This is a good area for walking, cycling, riding, climbing and fishing. Used by tour operators (80 pitches). Reception at the site is a joy to behold. Set in an attractive courtyard, within the farmhouse, it has a central fountain and masses of tubs and baskets of colourful flowers.

Facilities

Well appointed sanitary blocks with facilities for disabled people, are well maintained but cleaning is variable. . Laundry. Shop. Bar, restaurant, snack bar, takeaway. Barbecue areas. Swimming pools. Large, well equipped and fenced playground. Games room, tennis, volleyball, table tennis and boules. Well planned animation and entertainment programme, designed to appeal to families. No barbecues. Off site: Riding 2 km.

Open: 14 May - 2 September.

Directions

From Alès take D16 through Salindres, continue towards Allègre, until signs for Fumades (and thermal springs) on the right.

Charges 2007

Per unit incl. 2 persons and electricity	€ 16,00 - € 30,00
extra person	€ 3,00 - € 7,00
child (under 7 yrs)	€ 2,50 - € 4,00
pet	€ 4,30

Domaine des Fumades

A beautiful oasis situated between the Ardeche and the Mediterranée. Chalets, mobile homes and pitches. Mini club during the season, swimming pools, Jacuzzis, heated indoor swimming pool.

Domaine des Fumades
30500 ALLEGRE
Tél : 33 (0) 466 24 80 78
Fax : 33 (0) 466 24 82 42
www.campings-franceloc.com

Gard

FR30030 Camping Abri de Camargue

320 route du Phare de l'Espiguette, Port Camargue, F-30240 Le Grau-du-Roi (Gard)

Tel: **04 66 51 54 83**. Email: **contact@abridecamargue.fr**

This pleasant site has an attractive pool area overlooked by the bar with its outdoor tables on a pleasant sheltered terrace. The larger outdoor pool has surrounds for sunbathing and the smaller indoor one is heated. With 277 level pitches, there are 51 for touring units, mainly of 100 sq.m. (there are also smaller ones). Electricity and water are available on most, and the pitches are well maintained and shaded, with trees and flowering shrubs, quite luxuriant in parts. Recent additions include an air-conditioned cinema room and a club for children in high season.

Facilities

Well appointed toilet blocks and facilities for disabled visitors. Motorcaravan services. Shop. Bar, TV, restaurant, takeaway (all open all season). Heated indoor pool, outdoor pool and paddling pool. Cinema. Entertainment programme. High quality play area. Volleyball. Table tennis. Children's club. Petanque. New music room for young people in high season. Off site: Tennis 800 m. Riding, bicycle hire 1 km. Fishing 2 km. Golf 5 km. Nearest beach Port Camargue (900 m). L'Espiguette is 4 km. (free bus passes the gate – July/Aug). Boat, surfboard hire nearby.

Open: 1 April - 30 September.

Directions

Site is 45 km. southwest of Nimes. From A9 autoroute, exit 26, Gallargues to Le Grau-du-Roi. From bypass follow signs Port Camargue and Campings. Then follow Rive gauche signs towards Phare l'Espiguette. Site is on right opposite Toboggan Park. GPS: N43:31.350 E04:08.947

Charges 2008

Per unit incl. 1 or 2 persons	€ 27,00 - € 54,00
incl. 3-5 persons	€ 31,00 - € 59,00
pet	€ 7,00
Campsite access card deposit of € 15.	

FR30070 Castel Camping le Château de Boisson

Boisson, F-30500 Allègre-Les Fumades (Gard)

Tel: **04 66 24 82 21**. Email: **reception@chateaudeboisson.com**

Château de Boisson is a quiet family site within easy reach of the Cévennes, Ardèche or Provence. Reception at the entrance is new, light and cool, built from the stone in the local style. The site is hilly so the pitches are on two levels, many of which slope slightly and all have 5A electricity. Five have personal bathrooms. Rock pegs are essential. Trees provide some shade. The large attractive swimming pool with a slide and paddling pool is at the castle in a sunny location and there is also an indoor pool (all season) of excellent quality. The restaurant in the castle is cool and elegant with tables also available outside on the shady terrace. It is set in the grounds of the château, beside the small medieval village of Boisson.

Facilities

Refurbished, clean and well maintained toilet blocks. Washing machines, baby room, facilities for disabled visitors. Small shop. Good restaurant, bar, snacks (all season). Internet, WiFi. Play area. Indoor (all season) and outdoor pools (1/5-29/9). Bridge tournaments in low season. Painting classes. Tennis, boules, volleyball, basketball. Animation in July and Aug for 4-12 yr olds, outdoor competitions for adults. No dogs. No barbecues. Appartments to rent in the castle.

Open: Easter - 29 September.

Directions

From Alès take D16 northeast towards Salindres and Auzon. After Auzon turn right across river, immediately left, signed Barjac and site. Shortly turn right, site signed. Only route for trailers and motorcaravans. Do not drive through the village of Boissons. GPS: N44:12.551 E04:15.400

Charges 2007

Per unit incl. 2 persons and electricity	€ 19,00 - € 33,00
with water and drainage	€ 22,00 - € 37,00
with own sanitary unit	€ 25,00 - € 40,00
dog (not allowed 7/7-18/8)	€ 3,20

Castel Camping Château de Boisson
Cevennes - Ardèche
Tel : +33 (0) 466 248 561
www.chateaudeboisson.com
LES ★★★★ CASTELS
Hôtellerie de Plein Air

FR30040 Flower Camping Mas de Mourgues

Gallician, F-30600 Vauvert (Gard)

Tel: **04 66 73 30 88**. Email: **info@masdemourgues.com**

This is an English-owned campsite on the edge of the Petite Camargue region, popular with those who choose not to use the autoroutes. It can be hot here, the Mistral can blow and you may have some road noise, but having said all that, the previous owners and the present owners, the Foster family, have created quite a rural idyll. There are 80 pitches with 70 for touring and 62 with 10A electricity. Originally a vineyard on stony ground, some of the vines are now used to mark the pitches, although many other varieties of trees and shrubs have been planted.

Facilities

Two small toilet blocks provide for all needs. Facilities for disabled visitors. Washing machine. Motorcaravan service point. Chips and panini to takeaway. Reception keeps essentials and bottled water. Bread to order (evening before). Communal barbecue but gas or electric ones are allowed. Apartments, mobile homes and tents to rent. Off site: Fishing 2 km. (licence not required). Riding 8 km. Golf 20 km. Bicycle hire and boat launching 25 km. Beach 27 km.

Open: 1 April - 30 September.

Directions

Leave A9 autoroute at exit 26 (Gallargues) and follow signs for Vauvert. At Vauvert take N572 towards Arles and St Gilles. Site is on left after 4 km. at crossroads for Gallician.

Charges guide

Per unit incl. 2 persons	€ 11,00 - € 13,00
extra person	€ 3,00 - € 4,00
child (0-10 yrs)	€ 1,50 - € 2,00
electricity	€ 2,50
dog	€ 1,50 - € 1,70

FR30080 Kawan Village le Mas de Reilhe

F-30260 Crespian (Gard)

Tel: **04 66 77 82 12**. Email: **info@camping-mas-de-reilhe.fr**

This is a comfortable family site nestling in a valley with 95 pitches (76 for tourers), most have electricity (6/10A), some also have water and waste water and some of the upper ones may require long leads. The large lower pitches are separated by tall poplar trees and hedges, close to the main facilities but may experience some road noise. The large terraced pitches on the hillside are scattered under mature pine trees, some with good views, more suited to tents and trailer tents but with their own modern sanitary facilities. The heated swimming pool is in a sunny position and overlooked by the attractive bar/restaurant. There are no shops in the village, the nearest being at the medieval city of Sommières 10 km. away (and well worth a visit). From here you can explore the Cevennes gorges, enjoy the Mediterranean beaches, visit the Petite Camargue or Nimes with its Roman remains from le Mas de Reilhe. The entertainment in July and August is for children with just the occasional competition for adults.

Facilities

Good toilet facilities with washbasins in cabins and pre-set showers. Dishwashing and laundry sinks. Washing machine. Reception with limited shop (bread can be ordered). Bar (6/4-23/9), takeaway and restaurant (1/6-15/9). Small play area on grass. Pentaque. Heated swimming pool (all season). Internet access (WiFi on each pitch on payment). Motorcaravan services. Off site: Tennis 500 m. Fishing 3 km. Riding 5 km. Bicycle hire 10 km. Golf 25 km. The sea and the gorges are 30 km.

Open: 6 April - 23 September.

Directions

From the A9 take exit 'Nimes ouest' signed Alès, then onto the D999 towards Le Vigan. The site is on the N110 just north of the junction with the D999 at the southern end of the village of Crespian.

Charges 2008

Per unit incl. 2 persons	€ 14,00 - € 20,00
extra person	€ 3,50 - € 5,50
child (2-6 yrs)	€ 2,00 - € 3,50
electricity (6/10A)	€ 3,30 - € 4,30

Camping Cheques accepted.

FR30110 Camping du Mas de Rey

Arpaillargues, F-30700 Uzès (Gard)

Tel: **04 66 22 18 27**. Email: **info@campingmasderey.com**

A warm welcome from the English speaking Maire family is guaranteed at this small, unsophisticated 70 pitch site. The owners have made the site 'green' with ecologically aware measures (for example, solar heating). Most of the large (150 sq.m.) pitches are separated by bushes, many are shaded and all have 10A electricity. Due to the wonderful climate, grass can at times be hard to find. The reception, bar, restaurant and shop are in the same large airy building. New chalets for 2007. The owners are always willing to give advice on the numerous things to see and do in the area.

Facilities

Two well maintained unisex toilet blocks, one quite new with solar heating, facilities for the disabled, baby room and en-suite family cubicles. Dishwashing and laundry facilites. Shop (high season only but bread to order all season). Takeaway meals and a terrace restaurant with french meals (1/7-31/8). New Swimming pool and paddle pool from April 2008 (1/5-15/10, closed lunch-times). Off site: Riding 5 km. Golf and fishing 3 km. Canoeing 10 km. Nîmes, Avignon and the Pont du Gard all near.

Open: 20 March - 15 October.

Directions

From D981 in Uzès take the D982 westwards signed Arpaillargues, Anduze, Sommieres, Moussac. Site is 3 km. on the left, well signed. GPS: N43:59.903 E04:23.055

Charges 2007

Per unit incl. 2 persons	€ 14,00 - € 17,50
extra person	€ 4,40 - € 5,50
child (under 7yrs)	€ 2,80 - € 3,50
electricity	€ 2,40 - € 3,00

Credit cards accepted in July/Aug. only

FR30100 Camping Naturiste de la Sablière

Domaine de la Sablière, Saint Privat de Champclos, F-30430 Barjac (Gard)

Tel: **04 66 24 51 16**. Email: **contact@villagesabliere.com**

Spectacularly situated in the Cèze Gorges, this naturist site with a surprising 497 pitches, 240 for touring, tucked away within its wild terrain offers a wide variety of facilities, all within a really peaceful, wooded and dramatic setting. The pitches themselves are mainly on flat stony terraces, attractively situated among a variety of trees and shrubs (some with a low overhang). Many are of a good size and have electricity (6/10A), very long leads may be needed. Nudity is obligatory only around the pool complex. You must expect some fairly steep walking between the pitches and facilities. Those with walking difficulties may not find this site appropriate, although cars can be used in low season and there is a minibus shuttle service in July and August. An excellent pool complex provides a children's pool area and two large pools, one of which is heated and can be covered by a sliding dome, sunbathing terraces, saunas and a bar. A large varity of activities is provided including book binding, pottery and yoga. This is a family run and orientated site and the owner, Gaby Cespedes, provides a personal touch that is unusual in a large site. Member France 4 Naturisme.

Facilities

Six good unisex sanitary blocks have excellent free hot showers in typical open plan, naturist style, washbasins (cold water), baby baths and facilities for people with disabilities. Laundry. Good supermarket. Bar (1/4-22/9). Excellent open air, covered restaurant and takeaway (1/4-22/9). Small café/crêperie. Swimming pool complex (all season). Fitness room. Tennis. Minigolf. Activity and entertainment programme. Torch useful. Barbecues are not permitted. Off site: Bicycle hire 8 km. Riding 10 km.

Open: 1 April - 1 October.

Directions

From Barjac take D901 east for 3 km. Turn right at site sign just before St Privat-de-Champclos and follow site signs along winding country lane to site entrance in 4 km. GPS: N44:16.021 E04:21.125

Charges 2007

Per pitch incl. 2 persons	€ 19,00 - € 37,00
extra person	€ 5,00 - € 7,00
child (4-8 yrs)	free - € 1,80

Camping Cheques accepted.

FR30150 Camping les Sources

Route de Mialet, F-30270 Saint Jean-du-Gard (Gard)

Tel: **04 66 85 38 03**. Email: **camping-des-sources@wanadoo.fr**

This is a lovely, small, family run site situated in the foothills of the beautiful Cévennes. There are 92 average to good sized, slightly sloping pitches on small terraces with 80 used for touring units, all with electricity (6/10A). They are separated by a variety of flowering shrubs and trees offering good shade. Near the entrance is the attractive reception, bar, restaurant and terrace overlooking the swimming pools and children's play area. In May. The emphasis here is on quiet family holidays.

Facilities

Two well appointed, modern toilet blocks with washbasins in cabins and special facilities for babies and disabled visitors. Washing machine. Motorcaravan service point. Bar/restaurant with takeaway and small shop (all open all season). Good swimming and paddling pools (from late May). Play area. Barbecues are not permitted. Occasional children's activities and family evening meals. Off site: St Jean-du-Gard 1.5 km. Fishing and bathing 1.5 km. Riding 12 km. Bicycle hire 14 km. Golf 20 km.

Open: 1 April - 30 September.

Directions

From Alés take D907 through Anduze to St Jean-du-Gard. Take the ring road towards Florac. Turn right at lights on D983, then right on D50 (site signed). Very shortly, on sharp right bend, fork right (site signed) and descend to site. Take care not to overshoot the entrance, as access is impossible from the north.

Charges 2007

Per unit incl. 2 persons	€ 13,00 - € 19,00
incl. electricity	€ 14,50 - € 22,00
extra person	€ 3,20 - € 4,50

Check real time availability and at-the-gate prices...

www.**alanrogers**.com

FR30120 Camping Campeole Ile des Papes

Barrage de Villeneuve, F-30400 Villeneuve-lez-Avignon (Gard)
Tel: 04 90 15 15 90. Email: ile.papes@wanadoo.fr

Quite a new site, Camping Ile des Papes is large, open and very well equipped. Avignon and its Palace and museums are 8 km. away. The site has an extensive swimming pool area and a fishing lake with beautiful mature gardens. The railway is quite near but noise is not too intrusive. The 450 pitches are of a good size on level grass and all have electricity, 150 taken by mobile homes or chalets. Games and competitions for all ages are organised in high season.

Facilities

Toilet blocks of very good quality include baby rooms. Washing machines. Motorcaravan services. Well stocked shop (limited hours in low seasons). Bar and restaurant. Two large swimming pools and one for children. Play area. Lake for fishing. Archery, tennis, table tennis, volleyball, minigolf and basketball (all free). Bicycle hire. Off site: Riding 3 km.

Open: 25 March - 20 October.

Directions

From Avignon take N100 Nîmes road towards Bagnoles-sur-Cèze, after crossing Rhône turn right. Turn left along river bank, follow signs for Roquemaure (D980). After 6 km. turn right on the D228, signed Barrage de Villeneuve, site is 1 km. GPS: N43:59.631 E04:49.081

Charges guide

Per unit incl. 2 persons	€ 16,00 - € 23,00
extra person	€ 4,50 - € 6,30
child (2-5 yrs)	free - € 3,70
electricity (6A)	€ 3,90
Various special offers.	

CAMPING ★ ★ ★ ★
I'LE DES PAPES

Barrage de Villeneuve - 30400 Villeneuve-lez-Avignon
Tel : 490 151 590 - Fax : 490 151 591
E-mail : ile.papes@wanadoo.fr

Campéole Ile des Papes is an International modern and very comfortable campsite, located on a 20ha private island dedicated to relaxation and well-being. Ideal for families with young children, but also for holidays for groups, you will use this splendid campsite as a starting-point to radiate in the heart of the Provence, Ardeche and the Roussillon. Ile des Papes is in the Provence countryside, on the edges of the Rhône, 6 km from the town center of Avignon (direct road along the river). In July, you will enjoy the artistic atmosphere and the shows for every age during the famous Festival d'Avignon.

www.avignon-camping.com

FR30170 Camping la Sousta

Avenue du Pont du Gard, F-30210 Remoulins (Gard)
Tel: 04 66 37 12 80. Email: info@lasousta.com

With a long season, La Sousta is a former municipal site set under tall trees and with a ten minute walk of the famous Pont du Gard, a World Heritage site. The 300 pitches (including 64 mobile homes to rent) are mainly level and numbered, but are not very clearly defined. The reception office provides plenty of tourist information and coach trips are organised in high season to various places of interest. A large swimming pool set in a sunny location has surrounding grassy areas for sunbathing. A footpath leads to a private beach on the river.

Facilities

The four toilet blocks are well equipped with clean facilities with mainly British style WCs, baby bath and showers, and facilities for disabled people. Washing machines and dryer. Bar. Snack bar and takeaway (all 1/4-30/9). Swimming and paddling pools (1/5-31/10). Various play areas. Volleyball, tennis and football field. Bicycle hire. Weekly disco in July/Aug. Entertainment and canoes trips organised. Communal barbecue areas.

Open: 1 March - 31 October.

Directions

Site is signed from the centre of Remoulins. From N100 follow signs for Beaucaire and Nimes, then site signs. Site is beside the D981, just before Pont du Gard. GPS: N43:56.56 E04:32.42

Charges 2007

Per unit incl. 2 persons	€ 11,60 - € 19,50
incl. electricity	€ 15,80 - € 22,50
extra person (over 7 yrs)	€ 3,00 - € 6,50
dog	free - € 2,00

FR30140 Camping la Soubeyranne

Route de Beaucaire, F-30210 Remoulins (Gard)

Tel: 04 66 37 03 21. Email: soubeyranne@franceloc.fr

Owned by the group FranceLoc, this site is well positioned for visiting the Pont du Gard, Nîmes and Uzès, famed for their Roman connections. It is approached by a short tree-lined avenue which leads to reception. The 217 pitches offer extremely generous amounts of shade and keeping the 6 hectares watered involves over 5 km. of hose pipe. The touring pitches, of which there are 126, are large, level, numbered and separated, and all have 6A electricity connections. An animation programme (July/Aug) is aimed mainly at young children (teenagers may find the site rather quiet). Whilst quiet in some respects, train noise both by day and night can be an irritant.

Facilities

Two well appointed, unisex toilet blocks are basic but clean and give more than adequate facilities and include washbasins in cubicles. Provision for dishwashing, laundry, water and refuse points is equally generous. Motorcaravan service point. Fridges for hire. Small shop selling basics. Restaurant, bar and takeaway (all from 31/3-6/9) - menu not extensive but adequate and moderately priced. Heated swimming pool complex (31/3-6/9) with 20 x 10 m. pool and smaller toddlers' pool (unsupervised), and partly shaded. Play area including trampoline. Infatable castle. Mini golf. Table tennis, boules, tennis and volleyball. Bicycle hire. Off site: Fishing 1 km. Remoulins 1.5 km.

Open: 31 March - 6 October.

Directions

From Uzès take D981 to Remoulins, turn right at lights over river bridge, left at roundabout, then left (signed D986 Beaucaire). Site is 1.5 km. further on left. GPS: N43:55.320 E04:33.470

Charges 2007

Per unit incl. 2 persons	€ 14,80 - € 24,00
electricity	€ 4,00
extra person	€ 4,60 - € 7,00
child (under 7 yrs)	€ 2,50 - € 4,20
animal	€ 4,15 - € 4,30
Camping Cheques accepted.	

Domaine de La Soubeyranne

Shady pitches, mobile homes, heated indoor pool, waterslides, paddling pool, volleyball, table tennis, boules, mountain biking, entertainment.

Route de Beaucaire
30210 Remoulins
*Tél. 0033(0)4 66 37 03 21
Fax. 0033(0)4 66 37 14 65*
www.campings-franceloc.com

Gard

FR30180 Camping Mas de la Cam

Route de St André de Valborgne, F-30270 Saint Jean-du-Gard (Gard)

Tel: 04 66 85 12 02. Email: camping@masdelacam.fr

Camping Mas de la Cam is rather unusual in that all the pitches are used for touring. It is a very pleasant and spacious site with well trimmed grass and hedges and a profusion of flowers and shrubs. Lying alongside the small Gardon river, the banks have been left free of pitches giving neat grass for sunbathing and some trees for shade, whilst children can amuse themselves in the water (no good for canoes). Slightly sloping, the 200 medium to large pitches are on level terraces, some with varying amounts of shade, electricity (6A). There is no evening entertainment.

Facilities

High quality toilet blocks provide a baby bath and facilities for disabled visitors. Washing machines. Bar/restaurant, terrace. Small shop. Attractive large swimming (heated) and paddling pools. Huge play and sports areas, multisports court for football, volleyball and basketball. Club, used in low season for bridge, in high season as games room. Fishing. Off site: St Jean-du-Gard (3 km.) with shops, market. Bus twice a day. Riding 5 km. Bicycle hire 15 km.

Open: 28 April - 20 September.

Directions

Site is 3 km. northwest of St Jean-du-Gard in direction of St André de Valborgne on D907, site signed, fork left, descend across a narrow unfenced bridge to site. Site entrance not accessible from north.

Charges 2007

Per unit incl. 2 persons	€ 14,00 - € 23,00
with electricity	€ 17,00 - € 27,00
extra person	€ 3,30 - € 5,70
child (under 7 yrs)	free - € 3,80

FR30160 **Camping Caravaning le Boucanet**

B.P. 206, F-30240 Le Grau-du-Roi (Gard)

Tel: **04 66 51 41 48**. Email: **contact@campingboucanet.fr**

On the beach between La Grande Motte and Le Grau-du-Roi. Many trees have been planted and are growing but as yet most are not tall enough to give much shade. As to be expected, the 458 pitches are sandy but level. The 317 for touring are separated by small bushes, most with electricity (6A). Plenty of flowers decorate the site and the pleasant restaurant (open lunchtimes and evenings) overlooks the large pool (heated at beginning and end of season). An excellent shopping arcade provides groceries, fruit, newspapers, a butcher and cooked meats, rotisserie and pizzas. In July and August organised activities include games, competitions, gymnastics, water polo, jogging and volleyball for adults. There is access to the river for fishing and horse riding on the white horses of the Camargue is to be found within a few kilometres.

Facilities

The toilet blocks include facilities for disabled people. Baby rooms. Washing machines, dryers, irons and fridge hire. Motorcaravan services. Range of shops. Restaurant (1/5). Takeaway (June to end Aug). Bar, snacks. Large swimming pool, paddling pool. Play area on sand, miniclub in July/Aug. Table tennis, tennis. Bicycle hire. No dogs. Off site: Riding 500 m. Golf 1.5 km. Shops, restaurants and bars within 3 km.

Open: 7 April - 7 October.

Directions

Site is between La Grande Motte and Le Grau-du-Roi on the D255 coastal road, on the seaward side of the road.

Charges 2007

Per unit incl. 2 persons	€ 17,00 - € 34,00
electricity	€ 3,50 - € 3,70
pitch on first row of beach, plus	€ 5,00 - € 6,00
extra person	€ 6,00 - € 8,70
child (under 7 yrs)	€ 4,50 - € 7,70

Camping Cheques accepted.

CAMPINGS FranceLoc

Domaine du Boucanet

Pitches, mobile homes, heated swimming pool (1 indoor pool), many sports and leisure activities during the season on this family site ideal for relaxation!

B.P. 206
30240 Le Grau du Roi
Tél. 0033(0)4 66 51 41 48
Fax. 0033(0)4 66 51 41 87
www.campings-franceloc.com

Méditerranée

FR30210 **Camping de l'Arche**

Porte des Cévennes, F-30140 Anduze (Gard)

Tel: **04 66 61 74 08**. Email: **campingarche@wanadoo.fr**

Camping de l'Arche is situated in the valley of the Gardon river, in the beautiful Cevennes National Park. An attractive pebble river beach runs the length of the site. The 250 large pitches are shady and mostly divided by hedges, with 222 used for touring units, all with electricity (6A). In the centre of the site are a bar and restaurant with a terrace for outdoor dining. An innovative new pool complex integrates indoor and outdoor swimming areas, outdoor slides and spa facilities, together with another bar. In cooler periods, the indoor pool can be closed off and heated.

Facilities

Six toilet blocks are spread around the site. Facilities include washbasins in cabins and controllable showers. Baby rooms. Facilities for disabled people. Motorcaravan service point. Shop (5/5-14/9). Bar/restaurant (5/5-14/9). Swimming pool complex (all season). Entertainment and activities organised in high season. Hairdresser. Play area. Bicycle hire. Gas or electric barbecues only. WiFi internet access. Off site: Bus 500 m. Golf and riding 10 km.

Open: 15 March - 30 September.

Directions

From Alès via N110 towards Montpellier. In St Christol-les-Alès turn on D910 to Anduze. Turn right after the bridge over the Gardon river and follow river for 3 km. Turn left to site at Hotel des Cévennes.

Charges 2007

Per unit incl. 2 persons	€ 13,00 - € 25,00
incl. electricity and services	€ 13,00 - € 29,50
extra person	€ 2,95 - € 6,20
child (2-10 yrs)	€ 1,95 - € 4,00

FR30190 Camping International des Gorges du Gardon
Chemin de la Barque Vieille, F-30210 Vers-Pont-du-Gard (Gard)
Tel: 04 66 22 81 81. Email: camping.international@wanadoo.fr

Probably the main attraction in the Gardon area of France is the Pont du Gard, an amazing Roman aqueduct built around 50AD. It provides 200 level, mostly good-sized pitches, 180 for touring. Many are on stony terraces in a woodland setting offering good shade while others are more open, all with electricity (10-15A). Rock pegs are essential. There is direct access to the river where swimming is permitted, although in summer the water level may be a little low. Attractive, heated swimming and paddling pools (unsupervised) provide an alternative. The owners, Joseph and Sylvie Gonzales speak a little English, and visitors will always receive a warm and friendly welcome. Joseph previously owned a restaurant and we highly recommend his site restaurant. Tourist information is in the reception (open all day) and Sylvie will share her local knowledge if you need any additional help. There are other attractions worthy of a visit, such as the medieval village of Castillon-du-Gard perched on a rocky peak with narrow cobbled streets, and Collias at the bottom of the gorge from where you can hire canoes.

Facilities
Two toilet blocks provide facilities for disabled visitors. Baby room. Washing machine, dishwashing and laundry sinks. Bar and good restaurant (table service and takeaway). Heated swimming, paddling pools (unsupervised). Play areas. Table tennis. Games room and TV. Organised family entertainment during July/Aug. Canoeing arranged. Off site: Many old towns and villages with colourful markets (Uzès Saturday 10 km). Historic cities of Nîmes and Avignon. Good area for walking and cycling.
Open: 15 March - 31 October.

Directions
Exit A9 at Remoulins, then take D981 towards Uzès. About 4 km. after Remoulins, just after the junction for the Pont du Gard, turn left, site signed and follow signs to site (a few hundred metres).

Charges 2007
Per unit incl. 2 persons	€ 12,50 - € 18,50
extra person	€ 4,00 - € 6,50
child (under 7 yrs)	€ 2,70 - € 4,00
electricity	€ 3,20
dog	€ 2,00

Camping International Les Gorges du Gardon

30210 vers pont du gard / tel. 33 466 228 181 · fax. 33 466 229 012
www.le-camping-international.com   camping.international@wanadoo.fr

FR30220 Camping les Genêts d'Or
Route de Carmignan, F-30200 Bagnols sur Cèze (Gard)
Tel: 04 66 89 58 67. Email: info@camping-genets-dor.com

Les Genêts d'Or is situated where the two regions of the Cévennes and the Ardèche meet. The site is in woodland on the banks of the river Cèze, surrounded by forested hills and vineyards. The site has its own pebble river beach and, if you prefer, a good swimming pool. There are 105 pitches (95 for touring), all with 3-10A electricity and plenty of shade. The site owners are the Quarre family. Mme. Quarre speaks Dutch and English and runs the reception and a very good restaurant. The Cèze offers good fishing and the hilly countryside is ideal for mountain biking or walking.

Facilities
Two modern toilet blocks provide good, comfortable facilities including controllable showers and washbasins in cabins. Facilities for disabled people. Baby room. Shop (20/5-15/9). Bar and outdoor restaurant (10/5-15/9). Snack bar (10/5-15/9). Swimming pool (10/4-30/9). Play area. Weekly disco for children (high season). Fishing. Only gas and electric barbecues permitted. Dogs are not accepted July/Aug. Off site: Riding and bicycle hire 2 km.
Open: 1 April - 30 September.

Directions
From A7 autoroute (Montelimar - Valence) take exit 19 (Bollene), then D994 towards Pont St Esprit and on to Bagnols via the N86. Entering Bagnols, turn left just before Total service station and turn left for Carmigan. GPS: N44:10.424 E04:38.205

Charges 2007
Per unit incl. 2 persons	€ 21,20
extra person	€ 4,37
electricity (3/8A)	€ 3,00

FR30200 **Camping Cévennes-Provence**

Corbés-Thoiras, F-30140 Anduze (Gard)

Tel: **04 66 61 73 10**. Email: **marais@camping-cevennes-provence.com**

Whenever a new guest arrives at this spectacular and family owned site, one of the seven members of the family takes time to drive the visitors around to enable them to choose what suits their particular needs. From a place on the river bank, to the highest pitch some 330 feet higher, the emphasis is on calmness and tranquility. There are 250 pitches on the various levels, 200 with electricity. The river is very popular for swimming and in a separate section for enjoying the rough and tumble of a small 'rapids'. There are no activities arranged on site. However, the family will spend time with any visitor who wishes to explore off site, perhaps negotiating a discount on their behalf. The philosophy is furthered in many different ways. For instance, there is a special area, away from the main site, where teenagers can safely 'let off steam'. This is easily accomplished in the 30 hectares of this natural and unusual site. The family's ethos is perhaps summed up in the way that shrub beds in the minigolf area are sown with culinary herbs, which guests are encouraged to cut and use.

Facilities

The 10 toilet blocks are excellent with modern equipment and are kept exceptionally clean. Good facilities for disabled visitors. Large and well equipped shop. Restaurant, takeaway and bar (26/4-15/9). Comprehensive play area. Minigolf. Volleyball. River bathing and fishing. Many activities off site willingly arranged at reception. Internet point including WiFi. Off site: Bicycle hire 3 km. Riding 4 km. Golf 10 km. Adventure and discovery park on opposite bank of river offering many sports facilities.

Open: 20 March - 1 November.

Directions

From Anduze on the D907 take D284 alongside the river. Site is signed on right about 3 km. from the town. Take care on the approach – there is a narrow lane for 100 m, then a narrow bridge to cross, but visibility is good. GPS: N44:04.666 E03:57.883

Charges 2008

Per unit incl. 2 persons	€ 13,85 - € 19,80
extra person	€ 3,30 - € 4,70
child (2-7 yrs)	€ 2,25 - € 3,20
electricity (3-10A)	€ 2,15 - € 4,30

Camping-Caravaning "CEVENNES PROVENCE"

At your service for 50 years...

Open from 20/03 to 01/11

Calm, shaded Places with open view Fishing, pedestrian path Swimming in river: direct access and private beach

Corbès - Thoiras F30140 Anduze Gard Ø: 00 334 66 61 73 10 www.camping-cevennes-provence.fr

FR30250 **Camping Universal**

Chemin de Belbuis, F-30430 Rochegude (Gard)

Tel: **04 66 24 41 26**. Email: **camping-universal@hotmail.fr**

Camping Universal has recently been taken over by Christelle and Cedric Jamard who offer an enthusiastic welcome to their delightful site and are keen to have more British visitors. Thoughtfully landscaped for shade and privacy in most areas, the 90 grass pitches are level and all have electrical connections (6/10A). There is easy access around the site but some of the outer pitches are accessed across grass. The site has two outdoor swimming pools, a small bar and restaurant area offering a limited but good value menu, large sports playing field and direct access to the River Ceze.

Facilities

Clean but dated sanitary facilities. Laundry room and dishwashing facilities. Fridge rental. Bar and restaurant. Shop with bread, milk, gas supplies and local wine. WiFi. Swimming pool complex with paddling pool, poolside bar and sunbathing terrace. Play area. Sports field. Pentanque. Fishing. River swimming. Animation programmes (July/Aug). Bicycle hire. Charcoal barbecues are not permitted. Off site: Supermarket 2 km.

Open: 30 March - 30 September.

Directions

From Ales, take D904 north (Saint-Ambroix), then take D51 (Saint-Denis). Pass through Saint-Denis and turn east on D187 in about 4 km. Turn left in 200 m at campsite sign.

Charges 2007

Per person	€ 3,00 - € 6,00
pitch	€ 6,00 - € 11,00
electricity (6A)	€ 3,00

Credit cards only accepted during July/Aug.

FR30230 Camping le Val de l'Arre

Route du Pont de la Croix, F-30120 Le Vigan (Gard)

Tel: 04 67 81 02 77. Email: valdelarre@wanadoo.fr

Camping Val de l'Arre is situated along the Arre river, a tributary of the Herault river, and in the centre of the Cevennes National Park. The site is well managed by M. & Mme. Triaire and his Dutch wife, who between them speak English, Dutch and Spanish, as well as French. There are 180 pitches, 156 for touring of which most have electricity (10A). On well drained grass, there is shade from deciduous trees. There is a pleasant swimming pool with an outdoor bar. A pebble beach at the river bank provides opportunities for play and fishing enthusiasts will certainly also appreciate the river. There are numerous possibilities for outdoor activities such as white water rafting, canoeing or mountain biking. Qualified guides may take you on mountain expeditions on foot or by bicycle. The nearby Les Grottes des Demoiselles, are some of France's foremost caves. There is also the opportunity to taste the great wines of the Herault region.

Facilities

Three toilet blocks are well spaced around the site. Washbasins, both open style and in cabins, and controllable showers. Facilities for babies and disabled visitors. Washing machines. Shop (1/6-31/8). Open air bar with snacks (1/6-31/8). Swimming and paddling pools (1/6-31/8). Boules. Play area. Guided walks organised. Off site: Bicycle hire 2.5 km. Riding 8 km. Golf 25 km.

Open: 1 April - 30 September.

Directions

Coming from A75 (Millau - Beziers) leave at exit 48 and follow D7 and D999 to Le Vigan. From Montpellier take D986 to Ganges, then D999 to Le Vigan. Site is signed in the town. GPS: N43:59.524 E03:38.244

Charges guide

Per unit incl. 2 persons	€ 11,00 - € 14,50
extra person	€ 3,00 - € 4,50
child (0-6 yrs)	€ 2,00 - € 2,50
electricity	€ 3,00

Le Val de l'Arre ★★★

Cosy and shady family campsite in the south of the Cevennes region, situated at the Arre riverside. Many walking paths are close at hand for a day trip or excursion. We offer a swimming pool, modern sanitary facilities, a playground, WIFI, shop and a snack bar/restaurant with terrace. Mobile homes for rent. All ready to give you a relaxing and comfortable holiday.

Le Val de l'Arre - Route Du Pont de la Croix - Roudoulouse - 30120 Le Vigan
Tel: 0033 467 810 277 - Fax: 0033 467 817 123
E-mail: valdelarre@wanadoo.fr - www.valdelarre.com

FR30290 Castel Camping Domaine de Massereau

Les Hauteurs de Sommieres, route d'Aubais, F-30250 Sommieres (Gard)

Tel: 04 66 53 11 20. Email: info@massereau.fr

A member of the Castels group, de Massereau was opened in August 2006 and is set within a 50 hectare vineyard dating back to 1804. Of its 89 pitches, 42 are available for tourers. Pitch sizes range from 150-250 sq.m. but the positioning of trees on some of the pitches severely limits the useable space. The large modern sanitary block is thoughtfully designed with superb facilities for disabled visitors and children. There is an attractive pool complex and a wide range of leisure facilities for all ages. The restaurant offers a reasonable range of good value cuisine and there is a well stocked shop including the vineyard's wines. Good English is spoken.

Facilities

The modern toilet block has excellent facilities for children and disabled visitors. Laundry area. Motorcaravan service point. Well stocked shop and newspapers. Restaurant. Bar. Pizzeria and outdoor grill. Takeaway service. Outdoor pool with slide. Play area. Trampoline. Minigolf. Bicycle hire. Fitness trail. Short tennis. TV room. Barbecue hire. Cooker and fridge hire. Gas. WIFI. Charcoal barbecues are not allowed. Off site: Fishing 3 km. Riding 3 km. Golf 30 km. Sailing 30 km.

Open: 27 March - 15 November.

Directions

From the south on A9 take exit 27 and D12 towards Sommieres. Site is 5 km. on right. From the north, there is a width and weight restriction in Sommieres. To avoid this remain on the N110 and then take the N2110 into Sommieres, crossing the river and turn right onto the D12. Site is on left in 1 km. GPS: N43:27.100

Charges 2007

Per unit incl. 2 persons	€ 11,00 - € 27,00
extra person	€ 3,00 - € 8,00

FR30360 Camping Castel Rose

610 chemin de Recoulin, Anduze F-30140 (Gard)

Tel: **04 66 61 80 15**. Email: **castelrose@wanadoo.fr**

This site in the heart of the Verdon Regional nature Park, originally a municipal site, is a good example of what can be achieved by dedication and imagination. On the lowest reaches of a hill the 81 attractive, small pitches are delineated by shrubs and small trees offering good shade, 54 with 6A electricity. The two toilet blocks are tiled and decorated in imaginative. Riez is a charming Provençal village with markets, all the usual facilities and shops; including bike hire, allowing one to explore this ancient and historical area. No large outfits and twin axle caravans.

Facilities	Directions
Two attractive, well appointed toilet blocks include facilities for campers with disabilities. Small play area. Off site: Village shops, bicycle hire 500 m. Riding 3 km. Lake beach, fishing, sailing 10 km.	Riez is between Gréoux and Moustiers on the D952. The site is 500 m. southeast of Riez. Follow signs for site and Municpal tennis courts. GPS: N44:03.833 E03:58.617
Open: 7 April - 16 September.	**Charges 2007**

Charges 2007	
Per unit incl. 2 persons	€ 10,80 - € 13,20
extra person	€ 2,80 - € 3,60
child (under 7 yrs)	€ 2,00 - € 2,40
electricity (6A)	€ 2,95

FR30380 Yelloh! Village les Secrets de Camargue

Route de l'Espiguette, F-30240 Le Grau-du-Roi (Gard)

Tel: **04 66 73 97 39**. Email: **info@yellohvillage-secrets-de-camargue.com**

Les Secrets de Camargue is a recent addition to the Yelloh! Village group and has the unusual feature that it is reserved for over 18s and for families with children under 3 years old. There are 47 touring pitches (all with 6A electricity) and 130 mobile homes. The heart of the site is the Lodge Club which faces the pool and the surrounding sand dunes. The Lodge Club houses the site's bar and restaurant and it is also here that evening entertainment is organised throughout the high season. The nearest beach, L'Espiguette, is just 1.5 km. away and is said to be one of the largest in the south of France.

Facilities	Directions
Small shop. Restaurant. Bar. Takeaway. Swimming pool. Aqua gym. Activities and entertainment. Volleyball. Facilities for disabled visitors. Mobile homes and chalets for rent. Off site: Free use of facilities at the the nearby Camping Les Petits Camarguais. Nearest beach 1.5 km. Aigues Mortes and Le Grau du Roi. Fishing. Golf. Riding. Watersports.	Leave the A9 at exit for Gallargues and head for Aigues Mortes on the D979. Continue to Le Grau du Roi and then follow signs to Port Camargue on the D62, continuing to join the D255. Site is well signed from this point.
	Charges 2007
Open: 19 April - 5 October.	

Charges 2007	
Per unit incl. 2 persons	€ 17,00 - € 42,00
extra person	€ 3,00 - € 7,50

FR30390 Yelloh! Village les Petits Camarguais

F-30240 Le Grau du Roi (Gard)

Tel: **04 66 73 97 39**. Email: **info@yellohvillage-petits-camarguais.com**

Les Petits Camarguais is sister site to FR30020 and is also a member of the Yelloh! Village group. This 'accommodation only' site has no touring pitches but has been recommended to us and we plan to undertake a full inspection in 2008. There are 219 mobile homes and chalets here and a good range of facilities including an impressive swimming pool complex with slides, whirlpools and a balneotherapy beach. In high season there is a free shuttle to the nearest beach (1.8 km. distant). The beach is L'Espiguette, reputedly the largest French Mediterranean beach!

Facilities	Directions
Mobile homes and chalets for rent (no touring pitches). Shop. Bar. Restaurant. Takeaway. Swimming pool complex with slides, paddling pools, counter current swimming, water games and a balneotherapy beach. Aquagym in high season. Volleyball. Mini football. Activity and entertainment programme. Off site: Nearest beach 1.8 km. (free shuttle in peak season). Riding. Sea fishing. Golf. Casino. Lunapark fairground. Seaquarium park.	Leave the A9 autoroute at the Gallargues exit and head for Aigues Mortes on the D979. Continue to Le Grau du Roi and then follow signs to Port Camargue on the D62, continuing to join the D255b. The site is well signed from this point.
	Charges 2008
Open: 5 April - 19 September.	There are no touring pitches at this site. Contact site for details of accommodation to rent.

FR34020 Camping le Garden

44 place des Tamaris, F-34280 La Grande Motte (Hérault)

Tel: **04 67 56 50 09**. Email: **campinglegarden@orange.fr**

Le Garden is a mature site, situated 300 m. back from a fine sandy beach and with all the choice of sports, entertainment and other facilities of the popular holiday resort of La Grand Motte. With space for 86 caravans and 118 mobile homes, the 100 sq.m. pitches are hedged with good shade on sandy/grass base. All have electricity (10A), water and waste water drains. The fine sandy beach and port are only 300 m. away, with a shopping complex, bar and restaurant next to site.

Facilities

Three well situated toilet blocks, smartly refurbished in Mediterranean colours, include washbasins in cabins and baby bath. Dishwashing and laundry sinks. Washing machines. Unit for disabled people. Shop to one side of the site with groceries, cigarettes, newspapers, boutique, etc., restaurant, bar and takeaway service (from 15/5). Swimming pool and paddling pool (from 15/5). Children's play area. Table tennis. Off site: Tennis courts, a riding club, a casino and a nightclub nearby.

Open: 1 April - 15 October.

Directions

Entering La Grande Motte from D62 dual-carriageway, keep right following signs for 'campings' and petite Motte. Turn right at traffic lights by the Office de Tourism and right again by the Bar Le Garden and site almost immediately on right. GPS: N43:33.793 E04:04.367

Charges 2007

Per unit incl. 1-3 persons	€ 27,50
with electricity, water and drainage	€ 37,50
extra person	€ 9,00
Bracelet required for pool € 10.	

FR34030 Camping International le Napoléon

Avenue de la Méditérranée, F-34450 Vias-Plage (Hérault)

Tel: **04 67 01 07 80**. Email: **reception@camping-napoleon.fr**

Le Napoléon is a smaller, family run site situated in the village of Vias-Plage bordering the Mediterranean. Vias-Plage is hectic to say the least in season, but once through the security barrier and entrance to Le Napoléon, the contrast is marked -; tranquillity, yet still only a few yards from the beach and other attractions. It has a Californian style pool, amphitheatre for entertainment and other new facilities, but thoughtful planning and design ensure that the camping area is quiet. With good shade from many tall trees, the 239 mainly small, hedged pitches (134 for touring), most have electricity. There are no British tour operators on the site. The town of Vias itself is set further back from the sea, in the wine-growing area of the Midi, an area which includes the Camargue, Béziers and popular modern resorts such as Cap d'Agde.

Facilities

Sanitary blocks are of a reasonable standard. Baby bath. Facilities for disabled people. Laundry. Motorcaravan services. Fridge hire. Supermarket. Bar. Restaurant/pizzeria. Heated swimming pool with lively piped music. Gym/fitness room. Sauna, sun room. Bicycle hire. Tennis, archery, volleyball, basketball, boules. TV. Rooms for young campers. Children's club. Amphitheatre, wide range of free entertainment until midnight. Disco outside site (Easter-Sept). Off site: Shops, restaurants, and laundry etc. immediately adjacent. Fishing nearby. Riding 1 km. Golf 5 km.

Open: 5 April - 30 September.

Directions

From autoroute take exit for Vias. From town, take D137 towards Vias-Plage. Site is on the right near the beach; watch carefully for turning between restaurant and shops. GPS: N43:17.508 E03:24.991

Charges 2008

Per unit incl. 2 persons and electricity	€ 19,00 - € 39,00
extra person (over 4 yrs)	€ 6,00 - € 7,00
dog	€ 3,50 - € 4,00

FR34070 Yelloh! Village le Sérignan Plage

Mobile homes ▶ page 508

Le Sérignan Plage, F-34410 Sérignan (Hérault)

Tel: **04 66 73 97 39**. Email: **info@yellohvillage-serignan-plage.com**

A large, friendly, family-orientated site with direct access to superb sandy beaches, including a naturist beach. Those looking for 'manicured' sites may be less impressed, as its situation on 'the littoral' close to the beach makes it difficult to keep things neat and tidy. It has 273 mainly good sized, level touring pitches, including some (with little shade) actually alongside the beach, coupled with perhaps the most comprehensive range of amenities we've come across. Perhaps the most remarkable aspect is the cluster of attractive buildings which form the 'heart' of this site with courtyards housing many of the amenities. The hugely enthusiastic owners, Jean-Guy and Katy continually surprise us with new ideas and developments. New for 2004 was a superb 2800 sq.m. 'Spa Water Fitness centre' with more new pools, a fitness centre and jacuzzi. The amenities are just too extensive to describe in detail, but they include a pool complex, with slides surrounded by large grassy sunbathing areas with sun loungers and another indoor pool. Sérignan Plage exudes a strongly individualistic style which we find very attractive.

Facilities

Several modern blocks of individual design, with good facilities, including showers with washbasin and WC. Facilities for disabled people. Washing machines. Maintenance variable. Supermarket, bakery, newsagent, ATM. Poissonnerie, boucherie (7/6-8/9). Launderette. Hairdresser. Bars, restaurant, takeaway. Children's activities, evening entertainment. Heated indoor and outdoor pool with lifeguards in the main season (24/4-21/9). Sporting activities organised. Bicycle hire. Off site: Riding 2 km. Golf 10 km. Bicycle hire. Sailing and windsurfing school on beach (lifeguard in high season).

Open: 24 April - 21 September.

Directions

From A9 exit 35 (Béziers Est) follow signs for Sérignan, D64 (9 km). Before Sérignan, turn left, Sérignan Plage (4 km). At small sign (blue) turn right. At T-junction turn left over small road bridge and after left hand bend. Site is 100 m.

Charges 2008

Per unit incl. 1 or 2 persons and electricity (6A)	€ 14,00 - € 44,00
extra person	€ 5,00 - € 8,00
pet	€ 3,00 - € 4,00

Low season offers.
Discounts in low season for children under 7 yrs.

FR34080 Camping le Sérignan Plage Nature

F-34410 Sérignan (Hérault)

Tel: **04 67 32 09 61**. Email: **info@leserignannature.com**

Benefiting from many improvements, Sérignan Plage Nature is a characterful family-orientated site beside a superb sandy naturist beach. At present it has some 254 good sized touring pitches, on level grass and with plenty of shade except for those beside the beach. A friendly bar and restaurant are housed in the Romanesque style buildings which form the 'heart' of the site, including the setting for evening entertainment. Jean-Guy and Katy have some ambitious plans for both their sites, which may involve significant developments on Sérignan Plage Nature in particular, including a new 'aqua-village' with pools, fitness centre, jacuzzi, etc. In recent years the site has been developed by Jean-Guy and Katy Amat, but was originally owned by Jean-Guy's father, who retains an interest and who has been the mastermind behind the award-winning environmentally friendly irrigation system which serves both this site and Camping Sérignan Plage, the adjoining 'textile' site whose extensive range of facilities are also available to visitors here. These developments will probably take a couple of years to complete, so it may be worth checking out the latest state of play before you book or visit. Member 'France 4 Naturisme'.

Facilities

The toilet blocks of differing designs have all been refurbished, and all offer modern facilities with some washbasins in cabins and both British and Turkish style WCs. All is clean and well maintained. Washing machines. Supermarket. Market for fresh fruit and vegetables, newsagent/souvenir shop and ice cream kiosk. Small bar-café. Evening entertainment. Children's disco. Off site: Riding 1.5 km.

Open: 24 April - 21 September.

Directions

From A9 exit 35 (Béziers Est) towards Sérignan, D64 (9 km). Before Sérignan, take road to Sérignan Plage. At small sign (blue) turn right for 500 m. At T-junction turn left over bridge, site is 75 m. immediately after left hand bend (the second naturist site). GPS: N43:15.470 E03:19.130

Charges 2008

Per unit incl. 1 or 2 persons and electricity	€ 16,00 - € 42,00
extra person	€ 6,00 - € 8,00
dog	€ 4,00

Special discounts in low season.
Camping Cheques accepted.

Le Sérignan Plage

The magic of
the Mediterranean

Passerelles

Imagine – hot sunshine, blue sea, vineyards, olive and eucalyptus trees, alongside a sandy beach – what a setting for a campsite – not just any campsite either !

With three pool areas, one with four toboggans surrounded by sun bathing areas, an indoor pool for baby swimmers plus a magnificent landscaped, Romanesque spa-complex with half Olympic size pool and a superb range of hydro-massage baths to let you unwind and re-charge after the stresses of work.

And that's not all – two attractive restaurants, including the atmospheric "Villa" in its romantic Roman setting beside the spa, three bars, a mini-club and entertainment for all ages, all add up to a fantastic opportunity to enjoy a genuinely unique holiday experience.

Le Sérignan-Plage - F-34410 SERIGNAN
Tel: 00 33 467 32 35 33 - Fax: 00 33 467 32 26 36
info@leserignanplage.com - www.leserignanplage.com

FR34230 Camping le Plein Air des Chênes
Route de Castelnau, F-34830 Clapiers (Hérault)

Tel: 04 67 02 02 53. Email: pleinairdeschenes@free.fr

Situated just outside the village of Clapiers, about 5 km. from the interesting city of Montpellier, yet merely 15 km. from the beach, this is one of few campsites which provides something for everyone, especially for those who prefer to spend their holidays without ever leaving the campsite. There are 130 touring pitches with 6A electricity (some large with individual toilet cabin), all in a shaded terraced setting. The site boasts an amazing landscaped swimming pool complex, with multi-lane toboggan, four pools and surrounding facilities such as bars and restaurants. It is also open to the public and obviously very popular and it could be noisy.

Facilities

Three well equipped modern toilet blocks of circular design provide washbasins in cabins and facilities for disabled people. Three washing machines. Restaurant open to the public (all year). Bar, poolside bar, café/takeaway (1/6-15/9). Swimming pools (1/6-15/9). Four tennis courts. Multisports court. Play area. Miniclub, evening entertainment in main season. Internet. Off site: Golf 10 km. Beaches and Fishing 15 km.

Open: All year.

Directions

Site is north of Montpellier, 8 km. from A9. Exit 28 on N113 towards Montpellier passing Vendargues. Follow signs for Millau on D65, then Clapiers and follow site signs. GPS: N43:39.047 E03:53.456

Charges 2007

Per unit incl. 2 persons and electricity	€ 23,00 - € 37,00
extra person	€ 2,00 - € 6,50

Camping Cheques accepted.

FR34050 Camping Naturiste le Mas de Lignières
Cesseras-en-Minervois, F-34210 Olonzac (Hérault)

Tel: 04 68 91 24 86. Email: lemas1@tiscali.fr

A naturist site hidden in the hills of the Minervois, only 3 km. from the medieval town of Minerve. There are marvellous views to the Pyrénées, the Corbières and the coast at Narbonne. The owners Jeanne and Gilles, offer a warm welcome and promote an enjoyable family atmosphere. The site has 50 large pitches (electricity 6/10A), and 25 super pitches. Mainly on level grass, separated by mature hedges giving considerable privacy. Some smaller pitches are available for tents, with cars parked elsewhere. There is natural shade and a variety of flora and fauna including four types of orchid.

Facilities

Clean toilet block has open wash basins and showers, facilities for disabled people. Washing machine. Simple shop. Bread (15/6 -15/9). Bar (15/7-15/8). Swimming pool, sliding cover for use when cold. Paddling pool. Room for general use with TV, library, separate provision for young people. Playground. Tennis, volleyball, boules. Torch useful. Only gas barbecues. Off site: Sailing, riding and canoeing nearby – Lac de Jouarres. Canal du Midi.

Open: 1 May - 2 October.

Directions

From A61 take exit for Lézignan-Corbières, D611 to Homps, then D910 to Olonzac. Through village following signs to Minerve (D10). In 4 km. Turn left to Cesseras (D168). At Cesseras follow signs Fauzan for 4 km. on right, narrow, winding road.

Charges 2007

Per pitch incl. 2 persons and electricity (6A)	€ 22,00 - € 25,00
extra person	€ 4,00

FR34060 Hotel de Plein Air L'Oliveraie
Chemin de Bedarieux, F-34480 Laurens (Hérault)

Tel: 04 67 90 24 36. Email: oliveraie@free.fr

Situated at the foot of the Cevennes, L'Oliveraie has many attractive features and is open all year. Don't assume that the extensive range of sport and recreation available here means that it is all hectic activity – it is surprisingly peaceful. Most of the 116 hedged pitches are large and all have electricity (6/10A). Arranged in rows on two levels, those on the higher level are older and have more shade from mature trees (mainly olives). The ground is stony. The large leisure area is slightly apart from the pitches on the lower area, overlooked by the bar.

Facilities

Smart, modern toilet block, baby bathroom, washing machine. Small, well stocked shop. Bar/restaurant, pizzas. Indoor bar, used for films and activities for younger children (all 1/7-31/8). Good sized pool (1/6-30/9). Tennis with practice wall. Bicycle hire. Good play area for under 13s. Barbecue area. Archery. Off site: Local shops at Laurens 1 km.

Open: All year.

Directions

Site is signed 2 km. north of Laurens off the D909 (Béziers - Bédarieux) road. GPS: N43:32.080 E03:11.235

Charges 2007

Per unit incl. 1 or 2 persons	€ 9,00 - € 23,60
extra person	€ 5,00
electricity (6-10A)	€ 3,20 - € 4,60

FR34110 Yelloh! Village le Club Farret

F-34450 Vias-Plage (Hérault)

Tel: 04 66 73 97 39. Email: info@yellohvillage-club-farret.com

Mobile homes ▶ page 508

Well maintained and with welcoming, helpful staff, everywhere is neat and tidy. It is a large, busy site but the atmosphere is very relaxed. There are 756 good size, level, grassy pitches, with 370 for touring with 6A electricity. and there is some shade from many trees. The large heated pool has lots of sunbathing room. The safe beach is alongside the site so some pitches have sea views. There is a wide range of entertainments and the activities include an extensive art programme. The restaurant is high above the pool with views of the sea, everything is open all season. This superb site of excellent quality has been developed by the Giner family with love and care over the last 40 years. There is no advance booking for the touring pitches -; they say that they rarely turn anyone away and will give details of availability. If you wish you can try your hand at catamaran sailing or windsurfing -; free of charge for one hour. Activities include pottery, silk painting, mosaics and water colours. The mobile home areas are very smart, and have been attractively landscaped, with African or Balinese themes. Tour operators occupy 14% of the pitches.

Facilities

Very clean toilet blocks, children's toilets, baby rooms, facilities for disabled customers. Washing machines. Dog shower. Well stocked supermarket. Hairdresser. Bars with pizzas, snacks, takeaway. Restaurant. Heated swimming pool complex with lifeguard all season. Play areas. Miniclub (5-10 yrs). Teenagers' club (11-15 yrs). Tennis, table tennis, archery, volleyball, football, programme of games. Multisports court. Bicycle hire. Off site: Riding 1 km. Golf 10 km. Sailing and windsurfing on beach.

Open: 24 April - 11 October.

Directions

Site is south of Vias at Vias-Plage. From N112 (Béziers - Agde) take D137 signed Vias-Plage. Site is signed on the left. GPS: N43:17.462 E03:25.147

Charges 2008

Per unit incl. 1 or 2 persons   € 14,00 - € 44,00

L'Esprit de Famille

At Club Farret, the family spirit is allowed free rein. The high quality pitches and accommodations set among tenderly cared-for flowery gardens ensure that you will have a pleasant stay in a comfortable home-from-home.

From April to October, everyone can choose their own leisure activities and take full advantage of the pleasures of the pool that is heated in cooler weather, and of course of the beach that is only a stone's throw away. **Request our brochure as soon as possible by e-mail, telephone or letter!**

New 2008: booking for pitches

OPEN FROM 24TH APRIL TO 11TH OCTOBER 2008

Le Club Farret
CAMPING PLAGE
Languedoc - Méditerranée
L'Esprit DE Famille

Le Club Farret - 34450 VIAS PLAGE
Tel. : +33 (0)4 67 21 64 45 - Fax : +33 (0)4 67 21 70 49
E-mail : farret@wanadoo.fr - www.farret.com

yelloh! VILLAGE

FR34090 Camping Caravaning Domaine de la Yole

B.P. 23, F-34350 Valras Plage (Hérault)

Tel: **04 67 37 33 87**. Email: **layole34@aol.com**

A busy happy holiday village with over 1,100 pitches could seem a little daunting. There are 590 pitches for touring. Most pitches are of a good size, all are level, hedged and have electricity, water and waste water points and, very importantly for this area, they all have shade. The extensive pool area is attractive with lots of sunbathing areas and the impressive activities are located in a central area. The beach, a long stretch of beautiful sand, is 500 m. away and here is trampolining, paragliding and jet-skis. This is a busy site with something for all the family.

Facilities

Well maintained toilet blocks include baby rooms. Facilities for families and/or disabled visitors. Washing facilities. Motorcaravan service points. Shops. Restaurant, terrace, amphitheatre for daily entertainment (in season). Two large pools, paddling pool, all supervised. Tennis courts. Play areas. Children's club. Minigolf. Boules. Off site: Fishing or riding 1 km. Beach 500 m, path from site.

Open: 29 April - 23 September.

Directions

From A9 autoroute take Béziers Ouest exit for Valras-Plage (13-14 km) and follow Casino signs. Site is on left, just after sign for Vendres-Plage.

Charges 2007

Per unit incl. 2 persons	€ 18,00 - € 37,35
extra person	€ 5,70 - € 6,30
child (7-16 yrs)	free - € 3,75
child (under 7 yrs)	free - € 1,90

FR34130 Kawan Village le Neptune

46 Boulevard du St Christ, F-34300 Agde (Hérault)

Tel: **04 67 94 23 94**. Email: **info@campingleneptune.com**

Camping Neptune is a rare find in this area. This small, family run site with only 165 pitches makes a delightful change. The pitches are mostly separated by flowering bushes, with some shade, most with 6/10A electricity. The Fray family are welcoming and, even though in a busy area, this site is an oasis of calm, suited to couples and young families. Alongside the D32 there may be a little daytime road noise. The swimming pool is in a sunny position overlooked by the bar.

Facilities

Two toilet blocks provide roomy pre-set showers, washbasins in cabins, three cold showers for hot weather. Laundry and dishwashing sinks. Two washing machines, dryer. Small shop, bar (both 15/5-30/9). Heated swimming pool heated, bracelets required. Table tennis, field for sports. Boat mooring facility on the River Hérault across the road. Only one dog allowed. No barbecues. Off site: Beach 1.5 km. Golf and riding 1.5 km.

Open: 1 April - 30 September.

Directions

From A9 exit 34 follow signs for (Agde, Bessau, Vias), then Cap d'Agde. Exit for Grau d'Agde. At roundabout (with statue) follow signs for Grau d'Agde, and again at second roundabout (left). Keep straight on to fifth roundabout where left and under bridge. Site is 600 m. on left. GPS: N43:17.882 E03:27.377

Charges 2007

Per unit incl. 2 persons	€ 16,80 - € 24,20
with electricity	€ 18,90 - € 28,90
extra person	€ 4,70 - € 5,60
Camping Cheques accepted.	

FR34150 Yelloh! Village les Méditerranées

262 avenue des campings, F-34340 Marseillan Plage (Hérault)

Tel: **04 66 73 97 39**. Email: **info@yellohvillage-mediterranees.com**

Marseillan Plage is a small, busy resort east of Cap d'Adge and it enjoys a super position immediately beside a long gently shelving sandy beach. It is a good quality site set under tall trees with neat hedges separating the 520 pitches (370 for tourers), on sandy soil all having water and electricity (6A). Many newer pitches and the hardstanding pitches have little shade. Amenities and facilities are generally of excellent quality and include a strikingly attractive bar area overlooking the beach with a raised stage for entertainment. This is a well run, family owned site with lots to offer.

Facilities

Impressive toilet blocks, (2 newly renovated) including some en-suite showers and washbasins, facilities for disabled visitors, dog shower. Motorcaravan services. Bar, restaurant. Shop all season. Pool complex (all season). Play area, fitness centre, multi-purpose ball court. Weekly films, variety of organised games, competitions, dances, discos. WiFi. Bicycle hire. Off site: Shops at Charlemagne across the road. Riding, bicycle hire 500 m. Golf 5 km.

Open: 25 April - 27 September.

Directions

From A9 autoroute exit 34, follow N312 to Agde then take N112 towards Sete. Watch for signs to Marseillan Plage from where site is well signed. GPS: N43:18.522 E03:32.501

Charges 2008

Per unit incl. 2 persons, water and electricity	€ 14,00 - € 44,00
extra person (over 1 yr)	€ 6,00 - € 8,00

Check real time availability and at-the-gate prices...

www.**alanrogers**.com

FR34180 Camping la Borio de Roque

Route de la Salvetat, F-34220 Saint Pons-de-Thomières (Hérault)

Tel: **04 67 97 10 97**. Email: **info@borioderoque.com**

La Borio de Roque is a peaceful site in a very rural location hidden in a wooded valley 4 km. from St Pons. It lies at the end of a 1.5 km. rough track but it is well worth the effort and it is set around a lovely restored farmhouse with the outbuildings made into four very attractive gites. The 25 large, individually shaped, terraced pitches have 10A electricity and some shade. Some are private to which the owners will escort you. When the site was developed, many different varieties of trees were planted which has created a very attractive environment. The site is under new ownership. Children are encouraged to help with feeding and grooming the goats, sheep and horses. There are numerous walks and tracks for mountain bikes from the site and your Dutch hosts will be only too happy to advise on routes. St Pons (4 km.) is an attractive small town with bars, restaurants and a museum. La Borio is especially suited to couples and young families – not a site for teenagers who like lots of entertainment.

Facilities

Toilet block, baby bath. Use of large freezer. Bread all season. Local wine, home produced goat's cheese, honey, cherry jam for sale. Set menu four times weekly (to order) in high season and eaten with the family in the bar/barn, a very popular event. Swimming pool (from 1/6), small fishing lake. Small grassy play area. Barbecue areas. Not suitable for American motorhomes. Off site: Bicycle hire 5 km. Golf and riding 20 km. Beach 50 km.

Open: 15 May - 15 September.

Directions

St Pons-de-Thomières is on the N112 northwest of Béziers. Site is 4.5 km. north of the town on the D907 signed Salvetat, on the right on a bend, then 1.5 km. on a rough track (signed).
GPS: N43:30.656 E02:44.789

Charges 2007

Per person	€ 3,50 - € 4,50
child (under 7 yrs)	€ 2,50 - € 3,50
pitch incl. electricity	€ 10,75 - € 12,00
vehicle	€ 2,00 - € 2,25

No credit cards.

FR34170 Camping Caravaning les Mimosas

Port Cassafières, F-34420 Portiragnes Plage (Hérault)

Tel: **04 67 90 92 92**. Email: **les.mimosas.portiragnes@wanadoo.fr**

Les Mimosas is quite a large site with 400 pitches – 200 for touring units, the remainder for mobile homes – in a rural situation. The level, grassy pitches are of average size, separated and numbered, all with 6A electricity (long leads may be required), some have good shade others have less. The pool area, a real feature of the site, includes a most impressive wave pool, various toboggans, a large swimming pool and a paddling pool (seven pools in all) with lots of free sun beds. This is a friendly, family run site with families in mind.

Facilities

Modern toilet blocks, baby rooms, children's toilets, good disabled facilities (whole site wheelchair friendly). En-suite facilities on payment. Laundry facilities. Motorcaravan services. Fridge hire. Large shop. Bar, snacks all season, restaurant (from 1/6). Swimming pool complex (early June). Play area. Boules. Gym with instructor and sauna. Bicycle hire. No barbecues. Off site: Fishing and riding 1 km. Portiragnes Plage 2 km. Golf 10 km.

Open: 20 May - 9 September.

Directions

From A9 exit 35 (Béziers Est) take N112 south towards Serignan (1 km). Large roundabout follow signs for Cap d'Agde, watch carefully for D37, Portiragnes (1-2 km), follow signs for Portiragnes Plage. Site is signed. GPS: N43:17.492 E03:22.409

Charges 2007

Per unit incl. 2 persons	€ 22,00 - € 31,00
with electricity	€ 25,00 - € 35,00
extra person	€ 5,00 - € 9,00

FR34190 **Kawan Village les Champs Blancs**

Route de Rochelongue, F-34300 Agde (Hérault)

Tel: **04 67 94 23 42**. Email: **champs.blancs@wanadoo.fr**

Les Champs Blancs is set in high trees, 2 km. from Agde and 2 km. from the sea in a cooler, shady environment. The 169 level, sandy, touring pitches are bordered with bushes and plenty of trees, all with 10A electricity and 60 have private sanitary cabins. The pool area has been augmented by a super irregular pool, with toboggans, cascade, Jacuzzi, bridges and palms but retaining the original pool and paddling pool. Games, shows and competitions are arranged in July and August. The area nearest the road is bordered by trees to deaden possible road noise.

Facilities

Refurbished toilet blocks, unit for disabled visitors, 60 en-suite private cabins containing WC, shower and washbasin with outside sink for dishes. Washing machines, dryers. Motorcaravan services. Well stocked shop in high season, only bread low season. Bar (from 1 June). Restaurant (20/6-15/9). Swimming complex. Good play area, minigolf, tennis. Multicourt. Off site: Riding 1 km. Golf 1.5 km. Beach 2 km.

Open: 8 April - 30 September.

Directions

From A9 exit 34, follow N312 for Adge, joins N112 Béziers - Sète road. Cross bridge over river, take first turni (Rochelongue), turn right, next left, then next left (signed Adge). Site on left before another bridge back over N112. GPS: N43:17.821 E03:28.528

Charges 2007

Per pitch incl. 2 persons	€ 19,00 - € 40,00
with individual sanitary facilities	€ 21,00 - € 47,00
extra person	€ 10,00

Camping Cheques accepted.

FR34200 **Camping Club Californie Plage**

Côte Ouest, F-34450 Vias-Plage (Hérault)

Tel: **04 67 21 64 69**. Email: **californie.plage@wanadoo.fr**

With the benefit of direct access to a sandy cove, with a few, much sought-after pitches overlooking the sea, this is a fairly typical holiday-style campsite with a range of good quality facilities. These include a covered pool on the site and situated across the road in the grounds of its sister site is a superb tropical swimming pool complex with the inevitable toboggans etc. and even a naturist swimming pool (1/7-31/8). All are mainly on level sandy ground, separated by low hedging, electricity (3-10A) and there is a fair amount of shade from poplars.

Facilities

Good standard sanitary facilities. Washbasins in cabins, baby rooms, facilities for disabled visitors. Washing machines, dryer. Shop. Bars. Restaurant, takeaway. Beach café, tapas, fish dishes. Covered pool (1/4-31/10). Range of pools on sister site across road (1/7-31/8). Tennis. Bicycle hire. Games room. Play area. Sports nets. Archery. Extensive entertainment programme, children's activities in July/Aug. Off site: Riding 5 km. Golf 10 km.

Open: 1 April - 31 October.

Directions

From N112 Béziers-Agde road take D137 Vias-Plage turn. Watch for signs to 'Cote Ouest' and follow campsite signs thereafter. GPS: N43:17.400 E03:23.890

Charges 2007

Per unit incl. 1 or 2 persons and electricity (6A)	€ 12,50 - € 33,00
extra person (4 yrs and over)	€ 3,00 - € 5,00

No credit cards.

FR34210 **Camping les Berges du Canal**

Promenade les Vernets, F-34420 Villeneuve-les-Béziers (Hérault)

Tel: **04 67 39 36 09**. Email: **contact@lesbergesducanal.com**

There are surprisingly few campsites which provide an opportunity to enjoy the rather special ambience for which the Canal du Midi is renowned, so we were really pleased to discover this delightful site right alongside the canal at Villeneuve-les-Béziers. There are 75 level pitches on sandy grass of average size, mostly with 10A electricity, in a peaceful and shady situation, separated from the canal by an access road. There is a pleasant pool complex, one of the two pools being fitted with a jacuzzi-style facility, but there are no slides thereby ensuring that it is relatively peaceful.

Facilities

A fully equipped toilet block has mainly British-style WCs, some Turkish style and some washbasins in cabins. Facilities for the disabled (with key) and children. Beauty therapist visits weekly. Dishwashing and laundry facilities. Motorcaravan service point. Two pools. Bar/snack-bar (serving breakfast too). Small restaurant. Evening entertainment in high season. Off site: Attractive old village centre of Villeneuve-les-Béziers. Beach at Portiragnes Plage. Riding 5km. Canal du Midi.

Open: 15 April - 15 September.

Directions

From A9 exit 35, follow signs for Agde, at first roundabout take N112 (Béziers). First left onto D37 signed Villeneuve-les-Béziers and Valras Plage. Pass traffic lights, left at roundabout and follow site signs (take care at junction beside bridge). GPS: N43:18.990 E03:17.080

Charges 2007

Per unit incl. 2 persons	€ 14,00 - € 19,00
with electricity	€ 16,00 - € 23,00
extra person	€ 2,50 - € 4,50

FR34220 **Camping la Creole**

74 avenue des Campings, F-34340 Marseillan Plage (Hérault)

Tel: **04 67 21 92 69**. Email: **campinglacreole@wanadoo.fr**

This is a surprisingly tranquil, well cared for small campsite in the middle of this bustling resort that will appeal to those seeking a rather less frenetic ambience typical of many sites in this area. Essentially a family orientated site, it offers around 110 good-sized, level grass pitches, all with 6A electricity and mostly with shade from trees and shrubs. It also benefits from direct access to an extensive sandy beach and the fact that there is no swimming pool or bar actually contributes to the tranquillity. It may even be seen as an advantage for families with younger children. The beach will be the main attraction here no doubt, and the town's extensive range of bars, restaurants and shops are all within a couple of minutes walk.

Facilities

Toilet facilities are housed in a traditional building, modernised inside to provide perfectly adequate, if not particularly luxurious facilities including some washbasins in private cabins, a baby room and dog shower. Small play area. Table tennis. In high season beach games, dances, sangria evenings etc, are organised, all aimed particularly towards families. Barbecue area. Bicycle hire. Off site: Local market day Tuesday. Riding 1 km.

Open: 1 April - 12 October.

Directions

From A9 exit 34 take N312 towards Agde, then N112 towards Sète keeping a look-out for signs to Marseillan Plage off this road. Site is well signed in Marseillan Plage. GPS: N43:18.765 E03:32.779

Charges 2008

Per unit incl. 2 persons	€ 13,50 - € 25,75
extra person	€ 2,50 - € 4,80
electricity	€ 2,70
dog	€ 2,00 - € 3,00

CAMPING ★★★

LA CREOLE

Direct access to the beach
Located in the Heart of Marseillan-Plage
Mobile home to rent
Low prices in low season
Open from 2/04 to 10/10

74 avenue des campings
34340 Marseillan-Plage
Tel : +33 (0)4 67 21 92 69
Fax : +33 (0)4 67 26 58 16

campinglacreole@wanadoo.fr
www.campinglacreole.com

FR34260 **Kawan Village Beau Rivage**

F-34140 Méze (Hérault)

Tel: **04 67 43 81 48**. Email: **reception@camping-beaurivage.fr**

Beau Rivage is situated on the inland shore of the 4.5 km. by 19.5 km. Etang du Thau. This inland salt lake, lying parallel to the Mediterranean and separated by a very narrow strip of land, is well known for its oyster beds. It also popular for fishing, diving and watersports. The campsite on the edge of the town is within easy walking distance in the direction of Sète. The site has 150 level, sandy-grass pitches all with 6A electricity, plus 35 with mobile homes. The main features of the site are a pleasant pool and paddling pool with a bar and snack restaurant for the high season. Sète is well worth visiting with colourful houses overlooking its many canals, its fish market and 'water jousting', a feature of the town.

Facilities

One fully equipped small toilet block is open all season and a larger block for the main season. Baby bath. Facilities for disabled people. Washing machine. Motorcaravan service point. Bar providing snacks and simple takeaway food (July/Aug). Heated swimming and paddling pools (all season). Play area. Volleyball. Activities in July and August. Communal barbecues. Off site: Restaurant 300 m. Supermarket 200 m. Beach 500 m. All facilities of the town within easy walking distance. Tennis and bicycle hire 1 km.

Open: 5 April - 20 September.

Directions

From A9 autoroute take exit 33 for Sète. Follow RN113 for Poussan, Bouzigues and Mèze. Continue for 5 km. to outskirts of Mèze and site is on left just after a petrol station. The entrance is between the petrol station and a pottery (not too easy to see).

Charges 2008

Per unit incl. 2 persons	€ 18,00 - € 35,00
extra person	€ 4,00 - € 7,00
child (0-4 yrs)	free
dog	€ 3,00

421

FR34290 Yelloh! Village Mer et Soleil

Route de Rochelongue, F-34300 Cap d'Agde (Hérault)

Tel: **04 66 73 97 39**. Email: **info@yellohvillage-mer-et-soleil.com**

Close to Cap d'Agde, this is a popular, well equipped site with many facilities. The pool area is particularly attractive with large palm trees, a whirlpool, slides and a gym. An upstairs restaurant overlooks this area and the entertainment stage next to it. There are 500 pitches, around half taken by mobile homes and chalets (some to let, some privately owned). The touring pitches are hedged and have good shade, all with 6A electricity. A path from the back of the site leads to a 1 km. long path leading to the white sandy beach at Rochelongue.

Facilities

One large toilet block plus three smaller ones are fully equipped. Attractive units for children with small toilets, etc. Units for disabled visitors. Motorcaravan service point. Washing machine. Shop. Bar and restaurant. Swimming pools. Gym. Tennis. Archery. Sporting activities and evening entertainment. Off site: Beach 1 km. Riding 1 km. Sports complex opposite site.

Open: 5 April - 11 October.

Directions

From A9 exit 34, follow N312 for Agde. It joins the N112 Béziers - Sète.road. Cross bridge over Hérault river and turn right for Rochelongue. Turn left at next roundabout and site is a little further on the right. GPS: N43:17.171 E03:28.680

Charges 2007

Per unit incl. 2 persons	€ 17,00 - € 41,00
extra person	€ 3,20 - € 7,00

FR34470 Camping le Fou du Roi

Chemin des Codoniers, F-34130 Lansargues (Hérault)

Tel: **08 74 56 00 27**. Email: **contact@campinglefouduroi.com**

Beside the mellow stone village of Lansargues on the edge of the Camargue, Le Fou du Roi was taken over by the Brunel family two years ago. They have done much to update it with a new reception/bar area complete with an attractive Tahitian style construction which can be left open or closed depending on the weather. Altogether this a lovely little site. There are 82 pitches with 30 for touring units with 10A electricity, arranged in light shade amongst the vineyards. A small pool and play area for children make it a very comfortable site with a nice long season.

Facilities

Two toilet blocks, the first modern and fully equipped, the second not open when we visited. Facilities for disabled visitors. Washing machine and dryer. Motorcaravan service point. Small shop (July/Aug). Bar, simple snacks and takeaway (fully open July/Aug). Swimming pool (1/5-15/9). Play area. Only gas barbecues are permitted (communal area provided). Off site: Fishing and riding 3 km. Golf 4 km. Tennis in village. Village within easy walking distance with restaurants and shops.

Open: 30 March - 14 October.

Directions

From A9 exit 27 follow signs for Lunel and from there pick up D24 going south. Lansargues is 7 km. Do not take 'village centre' sign but continue past and pick up site sign just past village on right.

Charges 2007

Per unit incl. 2 persons	€ 13,00 - € 17,00
extra person	€ 3,00 - € 5,00
child (under 7 yrs)	free - € 2,50
electricity	€ 4,00

FR34390 Yelloh Village Aloha

F-34410 Sérignan Plage (Hérault)

Tel: **04 67 39 71 30**. Email: **info@yellohvillage-aloha.com**

A well run, orderly site beside the beach at Sérignan Plage, Aloha offers a wide range of good quality facilities all open when the site is open. There are 472 pitches with over 170 mobile homes for hire in attractively landscaped settings. The 295 pitches for touring units are of good size, regularly laid out on level, sandy grass. Easily accessed from tarmac roads, all have 10A electricity. Half are on one side of the small beach road with the swimming pools and other facilities, the other half are somewhat quieter with more grass but less shade across the road.

Facilities

Seven toilet blocks, three are large, offer all modern facilities and are well equipped for children. Laundry. Motorcaravan service point. Supermarket with fresh produce. Bakery, newsagent, bazaar, hairdresser. Bar, restaurant, snack-bar, pizzeria, takeaway. Large heated pool and fun pools. Playground. Tennis. Multisports. Beach and sailing club. Bicycle hire. Range of activities for children and adults. Evening entertainment. Off site: Riding 800 m. Boat launching 8 km. Golf 20 km.

Open: 26 April - 14 September.

Directions

From A9 exit 35 (Béziers Est) follow signs for Sérignan then Sérignan-Plage (D64, about 10 km). Once arrived at Serignan-Plage continue straight. Follow the sign for Aloha to right after the pink building. GPS: N43:16.400 E03:20.900

Charges 2007

Per unit incl. 2 persons and electricity	€ 17,00 - € 43,00
extra person	€ 5,00 - € 6,00
child (0-4 yrs)	free

FR34400 Camping les Sablons

F-34420 Portiragnes Plage (Hérault)

Tel: **04 67 90 90 55**. Email: **contact@les-sablons.com**

Les Sablons is an impressive and popular site with lots going on. Most of the facilities are arranged around the entrance with shops, a restaurant, bar and a large pool complex with no less than five slides, three heated pools and large stage for entertainment. There is also direct access to the white sandy beach at the back of the site close to a small lake. There is good shade on the majority of the site, although some of the newer touring pitches have less shade but are nearer the gate to the beach. On level sandy grass, all have 6A electricity. Of around 800 pitches, around half are taken by a range of mobile homes and chalets (many for hire, some by British tour operators). A wide range of sporting activities, and evening entertainment is arranged with much for children to do. In fact, this is a real holiday venue aiming to keep all the family happy.

Facilities

Well equipped, modernised toilet blocks include large showers some with washbasins. Baby baths and facilities for disabled visitors. Supermarket, bakery and newsagent. Restaurant, bar and takeaway. Pool complex. Entertainment and activity programme with sports, music and cultural activities. Beach club. Tennis. Archery. Play areas. Electronic games. ATM Internet access. Bicycle hire. Off site: Riding 200 m.

Open: 1 April - 30 September.

Directions

From A9 exit 35 (Béziers Est) follow signs for Vias and Agde (N112). After large roundabout pass exit to Cers then take exit for Portiragnes (D37). Follow for about 5 km. and pass over Canal du Midi towards Portiragnes Plage. Site is on left after roundabout. GPS: N43:16.800 E03:21.800

Charges 2008

Per unit incl. 2 persons	€ 16,00 - € 45,00
extra person (max.6)	€ 6,00 - € 8,00
child (0-4 yrs)	free - € 4,00
dog	€ 2,00 - € 4,00

FR34370 Camping Blue Bayou

Vendres Plage Ouest, F-34350 Valras Plage (Hérault)

Tel: **04 67 37 41 97**. Email: **bluebayou@infonie.fr**

A very pleasant site, Blue Bayou is situated at the far end of Vendres Plage near Le Grau Vendres (the port of Vendres). It is therefore in a much quieter location than many other sites, away from the more hectic, built-up areas of Vendres and Valras Plage The beach is 300 metres across sand dunes and there are open views from the site creating a feeling of spaciousness. There are 256 pitches, all with 10A electricity, with 74 privately owned mobile homes and 92 to let, including some chalets. The level, grassy touring pitches are large, some with their own sanitary arrangements. Light shade is provided by a mixture of trees. The restaurant and bar area is very attractive, overlooking two swimming pools, one with a toboggan, joined by a bridge where lifeguards station themselves. The site is under new ownership with all the family involved and you are made to feel very welcome. The site would make a very good choice for couples and families.

Facilities

Individual toilet units for about half the touring pitches. Two separate blocks are fully equipped. Baby bath. Facilities for disabled people. Laundry. Bar, restaurant and takeaway (open on demand in early season). Swimming pool (heated all season). Multisport court. Play area. Bicycle hire. Off site: Fishing, boat launching and riding 1 km. Golf 25 km.

Open: 8 April - 30 September.

Directions

From A9 exit 36 (Béziers Ouest) follow directions for Valras Plage and Vendres Plage over four roundabouts. At fifth roundabout (Port Conchylicole) follow sign for Vendres Plage Ouest and site is 500 m. on the left past the Ranch and tourist office. GPS: N43:13.380 E03:14.370

Charges 2007

Per unit incl. 2 persons	€ 19,00 - € 37,00
with private sanitary facility	€ 23,00 - € 45,00
extra person	€ 5,00 - € 9,00
child (0-2 yrs)	free

FR34500 Camping l'Oasis Palavasienne

Route de Palavas, F-34970 Lattes (Hérault)

Tel: **04 67 15 11 61**. Email: **oasis.palavasienne@wanadoo.fr**

This is a comfortable site in an area where the residents of Montpellier escape for their summer weekends. The site is dominated by its impressive high level reception area, restaurant, bar and swimming pool, with access by lift for people with disabilities. Behind this, the site stretches to the river which lies hidden behind a high bank and gated fence. The site is green and shady with 250 sandy grass pitches with 100 for touring units mixed amongst mobile homes and chalets to let. The site seems surprisingly tranquil considering the dual carriageway to Palavas runs past the front.

Facilities

Two toilet blocks, all have modern fittings, the main one brightly decorated. En-suite facilities for the disabled, babies and children. Washing machine. Shop and bar (June - late Aug). Restaurant and takeaway (July/Aug). Heated swimming and paddling pools (1/4-1/10). Sauna. Gym. Play area. Bicycle hire. Internet access. Communal barbecue area provided. Off site: Fishing 50 m. Golf and riding 1 km. Boat launching, beach with windsurfing and waterskiing 3 km.

Open: 1 May - early September.

Directions

From the A9 take exit 30 (Lattes, Palavas). Follow dual-carriageway past exit for Lattes and take next (site signed), over bridge, right at roundabout to site immediately on the left.

Charges 2007

| Per unit incl. 2 persons and electricity (7A) | € 16,00 - € 28,00 |
| extra person | € 3,00 - € 5,00 |

FR34430 Camping l'Occitanie

B.P. 29, F-34350 Valras Plage (Hérault)

Tel: **04 67 39 59 06**. Email: **campingoccitanie@wanadoo.fr**

L'Occitanie is a good value site, particularly for low season visits, and is within walking distance of Valras Plage. The site is virtually a straight road from the autoroute exit (12 km). On arrival, don't be put off by the entrance (it could be more inspiring). You can find a more open pitch in the higher part of the site which is lightly wooded with some views of the surrounding countryside, or choose the lower area with plenty of shade which French visitors seem to do. A right of way divides the site into two parts. The bar, restaurant and pool make a nice social area in the higher part. There are 400 pitches with 30 privately owned mobile homes and 58 for hire. All pitches have 6A electricity and are of reasonable size on level rough grass. The town is a 20 minute walk and the beach 1 km. It is therefore a relatively peaceful location and seems to attract a mix of visitors.

Facilities

Five toilet blocks are fully equipped and opened as required. En-suite unit with ramped access for disabled visitors. Baby bath. Washing machine. Motorcaravan service point. Bar, restaurant and takeaway. Swimming and paddling pools. Play area. Minigolf. Day time activities for children and sports for adults in high season and some evening entertainment.

Open: 31 May - 6 September.

Directions

From A9 exit 35 (Béziers Est) follow signs for Valras Plage (12 km). Continue straight on at roundabout beside McDonalds and Hyper U and again at next one towards Valras. Then turn immediately left into site. GPS: N43:15.424 E03:17.150

Charges 2008

Per unit incl. 2 persons and electricity	€ 17,00 - € 29,00
extra person	€ 2,00 - € 5,00
child (0-7 yrs)	free - € 3,00

FR34440 Camping les Tamaris

140 avenue d'Ingril, F-34110 Frontignan-Plage (Hérault)

Tel: **04 67 43 44 77**. Email: **les-tamaris@wanadoo.fr**

This is a super site, unusually situated on a strip of land that separates the sea from the étang or inland lake, and therefore Fontignan Ville from Fontignan Plage. The design of the site is unusual which adds to its attractiveness. The pitches are laid out in hexagons divided by tall hedging and colourful shrubs. In total, there are 250 pitches with 100 taken by mobile homes which are let by the site. All have 10A electricity and are on level sandy grass. Direct access to the sandy beach is possible via three gates.

Facilities

Three modern toilet blocks with en-suite showers and washbasins. Excellent facilities for childen. Unit for disabled visitors. Motorcaravan service point. Shop. Bar, restaurant and takeaway (all season). Swimming pool (from 1/5). Hairdresser. Gym. Play area. Mini-club. Archery. Bicycle hire. Internet access. Entertainment for all ages. Off site: Riding 150 m. Sailing 1 km. Boat launching 2.5 km. Golf 15 km.

Open: 1 April - 22 September.

Directions

From the north on the A9 take exit 32 and follow N112 towards Sète and Frontignan. After 16 km. ignore sign for Frontignan town and contine to Frontignan Plage following site signs along the road between the sea and étang. From the south use exit 33 and follow N300 to roundabout beside the port of Sète (11 km). Turn left on N112 and take second exit for Frontignan Plage.

Charges 2007

Per unit incl. 2 persons	€ 24,00 - € 38,00
extra person	€ 4,00 - € 8,00
dog	€ 1,50 - € 3,00

FR34450 Sunêlia Domaine de la Dragonnière

Mobile homes ▶ page 507

RN 112, F-34450 Vias-sur-Mer (Hérault)

Tel: **04 67 01 03 10**. Email: **dragonniere@wanadoo.fr**

La Dragonnière is a busy family site, located between the popular resorts of Vias and Portiragnes. There are no fewer than nine swimming pools here and a lively entertainment programme in high season. Many of the pitches are occupied by mobile homes and chalets but there are around 200 reasonably sized touring pitches, all offering some shade. The pitches all have electrical connections (6A) and many also offer water and drainage. La Dragonnière lies 5 km. from the nearest beach and a free shuttle operates in peak season. This is an ideal site for families with teenagers searching for a wide range of activities. The beach is doubtless the main appeal here but there is s a great deal to visit in the area. Popular excursions include the nearby Canal du Midi, the Sigean animal reserve and the cities of Montpellier and Beziers. Alternatively, given the very impressive range of facilities, including a good supermarket, some may prefer to spend all their time on site.

Facilities

Well maintained toilet blocks include facilities for babies and disabled people. Laundry. Supermarket. Two swimming pool complexes with children's pools. Bar and restaurant complex, with good range of meals. Play area. Sauna and gym. Tennis. Multisport pitch. Excursions reserved at reception. Sports competitions, children's club and evening entertainment in high season, including talent shows, regular discos and cabaret evenings. Mobile homes and chalets for rent. Off site: Nearest beach 5 km. (free shuttle in peak season). Fishing 4 km. Golf 12 km.

Open: 15 March – 6 October.

Directions

Take the Beziers Est exit from the A9 autoroute. Follow directions to Villenevue, Serignan and Valras Plage. After 800 m. at the large roundabout, follow signs to Vias aéroport on the N112. After a further 7 km, the campsite can be found on the right.

Charges 2008

Per unit with 3 persons, water, waste water and electricity	€ 19,00 - € 42,00
extra person	€ 6,00 - € 7,00
dog	€ 5,50

FR66000 Camping Caravaning de Pujol

Route du Tamariguer, F-66700 Argelès-sur-Mer (Pyrénées-Orientales)

Tel: **04 68 81 00 25**

Le Pujol is an attractive, well cared for site. There are various loud open air discos and activities in the area until the early hours. Pujol may be the best chance of avoiding the hectic seaside sites in otherwise attractive Argelès. There are 312 very large flat, grassy pitches, most with 6A electricity. The site's pride and joy is a delightful pool complex with semi-tropical shrubs and fountains. The bar is for the family, not overrun by youngsters. They are catered for in a covered meeting area opposite. There is some road noise near the entrance to the site.

Facilities

Well kept fully equipped toilet blocks. Baby bath. Washing machines. Small supermarket (1/6-15/9). Good restaurant, friendly family bar (1/6-15/9). Large L-shaped swimming pool, children's pool, spa pool (1/6-15/9). Table tennis. Small multi-gym. Boules. Minigolf. Playground. Games room. Gas or electric barbecues only. Off site: Riding 500 m. Fishing, bicycle hire 1 km. Argelès Plage and quiet resort of Racou short distance.

Open: 1 June - 15 September.

Directions

From autoroute take Perpignan-Nord exit and follow N114 from Perpignan and use exit 10 for Argelès, Cross first roundabout onto Chemin de Neguebous (avoiding town). Turn left at second roundabout and site is 200 m. on right opposite Tour de Pujol.

Charges 2008

Per pitch incl. 2 adults	€ 24,00
with electricity	€ 3,00
extra person	€ 6,00
Less 20% in June and Sept. No credit cards.	

FR34460 Camping Club International de l'Hérault

Route de la Tamarissière, F-34300 Agde (Hérault)

Tel: 04 67 94 01 01. Email: infos@interdelherault.com

This comfortable site beside the Hérault river is opposite the town of Agde with its famous black cathedral. The site was taken over by the Caron family last year. With one of their sons, Ludovic who manages the site, they have built a super new pool complex and generally upgraded the facilities, whilst the other son, a trained chef, manages the modern restaurant. The 417 level grassy hedged pitches are of reasonable size with 180 available for touring units. All have 6/10A electricity. This is a well run, family orientated site in a quiet situation, albeit with a little road and rail noise possible in high season. The family's enthusiasm for their new project and their wish to make this a truly international site with a wide range of facilities and entertainment should be a recipe for success. It enjoys a quiet situation close to Agde city and to the beach at Tamarissière with its pedestrian ferry connection to the fishing port and village of Grau d'Agde. A free shuttle bus service to the beach is offered in July and August.

Facilities

Two sanitary blocks are of older design but are fully equipped. Access for disabled people. Baby bath. Laundry. Gas. Shop. Bar, restaurant and takeaway (all season). Super pool complex with cascade and bridge separating the paddling pool (heated 1/5-31/8. Separate water slide. Tennis. Games room. TV in bar. Playground. Sporting activities. Entertainment for adults and children. Chalets and mobile homes to let or buy. Off site: Fishing outside site in river. Beach 2.5 km. Riding and boat launching 2 km. Golf 4 km.

Open: 1 May - 31 August.

Directions

From A9 use exit 34 and follow N112 towards Sète and Agde. Exit at junction for Tamarissiere and Agde centre. Follow signs for Agde centre and site, first left and site on right 500 m.

Charges 2007

Per unit incl. 2 persons and electricity	€ 17,00 - € 35,00
extra person	€ 4,00 - € 7,00
child (4-10 yrs)	€ 3,00 - € 4,00

Pitches for tents and caravans, chalets of Mobil homes for rent
Near the beach. Free shuttle service in July and August.
Animation for young and old
Swimming pool with water slide
For more information
www.interdelherault.com of 33 4 67 94 01 01
Camping Club International de l'Hérault
Route de la Tamarissière • 34300 AGDE

AGDE - CAP D'AGDE – MEDITERRANEE

FR66090 Camping Mar Estang

Route de St Cyprien, F-66140 Canet-en-Roussillon (Pyrénées-Orientales)

Tel: 04 68 80 35 53. Email: marestang@wanadoo.fr

Le Mar Estang is a large, 'all singing all dancing' site with something for everyone. Situated on the edge of Canet, between the Etang (part of the Réserve Naturelle de Canet/ St Nazaire) and the sea, there is access to the beach from the site by a tunnel under the road. If you don't fancy the beach, there are four swimming pools to choose from, complete with fun pool, water slides and a heated covered pool. There are 600 pitches, some 200 used for mobile homes or Bengali tents, with 5A electricity, some degree of shade and on sandy ground.

Facilities

Nine well equipped sanitary blocks well placed around the site. Facilities for babies. Laundry. Motorcaravan service point. Shop, bars, restaurant and takeaway open when site is open. Pools, jacuzzi and solarium. Fitness club. Entertainment. Disco. Communal barbecue. Sailing club. Tennis. Bicycle hire. Play areas. Direct access to beach. Off site: Riding nearby. Canet 500 m. with tourist train in high season. Perpignan 10 km.

Open: 29 April - 23 September.

Directions

Take exit 41 from A9 autoroute and follow signs for Canet. On outskirts of town follow signs for St Cyprien/Plage Sud. Site is very clearly signed on southern edge of Canet Plage.
GPS: N42:40.542 E03:01.881

Charges 2007

Per unit incl. 2 persons	€ 15,00 - € 30,00
extra person	€ 7,00 - € 12,00
electricity (5A)	€ 5,00 - € 7,00

Check real time availability and at-the-gate prices...

www.alanrogers.com

FR66030 Camping Cala Gogo

Avenue Armand Lanoux, les Capellans, F-66750 Saint Cyprien-Plage (Pyrénées-Orientales)

Tel: 04 68 21 07 12. Email: camping.calagogo@wanadoo.fr

This is an excellent, well organised site and it is agreeably situated by a superb sandy beach with a beach bar and boat launching. There are 450 average sized, level, pitches for touring, electrical connections (6A) everywhere and some shade. The site has a most impressive pool complex carefully laid out with palm trees in ample sunbathing areas. The large bar complex becomes very busy in season and dancing or entertainment is arranged on some evenings on a large stage recently built alongside the bar. A feature of the site is the provision of special beach buggies for the handicapped. A large Aquapark, reputed to be amongst the best in southern France, is nearby. Used by tour operators (148 pitches). There are 50 chalets and mobile homes to rent.

Facilities	Directions
High standard, fully equipped toilet blocks. Good supermarket, small shopping mall. Sophisticated restaurant with excellent cuisine, self-service restaurant, simple menu, takeaway. Bar, small beach bar, high season. Disco. TV. Three adult pools plus one for children, water-jets, Jacuzzi, waterfall. Children's play area, remote control cars for children. Tennis, table tennis, playground. Events and sports organised in season. Torches useful. Off site: Fishing, riding, bicycle hire and golf within 5 km. Boat excursions and courses in skin-diving, windsurfing or sailing nearby.	Using D81 (southward) avoid St Cyprien-Plage and continue towards Argelès. Turn right at roundabout signed Le Port and Aquapark and pick up site signs. Site is just past the Aquapark.

Charges 2007

Per person (over 5 yrs)	€ 8,20
pitch	€ 12,00
electricity (6A)	€ 3,30
dog	€ 3,70

Open: 12 May - 22 September.

FR66040 Camping le Soleil

Route du Littoral, F-66702 Argelès-sur-Mer (Pyrénées-Orientales)

Tel: 04 68 81 14 48. Email: camping.lesoleil@wanadoo.fr

Le Soleil has direct access to the sandy beach. It is a busy, popular, family owned site which has grown recently into a small village. It has over 800 pitches of ample size, and around 550 are used for touring units, on sandy/grassy ground and with a mixture of trees and shrubs providing some shade, all with electricity (6A). Access for caravans sometimes needs care on the narrow access roads. The site has a wide range of amenities, including an impressive pool complex, all facilities open when the site is open. Spain and the Pyrénées are near enough for excursions. There are over 200 pitches used by tour operators and 70 occupied by mobile homes. English is spoken and there is a comprehensive reservation system (advised for most of July/Aug).

Facilities	Directions
Seven toilet blocks of the type with external access to individual units. Some family cabins with washbasins, showers. Washing machines. Supermarket, general shop, press, tabac, restaurant, takeaway. ATM machine. Internet. Bar with disco (July/Aug), beach bar. California type swimming pool complex and entertainment area. Adventure playground. TV room. Tennis. Riding in high season (charge). No dogs. Off site: Fishing and mooring boats on the adjacent river. Golf 5 km.	Site is at north end of the beach, about 1 km. from Argelès-Plage village.

Charges 2007

Per person (over 5 yrs)	€ 8,20
pitch	€ 12,30
electricity (6A)	€ 3,30

Less 20% outside July/Aug.
Swimming pool deposit € 15.24 per pitch.

Open: 13 May - 23 September.

FR66050 Kawan Village le Haras

Domaine Saint Galdric, F-66690 Palau del Vidre (Pyrénées-Orientales)

Tel: 04 68 22 14 50. Email: haras8@wanadoo.fr

A distinctly 'French' style site, Le Haras is midway between the coast (about 8 km.) and the Pyrénées, in quiet countryside away from the bustle of the coastal resorts. Le Haras has 75 pitches with electricity, 18 fully serviced, arranged informally in bays of four, in the grounds of an old hunting lodge. A mixture of trees, shrubs and flowers provides colour and shade. Some access roads are narrow. There is an attractive pool complex with a bar and a courtyard area beside the restaurant and large function room. Rail noise is possible, although this is screened by large trees.

Facilities

Fully equipped toilet blocks, Renovation of smaller block near the pool planned. Covered dishwashing and laundry sinks. Washing machines. Fridge hire. Bar. Restaurant, open to public (all year). Takeaway. Swimming, paddling pools (1/5-15/9). Play area. No charcoal barbecues. Internet access. Off site: Three bakers in the village. Beaches 10 minutes drive. Fishing 500 m. Riding 2 km. Bicycle hire 6 km. Golf 7 km.

Open: 20 March - 20 October.

Directions

From A9, exit 43 (Le Boulou) follow D618 towards Argelès for 13 km. On bypassing St André, turn left, Palau-del-Vidre (D11). Bear right through village, on D11 towards Elne. Site on right at end of village.

Charges 2007

Per pitch incl. two persons	€ 14,00 - € 24,50
extra person	€ 3,50 - € 5,20
electricity (5A)	€ 4,00

Camping Cheques accepted.

FR66080 Camping les Fontaines

Route de St Nazaire, F-66140 Canet-en-Roussillon (Pyrénées-Orientales)

Tel: 04 68 80 22 57. Email: campinglesfontaines@wanadoo.fr

If you are looking for a different experience more in tune with nature you will perhaps enjoy Les Fontaines. The present owners took over a very run down site in 2003 and have spent much money, time and energy on improving it. The site itself borders 'La Réserve Naturelle de l'Etang de Canet-St Nazaire and is set amongst open fields with views of the Canigou and other mountains. The 160 pitches are large and level with 10A electricity but lack shade, although much planting has been carried out. It could therefore be very hot in high season and the pool is a very welcome addition.

Facilities

An unusual white castellated houses a fully equipped sanitary block. Baby bath. Facilities for disabled people. Washing machine. Swimming pool with paddling pool (1/6-30/9). Bar. Communal barbecues (only gas or electric on pitch). Play area. Farm to visit. Some mobile homes to rent. Off site: Beach, fishing and boat launching 4.5 km. Riding 5 km. Bicycle hire 3 km. Golf 11 km. Villages of St Nazaire and Elne.

Open: 1 May - 30 September.

Directions

Leave A9 at Perpigan Nord and follow directions for Canet for about 20 km. Then pick up the D11 Perpigan road and take first exit (5) for Canet village. Go under bridge, straight over roundabout and continue for about 1.5 km. to site on left.

Charges 2007

Per unit incl. 2 persons	€ 12,00 - € 24,00
extra person	€ 2,00 - € 5,00
electricity	€ 3,50

FR66020 Kawan Village Caravaning Ma Prairie

Route de St Nazaire, F-66140 Canet-en-Roussillon (Pyrénées-Orientales)

Tel: 04 68 73 26 17. Email: ma.prairie@wanadoo.fr

Ma Prairie is an excellent site and its place in this guide goes back over 30 years. Then it was simply a field surrounded by vineyards. The trees planted then have now matured, more have been planted, along with colourful shrubs providing a comfortable, park-like setting with some 260 pitches, all with electricity and 35 with water and drainage. It is a peaceful haven some 3 km. back from the sea but within walking distance of Canet village itself. The Gil family provide a warm welcome.

Facilities

Fully equipped toilet blocks, baby bath. Washing machines and dryers. No shop but bread can be ordered. Covered snack bar and takeaway. Air-conditioned bar and restaurant. Large adult pool, splendid children's pool. Play area. Tennis. Bicycle hire. Volleyball.TV. Billiards. Amusement machines. Dancing three times weekly, busy daily activity programme in season. Caravan storage. Off site: Supermarket 400 m. Riding 600 m. Golf 6 km. Canet Village within walking distance with all amenities.

Open: 5 May - 25 September.

Directions

Leave autoroute A9 at Perpignan North towards Barcarès. Site access is from the D11 Perpignan road (exit 5), close to the junction with D617 in Canet-Village. Go under bridge, right at roundabout the left to site.

Charges 2007

Per unit incl. 2 persons	€ 17,00 - € 30,00
extra person	€ 4,00 - € 7,00
electricity (10A)	€ 4,00 - € 5,00

Camping Cheques accepted.

FR66070 Yelloh! Village le Brasilia

Mobile homes ▶ page 508

B.P. 204, F-66141 Canet-en-Roussillon (Pyrénées-Orientales)
Tel: 04 66 73 97 39. Email: info@yellohvillage-brasilia.com

An impressive family site beside the beach and well managed, Le Brasilia is pretty, neat and well kept with an amazingly wide range of facilities. There are 763 neatly hedged pitches all with electricity varying in size from 100-150 sq.m. Some of the longer pitches are suitable for two families together. With a range of shade from pines and flowering shrubs, less on pitches near the beach, there are neat access roads (sometimes narrow for large units). Over 100 of the pitches have mobile homes or chalets to rent. The sandy beach here is busy, with a beach club (you can hire windsurfing boards) and a naturist section is on the beach to the west of the site. There is also a large California type pool. The village area of the site provides bars, a busy restaurant, entertainment (including a night club) and a range of shops. In fact you do not need to stir from the site which is almost a resort in itself also providing a cash dispenser, exchange facilities, telephone, post office, gas supplies and even weather forecasts. It does have a nice, lively atmosphere but is orderly and well run – very good for a site with beach access. Although it is a large site it does not seem so. A 'Yelloh Village' member. Member of Leading Campings Group.

Facilities

Ten modern sanitary blocks are very well equipped and maintained, with British style WCs (some Turkish) and washbasins in cabins. Good facilities for children and for disabled people. Laundry room. Hairdresser. Bars and restaurant. Swimming pool with lifeguards (heated). Play areas. Sports field. Tennis. Sporting activities. Library, games and video room. Internet café. Daily entertainment programme. Bicycle hire. Fishing. Torches useful. Off site: Riding 5 km. Golf 12 km.

Open: 26 April - 27 September.

Directions

From A9 exit 41 (Perpignan Centre/Rivesalts) follow signs for Le Barcarès/Canet on D83 for 10 km, then for Canet (D81). At first Canet roundabout, turn fully back on yourself (direction Sainte-Marie) and watch for Brasilia sign almost immediately on right. GPS: N42:42.280 E03:02.090

Charges 2007

Per unit incl. 2 persons and electricity (6A)	€ 17,00 - € 43,00
extra person	€ 4,60 - € 8,00
child (1-4 yrs)	free - € 4,00

LE BRASILIA, YOUR PENINSULA, YOUR SECRET

Enjoy this site with water at your feet, an eye-full of blue skies, a floral rainbow and a beach. Oh how lucky you are! But hush... it's your secret, a secret hidden amongst a 15-hectare pine wood with a heated swimming pool, tennis courts, fields for a multitude of sports, entertainment for both adults and children, shops, restaurant-bar, cabaret and discotheque. For your ultimate well being, mobile homes and homes with a garden ewait you.

Camping Village Le Brasilia
BP 204 - 66141 Canet-en-Roussillon Cedex
tel. 00 33 (0)4 68 80 23 82
fax 00 33 (0)4 68 73 32 97
e-mail: camping-le-brasilia@wanadoo.fr
www.brasilia.fr
le Brasilia ★★★★

FR66100 Camping Caravaning la Pergola

F-66478 Sainte Marie la Mer (Pyrénées-Orientales)
Tel: 04 68 73 03 07. Email: info@campinglapergola.com

La Pergola is an attractive tranquil campsite with 180 pitches which include 140 for tourers, all with 10A electricity. It is located in a mainly residential area of this up-and-coming and, at times, quite lively, seaside resort. Family-run, and orientated towards family holidays, it offers a choice of mainly large pitches, some with lots of shade and some with less. It has a very pleasant ambience, a nice quiet pool area and it will undoubtedly appeal to families with younger children in particular.

Facilities

Three modern toilet blocks include facilities for babies and disabled visitors. Bar (mid June-Aug). Takeaway (July/Aug). Swimming and paddling pools (mid June-Aug; no toboggans). TV. Play Area. Some evening entertainment in high season. Off site: Beach 500 m.

Open: 1 June - 30 September.

Directions

From A9 take exit 41 and follow signs towards Canet via the D83 and D81 until a roundabout signed Ste Marie-la-Mer Plage. Turn left into Ste Marie Plage and follow campsite signs.

Charges guide

Per unit incl. 2 persons	€ 19,60 - € 24,50
incl. electricity	€ 22,00 - € 27,50
extra person	€ 5,20 - € 6,50

FR66110 Camping le Dauphin

Route de Taxo-d'Avall, F-66704 Argelès-sur-Mer (Pyrénées-Orientales)

Tel: **04 68 81 17 54**. Email: **info@campingledauphin.com**

Near Taxo in the quieter, northern part of Argelès (a somewhat frenzied resort in season), this family owned site on flat, grassy parkland with plenty of tall trees enjoys good views of the Pyrénées from the terrace area surrounding its excellent complex of swimming pools. There are 346 level, grassy well shaded pitches, all with 10A electricity and some with individual sanitary units. Located some 1.5 km. from the town and beach, there is a regular connecting 'road train' service to and fro throughout the day and evening until midnight. There are 168 pitches taken by mobile homes and chalets either privately owned or for rent. Tour operators use 76 of the pitches.

Facilities

A central sanitary block, although mature, provides all essential facilities including washbasins en-suite. One third of the pitches have their own fully equipped individual sanitary unit. Shops. Bar/restaurant, pizzeria with takeaway (all 17/5-6/9). Two large swimming pools and paddling pool (small charge). Two play areas. Tennis courts. Minigolf. Multisport court, sports ground and games room. Entertainment programme in high season. Torches useful in some areas. Off site: Riding 1 km. Fishing 2 km.

Open: 17 May - 20 September.

Directions

Site is on north side of Argelès. From autoroute take exit Perpignan-Nord for Argelès and follow directions for Plage-Nord and Taxo-d'Avall (similarly from the N114).

Charges 2008

Per unit incl. 2 persons and electricity	€ 16,00 - € 25,90

FR66130 Hotel de Plein Air l'Eau Vive

Chemin de St Saturnin, F-66820 Vernet-les-Bains (Pyrénées-Orientales)

Tel: **04 68 05 54 14**. Email: **info@leauvive.com**

Enjoying dramatic views of the Pic du Canigou (3,000 m.), this small site is 1.5 km. from the centre of Vernet-les-Bains in the Pyrénées. It is approached via a twisting road through a residential area. The 70 tourist pitches, with electricity (4/10A) and 45 fully serviced, are on a slight slope, part hedged and some terraced, with a separate tent field. Most pitches have some shade. Although there is no swimming pool, the site has a very attractive, natural pool with water pumped from the nearby stream, with a small beach.

Facilities

First class toilet facilities and provision for disabled people. Washing machine. Bread, main season. Bar/reception, pool table, library. Snack bar, takeaway (15/5-15/9). A 'meal of the day' can be ordered. Play area. Natural pool for children. Sports field. Basketball. Bicycle hire. Off site: Fishing 200 m. Swimming pool, thermal centre in village 1 km. Nearby medieval, walled town of Ville Franche de Conflent, Grottes des Canalettes, Fort Libena with its many steps are well worth visiting. Organised rafting, canoeing, hydrospeed trips.

Open: 16 December - 25 October.

Directions

Following N116 towards Andorra. At Ville Franche, turn south, D116, for Vernet-les-Bains. After 5 km, keep right avoiding town. Turn right over bridge towards Sahorre. Immediately turn right, Ave de Saturnin for about 1 km. beyond houses, site signed.

Charges 2007

Per unit incl. 2 persons	€ 12,50 - € 21,50
incl. electricity	€ 15,00 - € 25,00
extra person (over 4 yrs)	€ 1,50 - € 2,50
animal	€ 1,50 - € 2,50

Credit cards accepted 15/6-15/9 only.
Camping Cheques accepted.

FR66230 Camping Caravaning le Romarin

Route de Sorède, chemin des Vignes, F-66702 Argelès-sur-Mer (Pyrénées-Orientales)

Tel: **04 68 81 02 63**. Email: **contact@camping-romarin.com**

In an area dominated by 'all-singing, all-dancing' holiday sites, we were pleased to discover, almost by accident, this charming little gem of a site tucked away some 2 km. behind the busy resort of Argelès. Essentially a site for families with younger children, or for adults seeking peace and quiet, it provides 110 good sized touring pitches, with electricity (6-10A) set among pine, eucalyptus, oak and mimosa trees. Ideal for exploring this area, especially the Albères range of Pyrénéen mountains and the ancient city of Perpignan.

Facilities

Good, large toilet block provides a mix of British and Turkish WCs, showers, washbasins in cabins, washing machine. Snack bar (mid June - end Sept). Swimming pool (mid June - mid Sept). Play area. Table tennis. Some traditional (local) family entertainment in high season. Off site: Riding and bicycle hire 2 km. Fishing 4 km. Golf 8 km. Within reach of shops, supermarket 2 km., all the attractions of Argelès, both village and Plage.

Open: 15 May - 30 September.

Directions

From A9 exit 42 (Perpignan Sud), N114 towards Argelès for 25 km, exit 11a. At roundabout, signed St André, for 300 m. Acute left turn (site signed). After 2 km, T junction, turn left, D11. Shortly take third left (site signed), follow lane to site.

Charges 2008

Per unit incl. 2 persons and electricity	€ 15,00 - € 34,50
extra person	€ 2,00 - € 4,00
child (2-5 yrs)	free - € 2,50
dog	free - € 2,00

CAMPING LE ROMARIN

Great pleasure in a small camping site, in the middle of olive groves, between the sea and the mountain, you will enjoy your stay in natural surroundings. Welcome to the Romarin

Route de Sorède - Chemin des Vignes - F-66702 Argelès-sur-Mer - France
Tél.: 04 68 81 02 063 - Fax: 04 68 81 57 43
Email: contact@camping-romarin.com - www.camping-romarin-com

FR66160 Camping la Palmeraie

Boulevard de la Plage, F-66440 Torreilles-Plage (Pyrénées-Orientales)

Tel: **04 68 28 20 64**. Email: **info@camping-la-palmeraie.com**

La Palmeraie is a very attractive, top quality campsite situated some 600 metres from the beach at Torreilles-Plage. Arguably the prettiest campsite in the area, there is an abundance of foliage, including a variety of trees and flowering shrubs which provide ample shade – unusual in a situation on the littoral and so close to the sea. The site is a credit to the owners. The 110 touring pitches (out of a total of 240 in all) are generally on the large side. All the facilities, including an attractive pool and surrounding sunbathing area, are of a good quality and lend an air of elegance to this excellent campsite.

Facilities

Three well equipped, modern sanitary blocks are traditional in style with modern fittings. Facilities for disabled visitors and children. Laundry facilities. Fridge hire. Shop. Bar, restaurant and takeaway (all open when site is open). Swimming and paddling pools. Play area. Games room. Multisport court. Safety depost. Internet access. Evening entertainment and organised sports activities in July/Aug. Children's club (6-12 yrs). Off site: Beach 600 m. Riding 500 m. Sailing, beach club, minigolf and other activities in the local area.

Open: 27 May - 30 September.

Directions

From A9 take exit 41 and follow signs for Canet via D81 and D83. Once on D83 look for signs for Torreilles Plage. Site is on right hand side as you approach from the roundabout on the D83.

Charges guide

Per unit incl. 2 persons	€ 15,70 - € 24,50
extra person	€ 5,00 - € 7,50
child (3-7 yrs)	€ 4,00 - € 5,50
electricity (5/10A)	€ 3,50 - € 6,60

433

FR66180 Mas Llinas Camping

F-66160 Le Boulou (Pyrénées-Orientales)

Tel: **04 68 83 25 46**. Email: **info@camping-mas-llinas.com**

This is a simple, peaceful and well maintained site with a relaxed feel and helpful, friendly owners. The highest terraces on this campsite have commanding views over the valley and to the surrounding mountains. The roads up to the level, terraced, hillside pitches (100) are paved. Some pitches are large, some grassy and a few hedged for privacy, many with outstanding views and lovely trees (electricity 5/6A). Rock pegs advised. The reception is near the bar/café that serves a very limited range of snacks and some local produce, including the wine of the region.

Facilities

One clean and modern toilet block, the other recently refurbished. Facilities for disabled campers. Washing machine. Motorcaravan services. Limited bar/café (mid June to end Sept). Bread (July/Aug). Small swimming pool (mid May - Oct). Volleyball. Table tennis. Games room. Electronic games. Torches necessary. Riding. Bicycle hire. Only gas barbecues. Off site: VTT with guide. Fishing 5 km. Golf 25 km. The site is close to the border and its associated shopping opportunities.

Open: 1 March - 30 November.

Directions

Le Boulou is 26 km. north of Spanish border. South from Perpignan, A9 or N9 to Le Boulou (30 km). Site well signed from town, on northern outskirts, approached via light commercial area. Follow road uphill for about 2 km. GPS: N42:32.50 E02:50.05

Charges 2008

Per person	€ 4,20 - € 5,20
child (under 10 yrs)	€ 2,70
pitch	€ 4,70 - € 6,60
electricity (5/10A)	€ 3,60 - € 4,60

FR66150 Castel Camping les Criques de Porteils

RD 114, route de Coullioure, F-66701 Argelès-sur-Mer (Pyrénées-Orientales)

Tel: **04 68 81 12 73**. Email: **criquesdeporteils@wanadoo.fr**

This is an amazing site situated on the cliff top with views across the sea to Argelès, set against a backdrop of mountains and close to Collioure, the artist's paradise. What more could you ask? Under new ownership, the facilities are being renovated and some of the pitches being redesigned for easier access. There are around 275 of varying sizes and shapes due to the nature of the terrain, level in places up and down in others. Most have sea views and 5A electricity available. There are three small coves of grey sand accessed by steep steps (gated).

Facilities

Two renovated toilet blocks, fully equipped with super children's room, all small equipment and colourful. Laundry room with internet point. Motorcaravan service point. Shop. Bar. Restaurant with takeaway. Swimming pool. Play area. Sports field. Off site: Collioure 5 mins.

Open: 1 April - 9 September.

Directions

Exit A9 at Perpigan Sud or Le Boulou. Head for Argelès to pick up signs for 'Collioure par la Corniche'. Watch for site signs coming into a bend as you come down a hill by hotel. GPS: N42:32.000 E03:04.001

Charges 2007

Per unit incl. 2 persons	€ 14,00 - € 29,00
extra person	€ 6,00 - € 9,00
electricity	€ 3,00 - € 6,00

FR66190 Sunêlia les Tropiques

Boulevard de la Méditerranée, F-66440 Torreilles-Plage (Pyrénées-Orientales)

Tel: **04 68 28 05 09**. Email: **contact@camping-les-tropiques.com**

Les Tropiques makes a pleasant holiday venue, only 400 metres from a sandy beach and also boasting two pools. There are 450 pitches with 200 given over to mobile homes and chalets. Pleasant pine and palm trees with other Mediterranean vegetation give shade and provide an attractive environment. Activities are provided for all including a large range of sports, caberets and shows but an identity bracelet for entry to the site is obligatory in high season (small payment required).

Facilities

Modern, fully equipped sanitary facilities, provision for disabled visitors. Launderette. Shop and bar (1/5-15/9), restaurant, takeaway, pizzeria (all 1/6-15/9). Heated pool, another pool (15/5-30/9), paddling pool. Tennis, football, volleyball. Archery (1/7-31/8). TV, billiards room. Play area. Disco (every evening), club for 6-12 year olds in July/Aug. Bicycle hire (15/6-15/9). Off site: Minigolf 300 m. Windsurf board hire, sea fishing 400 m. Riding 400 m. Microlights, karting 1.5 km. Diving, water-skiing 4 km. Golf 15 km.

Open: 31 March - 7 October.

Directions

From A9 exit Perpignan Nord, follow D83 towards Le Barcarès for 9 km. Take D81 south towards Canet for 3 km. turn left at roundabout for Torreilles-Plage. Site is the last but one on left.

Charges 2007

Per unit incl. 2 persons	
with electricity	€ 17,00 - € 35,50
extra person	€ 3,70 - € 8,20
child (0-13 yrs)	€ 2,50 - € 5,80
animal	€ 4,00

FR66250 **Huttopia Font-Romeu**

Route de Mont-Louis, F-66120 Font-Romeu (Pyrénées-Orientales)

Tel: **04 68 30 09 32**. Email: **font-romeu@huttopia.com**

This is a large, open site of some seven hectares, nestling on the side of the mountain at the entrance to Font-Romeu. This part of the Pyrénées offer some staggering views and the famous Mont Louis is close by. An ideal base for climbing, hiking or cycling, it would also provide a good stop over for a night or so whilst traveling between Spain and France or to or from Andorra into France. The terraced pitches are easily accessed, with those dedicated to caravans and motorcaravans at the top of the site, whilst tents go on the lower slopes. Trees provide shade to many of the pitches from the sun which can be quite hot at this altitude. Facilities on site are limited to very good toilet blocks and a very large games room and assembly hall which is used by those in tents when it rains.

Facilities

Two toilet blocks, one behind reception, the other in the centre of the tent pitches. Traditional in style, they are bright and clean with modern fittings. Toilet for children and excellent facilities for disabled visitors. Washing machines and dryers at each block. large games hall. Only gas barbecues are permitted. Off site: Opportunities for walking and climbing are close by as are golf, riding, fishing, cycling and tennis. The small town of Font-Romeu is very near with all the usual shops and banking facilities.

Open: 4 July - 28 September.

Directions

Font-Romeu is on the D118, some 12 km. after it branches off the N116 heading west, just after Mont Louis. This is an interesting road with magnificent views and well worth the climb. The site is just before the town, on the left and accessed off the car park.

Charges 2007

Per person	€ 3,50 - € 4,00
child (2-7 yrs)	€ 2,00 - € 2,50
pitch	€ 5,00 - € 6,00
electricity (6A)	€ 3,20

UTTOPIA

tel: +33 (0) 4 37 64 22 33 www.huttopia.com

FR66220 **Camping du Stade**

Avenue du 8 Mai 1945, F-66702 Argelès-sur-Mer (Pyrénées-Orientales)

Tel: **04 68 81 04 40**. Email: **info@campingdustade.com**

Quieter and more peaceful family orientated sites are rare in this immediate area, so we were pleasantly surprised to discover one in a pleasant shady setting midway between the village and the beach resort – less than 1 km. from both. The 180 good sized pitches, (most with electricity) are in green surroundings with plenty of shade. This traditionally French campsite, could be a quiet haven for those who want to relax at the end of the day without the distraction of a noisy pool and bar, but who want to be close to all the various attractions offered by this resort.

Facilities

With so much within easy walking distance the site itself has few facilities, but it does have two good quality, part modern, part traditional, well-maintained toilet blocks with good sized showers, washbasins in cabins, etc. Unit for disabled people, facilities for babies, covered dishwashing area and washing machine. Snack-bar and takeaway (high season only). Adventure-style play area. Table tennis. Off site: Beach, shops, bars and restaurants all within walking distance.

Open: 1 April - 30 September.

Directions

From A9 exit 42 (Perpignan Sud) take N114 towards Argelès, then exit 10 for Pujols and Argelès. Follow signs towards Centre, Plage. First roundabout straight on (Ave Molliere). At next small roundabout turn left, site immediately on left.

Charges 2007

Per unit incl. 2 persons and electricity	€ 17,10 - € 23,00
extra person	€ 3,60 - € 5,10
child (0-5 yrs)	€ 2,30 - € 3,30

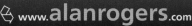

FR66290 Camping Club le Floride et l'Embouchure

Route de Saint Laurent, F-66423 Le Barcarès (Pyrénées-Orientales)

Tel: **04 68 86 11 75**. Email: **campingfloride@aol.com**

Essentially a family run enterprise, Le Floride et L'Embouchure is really two sites in one – L'Embouchure the smaller one with direct access to the beach and Le Floride on the opposite side of the fairly busy road into Le Barcarès village. Apart from having some very unusual accommodation to rent (the 'Bungahomes') and a few pitches with their own individual sanitary facility, the sites are fairly unremarkable, albeit within a very friendly family-centred environment, very popular with Dutch visitors. In total there are 632 pitches, all with 10A electricity. The site is relatively inexpensive, especially outside the July/August peak period. It offers a comfortable, if unpretentious, holiday opportunity with reasonably sized pitches (300 for touring units) and ample shade. In the case of L'Embouchure, there is direct access to a popular beach, but Le Floride has the pool complex complete with toboggan.

Facilities

Four fully equipped toilet blocks on Le Floride and two on L'Embouchure where 50 pitches near the beach have individual facilities. Shop, bar, restaurant and takeaway (all 15/6-5/9). Three swimming pools (one heated outside July/Aug). Play area. Entertainment programme (July/Aug). Charcoal barbecues are not permitted. Off site: Fishing 1 km. Riding 1.5 km. Bicycle hire 3 km. Beach 100 m.

Open: 1 April - 30 September.

Directions

From A9 take exit 41 (Perpignan Nord) and follow signs for Canet and Le Barcarès via D83. At J9 follow D81 (Canet) then next left into Le Barcarès Village. Site is 1 km. on the left and right sides of the road.

Charges 2007

Per unit incl. 2 persons	
and electricity	€ 12,50 - € 34,00
incl. individual sanitary facility	€ 16,00 - € 42,00
extra person	€ 2,60 - € 6,20
child (1-4 yrs)	free - € 3,60

FR66260 Camping la Massane

25 avenue Molière, F-66702 Argelès-sur-Mer (Pyrénées-Orientales)

Tel: **04 68 81 06 85**. Email: **camping.massane@infonie.fr**

Set a little bit back from the seafront, La Massane is one of the traditional older sites with good views of the Canigou and a pool open for a longer season. With 184 pitches and only 26 taken by mobile homes, it could make a good, quiet and relaxing choice. In July and August it will be a little more hectic (as is the whole resort) with a bar and some family entertainment. Other amenities are within walking distance. Pitches are divided, level and semi-grassed with a mixture of shade from tall trees or shrubs. Electricity (6/10A) is available.

Facilities

Two toilet blocks, one large and modernized with a baby room and facilities for disabled visitors. A smaller, traditional block is used early in the season. Laundry room. Swimming pool (heated 15/4-30/9) with paddling pool. Shop, bar, takeaway and entertainment July/Aug only. Play area. Charcoal barbecues not permitted. Off site: Village of Argelès. Beach 1 km. Bicycle hire 1 km. Spain, Collieure and the Pyrénées within driving distance.

Open: 15 March - 15 October.

Directions

From the A9 take exit 42 (Perpignan Sud) and follow N114 for Argelès to exit 10.for Pujols. At first roundabout take 'Centre Plage'. Pass school on left and site is almost immediately on left. GPS: N42:33.043 E03:01.876

Charges 2008

Per unit incl. 2 persons	
and electricity	€ 11,00 - € 25,00
extra person	€ 2,50 - € 5,00
child (0-4 yrs)	free - € 2,00
dog	free - € 2,00

FR66300 Yelloh! Village le Pré Catalan

Route de St Laurent, F-66420 Le Barcarès (Pyrénées-Orientales)

Tel: **04 66 73 97 39**. Email: **info@yellohvillage-pre-catalan.com**

The green foliage from the mixed trees and the flowering shrubs makes the site very attractive and an avenue of palms is particularly spectacular. There has been a campsite on the spot since 1960 but the present owners, the Galidie family, took over in 1982 and the site is now run by their son Francois and his English wife Jenny. With 250 pitches in total, there are 180 taken by mobile homes and chalets, half to let and half privately owned. These are mixed amongst the touring pitches which are on level, sandy ground, clearly divided by hedging and with 10A electricity. The newer part has been planted in the same way as the original areas. It has less shade but enjoys views across to the mountains. The facilities are opened all season but hours are adapted according to the number of visitors on site. An upstairs bar has a long terrace which overlooks the pool area. A footpath of just less than 1 km. leads to the sandy beach. All in all, this a pleasant and comfortable place to stay.

Facilities

Good modern facilities include small showers for children. Laundry. Small shop. Bar, restaurant and takeaway (all season). Heated swimming pool and paddling pool. Excellent play area. Tennis. Archery. Internet access. Library. Activities for children with miniclub and evening entertainment (July/Aug). Only gas barbecues. Off site: Beach 900 m. River fishing 1 km. Riding 1.5 km. Boat launching 3 km. Nearby La Réserve Africaine de Sigean and Le Château de Salses.

Open: 30 April - 20 September.

Directions

From A9 exit 41 (Perpignan Nord), follow signs for Le Barcarès and Canet (D81). At junction 9 take the D81 (Canet), then first left to Le Barcarès (D90). Site is on left after 500 m. next to Le California. Follow narrow lane to site entrance.

Charges 2007

Per unit incl. 2 persons	€ 13,00 - € 32,00
extra person	€ 4,00 - € 7,50
child (3-6 yrs)	€ 2,00 - € 4,00
electricity	€ 4,00

66420 Le Barcarès - Tel : 0033 468 86 12 60
Internet : www.precatalan.com - Email : info@precatalan.com

2 heated swimming pools of which one is a children's pool, bar, snack, restaurant, shop, animation for all ages. Our services are available from the opening date. Beach at 900 meter on foot. French/English owned.

FR66200 Camping les Marsouins

Avenue de la Retirada, F-66702 Argelès-sur-Mer (Pyrénées-Orientales)

Tel: **04 68 81 14 81**. Email: **marsouin@campmed.com**

Les Marsouins is a large site situated on the beach road out of Argelès. There are 587 pitches in total. The 430 good size, grassy, level pitches, electricity (5A), for touring are divided by hedging and tall trees give some shade. An outdoor entertainment area is located at the entrance beside the bar and restaurant (for high season entertainment). The lagoon style heated pool and paddling pool (no water slides) have ample space for sunbathing. The site is well situated for easy access to the good sandy beach, with activities like windsurfing and sea kayaking possible (free 15/5-30/9).

Facilities

Fully equipped toilet blocks provide facilities for disabled visitors. Washing machine and iron. Motorcaravan services. Shop (26/5-8/9). Bar, self-service restaurant (16/6-5/9), takeaway (1/4-30/9). Mini-market (8/6-7/9). Heated swimming pool (15/04-29/9). Large play area. Children's club, organised activities (24/6-1/9). Tennis. Range of evening entertainment (30/5-30/8). Off site: Beach 800 m. Riding next door. Boat launching 2 km. Golf 7 km.

Open: 9 April - 22 September.

Directions

From A9 autoroute take Perpignan Sud exit. Follow signs for Argelès (RN114) from exit 10 and follow signs for Pujols at roundabout then Plage Nord at next roundabout. Site is 1.5 km. on left. GPS: N42:33.827 E03:02.044

Charges 2007

Per unit incl. 2 persons and 5A electricity	€ 14,00 - € 29,00
with water and drainage	€ 15,50 - € 30,50
extra person (over 5 yrs)	€ 4,00 - € 5,50

FR66560 Camping la Sirène

Route De Taxo, F-66702 Argelès-sur-Mer (Pyrénées-Orientales)

Tel: **04 68 81 04 61**. Email: **contact@camping-lasirene.fr**

From the moment you step into the hotel-like reception area you realize that this large site offers the holiday maker everything they could want in a well managed and convenient location close to Argelès sur Mer and the beaches. The 740 mobilehomes and chalets vary in standard but all are less than five years old, very clean, comfortable and located on neat tidy pitches. There are also some touring pitches. In the summer there are 170 staff on duty to ensure your stay is as enjoyable as they can make it. All the shops and amenities are near reception making the accommodation areas quite peaceful and relaxing.

Facilities	Directions
Restaurant, bar and takeaway. Large shop (all season). Large aquapark, paddling pools, slides, jacuzzi. Games room. Multisports field, tennis, archery, minigolf, football. Theatre, evening entertainment, discos, show time spectacular. Off site: Resort of Argelès sur Mer and its beaches 2 km, as is karting, ten pin bowling, amusement park and the sites private beach club Emeraude. Interesting old town of Collioure close by.	Leave A9 motorway, junction 42, take D114, towards Argelès. Leave D114, junction 10 and follow signs for Plage Nord. Site signed after first roundabout. Site on right 2 km. after last roundabout.

Open: 7 April - 28 September.

Charges 2008

Per unit with 3 persons	
and electricity	€ 26,00 - € 43,00
extra person	€ 6,00 - € 9,00
child (under 5 yrs)	€ 4,00 - € 6,00

FR66570 Camping l'Hippocampe

Route de Taxo, F-66702 Argelès-sur-Mer (Pyrénées-Orientales)

Tel: **04 68 81 04 61**. Email: **contact@camping-lasirene.fr**

A sister site to La Sirène just opposite, this site has some touring pitches along with 170 mobile home and chalet pitches and is aimed at families with young children and adults looking for a quieter site. The mobile homes and chalets are all modern, well maintained and have space around them to provide privacy. The pool on site is dedicated to the smaller children and is a great place for them to gain confidence in the water whilst still being able to play. Entertainment, shops, bars and the full range of activities offered by La Sirène, just across the road

Facilities	Directions
Pool and laundry. Shop, small bar (all season). All other facilities are at La Sirène just across the road. Off site: Beach, Argelès sur Mer within 2 km. Karting, ten pin bowling, amusement park and horse riding within 1 km.	Leave A9 junction 42. Take D114, Argelès road. Leave D114 junction 10, follow signs for Plage Nord. Site signed after the first roundabout, on left 2 km. after last roundabout.

Open: 6 April - 28 September.

Charges 2008

Per unit incl. 3 persons	
and electricity	€ 26,00 - € 43,00
extra person	€ 6,00 - € 9,00
child (under 5 yrs)	€ 4,00 - € 6,00

FR66590 Camping le Bois du Valmarie

F-66702 Argelès-sur-Mer (Pyrénées-Orientales)

Tel: **04 68 81 04 61**. Email: **contact@camping-lasirene.fr**

Le Bois de Valmarie is a member of the same group of sites as La Sirene (FR66560) and L'Hippocampe (FR66570). The site is located 3 km. to the north of the town. Please note, however, the 181 pitches on this site are all occupied by mobile homes and chalets, the majority of which are available for booking. There are no touring pitches. The site has a pleasant woodland location and an impressive range of amenities including a large swimming pool complex with waterslides and a separate children's pool. The sea is just 50 m. from the site entrance with a sandy beach and within easy walking distance. This is a lively site in high season with a programme of evening entertainment.

Facilities	Directions
Supermarket. Restaurant. Bar. Beach shop. Takeaway food. Swimming pool with waterslides and separate children's pool. Play area. Mobile homes for rent. Off site: Argelès town centre 3 km. Diving club. Blue Bear activity club. Emeraude Beach Club.	Leave autoroute at Perpignan Sud exit and join the N114 southbound toward Argelès. Take exit 13 and follow signs to Le Racou. Site is well signed from here.

Open: 7 April - 28 September.

CAMPINGS
CLUBS ★★★★
ARGELÈS/MER
MÉDITERRANÉE

A SIRÈNE • LE BOIS DE VALMARIE • L'HIPPOCAMPE

Quick and easy,
**your reservation
in just one
click on:**

route de Taxo
66702 Argelès-sur-Mer
Tél. : +33 (0)4 68 81 04 61
Fax : +33 (0)4 68 81 69 74
e-mail : contact@camping-lasirene.fr

www.camping-lasirene.fr

FR66310 Camping le Rotja

F-66820 Fuilla (Pyrénées-Orientales)

Tel: **04 68 96 52 75**. Email: **campinglerotja.ellenetwim@wanadoo.fr**

La Rotja is a pretty, Dutch-owned site, set up a little valley above the fortified old town of Villefranche-de-Conflent and watched over by the impressive, snow-capped Pic d'Canigou. The older part of the site is semi-wooded with wonderful silver birches, whilst the newer part further up the hill is more open and terraced. There is room for 100 fairly level pitches, 80 with electricity, and one can chose a shaded place or not. A small pool at the top of the site is very welcome in high season. Trips are organized into the mountains, along with barbecue evenings. A small bar doubles as reception and a rustic outside area allows 'al fresco' enjoyment of the daily menu. The site has a wonderful situation and whilst having all 'mod cons', the naturalness of the area has been retained. The spa town of Vernet-le-Bains in the next valley is worth visiting, as is the celebrated Fort Libéria, or walk around the walls of Villefranche-de-Conflent or even enjoy a jaunt on the Petit Train Jaune to enjoy the magnificent scenery.

Facilities

Two toilet blocks, both fully equipped. The older one beside the bar area can be heated, a larger, more modern one is in the new area. Facilities for disabled visitors and babies. Bar, outside restaurant (15/5-30/9). Swimming and paddling pools (1/5-30/9). Gas barbecues only. Bicycle hire. Off site: Tennis 100 m. Fishing 300 m. Riding 7 km. Beach 55 km. Rafting, canyoning, hydro-speed and 'parc-aventure' possible with trained guides. Walking, VTT.

Open: 1 April - 31 October.

Directions

Follow the N116 from Perpignan (route to Andorra). After about 50 km. bypass Prades and continue to Villefranche-de-Conflent. Follow around and past it to take left turn signed Fuilla and Sahorre. After 2 km. turn right at village to site.

Charges 2008

per unit incl. 2 persons	€ 13,25 - € 18,25
incl. electricity	€ 15,50 - € 20,50
extra person	€ 2,75 - € 3,75
child (0-7 yrs)	€ 1,75 - € 2,75

FR66610 Camping le Bois de Pins

Route d'Opoul, F-66600 Salses-le Château (Pyrénées-Orientales)

Tel: **04 68 38 68 44**. Email: **info@leboisdepins.com**

This is an all year site located two kilometres from the village of Salses, best known for its 15th century fortified chateau. Le Bois de Pins is a small site which has been recommended by our French agent and we are planning a full inspection in 2008. There are 66 large and well shaded pitches, most with electrical connections (9A). This is a relatively simple site with few amenities and, given its proximity to the A9 autoroute, it may be a good choice for an overnight stop en-route further south.

Facilities

Small shop. Takeaway food. Playground. Off site: Salses le Château 2 km. Perpignan 15 km. Nearest beaches 10 km. Fishing lake 2 km. Walking and cycle routes.

Open: All year.

Directions

From the A9 exit 41 (Salses) follow signs to Salses using the N9. In Salses follow signs to Opoul and site is well signed from this point.

Charges 2007

Per unit incl. 2 persons	€ 9,00 - € 17,00
extra person	€ 3,00 - € 5,00
child (under 12 yrs)	€ 1,00 - € 3,00
electricity (9A)	€ 3,00

MAP 15 & 16

Bathed in sunshine from early spring to late autumn, surrounded by stunning scenery, cosmopolitan towns and superb sandy beaches, no wonder this is one of France's most sought-after destinations.

THIS SECTION COVERS THE EASTERN COASTAL REGION OF THE MEDITERRANEAN. WE INCLUDE TWO DÉPARTEMENTS FROM THE OFFICIAL REGION OF PROVENCE AND THE REGION OF CÔTE D'AZUR: 13 BOUCHES-DU-RHÔNE, 83 VAR, 06 ALPES-MARITIME

The glittering Côte d'Azur, perhaps better known as the French Riviera, is a beautiful stretch of coast studded with sophisticated towns such as the famous Monte Carlo, Nice, and Cannes, not forgetting the other famous and arguably the most glamorous resort of St Tropez. With its vast expanses of golden sandy beaches and long lazy hours of sunshine, this is a paradise for sun worshippers and beach enthusiasts. It's a spectacular coast of rugged coves, sweeping beaches and warm seas.

The quaint harbours and fishing villages have become chic destinations, now full of pleasure yachts, harbour-side cafés and crowded summertime beaches. Further up in the hills are quieter tiny medieval villages with winding streets and white-walled houses with terracotta roofs, which have attracted artists for many years. In St Paul-de-Vence visitors browse through shops and galleries set on narrow winding cobblestone streets and inland Grasse is the perfume capital of the world, surrounded by the Provencal lavender fields and shady olive groves which pervade the air with a magical scent at certain times of the year.

Places of interest

Aix-en-Provence: old town with 17th-18th century character, Paul Cézanne and Tapestry museums.

Cannes: popular for conventions and festivals, Cannes Film Festival, la Croisette, old city.

Monte Carlo: main city of Monaco, casinos, gardens, Napoleon Museum. Motorsport circuit.

Cuisine of the region

Aigo Bouido: garlic and sage soup.

Bouillabaisse: fish soup.

Rouille: an orange coloured sauce with peppers, garlic and saffron.

Bourride: a creamy fish soup.

Pissaladière: Provençal bread dough with onions, anchovies and olives.

Pistou (Soupe au): vegetable soup bound with *pommade*.

Pommade: a thick paste of garlic, basil, cheese and olive oil.

Ratatouille: aubergines, courgettes, onions, garlic, red peppers and tomatoes in olive oil.

Salade Niçoise: tomatoes, beans, potatoes, black olives, anchovy, lettuce, olive oil and tuna fish.

FR06010 Camping Domaine Sainte-Madeleine

Route de Moulinet, F-06380 Sospel (Alpes-Maritimes)

Tel: **04 93 04 10 48**. Email: **camp@camping-sainte-madeleine.com**

Domaine Sainte Madeleine is an attractive, peaceful site, with swimming pool, in spectacular mountain scenery. It is about 20 km. inland from Menton, and very near the Italian border. The approach to this site involves a 17 km. climb with hairpin bends and then a choice of going through the pass or an 800 m. long tunnel (3.5 m. high, 3 m. wide). Situated on a terraced hillside with mountain views towards Italy, manoeuvring within the site presents no problem as the pitches are on level, well drained grass. The lower ones have shade but those higher up on the hill have none. Electricity is available to 60 of the 66 pitches.

Facilities

Good quality toilet block with hot showers (token required). Hot water (often only warm) for dishwashing and laundry sinks drawn from single tap. Washing machines. Motorcaravan services. Gas supplies. Bread can be ordered. Pool (140 sq.m. and heated in spring and autumn). Off site: The attractive town of Sospel is 4 km. with many restaurants, bars, cafés and shops. Tennis, riding and a centre for mountain biking. Fishing 1 km.

Open: 31 March - 30 September.

Directions

From A8 take Menton exit towards Sospel from where you turn onto the D2566 (route de Moulinet). Site is 4 km. north of Sospel on the left.

Charges 2007

Per unit incl. 2 persons	€ 19,00
extra person	€ 4,20
child (under 6 yrs)	€ 2,40
electricity (10A)	€ 2,90

Less 15% outside July/Aug. No credit cards.

FR06020 Camping le Vallon Rouge

Route de Gréolières, F-06480 La Colle-sur-Loup (Alpes-Maritimes)

Tel: **04 93 32 86 12**. Email: **auvallonrouge@aol.com**

In the valley of the Loup river, a pleasant holidaying area, this small site is close to the Côte d'Azur, but away from all the bustle of the Mediterranean coast. There is the opportunity for total relaxation amongst the cork, oak, pine and mimosa. The three hectare site is quite flat with many umbrella pines for shade, with 103 separated pitches for touring caravans and tents. An average of 80 sq.m. in size, all have electricity, with those in one area also having water and drainage. Some pitches are on the banks of the Loup.

Facilities

Two toilet blocks are kept clean and include washbasins in cubicles and spacious showers. Facilities for disabled people and babies. Laundry areas and washing machines. Small shop. Bar/restaurant and takeaway. New pool complex (all season). Playground. Electronic games. Fishing. Only gas barbecues are permitted. Off site: Riding or golf 4 km. Beach, Cros de Cagnes 7 km.

Open: 5 April - 27 September.

Directions

Leave A8 at exit 47 on D6 towards Grasse. Follow signs and site is on the right. Larger units should stop at the top access gate and ask for assistance.

Charges 2007

Per unit with electricity	€ 13,20 - € 23,20
person	€ 3,00 - € 4,30
child (5-18 yrs)	€ 3,00 - € 3,20

Camping Cheques accepted.

FR06030 Camping Caravaning Domaine de la Bergerie

1330 chemin de la Sine, F-06140 Vence (Alpes-Maritimes)

Tel: **04 93 58 09 36**. Email: **info@camping-domainedelabergerie.com**

La Bergerie is a quiet, family owned site, situated in the hills 3 km. from Vence and 10 km. from the sea at Cagnes-sur-Mer. This extensive, natural, lightly wooded site is in a secluded position about 300 m. above sea level. Most of the pitches are shaded and all are of a good size. There are 450 pitches, 224 with electricity (2/5A), water and drainage. Some of the pitches are a little distance from the toilet blocks. There are no organised activities and definitely no groups allowed.

Facilities

Refurbished toilet blocks, excellent provision for disabled people (pitches near the block are reserved for disabled people). Good shop, small bar/restaurant, takeaway (all 1/5-30/9). Large swimming pool, paddling pool, spacious sunbathing area (1/5-30/9). Playground. Bicycle hire. Table tennis, tennis courts, 12 shaded boules pitches (lit at night) with competitions in season. No barbecues. Off site: Riding and fishing 10 km. Golf 18 km. Hourly bus service (excl. Sundays) from site to Vence.

Open: 25 March - 15 October.

Directions

From A8 exit 47 take Cagnes-sur-Mer road towards Vence. Site west of Vence - follow 'toutes directions' around town, join D2210 Grasse road. In 2 km. at roundabout, turn left, follow site signs, 1 km. Site on right in light woodland. GPS: N43:42.421 E07:05.258

Charges 2007

Per unit incl. 2 persons	€ 15,00 - € 21,00
with electricity (2A)	€ 18,00 - € 25,00
with full services	€ 23,00 - € 31,00
extra person	€ 5,00

Camping Cheques accepted.

FR06080 Camping Caravaning les Cigales

505 Avenue de la Mer, F-06210 Mandelieu-la-Napoule (Alpes-Maritimes)

Tel: 04 93 49 23 53. Email: **campingcigales@wanadoo.fr**

Mobile homes ▶ page 509

It is hard to imagine that such a quiet, peaceful site could be in the middle of such a busy town and so near Cannes. The entrance (easily missed) has large electronic gates that ensure that the site is very secure. There are only 115 pitches (40 mobile homes) so this is quite a small, personal site. There are three pitch sizes, from small ones for tents to pitches for larger units and all have electricity (6A), some fully serviced. All are level with much needed shade in summer, although the sun will get through in winter when it is needed. The site is alongside the Canal de Siagne and for a fee, small boats can be launched at La Napoule, then moored outside the campsite's side gate. Les Cigales is open all year so it is useful for the Monte Carlo Rally, the Cannes Film Festival and the Mimosa Festival, all held out of the main season. English is spoken.

Facilities

Well appointed, clean, heated toilet blocks. Facilities for babies and disabled visitors. Washing machine. Motorcaravan services. Restaurant and takeaway (May - Oct). Heated swimming pool and large sunbathing area (April - Oct). Small play area. Table tennis. Two games machines. Canal fishing. Off site: Beach 800 m. The town is an easy walk. Two golf courses within 1 km. Railway station 1 km. for trains to Cannes, Nice, Antibes, Monte Carlo. Hypermarket 2 km. Bus stop 10 minutes.

Open: All year.

Directions

From A8, exit 40, bear right. Remain in right hand lane, continue right signed Plages-Ports, Creche-Campings. Casino supermarket on right. Continue under motorway to T-junction. Turn left, site is 60 m. on left opposite Chinese restaurant.

Charges 2007

Per person	€ 6,00
child (under 5 yrs)	€ 3,00
tent	€ 6,50 - € 13,50
caravan or motorcaravan	€ 14,00 - € 23,50

FR06050 Camping la Vieille Ferme

296 boulevard des Groules, F-06270 Villeneuve-Loubet-Plage (Alpes-Maritimes)

Tel: 04 93 33 41 44. Email: **info@vieilleferme.com**

Open all year, in a popular resort area, La Vieille Ferme is a family owned site with good facilities. It has 113 level gravel-based touring pitches, 95 fully serviced and the majority separated by hedges. Some are only small, simple pitches for little tents. There is also a fully serviced pitch on tarmac for motorhomes. There are special winter rates for long stays with quite a few long stay units on site. The entrance to the site is very colourful with well tended flower beds. English is spoken at reception and the whole place has a very friendly feel to it.

Facilities

Modern, heated, well kept toilet blocks, children's toilets, baby room, facilities for disabled people. Motorcaravan services. Washing machines, dryer. Shop (Easter - Sept). Machine with drinks, sweets, ices in TV room. Gas, bread, milk to order. Refrigerator hire. Swimming pool, children's pool, heated and covered for winter use (closed mid Nov-mid Dec), Jacuzzi. Internet. Table tennis, basketball, boules. Games, competitions organised in July/Aug. Off site: Bus from outside site. Fishing 1 km. Golf 2 km. Marineland water park.

Open: All year.

Directions

From west, A8, exit 44 Antibes, D35, 3.5 km. Left towards Nice, N7. After 3.5 km. turn left for site between Marine Land and Parc de Vaugrenier. Site is 150 m. on right. Avoid N98 Route du Bord de Mer.

Charges 2007

Per unit incl. 2 persons	€ 17,50 - € 28,50
extra person	€ 3,70 - € 5,00
child (under 5 yrs)	€ 2,50 - € 3,00
electricity (2-10A)	€ 2,50 - € 5,50
dog	€ 1,50

FR06070 Domaine Naturiste Club Origan

F-06260 Puget-Theniers (Alpes-Maritimes)

Tel: **04 93 05 06 00**. Email: **origan@wanadoo.fr**

Origan is a naturist site set in the mountains behind Nice, at a height of 500 m. The access road is single track and winding with a few passing places, so arrival is not recommended until late afternoon. The site's terrain is fairly wild and the roads stony and it is not suitable for caravans longer than six metres due to the steep slopes, although the site will assist with a 4x4 vehicle if requested. The 100 touring pitches, in three areas, are of irregular size and shape with good views. Electricity connection (6A) is possible on most pitches (by long cable). Member 'France 4 Naturisme'.

Facilities

Sanitary facilities, are clean and of a standard and type associated with most good naturist sites - mostly open plan hot showers. Laundry facilities. Shop (1/6-30/8). Bar/restaurant. Takeaway. Heated swimming pools. Jacuzzi and sauna. Disco. Tennis. Fishing. Bicycle hire. Organised activities for all (high season). Only gas or electric barbecues are permitted. Torches advised. Off site: Puget-Theniers offers bars, cafés, shops, etc.

Open: 15 April - 30 September.

Directions

Heading west on the N202, just past the town of Puget-Theniers, turn right at camp sign at level crossing; site is 1 km.

Charges 2007

Per unit incl. 2 persons and electricity	€ 15,00 - € 31,00
extra person	€ 3,00 - € 7,00
child (3-8 yrs)	€ 2,00 - € 6,00

Camping Cheques accepted.

FR06090 Camping Caravaning les Gorges du Loup

965 chemin des Vergers, F-06620 Le Bar sur Loup (Alpes-Maritimes)

Tel: **04 93 42 45 06**. Email: **info@lesgorgesduloup.com**

Les Gorges du Loup is situated on a steep hillside above Grasse. The one kilometre lane which leads to the site is narrow with passing places. The 70 pitches are on level terraces, all with electricity and many have stupendous views. Some pitches are only suitable for tents and the site roads are quite steep. A quiet family site, there is no organised entertainment. Grasse (9 km.) is surrounded by fields of lavender, mimosa and jasmine and has been famous for the manufacture of perfume since the 16th century. The very friendly and enthusiastic owners provide 4x4 assistance.

Facilities

Clean toilet blocks with washbasins and hot showers, dishwashing and laundry sinks have only a single hot tap. Washing machine and iron. Reception, small shop, bread. Small bar/restaurant with terrace, takeaway (all 3/6-8/9). Pool, small slide, diving board, but no pool for small children. Basketball, volleyball, skittles. TV room, board games, library. Children's climbing frame, slide. No charcoal barbecues. Chalets, mobile homes for hire. Off site: Bar-de-Loup with its few shops, restaurants is only a 500 m. walk.

Open: 1 April - 30 September.

Directions

From Grasse, D2085 Nice road. D3 briefly to Châteauneuf Pré du Lac. D2210 to Pont-de-Loup, Vence. Site signed on right. Pass village of Bar-sur-Loup on left, after sharp right turn, follow narrow access road 750 m. (passing places). GPS: N43:42.148 E06:59.726

Charges 2007

Per unit incl. 2 persons	€ 14,50 - € 24,20
extra person	€ 4,20
electricity (4/10A)	€ 3,20 - € 4,20

No credit cards.

FR06100 Camping les Pinèdes

Route du Pont de Pierre, F-06480 La Colle-sur-Loup (Alpes-Maritimes)

Tel: **04 93 32 98 94**. Email: **camplespinedes06@aol.com**

Les Pinèdes is seven kilometres inland from the busy coast, at the centre of all the attractions of the Côte d'Azur, yet far enough away to be a peaceful retreat at the end of a busy day. It is terraced on a wooded hillside where olives and vines used to grow, All the level pitches have electricity (3-10A), most also with water and they are separated by low bushes. There are plans for 12 new pitches at the top of the site and also a small children's pool. The restaurant at the site entrance has an excellent reputation. In May the evenings are alive with fireflies. A 'Sites et Paysages' member.

Facilities

Two excellent new toilet blocks. One block has facilities for disabled visitors. Baby room. Shop, bakery. Bar, restaurant, takeaway. Swimming pool. Play area. Archery, boules. Entertainment for young and old, July/Aug. Weekly walks in the hills June - September (light breakfast carried by the donkeys). Off site: River fishing 50 m. Village 1 km. St Paul de Vence is 15 minutes away.

Open: 15 March - 30 September.

Directions

From A8 take D2 towards Vence. At Colle sur Loup roundabout take D6 signed Grasse, site on right in 3 km. at large sign after the restaurant entrance.

Charges 2007

Per tent incl. 2 persons	€ 14,00 - € 24,50
caravan or motorcaravan	€ 16,00 - € 27,00
extra person	€ 4,00 - € 5,00
electricity (3-10A)	€ 3,20 - € 4,50

FR06140 Ranch Camping

Chemin Saint Joseph, F-06110 Le Cannet (Alpes-Maritimes)

Tel: **04 93 46 00 11**. Email: **dstallis@free.fr**

Ranch Camping is a well run 'French flavoured' site. The ambience here is calm and there is relatively little by way of entertainment or leisure amenities. The site is very well located for the beaches of Cannes just 2 km. away; a regular bus service runs past the site entrance. Despite its urban setting the site enjoys a tranquil position on a wooded hillside. There are 102 touring pitches which are generally level and well shaded, all with 6A electrical connections. The swimming pool is quite small and can be covered in low season. Other leisure facilities are nearby.

Facilities

Principal toilet block has been recently refurbished, whereas the second block is of 'portacabin' style. Both very clean and well maintained. Facilities for disabled people. Washing machines and dryers. Small shop. Swimming pool (covered in low season). Play area. Games room. Mobile homes, rooms to rent. Off site: Beach 2 km. Bus stop at site entrance (regular service to Cannes and beaches). Tennis 200 m. Fishing, bicycle hire 2 km. Golf 4 km.

Open: 1 April - 30 October.

Directions

From A8 exit 42 follow signs to Le Cannet, then L'Aubarède to the right (D809). Follow this road until signs for La Bocca and site is signed from here. GPS: N43:33.529 E06:58.396

Charges 2007

Per unit incl. 1 person	€ 11,00 - € 17,00
extra person	€ 6,00
child (5-10 yrs)	€ 3,00

FR06120 Camping Green Park

159 Vallon des Vaux, F-06800 Cagnes-sur-Mer (Alpes-Maritimes)

Tel: **04 93 07 09 96**. Email: **info@greenpark.fr**

Green Park has many facilities of a high standard and the family owners are justifiably proud. Situated just over 4 km. from the beaches at Cagnes-sur-Mer, Green Park is at the centre of the Cote d'Azur. The newer part of the site keeps all the family occupied with activities for children, teenagers and adults, while on the other side of the road is a quieter, traditional site, with limited facilities. There are 78 touring pitches mainly on grass, with electricity and 24 are fully serviced. The site has two swimming pools, one on each side of the quiet road.

Facilities

All the toilets are modern and mostly British, with facilities for children and disabled visitors (the disabled facilities are superb). Showers and washbasins are modern and kept very clean. Dishwashing and laundry sinks and three washing machines. Bar, restaurant and takeaway (28/4-24/9). Two swimming pools (all season, one heated 5/5-24/9). Internet point. Games room. Electronic barrier (€5 card deposit) and a gate keeper on duty all night. Off site: Beach 4 km. Golf and riding 9 km.

Open: 31 March - 15 October.

Directions

From Aix, A8, exit 47 onto N7 towards Nice. Straight on at traffic lights, by racecourse, for 2 km. Turn left towards Val Fleuri, Av. du Val Fleuri. Over roundabouts to Chemin Vallon des Vaux, site on right 2 km. Avoid the town centre. GPS: N43:41.355 E07:09.409

Charges 2007

Per unit incl. 2 persons	€ 13,00 - € 44,00
extra person	€ 4,60 - € 6,00
child (7-17 yrs)	€ 3,90 - € 4,50
electricity	€ 5,50 - € 6,50

445

FR06190 Parc Saint James le Sourire

Route de Grasse, F-06270 Villeneuve-Loubet (Alpes-Maritimes)

Tel: **04 93 20 96 11.** Email: **info@camping-parcsaintjames.com**

This campsite has been recommended by our agent in France and we intend to undertake a full inspection next year. Le Sourire is a member of the Parc Saint James group. There are 411 pitches here and many are occupied by mobile homes and chalets. There are however 241 touring pitches dispersed throughout the wooded terrain. The site is close to the impressive La Vanade sports complex which has a massive range of activities including no fewer than 55 tennis courts, a riding centre and a 9-hole golf course. There are a good range of activities on site too, including a large swimming pool with a regular programme of aqua gym, water polo and other activities.

Facilities	Directions
Laundry. Supermarket. Swimming pool and separate children's pool. Bar and restaurant. Takeaway. Play area. TV room. Gym. Games room. Sports competitions. Children's club. Evening entertainment. Disco. Off site: Cannes and Nice. Nearest beaches 4 km. Marineland water park. Leisure park at La Vanade.	Take the Villeneuve Loubet exit from the A8 autoroute and follow signs to Grasse joining the D2085. The site can be found on the left, 2 km. from Villeneuve Loubet.

Open: 15 May – 15 September.

Charges 2007

Per unit incl. 2 persons and electricity	€ 17,00 - € 28,00
extra person	€ 2,50 - € 4,50
child (under 10 yrs)	€ 1,50 - € 4,00

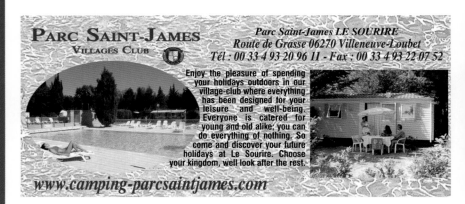

PARC SAINT-JAMES
VILLAGES CLUB

Parc Saint-James LE SOURIRE
Route de Grasse 06270 Villeneuve-Loubet
Tél : 00 33 4 93 20 96 11 - Fax : 00 33 4 93 22 07 52

Enjoy the pleasure of spending your holidays outdoors in our village-club where everything has been designed for your leisure and well-being. Everyone is catered for young and old alike; you can do everything or nothing. So come and discover your future holidays at Le Sourire. Choose your kingdom, we'll look after the rest.

www.camping-parcsaintjames.com

FR06180 Camping les Rives du Loup

Mobile homes ▶ page 509

2666b route de la Colle, Tourettes-sur-Loup, F-06140 Vence (Alpes-Maritimes)

Tel: **04 93 24 15 65.** Email: **info@rivesduloup.com**

When we arrived here in June, many of the residents were just about to tuck in to fish, chips and mushy peas at the site's restaurant. The English owners attract many long-stay British residents, but lately the location and the quiet, friendly atmosphere have increasingly attracted other nationalities. Les Rives du Loup is predominately a mobile home park but there are 14 pitches (out of a total of 116), which can accommodate touring units. Situated in the pass north of Colle-sur-Loup, the site is some 15 km. from the beaches and 6 km. west of Tourettes.

Facilities	Directions
Single sanitary block provides toilets, washbasins and showers. Facilities for disabled campers. Bar, restaurant and very small shop. Swimming pool. Play area. Activities for children (high season). Off site: Bar-sur-Loup, Antibes, Nice.	From Vence follow signs to Tourettes-sur-Loup and then onwards towards Bar-sur-Loup. Just before entering this village turn left down the D6, towards Colle-sur-Loup. Site is 2.6 km. on with a steep access down to reception.

Open: Easter - 30 September.

Charges 2007

Per unit incl. 2 persons	€ 14,50 - € 23,50
extra person	€ 4,50
child (5-18 yrs)	€ 3,50
electricity (5A)	€ 3,50

FR13040 Camping Monplaisir

Chemin de Monplaisir, F-13210 Saint Rémy-De-Provence (Bouches du Rhône)

Tel: **04 90 92 22 70**. Email: *reception@camping-monplaisir.fr*

Only a kilometre from the centre of St Rémy, in the foothills of the Alpilles mountains, this is one of the most pleasant and well run sites we have come across. Everything about the site is of a high standard and quality. The good impression created by the reception and shop continues through the rest of the site. In all there are 130 level grass pitches with 8 taken by smart mobile homes, with 6A electricity everywhere. Flowering shrubs and greenery abounds, roads are tarmac and all is neat and tidy. There are five toilet blocks strategically placed for all areas, two heated and one larger, but all unisex. The recreation area with a swimming pool (18 x 10 m.), jacuzzi and paddling pool is overlooked by the bar area. Open in July and August, it provides light meals and snacks and some entertainment. St Rémy is a very popular town and the site was full when we visited in mid June.

Facilities

Five good quality toilet blocks all have some washbasins in cabins. Family rooms and en-suite facilities for disabled people in two. Washing machines. Two motorcaravan service points. Shop with essentials (good cheese and cold meat counter), also providing takeaway pizzas (all season). Bar with snacks (July/Aug). Swimming pool (1/5-30/11). Play area. Table tennis. Boules. Off site: St Rémy 1 km. Les Baux 5 km. Bicycle hire 1 km. Riding 5 km. Fishing 2 km. Golf 10 km.

Open: 1 March - 3 November.

Directions

From St Rémy town centre follow signs for Arles and Nîmes. At roundabout on western side of town take D5 signed Maillane and immediately left by a supermarket. Site is signed and is on the left a little further on.

Charges 2007

Per unit incl. 2 persons	€ 13,00 - € 18,20
child (2-7 yrs)	€ 2,20 - € 4,20
electricity	€ 3,40
dog	€ 1,70

CAMPING MONPLAISIR

- Overflowing swimming and paddling pool
- Snack bar in high season, Laundry
- 130 pitches, 2.8 ha of comfort, quietness and garden area
- Boules, children's games, table tennis, grocery
- Chalets & mobile homes to let

CHEMIN MONPLAISIR - F-13210 ST. RÉMY DE PROVENCE - FRANCE
TEL : +33 (0)4 90 92 22 70 - FAX : +33 (0)4 90 92 18 57
www.camping-monplaisir.fr
reception@camping-monplaisir.fr

FR13010 Camping Municipal les Romarins

Route de Saint Remy, F-13520 Maussane (Bouches du Rhône)

Tel: **04 90 54 33 60**. Email: *camping_municipal_maussane@wanadoo.fr*

A well kept, neat municipal site, Les Romarins has been in the guide for several years and remains popular with our readers. Tarmac access roads lead to 145 good sized grassy pitches separated by hedges and bushes, all with electrical connections (4A). The municipal swimming pool (with discounts) is near and shops and restaurants are in the pleasant little town. Les Baux and St Remy-de-Provence are tourist attractions not to be missed, especially St Remy's Roman ruins. Les Romarins is popular and becomes very busy from 1 July - late August.

Facilities

Three toilet blocks, two refurbished, showers (on payment). Baby room, washing machine, laundry and facilities for disabled visitors. An older block open for July and August. Plans for refurbishment. Motorcaravan services. Municipal swimming pool (50 m. from site) free to campers 15/6-31/8. Play area. Free tennis. Reading room. Internet access. Off site: Bicycle hire or golf 1 km. Fishing or riding 3 km.

Open: 15 March - 15 October.

Directions

Site is within the little town of Maussane on the eastern edge.

Charges guide

Per unit incl. 1 or 2 persons plus 1 child	€ 16,00 - € 17,60
extra person	€ 3,70 - € 4,10
child	€ 2,10 - € 2,60
dog	€ 2,50
electricity	€ 3,20
Less 10-20% for longer stays.	

FR13030 **Camping le Nostradamus**

Route d'Eyguières, F-13300 Salon-de-Provence (Bouches du Rhône)

Tel: 04 90 56 08 36. Email: gilles.nostra@wanadoo.fr

Only some five kilometres from Salon-de-Provence, near the village of Eyguières, this is a very pleasant campsite with grassy, shaded pitches due to the many trees which have been preserved here as a result of the imaginative irrigation scheme developed by the owners in the 18th century. The campsite edging the canal was first opened 42 years ago as a farm site but has now been developed to offer 83 hedged pitches including 10 used for mobile homes. There are 20 with full services, the rest having electricity connections (4/6/10A). This is a family site but having said that the canal is unfenced. You can swim or fish in it or even paddle in the adjoining stream.

Facilities

One large block with showers and toilets upstairs, and one small toilet block both provide all modern facilities including an en-suite units for babies and children and another for disabled visitors (key). Washing machine (key). Motorcaravan service point. Shop (basic essentials) and bar (1/3-31/10) Takeaway/restaurant (limited in early season). Swimming and paddling pools (15/5-30/9). Play area outside entrance. Table tennis. Volleyball. Petanque. Fishing. Off site: Riding 5 km. Golf 12 km.

Open: 1 March - end October.

Directions

From A7 autoroute take exit 26 (Senas) and follow N538 south for 5 km. Then take D175 west and pick up the D17 going south to Salon. Site is at junction of the D17 and CD72 with the entrance off the CD72. From A54 exit 13 go north towards Eyguières and take first right on CD72 (site signed). Entrance is just before the T-junction with the D17. GPS: N43:40.380 E05:03.500

Charges 2007

| Per unit incl. 2 persons | € 12,90 - € 17,10 |
| electricity | € 2,95 - € 5,95 |

FR13050 **Camping Mas de Nicolas**

Avenue Plaisance du Touch, F-13210 Saint-Rémy-de-Provence (Bouches du Rhône)

Tel: 04 90 92 27 05. Email: camping-masdenicolas@nerim.fr

The site has a very spacious feel to it, due mainly to the central area of gently sloping grass, dotted with shrubs, that is kept clear of pitches and used for leisure and sunbathing. The 140 pitches are separated by hedges, 120 with electricity, water and drainage, and access roads are wide. Some pitches are an irregular shape and some are sloping, but many have views and they are mostly organised into groups of two and four. There is an attractive pool area with new 'Balneotherapie et Remise en form', or as we would call it a spa and gym.

Facilities

Good, modern toilet blocks including baby bathroom. Plans to refurbish one block. Dishwashing and laundry sinks, washing machines. Small bar (May-Sept), occasional Swimming pool (15/5-15/9). Sauna, steam room, spa bath, gym. Play area. Internet. Off site: Bicycle hire, riding 1 km. Fishing 2 km. Golf 15 km.

Open: 1 March - 31 October.

Directions

St Rémy de Provence is located where the D571 from Avignon connects with the D99 Tarascon - Cavaillon road. Site is signed from the village on the north side. Leave A7 at Cavaillon or Avignon-Sud.

Charges 2008

| Per unit incl. 2 persons and electricity | € 17,30 - € 22,50 |
| extra person | € 4,50 - € 6,30 |

FR13060 **Camping les Micocouliers**

445 route de Cassoulen, F-13690 Graveson-en-Provence (Bouches du Rhône)

Tel: 04 90 95 81 49. Email: micocou@free.fr

M. et Mme. Riehl started work at Les Micocouliers in 1997 and they have developed a comfortable site. On the outskirts of the town it is only 10 km. from St Rémy and Avignon. A purpose built, terracotta 'house' in a raised position provides all the facilities. The 65 pitches radiate out from here with the pool and entrance to one side. The pitches are on level grass, separated by small bushes, and shade is developing. Electricity connections are possible (4-13A). There are a few mobile homes.

Facilities

Unisex facilities in one unit provide toilets and facilities for disabled visitors (by key), another showers and washbasins in cabins and another dishwashing and laundry facilities. Reception and limited shop (July/Aug) are in another. Swimming pool (12 x 8 m; 5/5-15/9). Paddling pool (1/7-31/8). Play area. Table tennis. Volleyball. Off site: Fishing 5 Km. Bicycle hire 1 km. Riding next door. Golf 5 km. Beach 60 km. at Ste Marie de la Mer.

Open: 15 March - 15 October.

Directions

Site is southeast of Graveson. From the N570 at new roundabout take D5 towards St Rémy and Maillane and site is 500 m. on the left.

Charges 2007

Per unit incl. 2 persons	€ 13,70 - € 17,30
extra person	€ 4,50 - € 5,70
child (2-12 yrs)	€ 2,50 - € 4,50
electricity	€ 3,50 - € 6,30
Camping Cheques accepted.	

FR13120 Airotel Parc de Chantecler

41 ave du Val Saint André, F-13100 Aix-eneProvence (Bouches du Rhône)

Tel: **04 42 26 12 98**. Email: **info@campingchantecler.com**

Cézanne is amongst Aix's most famous former residents, but many just see the town as a stop on the journey south. This good, quiet campsite might change that image; on the southeast edge of the town, close to the motorway it is only minutes by the good bus service from the city centre. The site provides 240 pitches (160 for tourers) in mature woodland with good facilities. Under the new leadership of Serge Carcolse, the site is destined to change for the good whilst retaining the best that already exists. Cézanne's studio is amongst the numerous places to visit in Aix.

Facilities

Four sanitary blocks provide ample WCs, washbasins and hot showers around the site. Facilities for disabled campers. Motorcaravan service point. Bar and restaurant (1/7-30/8). Swimming pool (1/5-15/9). Tennis. Volleyball. Boules. Internet access and WiFi. Mobile homes to rent. Barbecues are not permitted. Off site: Bus service 200 m. Aix-en-Provence 2 km. Riding 2 km. Golf 5 km.

Open: All year.

Directions

Leave the A8 at exit 31 (Aix-Sud) and at roundabout turn right. At second set of lights turn left and within 300 m. at roundabout turn right to the site in 200 m. GPS: N43:30.989 E05:28.512

Charges 2007

Per person	€ 5,40 - € 5,80
child (under 7 yrs)	€ 3,40 - € 3,60
pitch	€ 6,10 - € 7,00
electricity (5A)	€ 3,40 - € 3,70

FR83010 Camping Caravaning les Pins Parasols

Route de Bagnols, F-83600 Fréjus (Var)

Tel: **04 94 40 88 43**. Email: **lespinsparasols@wanadoo.fr**

Not everyone likes very big sites and Les Pins Parasols with its 189 pitches is of a comfortable size which is quite easy to walk around. It is family owned and run. Although on very slightly undulating ground, virtually all the pitches (all have electricity) are levelled or terraced and separated by hedges or bushes with pine trees for shade. There are 48 pitches equipped with their own fully enclosed, sanitary unit, with WC, washbasin, hot shower and dishwashing sink. These pitches naturally cost more but may well be of interest to those seeking extra comfort. The nearest beach is the once very long Fréjus-Plage (5.5 km) now reduced a little by the new marina, and adjoins St Raphaël. Used by tour operators (10%).

Facilities

Average quality toilet blocks (one heated) providing facilities for disabled people. Small shop with reasonable stocks, restaurant, takeaway (both 15/4-30/9). General room, TV. Swimming pool, attractive rock backdrop, separate long slide with landing pool, small paddling pool (heated). Half-court tennis. Off site: Bicycle hire or riding 2 km. Fishing 6 km. Golf 10 km. Bus from the gate into Fréjus 5 km. Beach 6 km.

Open: 5 April - 27 September.

Directions

From A8 take exit 38 for Fréjus Est. Turn right immediately on leaving pay booths on a small road which leads across to D4, then right again and under 1 km. to site.

Charges 2007

Per unit incl. 2 persons and electricity	€ 17,40 - € 26,10
pitch with sanitary unit	€ 22,00 - € 32,50
extra person	€ 4,40 - € 6,10
child (under 7 yrs)	€ 2,90 - € 3,70
dog	€ 1,80 - € 2,70

Check real time availability and at-the-gate prices...

www.**alanrogers**.com

FR83020 Castel Camping Caravaning Esterel

Mobile homes ▶ page 509

Avenue des Golf, F-83530 Saint Raphaël – Agay (Var)

Tel: **04 94 82 03 28**. Email: **contact@esterel-caravaning.fr**

Esterel is a quality caravan site east of St Raphaël, set among the hills at the back of Agay. The site is 3.5 km. from the sandy beach at Agay where parking is perhaps a little easier than at most places on this coast. It has 230 pitches for tourists, for caravans but not tents, all have electricity and water tap, 18 special ones have their own en-suite washroom adjoining. Pitches are on shallow terraces, attractively landscaped with good shade and a variety of flowers, giving a feeling of spaciousness. Some 'maxi-pitches' from 110-160 sq.m. are available with 10A electricity. Developed by the Laroche family for over 30 years, the site has an attractive, quiet situation with good views of the Esterel mountains. A member of 'Les Castels' group. Wild boar occasionally come to the perimeter fence to be fed by visitors. This is a very good site, well run and organised in a deservedly popular area. A pleasant courtyard area contains the shop and bar, with a terrace overlooking the attractively landscaped (floodlit at night) pool complex.

Facilities

Excellent refurbished, heated toilet blocks. Individual toilet units on18 pitches. Facilities for disabled people. Laundry room. Motorcaravan services. Shop. Gift shop. Takeaway. Bar/restaurant. Five circular swimming pools (two heated), one for adults, one for children, three arranged as a waterfall (1/4-30/9). Disco. Archery. Minigolf. Tennis. Pony rides. Petanque. Squash. Playground. Nursery. Bicycle hire. Internet access. Organised events in season. No barbecues. Off site: Golf nearby. Trekking by foot, bicycle or by pony in L'Esterel forest park. Fishing, beach 3 km.

Open: 1 April - 6 October.

Directions

From A8, exit Fréjus, follow signs for Valescure, then for Agay, site on left. The road from Agay is the easiest to follow but it is possible to approach from St Raphaël via Valescure.
GPS: N43:27.253 E06:49.945

Charges 2007

Per unit incl. 2 persons,	
standard pitch	€ 23,00 - € 38,00
'maxi' pitch	€ 28,00 - € 47,00
deluxe pitch	€ 32,00 - € 51,00
extra person	€ 8,50
child (1-7 yrs)	€ 6,50

FR83040 Camping Club la Bastiane

1056 chemin de Suvières, F-83480 Puget-sur-Argens (Var)

Tel: **04 94 55 55 94**. Email: **info@labastiane.com**

With a shady woodland setting, La Bastiane is a well established site with good amenities, well located for exploring the Cote d'Azur and with easy access to nearby beaches. There are 180 pitches here of which 100 are reserved for touring. They are generally of a good size and are all supplied with electrical connections (6A). The terrain is somewhat undulating but most of the pitches are on level terraces. There is a good swimming pool and a range of amenities including a shop, bar and restaurant. The site becomes lively in peak season with many activities including sports tournaments, discos, a children's club and excursions to nearby places of interest such as Monaco and the Gorges de Verdon.

Facilities

Four toilet blocks, three of modern construction, one refurbished. Facilities for disabled visitors. Washing machines, dryers. Shop. Bar. Takeaway. Restaurant. Heated swimming pool. Tennis. Multisport terrain. Children's club. Play area. Games/TV room. Bicycle hire. Evening entertainment in peak season. Excursion programme. Only electric barbecues. One dog only. Mobile homes and chalets for rent. Off site: Beach 7 km. Lake beach 8 km. Riding 500 m. Fishing 3 km. Golf 9 km.

Open: 24 March - 21 October.

Directions

Leave A8 at exit 37 (Puget), take right turn at first roundabout (signed Roquebrune), join N7. Turn right, first traffic lights (200 m), then left at T-junction. Site signed from here, on the right 2.5 km. from the motorway.

Charges 2008

Per unit incl. 2 persons,	
electricity	€ 15,34 - € 37,34
extra person	€ 3,30 - € 7,17
child (3-13 yrs)	€ 2,20 - € 4,50
pet (max. 1)	€ 1,90 - € 4,00

FR83050 Camping Résidence du Campeur

D7 (B.P. 12), F-83371 Saint Aygulf (Var)

Tel: **04 94 81 01 59**. Email: **info@residence-campeur.com**

This excellent site near the Côte d'Azur will take you away from all the bustle of the Mediterranean coast. Spread out over ten hectares, there are separate areas for mobile homes and touring caravans and tents, with pitches arranged along avenues. The touring pitches average 100 sq.m. in size and all have electricity connections and private sanitary facilities. Unfortunately washbasins double as dishwashing sinks. The bar/restaurant is surrounded by a shady terrace, whilst friendly staff provide an excellent service. A pleasant pool complex is available for those who wish to stay on site instead of going swimming in the nearby lake or from the Mediterranean beaches. Activities are organised daily during the summer season and the site has it's own open air cinema.

Facilities

Private toilet blocks are cleaned at regular intervals and include a washbasin, shower and WC. Laundry area with washing machines. Well stocked supermarket. Bar/restaurant. Takeaway. Good pool complex (1/4-30/9). Three tennis courts. Minigolf. Volleyball. Only gas or electric barbecues are permitted. Off site: Riding, golf and bicycle hire nearby. Beach and St Aygulf 2.5 km. Water skiing nearby.

Open: 1 April - 30 September.

Directions

Leave A8 at Le Muy exit (no. 36) on N555 towards Draguignan then onto the N7 towards Fréjus. Turn right on D7 signed St Aygulf and site is on the right about 2.5 km. before the town.

Charges 2007

Per unit	€ 27,48 - € 45,80

Camping - Club ★★★★
RESIDENCE DU CAMPEUR

At 2,5 km from sandy beaches, discover this charming site offering plenty of shade. Excellent facilities for your comfort: supermarket, bar, restaurant, cinema (open air), disco, games room, mini golf, multi sport field, pétanque, archery. Animation and Mickey club in July and August.

B.P 12 Les grands châteaux de Villepey
83371 Saint-Aygulf cedex
Tél : 00 33 (0)4.94.81.01.59
Fax : 00 33 (0)4.94.81.01.64
www.residence-campeur.com
Email : info@residence-campeur.com

Heated swimming pool

Open from 22 March till 30 September

Provence Côte d'Azur

**Mobile homes for rent
PRIVATE SANITARY BLOCK**

FR83080 Au Paradis des Campeurs

La Gaillarde-Plage, F-83380 Les Issambres (Var)

Tel: **04 94 96 93 55**

Family owned and run, it now has 180 pitches, all with 6A electricity and 132 with water tap and drain. The original pitches vary in size and shape but all are satisfactory and most have some shade. The newer pitches are all large but at present have little shade although trees and bushes have been planted and shade is developing. There is no entertainment which gives peaceful nights. The gates are surveyed by TV (especially the beach gate) and a security man patrols all day. The site has become popular, it is essential to book for June, July and August. Having direct access to a sandy beach (via an underpass) and being so well maintained are just two of the reasons which make Au Paradis so popular.

Facilities

Excellent, refurbished, well maintained toilet blocks, facilities for babies, children, shower at suitable height. En-suite for disabled visitors. Washing machines, dryer. Motorcaravan services. Shop, restaurant, takeaway service, open all season. TV room. Internet and WiFi. Excellent play areas, catering for the under and over 5s, top quality safety bases. Boules. Car wash area. Off site: Bicycle hire 2.5 km. Riding 3 km. Golf 6 km.

Open: 28 March - 16 October.

Directions

Site is signed from N98 coast road at La Gaillarde, 2 km. south of St Aygulf. GPS: N43:21.956 E06:42.738

Charges 2007

Per unit incl. 2 persons	€ 14,00 - € 22,00
with water and drainage	€ 16,00 - € 26,00
extra person	€ 6,00
child (under 4 yrs)	€ 3,00
electricity (6A)	€ 3,50

FR83030 Camping Caravaning Leï Suves

Mobile homes ▶ page 510

Quartier du Blavet, F-83520 Roquebrune-sur-Argens (Var)

Tel: 04 94 45 43 95. Email: camping.lei.suves@wanadoo.fr

This quiet, pretty site is a few kilometres inland from the coast, 2 km. north of the N7. Close to the unusual Roquebrune rock, it is within easy reach of St Tropez, Ste Maxime, St Raphaël and Cannes. The site entrance is appealing -; wide and spacious, with a large bank of well tended flowers. Mainly on a gently sloping hillside, the 310 pitches are terraced with shade provided by the many cork trees which give the site its name. All pitches have electricity and access to water. A pleasant pool area is beside the bar/restaurant and entertainment area. It is possible to walk in the surrounding woods as long as there is no fire alert. A good number of the pitches are used for mobile homes.

Facilities

Modern, well kept toilet blocks include washing machines, facilities for disabled visitors. Shop. Good sized swimming pool, paddling pool. Bar, terrace, snack bar, takeaway (all 1/4-30/9). Outdoor stage near the bar for evening entertainment, high season. Excellent play area. Table tennis, tennis, sports area. Internet terminal. Only gas barbecues. Off site: Bus stop at site entrance. Riding 1 km. Fishing 3 km. Bicycle hire 5 km. Golf 7 km. Beach at St Aygulf 15 km.

Open: 1 April - 15 October.

Directions

Leave autoroute at Le Muy and take N7 towards St Raphaël. Turn left at roundabout onto D7 heading north signed La Boverie (site also signed). Site on right in 2 km. GPS: N43:28.677 E06:38.324

Charges 2008

Per unit incl. 2 persons	€ 19,00 - € 34,50
incl. 3 persons	€ 21,00 - € 37,00
extra person	€ 4,50 - € 7,50
electricity	€ 4,50

Leï Suves is beautifully located at the Cote d'Azur close to Saint-Tropez Sainte Maxime, Saint-Raphaël and Cannes.

Camping Caravaning ★★★★
Leï Suves
Quartier du Blavet
83520
Roquebrune sur Argens
Tél : (0033) 4 94 45 43 95
Fax : (0033) 4 94 81 63 13

www.camping-lei-suves.com

Roquebrune sur Argens Provence

Check real time availability and at-the-gate prices...

www.alanrogers.com

FR83060 Camping Resort la Baume – la Palmeraie

Mobile homes ▶ page 510

Route de Bagnols, F-83618 Fréjus (Var)

Tel: **04 94 19 88 88**. Email: **reception@labaume-lapalmeraie.com**

La Baume is large, busy site about 5.5 km. from the long sandy beach of Fréjus-Plage, although with its fine and varied selection of swimming pools many people do not bother to make the trip. The pools with their palm trees are remarkable for their size and variety (water slides, etc.) – the very large 'feature' pool a highlight. Recent additions are an aquatic play area and two indoor pools with a slide and a spa area. The site has nearly 250 adequately sized, fully serviced pitches, with some separators and most have shade. Although tents are accepted, the site concentrates mainly on caravanning. It becomes full in season. Adjoining La Baume is its sister site La Palmeraie, providing self-catering accommodation, its own landscaped pool and offering some entertainment to supplement that at La Baume. There are 500 large pitches with mains sewerage for mobile homes. La Baume's convenient location has its 'downside' as there is some traffic noise on a few pitches from the nearby autoroute – somewhat obtrusive at first but we soon failed to notice it. It is a popular site with tour operators.

Facilities

Seven refurbished toilet blocks. Supermarket, several shops. Two bars, terrace overlooking pools, TV. Restaurant, takeaway. Six swimming pools (heated all season, two covered, plus steam room and jacuzzi). Fitness centre. Tennis. Archery (July/Aug). Organised events, daytime and evening entertainment, some English. Amphitheatre. Skateboard park. Discos all season. Children's club (all season). Off site: Bus to Fréjus passes gate. Riding 2 km. Fishing 3 km. Golf 5 km. Beach 5 km.

Open: 1 April - 30 September, with full services.

Directions

From west, A8, exit Fréjus, take N7 southwest (Fréjus). After 4 km, turn left on D4 and site is 3 km. From east, A8, exit 38 Fréjus and follow signs for Cais. Site is signed. GPS: N43:27.599 E06:43.229

Charges 2007

Per unit incl. 2 persons, 6A electricity, water and drainage	€ 18,00 - € 39,00
extra person	€ 4,00 - € 10,00
child (under 7 yrs)	free - € 6,00
dog	€ 4,00 - € 5,00
car	€ 4,00 - € 5,00

Min. stay for motorhomes 3 nights. Large units should book.

FR83100 Camping de la Plage

RN98, F-83310 Grimaud (Var)

Tel: **04 94 56 31 15**. Email: **campingplagegrimaud@wanadoo.fr**

A site on the beach is always in great demand, and Camping de la Plage is no exception, consequently it becomes very crowded. The site is divided into two parts by the N98 although a dangerous crossing is avoided by an underpass. The pitches away from the beach will be the more peaceful. They are mostly of a good size, with the ones over the road having more grass and more shade. There is some traffic noise on the pitches close to the busy road. All pitches have electricity (2-10A) but long leads may be required. Ste Maxime is 6 km. and it is not very far to all the familiar names of the south of France – St Tropez, Port Grimaud, Fréjus and St Aygulf.

Facilities

Three toilet blocks of varying quality but well equipped and clean. Baby bath. Large supermarket (all season). Bar, restaurant, takeaway (from May). Tennis. Small play area. Off site: Bicycle hire 2 km. Golf and riding 3 km. Boat hire nearby.

Open: Two weeks before Easter - 6 October.

Directions

Site is on N98 main coast road about 6 km. southwest of Ste Maxime. Take care – this road is very busy in main season. GPS: N43:16.913 E06:35.159

Charges 2007

Per unit with 2 persons	€ 22,00 - € 27,00
extra person	€ 5,80 - € 6,80
child (under 7 yrs)	€ 2,90 - € 3,40
electricity (2-10A)	€ 4,00 - € 8,50
animal	€ 1,80

Check real time availability and at-the-gate prices...

 www.**alanrogers**.com

La Baume ★★★★
Camping - Caravaning

La Palmeraie ★★
Résidence de Tourisme

Fréjus Côte d'Azur

ed sanitary blocks, marked-out
es, 6 swimming pools, covered
ed swimming pool, 6 water-slides.
ometers from the sandy beaches of
s and Saint Raphaël.

On going entertainment
Cabaret, Show, Disco,
Children's club during the season

Le Sud Grandeur Nature

Heated swimming pool

covered
heated
mming-pool

Provençal chalet,
mobil-homes 4/6 persons
and appartments 6 of 10 persons for hire

al rates in low season

FR83090 **RCN Domaine de la Noguière**

Route de Fréjus, F-83490 Le Muy (Var)

Tel: **04 94 45 13 78**. Email: **info@rcn-domainedelanoguiere.fr**

A Dutch company, RCN runs a chain of good campsites in the Netherlands. They now operate five sites in France, all with Dutch managers who speak good French and English. Les Domaine de la Noguière is located amongst beautiful Provençal scenery with lavender fields, yellow mimosa trees and reddish brown rocks. The Mediterranean beaches at the famous resorts of Fréjus and St Raphaël are only 16 km. There are 200 pitches all with 6A electricity, arranged on small terraces on the slightly sloping ground. At the entrance to the site there is a reception area, a shop and a restaurant serving regional specialities.

Facilities	Directions
Toilets are fully tiled with individual cabins and access for disabled visitors. Washing machines, dryers and ironing area. Bar/restaurant with terrace. Small meeting room with library, snooker table, table football and large TV. Swimming pool with large slides. Tennis. Boules. Football and volleyball pitches.	From the A8, take exit 37 toward Roquebrune sur Argens and Puget sur Argens (this is the second exit towards Roquebrune, drive past exit 36). At roundabout, take first right toward Roquebrune and Le Muy (N7). Continue for 8 km. to site on the right.

Open: 24 March - 3 November.

Charges 2008

Per unit incl. 2 persons, electricity and water € 18,00 - € 45,50
Camping Cheques accepted.

FR83110 **Camping de la Baie**

Boulevard Pasteur, B.P. 12, F-83240 Cavalaire-sur-Mer (Var)

Tel: **04 94 64 08 15**. Email: **campbaie@club-internet.com**

This busy site is only a short walk from the main street of the popular holiday resort of Cavalaire with it's harbour, restaurants and shops. A long, sandy beach runs right round the bay and there are plenty of watersport activities nearby. The site is only 400 metres from the beach, very well positioned for a family holiday. The 253 individual touring pitches are on slightly sloping, sandy ground with terracing and good access roads, and all have electricity hook-ups (10A). Trees give plenty of shade. The remaining 190 pitches are used for mobile homes and chalets. English is spoken.

Facilities	Directions
Four main modern toilet blocks include washbasins in cabins, and four smaller units have open washbasins behind. Toilets are mainly British style, with some Turkish. Launderette. Small shop. Restaurant. Bar. Takeaway. Entertainment with dance evenings. Kidney-shaped pool (Easter - end Nov)l and new jacuzzi. Playground. Off site: Bicycle hire 200 m. Beach 400 m. Golf 10 km.	Take D559 to Cavalaire-sur-Mer (not Cavalière, some 4 km. away). Site is signed by yellow signs from the main street, some 400 m. north of the harbour. GPS: N43:10.176 E06:31.816

Open: 15 March - 15 November.

Charges 2007

Per unit incl. 1-3 persons	€ 22,00 - € 41,80
extra person	€ 6,00 - € 10,70
electricity	€ 4,90

FR83120 **Camp du Domaine**

La Favière B.P. 207, F-83230 Bormes-les-Mimosas (Var)

Tel: **04 94 71 03 12**. Email: **mail@campdudomaine.com**

Camp du Domaine, three kilometres south of Le Lavandou, is a large, attractive beach-side site with 1,200 pitches set in 45 hectares of pine woods, although surprisingly it does not give the impression of being so big. Most pitches are reasonably level and 800 have 10A electricity. The most popular pitches are at the beach, but the ones furthest away are, on the whole, larger and have more shade amongst the trees, although many of them are more suitable for tents. The beach is the attraction however and everyone tries to get close. American motorhomes not accepted.

Facilities	Directions
Ten modern, well used but clean toilet blocks. Mostly Turkish WCs. Facilities for disabled visitors (but steep steps). Children and baby room. Washing machines. Fridges to hire. Well stocked supermarket, bars, pizzeria (all open all season). Excellent play area. Boats, pedaloes for hire. Watersports. Games, competitions July/Aug. Children's club. Tennis. Multisports courts. Barbecues are strictly forbidden. Dogs are not accepted 3/7-31/8. Off site: Bicycle hire 500 m. Riding or golf 15 km.	Just outside and to west of Le Lavandou, at roundabout, turn off D559 towards the sea on road signed Favière. After some 2 km. turn left at site signs. GPS: N43:07.080 E06:21.076

Open: 15 March - 31 October.

Charges 2007

Per unit incl. 2 persons	€ 18,00 - € 29,00
with electricity and water	€ 26,00 - € 35,50
extra person	€ 5,40 - € 7,50
child (under 7 yrs)	€ 1,00 - € 3,80

FR83170 Camping Domaine de la Bergerie

Mobile homes ▶ page 510

Vallée du Fournel, route du Col du Bougnon, F-83520 Roquebrune-sur-Argens (Var)
Tel: 04 98 11 45 45. Email: info@domainelabergerie.com

This excellent site near the Côte d'Azur will take you away from all the bustle of the Mediterranean to total relaxation amongst the cork, oak, pine and mimosa in its woodland setting. The 60 hectare site is quite spread out with semi-landscaped areas for mobile homes and, grassy avenues of 200 separated pitches for touring caravans and tents. All pitches average over 80 sq.m. and have electricity, with those in one area also having water and drainage. The restaurant/bar, a converted farm building, is surrounded by shady patios, whilst inside it oozes character with high beams and archways leading to intimate corners. Activities are organised daily and, in the evening, shows, cabarets, discos, cinema, karaoke and dancing at the amphitheatre prove popular (possibly until midnight). A superb new pool complex supplements the original pool adding more outdoor pools with slides and a river feature, an indoor pool and a fitness centre with jacuzzi, sauna, turkish bath, massage, reflexology and gym.

Facilities

Four toilet blocks (all refurbished in 2007) are kept clean and include washbasins in cubicles, facilities for disabled people and babies. Supermarket. Bar/restaurant. Takeaway. Pool complex (5/4-30/9) with indoor pool and fitness centre (body building, sauna, gym, etc). Tennis courts. Archery. Roller skating. Minigolf. English speaking childrens club. Mini-farm for children. Fishing. Only gas barbecues are permitted. Off site: Riding or golf 2 km. Bicycle hire 7 km. Beach, St Aygulf or Ste Maxime 7 km. Water skiing and rock climbing nearby.

Open: 25 April - 30 September.
Mobile homes 15 February - 15 November.

Directions

Leave A8 at Le Muy exit on N7 towards Fréjus. Go on for 9 km. then right onto D7 signed St Aygulf. Continue for 8 km. and then right at roundabout on D8; site is on the right. GPS: N43:24.547 E06:40.481

Charges 2008

Per unit incl. 2 persons and electricity (6A)	€ 18,50 - € 40,00
2 persons and electricity, water and drainage	€ 24,00 - € 45,00
extra person	€ 5,00 - € 9,00
child (under 7 yrs)	€ 3,60 - € 6,50
electricity (10A)	€ 2,00 - € 3,00

FR83070 Caravaning l"Etoile d'Argens

F-83370 Saint Aygulf (Var)

Tel: **04 94 81 01 41**. Email: **info@etoiledargens.com**

First impressions of L'Etoile d'Argens are of space, cleanliness and calm. This is a site run with families in mind and many of the activities are free, making for a good value holiday. There are 493 level, fully serviced, grass pitches (265 for touring units – 10A electricity), separated by hedges, with five sizes, ranging from 50 sq.m. (for small tents) to 250 sq.m. mainly with good shade. The pool and bar area is attractively landscaped with olive and palm trees on beautifully kept grass. Two heated pools (one for adults, one for children) – both very much with families in mind. Reception staff are very friendly and English is spoken. The exceptionally large pitches could easily take two caravans and cars or one family could have a very spacious plot with a garden like atmosphere. The river runs alongside the site with a free boat service to the beach (15/6-15/9). This is a good family site for the summer but also good in low season for a quiet stay in a superb location with excellent pitches. Tour operators take 85 pitches and there are 175 mobile homes but for a large site it is unusually calm and peaceful even in July.

Facilities	Directions
Over 20, well kept, small toilet blocks. Supermarket and gas supplies. Bar, restaurant, pizzeria, takeaway. Two adult pools (heated 1/4-20/6), paddling pool, jacuzzi, solarium. Floodlit tennis with coaching. Minigolf (both free in low season). Aerobics. Archery (July/Aug). Football and swimming lessons. Boules. Good play area. Children's entertainment (July/Aug). Activity programme with games, dances and escorted walking trips to the surrounding hills within 3 km. Off site: Golf and riding 2 km. Beach 3.5 km.	From A8 exit 36, take N7, Le Muy, Fréjus. After 8 km. at roundabout take D7 signed Roquebrune, St Aygulf. In 9.5 km. (after roundabout) turn left signed Fréjus. Site signed. Ignore width and height limit signs as site is before limit (500 m). GPS: N43:24.947 E06:42.326

Open: 1 April - 30 September, with all services.

Charges 2007

Per tent pitch (100 sq.m.) with electricity and 2 persons	€ 20,00 - € 46,00
comfort pitch (130 sq.m.) incl. 3 persons with water and drainage	€ 32,00 - € 58,00
luxury pitch incl. 4 persons 180 sq.m	€ 38,00 - € 68,00
extra person	€ 5,00 - € 8,50
child (under 7 yrs)	€ 4,00 - € 6,50

FR83130 Flower Camping le Beau Vezé

Route de la Moutonne, F-83320 Carqueiranne (Var)

Tel: **04 94 57 65 30**. Email: **info@camping-beauveze.com**

Le Beau Vezé is a quiet site, some way inland from the busy resort of Hyères. The owner tries to keep it as a family site with its quiet position, although the superb beaches and hectic coastal areas are within easy reach. On a steep hillside it has terraced pitches and a plateau with more pitches on the top. The 150 pitches are well shaded but unfortunately some will be rather difficult to manoeuvre onto due to over-hanging trees and could be difficult for motorcaravans. There is some road noise on the lower pitches.

Facilities	Directions
Reasonable standard sanitary blocks two heated, although maintenance may be variable. Some showers with washbasin. Baby room. Washing machines. Bar/restaurant, takeaway. Bread. Medium sized pool, paddling pool. Play area. Minigolf, table tennis, volleyball, boules, tennis. Bicycle hire. Jetski hire. Walking tours, visits to vineyard. Evening entertainment in restaurant. Off site: Fishing 3km. Bicycle hire 0.5km. Riding 2 km. The lovely old town of Hyères is only 8 km.	From A57 take exit for Toulon Est and follow D559 between Carqueiranne and Le Pradet. Take D76 northwards signed La Moutonne and site is signed on right of D76.

Open: 15 May - 15 September.

Charges 2007

Per unit incl. 2 persons	€ 27,00
extra person	€ 5,50 - € 6,30
child (under 10 yrs)	€ 3,50 - € 4,60
electricity (6A)	€ 4,00
animal	€ 2,50

No credit cards.

2008

L'Etoile d'Argens

✵ ✵ ✵ ✵ *Camping-Caravaning*

ESE COMMUNICATION - DRAGUIGNAN - 04 94 67 06 00

www.etoiledargens.com

E-mail : info@etoiledargens.com

83370 St Aygulf - Tél. +33 4 94 81 01 41

FR83140 Camping les Lacs du Verdon

Domaine de Roquelande, F-83630 Régusse (Var)

Tel: **04 94 70 17 95**. Email: **info@lacs-verdon.com**

In beautiful countryside and within easy reach of the Grand Canyon du Verdon and its nearby lakes, this site is only 90 minutes from Cannes. This bustling and possible noisy campsite is suitable for active families and teenagers. The 30 acre wooded park is divided in two by a minor road. The 480 very stony, but level pitches (rock pegs advised) are marked and separated by stones and trees. 130 pitches are for tourists, many an irregular shape, but all are of average size with 10A electricity (long leads may be necessary).

Facilities

Modernised toilet blocks have mainly have British style WCs and some washbasins in cubicles. Laundry and dishwashing facilities. Motorcaravan service point. Shop. Bar. Restaurant and pizzeria. TV and teenage games. Discos, dances and theme nights. Excellent swimming pool/paddling pool complex. Artificial grass tennis courts. Volleyball. Bicycle hire. Playground. Entertainment programme. Only electric barbecues are permitted. Off site: Régusse 2.5 km. Aups 7 km. Riding 10 km. Fishing, beach, sailing and windsurfing at Saint Croix 15 km.

Open: 29 April - 23 September.

Directions

Leave A8 motorway at St Maximin and take the D560 northeast (Barjols). At Barjols turn left on the D71 (Montmeyan), turn right on D30 (Régusse) and follow site signs. GPS: N43:39.612 E06:09.064

Charges guide

Per pitch incl. 1 or 2 persons	€ 18,00 - € 27,00
extra person	€ 5,00 - € 7,50
child (3-7 yrs)	€ 4,00 - € 6,00
electricity (10A)	€ 4,00
dog	€ 3,00

FR83160 Parc Camping les Cigales

721 chemin du Jas de la Paro, F-83490 Le Muy (Var)

Tel: **04 94 45 12 08**. Email: **contact@les-cigales.com**

Parc Les Cigales is a pleasant site benefiting from the shady environment of cork umbrella pines, further enhanced by olives, palm trees and colourful shrubs. The terrain is typical of the area with rough, sloped and stony, dry ground but the pitches are of a good size, terraced where necessary and nestling amongst the trees. There are 163 pitches in total with 35 mobile homes to rent. The restaurant/bar area overlooks the attractive pool complex including a children's pool with sloping beach effect. Convenient for the autoroute, this is a spacious family site away from the coast.

Facilities

Modern sanitary blocks of varying size, facilities for disabled people. Laundry area, washing machines, ironing boards. Shop (1/5-30/8). Restaurant/bar, patio. Heated pool complex. Adventure play area. Survival courses. Riding. Canoeing. Evening entertainment in season, disco twice weekly, daytime activities for children and senior citizens. Internet. No charcoal barbecues. Off site: Le Muy 2 km. Sunday market. Fishing 2 km. Golf 10 km.

Open: 1 April - 31 October.

Directions

From A8, Le Muy exit, site is signed (west of Le Muy on N7, 2 km). It is necessary to cross the dual-carriageway as you approach the toll booth from Le Muy. Site entrance is well signed. GPS: N43:27.492 E06:32.728

Charges 2008

Per unit incl. 2 persons	€ 12,00 - € 29,50
extra person	€ 3,00 - € 8,50
electricity (6-10A)	€ 3,00 - € 5,00

FR83380 Camping des Prairies de la Mer

RN 98 Quartier Saint Pons, les Mûres, F-83310 Grimaud (Var)

Tel: **04 94 79 09 09**. Email: **prairies@riviera-villages.com**

This busy site is in the pleasant and popular holiday resort of Port Grimaud where there is a luxurious harbour, restaurants and shops. A long, sandy beach runs right round the bay. The site is right on the beach and is very well equipped for a family holiday. In fact, it is a complete holiday resort, even including its own amusement park for children. There are 500 individual touring pitches on flat, sandy ground, all with electricity. A further 900 pitches are used for mobile homes and chalets. Trees have grown well to give plenty of shade and but there is no swimming pool.

Facilities

Nine modern toilet blocks with three near the touring pitches include washbasins in cabins. Toilets are all British style, Launderette. Large shopping complex. Bar. Italian style restaurant (all season). Takeaway. Entertainment programme. Play area. Sports ground. TV room. Bicycle hire. Sailing and diving schools. Miniclub. ATM. Excursions. Beach. Off site: Golf 3 km. Riding 2 km.

Open: 1 April - 8 October.

Directions

From the A8 (Aix-en-Provence - Cannes) exit 36 (Le Muy) take the D25 to St Maxime, then the coast road N98 towards St Tropez. Site is 6 km. on the left. GPS: N43:16.628 E06:34.910

Charges 2007

Per unit incl. 2 persons	€ 18,00 - € 42,00
extra person	€ 3,00 - € 7,00
electricity	free - € 5,00

FR83190 Camping la Presqu'île de Giens

Mobile homes ▶ page 511

153 route de la Madraque-Giens, F-83400 Hyères (Var)

Tel: **04 94 58 22 86**. Email: **info@camping-giens.com**

La Presqu'île de Giens a good family campsite at the southern end of the Giens peninsula. The site is well maintained and extends over 17 acres of undulating terrain. Of the site's 460 pitches, 170 are reserved for touring. These are generally of a good size and well shaded -; there is a separate area of smaller pitches reserved for tents. Electrical connections (16A) are available on all pitches. In high season this becomes a lively site with a well-run children's club (small charge) and an evening entertainment programme including discos, singers and dancers. Although there is no swimming pool, the site lies between two sandy beaches, and in July and August a free shuttle bus runs to the nearest, 800 metres away. Excursions are organised to the adjacent islands of Porquerolles, Port Cros and Le Levant. There is a beautiful walking trail set out all around the peninsula.

Facilities

Five toilet blocks, three very good new ones (heated in low season), and two refurbished with a higher proportion of 'Turkish' style toilets. All clean and well maintained. Facilities for disabled visitors. Washing machines and dryers. Shop. Bar, restaurant, takeaway food. Play area. Children's club. Evening entertainment. Sports pitch. Diving classes. Sports tournaments. Excursion programme. Only electric barbecues are permitted. Off site: Beach 800 m. Fishing 1 km. Bicycle hire 3 km. Riding 10 km. Golf 15 km. 'Golden islands' excursions.

Open: 22 March - 5 October.

Directions

From the west, leave A57 at Hyères and continue to Hyères on the A570. At Hyères follow signs to Giens - Les Iles (D97). At end of this road, after 11 km. turn right towards Madraque. Site on left side of road. GPS: N43:02.458 E06:08.583

Charges 2008

Per unit incl. 2 persons	€ 13,50 - € 20,90
extra person	€ 4,10 - € 6,60
child (0-5 yrs)	free
electricity	€ 4,90 - € 5,70
pet	€ 2,80

Camping Cheques accepted.

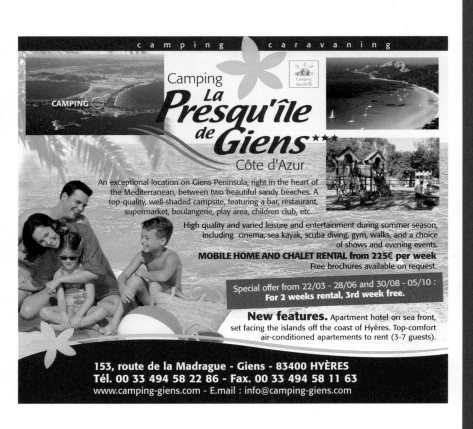

FR83210 Yelloh! Village les Tournels

Route de Camarat, F-83350 Ramatuelle (Var)

Tel: **04 66 73 97 39**. Email: **info@yellohvillage-les-tournels.com**

Les Tournels is a large site set on a hillside and pitches have panoramic views of the Gulf of St Tropez and Pampelonne beach. The hillside is covered in parasol pines and old olive trees. The pitches are reasonably level, shady, variable size, most with electricity (long leads). The swimming pool, play area, shop and bar maybe some distance away. Recent additions include a superb new spa centre with gym, sauna and jacuzzi, with an excellent pool alongside, all reserved for over 18s.

Facilities

Well equipped toilet blocks, some heated, baby baths, children's WCs, facilities for disabled visitors. Washing, drying machines, refrigerators to rent. Bar/restaurant (1/4-15/10). Takeaway. Bar, disco well away from most pitches. Restaurant. Large heated swimming pool (1/4-20/10). Fitness centre and pool. Good quality play area. Boules. Archery. Mini-club for children over 5 years. Safety deposit boxes. Only gas barbecues. Off site: Shopping centre 500 m, shuttle bus service. Golf 6 km. Beach 1.5 km.

Open: 13 March - 7 January.

Directions

From A8 exit 36 take D25 to Ste Maxime, then D98 towards St Tropez. On outskirts of St Tropez, take D93 to Ramatuelle. Site is signed on left in 9 km. GPS: N43:12.315 E06:39.043

Charges 2007

Per unit incl. 2 persons with	
electricity and water	€ 17,00 - € 40,00
extra person	€ 6,00 - € 8,00
child (2-7 yrs)	free - € 4,00
animal	€ 3,00 - € 4,00

FR83230 Kawan Village du Colombier

Route de Bagnols-en-Forêt, 1052 rue des Combattants d'AFN, F-83600 Fréjus (Var)

Tel: **04 94 51 56 01**. Email: **info@domaine-du-colombier.com**

Domaine du Colombier is located between Cannes and St Tropez, 2 km. from the centre of Fréjus and 4 km. from the sandy beaches of Fréjus Saint-Raphaël. There are 70 touring pitches, ranging in size from 80-150 sq.m. and all with 16A electricity. In recent years there has been much investment in high quality facilities. An attractive pool complex includes a heated pool (600 sq.m), a large paddling pool, water slides and jacuzzis and is surrounded by sun loungers, a fitness area and a restaurant. Plenty of activities and excursions are arranged all season, the site caters principally for families.

Facilities

Three well maintained, fully equipped toilet blocks (two heated and with baby rooms). Facilities for disabled visitors. Laundry. Well stocked shop. Bar/restaurant, takeaway. Soundproofed nightclub. Large heated swimming pool with paddling pool, slides and jacuzzis (all season). Fitness facilities. Internet access and WiFi. Three play areas and four sports areas. Fridge, safe and barbecue hire. Off site: Bus stop 50 m.

Open: 31 March - 15 October.

Directions

From A8 exit 37, follow signs for Fréjus, turning left at second lights (D4) and site is 1 km. on the right. From A8 exit 38 east (Nice) straight on at three roundabouts, then right at fourth and fifth. Site is 300 m. on right. GPS: N43:26.750 E06:43.636

Charges 2007

Per unit incl. up to 3 persons	€ 26,00 - € 30,00
extra person	€ 5,00 - € 8,00

Camping Cheques accepted.

FR83240 Camping Caravaning Moulin des Iscles

Quartier La Valette, F-83520 Roquebrune-sur-Argens (Var)

Tel: **04 94 45 70 74**. Email: **moulin.iscles@wanadoo.fr**

Moulin des Iscles is a small, pretty site beside the river Argens with access to the river in places for fishing, canoeing and swimming with some sought after pitches overlooking the river. The 90 grassy, level pitches have water and electricity (6A), A nice mixture of deciduous trees provides natural shade and colour and the old mill house is near the entrance, which has the security barrier closed at night. This is a quiet site with little on site entertainment, but with a pleasant restaurant.

Facilities

Fully equipped toilet block, plus small block near entrance, ramped access for disabled visitors. Some Turkish style toilets. Washbasins have cold water. Baby bath and changing facilities. Washing machine. Restaurant, home cooked dish-of-the-day. Well stocked shop. Library - some English books. TV, pool table, table tennis. Play area, minigolf, boules all outside the barrier. Internet terminal. Canoeing possible. Off site: Riding and golf 4 km. Bicycle hire 1 km. (cycle way to St Aygulf). Beach 9 km.

Open: 1 April - 30 September.

Directions

From A8, exit Le Muy, follow N7 towards Fréjus for 13 km. Cross over A8 and turn right at roundabout through Roquebrune sur Argens towards St Aygulf for 1 km. Site signed on left. Follow private unmade road for 500 m. GPS: N43:26.708 E06:39.470

Charges 2007

Per unit incl. 2 or 3 persons	€ 19,80
extra person	€ 3,20
electricity	€ 2,70

Camping Cheques accepted.

FR83200 Kawan Village les Pêcheurs

F-83520 Roquebrune-sur-Argens (Var)

Tel: **04 94 45 71 25**. Email: **info@camping-les-pecheurs.com**

Mobile homes ▶ page 511

Les Pêcheurs will appeal to families who appreciate natural surroundings together with many activities, cultural and sporting. Interspersed with mobile homes, the 150 good sized touring pitches (electricity 6/10A) are separated by trees or flowering bushes. The Provencal style buildings are delightful, especially the bar, restaurant and games room, with its terrace down to the river and the site's own canoe station (locked gate). Across the road is a lake used exclusively for water skiing with a sandy beach, a restaurant and minigolf. This popular Riviera site has some new spa facilities including steam pool and sauna. Developed over three generations by the Simoncini family, this peaceful, friendly site is set in more than four hectares of mature, well shaded countryside at the foot of the Roquebrune Rock. Activities include climbing the 'Rock' with a guide. We became more and more intrigued with stories about the Rock and the Holy Hole, the Three Crosses and the Hermit all call for further exploration which reception staff are happy to arrange, likewise trips to Monte Carlo, Ventimigua (Italy) and the Gorges du Verdon, etc. The medieval village of Roquebrune is within walking distance.

Facilities

Modern, refurbished, well designed toilet blocks, baby baths, facilities for disabled visitors. Washing machines. Shop. Bar, restaurant, games room (all open all season). Heated outdoor swimming pool (all season), separate paddling pool (lifeguard in high season), ice cream bar. Spa facilities. Playing field. Fishing. Canoeing, water skiing. Activities for children and adults (high season), visits to local wine caves. Rafting and diving schools. Only gas or electric barbecues. WiFi in reception, bar/restaurant and pool area. Off site: Bicycle hire 1 km. Riding 5 km. Golf 5 km. (reduced fees).

Open: 1 April - 30 September.

Directions

From A8 take Le Muy exit, follow N7 towards Fréjus for 13 km. bypassing Le Muy. After crossing A8, turn right at roundabout towards Roquebrune-sur-Argens. Site is on left after 1 km. just before bridge over river.

Charges 2008

Per unit incl. 2 persons	
and electricity	€ 22,00 - € 40,00
incl. 3 persons	€ 24,50 - € 42,50
extra person	€ 4,00 - € 6,70
child (5-10 yrs)	€ 3,20 - € 5,50
dog (max. 1)	€ 3,10

Camping Cheques accepted.

Check real time availability and at-the-gate prices...
www.**alanrogers**.com

FR83250 **Kawan Village Douce Quiétude**

3435 boulevard Jacques Baudino, F-83700 Saint Raphaël (Var)

Tel: **04 94 44 30 00**. Email: **sunelia@douce-quietude.com**

Douce Quiétude is five kilometres from the beaches at Saint Raphaël and Agay but is quietly situated at the foot of the Estérel massif. There are 400 pitches, only 70 of these are for touring set in pleasant pine woodland or shaded, green areas. The pitches are of a comfortable size, separated by bushes and trees with electricity (6A), water, drainage and telephone/TV points provided. This mature site offers a wide range of services and facilities complete with a pool complex. It can be busy in the main season yet is relaxed and spacious.

Facilities

Fully equipped modern toilet blocks, facilities for babies and disabled visitors. Launderette. Bar, restaurant, takeaway, pizzeria (3/4-3/9). Shop. Three swimming pools (two heated), water slide, Jacuzzi. Play area. Children's club, activities for teenagers (all July/Aug). Sports area. Games room. Tennis. Minigolf. Archery. Fitness centre, sauna. Evening entertainment, shows, karaoke, discos (July/Aug). Mountain bike hire. Only gas barbecues. Off site: Bus route 1 km. Golf and riding 2 km. Windsurf hire and sea fishing 5 km.

Open: 3 April - 2 October.

Directions

From A8 exit 38 (Fréjus/St Raphaël) take the D100, signed Valescure then Agay. Follow site signs (round the back of Fréjus/St Raphael). Access via N98 coast road turning north at Agay on the D100. Pass Esterel Camping, then site signed. GPS: N43:26.836 E06:48.360

Charges 2007

Per unit incl. 2 persons and electricity	€ 18,00 - € 47,50
extra person	€ 5,00 - € 9,00

Camping Cheques accepted.

FR83260 **Camping Château de l'Eouvière**

Route de Tavernes, F-83670 Montmeyan (Var)

Tel: **04 94 80 75 54**. Email: **contact@leouviere.com**

This spacious site is in the grounds of an 18th century château, close to the magnificent hill village of Montmeyan. Many of the terraced pitches, mostly behind the château, have magnificent views. The 80 large touring pitches are part grassy, part stony with varying amounts of shade from mature trees, all have electricity points. Entrance to the site is very steep and may cause problems for some. The owner will assist with his 4 x 4 vehicle any visitor experiencing difficulty in siting their unit. This is a quieter site for those seeking the 'real' France.

Facilities

Main refurbished toilet block (may be stretched in high season) has all the necessary facilities. Disabled facilities. Washing machine, iron. Bar (15/4-15/10), restaurant (15/6-15/10), shop (1/7-31/8). Pool, sunbathing area. Small play area, paddling pool (some distance from the pool). Entertainment and children's activities in high season. Virtually soundproof disco in the cellars of château. Off site: Montmeyan 1 km. Beach at Lake Quinson (7 km).

Open: 15 April - 15 October.

Directions

Leave A8 autoroute at St Maximin and take D560 to Barjols, then D71 to Montmeyan. At roundabout on entering village, take D13 southeast signed Cotignac and site entrance is very shortly on the right.

Charges 2007

Per person	€ 6,00 - € 7,00
child (under 7 yrs)	€ 4,00 - € 5,00
pitch	€ 6,00 - € 9,00
electricity	€ 4,00

FR83290 **Camping de Saint-Aygulf Plage**

270 avenue Salvarelli, F-83370 Saint Aygulf-Plage (Var)

Tel: **04 94 17 62 49**. Email: **info@camping-cote-azur.com**

This is a large, well run and self-sufficient campsite with a range of good facilities and direct access to the beach. The pitches are well marked, flat and arranged in long rows, many with good shade from the pine trees. There are 1,100 in total, with 700 for touring units and the remainder used for mobile homes and chalets. Electricity is available on 500 touring pitches. Although there is no swimming pool on the site. Direct access to the beach makes this is a fine family holidaying campsite.

Facilities

Four large toilet blocks provide good, clean facilities. No facilities for disabled visitors. Laundry facilities. Supermarket. Bakery. Two restaurants. Bar/patio. Stage for discos and entertainmanet. Pizzeria and takeaways. Multi-sports court. Play areas. First aid. Caravan storage. Beach. Only gas and electric barbecues are permitted. Off site: Bicycle hire 100 m. Riding 1 km. Golf 6 km.

Open: 1 May - 19 September
(chalets, mobile homes 29 March - 25 October).

Directions

From A8 take exits for Puget or Fréjus and RN7 to Fréjus town. Follow signs to sea front and join RN98. Saint Aygulf is 2 km. towards St Tropez. Site signed and is behind Hotel Van der Valk. GPS: N43:23.574 E06:43.608

Charges 2007

Per unit incl. 2 persons	€ 11,50 - € 40,00
incl. electricity	€ 14,50 - € 50,00
extra person	€ 3,00 - € 8,00

FR83220 Kawan Village Cros de Mouton

Mobile homes ⊙ page 511

P.O. 116, F-83240 Cavalaire-sur-Mer (Var)

Tel: **04 94 64 10 87**. Email: **campingcrosdemouton@wanadoo.fr**

Cros de Mouton is a reasonably priced campsite in a popular area. High on a steep hillside, about 2 km. from Cavalaire and its popular beaches, the site is a calm oasis away from the coast. There are stunning views of the bay but, due to the nature of the terrain, some of the site roads are very steep (the higher pitches with the best views are especially so). There are 199 large, terraced pitches (electricity 10A) under cork trees with 73 suitable only for tents with parking close by, and 80 for touring caravans. English is spoken by the welcoming and helpful owners. The restaurant terrace and the pools share the wonderful view of Cavalaire and the bay. Olivier and Andre are happy to take your caravan up with their 4 x 4 Jeep if you are worried.

Facilities

Clean, well maintained toilet blocks have all the usual facilities including those for disabled customers (although site is perhaps a little steep in places for wheelchairs). Washing machine. Shop. Bar/restaurant, reasonably priced meals, takeaways. Swimming and paddling pools with lots of sun beds on the terrace and small bar for snacks and cold drinks. Small play area. Games room. Off site: Beach 1.5 km. Bicycle hire 1.5 km. Riding 3 km. Golf 15 km.

Open: 15 March - 9 November.

Directions

Take the D559 to Cavalaire-sur-Mer (not Cavalière 4 km. away). Site is about 1.5 km. north of the town, very well signed from the centre. GPS: N43:10.933 E06:30.966

Charges 2008

Per person	€ 6,30 - € 7,90
child (under 7 yrs)	€ 4,10 - € 4,30
pitch	€ 6,30 - € 7,90
electricity (10A)	€ 4,10 - € 4,50
dog	free - € 2,00

Camping Cheques accepted.

Check real time availability and at-the-gate prices...
www.**alanrogers**.com

FR83300 Camping Clos Sainte-Thérèse

Route de Bandol, F-83270 Saint Cyr-sur-Mer (Var)

Tel: **04 94 32 12 21**. Email: **camping@clos-therese.com**

This is a very attractive, family run campsite set in hilly terrain four kilometres from the beaches of Saint Cyr. The terraced pitches are level, some with sea views, the friendly owners offering a tractor service if required. There is good shade from pines, olives and evergreen oaks. There are 86 pitches for touring units, all with electricity and 30 for chalets or mobile homes. Five pitches are fully serviced. The landscaped pool complex is pretty and well kept, with a small slide, jacuzzi and a separate paddling pool. This is a friendly, small site, ideal for couples or families with young children.

Facilities

Clean, well maintained toilet facilities. Fridge hire. Shop. Bar, restaurant (15/6-15/9). Swimming pools (one heated), children's pool. Games room. Table tennis. TV room and library. Boules. Play area. Activities in high season. Off site: Golf course (9 and 18 holes, driving range), tennis courts opposite site. Bicycle hire 2 km. Beach 4 km. Fishing 4 km. Riding 8 km.

Open: 1 April - 30 September.

Directions

From A50 take D559 to Saint Cyr. Continue towards Bandol and site is 3 km. on the left. GPS: N43:09.587 E05:43.772

Charges 2007

Per unit incl. 2 persons	€ 15,00 - € 21,50
extra person	€ 3,40 - € 5,20
electricity (4-10A)	€ 3,35 - € 5,00

Camping Cheques accepted.

FR83310 Camping l'Argentière

D48 chemin de l'Argentiere, F-83310 Cogolin (Var)

Tel: **04 94 54 63 63**. Email: **campinglargentiere@wanadoo.fr**

This jewel of a site is in a pleasant setting and the intervening wooded area seems to give it sufficient screening to make the campsite itself quite peaceful. It is only 5 km. from the beach at Gogolin or St Tropez, so its position is handy for one of the showplaces of the Riviera, but away from the hustle and bustle of the beach resorts. There are 150 good sized touring pitches (out of 238 with the others used for mobile homes to rent). All have electricity although long leads may be necessary.

Facilities

Two of three toilet blocks are near the touring pitches and are well kept and clean. Washbasins have warm water (some in cabins) with hot water for dishwashing and laundry. Washing machines (near site entrance). Water has to be taken from the sanitary block. Large swimming pool beside an attractive terrace bar serving snacks. Table tennis. Play equipment. Barbecues are not permitted. Off site: Shops close. Fishing, bicycle hire and riding 2 km. Golf 5 km.

Open: 1 April - 30 September.

Directions

From the A8 take exit 36 (Le Muy), then, D25 to Ste Maxime and the coast road N98 towards St Tropez. After Grimaud keep following signs for Cogolin. When near that village follow D48 towards St Maur-en-Collobrière, then signs to site in the suburb of L'Argentière. GPS: N43:15.365 E06:30.744

Charges 2007

Per unit incl. 2 persons	€ 14,00 - € 26,00
extra person	€ 3,00 - € 4,00
electricity (3-10A)	€ 2,00 - € 6,00

FR83320 Campasun Parc Mogador

167 chemin de Beaucours, F-83110 Sanary-sur-Mer (Var)

Tel: **04 94 74 53 16**. Email: **mogador@campasun.com / campasun@free.fr**

This site in the Mediterranean countryside is very much geared for family holidays with children. Some 20 minutes on foot from the beach, the site has a very large and well kept pool area and a stage for entertainment. Somewhat smaller than other sites of this type, there are 180 good sized pitches (160 for touring units). The ground is mainly level, if rather stony and sandy. Variable shade is available and all pitches have 10A electricity. There are plans to enlarge some of the smaller, 80 sq.m. pitches. The attractive pool, is surrounded by ample paved sunbathing areas.

Facilities

Two large, super de-luxe toilet blocks, one including washbasins and showers in cabins. The high-tech toilets are automatically cleaned and disinfected after every use. Laundry. Motorcaravan services. Restaurant with varied and full menu (15/5-30/10), also snacks, pizzas and takeaway. TV room also used for entertainment shows, cabarets, etc. Swimming pool and paddling pool, solarium. Boules. Miniclub for children and evening entertainment in season. Dogs are not accepted. Off site: Beach 800 m. Golf 6 km. Fishing 800 m.

Open: 1 May - 30 October.

Directions

Take Bandol exit 12 from A50 and head for Six Fours on the N 559. Arriving at Sanary-sur-Mer turn left towards Beaucours and site is on left after 100 m.

Charges 2007

Per unit incl. 2 persons and electricity (6A)	€ 16,00 - € 41,00
extra person	€ 5,00 - € 7,00
child (1-7 yrs)	€ 4,00 - € 6,00

FR83360 La Pierre Verte Camping Village

Route de Bagnols-en-Forêt, F-83600 Fréjus (Var)

Tel: 04 94 40 88 30. Email: info@campinglapierreverte.com

This attractive, terraced site, set on a hillside under umbrella pines, has been gradually and thoughtfully developed. The genuine, friendly welcome means many families return year upon year, bringing, in turn, new generations. The site is divided into terraces, each with its own toilet block. All the generously sized pitches (200 for tourists) enjoy good shade from trees and have electricity (6A). For those seeking to 'get away from it all' in an area of outstanding natural beauty, there can be few more tranquil sites, but the many beaches, watersports and excursions the Gulf of St Tropez has to offer can also be enjoyed. For those staying on site, there are two large, heated swimming pools with large sunbathing areas and exciting water slides. Not far away, some exhilarating hanggliding and parascending can be enjoyed.

Facilities

Five toilet blocks with mostly British style WCs and washbasins in cubicles are extremely clean and accessible from all levels. Baby bath. Laundry facilities. Bread available each morning. Bar with reasonably priced takeaway service. Heated swimming pools (25 x 15 m. and 15 x 15m.) and paddling pool. Play area Boules. Games room. Fridge hire. Entertainment and activities in high season. Barbecues are not permitted. Off site: A few shops 2 km. Nearest shopping centre Frejus 8 km. Riding 1 km. Bicycle hire 5 km. Fishing 8 km. Golf 12 km.

Open: 5 April - 29 Spetember.

Directions

From the A8 (Aix-en-Provence - Nice) take exit 38 onto D4 towards Bagnols-en-Forêt. Site lies along this road past a military camp.

Charges 2007

Per unit incl. 2 persons	€ 16,00 - € 28,00
incl. electricity	€ 22,00 - € 32,00
extra person	€ 5,00 - € 7,00
child (2-6 yrs)	€ 4,00 - € 5,00

FR83340 Camping Bonporteau

RD 559 B.P. 18, F-83240 Cavalaire-sur-Mer (Var)

Tel: 04 94 64 03 24. Email: contact@bonporteau.fr

This terraced site is situated northeast of and above the pleasant and popular holiday resort of Cavalaire where there is a harbour, restaurants and shops. A long, sandy beach runs right round the bay and there are plenty of watersport activities nearby. The site is only 200 metres from the beach, very well positioned for a family holiday, and only a short walk from a very good hypermarket. The 170 individual touring pitches are on sloping, sandy ground with terracing and good access roads, and all have electricity hook-ups (10A). The remaining 70 pitches are used for mobile homes and chalets.

Facilities

Three main toilet blocks are modern and include washbasins in cabins, Toilets are mainly British style. Launderette. Small shop. Small but attractive, restaurant (1/4-30/9). Bar. Takeaway. Entertainment with dance evenings. Swimming pool with terrace (15/3-30/9) and small paddling pool. Playground. Table tennis. TV and games room. Off site: Beach 200 m. Bicycle hire 800 m. Riding 2 km. Golf 20 km.

Open: 15 March - 15 October.

Directions

Take D559 to Cavalaire-sur-Mer (not Cavalière, some 4 km. away). Site is signed by yellow signs from the main road before entering the town.

Charges 2007

Per unit incl. 1-3 persons	€ 19,00 - € 36,50
incl. services	€ 25,00 - € 52,85
extra person	€ 5,00 - € 9,00
child	€ 2,50 - € 4,50

FR83350 Sélection Camping

12 boulevard de la Mer B.P. 88, F-83420 La Croix Valmer Plage (Var)

Tel: **04 94 55 10 30.** Email: **camping-selection@wanadoo.fr**

This site is only a short walk from the main street of the pleasant and popular holiday resort of La Croix Valmer where there is a harbour, restaurants and shops. There are plenty of watersport activities nearby A sandy beach is only 400 metres from the site, which is a good choice for a family holiday. The 136 individual touring pitches are on sloping, sandy ground with terracing and good access roads, All have electricity hook-ups (10A). There are a further 67 pitches used for mobile homes and chalets. Trees have grown well to give plenty of shade.

Facilities

Three main toilet blocks include washbasins in cabins. Toilets are mainly British style, with some Turkish. Launderette. Small shop. Restaurant (all season), bar and takeaway (form 1/5). Kidney-shaped pool (1/5-1/10). Some evening entertainment (July/Aug). Playground. Dogs are not accepted in July/Aug. Only gas or electric barbecues. Off site: Beach 400 m. Bicycle hire 200 m.

Open: 15 March - 15 October.

Directions

From the A8 (Aix-en-Provence - Fréjus) take exit 36 (Le Muy), then D25 towards Ste Maxime and then N98 towards St Tropez. At roundabout turn right following signs. GPS: N43:11.664 E06:33.308

Charges 2007

Per unit incl. 1-3 persons	€ 22,00 - € 31,50
extra person	€ 6,20 - € 9,50
electricity (120A)	€ 5,00

FR83420 Parc et Plage

Parcs Residentiels ▶ page 516

28 rue des Langoustiers, l'Ayguade, F-83400 Hyères Les Palmiers (Var)

Tel: **04 94 66 31 77.** Email: **contact@parc-plage.com**

Pitches at this campsite are exclusively for chalet accommodation.

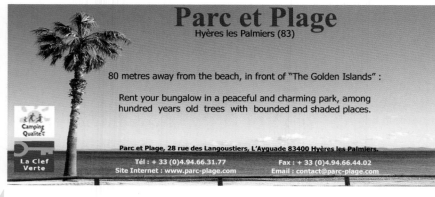

FR83370 Camping le Fréjus

Route de Bagnols, F-83600 Fréjus (Var)

Tel: **04 94 19 94 60.** Email: **contact@lefrejus.com**

Set on a hillside away from busy Fréjus, this attractively terraced site was developed over 35 years from a farm into a modern, pleasant campsite where there is a warm and genuine welcome. Divided into slightly sloping terraces, its 190 rather small pitches enjoy good shade from trees and have access to 6A electricity. In high season one terrace is reserved as a simple camping area for young people (reservation not required). Whether you choose to drive, walk or cycle, there is plenty of wonderful scenery to discover in the immediate vicinity, whilst not far away beautiful beaches can be enjoyed.

Facilities

Three clean and well positioned toilet blocks have mostly British style WCs and washbasins in cubicles. Baby bath. Laundry facilities. Well stocked shop in high season, bread from bar at other times. Bar (1/5-31/8) with reasonably priced takeaway. Heated swimming pool (1/5-31/8). Simple play area. Tennis. Barbecues are not permitted. Off site: Fréjus 6 km. Bicycle hire 3 km. Fishing 6 km. Riding 2 km. Beach 6 km.

Open: All year excl. 16 December - 15 January.

Directions

From the A8 (Aix-en-Provence - Nice) take exit 38 onto D4 towards Fréjus. Site lies along this road on the right. GPS: N43:27.877 E06:43.451

Charges 2007

Per unit incl. 2 persons and electricity (6A)	€ 16,00 - € 30,50
extra person	€ 4,60 - € 6,60
child (2-8 yrs)	€ 2,50 - € 3,10

Check real time availability and at-the-gate prices...

www.**alanrogers**.com

FR83400 Club Holiday Marina

Le Ginestrel RN 98, F-83310 Grimaud (Var)

Tel: **04 94 56 08 43**. Email: **info@holiday-marina.com**

Owned and operated by an English family this site is an established favourite with British families. It is located in the busy holiday area of the Gulf of St Tropez. The site has a large and well kept pool area and its own adjacent moorings for small yachts. Smaller than many sites in this area, there are 230 good sized pitches of which 49 for touring units. Each of these has its own spacious bathroom with a good shower, washbasin and WC and a shared outdoor sink. On level, rather sandy ground, with variable shade, all have 20A electricity. Cars are parked separately to reduce noise. The roads are paved with flattened cobblestones with lighting built in. An attractive pool is surrounded by ample paved sunbathing areas with some shade from trees and a roomy dining terrace with heating for cool evenings in low season. Although having all the facilities, activities and entertainment expected of a holiday site, the atmosphere is relaxed and much less frenzied than at similar sites.

Facilities

Private toilet blocks include washbasin, shower and WC, heated in low seasons. Dishwashing sinks. Laundry. Two restaurants with varied and full menu (15/6-31/8). Snacks and takeaway. Separate building houses a bar and games room. TV room. Swimming and paddling pools. Mini-club for children and evening entertainment in season. Fishing in adjacent canal. Off site: Beach 850 m. Golf 4 km.

Open: March - December.

Directions

From the A8 (Aix-en-Provence - Cannes) take exit 36 (Le Muy) and D25 to St Maxime. Follow N98 coast road towards St Tropez and site is 10 km. after very busy roundabout at Grimaud.

Charges 2007

Per unit incl. 2 persons and electricity	€ 19,00 - € 49,00
family rate	€ 29,00 - € 59,00
extra person	€ 5,00 - € 19,00

Camping Club Holiday Marina

We are a friendly safe site, ideal for families. Just 900 m from the beaches of Port Grimaud. Our holiday Home rentals come in 4 catagories from 25 m2 to 40 m2 and alle our camping emplacements come with their own private fully equipped bathroom with a water and 20 amp electrical hook up.
Facilities include pool, Jacuzzi, bar, restaurant, shop, hire shop, play area, kids club, boat moorrings with direct access to the mediterran sea and much more.
Opening dates March to December 2008

RN 98 Le Ginestel - F-83310 Grimaud - France   Tel: +33 (0)4 94 56 08 43 - Fax: +33 (0)4 94 56 23 88
Web site: www.holiday-marina.com   Email: info@holiday-marina.com

FR83410 Camping Club le Ruou

Les Esparrus RD560, F-83690 Villecroze - Les Grottes (Var)

Tel: **04 94 70 67 70**. Email: **info@leruou.com**

This is a family oriented site in the Provencal countryside, very much geared for family holidays with children. Some 45 minutes by car from the coast at Fréjus, the site has a large and well kept pool area and a mobile stage for entertainment. Smaller than some other sites of this type, there are 110 good sized pitches (52 for touring units). On mainly terraced, rather stony, ground with good shade, all have 6/10A electricity. Some of the pitches for caravans are along a steep path but there is a 4 x 4 available to assist.

Facilities

One new super de-luxe toilet block includes washbasins in cabins. Facilities for babies and disabled visitors. Laundry facilities. Snacks and takeaway (15/6-31/8). The main building houses a bar and entertainment room with TV. Area for shows, cabarets, etc. with mobile stage. Two swimming pools. Riding. Tennis. Boules. Miniclub for children and evening entertainment in season. Off site: Beach 30 km. Riding and bicycle hire 5 km. Fishing 10 km. Golf 17 km.

Open: 1 April - 30 October.

Directions

Directions: Villecroze-les-Grottes is northwest of Fréjus. From the A8 (Toulon - Mandelieu-la-Napoule) take exit 13 onto the N7 towards Le Muy. At Les Arcs turn left on D555 (Draguignan), then onto D557 to Villecroze. Site is on the left side of this road. GPS: N43:33.333 E06:18.000

Charges 2007

Per unit incl. 2 persons	€ 14,30 - € 27,00
extra person	€ 3,30 - € 5,50
electricity (6/10A)	€ 2,20 - € 5,30
Camping Cheques accepted.	

Check real time availability and at-the-gate prices...

 www.**alanrogers**.com

FR83610 Parc Saint James Oasis

Route de la Bouverie, F-83480 Puget-sur-Argens (Var)

Tel: **04 98 11 85 60**. Email: **oasis@camping-parcsaintjames.com**

This campsite has been recommended by our agent in France and we intend to undertake a full inspection next year. Oasis Village is a member of the Parc Saint James group and the 450 pitches here are all occupied by mobile homes and chalets. The site extends over 42 hectares of pine and oak woods with an attractive Provençal village at the centre, housing various shops and the site's restaurant. The swimming pool is impressive and understandably popular. Various activities and sports are available free of charge and during the high season, water polo is organised. At the end of the day, the Provençal style restaurant is a pleasant place to enjoy a meal and the site's regular entertainment programme.

Facilities

Laundry. Supermarket. Large swimming pool complex with children's pool. Bar and restaurant. Takeaway. Play area. TV room. Gym. Tennis. Sports competitions. Children's club. Evening entertainment. Disco. Off site: Frejus and St Raphaël. Aquatica water park. Riding 4 km. Golf 5 km. Nearest beaches 8 km.

Open: 31 March - 22 September.

Directions

Take the Puget sur Argens exit from the A8 autoroute and join the N7 in the direction of Le Muy. After 2.5 km. turn right into the Route de la Bouverie. The site can be found after a further 1.5 km. on the right.

FR83620 Parc Saint James Gassin

Route de Bourrian, F-83580 Gassin (Var)

Tel: **04 94 55 20 20**. Email: **gassin@camping-parcsaintjames.com**

This campsite has been recommended by our agent in France and we intend to undertake a full inspection next year. Gassin Village is a member of the Parc Saint James group and open for a long season. The majority of the pitches at Gassin are occupied by mobile homes and chalets but there are also 120 touring pitches. These are attractively located around the wooded 30 hectare estate and overlook the Golfe de St Tropez and the small village of Gassin. There is a good range of activities here, many concentrated around the large swimming pool. In high season, the activity and entertainment programme is popular and includes soirées on the site's attractive bar terrace. Gassin Village lies close to many places of interest – St Tropez is close at hand, as well as Ramatuelle with its famous beach of Pampelone. The site is also well located for excursions on foot; Gassin is justifiably popular with superb views over the gulf. This is also a good site for children with a miniclub and play area.

Facilities

Laundry. Supermarket. Swimming pool and separate children's pool. Bar and restaurant. Takeaway. Play area. TV room. Gym. Tennis training wall. Games room. Children's club. Evening entertainment. Disco. Mobile homes and chalets for rent. Off site: St Tropez, Port Grimaud and Cogolin. Nearest beaches 5 km. Riding. Fishing. Walking trails.

Open: 6 January - 24 November.

Directions

Take the Le Muy exit from the A8 autoroute and follow signs to St Tropez and La Croix-Valmer. Pass Sainte Maxime and continue towards St Tropez on the N98 and follow signs to Gassin. The site is well signed.

Charges 2007

Per unit incl. 2 persons	
and electricity	€ 18,00 - € 35,00
extra person	€ 2,50 - € 5,00
child (under 10 yrs)	€ 1,50 - € 4,00

PARC SAINT-JAMES
VILLAGES CLUB

Parc Saint-James
GASSIN

Route de Bourrian
83580 Gassin
Tél : 00 33 4 94 55 20 20
Fax : 00 33 4 94 56 34 77

Enjoy the pleasure of spending your holidays outdoors in our village-clubs where everything has been designed for your leisure and well-being. Everyone is catered for young and old alike; you can do everything of nothing. So come and discover your future holidays at Gassin or Oasis. Choose your kingdom, well look after the rest.

Route de Bouverie
83480 Puget sur Argens
Tél : 00 33 4 98 11 85 60
Fax : 00 33 4 98 11 85 79

2 campsites Riviera-Côte d'Azur

23, 27 rue Victor Pauchet 92420 Vaucresson
Tél : 00 33 1 47 95 53 63/62
Fax : 00 33 1 47 95 53 68
www.camping-parcsaintjames.com
E-mail : info@camping-parcsaintjames.com

FR83440 **Domaine de la Malissonne**

F-83740 La Cadière d'Azur (Var)

Tel: **04 94 90 10 60**. Email: **info@domainemalissonne.com**

This pleasant site is part of the FranceLoc group and is a park for caravan holiday homes with over 200 mobile homes. There are just four pitches without electricity for touring campers and these are really only for tents. Although the site is close to the A50 we heard little noise and site does provide a good base for touring the western Var and Bouche du Rhône departments. Surrounded by vineyards, this sloping site is very well maintained. It is a quiet and restful environment, yet is only minutes from the coast at Les Lecques. Jean Marc, the son of the former owners, manages the site to perfection.

Facilities

Two good sanitary blocks. Launderette. Bar. Restaurant and shop. Three swimming pools. Fitness area. Play area. Gym. Volleyball. Boules. Archery. Minigolf. Animation in high season. TV room and electronic games room. WiFi. Dogs are not accepted 1/7-30/8. Off site: Massif de la Sainte Baume.

Open: 1 March - 13 November.

Directions

Site is on the D66 about 2 km. west of Cadière. Leave the A50 at exit 11 and go towards the town. Then follow signs to the site which itself is close to a motorway bridge. GPS: N43:12.142 E05:44.294

Charges 2007

Per unit incl. 2 persons	€ 20,50 - € 27,50
extra person	€ 6,10
child (under 7 yrs)	€ 4,50

FR83510 **Camping la Pinède**

Chemin des Mannes, F-83240 Cavalaire-sur-Mer (Var)

Tel: **04 94 64 11 14**

La Pinede is an attractive small site, the appeal being in its proximity to the local town, superb beaches and excellent off site facilities making it ideal for motorcaravanners without additional transport. Laurent is proud of his site and this is reflected in the number of campers who return year after year to this delightful stretch of the Cote d'Azur. Everything you could want is within a 500 m. walk. There are 140 pitches of mixed size, screened with trees and beautiful flowering hedges. This is a good value site for the area and excellent English is spoken. The local town of Cavalaire-sur-Mer has much to offer visitors and is well placed for visits further afield to Saint Tropez and Cannes. With several Blue Flag beaches, the area is renowned for crystal clear seas and sandy beaches. The lack of on-site facilities will not appeal to some but ensures that the site is fairly tranquil. Keen to welcome more English and Dutch visitors, this site is worth visiting just for the scenic coastal drive to get to it.

Facilities

Recently modernised sanitary block. Laundry and dishwashing areas. Bread service. Gas supplies. Fridge hire. Play area. Petanque. Charcoal barbecues are not allowed. Off site: Supermarket 400 m. Boat hire and launching 500 m. Beach 300 m. Riding 2 km. Tennis 4 km. Golf 14 km.

Open: 15 March - 15 October.

Directions

Following the N98 from Hyères, take D559 towards Le Lavandou. Follow D559 coast road for 20 km. On reaching Cavalaire-sur-Mer, turn left at roundabout into Chemin des Mannes. Site is 50 m on left. Site is signed on entry to town.

Charges 2007

Per unit incl. 2 persons	€ 15,00 - € 21,00
extra person	€ 5,00
child (1-7 yrs)	€ 3,10
electricity (5A)	€ 3,00

MAP 16

The island of Corsica is both
dramatic and beautiful. The
scenery is spectacular with
bays of white sand lapped
by the clear blue waters of the
Mediterranean. At certain times
of the year the entire island is ablaze
with exotic flowers, aided by Corsica's
excellent sunshine record.

Corsica

DÉPARTEMENTS: 2A CORSE-SUD; 2B HAUTE-CORSE

MAJOR CITIES: AJACCIO AND BASTIA

Corsica is regarded by some as the jewel of
the Mediterranean islands and is made up
of two départements: Haute Corse (upper
Corsica) and Corse du Sud (southern
Corsica). The island has endured a bloody
history, having being much disputed the
Greeks, Romans and Lombards. Five
hundred years of Italian rule has influenced
the look of the island with Italian-style
hilltop hamlets and villages developed
alongside mountain springs. Many of the
villages feature rustic, unadorned churches
and also a few Romanesque examples too.

The variety of scenery is spectacular.
Across much of the island one can discover
dramatic gorges, glacial lakes, gushing
mountain torrents and magnificent pine
and chestnut forests.You'll also experience
the celebrated perfume of the Corsican
maquis: a tangled undergrowth of fragrant
herbs, flowers and bushes that fills the
warm spring and summer air. The highest
mountains lie to the west, while the
gentler ranges, weathered to strange
and often bizarre shapes, lie to the south
and a continuous barrier forms the island's
backbone.

Places of interest

Ajaccio: a dazzling white city full of
Napoleonic memorabilia.

Bastia: historic citadel towering over the
headland. The old town has preserved its
streets in the form of steps connected by
vaulted passages, converging on the Vieux
port (the old port). The new port is the real
commercial port of the island.

Cuisine of the region

Brocchui: sheeps' milk cheese is used much
in cooking in both its soft form (savoury or
sweet) or more mature and ripened.

Capone: local eels, cut up and grilled on
a spit over a charcoal fire.

Dziminu: fish soup, like bouillabaise but
much hotter. Made with peppers and
pimentos.

Figatelli: a sausage made of dried
and spiced pork with liver. Favourite
between-meal snack.

Pibronata: a highly spiced local sauce.

Prizzutu: a peppered smoked ham;
resembles the Italian prosciutto, but with
chestnut flavour added.

Corsica

FR20000 Camping Pertamina Village

RN 198, F-20169 Bonifacio (Corse-du-Sud)

Tel: **04 95 73 05 47**. Email: **pertamina@wanadoo.fr**

Whether or not you are using the ferry to Sardinia, Bonifacio deserves a visit and this is a convenient site for a night stop or longer stay. The 120 pitches, many in delightful settings, have electricity (3A), are partially terraced and are hedged with trees and bushes, providing shade. They are fairly flat and vary in size, many being well over 100 sq.m. A central feature of the site is the large attractive swimming pool, surrounded by terraces. The bar, restaurant, pizzeria/grill and creperie are on a series of terraces above the pool and patios. This site will suit campers who like a large pool complex and do not mind a drive to the beach.

Facilities

Two toilet blocks include washbasins in semi-private cubicles, British and Turkish style WCs, washing machines plus drying and ironing facilities. Motorcaravan service point at entrance (public). Shop. Takeaway. Bar, restaurant,pizzeria/grill serving set meals and á la carte menu at reasonable prices (shorter opening hours in May, June and Oct). Swimming pool. Tennis. Play area. TV room. Excellent gym. Off site: Bonifacio 4 km.

Open: Easter - 15 October.

Directions

Site is on the RN198 road, 4 km. north of Bonifacio to the east. Well signed as Pertamina Village.

Charges 2007

Per unit incl. 2 persons	
with electricity	€ 19,50 - € 30,00
extra person	€ 6,50 - € 9,50
child (under 8 yrs)	free - € 5,80
Camping Cheques accepted.	

FR20060 Camping la Vetta

Route de Bastia, la Trinité, F-20137 Porto-Vecchio (Corse-du-Sud)

Tel: **04 95 70 09 86**. Email: **info@campinglavetta.com**

This is a site not to be missed in Corsica, the English/French owners Nick and Marieline Long having created a very friendly and peaceful country park setting for their campsite to the north of La Trinité village. The 8.5 hectares of well maintained campsite are part sloping, part terraced with an informal pitch allocation system. It seems to stretch endlessly. The abundance of tree varieties including many cork oaks give shade to 111 pitches which all have 10A electricity. The site has a brilliant new lagoon style pool, all landscaped and serviced by its own snack bar and creperie.

Facilities

Spotless, traditional style toilet facilities have plenty of hot water. Dishwashing and laundry facilities. Shop (July/Aug), gas supplies. Excellent restaurant, patio, bar (July/Aug). Swimming pool, paddling pool and water play area (all season). Play area. TV. Entertainment in high season. Off site: Beach 1.5 km. Supermarket 2 km. Fishing and watersports 1.5 km. Riding 4 km. Bicycle hire 5 km. Golf 7 km. Public transport 800 m.

Open: 1 June - 1 October.

Directions

Site is in La Trinité village, off the RN198 (east side), north of Porto-Vecchio.

Charges 2007

Per person	€ 6,00 - € 7,50
child (under 7 yrs)	€ 3,00 - € 4,00
pitch	€ 4,50 - € 7,00
electricity	€ 3,00

FR20070 Camping Caravaning Santa Lucia

Lieudit Mulindinu, F-20144 Sainte Lucie-de Porto-Vecchio (Corse-du-Sud)

Tel: **04 95 71 45 28**. Email: **information@campingsantalucia.com**

Camping Santa Lucia is a very small, friendly, family run site in a delightful southern Corsican setting, where little English is spoken. Behind the little reception hut is an unsophisticated restaurant and bar which have terraces overlooking the pool. It is very pleasant in the evenings when ornamental lamps light up the area. There are 160 pitches, 60 with 6A electrical connections and 18 serviced pitches. Some of the pitches are in enclosed bays created from huge boulders, making them very private. This site is only minutes by car from Porto Vecchio and with very reasonable prices, will suit many.

Facilities

Two clean and pleasant toilet blocks include British style toilets, some washbasins in cubicles. Washing and laundry facilites. Disabled facilities. Bread to order. Bar (15/6-15/9). Restaurant and takeaway (1/7-31/8). Swimming and paddling pools. Play area and high season miniclub for children. Minigolf. Communal barbecues. Satellite TV. WiFi. Off site: Beach, fishing and watersports 5 km. Golf 20 km. Supermarket opposite site.

Open: 15 May - 10 October.

Directions

Site is at south end of Sainte-Lucie-de-Porto-Vecchio village, off N198 and well signed.

Charges 2007

Per person	€ 5,00 - € 7,00
child (2-10 yrs)	free - € 3,30
pitch	€ 3,20 - € 4,75
with electricity	€ 5,00 - € 7,50

FR20220 Camping les Oliviers

F-20150 Porto (Corse-du-Sud)

Tel: 04 95 26 14 49. Email: lesoliviersporto@wanadoo.fr

This attractive and modern, resort style campsite is by the Bay of Porto, set alongside a charming river suitable for fishing and swimming. The surrounding area is listed as a World heritage site. It is located on the difficult to access and remote west coast of Corsica and reservations are essential. The site is is on very steep slopes and has 190 mainly small and terraced touring pitches, with 64 having electricity (10A). The quality of the pitches reflect the rugged terrain, large units will find the few motorhome pitches very challenging to access.

Facilities

Toilet facilities are unisex and in four blocks spread throughout the site. Some washbasins in cubicles, British style WCs. Washing machines. No facilities for disabled visitors and unsuitable for those with mobility difficulty. Fridge hire. Bread supplies. Restaurant, pizzeria and bar. Swimming pool, gym, sauna, massage and Turkish bath. Play area. Internet access. Fishing. Torches useful. Corsican trek agency. Off site: Supermarket 50 m. Bicycle hire 200 m. Golf 1.5 km. Riding 30 km.

Open: 28 March - 7 November.

Directions

When approaching Porto from the North the road crosses a bridge over the river. Les Oliviers is on the left, well signed.

Charges 2007

Per person	€ 6,50 - € 8,80
child (under 7 yrs)	€ 3,20 - € 4,50
car and caravan with electricity	€ 11,50 - € 14,00
motorcaravan with electricity	€ 9,00 - € 10,50

FR20230 Camping le Sagone

Route de Vico, F-20118 Sagone (Corse-du-Sud)

Tel: 04 95 28 04 15. Email: sagone.camping@wanadoo.fr

Situated outside the bustling seaside resort of Sagone, surrounded by protective hills, this campsite which used to be a fruit farm is in an ideal location for exploring Corsica's wild and rocky west coast or its mountainous interior. The large site borders a pleasant river and has 300 marked, shaded pitches, 250 with electricity (6A). There are 105 bungalows offered for rent, which are generally separated.Animation takes place in the central area by the pool during the high season.

Facilities

Clean, fully equipped toilet blocks. Washbasins in cubicles. Facilities for disabled people. Baby baths. Washing machines, dryers. Motorcaravan services. Large supermarket (all year). Restaurant, pizzeria, bar, games room. Swimming pool (June - Sept). Half court tennis. Play area. Sub-aqua experience in pool. Communal barbecues. Satellite TV. Internet. Car wash. New putting and golf practise area. Off site: Riding 500 m. Diving, windsurfing, mountain biking, fishing, bicycle hire.

Open: 1 May - 30 September.

Directions

From Ajaccio take the RD81 in direction of Cergése and Calvilby (by coast road). In Sagone take RD70 in direction of Vico, Sagone can be found on left after 1.5 km. next to supermarket.

Charges 2007

Per unit incl. 2 persons	€ 14,50 - € 23,00
extra person	€ 4,50 - € 7,70
child (under 12 yrs)	€ 2,25 - € 3,90
electricity	€ 3,00

Camping Cheques accepted.

FR20240 Camping Rondinara

Suartone, F-20169 Bonifacio (Corse-du-Sud)

Tel: 04 95 70 43 15. Email: reception@rondinara.fr

The views from every pitch in this site are stunning, either coastal or the rolling hills and cliffs inland. The 'great outdoors' describes this campsite which is away from the any tourist over-development and is at one with nature. The natural and informal pitches sit on the hillside above a superb bay with sheltered water, fine silver sand and safe swimming. Most pitches have shade but most tree foliage is relatively low as yet. Large boulders make natural divisions and some pitches need long leads for the 6A electricity. The beach is a 400 m. walk down a rough track through the maquis.

Facilities

Three excellent, modern toilet blocks are very clean and offer hot water throughout, hot showers and single sex British style toilets. Motorcaravan service point. Shop. Pizza restaurant. Bar. Swimming pool. Play area. Games room. Animation and family activities. Torches are essential. Off site: Fishing 400 m. Golf 15 km. Riding 15 km. Boat launching 400 m. Beach 400 m. Sailing 15 km.

Open: 15 May - 30 Spetember.

Directions

Site is mid-way between Bonifacio and Porto Vecchio off the RN 198. Take the D158 to Baie de la Rondinara for 7 km. The road is rough and narrow but large units will have no trouble negotiating it.

Charges 2007

Per person	€ 5,50 - € 6,90
child (2-12 yrs)	€ 2,80 - € 3,30
pitch	€ 5,50 - € 10,20

FR20250 **Camping Campo di Liccia**

Lieu-dit Parmentil, route de Porto-Vecchio, F-20169 Bonifacio (Corse-du-Sud)

Tel: **04 9573 03 09**. Email: **info@campingdiliccia.com**

A small, pleasant family site, La Liccia has a good ambience. It is fresh and clean and the owners have spent much time and money achieving high standards. We found this site to be a breath of fresh air compared to many other small sites on the island. The 150 flat touring pitches are informally arranged under mature trees with 4/10A electricity in different designated areas of site. A swimming and paddling pool near reception is pleasant (but no lifeguard). The pool is overlooked by the terraced patios of the restaurant and bar which are built around a lovely old tree.

Facilities

Two sanitary blocks have modern facilities including those for disabled campers. Hot water is available at all points and the blocks are kept very clean. Baby room. Washing machines. Motorcaravan service point. Bar/restaurant (June - Sept). Swimming pool and paddling pool (no lifeguard). Play area. WiFi. Animation in high season. Torches useful. Off site: Beach and fishing 4 km. Riding and bicycle hire 4 km. Golf 20 km. Boat launching 5 km.

Open: Easter - 15 October.

Directions

Site is north of Bonifacio on the RN198. Drive 4 km. north and look for the signs on the left.

Charges 2007

Per person	€ 4,40 - € 6,00
child (under 10 yrs)	€ 1,85 - € 2,70
pitch	€ 3,60 - € 7,55

FR20010 **Camping Arinella Bianca**

Route de la Mer, F-20240 Ghisonaccia (Haute-Corse)

Tel: **04 95 56 04 78**. Email: **arinella@arinellabianca.com**

Arinella is a lively, family oriented site on Corsica's east coast. The 415 level, grassy, good size, irregular shape pitches (198 for touring units) have a variety of trees and shrubs providing ample shade and 6A electricity (long leads needed). Some pitches overlook the attractive lakes which have fountains and are lit at night. The site has direct acess to a huge long beach of soft sand. The brilliantly designed resort style pools and paddling pool, overlooked by an attractive large restaurant, terraced bar and entertainment area, form the hub of Arinella Bianca.

Facilities

Four open plan sanitary blocks provide showers, (some with dressing area), washbasins in cabins, mainly British style WCs. Open air dishwashing areas. Laundry, washing machines, ironing boards. Motorcaravan services. Shop, bar, terrace, restaurant, amphitheatre, snack bar (all 10/5-15/9). Swimming pool (from 1/5). Windsurfing. Canoeing. Fishing. Tennis. Riding. Children's miniclub. Play area. Disco. Good entertainment programme in the main season. Communal barbecue area. Off site: Sailing 500 m. Boat launching 2 km.

Open: Mid April - 30 September.

Directions

Site is 4 km. east of Ghisonaccia. From N198 in Ghisonaccia look for sign 'La Plage, Li Mare'. Turn east on D144 at roundabout just south of town. Continue for 3.5 km. to further roundabout where site is signed to right. Site is 500 m. Watch for speed bumps on approach road and on site.

Charges 2007

Per unit incl. 2 persons	€ 21,00 - € 36,00
extra person	€ 7,00 - € 9,80
electricity (6A)	€ 4,20

Camping Cheques accepted.

FR20030 **Camping Merendella**

Moriani-Plage, F-20230 San-Nicolao (Haute-Corse)

Tel: **04 95 38 53 47**. Email: **merendel@club-internet.fr**

This attractive family run site has the advantage of direct access to a pleasant, long sandy beach. It is peacefully situated on level grass with many well tended trees and shrubs providing shade and colour. Level green sites such as this are unusual in Corsica and are ideal for families or those with mobility problems. There are 196 pitches, all with electricity (2/5A, long leads required) and a minimum of 100 sq.m. There is a dedicated night parking area if you arrive late. An excellent bar, restaurant/pizzeria is close to the site entrance (takeaway pizzas are available).

Facilities

Modern blocks, two individual cabin units near the beach. Washbasins in private cubicles. British and Turkish style WCs. Facilites for disabled people. Motorcaravan services. Shop. Bar/restaurant, pizzeria. Diving centre. Play area. Torches essential. No pets. Off site: Restaurant outside gate. Town 800 m. with usual amenities. Tennis and riding 2 km. Bicycle hire 800 m.

Open: 15 May - 30 September.

Directions

Site is to seaward side of the RN198, 800 m. south of Moriani Plage.

Charges 2007

Per person	€ 6,35 - € 7,50
caravan and car	€ 6,15 - € 6,95
motorcaravan	€ 5,95 - € 7,10
electricity (2/5A)	€ 3,30 - € 4,30

FR20040 Riva Bella Nature Resort & Spa

B.P. 21, F-20270 Alèria (Haute-Corse)

Tel: 04 95 38 81 10. Email: **riva-bella@wanadoo.fr**

Mobile homes ▶ page 512

TRAVEL SERVICE SITE
TO BOOK CALL 01580 214000
Advice & low ferry-inclusive prices

This is a relaxed, informal, spacious naturist site alongside an extremely long and beautiful beach. Riva Bella is naturist camping at its very best, with great amenities. It offers a variety of pitches, situated in beautiful countryside and seaside. The site is divided into several areas with 200 pitches and bungalows, some alongside the sandy beach with little shade, others in a wooded glade with ample shade. The huge fish-laden lakes are a fine feature of this site. Although electricity is available in most parts, a long cable may be needed. The ground is fairly flat with terracing for tents.

Facilities

High standard toilet facilities. Provision for disabled people, children and babies. Laundry. Large shop (1/5-18/10). Fridge hire. Restaurant with lake views (all season) with reasonable prices. Excellent beach/snack bar. Bar. Watersports, sailing school, fishing, sub-aqua. Balneotherapy centre. Sauna. Volleyball, aerobics, table tennis, giant draughts, archery. Fishing. Mountain bike hire. Half-court tennis. Walk with llamas. Internet. WiFi. Professional evening entertainment programme. Off site: Riding 2 km.

Open: 1 April - 1 November.

Directions

Site is 12 km. north of Aleria on N198 (Bastia) road. Watch for large signs and unmade road to site and follow for 4 km.

Charges 2007

Per unit incl. 2 persons	€ 17,00 - € 32,50
extra person	€ 4,00 - € 8,50
child (3-8 yrs)	€ 2,00 - € 5,00
dog	€ 3,00 - € 3,00

Special offers and half-board arrangements available. Camping Cheques accepted.

FR20080 Camping Bagheera Naturisme

Route 198, F-20230 Bravone (Haute-Corse)

Tel: 04 95 38 80 30. Email: **bagheera@bagheera.fr**

An extremely long private road leads you to this naturist site which is alongside a 3 km. fine sand beach and has been run by the same family for 30 years. There are 190 pitches which are separated from the numerous bungalows. Well shaded under huge eucalyptus trees, all have 10A electricity (long leads may be necessary). Some beach-side pitches have sea views but most others are further back from the sea. All pitches are on sandy grass and are kept clean and neat. Large units will have no problems with access here. The restaurant and beach bar have superb panoramic views of the sea.

Facilities

Four sanitary blocks (one new for 2008) offer hot water throughout. Washing machines. Excellent restaurant and bar. Comprehensive beach snack bar and bar. Pizzeria. Shop. All amenities (1/6-30/10). Pool. New play area. Gym. Massage. Sauna. Sub-aqua diving. Tennis. Bicycle hire. Fishing. Entertainment all season. TV. Internet. Off site: Riding. Boat launching 15 km. Town 11 km.

Open: 1 April - 30 October (bungalows all year).

Directions

Site is between Bastia and Aleria near Bravone, 7 km. north of Aleria on the N198. It is well signed off the N198. Follow site road 4 km. east to beach.

Charges 2007

Per unit incl. 2 persons	€ 16,00 - € 22,40
extra person	€ 3,60 - € 5,80
child (3-15 yrs)	€ 1,60 - € 3,25

FR20110 Camping Restonica

Faubourg Saint Antoine, F-20250 Corte (Haute-Corse)

Tel: 04 95 46 11 59. Email: **vero.camp@worldonline.fr**

Tucked away alongside the pretty Restonica river and near the Pont Neuf leading into the stunning mountainside old city of Corte, Camping Restonica is ideally placed for tourists wanting to visit Corte or travel on the popular inland mountain railway (the station is only a few hundred metres from the site). This is a small, simple site catering for those who want to enjoy the many delights of Corte. The entrance is steep but manageable for all but very large units, there are flat pitches for campers and caravans in the middle of the site, and many beautiful terraced pitches for tents dotted along the river bank under shady trees.

Facilities

Single, central toilet block is unisex and somewhat dated, although very clean. Toilet for disabled visitors but site not really suitable. Washing machine. Bread to order. Bar and snack bar. River fishing. Off site: Sightseeing. Famous train journeys across Corsica. Museum. Only university in Corsica (politically significant).

Open: 15 April - 30 September.

Directions

Approaching Corte, turn left at first roundabout onto Ave du 9 Septembre. Site is 300 m. on the right. It is signed from the roundabout and at the top of the steep, narrow access road.

Charges 2007

Per person	€ 6,50
pitch	€ 5,00 - € 7,50

No credit cards.

Check real time availability and at-the-gate prices...

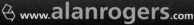

www.**alanrogers**.com

FR20140 Camping Dolce-Vita

Route de Bastia, F-20260 Calvi (Haute-Corse)
Tel: 04 95 65 05 99

Tucked under mature trees, this family site has direct access to the river and across a little bridge to a soft sandy beach with fabulous views of Calvi. It is rustic, as are all sites on the west coast, but is a cut above most. Small boats may be moored by the river bridge (caution with children) and the sea is 30 m. away. A pleasant, traditional restaurant and bar are in the centre of the site. There are 250 informal touring pitches, in shade with 10A electricity (long leads required in some areas).

Facilities

Three sanitary blocks are dated but well looked after and clean. Solar powered for hot water and British style toilets. Push-button hot showers. Basic baby area. Shop. Bar and restaurant with TV and pleasant patio. Pizzeria. (May-Sept). Play area. Tennis. Communal barbecue area. Torches are required. Mooring for small boats. Fishing. Off site: Beach 30 m. Riding 1 km. Boat launching 3 km. Town 3 km.

Open: 1 May - 30 September.

Directions

Site is north of Bastia on RN197. On approach to the town from the north it is well signed, 3 km. from town down a minor road towards l'Ile Rousse and the beach.

Charges 2007

Per person	€ 8,30
child (under 7 yrs)	€ 4,00
pitch	€ 2,80 - € 6,60

No credit cards.

FR20150 Camping d'Olzo

L.D. Strutta, F-20217 Saint-Florent (Haute-Corse)
Tel: 04 95 37 03 34. Email: info@campingolzo.com

The friendly Barenghi family who own this site are delightful. They are pleased to welcome you to their compact site and Dutch, Italian and English are spoken. The site is flat and very peaceful with a wide variety of trees, including gums and olives, which offer shade to most of the informal pitches. There is ample room to manoeuvre for large units. All 60 pitches have electricity (10A) and are not far from the central sanitary block or the facilities which are grouped near reception. The site is a short walk from the beach. A swimming pool is planned for the site.

Facilities

Single central block has unisex toilets (Turkish and British style) and single sex hot showers. Water at the sinks is cold. Everything is kept very clean and smart. Washing machines. Motorcaravan services. Facilities for disabled campers. Small shop (July/Aug), bread to order. Restaurant/pizzeria and bar. Internet access. Play area. Communal barbecue area. Off site: Town of St Florent with usual facilities. Riding 500 m. Bicycle hire 2 km. Boat launching 2 km. Sailing 2 km.

Open: 1 April - 30 September.

Directions

From Bastia take the D81 west to St Florent. After some 30 minutes the site is well signed as you enter the village on the right.

Charges 2007

Per person	€ 5,30 - € 6,00
child (under 10 yrs)	€ 2,50 - € 3,50
pitch	€ 2,50 - € 7,00

FR20160 Camping Paradella

Route de la Forêt de Bonifato, Suare, F-20214 Calenzana (Haute-Corse)
Tel: 04 95 65 00 97. Email: info@camping-paradella.com

This site is owned by Antoine Hatt, once a winemaker, but now keen that you enjoy this out of town site with its natural surroundings. The facilities here are of a high standard and it has a new, fresh look, unlike many of the traditional sites on this coast. It is a back to nature site with 130 touring pitches, all with access to 3A electricity. Access is good, even for large units and the pitches are neat, shaded and level. One central tarmac road serves the pitches and the sanitary block is centrally placed. The site is very peaceful, other than a little road noise on one side.

Facilities

One central, modern sanitary block is very clean with British style toilets and hot showers. Hot water for sinks and laundry. Astro-turf ramps to facilities for disabled campers. Washing machines. Separate small kitchen for groups. Very good motorcaravan service point. Shop. Bar and snack bar/restaurant.(June - Sept). Pizzeria (June - Sept). Pool with pleasant patio (May - Sept). Satellite TV. Open sports area. Off site: Fishing 7 km. Riding 1 km. Bicycle hire 8 km. Beach, sailing 7 km.

Open: 1 May - 30 September.

Directions

Site is off the RN197 north of Calvi. Take the GR20 towards Suare and the 'Forêt de Bonifacio'. Site is well signed 7 km. along this road.

Charges 2007

Per person	€ 5,60 - € 6,40
child (under 7 yrs)	€ 2,00 - € 3,40
pitch	€ 5,60 - € 9,00
electricity	€ 3,20

FR20170 Camping Paduella

Route de Bastia, F-20260 Calvi (Haute-Corse)

Tel: **04 95 65 06 16**

Camping Paduella is a beautifully maintained, simple site which has been run by the friendly Peretti family for 40 years. As it is a popular site, it is best to book ahead for high season. There is a wide choice of pleasant pitches, some shaded under pines, others grassed and hedged with less shade. All are well maintained on level terraces with good access. The lovely white sand beach is 300 m. away and the picturesque town of Calvi is a delightful 30 minute walk. There is a fairly busy road and light railway to cross to get to the beach but most of the walk is through the shaded beach parkland.

Facilities

Two centrally located spotless modern sanitary blocks (British style WCs). Well equipped showers. Laundry with washing machines, ironing board. Small shop with basic supplies and fresh bread. Pizzeria and bar. Internet access. Play area. Sports ground. Fridge hire can be arranged. Off site: Supermarket and ATM 200 m. Riding and bicycle hire 700 m. Boat launching and marina 1 km. Adventure activities 200 m. Scuba diving, rowing and sailing nearby.

Open: 1 May - 15 October.

Directions

From the north, site is just before the town of Calvi. It is directly off the RN197 on the left and is well signed.

Charges 2007

Per person	€ 6,00 - € 7,30
child	€ 3,00 - € 3,65
pitch	€ 9,60 - € 10,60

No credit cards.

FR20180 Camping la Pinède

Route de la Pinède, F-20260 Calvi (Haute-Corse)

Tel: **04 95 65 17 80**. Email: **info@camping-calvi.com**

Camping La Pinède is a well ordered, family site of 185 touring pitches, all with 4-16A electricity. The pitches are marked and level (although the pine roots are a nuisance in places). There is access for large units in some areas. Water points are spread around the site and everything is kept tidy and clean. Under the mature pines it can be quite dark but there are plenty of alternatives in the light. The site is divided into areas of accommodation – pitches for tour operators, mobile homes and tourers. Unusually all facilities are in separate buildings.

Facilities

Three well maintained and well placed concrete sanitary buildings offer hot showers and facilities for disabled campers. Washing machines. Clean and fresh, the blocks are better than most on the west coast. Motorcaravan service point. Shop (June - Sept). Bar. Restaurant (May - Sept). Pool (no lifeguard). Internet access. Play area. Tennis. Off site: Fishing 200 m. Riding 500 m. Golf 22 km. Beach 200 m. Bicycle hire 2 km.

Open: 1 April – 31 October.

Directions

Site is north of Calvi off the RN197, just south of the D251 road to the airport. Look for signs off the roundabout here and take care along a narrow road with leaning fir trees.

Charges 2007

Per person	€ 6,50 - € 8,50
child (under 7 yrs)	€ 3,50 - € 4,50

FR20050 Camping Naturiste Club la Chiappa

Mobile homes ▶ page 512

F-20137 Porto-Vecchio (Corse-du-Sud)

Tel: **04 95 70 00 31**. Email: **chiappa@wanadoo.fr**

This is a large naturist campsite on the Chiappa peninsula with 220 pitches for tourers and tents, plus 250 bungalows. A few touring pitches have sea views and are taken first in high season. The pitches are informally marked and have a variety of shapes and sizes, some with difficult slopes and access, especially for large units. (75-125 sq.m.). Cars are parked separately. Very long electricity leads are necessary here for most pitches (10A) electricity. The beaches are between long rocky outcrops and it is generally safe to swim, or alternatively enjoy the swimming pool by the main beach.

Facilities

The sanitary facilities were tired and in need of refurbishment when we visited. Washing machines. Motorcaravan service point. Well stocked shop. Two bars and restaurants with snacks. Baby sitting service. Swimming pool. Play area for children. Riding. Tennis. Minigolf. Fishing. Diving, windsurfing and sailing schools. Keep fit, yoga, sauna (extra cost). Bistro. Satellite TV. Internet access. Torches essential. Off site: Excursions. Car rental. Bus to La Chiappa once a week (10 persons).

Open: 12 May - 6 October.

Directions

From Bastia, N198 heading south, take Porto-Vecchio bypass (signed Bonofaccio). At southern end, take first left signed Pont de la Chiappa, unclassified road. After 8 km. site signed. Turn left and follow rough track for 2 km. to site.

Charges guide

Per person	€ 8,00 - € 10,00
child (5-13 yrs)	€ 3,50 - € 4,50
pitch incl. electricity	€ 11,00 - € 13,50

Less for longer stays in low season.

Accommodation

Over recent years many of the campsites featured in this guide have added large numbers of high quality mobile homes and chalets. Many site owners believe that some former caravanners and motorcaravanners have been enticed by the extra comfort they can now provide, and that maybe this is the ideal solution to combine the freedom of camping with all the comforts of home.

Quality is consistently high and, although the exact size and inventory may vary from site to site, if you choose any of the sites detailed here, you can be sure that you're staying in some of the best quality and best value mobile homes available.

Home comforts are provided and typically these include a fridge with freezer compartment, gas hob, proper shower – often a microwave and radio/cassette hi-fi too but do check for details. All mobile homes and chalets come fully equipped with a good range of kitchen utensils, pots and pans, crockery, cutlery and outdoor furniture. Some even have an attractive wooden sundeck or paved terrace – a perfect spot for outdoors eating or relaxing with a book and watching the world go by.

Regardless of model, colourful soft furnishings are the norm and a generally breezy décor helps to provide a real holiday feel.

Although some sites may have a large number of different accommodation types, we have restricted our choice to one or two of the most popular accommodation units (either mobile homes or chalets) for each of the sites listed.

The mobile homes here will be of modern design, and recent innovations, for example, often include pitched roofs which substantially improve their appearance.

Design will invariably include clever use of space and fittings/furniture to provide for comfortable holidays – usually light and airy, with big windows and patio-style doors, fully equipped kitchen areas, a shower room with shower, washbasin and WC, cleverly designed bedrooms and a comfortable lounge/dining area (often incorporating a sofa bed).

In general, modern campsite chalets incorporate all the best features of mobile homes in a more traditional structure, sometimes with the advantage of an upper mezzanine floor for an additional bedroom.

Our selected campsites offer a massive range of different types of mobile home and chalet, and it would be impractical to inspect every single accommodation unit. Our selection criteria, therefore, primarily takes account of the quality standards of the campsite itself. However, there are a couple of important ground rules

- ☑ Featured mobile homes must be no more than 5 years old, and chalets no more than 10 years old.

- ☑ All listed accommodation must, of course, fully conform with all applicable local, national and European safety legislation.

For each campsite we given details of the type, or types, of accommodation available to rent, but these details are necessarily quite brief. Sometimes internal layouts can differ quite substantially, particularly with regard to sleeping arrangements, where these include the flexible provision for 'extra persons' on sofa beds located in the living area. These arrangements may vary from accommodation to accommodation, and if you're planning a holiday which includes more people than are catered for by the main bedrooms you should check exactly how the extra sleeping arrangements are to be provided!

Charges

An indication of the tariff for each type of accommodation featured is also included, indicating the variance between the low and high season tariffs. However, given that many campsites have a large and often complex range of pricing options, incorporating special deals and various discounts, the charges we mention should be taken to be just an indication. We strongly recommend therefore that you confirm the actual cost when making a booking.

We also strongly recommend that you check with the campsite, when booking, what (if anything) will be provided by way of bed linen, blankets, pillows etc. Again, in our experience, this can vary widely from site to site.

On every campsite a fully refundable deposit (usually between 150 and 300 euros) is payable on arrival. There may also be an optional cleaning service for which a further charge is made. Other options may include sheet hire (typically 30 euros per unit) or baby pack hire (cot and high chair).

FR29010 Castel Camping le Ty-Nadan

Route d'Arzano, F-29310 Locunolé (Finistère)   Open: 1 April - 7 September

For our full description of this campsite ▶ see page 29

AR1 – IRM – Mobile Home

Sleeping: 2 bedrooms, sleeps 6: 1 double, 2 single beds, sofa bed, pillows & blankets provided

Living: living/kitchen area, heating, shower & WC

Eating: fitted kitchen with hob, oven, fridge

Outside: table & chairs, 2 sun loungers, parasol

Pets: accepted

AR2 – WOODEN CHALET – Chalet

Sleeping: 2 bedrooms, sleeps 6: 1 double, 2 single beds, sofa bed, pillows & blankets provided

Living: living/kitchen area, heating, shower & WC

Eating: fitted kitchen with hob, fridge

Outside: table & chairs, 2 sun loungers, parasol

Pets: accepted

Weekly Charge	AR1	AR2
Low Season (from)	€ 357	€ 406
High Season (from)	€ 924	€ 1092

FR29050 Castel Camping l'Orangerie de Lanniron

Château de Lanniron, F-29336 Quimper (Finistère)   Open: 1 April - 31 October

For our full description of this campsite ▶ see page 30

AR1 – ZEN – Mobile Home

Sleeping: 3 bedrooms, sleeps 6: 1 double, 2 single beds, bunk bed, pillows & blankets provided

Living: living/kitchen area, heating, air conditioning, shower & separate WC

Eating: fitted kitchen with hob, microwave, coffee machine, fridge/freezer

Outside: table & chairs, 2 sun loungers, parasol, BBQ

Pets: not accepted

AR2 – CONFORT – Mobile Home

Sleeping: 2 bedrooms, sleeps 4/6: double, 2 single beds, bunk bed, sofa bed, pillows & blankets provided *(bed linen, childrens bed and chair for rent)*

Living: living/kitchen area, heating, radio, shower & separate wc

Eating: fitted kitchen with hob, microwave, coffee machine, fridge/freezer

Outside: table & chairs, 2 sun loungers, parasol, BBQ

Pets: not accepted

Weekly Charge	AR1	AR2
Low Season (from)	€ 448	€ 378
High Season (from)	€ 672	€ 595

FR29080 Camping le Panoramic

Route de la Plage-Penker, F-29560 Telgruc-sur-Mer (Finistère)   Open: 1 June - 15 September

For our full description of this campsite ▶ see page 31

AR1 – TRIGANO ELEGANTE 33 – Mobile Home

Sleeping: 3 bedrooms, sleeps 6: 1 double, 2 single beds, pillows & blankets provided

Living: living/kitchen area, heating, shower & WC

Eating: fitted kitchen with hob, fridge

Outside: table & chairs, 2 sun loungers, parasol, BBQ

Pets: accepted

AR2 – TRIGANO ELEGANTE 25 – Mobile Home

Sleeping: 2 bedrooms, sleeps 6: 1 double, 2 single beds, sofa bed, pillows & blankets provided

Living: living/kitchen area, heating, shower & WC

Eating: fitted kitchen with hob, fridge

Outside: tables & chairs, sun lounger, parasol, BBQ

Pets: accepted

Weekly Charge	AR1	AR2
Low Season (from)	€ 300	€ 250
High Season (from)	€ 660	€ 580

FR29090 Camping le Raguenès-Plage

19 rue des Iles, Raguenès, F-29920 Névez (Finistère)　　　　**Open:** 30 March - 23 September

For our full description of this campsite ▶ **see page 32**

AR1 – VARIANTE – Mobile Home

Sleeping: 2 bedrooms, sleeps 5: 1 double, 2 single beds, sofa bed, pillows & blankets provided

Living: living/kitchen area, heating, air conditioning, shower & separate WC

Eating: fitted kitchen with microwave, oven, coffee machine, fridge/freezer

Outside: table & chairs, 2 sun loungers, parasol, BBQ

Pets: not accepted

AR2 – O'HARA COTTAGE – Mobile Home

Sleeping: 2 bedrooms, sleeps 4/5: 1 double, 2 single beds, sofa bed, pillows & blankets provided *(bed linen, childrens bed and chair for rent)*

Living: living/kitchen area, heating, air conditioning, shower & separate wc

Eating: fitted kitchen with hob, microwave, coffee machine, fridge/freezer

Outside: table & chairs, 2 sun loungers, parasol, BBQ

Pets: not accepted

Weekly Charge	AR1	AR2
Low Season (from)	€ 320	€ 340
High Season (from)	€ 699	€ 740

FR29180 Camping les Embruns

Rue du Philosophe Alain, Le Pouldu, F-29360 Clohars-Carnoet (Finistère)　　**Open:** 7 April - 15 September

For our full description of this campsite ▶ **see page 36**

AR1 – CAMPITEL – Chalet

Sleeping: 3 bedrooms, sleeps 6: 2 doubles, bunk bed, sofa bed

Living: living/kitchen area, heating, shower & WC

Eating: fitted kitchen with hob, oven, coffee machine, fridge

Outside: table & chairs

Pets: accepted (with supplement)

AR2 – EMBRUNS – Mobile Home

Sleeping: 2 bedrooms, sleeps 4/6: 1 double, 2 single beds, sofa bed

Living: living/kitchen area, heating, shower & WC

Eating: fitted kitchen with hob, oven, coffee machine, fridge

Outside: table & chairs, parasol

Pets: accepted (with supplement)

Weekly Charge	AR1	AR2
Low Season (from)	€ 330	€ 330
High Season (from)	€ 680	€ 690

FR35000 Camping le Vieux Chêne

Baguer-Pican, F-35120 Dol-de-Bretagne (Ille-et-Vilaine)　　　　**Open:** 31 March - 22 September

For our full description of this campsite ▶ **see page 46**

AR1 – REVE CONFORT – Chalet

Sleeping: 2 bedrooms, sleeps 6: 1 double, 2 single beds, bunk bed, sofa bed, pillows & blankets provided

Living: living/kitchen area, heating, shower & separate WC

Eating: fitted kitchen with hob, oven, coffee machine, fridge/freezer

Outside: table & chairs

Pets: accepted (with supplement)

AR2 – COTTAGE DE BRETAGNE – Chalet

Sleeping: 2 bedrooms, sleeps 6: 1 double, 2 single beds, bunk bed, sofa bed, pillows & blankets provided

Living: living/kitchen area, heating, shower & separate wc

Eating: fitted kitchen with hob, oven, fridge/freezer

Outside: table & chairs

Pets: accepted (with supplement)

Weekly Charge	AR1	AR2
Low Season (from)	€ 400	€ 440
High Season (from)	€ 820	€ 700

483

FR44090 Camping Château du Deffay

B.P. 18 Le Deffay, F-44160 Pontchâteau (Loire-Atlantique)   **Open:** 1 April - 31 October

For our full description of this campsite ▶ **see page 53**

AR1 – MOBILE HOME 5 PERSONS – Mobile Home

Sleeping: 2 bedrooms, sleeps 5: 1 double, 1 single bed, bunk bed, pillows & blankets provided

Living: living/kitchen area, heating, radio, shower & separate WC

Eating: fitted kitchen with hob, microwave, coffee machine, fridge/freezer

Outside: table & chairs, 2 sun loungers, parasol, BBQ

Pets: not accepted

AR2 – CHALET 4/6 PERSONS – Chalet

Sleeping: 2 bedrooms, sleeps 6: 1 double, 2 bunk beds, sofa bed, pillows & blankets provided
(bed linen, childrens bed and chair for rent)

Living: living/kitchen area, heating, radio, shower & WC

Eating: fitted kitchen with hob, dishwasher, microwave, coffee machine, grill, fridge/freezer

Outside: table & chairs, 2 sun loungers, parasol, BBQ

Pets: not accepted

Weekly Charge	AR1	AR2
Low Season *(from)*	€ 209	€ 225
High Season *(from)*	€ 379	€ 399

FR44100 Sunêlia le Patisseau

29 rue du Patisseau, F-44210 Pornic (Loire-Atlantique)   **Open:** 8 April - 6 November

For our full description of this campsite ▶ **see page 51**

AR1 – CHALET 6 – Chalet

Sleeping: 2 bedrooms, sleeps 6: 1 double, 2 single beds, sofa bed, pillows & blankets provided

Living: living/kitchen area, heating, shower & WC

Eating: fitted kitchen with hob, microwave, fridge

Outside: table & chairs, parasol

Pets: not accepted

AR2 – MOBILE HOME 6 – Mobile Home

Sleeping: 2 bedrooms, sleeps 6: 1 double, 2 single beds, sofa bed, pillows & blankets provided

Living: living/kitchen area, heating, shower & WC

Eating: fitted kitchen with hob, microwave, fridge

Outside: table & chairs, parasol

Pets: not accepted

Weekly Charge	AR1	AR2
Low Season *(from)*	€ 430	€ 430
High Season *(from)*	€ 889	€ 889

FR44180 Camping de la Boutinardière

Rue de la Plage de la Boutinardière, F-44210 Pornic (Loire-Atlantique)   **Open:** 4 April - 4 October

For our full description of this campsite ▶ **see page 56**

AR1 – MOBILE HOME 5 PERSONS – Mobile Home

Sleeping: 2 bedrooms, sleeps 4/6: 1 double, 2 single beds, sofa bed, pillows & blankets provided

Living: living/kitchen area, heating, shower & WC

Eating: fitted kitchen with hob, fridge

Outside: table & chairs, parasol

Pets: not accepted

AR2 – MOBILE HOME 6 PERSONS – Mobile Home

Sleeping: 3 bedrooms, sleeps 6: 1 double, 4 single beds, pillows & blankets provided

Living: living/kitchen area, heating, shower & WC

Eating: fitted kitchen with hob, fridge

Outside: table & chairs, parasol

Pets: not accepted

Weekly Charge	AR1	AR2
Low Season *(from)*	€ 280	€ 350
High Season *(from)*	€ 800	€ 880

Check real time availability and at-the-gate prices...

www.**alanrogers**.com

FR44190 Camping le Fief

57, chemin du Fief, F-44250 St Brévin-les-Pins (Loire-Atlantique)   **Open:** 22 March - 5 October

For our full description of this campsite **see page 58**

AR1 – COTTAGE – Mobile Home

Sleeping: 3 bedrooms, sleeps 6: 1 double, 4 single beds

Living: living/kitchen area, shower & WC

Eating: fitted kitchen with hob, microwave, fridge

Outside: table & chairs

Pets: accepted (with supplement)

AR2 – COTTAGE – Mobile Home

Sleeping: 2 bedrooms, sleeps 6: 1 double, 2 single beds

Living: living/kitchen area, shower & WC

Eating: fitted kitchen with hob, microwave, fridge

Outside: table & chairs

Pets: accepted (with supplement)

Weekly Charge	AR1	AR2
Low Season *(from)*	€ 364	€ 364
High Season *(from)*	€ 910	€ 861

FR44210 Camping l'Océan

44490 Le Croisic (Loire-Atlantique)   **Open:** 5 April - 30 September

For our full description of this campsite **see page 56**

AR1 – COTTAGE OCÉAN – Mobile Home

Sleeping: 2 bedrooms, sleeps 4/6: 1 double, 2 single beds, sofa bed, pillows & blankets provided

Living: living/kitchen area, heating, shower & WC

Eating: fitted kitchen with hob, fridge

Outside: table & chairs, parasol

Pets: not accepted

AR2 – OCEAN GRAND CONFORT – Mobile Home

Sleeping: 3 bedrooms, sleeps 6: 1 double, 4 single beds, pillows & blankets provided

Living: living/kitchen area, shower & WC

Eating: fitted kitchen with hob, fridge

Outside: table & chairs, parasol

Pets: not accepted

Weekly Charge	AR1	AR2
Low Season *(from)*	€ 390	€ 435
High Season *(from)*	€ 850	€ 950

FR44220 Parc de Léveno

Route de Sandun, F-44350 Guérande (Loire-Atlantique)   **Open:** 5 April - 30 September

For our full description of this campsite **see page 56**

AR1 – COTTAGE 2 ROOMS – Mobile Home

Sleeping: 2 bedrooms, sleeps 6: 1 double, 2 single beds, sofa bed, pillows & blankets provided

Living: living/kitchen area, heating, shower & WC

Eating: fitted kitchen with hob, fridge

Outside: table & chairs, parasol

Pets: not accepted

AR2 – COTTAGE 3 ROOMS – Mobile Home

Sleeping: 3 bedrooms, sleeps 6: 1 double, 4 single beds, pillows & blankets provided

Living: living/kitchen area, shower & WC

Eating: fitted kitchen with hob, fridge

Outside: table & chairs, parasol

Pets: not accepted

Weekly Charge	AR1	AR2
Low Season *(from)*	€ 250	€ 275
High Season *(from)*	€ 750	€ 790

FR56280 Airotel les Sept Saints

B.P. 14, F-56410 Erdeven (Morbihan) Open: 31 March - 23 September

For our full description of this campsite (▶) **see page 71**

AR1 – GRAND CONFORT – Mobile Home

Sleeping: 2 bedrooms, sleeps 4/6: 1 double, 2 single beds, sofa bed

Living: living/kitchen area, shower & WC

Eating: fitted kitchen with hob, fridge

Outside: table & chairs, parasol, BBQ

Pets: accepted

AR2 – CHALET – Chalet

Sleeping: 2 bedrooms, sleeps 6: 1 double, 2 single beds, sofa bed

Living: living/kitchen area, heating, TV, shower & WC

Eating: fitted kitchen with hob, fridge

Outside: table & chairs, parasol, BBQ

Pets: accepted

Weekly Charge	AR1	AR2
Low Season (from)	€ 300	€ 330
High Season (from)	€ 760	€ 790

FR14070 Camping de la Vallée

88 rue de la Vallée, F-14510 Houlgate (Calvados) Open: 29 March - 2 November

For our full description of this campsite (▶) **see page 77**

AR1 – BUNGALOW 4 PERSONS – Mobile Home

Sleeping: 2 bedrooms, sleeps 4: 1 double, 2 single beds, pillows & blankets provided

Living: living/kitchen area, heating, shower & separate WC

Eating: fitted kitchen with hob, fridge

Outside: table & chairs, 2 sun loungers, parasol, BBQ

Pets: accepted (with supplement)

AR2 – BUNGALOW 6 PERSONS – Mobile Home

Sleeping: 2 bedrooms, sleeps 6: 1 double, 2 single beds, sofa bed

Living: living/kitchen area, heating, shower & separate WC

Eating: fitted kitchen with hob, fridge

Outside: table & chairs, 2 sun loungers, parasol, BBQ

Pets: accepted (with supplement)

Weekly Charge	AR1	AR2
Low Season (from)	€ 300	€ 370
High Season (from)	€ 690	€ 690

FR14160 Camping Bellevue

Route des Dives, F-14640 Villers sur Mer (Calvados) Open: 5 April - 30 September

For our full description of this campsite (▶) **see page 79**

AR1 – OCEANE OAKLEY PACIFIQUE – Mobile Home

Sleeping: 2 bedrooms, sleeps 4: 1 double, 2 single beds, pillows & blankets provided

Living: living/kitchen area, heating, shower & WC

Eating: fitted kitchen with hob, microwave, fridge

Outside: table & chairs, parasol

Pets: not accepted

AR2 – TAMARIS – Mobile Home

Sleeping: 3 bedrooms, sleeps 6: 1 double, 4 single beds, pillows & blankets provided

Living: living/kitchen area, heating, shower & WC

Eating: fitted kitchen with hob, microwave, fridge

Outside: table & chairs, parasol

Pets: not accepted

Weekly Charge	AR1	AR2
Low Season (from)	€ 290	€ 330
High Season (from)	€ 610	€ 660

FR27070 Camping l'Ile de Trois Rois

FR27700 Les Andelys (Eure)   **Open:** 13 March - 14 November

For our full description of this campsite ▶ **see page 83**

AR1 – Mobile Home

Sleeping: 2 bedrooms, sleeps 4: 1 double, 2 single beds

Living: living/kitchen area, heating, shower & WC

Eating: fitted kitchen with hob, fridge

Outside: table & chairs

Pets: not accepted

Weekly Charge	AR1
Low Season *(from)*	€ 280
High Season *(from)*	€ 480

FR80060 Camping le Val de Trie

Bouillancourt-sous-Miannay, F-80870 Moyenneville (Somme)   **Open:** 21 March - 15 October

For our full description of this campsite ▶ **see page 101**

AR1 – MORÉVA – Mobile Home

Sleeping: 2 bedrooms, sleeps 6: 1 double, 2 single beds, sofa bed , pillows & blankets provided

Living: living/kitchen area, heating, shower & separate WC

Eating: fitted kitchen with hob, microwave, coffee machine, fridge/freezer

Outside: table & chairs, parasol, BBQ

Pets: not accepted

AR2 – PRIVILEGE ZEN – Mobile Home

Sleeping: 3 bedrooms, sleeps 6: 1 double, 2 single beds,bunk bed, pillows & blankets provided *(bed linen and childrens chair for rent)*

Living: living/kitchen area, heating, radio, shower & separate WC

Eating: fitted kitchen with hob, microwave, dishwasher, coffee machine, fridge/freezer

Outside: table & chairs, 2 sun loungers, parasol, BBQ

Pets: not accepted

Weekly Charge	AR1	AR2
Low Season *(from)*	€ 259	€ 365
High Season *(from)*	€ 595	€ 693

FR80070 Camping la Ferme des Aulnes

1 rue du Marais, Fresne-sur-Authie, F-80120 Nampont-St Martin (Somme)   **Open:** 22 March - 3 November

For our full description of this campsite ▶ **see page 103**

AR1 – CONFORT – Mobile Home

Sleeping: 2 bedrooms, sleeps 5: 1 double, 2 single beds, sofa bed, pillows & blankets provided

Living: living/kitchen area, heating, TV, shower & separate WC

Eating: fitted kitchen with hob, microwave, coffee machine, fridge/freezer

Outside: table & chairs, parasol, BBQ

Pets: accepted (with supplement)

AR2 – PRIVILEGE – Mobile Home

Sleeping: 3 bedrooms, sleeps 6: 1 double, 2 single beds, pillows & blankets provided *(bed linen, childrens bed and chair for rent)*

Living: living/kitchen area, heating, TV (with DVD player), radio, hair dryer, shower & separate WC

Eating: fitted kitchen with hob, microwave, oven/grill, dishwasher, coffee machine, fridge/freezer

Outside: table & chairs, parasol, BBQ

Pets: accepted (with supplement)

Weekly Charge	AR1	AR2
Low Season *(from)*	€ 490	€ 590
High Season *(from)*	€ 690	€ 790

FR77020 Camping le Chêne Gris

24, place de la Gare de Faremoutiers, F-77515 Pommeuse (Seine-et-Marne)   **Open**: 25 April - 11 September

For our full description of this campsite **see page 108**

AR1 – BALI – Mobile Home

Sleeping: 2 bedrooms, sleeps 6: 1 double, 2 single beds, bunk bed, sofa bed , pillows & blankets provided

Living: living/kitchen area, heating, air conditioning, safe, shower & separate WC

Eating: fitted kitchen with hob, microwave, coffee machine, fridge/freezer

Outside: table & chairs, parasol

Pets: not accepted

AR2 – TAHITI – Mobile Home

Sleeping: 2 bedrooms, sleeps 5: 1 double, 2 single beds, bunk bed, pillows & blankets provided *(bed linen for rent)*

Living: living/kitchen area, heating, air conditioning, safe, 2 showers & 2 WC's

Eating: fitted kitchen with hob, microwave, coffee machine, fridge/freezer

Outside: table & chairs, 2 sun loungers

Pets: not accepted

Weekly Charge	AR1	AR2
Low Season *(from)*	€ 413	€ 441
High Season *(from)*	€ 763	€ 798

FR77060 Le Parc de la Colline

Route de Lagny, F-77200 Torcy (Seine-et-Marne)   **Open**: All year

For our full description of this campsite **see page 110**

AR1 – O'HARA – Mobile Home

Sleeping: 2 bedrooms, sleeps 6: 1 double, 2 single beds, sofa bed , pillows & blankets provided

Living: living/kitchen area, heating, shower & WC

Eating: fitted kitchen with hob, fridge

Outside: table & chairs

Pets: accepted (with supplement)

AR2 – NEVA – Chalet

Sleeping: 2 bedrooms, sleeps 4: 1 double, 2 bunk beds, pillows & blankets provided

Living: living/kitchen area, heating, shower & WC

Eating: fitted kitchen with hob, fridge

Outside: table & chairs

Pets: accepted (with supplement)

Weekly Charge	AR1	AR2
Low Season *(from)*	€ 701	€ 687
High Season *(from)*	€ 785	€ 687

FR52030 Camping Lac de la Liez

Peigney, F-52200 Langres (Haute-Marne)   **Open**: 1 April - 15 October

For our full description of this campsite **see page 131**

AR1 – COUNTRY LODGE – Chalet

Sleeping: 2 bedrooms, sleeps 6: 1 double, 2 single beds, sofa bed, bunk bed, pillows & blankets provided

Living: living/kitchen area, heating, shower & separate WC

Eating: fitted kitchen with hob, microwave, coffee machine, fridge/freezer

Outside: table & chairs, 2 sun loungers, parasol

Pets: accepted (with supplement)

AR2 – ZEN – Mobile Home

Sleeping: 3 bedrooms, sleeps 6: 1 double, 4 single beds, pillows & blankets provided

Living: living/kitchen area, heating, radio, shower & separate WC

Eating: fitted kitchen with hob, microwave, coffee machine, fridge/freezer

Outside: table & chairs, 2 sun loungers, parasol

Pets: accepted (with supplement)

Weekly Charge	AR1	AR2
Low Season *(from)*	€ 350	€ 273
High Season *(from)*	€ 756	€ 630

FR88040 Camping Club Lac de Bouzey

19 rue du Lac, F-88390 Sanchey (Vosges)　　　　　　　　　　**Open:** All year

For our full description of this campsite ▶ see page 125

AR1 – ABI – Mobile Home

Sleeping: 2 bedrooms, sleeps 4/6: 1 double, 2 single beds, sofa bed

Living: living/kitchen area, shower & WC

Eating: fitted kitchen with hob, microwave, fridge

Outside: table & chairs, 2 sun loungers, parasol, BBQ

Pets: accepted (on request)

AR2 – ZEN – Mobile Home

Sleeping: 3 bedrooms, sleeps 6: 1 double, 4 single beds

Living: living/kitchen area, shower & WC

Eating: fitted kitchen with hob, microwave & fridge/freezer

Outside: table & chairs, 2 sun loungers, parasol, BBQ

Pets: accepted (on request)

Weekly Charge	AR1	AR2
Low Season *(from)*	€ 250	€ 440
High Season *(from)*	€ 630	€ 840

FR88130 Camping Vanne de Pierre

5, rue du camping, F-88100 St Dié-des-Vosges (Vosges)　　　　　　**Open:** All year

For our full description of this campsite ▶ see page 128

AR1 – COUNTRY LODGE – Chalet

Sleeping: 2 bedrooms, sleeps 4/6: 1 double, 2 single beds, sofa bed

Living: living/kitchen area, shower & WC

Eating: fitted kitchen with hob, microwave, fridge

Outside: table & chairs, 2 sun loungers, parasol

Pets: accepted (on request)

AR2 – ZEN – Mobile Home

Sleeping: 3 bedrooms, sleeps 6: 1 double, 4 single beds

Living: living/kitchen area, heating, TV, shower & WC

Eating: fitted kitchen with hob, microwave & fridge

Outside: table & chairs, 2 sun loungers, parasol

Pets: accepted (on request)

Weekly Charge	AR1	AR2
Low Season *(from)*	€ 400	€ 350
High Season *(from)*	€ 840	€ 770

FR17070 Camping les Gros Joncs

Les Sables Vignier, F-17190 Saint-Georges-d'Oleron (Charente-Maritime)　　**Open:** All year

For our full description of this campsite ▶ see page 137

AR1 – O'HARA M36 – Mobile Home

Sleeping: 2 bedrooms, sleeps 6: 1 double, 2 single beds, sofa bed

Living: living/kitchen area, shower & separate WC

Eating: fitted kitchen with hob, microwave, fridge

Outside: table & chairs

Pets: not accepted

AR2 – PARADIS – Chalet

Sleeping: 3 bedrooms, sleeps 6/8: 1 double, 3 single beds *(bed linen for rent)*

Living: living/kitchen area with satelite TV & telephone, shower & separate WC

Eating: fitted kitchen with hob, microwave, fridge/freezer

Outside: table & chairs

Pets: not accepted

Weekly Charge	AR1	AR2
Low Season *(from)*	€ 410	€ 522
High Season *(from)*	€ 967	€ 1233

FR17010 Camping Bois Soleil

2 avenue de Suzac, F-17110 St Georges-de-Didonne (Charente-Maritime) **Open:** 4 February - 2 November

For our full description of this campsite ▶ **see page 134**

AR1 – O'HARA COTTAGE CHARME – Mobile Home

Sleeping: 2 bedrooms, sleeps 4: 1 double, 2 single beds, pillows & blankets provided

Living: living/kitchen area, heating, shower & WC

Eating: fitted kitchen with hob, microwave, fridge

Outside: table & chairs, parasol

Pets: not accepted

AR2 – BURSTNER COTTAGE CONFORT – Mobile Home

Sleeping: 2 bedrooms, sleeps 5: 1 double, 3 single beds, pillows & blankets provided

Living: living/kitchen area, heating, shower & WC

Eating: fitted kitchen with hob, microwave, fridge

Outside: table & chairs, parasol

Pets: not accepted

Weekly Charge	AR1	AR2
Low Season (from)	€ 238	€ 218
High Season (from)	€ 780	€ 720

FR17280 Camping la Grainetière

Route de Saint-Martin, F-17630 La Flotte en Ré (Charente-Maritime) **Open:** 4 April - 30 September

For our full description of this campsite ▶ **see page 145**

AR1 – CONFORT – Chalet

Sleeping: 2 bedrooms, sleeps 4/5: 1 double, 2 single beds, sofa bed

Living: living/kitchen area, shower & separate WC

Eating: fitted kitchen with hob, microwave, coffee machine, fridge

Outside: table & chairs, parasol

Pets: accepted

AR2 – LUXE – Mobile Home

Sleeping: 3 bedrooms, sleeps 6: 1 double, 4 single beds, sofa bed, pillows & blankets provided

Living: living/kitchen area, shower & separate WC

Eating: fitted kitchen with hob, microwave, coffee machine, fridge

Outside: table & chairs, parasol

Pets: accepted

Weekly Charge	AR1	AR2
Low Season (from)	€ 220	€ 255
High Season (from)	€ 725	€ 615

FR85150 Camping la Yole

Chemin des Bosses, Orouet, F-85160 St Jean-de-Monts (Vendée) **Open:** 5 April - 26 September

For our full description of this campsite ▶ **see page 151**

AR1 – LOUISIANE FLORÈS 3 – Mobile Home

Sleeping: 3 bedrooms, sleeps 6: 1 double, 4 single beds, pillows & blankets provided

Living: living/kitchen area, heating, shower & WC

Eating: fitted kitchen with hob, microwave, fridge/freezer

Outside: table & chairs, 2 sun loungers, parasol

Pets: not accepted

AR2 – LOUISIANE FLORÈS 2 – Mobile Home

Sleeping: 2 bedrooms, sleeps 6: 1 double, 2 single beds, sofa bed, pillows & blankets provided
(bed linen, childrens bed and chair for rent)

Living: living/kitchen area, heating, shower & WC

Eating: fitted kitchen with hob, microwave & fridge/freezer

Outside: table & chairs, 2 sun loungers, parasol

Pets: not accepted

Weekly Charge	AR1	AR2
Low Season (from)	€ 430	€ 395
High Season (from)	€ 810	€ 780

FR85210 Camping les Ecureuils

Route des Goffineaux, F-85520 Jard-sur-Mer (Vendée)   **Open:** 5 April - 27 September

For our full description of this campsite **see page 153**

AR1 – D – Mobile Home

Sleeping: 2 bedrooms, sleeps 6: 1 double, 2 single beds, sofa bed , pillows & blankets provided

Living: living/kitchen area, heating, shower & separate WC

Eating: fitted kitchen with hob, microwave, coffee machine, fridge

Outside: table & chairs 2 sun loungers, parasol

Pets: not accepted

AR2 – E2 – Mobile Home

Sleeping: 3 bedrooms, sleeps 6: 1 double, 4 single beds, pillows & blankets provided
(bed linen, childrens bed and chair for rent)

Living: living/kitchen area, heating, shower & separate WC

Eating: fitted kitchen with hob, microwave, coffee machine, fridge

Outside: table & chairs, 2 sun loungers, parasol

Pets: not accepted

Weekly Charge	AR1	AR2
Low Season *(from)*	€ 460	€ 490
High Season *(from)*	€ 730	€ 780

FR85480 Camping Caravaning le Chaponnet

Rue du Chaponnet N-16, F-85470 Brem sur Mer (Vendée)   **Open:** Easter - 3 September

For our full description of this campsite **see page 160**

AR1 – CLASSIC – Mobile Home

Sleeping: 2 bedrooms, sleeps 6: 1 double, 2 single beds, sofa bed, pillows & blankets provided

Living: living/kitchen area, heating, shower & separate WC

Eating: fitted kitchen with hob, fridge

Outside: table & chairs, 2 sun loungers, parasol

Pets: accepted (with supplement)

AR2 – GITOTEL – Chalet

Sleeping: 2 bedrooms, sleeps 5: 1 double, 2 single beds, bunk bed, sofa bed, pillows & blankets provided

Living: living/kitchen area, shower & separate WC

Eating: fitted kitchen with hob, fridge

Outside: table & chairs, 2 sun loungers, parasol

Pets: accepted (with supplement)

Weekly Charge	AR1	AR2
Low Season *(from)*	€ 250	€ 275
High Season *(from)*	€ 740	€ 750

FR37060 Camping l'Arada Parc

Rue de la Baratière, F-37360 Sonzay (Indre-et-Loire)   **Open:** 22 March - 25 October

For our full description of this campsite **see page 174**

AR1 – SAMIBOIS – Chalet

Sleeping: 3 bedrooms, sleeps 6: 2 doubles, 1 bunk bed, pillows & blankets provided

Living: living/kitchen area, heating, shower & separate WC

Eating: fitted kitchen with hob, microwave, coffee machine, fridge/freezer

Outside: table & chairs, BBQ

Pets: accepted

AR2 – BURSTNER – Mobile Home

Sleeping: 2 bedrooms, sleeps 5: 1 double, 1 single bed, 1 bunk bed, pillows & blankets provided
(bed linen, childrens bed and chair for rent)

Living: living/kitchen area, heating, radio, shower & separate WC

Eating: fitted kitchen with hob, microwave, coffee machine, fridge/freezer

Outside: table & chairs, parasol, BBQ

Pets: accepted

Weekly Charge	AR1	AR2
Low Season *(from)*	€ 345	€ 295
High Season *(from)*	€ 645	€ 595

FR41020 Castel Camping Château de la Grenouillière

F-41500 Suèvres (Loir-et-Cher) Open: 26 April - 6 September

For our full description of this campsite **see page 178**

AR1 – MOBILE HOME CONFORT – Mobile Home	AR2 – GITOTEL – Chalet
Sleeping: 3 bedrooms, sleeps 6: 1 double, 4 single beds, sofa bed, pillows & blankets provided	**Sleeping:** 2 bedrooms, sleeps 6: 2 doubles, 1 single bed, sofa bed, pillows & blankets provided
Living: living/kitchen area, heating, shower & separate WC	**Living:** living/kitchen area, heating, shower & separate WC
Eating: fitted kitchen with hob, fridge	**Eating:** fitted kitchen with hob, fridge
Outside: table & chairs, parasol, BBQ	**Outside:** table & chairs, parasol, BBQ
Pets: not accepted	**Pets:** not accepted

Weekly Charge	AR1	AR2
Low Season *(from)*	€ 450	€ 400
High Season *(from)*	€ 830	€ 760

FR41010 Le Parc du Val de Loire

Route de Fleuray, F-41150 Mesland (Loir-et-Cher) Open: 5 April - 27 September

For our full description of this campsite **see page 182**

AR1 – O'HARA LUXE – Mobile Home	AR2 – STAR – Chalet
Sleeping: 2 bedrooms, sleeps 6: 1 double, 2 single beds, bunk bed, sofa bed, pillows & blankets provided	**Sleeping:** 3 bedrooms, sleeps 7: 1 double, 2 single beds, bunk bed, sofa bed, pillows & blankets provided
Living: living/kitchen area, heating, shower & separate WC	**Living:** living/kitchen area, heating, shower & separate WC
Eating: fitted kitchen with hob, microwave, coffee machine, fridge/freezer	**Eating:** fitted kitchen with hob, microwave, coffee machine, fridge/freezer
Outside: table & chairs, 2 sun loungers, parasol, BBQ (with supplement)	**Outside:** table & chairs, 2 sun loungers, parasol, BBQ
Pets: accepted (with supplement)	**Pets:** accepted (with supplement)

Weekly Charge	AR1	AR2
Low Season *(from)*	€ 195	€ 195
High Season *(from)*	€ 660	€ 630

FR41070 Camping Caravaning la Grande Tortue

3 route de Pontlevoy, F-41120 Candé-sur-Beuvron (Loir-et-Cher) Open: 5 April - 20 September

For our full description of this campsite **see page 181**

AR1 – IRM SUPER MERCURE – Mobile Home	AR2 – CLASS 4 – Chalet
Sleeping: 2 bedrooms, sleeps 5: 1 double, 2 single beds, bunk bed, pillows & blankets provided	**Sleeping:** 2 bedrooms, sleeps 6: 1 double, 2 single beds, bunk bed, pillows & blankets provided *(bed linen and childrens chair for rent)*
Living: living/kitchen area, heating, safe, shower & separate WC	**Living:** living/kitchen area, heating, safe, shower & separate WC
Eating: fitted kitchen with hob, microwave, coffee machine, fridge	**Eating:** fitted kitchen with hob, coffee machine, microwave, fridge
Outside: table & chairs, 2 sun loungers	**Outside:** table & chairs, 2 sun loungers
Pets: accepted	**Pets:** accepted

Weekly Charge	AR1	AR2
Low Season *(from)*	€ 321	€ 436
High Season *(from)*	€ 665	€ 728

FR49040 Camping de l'Etang

Route de St Mathurin, F-49320 Brissac (Maine-et-Loire)

Open: 1 May - 15 September

For our full description of this campsite ⊙ see page 185

AR1 – WILLERBY – Mobile Home

Sleeping: 2 bedrooms, sleeps 6: 1 double, 2 single beds, bunk bed, sofa bed, pillows & blankets provided

Living: living/kitchen area, heating, shower & separate WC

Eating: fitted kitchen with hob, fridge

Outside: table & chairs, sun lounger, parasol, BBQ

Pets: accepted (with supplement)

AR2 – CONCORDE – Mobile Home

Sleeping: 2 bedrooms, sleeps 5: 1 double, 2 single beds, bunk bed, sofa bed, pillows & blankets provided

Living: living/kitchen area, heating, shower & separate WC *(childrens chair for rent)*

Eating: fitted kitchen with hob, fridge/freezer

Outside: table & chairs, sun loungers, parasol, BBQ

Pets: accepted (with supplement)

Weekly Charge	AR1	AR2
Low Season *(from)*	€ 455	€ 350
High Season *(from)*	€ 650	€ 565

FR49060 Camping Parc de Montsabert

Montsabert, F-49320 Coutures (Maine-et-Loire)

Open: 12 April - 16 September

For our full description of this campsite ⊙ see page 184

AR1 – MOBILE HOME 4 PERSONS – Mobile Home

Sleeping: 2 bedrooms, sleeps 4: 1 double, 2 single beds

Living: living/kitchen area, shower & separate WC

Eating: fitted kitchen with hob, microwave, fridge

Outside: table & chairs, 2 sun loungers, parasol

Pets: accepted (with supplement)

AR2 – CHALET 1/4 PERSONS – Chalet

Sleeping: 2 bedrooms, sleeps 4: 1 double, 2 single beds *(childrens bed and chair for rent)*

Living: living/kitchen area, shower & WC

Eating: fitted kitchen with hob, microwave, fridge

Outside: table & chairs, 2 sun loungers, parasol

Pets: accepted (with supplement)

Weekly Charge	AR1	AR2
Low Season *(from)*	€ 290	€ 319
High Season *(from)*	€ 621	€ 755

FR86040 Camping le Futuriste

F-86130 St Georges-les-Baillargeaux (Vienne)

Open: All year

For our full description of this campsite ⊙ see page 191

AR1 – FABRE 2012 – Chalet

Sleeping: 2 bedrooms, sleeps 6: 1 double, 2 single beds, sofa bed , pillows & blankets provided

Living: living/kitchen area, heating, TV, shower & WC

Eating: fitted kitchen with hob, microwave, fridge

Outside: table & chairs

Pets: not accepted

AR2 – CHALET – Chalet

Sleeping: 2 bedrooms, sleeps 4: 1 double, 2 single beds

Living: living/kitchen area, heating, TV, shower & WC

Eating: fitted kitchen with hob, microwave & fridge/freezer

Outside: table & chairs

Pets: not accepted

Weekly Charge	AR1	AR2
Low Season *(from)*	€ 252	€ 275
High Season *(from)*	€ 323	€ 370

Check real time availability and at-the-gate prices...

www.**alanrogers**.com

FR58030 Castel Camping le Manoir de Bezolle

F-58110 Saint Pereuse-en-Morvan (Nièvre)　　　　　　　**Open:** Easter - 31 October

For our full description of this campsite ▶ **see page 198**

AR1 – MOBILE HOME – Mobile Home

Sleeping: 2 bedrooms, sleeps 4/6: 1 double, 2 single beds, sofa bed, pillows & blankets provided

Living: living/kitchen area, heating, shower & separate WC

Eating: fitted kitchen with hob, microwave, coffee machine, fridge/freezer

Outside: table & chairs, sun lounger, parasol, BBQ

Pets: not accepted

AR2 – CHALET – Chalet

Sleeping: 2-3 bedrooms, sleeps 4/6: 1 double, 2 single beds, sofa bed, pillows & blankets provided *(bed linen, childrens bed and chair for rent)*

Living: living/kitchen area, heating, shower & separate WC

Eating: fitted kitchen with hob, microwave, coffee machine, fridge

Outside: table & chairs, sun loungers, parasol, BBQ

Pets: not accepted

Weekly Charge	AR1	AR2
Low Season *(from)*	€ 260	€ 300
High Season *(from)*	€ 390	€ 650

FR71070 Castel Camping Château de l'Epervière

F-71240 Gigny-sur-Saône (Saône-et-Loire)　　　　　**Open:** 1 April - 30 September

For our full description of this campsite ▶ **see page 202**

AR1 – LOUISIANE ZEN – Mobile Home

Sleeping: 3 bedrooms, sleeps 6: 1 double, 2 single beds, bunk bed, pillows & blankets provided

Living: living/kitchen area, heating, TV, radio, shower & separate WC

Eating: fitted kitchen with hob, microwave, coffee machine, fridge/freezer

Outside: table & chairs, 2 sun loungers, parasol

Pets: not accepted

AR2 – APPARTMENT – Appartment

Sleeping: 2 bedrooms, sleeps 5: 1 double, 1 single bed, bunk bed, pillows & blankets provided *(bed linen, childrens bed and chair for rent)*

Living: living/kitchen area, heating, TV, shower & separate WC

Eating: fitted kitchen with hob, oven, coffee machine, fridge/freezer

Outside: table & chairs

Pets: not accepted

Weekly Charge	AR1	AR2
Low Season *(from)*	€ 373	€ 150
High Season *(from)*	€ 799	€ 395

FR25080 Camping les Fuvettes

F-25160 Malbuisson (Doubs)　　　　　　　　　　**Open:** 1 April - 1 October

For our full description of this campsite ▶ **see page 209**

AR1 – MOBILE HOME 800 – Mobile Home

Sleeping: 2 bedrooms, sleeps 4/5: 1 double, 2 single beds, sofa bed, pillows & blankets provided

Living: living/kitchen area, heating, shower & separate WC

Eating: fitted kitchen with hob, microwave, coffee machine, fridge/freezer

Outside: table & chairs, parasol

Pets: accepted (with supplement)

AR2 – CHALET 4/5 PERSONS – Chalet

Sleeping: 2 bedrooms, sleeps 5: 1 double, 3 single beds, pillows & blankets provided *(bed linen, childrens bed and chair for rent)*

Living: living/kitchen area, heating shower & WC

Eating: fitted kitchen with hob, microwave, coffee machine, fridge

Outside: table & chairs

Pets: accepted (with supplement)

Weekly Charge	AR1	AR2
Low Season *(from)*	€ 260	€ 295
High Season *(from)*	€ 550	€ 600

FR73030 Camping les Lanchettes

F-73210 Peisey-Nancroix (Savoie) **Open:** 15 December - 30 September

For our full description of this campsite ⊙ **see page 232**

AR1 – CHALET 1 – Chalet

Sleeping: 2 bedrooms, sleeps 4/5: 1 double, 2 single beds

Living: living/kitchen area, shower & WC

Eating: fitted kitchen with hob, oven, dishwasher, fridge

Outside: table & chairs, parasol

Pets: not accepted

AR2 – CHALET - BALLARIO – Chalet

Sleeping: 2 bedrooms, sleeps 4/6: 1 double, 4 single beds

Living: living/kitchen area, shower & separate WC

Eating: fitted kitchen with hob, oven, fridge

Outside: table & chairs & parasol

Pets: not accepted

Weekly Charge	AR1	AR2
Low Season (from)	€ 300	€ 300
High Season (from)	€ 580	€ 580

FR33110 Airotel Camping de la Côte d'Argent

F-33990 Hourtin-Plage (Gironde) **Open:** 17 May - 14 September

For our full description of this campsite ⊙ **see page 240**

AR1 – LOUISIANE SAVANNAH – Mobile Home

Sleeping: 2 bedrooms, sleeps 4/6: 1 double, 2 single beds, sofa bed, pillows & blankets provided

Living: living/kitchen area, shower & WC

Eating: fitted kitchen with hob, microwave, coffee machine, fridge/freezer

Outside: picnic table & benches, parasol

Pets: not accepted

AR2 – O'HARA SUPER FAMILY – Mobile home

Sleeping: 3 bedrooms, sleeps 6: 1 double, 4 single beds, pillows & blankets provided

Living: living/kitchen area shower & WC

Eating: fitted kitchen with hob, microwave, coffee machine, fridge/freezer

Outside: picnic table & benches, parasol

Pets: not accepted

Weekly Charge	AR1	AR2
Low Season (from)	€ 420	€ 476
High Season (from)	€ 945	€ 1015

FR33130 Yelloh! Village les Grands Pins

Plage Nord, F-33680 Lacanau-Océan (Gironde) **Open:** 26 April - 20 September

For our full description of this campsite ⊙ **see page 243**

AR1 – PREMIER – Mobile Home

Sleeping: 2 bedrooms, sleeps 4: 1 double, 2 single beds, pillows & blankets provided

Living: living/kitchen area, heating, shower & separate WC

Eating: fitted kitchen with hob, microwave, coffee machine, fridge

Outside: table & chairs, 2 sun loungers, parasol

Pets: accepted

AR2 – SUNSET – Mobile Home

Sleeping: 3 bedrooms, sleeps 6: 1 double, 4 single beds, pillows & blankets provided
(bed linen, childrens bed and chair for rent)

Living: living/kitchen area, heating, shower & separate WC

Eating: fitted kitchen with hob, microwave, dishwasher, fridge/freezer

Outside: table & chairs, 2 sun loungers, parasol

Pets: accepted

Weekly Charge	AR1	AR2
Low Season (from)	€ 224	€ 378
High Season (from)	€ 854	€ 1148

FR33220 Sunêlia le Petit Nice

Route de Biscarosse, F-33115 Pyla-sur-Mer (Gironde)   **Open:** 1 April - 30 September

For our full description of this campsite ▶ see page 245

AR1 – COTTAGE – Mobile Home

Sleeping: 2 bedrooms, sleeps 4: 1 double, 2 single beds, pillows & blankets provided

Living: living/kitchen area, heating, shower & WC

Eating: fitted kitchen with hob, fridge

Outside: table & chairs

Pets: accepted (with supplement)

AR2 – SUNÊLIA FAMILY – Mobile Home

Sleeping: 3 bedrooms, sleeps 6: 1 double, 2 single beds, bunk bed, pillows & blankets provided
(bed linen, childrens bed and chair for rent)

Living: living/kitchen area, shower & separate WC

Eating: fitted kitchen with hob, microwave, fridge

Outside: table & chairs

Pets: accepted (with supplement)

Weekly Charge	AR1	AR2
Low Season (from)	€ 392	€ 602
High Season (from)	€ 700	€ 1064

FR40100 Camping du Domaine de la Rive

Route de Bordeaux, F-40600 Biscarosse (Landes)   **Open:** 5 April - 7 September

For our full description of this campsite ▶ see page 254

AR1 – SAVANAH – Mobile Home

Sleeping: 2 bedrooms, sleeps 6: 1 double, 2 single beds, sofa bed, pillows & blankets provided

Living: living/kitchen area, heating, shower & WC

Eating: fitted kitchen with hob, microwave, fridge/freezer

Outside: table & chairs, 2 sun loungers, parasol

Pets: not accepted

AR2 – COTTAGE 3 – Mobile Home

Sleeping: 3 bedrooms, sleeps 6: 1 double, 4 single beds, pillows & blankets provided

Living: living/kitchen area, shower & WC

Eating: fitted kitchen with hob, microwave, fridge/freezer

Outside: table & chairs, parasol

Pets: not accepted

Weekly Charge	AR1	AR2
Low Season (from)	€ 306	€ 318
High Season (from)	€ 1008	€ 1001

FR40140 Camping Caravaning Lou P'tit Poun

110 avenue du Quartier Neuf, F-40390 St Martin de Seignanx (Landes)   **Open:** 1 June - 15 September

For our full description of this campsite ▶ see page 257

AR1 – FABRE REVE – Chalet

Sleeping: 2 bedrooms, sleeps 5: 1 double, 3 single beds

Living: living/kitchen area, shower & WC

Eating: fitted kitchen with hob, fridge

Outside: table & chairs, 2 sun loungers

Pets: not accepted

AR2 – IRM MERCURE – Mobile Home

Sleeping: 2 bedrooms, sleeps 5: 1 double, 2 single beds, sofa bed

Living: living/kitchen area, shower & WC

Eating: fitted kitchen with hob, fridge

Outside: table & chairs, 2 sun loungers

Pets: not accepted

Weekly Charge	AR1	AR2
Low Season (from)	€ 285	€ 275
High Season (from)	€ 695	€ 675

FR40180 Camping le Vieux Port

Plage sud, F-40660 Messanges (Landes)

Open: 18 March - 30 September

For our full description of this campsite ▶ see page 259

AR1 – MOBILE HOME

Sleeping: 2 bedrooms, sleeps 4: 1 double, 2 single beds, pillows & blankets provided

Living: living/kitchen area, heating, shower & WC

Eating: fitted kitchen with hob, oven, fridge

Outside: table & chairs, parasol

Pets: not accepted

AR2 – CHALET

Sleeping: 2 bedrooms, sleeps 4/5: 1 double, 3 single beds, pillows & blankets provided

Living: living/kitchen area, heating, shower & WC

Eating: fitted kitchen with hob, oven, fridge/freezer

Outside: table & chairs, 2 sun loungers, parasol

Pets: not accepted

Weekly Charge	AR1	AR2
Low Season (from)	€ 285	€ 360
High Season (from)	€ 690	€ 1000

FR40190 Le Saint Martin Airotel Camping

Avenue de l'Océan, F-40660 Moliets-Plage (Landes)

Open: 19 March - 11 November

For our full description of this campsite ▶ see page 258

AR1 – DUO – Chalet

Sleeping: 1 bedrooms, sleeps 3: 1 double, 1 single bed, pillows & blankets provided

Living: living/kitchen area, heating, safe, shower & separate WC

Eating: fitted kitchen with hob, microwave, coffee machine, fridge/freezer

Outside: table & chairs

Pets: accepted (with supplement)

AR2 – ZEPHYR – Chalet

Sleeping: 2 bedrooms, sleeps 5: 1 double, 2 single beds, one persons sofa bed, pillows & blankets provided

Living: living/kitchen area, heating, safe, shower & separate WC

Eating: fitted kitchen with hob, microwave, coffee machine, fridge/freezer

Outside: table & chairs, 2 sun loungers

Pets: accepted (with supplement)

Weekly Charge	AR1	AR2
Low Season (from)	€ 179	€ 527
High Season (from)	€ 525	€ 1250

FR40200 Yelloh! Village le Sylvamar

Avenue de l'Océan, F-40530 Labenne Océan (Landes)

Open: 26 April - 17 September

For our full description of this campsite ▶ see page 262

AR1 – COTTAGE 4/6 – Mobile Home

Sleeping: 2 bedrooms, sleeps 4/6: 1 double, 2 single beds, sofa bed, pillows & blankets provided

Living: living/kitchen area, heating, shower & separate WC

Eating: fitted kitchen with hob, microwave, coffee machine, fridge/freezer

Outside: table & chairs, 2 sun loungers, parasol

Pets: not accepted

AR2 – CHALET – Chalet VIP/Ocean

Sleeping: 2 bedrooms, sleeps 6: 1 double, 2 single beds, sofa bed, pillows & blankets provided *(bed linen, childrens bed and chair for rent)*

Living: living/kitchen area, heating, shower & WC

Eating: fitted kitchen with hob, microwave, coffee machine, dishwasher, fridge/freezer

Outside: table & chairs, 2 sun loungers, BBQ

Pets: not accepted

Weekly Charge	AR1	AR2
Low Season (from)	€ 203	€ 455
High Season (from)	€ 980	€ 1365

FR64110 Sunêlia Col d'Ibardin

F-64122 Urrugne (Pyrénées-Atlantiques) **Open:** 21 March - 2 November

For our full description of this campsite ▶ **see page 267**

AR1 – O'HARA 4 – Mobile Home

Sleeping: 2 bedrooms, sleeps 4: 1 double, 2 single beds pillows & blankets provided

Living: living/kitchen area, heating, shower & separate WC

Eating: fitted kitchen with hob, microwave, coffee machine, fridge/freezer

Outside: table & chairs, parasol

Pets: not accepted

AR2 – O'HARA 6 – Mobile Home

Sleeping: 3 bedrooms, sleeps 6: 1 double, 4 single beds, pillows & blankets provided

Living: living/kitchen area, heating, shower & separate WC

Eating: fitted kitchen with hob, microwave, coffee machine, fridge/freezer

Outside: table & chairs

Pets: not accepted

Weekly Charge	AR1	AR2
Low Season (from)	€ 336	€ 448
High Season (from)	€ 602	€ 700

FR64150 Airotel Residence des Pins

Avenue de Biarritz, F-64210 Bidart (Pyrénées-Atlantiques) **Open:** 7 May - 20 September

For our full description of this campsite ▶ **see page 269**

AR1 – O'HARA – Mobile Home

Sleeping: 2 bedrooms, sleeps 6: 1 double, 2 single beds, sofa bed

Living: living/kitchen area, heating, shower & WC

Eating: fitted kitchen with hob, fridge

Outside: table & chairs, 2 sun loungers, parasol

Pets: not accepted

AR2 – CHALET – Chalet

Sleeping: 2 bedrooms, sleeps 5: 2 doubles, 2 bunk beds

Living: living/kitchen area, shower & WC

Eating: fitted kitchen with hob, fridge

Outside: table & chairs, parasol

Pets: not accepted

Weekly Charge	AR1	AR2
Low Season (from)	€ 315	€ 294
High Season (from)	€ 735	€ 672

FR24010 Camping Château le Verdoyer

Champs Romain, F-24470 St Pardoux (Dordogne) **Open:** 26 April - 8 October

For our full description of this campsite ▶ **see page 286**

AR1 – ATLAS – Mobile Home

Sleeping: 2 bedrooms, sleeps 6: 2 doubles, 2 single beds, sofa bed, pillows & blankets provided

Living: living/kitchen area, heating, shower & WC

Eating: fitted kitchen with hob, microwave & fridge

Outside: table & chairs, 2 sun loungers, parasol

Pets: not accepted

AR2 – BÜRSTNER – Mobile Home

Sleeping: 2 bedrooms, sleeps 7: 1 double, 2 single beds, bunk bed, sofa bed, pillows & blankets provided

Living: living/kitchen area, heating, shower & WC.

Eating: fitted kitchen with hob, microwave, fridge

Outside: table & chairs, 2 sun loungers, parasol

Pets: not accepted

Weekly Charge	AR1	AR2
Low Season (from)	€ 270	€ 270
High Season (from)	€ 630	€ 630

499

Check real time availability and at-the-gate prices...

www.**alanrogers**.com

FR24020 Camping Caravaning les Granges

F-24250 Grolejac-en-Perigord (Dordogne)   **Open:** 26 April - 11 September

For our full description of this campsite ▶ see page 287

AR1 – REVE CONFORT – Mobile Home	AR2 – O'HARA – Mobile Home
Sleeping: 2 bedrooms, sleeps 4/5: 1 double, 2 single beds, sofa bed, pillows & blankets provided	**Sleeping:** 3 bedrooms, sleeps: 6, 1 double, 4 single beds, pillows & blankets provided
Living: living/kitchen area, heating, shower & separate WC	**Living:** living/kitchen area, heating, shower & separate WC
Eating: fitted kitchen with hob, microwave, coffee machine, fridge	**Eating:** fitted kitchen with hob, microwave, coffee machine, fridge
Outside: table & chairs, 2 sun loungers, BBQ	**Outside:** table & chairs, sun loungers, BBQ
Pets: accepted (with supplement)	**Pets:** accepted (with supplement)

Weekly Charge	AR1	AR2
Low Season *(from)*	€ 525	€ 525
High Season *(from)*	€ 767	€ 850

FR24090 Camping Soleil Plage

Caudon par Montfort, Vitrac, F-24200 Sarlat-la-Canéda (Dordogne)   **Open:** 11 April - 11 November

For our full description of this campsite ▶ see page 289

AR1 – REVE – Chalet	AR2 – SUPER MERCURE – Mobile Home
Sleeping: 2 bedrooms, sleeps 5/7: 1 double, 2 single beds, bunk bed, pillows & blankets provided	**Sleeping:** 2 bedrooms, sleeps 4/6: 1 double, 2 single beds, sofa bed, pillows & blankets provided *(bed linen, childrens bed and chair for rent)*
Living: living/kitchen area, heating, TV, shower & WC	**Living:** living/kitchen area, heating, shower & separate WC
Eating: fitted kitchen with hob, microwave, coffee machine, fridge	**Eating:** fitted kitchen with hob, coffee machine, fridge
Outside: table & chairs, 2 sun loungers, parasol, BBQ	**Outside:** table & chairs, 2 sun loungers, parasol, BBQ
Pets: accepted (with supplement)	**Pets:** accepted (with supplement)

Weekly Charge	AR1	AR2
Low Season *(from)*	€ 310	€ 280
High Season *(from)*	€ 800	€ 750

FR24130 Camping les Grottes de Roffy

Ste Nathalène, F-24200 Sarlat-la-Canéda (Dordogne)   **Open:** 26 April - 21 September

For our full description of this campsite ▶ see page 284

AR1 – O'HARA 2 BEDROOMS – Mobile Home	AR2 – O'HARA 3 BEDROOMS – Mobile Home
Sleeping: 2 bedrooms, sleeps 6/7: 1 double, 2 single beds, bunk bed, sofa bed, pillows & blankets provided	**Sleeping:** 3 bedrooms, sleeps 6/7: 1 double, 4 single beds, sofa bed, pillows & blankets provided *(bed linen, childrens chair for rent)*
Living: living/kitchen area, heating, shower & separate WC	**Living:** living/kitchen area, shower & separate WC
Eating: fitted kitchen with hob, microwave, coffee machine, fridge/freezer	**Eating:** fitted kitchen with hob, microwave, coffee machine, fridge/freezer
Outside: table & chairs, 2 sun loungers, parasol, BBQ	**Outside:** table & chairs, 2 sun loungers, parasol, BBQ
Pets: accepted	**Pets:** accepted

Weekly Charge	AR1	AR2
Low Season *(from)*	€ 270	€ 280
High Season *(from)*	€ 790	€ 860

Check real time availability and at-the-gate prices...

 www.**alanrogers**.com

FR24160 Camping le Grand Dague

Atur, F-24750 Périgueux (Dordogne)

Open: 5 May - 28 September

For our full description of this campsite see page 293

AR1 – BALI – Mobile Home

Sleeping: 2 bedrooms, sleeps 6: 1 double, 2 single beds, bunk bed, sofa bed, pillows & blankets provided

Living: living/kitchen area, heating, shower & separate WC

Eating: fitted kitchen with hob, microwave, fridge/freezer

Outside: table & chairs, 2 sun loungers, parasol

Pets: not accepted

AR2 – WAIKIKI – Mobile Home

Sleeping: 3 bedrooms, sleeps 6: 1 double, 4 single beds, sofa bed, pillows & blankets provided *(childrens bed and chair for rent)*

Living: living/kitchen area, heating, air conditioning, shower & separate WC

Eating: fitted kitchen with hob, microwave, fridge/freezer

Outside: table & chairs, 2 sun loungers, parasol

Pets: accepted

Weekly Charge	AR1	AR2
Low Season *(from)*	€ 180	€ 234
High Season *(from)*	€ 336	€ 441

FR24320 Camping les Peneyrals

Le Poujol, F-24590 St Crépin-Carlucet (Dordogne)

Open: 10 May - 13 September

For our full description of this campsite see page 295

AR1 – MERCURE – Mobile Home

Sleeping: 2 bedrooms, sleeps 4/5: 1 double, 2 single beds, sofa bed, pillows & blankets provided

Living: living/kitchen area, heating, shower & separate WC

Eating: fitted kitchen with hob, microwave, coffee machine, fridge

Outside: table & chairs, 2 sun loungers, parasol, BBQ

Pets: accepted (with supplement)

AR2 – EQUINOXE – Chalet

Sleeping: 3 bedrooms, sleeps 6/7: 1 double, 4 single beds, sofa bed, pillows & blankets provided *(bed linen for rent, childrens bed and chair for free - on demand)*

Living: living/kitchen area, heating, TV, shower & separate WC

Eating: fitted kitchen with hob, microwave, coffee machine, fridge

Outside: table & chairs, 2 sun loungers, parasol, BBQ

Pets: accepted (with supplement)

Weekly Charge	AR1	AR2
Low Season *(from)*	€ 300	€ 460
High Season *(from)*	€ 800	€ 940

FR46010 Castel Camping le Domaine de la Paille Basse

F-46200 Souillac-sur-Dordogne (Lot)

Open: 15 May - 15 September

For our full description of this campsite see page 307

AR1 – LUXE – Mobile Home

Sleeping: 2 bedrooms, sleeps 6: 1 double, 2 single beds, childrens bed, sofa bed

Living: living/kitchen area, shower & WC

Eating: fitted kitchen with hob, microwave, fridge

Outside: table & chairs, 2 sun loungers, parasol, BBQ

Pets: not accepted

AR2 – GRAND LUXE – Mobile Home

Sleeping: 3 bedrooms, sleeps 6: 1 double, 2 single beds, 2 bunk beds, pillows & blankets provided

Living: living/kitchen area, heating, radio, shower & WC

Eating: fitted kitchen with hob, fridge

Outside: table & chairs, 2 sun loungers, parasol, BBQ

Pets: not accepted

Weekly Charge	AR1	AR2
Low Season *(from)*	€ 270	€ 290
High Season *(from)*	€ 710	€ 810

FR47010 Camping Caravaning Moulin du Périé

F-47500 Sauveterre-la-Lemance (Lot-et-Garonne)　　　　　**Open:** 7 May - 20 September

For our full description of this campsite ◉ **see page 313**

AR1 – IRM SUPER MERCURE – Mobile Home

Sleeping: 2 bedrooms, sleeps 6: 2 doubles, 2 single beds, pillows & blankets provided

Living: living/kitchen area, heating, shower & WC

Eating: fitted kitchen with hob, fridge

Outside: table & chairs, parasol

Pets: not accepted

AR2 – HAVITAT RÊVE – Chalet

Sleeping: 2 bedrooms, sleeps 7: 2 doubles, 2 single beds, bunk bed, pillows & blankets provided

Living: living/kitchen area, heating, shower & WC

Eating: fitted kitchen with hob, fridge

Outside: table & chairs, parasol

Pets: not accepted

Weekly Charge	AR1	AR2
Low Season (from)	€ 343	€ 378
High Season (from)	€ 679	€ 721

FR47150 Domaine de Guillalmes

Condat, FR-47500 Fumel (Lot-et-Garonne)　　　　　**Open:** All year

For our full description of this campsite ◉ **see page 315**

AR1 – CHALET – Chalet

Sleeping: 2 bedrooms, sleeps 4/6: 1 double, 2 single beds, sofa bed, pillows & blankets provided

Living: living/kitchen area, heating, shower & separate WC

Eating: fitted kitchen with hob, fridge

Outside: table & chairs, paraslol

Pets: not accepted

Weekly Charge	AR1
Low Season (from)	€ 285
High Season (from)	€ 750

FR23010 Castel Camping le Château de Poinsouze

Route de la Châtre, BP 12, F-23600 Boussac-Bourg (Creuse)　　　**Open:** 10 May - 13 September

For our full description of this campsite　　see page 326

AR1 – IRM SUPER MERCURE 2 BEDROOMS – Mobile Home

Sleeping: 2 bedrooms, sleeps 4/6: 1 double, 2 single beds, sofa bed

Living: living/kitchen area, shower & separate WC

Eating: fitted kitchen with hob, fridge

Outside: table & chairs, parasol, BBQ

Pets: not accepted

AR2 – COUNTRY LODGE – Chalet

Sleeping: 2 bedrooms, sleeps 4/5; 1 double, 2 single beds, sofa bed

Living: living/kitchen area, shower & separate WC

Eating: fitted kitchen with hob, microwave, coffee machine, fridge

Outside: table & chairs, 2 sun loungers, parasol, BBQ

Pets: not accepted

Weekly Charge	AR1	AR2
Low Season (from)	€ 280	€ 320
High Season (from)	€ 570	€ 650

FR07120 Camping Nature Parc l'Ardéchois

Route touristique des Gorges, F-07150 Vallon-Pont-d'Arc (Ardèche)　　**Open:** Easter - 30 September

For our full description of this campsite　　see page 345

AR1 – LOUISIANE OAKLEY – Mobile Home

Sleeping: 2 bedrooms, sleeps 5: 1 double, 2 single beds, bunk bed, pillows & blankets provided

Living: living/kitchen area, heating, shower & WC

Eating: fitted kitchen with hob, fridge

Outside: table & chairs, 2 sun loungers, parasol

Pets: accepted (only in low season)

AR2 – LOUISIANE PACIFIQUE – Mobile Home

Sleeping: 2 bedrooms, sleeps 5: 1 double, 2 single beds, bunk bed, pillows and blankets provided

Living: living/kitchen area, heating, shower & WC

Eating: fitted kitchen with hob, microwave, fridge/freezer

Outside: table & chairs, 2 sun loungers, parasol

Pets: accepted (only in low season)

Weekly Charge	AR1	AR2
Low Season (from)	€ 443	€ 443
High Season (from)	€ 1030	€ 1030

FR07150 Camping Domaine de Gil

Route de Vals-les-Bains, Ucel, F-07200 Aubenas (Ardèche)　　　**Open:** 14 April - 23 September

For our full description of this campsite　　see page 346

AR1 – CONFORT – Mobile Home

Sleeping: 2 bedrooms, sleeps 4/5: 1 double, 2 single beds, sofa bed

Living: living/kitchen area, heating, shower & WC

Eating: fitted kitchen with hob, coffee machine, fridge

Outside: table & chairs, parasol

Pets: not accepted

AR2 – GRAND LUXE – Mobile Home

Sleeping: 3 bedrooms, sleeps 7: 1 double, 4 single beds, sofa bed, pillows & blankets provided

Living: living/kitchen area, shower & separate WC

Eating: fitted kitchen with hob, microwave, coffee machine, fridge

Outside: table & chairs, sun lounger, parasol

Pets: not accepted

Weekly Charge	AR1	AR2
Low Season (from)	€ 213	€ 290
High Season (from)	€ 610	€ 785

Check real time availability and at-the-gate prices...

www.**alanrogers**.com

FR26210 Camping les Bois du Chatelas

Route de Dieulefit, F-26460 Bourdeaux (Drôme)　　　　　　**Open:** 12 April - 28 September

For our full description of this campsite ▶ see page 358

AR1 – GOELAND – Chalet

Sleeping: 2 bedrooms, sleeps 5/7: 1 double, 3 single beds, sofa bed, blankets provided

Living: living/kitchen area, heating, shower & separate WC

Eating: fitted kitchen with hob, microwave, coffee machine, fridge/freezer

Outside: table & chairs

Pets: accepted

AR2 – TEXAS WATIPI – Mobile Home

Sleeping: 3 bedrooms, sleeps 7: 1 double, 4 single beds, sofa bed, blankets provided
(bed linen, childrens bed and chair for rent)

Living: living/kitchen area, heating, shower & separate WC

Eating: fitted kitchen with hob, microwave, coffee machine, fridge/freezer

Outside: table & chairs

Pets: accepted

Weekly Charge	AR1	AR2
Low Season *(from)*	€ 340	€ 300
High Season *(from)*	€ 755	€ 670

FR04010 Sunêlia Hippocampe

Route de Napoléon, F-04290 Volonne (Alpes-de-Haute-Provence)　　　　**Open:** 22 March - 30 September

For our full description of this campsite ▶ see page 363

AR1 – WATIPI COTTAGE/SUNELIA FAMILY – Mobile home

Sleeping: 3 bedrooms, sleeps 6: 1 double, 2 twin with 2 single beds, pillows & blankets provided

Living: living/kitchen area, heating, shower & WC (air conditioning on request)

Eating: fitted kitchen with cooking hob, microwave & fridge/freezer

Outside: 2 sun loungers, parasol

Pets: accepted

AR2 – IRM – Mobile Home

Sleeping: 2 bedrooms, sleeps 6: 1 double, 1 twin with 2 single beds, pillows & blankets provided

Living: living/kitchen area, heating, shower & WC

Eating: fitted kitchen with cooking hob & fridge

Outside: 2 sun loungers, parasol

Pets: accepted

Weekly Charge	AR1	AR2
Low Season *(from)*	€ 294	€ 294
High Season *(from)*	€ 917	€ 973

FR04020 Castel Camping le Camp du Verdon

Domaine du Verdon, F-04120 Castellane (Alpes-de-Haute-Provence)　　　**Open:** 15 May - 15 September

For our full description of this campsite ▶ see page 364

AR1 – WATIPI – Mobile Home

Sleeping: 2 bedrooms, sleeps 4: 1 double, 2 single beds, pillows & blankets provided

Living: living/kitchen area, shower & WC

Eating: fitted kitchen with cooking hob & fridge

Outside: table & chairs, 2 sun loungers

Pets: accepted

AR2 – TITOM – Chalet

Sleeping: 3 bedrooms, sleeps 6: 1 double, 2 single beds, bunk bed, pillows & blankets provided

Living: living/kitchen area, shower & WC

Eating: fitted kitchen with cooking hob & fridge

Outside: table & chairs, 2 sun loungers

Pets: accepted

Weekly Charge	AR1	AR2
Low Season *(from)*	€ 336	€ 364
High Season *(from)*	€ 630	€ 665

FR04100 Camping International

Route Napoleon, F-04120 Castellane (Alpes-de Haute-Provence)

Open: 31 March - 1 October

For our full description of this campsite ▶ **see page 364**

AR1 – SHELBOX – Mobile Home

Sleeping: 2 bedrooms, sleeps 5: 1 double, 1 single bed, bunk bed, pillows & blankets provided

Living: living/kitchen area, heating, shower & WC

Eating: fitted kitchen with cooking hob, microwave & fridge

Outside: table & chairs, 2 sun loungers

Pets: accepted

Weekly Charge	AR1
Low Season (from)	€ 190
High Season (from)	€ 650

FR84020 Domaine Naturiste de Bélézy

F-84410 Bédoin (Vaucluse)

Open: 21 March - 5 October

For our full description of this campsite ▶ **see page 373**

AR1 – NAUTILHOME – Mobile Home

Sleeping: 2 bedrooms, sleeps 5: 1 double, 2 single beds, single sofa bed, bed linen, pillows & blankets provided

Living: living/kitchen area, heating, safe, shower & separate WC

Eating: fitted kitchen with hob, microwave, coffee machine, fridge/freezer

Outside: table & chairs, 2 sun loungers, awning

Pets: not accepted

AR2 – EDEN – Chalet

Sleeping: 2 bedrooms, sleeps 5: 1 double, 3 single beds, pillows & blankets provided *(childrens bed and chair for rent)*

Living: living/kitchen area, heating, TV, safe, radio, shower & separate WC

Eating: fitted kitchen with hob, microwave, coffee machine, fridge/freezer

Outside: table & chairs, 2 sun loungers, awning

Pets: not accepted

Weekly Charge	AR1	AR2
Low Season (from)	€ 525	€ 651
High Season (from)	€ 896	€ 1029

FR09020 Camping l'Arize

Lieu-dit Bourtol, F-09240 La Bastide-de-Sérou (Ariège)

Open: 7 March - 12 November

For our full description of this campsite ▶ **see page 379**

AR1 – MH CONFORT 2 BEDROOMS – Mobile Home

Sleeping: 2 bedrooms, sleeps 6: 1 double, 2 single beds, sofa bed, pillows & blankets provided

Living: living/kitchen area, heating, shower & separate WC

Eating: fitted kitchen with hob, microwave, grill & fridge

Outside: table & chairs, parasol, BBQ

Pets: accepted (with supplement)

AR2 – LOUISIANE FLORÈS MH CONFORT PLUS

Sleeping: 2 bedrooms, sleeps 6: 1 double, 2 single beds, bunk bed, sofa bed, pillows & blankets provided *(bed linen for rent)*

Living: living/kitchen area, heating, shower & separate WC

Eating: fitted kitchen with hob, microwave, grill, fridge/freezer

Outside: table & chairs, parasol, BBQ

Pets: accepted (with supplement)

Weekly Charge	AR1	AR2
Low Season (from)	€ 343	€ 428
High Season (from)	€ 639	€ 719

FR32010 Le Camp de Florence

Route Astaffort, F-32480 La Romieu (Gers)

Open: 1 April - 11 October

For our full description of this campsite see page 383

AR1 – LOUISIANE ZEN – Mobile Home

Sleeping: 2 bedrooms, sleeps 6: 1 double, 2 single beds, sofa bed, pillows & blankets provided

Living: living/kitchen area, heating, shower & WC

Eating: fitted kitchen with hob, fridge/freezer

Outside: table & chairs, 2 sun loungers

Pets: accepted

AR2 – IRM DELUXE – Mobile Home

Sleeping: 2 bedrooms, sleeps 6: 2 doubles, sofa bed, pillows & blankets provided

Living: living/kitchen area, heating, shower & WC

Eating: fitted kitchen with hob, microwave, fridge

Outside: table & chairs, 2 sun loungers

Pets: accepted

Weekly Charge	AR1	AR2
Low Season *(from)*	€ 230	€ 250
High Season *(from)*	€ 670	€ 715

FR11070 Camping les Mimosas

Chaussée de Mandirac, F-11100 Narbonne (Aude)

Open: 21 March - 1 November

For our full description of this campsite see page 399

AR1 – PACIFIQUE – Mobile Home

Sleeping: 2 bedrooms, sleeps 4: 1 double, 2 single beds, pillows & blankets provided

Living: living/kitchen area, shower & WC

Eating: fitted kitchen with hob, microwave, coffee machine, fridge

Outside: table & chairs, 2 sun loungers

Pets: accepted

AR2 – FLORÈS – Mobile Home

Sleeping: 3 bedrooms, sleeps 6: 1 double, 4 single beds, pillows & blankets provided

Living: living/kitchen area, heating, air conditioning, shower & WC

Eating: fitted kitchen with hob, microwave, coffee machine, fridge/freezer

Outside: table & chairs, 2 sun loungers

Pets: not accepted

Weekly Charge	AR1	AR2
Low Season *(from)*	€ 252	€ 343
High Season *(from)*	€ 603	€ 819

FR11080 Camping la Nautique

La Nautique, F-11100 Narbonne (Aude)

Open: 15 February - 15 November

For our full description of this campsite see page 398

AR1 – TYPE VI – Mobile Home

Sleeping: 2 bedrooms, sleeps 6: 1 double, 2 single beds, sofa bed, pillows & blankets provided

Living: living/kitchen area, heating, radio, shower & separate WC

Eating: fitted kitchen with hob, microwave or oven with grill, coffee machine, fridge/freezer

Outside: table & chairs, 2 sun loungers, parasol

Pets: accepted (with supplement)

AR2 – TYPE X – Mobile Home

Sleeping: 2 bedrooms, sleeps 6: 1 double, 2 single beds, sofa bed, pillows & blankets provided *(bed linen, childrens bed and chair for rent)*

Living: living/kitchen area, heating, radio, shower & separate WC

Eating: fitted kitchen with hob, microwave or oven with grill, coffee machine, fridge/freezer

Outside: table & chairs, 2 sun loungers, parasol

Pets: accepted (with supplement)

Weekly Charge	AR1	AR2
Low Season *(from)*	€ 294	€ 350
High Season *(from)*	€ 630	€ 770

FR34450 Sunêlia Domaine de la Dragonnière

RN 112, F-34450 Vias-sur-Mer (Hérault)

Open: 15 March - 4 October

For our full description of this campsite ▶ see page 426

AR1 – LODGE VIP – Mobile Home

Sleeping: 2 bedrooms, sleeps 6: 1 double, 2 single beds, sofa bed, pillows & blankets provided

Living: living/kitchen area, heating, shower & separate WC

Eating: fitted kitchen with hob, microwave, coffee machine, fridge/freezer

Outside: table & chairs, 2 sun loungers

Pets: accepted (with supplement)

AR2 – LANKA – Chalet

Sleeping: 2 bedrooms, sleeps 7: 1 double, 3 single beds, sofa bed, pillows & blankets provided
(childrens bed and chair for rent)

Living: living/kitchen area, heating, shower & separate WC

Eating: fitted kitchen with hob, microwave, coffee machine, fridge/freezer

Outside: table & chairs

Pets: accepted (with supplement)

Weekly Charge	AR1	AR2
Low Season *(from)*	€ 350	€ 350
High Season *(from)*	€ 910	€ 910

Domaine de la
DRAGONNIÈRE
★★★★
Camping Village club
R.N 112
34450 Vias sur Mer
France
www.dragonniere.com

Tel : 0033 467 010 310
Fax : 0033 467 217 339

NEW FOR 2008
SLIDE AND KIDS PARADISE
9 pools of which 5 are heated
Disco. Restaurant - Snackbars
Supermarket - Animation
10 minutes from the beach,
free bus service to the beach
Sauna – Jacuzzi

Mobile homes and Bungalows
for hire :
March till June & September:
126 € tot 490€ / week *
July & August: :
196 € tot 1022 € / week *
*See rates

FR34070 Yelloh! Village le Sérignan Plage

Le Sérignan Plage, F-34410 Sérignan (Hérault)　　　　　**Open:** 24 April - 21 September

For our full description of this campsite　(>)　**see page 414**

AR1 – COTTAGE VIP – Mobile Home

Sleeping: 2 bedrooms, sleeps 4: 1 double, 2 single beds, pillows & blankets provided

Living: living/kitchen area, heating, fan, safe, shower & separate WC

Eating: fitted kitchen with hob, microwave, coffee machine, fridge/freezer

Outside: table & chairs, 2 sun loungers, parasol

Pets: not accepted

AR2 – VIP QUARTIER DES CABANES – Mobile Home

Sleeping: 3 bedrooms, sleeps 6: 1 double, 4 single beds, pillows & blankets provided
(bed linen and children's chair for rent)

Living: living/kitchen area, heating, safe, shower & separate WC

Eating: fitted kitchen with hob, microwave, coffee machine, dishwasher, fridge/freezer

Outside: table & chairs, 2 sun loungers, parasol

Pets: not accepted

Weekly Charge	AR1	AR2
Low Season *(from)*	€ 203	€ 252
High Season *(from)*	€ 1078	€ 1288

FR34110 Yelloh! Village le Club Farret

F-34450 Vias-Plage (Hérault)　　　　　**Open:** 29 March - 22 September

For our full description of this campsite　(>)　**see page 417**

AR1 – BALI – Mobile Home

Sleeping: 3 bedrooms, sleeps 6: 1 double, 4 single beds, pillows provided

Living: living/kitchen area, heating, air conditioning, safe, shower & separate WC

Eating: fitted kitchen with hob, microwave, coffee machine, fridge/freezer

Outside: table & chairs, 2 sun loungers, parasol

Pets: not accepted

AR2 – AFRICA – Mobile Home

Sleeping: 2 bedrooms, sleeps 4/6: 1 double, 2 single beds, sofa bed, pillows provided

Living: living/kitchen area, heating, shower & separate WC

Eating: fitted kitchen with hob, microwave, coffee machine, fridge/freezer

Outside: table & chairs, 2 sun loungers, parasol

Pets: not accepted

Weekly Charge	AR1	AR2
Low Season *(from)*	€ 301	€ 293
High Season *(from)*	€ 1085	€ 980

FR66070 Yelloh! Village le Brasilia

B.P. 204, F-66141 Canet-en-Roussillon (Pyrénées-Orientales)　　　　　**Open:** 26 April - 27 September

For our full description of this campsite　(>)　**see page 431**

AR1 – OKAVANGO – Mobile Home

Sleeping: 2 bedrooms, sleeps 6: 1 double, 2 single beds, bunk bed, pillows & blankets provided

Living: living/kitchen area, heating, safe, shower & WC

Eating: fitted kitchen with hob, microwave, grill, coffee machine, fridge/freezer

Outside: table & chairs, 2 sun loungers, parasol

Pets: accepted

AR2 – PINEDE – Bungalow

Sleeping: 2 bedrooms, sleeps 4: 1 double, 2 single beds, pillows & blankets provided
(bed linen, childrens bed for rent)

Living: living/kitchen area, heating, TV, shower & separate WC

Eating: fitted kitchen with hob, microwave, grill, coffee machine, fridge/freezer

Outside: table & chairs, 2 sun loungers, parasol

Pets: accepted

Weekly Charge	AR1	AR2
Low Season *(from)*	€ 259	€ 259
High Season *(from)*	€ 875	€ 875

FR06080 Camping Caravaning les Cigales

505 ave. de la Mer, F-06210 Mandelieu-la-Napoule (Alpes-Maritimes)　　　　　**Open:** All year

For our full description of this campsite　　see page 443

AR1 – O'HARA – Mobile Home

Sleeping: 2 bedrooms, sleeps 4: 1 double, 2 single beds, pillows & blankets provided

Living: living/kitchen area, heating, shower & WC

Eating: fitted kitchen with hob & fridge

Outside: terrace with tablel & chairs, parasol

Pets: accepted

AR2 – MOBILE HOME – Mobile Home

Sleeping: 2 bedrooms, sleeps 6: 1 double, 2 single beds, sofa bed, pillows & blankets provided

Living: living/kitchen area, shower & WC

Eating: fitted kitchen with cooking hob & fridge

Outside: table & chairs, 2 sun loungers, parasol

Pets: accepted

Weekly Charge	AR1	AR2
Low Season (from)	€ 375	€ 385
High Season (from)	€ 660	€ 680

FR06180 Camping les Rives du Loup

2666b route de la Colle, F-06140 Tourettes-sur-Loup (Alpes-Maritimes)　　**Open:** 1 April - 30 September

For our full description of this campsite　　see page 446

AR1 – FAMILY 3 – Mobile Home

Sleeping: 3 bedrooms, sleeps 6/8: 1 double, 4 single beds, sofa bed, pillows & blankets provided

Living: living/kitchen area, heating, shower & separate WC

Eating: fitted kitchen with hob, microwave, oven, grill, coffee machine, fridge/freezer

Outside: table & chairs, sun lounger, parasol

Pets: accepted (with supplement)

AR2 – FAMILY 2 – Mobile Home

Sleeping: 2 bedrooms, sleeps 6: 1 double, 2 single beds, sofa bed, pillows & blankets provided
(bed linen, childrens bed and chair for rent)

Living: living/kitchen area, heating, shower & separate WC

Eating: fitted kitchen with hob, microwave, oven, grill, coffee machine, fridge/freezer

Outside: table & chairs, sun lounger, parasol

Pets: accepted (with supplement)

Weekly Charge	AR1	AR2
Low Season (from)	€ 350	€ 300
High Season (from)	€ 695	€ 675

FR83020 Castel Camping Caravaning Esterel

Avenue des Golf, F-83530 St Raphaél – Agay (Var)　　　　　**Open:** 31 March - 6 October

For our full description of this campsite　　see page 450

AR1 – LA SUITE – Mobile Home

Sleeping: 2 bedrooms, sleeps 6: 1 double, 2 single beds, sofa bed

Living: living/kitchen area, heating, shower & WC

Eating: fitted kitchen with hob, oven & fridge/freezer

Outside: table & chairs, 2 sun loungers, parasol

Pets: accepted

AR2 – MINI LUXE – Mobile Home

Sleeping: 1 bedrooms, sleeps 4: 2 doubles, sofa bed

Living: living/kitchen area, shower & WC

Eating: fitted kitchen with hob, fridge

Outside: table & chairs, 2 sun loungers, parasol

Pets: accepted

Weekly Charge	AR1	AR2
Low Season (from)	€ 460	€ 220
High Season (from)	€ 930	€ 600

FR83030 Camping Caravaning Leï Suves

Quartier du Blavet, F-83520 Roquebrune-sur-Argens (Var)　　　　**Open:** 1 April - 15 October

For our full description of this campsite ● **see page 453**

AR1 – TYPE D – Mobile Home

Sleeping: 2 bedrooms, sleeps 6: 1 double, 2 single beds, sofa bed

Living: living/kitchen area, shower & WC

Eating: fitted kitchen with hob, oven, fridge

Outside: table & chairs

Pets: not accepted

Weekly Charge	AR1
Low Season *(from)*	€ 350
High Season *(from)*	€ 720

FR83060 Camping Caravaning de la Baume

Route de Bagnols, F-83618 Fréjus (Var)　　　　**Open:** 15 March - 20 September

For our full description of this campsite ● **see page 454**

AR1 – BASTIDON – Chalet

Sleeping: 2 bedrooms, sleeps 4/6: 1 double, 2 single beds, sofa bed

Living: living/kitchen area, shower & WC

Eating: fitted kitchen with hob, fridge

Outside: table & chairs, 2 sun loungers

Pets: not accepted

AR2 – PHOENIX – Mobile Home

Sleeping: 2 bedrooms, sleeps 6: 1 double, 2 single beds, sofa bed

Living: living/kitchen area, shower & WC

Eating: fitted kitchen with hob, fridge

Outside: table & chairs, 2 sun loungers

Pets: not accepted

Weekly Charge	AR1	AR2
Low Season *(from)*	€ 315	€ 315
High Season *(from)*	€ 896	€ 896

FR83170 Camping Domaine de la Bergerie

Route du Col du Bougnon, F-83520 Roquebrune-sur-Argens (Var)　　　　**Open:** 15 February - 15 November

For our full description of this campsite ● **see page 457**

AR1 – 4 COTTAGE – Mobile Home

Sleeping: 2 bedrooms, sleeps 4: 1 double, 2 single beds, pillows & blankets provided

Living: living/kitchen area, heating, fan, shower & separate WC

Eating: fitted kitchen with hob, microwave, oven, fridge/freezer

Outside: table & chairs, sun lounger

Pets: accepted (with supplement)

AR2 – COTTAGE 4/5 – Mobile Home

Sleeping: 2 bedrooms, sleeps 5: 1 double, 2 single beds, sofa bed, pillows & blankets provided *(bed linen, childrens bed and chair for rent)*

Living: living/kitchen area, heating, fan, shower & separate WC

Eating: fitted kitchen with hob, microwave, oven, fridge/freezer

Outside: table & chairs, sun lounger

Pets: accepted (with supplement)

Weekly Charge	AR1	AR2
Low Season *(from)*	€ 374	€ 396
High Season *(from)*	€ 937	€ 994

FR83190 Camping la Presqu'île de Giens

153, route de la Madraque-Giens, F-83400 Hyères (Var)

Open: 20 March - 5 October

For our full description of this campsite ▶ see page 461

AR1 – IRM EVASION – Mobile Home

Sleeping: 2 bedrooms, sleeps 4: 1 double, 2 single beds, pillows & blankets provided

Living: living/kitchen area, heating, shower & WC

Eating: fitted kitchen with hob, microwave, coffee machine, fridge/freezer

Outside: table & chairs

Pets: accepted

AR2 – GITOTEL COTTAGE – Chalet

Sleeping: 3 bedrooms, sleeps 6: 2 doubles, 2 single beds, pillows & blankets provided

Living: living/kitchen area, heating, shower & WC

Eating: fitted kitchen with hob, microwave, fridge/freezer

Outside: table & chairs, 2 sun loungers

Pets: accepted

Weekly Charge	AR1	AR2
Low Season (from)	€ 320	€ 370
High Season (from)	€ 680	€ 850

FR83200 Camping Caravaning les Pêcheurs

F-83520 Roquebrune-sur-Argens (Var)

Open: 1 April - 30 September

For our full description of this campsite ▶ see page 463

AR1 – SHELBOX PARADIS'HOME – Mobile Home

Sleeping: 2 bedrooms, sleeps 6: 1 double, 3 single beds, single persons sofa bed , pillows & blankets provided

Living: living/kitchen area, heating, shower & separate WC

Eating: fitted kitchen with hob, microwave, coffee machine, fridge/freezer

Outside: table & chairs, 2 sun loungers, parasol

Pets: accepted (with supplement)

AR2 – O'HARA O'PHEA 833 – Mobile Home

Sleeping: 2 bedrooms, sleeps 4/ 6: 1 double, 2 single beds, sofa bed, pillows & blankets provided

Living: living/kitchen area, heating, shower & separate WC

Eating: fitted kitchen with hob, microwave, coffee machine, fridge/freezer

Outside: table & chairs, 2 sun loungers, parasol

Pets: accepted (with supplement)

Weekly Charge	AR1	AR2
Low Season (from)	€ 330	€ 400
High Season (from)	€ 730	€ 815

FR83220 Camping Caravaning Cros de Mouton

P.O. 116, F-83240 Cavalaire-sur-Mer (Var)

Open: 15 March - 1 November

For our full description of this campsite ▶ see page 465

AR1 – IRM – Mobile Home

Sleeping: 2 bedrooms, sleeps 6: 1 double, 2 single beds, sofa bed, pillows & blankets provided

Living: living/kitchen area, heating, shower & WC

Eating: fitted kitchen with hob, microwave, fridge/freezer

Outside: table & chairs, parasol

Pets: accepted

AR2 – GITOTEL – Chalet

Sleeping: 2 bedrooms, sleeps 6: 2 doubles, 2 bunk beds, pillows & blankets provided

Living: living/kitchen area, heating, shower & WC

Eating: fitted kitchen with hob, microwave & fridge

Outside: table & chairs, parasol

Pets: accepted

Weekly Charge	AR1	AR2
Low Season (from)	€ 380	€ 380
High Season (from)	€ 690	€ 690

FR20050 Camping Naturiste Club la Chiappa

F-20137 Porto-Vecchio (Corse-du-Sud)

Open: 10 May - 11 October

For our full description of this campsite ▶ see page 479

AR1 – TYPE C – Bungalow

Sleeping: 2 bedrooms, sleeps 4: 4 single beds, pillows & blankets provided

Living: living/kitchen area, shower, WC

Eating: fitted kitchen with hob, fridge

Outside: table & chairs

Pets: accepted

AR2 – TYPE B – Bungalow

Sleeping: 1 bedrooms, sleeps 2: 2 single beds

Living: living/kitchen area, shower & WC

Eating: fitted kitchen with hob, fridge

Outside: table & chairs

Pets: accepted

Weekly Charge	AR1	AR2
Low Season *(from)*	€ 630	€ 420
High Season *(from)*	€ 1050	€ 700

FR20040 Riva Bella Nature Resort & Spa

B.P. 21, F-20270 Alèria (Haute-Corse)

Open: 29 March - 1 November

For our full description of this campsite ▶ see page 477

AR1 – CHALET 4 – Chalet

Sleeping: 2 bedrooms, sleeps 5: 1 double, 2 single beds, bunk bed

Living: living/kitchen area, heating, shower & WC

Eating: fitted kitchen with hob, fridge

Outside: table & chairs, 2 sun loungers, parasol

Pets: accepted

AR2 – CHALET 2 – Chalet

Sleeping: 2 bedrooms, sleeps 4: 1 double, 2 bunk bed, pillows & blankets provided

Living: living/kitchen area, heating, shower & WC

Eating: fitted kitchen with hob, fridge

Outside: table & chairs, 2 sun loungers, parasol

Pets: accepted

Weekly Charge	AR1	AR2
Low Season *(from)*	€ 462	€ 203
High Season *(from)*	€ 1043	€ 553

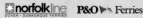

Parcs Résidentiels
de Loisirs

Recent years have seen a significant increase in the number of Parcs résidentiels de loisirs in France. In many ways, these parks resemble good campsites but with the important distinction that they do not have any touring pitches!

Amenities at the parks are invariably very impressive, often with top quality swimming pool complexes and fine restaurant facilities. However, all the pitches on these sites are occupied by either mobile homes or chalets, many of which are available for let.

These parks have been developed by their owners often with the expectation that their clients may be former campers or caravanners, or possibly those travelling from afar, with the common desire to combine the freedom of camping and caravanning with a high standard of home comforts.

We have chosen to include a small selection of the best parcs résidentiels, all of which are attractively located in popular regions of France. In every case, there will be a good choice of accommodation available for rent. We are, however, featuring 2 types of accommodation and give full details of what is provided in terms of living and sleeping accommodation, as well as an indication of the park's tariffs.

Check real time availability and at-the-gate prices...
www.alanrogers.com

FR12340 Résidence les Clédelles le Colombier

F-12130 Saint Geniez d'Olt (Aveyron)

Open: All year

Tel: 05 65 47 45 72. Email: cledelles.reservations@wanadoo.fr

Le Colombier is a residential park on the banks of the River Lot, just five minutes from the centre of the attractive village of St Geniez d'Olt in the heart of the Aveyron. The site is a member of the Les Clédelles group and has a range of chalets available for rent but there are no touring pitches. On site amenities include a swimming pool and club house with a snack bar. A number of local specialities are on offer here, including 'saucisse-aligot'. A wide range of activities are organised in high season, including a children's club and numerous excursions including canoeing and cycling trips.

Facilities

Variety of chalets for rent. Direct access to River Lot. Small shop. Swimming pool. Snack bar. Activities in high season. Children's club. Play area. Off site: Many cycle and walking trails. Good range of shops and restaurants in St Geniez d'Olt.

Directions

From the A75, take exit 41 and follow signs for St Geniez d'Olt. Site is close to the village centre and is well signed.

FR27060 Domaine de Marcilly

Route de Saint-Andre-de-l'Eure, F-27810 Marcilly-sur-Eure (Eure)
Tel: **02 37 48 45 42**. Email: **domainedemarcilly@wanadoo.fr**

Open: 12 April - 29 October

Just between Ile de France and Normandy, less than an hours drive from Paris, Domaine de Marcilly is beautifully located in a 15 hectare park, surrounded by pine, oak and birch trees. Although most pitches are dedicated to mobile homes, this park also welcomes motorcaravans and each pitch has a picnic table. Leisure facilities include a swimming pool and two tennis courts. There are paths and cycle routes through the parkland and surrounding countryside, as well as riding and fishing.

Facilities

The sanitary block provides hot showers and washbasins. Facilities for disabled visitors. Laundry facilities. Motorcaravan service point. Heated swimming pool (1/6-30/9). Boules. Tennis. Internet. TV. Animation and entertainment during high season. Off site: Local shops 900 m. Riding 3 km. Golf 10 km. Canoeing.

Directions

From Paris A13, A12 exit onto N12 for Houdan, take exit Goussainville, Havelu, Bu, then Marcilly. Site is on the D52 in the direction of St Andre.
GPS: N48:49.513 E01:19.422

AR1 – O'PHEA – Mobile Home

Sleeping: 2 bedrooms, sleeps 4/5: 1 double, 2 single beds, pillows & blankets provided

Living: living/kitchen area, heating, shower & WC

Eating: fitted kitchen with hob, microwave, oven, fridge

Outside: table & chairs, BBQ

Pets: accepted

AR2 – O'PHEA – Mobile Home

Sleeping: 3 bedrooms, sleeps 6: 1 double, 2 single beds, sofa bed, pillows & blankets provided

Living: living/kitchen area, heating, shower & WC

Eating: fitted kitchen with hob, microwave, oven, fridge

Outside: table & chairs, BBQ

Pets: accepted

Weekly Charge	AR1	AR2
Low Season *(from)*	€ 290	€ 320
High Season *(from)*	€ 560	€ 590

FR33300 Domaine Residentiel Naturiste la Jenny

F-33680 Le Porge (Gironde)
Tel: **05 56 26 56 90**. Email: **info@lajenny.fr**

Open: 12 May - 15 September

Situated at the heart of Europe's largest forest, yet within walking distance of the Atlantic beaches through the forest, La Jenny is a naturist site providing 750 high quality chalets, of which 500 are let on behalf of the owners. This is an ideal spot for a quiet and peaceful holiday, yet with a great deal on offer for those seeking a more lively holiday. With four pools covering an area of 1,000 sq m, a wide range of sports amenities, including golf, tennis and archery, there is always something to do.

Facilities

Supermarket, boulangerie and fish shop. Launderette. Restaurant. Pizzeria. Bar. Brasserie. Heated pool complex. Body care and fitness centres. Sauna. Yoga. Aqua gym. Children's club. Tennis and golf course. Bicycle hire. Pony club. Diving. Staffed play area. Off site: Fishing and watersports 300 m. Riding 4 km.

Directions

From the Bordeaux ring road take exit 8 signed Lacanau. Follow D107 to Lacanau via Le Temple and La Porge, then towards Lege/Cap Ferret on the D3 to La Jenny (on the right).
GPS: N44:50.660 W01:12.659

AR1 – LOUISIANE – Chalet

Sleeping: 3 bedrooms, sleeps 8: 2 doubles, bunkbed, sofa bed, pillows provided

Living: living/kitchen area, shower & separate WC

Eating: fitted kitchen with hob, microwave, oven, coffee machine, dishwasher, fridge

Outside: table & chairs

Pets: accepted (with supplement)

AR2 – TOURTERELLE – Chalet

Sleeping: 2 bedrooms, sleeps 6: 1 double, 2 single beds, sofa bed, pillows & blankets provided

Living: living/kitchen area, shower & separate WC

Eating: fitted kitchen with hob, microwave, oven, coffee machine, fridge

Outside: table & chairs

Pets: accepted (with supplement)

Weekly Charge	AR1	AR2
Low Season *(from)*	€ 1080	€ 700
High Season *(from)*	€ 1300	€ 800

FR63000 Les Chalets du Hameau du Lac

Lieu dit le Pré Bad, Le Lac Chambon, F-63790 Chambon sur Lac (Puy-de-Dôme)   **Open:** All year

Tel: **04 73 28 62 67**. Email: **auvergne-chalets-location@orange.fr**

Les Chalets du Hameau du Lac is a recently developed residential park on the banks of Lac Chambon in the heart of the Auvergne. The site has direct access to the lake and a range of chalets are available for rent here, some enjoying fine views across the lake. There are no touring pitches. Although there are few amenities on site, a wide range of leisure activities are on offer around the lake, including canoeing, pedaloes and waterskiing as well as inumerable walking and cycling opportunities.

Facilities	Directions
Variety of chalets for rent. Direct access to Lac Chambon. Play area. Small shop. Activities in high season. Off site: Sailing, windsurfing, water skiing. Many cycle and walking trails. Good range of shops and restaurants in Murol.	From the A75, take exit 6 for Plauzat, then the D978 to Champeix. Join the D996 to Murol, passing through St Nectaire. At Murol, continue on the D996 towards Chambon sur Lac and the chalet park is clearly indicated on the lakeside.

AR1 – CHALET – Chalet

Sleeping: 2 bedrooms, sleeps 6: 4 single beds, sofa bed, pillows & blankets provided

Living: living/kitchen area, heating, TV, shower & WC

Eating: fitted kitchen with hob, microwave, oven, grill, coffee machine, dishwasher, fridge/freezer

Outside: table & chairs

Pets: not accepted

	Weekly Charge	AR1
	Low Season (from)	€ 310
	High Season (from)	€ 680

FR83420 Parc et Plage

28 rue des Langoustiers, l'Ayguade, F-83400 Hyères Les Palmiers (Var)

Tel: **04 94 66 31 77**. Email: **contact@parc-plage.com**   **Open:** 1 March - 31 October

This exceptional mobile home park is just 200 metres from the beach and is set in an very attractive, landscaped park. There are 200 prestige caravan holiday homes, 110 of which are to rent, the remainder being privately owned. A shop, bar and restaurant on the site provide for the immediate needs of the residents, but both L'Ayguade and Hyères are not too far away. Whilst every unit is provided with its own facilities, there are also two excellent sanitary blocks on site. Access to the beach across the coast road is easy. If you are looking to buy or rent a mobile home, this would be a very good place to start the search. There is some noise from the nearby small airport.

Facilities	Directions
Two sanitary blocks supplement the private facilities. Shop, bar and restaurant. Bicycle hire. Mobile homes to rent or buy. Off site: Beach with sun beds and shades 200 m. Hyères, l'Ayguade and the Côte d'Azur.	Site is just off the D42 west of l'Ayguade between traffic lights and Hôtel de Plein Sud, about 1 km. from Hyères airport. GPS: N43:05.892 E06:09.998

AR1 – COTTAGE LUXE A – Mobile Home

Sleeping: 2 bedrooms, sleeps 4: 1 double, 2 single beds, sofa bed, pillows and blankets provided

Living: living/kitchen area, heating, air conditioning, shower & separate WC

Eating: fitted kitchen with hob, microwave, oven, grill, coffee machine, dishwasher, fridge/freezer

Outside: table & chairs, 2 sun loungers, parasol

Pets: accepted (with supplement)

AR2 – COTTAGE STANDARD C – Mobile Home

Sleeping: 3 bedrooms, sleeps 6/8: 1 double, 4 single beds, sofa bed, pillows & blankets provided

Living: living/kitchen area, heating, air conditioning, radio, TV, shower & separate WC

Eating: complete fitted kitchen with hob, microwave, oven, grill, coffee machine, fridge/freezer

Outside: table & chairs, 2 sun loungers, parasol

Pets: accepted (with supplement)

	Weekly Charge	AR1	AR2
	Low Season (from)	€ 385	€ 385
	High Season (from)	€ 1010	€ 1010

Check real time availability and at-the-gate prices...

www.alanrogers.com

The following sites are understood to accept caravanners and campers all year round. It is always wise to phone the site to check as the facilities available, for example, may be reduced.

Brittany
FR22020 Fleur de Bretagne
FR44320 Pierre Longue
FR56150 Haras

Normandy
FR27060 Marcilly
FR76090 Mun. Etennemare
Northern France
FR62120 Eté Indien

Paris & Ile de France
FR91010 Beau Village
FR75020 Bois de Boulogne
FR77020 Chêne Gris
FR77060 Colline
FR94000 Tremblay

Eastern France
FR10040 Noue des Rois
FR88020 Belle Hutte
FR88040 Lac de Bouzey
FR88050 Champé
FR88090 Lac de la Moselotte
FR88130 Vanne de Pierre

Vendée & Charente
FR17070 Gros Joncs
FR85890 Rouge-Gorge

Loire Valley
FR79020 Courte Vallée
FR36050 Vieux Chênes
FR45040 Hortus

FR49150 Thouet
FR53020 Malidor
FR86040 Futuriste

Burgundy
FR21060 Bouleaux
FR21090 Arquebuse

Savoy & Dauphiny Alps
FR74230 Giffre

Atlantic Coast
FR33090 Pressoir
FR33350 Chez Gendron
FR64040 Gaves

Dordogne & Aveyron
FR12310 Cascade
FR12340 Clédelles le Colombier
FR16040 Devezeau
FR24150 Deux Vallées
FR24410 Bois du Coderc
FR24480 Tailladis
FR24640 Nontron
FR46070 Plage (St Cirq-Lapopie)
FR47110 Cabri
FR47150 Guillalmes

Limousin & Auvergne
FR19080 Vianon
FR48070 Tivoli
FR63000 Chalets du Hameau
           du Lac
FR63060 Clos Auroy

Rhône Valley
FR01100 Vaugrais
FR26100 Sagittaire
FR26110 4 Saisons
FR69010 Lyon

Provence
FR05060 Pause
FR05080 Solaire
FR84080 Simioune

Midi-Pyrénées
FR09050 Prade (Sorgeat)
FR09080 Lac (Foix)
FR65080 Lavedan
FR65130 Pyrenevasion
FR65160 Monlôo

Mediterranean West
FR11110 Val d'Aleth
FR34060 Oliveraie
FR34230 Chênes
FR66610 Bois de Pins

Mediterranean East
FR06050 Vieille Ferme
FR06080 Cigales
FR13120 Chantecler

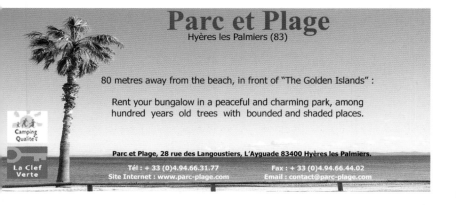

Dogs

For the benefit of those who want to take their dogs to France, we list here the sites which have indicated to us that they do not accept dogs or have certain restrictions. If you are planning to take your dog we do advise you to phone the site first to check – there may be limits on numbers, breeds, or times of the year when they are excluded.

FR01080	Etang du Moulin	FR29140	Kerlann	FR66040	Soleil
FR14090	Brévedent	FR30160	Boucanet	FR83320	Mogador
FR16020	Gorges du Chambon	FR40040	Paillotte	FR84020	Bélézy (Naturiste)
FR17010	Bois Soleil	FR46040	Moulin de Laborde	FR85210	Ecureuils
FR17020	Puits de l'Auture	FR64060	Pavillon Royal	FR85420	Bel
FR20030	Merendella	FR65160	Monlôo		
FR24040	Moulin du Roch	FR65170	Arrayade		

Sites that accept dogs but with certain restrictions:

FR04110	Verdon Parc	FR30220	Gênets d'Or	FR83040	Bastiane
FR07250	Plaine	FR33290	Le Tedey	FR83120	Domaine
FR17170	Les Charmilles	FR34130	Neptune	FR83200	Pêcheurs
FR17210	Interlude	FR35040	P'tit Bois	FR83350	Sélection
FR17290	Peupliers	FR40250	Grands Pins	FR83440	Malissonne
FR23010	Poinsouze	FR46190	Faurie	FR85000	Petit Rocher
FR24100	Moulinal	FR49060	Montsabert	FR85030	Loubine
FR24290	Moulin du Bleufond	FR50030	Lez-Eaux	FR85150	Yole
FR26030	Grand Lierne	FR64100	Etche Zahar	FR85440	Brunelles
FR29000	Mouettes	FR66290	Floride	FR85870	Baie d'Aunis
FR29380	Port de Plaisance	FR68080	Clair Vacances		
FR30070	Boisson	FR74060	Colombière		

Naturist Sites

We have had very favourable feedback from readers concerning our choice of naturist sites, which we first introduced several years ago. Apart from the need to have a 'Naturist Licence' (see below), there is no need to be a practising naturist before visiting these sites. In fact, at least as far as British visitors are concerned, many are what might be described as 'holiday naturists' as distinct from the practice of naturism at other times. The emphasis in all the sites featured in this guide at least, is on naturism as 'life in harmony with nature', and respect for oneself and others and for the environment, rather than simply on nudity. In fact nudity is really only obligatory in the area of the swimming pools.

Travelling

When taking your car (and caravan, tent or trailer tent) or motorcaravan to the continent you do need to plan in advance and to find out as much as possible about driving in the countries you plan to visit. Whilst European harmonisation has eliminated many of the differences between one country and another, it is well worth reading the short notes we provide in the introduction to each country in this guide in addition to this more general summary.

Of course, the main difference from driving in the UK is that in mainland Europe you will need to drive on the right. Without taking extra time and care, especially at busy junctions and conversely when roads are empty, it is easy to forget to drive on the right. Remember that traffic approaching from the right usually has priority unless otherwise indicated by road markings and signs. Harmonisation also means that most (but not all) common road signs are the same in all countries.

Your vehicle

Book your vehicle in for a good service well before your intended departure date. This will lessen the chance of an expensive breakdown. Make sure your brakes are working efficiently and that your tyres have plenty of tread (3 mm. is recommended, particularly if you are undertaking a long journey).

Also make sure that your caravan or trailer is roadworthy and that its tyres are in good order and correctly inflated. Plan your packing and be careful not to overload your vehicle, caravan or trailer – this is unsafe and may well invalidate your insurance cover (it must not be more fully loaded than the kerb weight of the insured vehicle).

Check all the following:

☐ GB sticker. If you do not display a sticker, you may risk an on-the-spot fine as this identifier is compulsory in all countries. Euro-plates are an acceptable alternative within the EU (but not outside). Remember to attach another sticker (or Euro-plate) to caravans or trailers. Only GB stickers (not England, Scotland, Wales or N. Ireland) stickers are valid in the EU.

☐ Headlights. As you will be driving on the right you must adjust your headlights so that the dipped beam does not dazzle oncoming drivers. Converter kits are readily available for most vehicle, although if your car is fitted with high intensity headlights, you should check with your motor dealer. Check that any planned extra loading does not affect the beam height.

☐ Seatbelts. Rules for the fitting and wearing of seatbelts throughout Europe are similar to those in the UK, but it is worth checking before you go. Rules for carrying children in the front of vehicles vary from country to country. It is best to plan not to do this if possible.

☐ Door/wing mirrors. To help with driving on the right, if your vehicle is not fitted with a mirror on the left hand side, we recommend you have one fitted.

☐ Fuel. Leaded and Lead Replacement petrol is increasingly difficult to find in Northern Europe.

Travelling continued

Compulsory additional equipment

The driving laws of the countries of Europe still vary in what you are required to carry in your vehicle, although the consequences of not carrying a required piece of equipment are almost always an on-the-spot fine.

To meet these requirements we suggest that you carry the following:

- ☐ Fire extinguisher
- ☐ Basic tool kit
- ☐ First aid kit
- ☐ Spare bulbs
- ☐ Two warning triangles – two are required in some countries at all times, and are compulsory in most countries when towing.
- ☐ High visibility vest – now compulsory in Spain, Italy and Austria (and likely to become compulsory throughout the EU) in case you need to walk on a motorway.

Insurance and Motoring Documents

Vehicle insurance

Contact your insurer well before you depart to check that your car insurance policy covers driving outside the UK. Most do, but many policies only provide minimum cover (so if you have an accident your insurance may only cover the cost of damage to the other person's property, with no cover for fire and theft).

To maintain the same level of cover abroad as you enjoy at home you need to tell your vehicle insurer. Some will automatically cover you abroad with no extra cost and no extra paperwork. Some will say you need a Green Card (which is neither green nor on card) but won't charge for it. Some will charge extra for the Green Card. Ideally you should contact your vehicle insurer 3-4 weeks before you set off, and confirm your conversation with them in writing.

Breakdown insurance

Arrange breakdown cover for your trip in good time so that if your vehicle breaks down or is involved in an accident it (and your caravan or trailer) can be repaired or returned to this country. This cover can usually be arranged as part of your travel insurance policy (see below).

Documents you must take with you

You may be asked to show your documents at any time so make sure that they are in order, up-to-date and easily accessible while you travel. These are what you need to take:

- ☐ Passports (you may also need a visa in some countries if you hold either a UK passport not issued in the UK or a passport that was issued outside the EU).
- ☐ Motor Insurance Certificate, including Green Card (or Continental Cover clause)
- ☐ DVLC Vehicle Registration Document plus, if not your own vehicle, the owner's written authority to drive.
- ☐ A full valid Driving Licence (not provisional). The new photo style licence is now mandatory in most European countries).

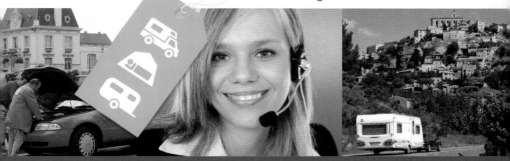

Travelling continued

Personal Holiday insurance

Even though you are just travelling within Europe you must take out travel insurance. Few EU countries pay the full cost of medical treatment even under reciprocal health service arrangements. The first part of a holiday insurance policy covers people. It will include the cost of doctor, ambulance and hospital treatment if needed. If needed the better companies will even pay for English language speaking doctors and nurses and will bring a sick or injured holidaymaker home by air ambulance.

The second part of a good policy covers things. If someone breaks into your motorhome and steals your passports and money, one phone call to the insurance company will have everything sorted out. If you manage to drive over your camera, it should be covered. NB – most policies have a maximum payment limit per item, do check that any valuables are adequately covered.

An important part of the insurance, often ignored, is cancellation (and curtailment) cover. Few things are as heartbreaking as having to cancel a holiday because a member of the family falls ill. Cancellation insurance can't take away the disappointment, but it makes sure you don't suffer financially as well. For this reason you should arrange your holiday insurance at least eight weeks before you set off.

Whichever insurance you choose we would advise reading very carefully the policies sold by the High Street travel trade. Whilst they may be good, they may not cover the specific needs of campers, caravanners and motorcaravanners.

Telephone **0870 405 4059** for a quote for our European Camping Holiday Insurance with cover arranged through Green Flag Motoring Assistance and Inter Group Assistance Services, one of the UK's largest assistance companies. Alternatively visit our website at **www.insure4campers.com**.

European Health Insurance Card (EHIC)

Important Changes since E111: Since September 2005 new European Health Insurance Cards have replaced the E111 forms .

Make sure you apply for your EHIC before travelling in Europe. Eligible travellers from the UK are entitled to receive free or reduced-cost medical care in many European countries on production of an EHIC. This free card is available by completing a form in the booklet 'Health Advice for Travellers' from local Post Offices. One should be completed for each family member. Alternatively visit www.dh.gov.uk/travellers and apply on-line. Please allow time to send your application off and have the EHIC returned to you.

The EHIC is valid in all European Community countries plus Iceland, Liechtenstein, Switzerland and Norway. If you or any of your dependants are suddenly taken ill or have an accident during a visit to any of these countries, free or reduced-cost emergency treatment is available - in most cases on production of a valid EHIC. Only state-provided emergency treatment is covered, and you will receive treatment on the same terms as nationals of the country you are visiting. Private treatment is generally not covered, and state-provided treatment may not cover all of the things that you would expect to receive free of charge from the NHS.

Remember an EHIC does not cover you for all the medical costs that you can incur or for repatriation - it is not an alternative to travel insurance. You will still need appropriate insurance to ensure you are fully covered for all eventualities.

Per night
FROM
€**29**
IN A COTTAGE*
FOR 4/6 PERS.

upreme comfort and the great outdoors:
oday your holidays with Yelloh ! Village can be
s colourful as your dreams.

elloh ! Village is the number 1 chain of top-of-the-range
amping-villages. There are 39 villages in different regions in
rance and two in Spain, offering quality services, and a wide
hoice of fully-equipped accommodation to rent: cottages,
halets, bungalows or mobile-homes.
ach Yelloh ! Village guarantees you:
Water on site: sea, ocean, swimming pool, river or lake.
An exceptional site and a carefully-tended natural environment.
Facilities, events, activities for all, from the first day of opening
right up until the site shuts.
Comfort and a choice of pitches and rented accommodation.
An attentive welcome, personalised information, on-line internet
reservation.

/ith Yelloh ! Village, you can discover or re-discover the extra
imension of the open air and live your holidays to the full, in
elloh ! Color.

Per night
FROM
€**14**
FOR CAMPING*

DOB Travel & Tourism - Fotos: D. Narbeburu / M. Huynh / DR

* see conditions on each campsite.

kawan
VILLAGES CAMPINGS

NEW

83 Quality Campsites
'At-The-Gate' Prices

A New Concept

Kawan Villages offers 83 great family campsites in France and 7 other countries. All are graded 3 or 4 star and all can be booked direct at the campsite's own 'at-the-gate' tariff. No surcharge, no premium, no hidden costs. You simply pay what you would pay at reception. Book on 01580 214017 for convenience and courteous, reliable service – at no extra cost!

High quality facilities, pleasant surroundings, great locations

Fully equipped mobile homes and chalets

Wonderful environment for children: safe, spacious, plenty to do

France

Spain

Portugal

Italy

Germany

Luxembourg

The Netherlands

Denmark

Sweden

1ᵉʳ Réseau Européen de Villages Campings

FREE BROCHURE
01580 214017

www.**kawan-villages**.co.uk

flower camping

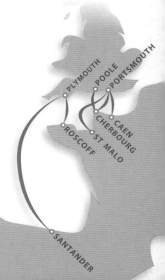

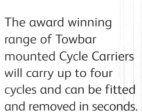

3 ISSUES FOR £1

Our practical titles are packed full of holiday tips, technical advice, reader reviews, superb photography…and much more! So subscribe to Practical Caravan or Practical Motorhome for just £1.

- **YOU** get your first 3 issues for £1
- **YOU** save 20% on the shop price after your trial ends
- **RISK-FREE** offer - you can cancel at any time
- **FREE** delivery, straight to your door!
- **EXCLUSIVE** subscriber offers and discounts

CALL 08456 777 812 NOW!

or visit **www.themagazineshop.com** quote code ALR08

Europe by car
Best fares by far

Best value fares

Up to 24 sailings per day

Easy access to main European destinations

Motorists only - no coach parties or foot passengers

CAMPING-ATTITUDE

Vacations should always be vacations !

Spend your vacation in a natural setting, bathed in sunlight, by water.
The 27 Village Center sites in three, main trends: Zen, leisure and discovery.
Up to you to choose!

Book your stay :

▶ +33 (0)4 99 57 21 21

www.village-center.com

Village center

A SELECTION OF CAMPSITES FOR EXPLORING FRANCE IN A WHOLE NEW WAY

Sites &
Paysages
DE FRANCE

SITES & PAYSAGES DE FRANCE, A SELECTION OF QUALITY CAMPSITES COVERING THE RICH DIVERSITY OF THE FRENCH REGIONS.

SITES & PAYSAGES de FRANCE offers campers and caravanners a carefully chosen selection of high quality, 3- and 4-star comfortable campsites across the country. Our campsites are situated in attractively landscaped, tree-shaded environments, with all the amenities for tents, caravans, camping-cars, mobile homes or chalet accommodation.
All are laid out with 'room to breathe' and located in areas of great natural beauty, with masses to do and see, from on-site sport and leisure activities, to nearby heritage visits…
not forgetting the sublime joys of authentic local French cuisine.

ASK US FOR YOUR FREE MAGAZINE

Information office:
Tél. 00 33 820 20 46 46 - www.sites-et-paysages.com
E-mail us at: contact@sites-et-paysages.com

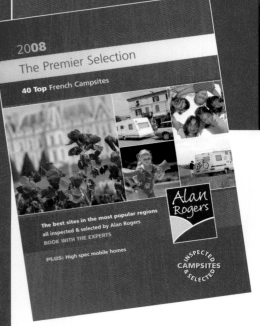

LES CASTELS

38 superb 4-star touring sites in exceptional settings across France

Welcome to Les Castels where the grounds of stunning castles, beautiful manors and charming country houses provide unique natural settings for some of the finest touring sites in France, all created by

LES CASTELS

★ ★ ★ ★

owners with a passion for the simpler things in life. You will be assured of a warm and courteous welcome, tranquil surroundings, great services and a taste of authentic French 'art de vivre'.

Courtesy, conviviality & hospitality
Choice, comfort and 4-star quality
Superb touring pitches
Excellent services & facilities

LES CASTELS 'PRIVILEGE CARD'
For special low-season rates contact us for details of the Les Castels 'Privilège card'

Contact us for a brochure and discover a Castels site that matches your idea of a perfect holiday destination.

Les Castels...discover a 'different France'

Les Castels - Manoir de Terre Rouge - 35270 Bonnemain - France
Tel. +33 02 23 16 03 20 / Fax +33 02 23 16 03 23
www.les-castels.com

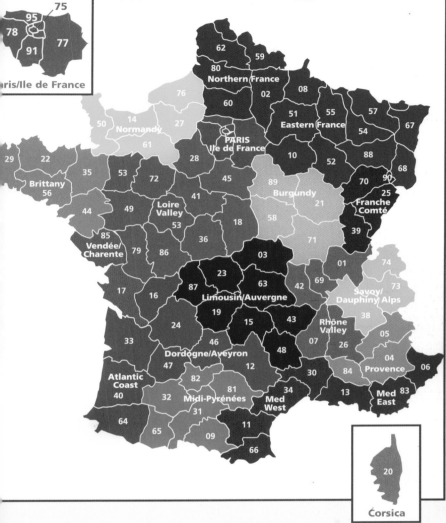

Corsica

For administrative purposes France is actually divided into 23 official Regions covering the 95 départements (similar to our counties).

However, theses do not always coincide with the needs of tourists (for example, the area we think of as the 'Dordogne' is split between two official regions. We have, therefore, opted to feature our campsites within unofficial 'tourist' regions.

We use the departement numbers as the first two digits of our campsite numbers so, for example, any site in the Manche departement will start with the number 50.

■ **Brittany** *(pages 17-73)*		░ Normandy *(pages 75-94)*		■ **Northern France** *(pages 95-105)*	
22	Côtes d'Armor	14	Calvados	59	Nord
29	Finistère	27	Eure	62	Pas-de-Calais
35	Ille-et-Vilaine	50	Manche	02	Aisne
56	Morbihan	61	Orne	60	Oise
44	Loire Atlantique	76	Seine Maritime	80	Somme

■ **Paris & Ile de France**
(pages 106-115)

75 Paris
77 Seine-et-Marne
78 Yvelines
91 Essone
92 Hauts-de-Seine
93 Seine-St-Denis
94 Val de Marne
95 Val d'Oise

■ **Eastern France**
(pages 116-132)

08 Ardennes
51 Marne
10 Aube
52 Haute-Marne
54 Meurthe-et-Moselle
55 Meuse
57 Moselle
88 Vosges
67 Bas-Rhin
68 Haut-Rhin

■ **Vendée & Charente**
(pages 133-167)

85 Vendée
17 Charente-Maritime

■ **Loire Valley**
(pages 169-193)

18 Cher
28 Eure-et-Loir
36 Indre
37 Indre-et-Loire
41 Loir-et-Cher
45 Loiret
49 Maine-et-Loire
53 Mayenne
72 Sarthe
79 Deux Sèvres
86 Vienne

■ **Burgundy**
(pages 194-206)

21 Côte d'Or
58 Nièvre
71 Saône-et-Loire
89 Yonne

■ **Franche-Comté**
(pages 207-214)

25 Doubs
39 Jura
70 Haute-Saône
90 Tre. de Belfort

■ **Savoy & Dauphiny Alps**
(pages 215-235)

38 Isère
73 Savoie
74 Haute-Savoie

■ **Atlantic Coast**
(pages 236-271)

33 Gironde
40 Landes
64 Pyrénées Atlantiques

■ **Dordogne & Aveyron**
(pages 272-316)

24 Dordogne
47 Lot-et-Garonne
12 Aveyron
46 Lot
16 Charente

■ **Limousin & Auvergne**
(pages 317-335)

19 Corrèze
23 Creuse
87 Haute-Vienne
03 Allier
15 Cantal
43 Haute-Loire
63 Puy-de-Dôme
48 Lozère

■ **Rhône Valley**
(pages 336-361)

01 Ain
07 Ardèche
26 Drôme
42 Loire
69 Rhône

■ **Provence**
(pages 362-377)

04 Alpes-de-Haute-Provence
05 Hautes-Alpes
84 Vaucluse

■ **Midi-Pyrénées**
(pages 378-394)

09 Ariège
31 Haute-Garonne,
32 Gers
65 Hautes-Pyrénées
81 Tarn
82 Tarn-et Garonne

■ **Mediterranean West**
(pages 395-440)

11 Aude
30 Gard
34 Hérault
66 Pyrénées-Orientales

■ **Mediterranean East**
(pages 441-472)

13 Bouches-du-Rhône
83 Var
06 Alpes-Maritime

■ **Corsica**
(pages 473-479)

20 Corse-Sud
Haute-Corse

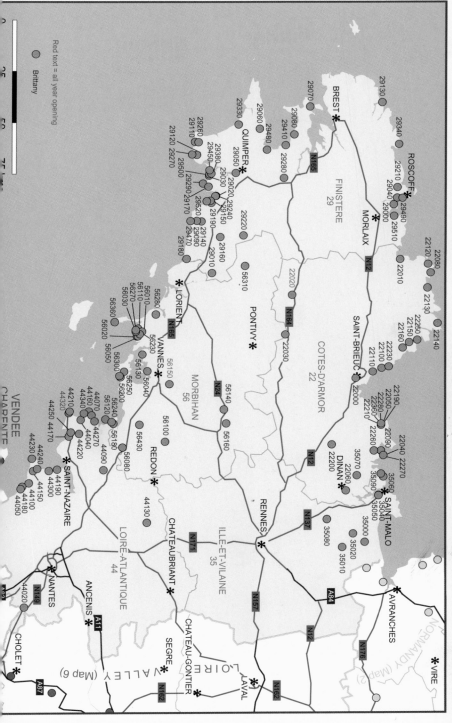

Red text = all year opening

Brittany

BREST

ROSCOFF

FINISTERE
29

MORLAIX

QUIMPER

SAINT-BRIEUC

CÔTES-D'ARMOR
22

DINAN

SAINT-MALO

PONTIVY

LORIENT

VANNES

MORBIHAN
56

REDON

RENNES

ILLE-ET-VILAINE
35

AVRANCHES

VIRE

CHATEAUBRIANT

LOIRE-ATLANTIQUE
44

CHATEAU-GONTIER

LAVAL

NORMANDY (Map 2)

VENDEE
CHARENTE

SAINT-NAZAIRE

NANTES

ANCENIS

SEGRE

CHOLET

LOIRE VALLEY (Map 6)

29130
29070
29340
29330
29060
29080
29480
29410
29280
29210
29040
29000
29490
29510
29260
29110
29120 29270
29750
29500
29290 29170
29520
29380 29050
29450
29030
29020 29240
29150
29190
29140
29090
29470
29180
29220
29160
29010
56310

22080
22120
22010
22130
22250
22150
22160
22140
22230
22100
22110
22000

22190
22050
22280
22210
22260
22090
22040 22270

35070
35000
35090 35060
35040 35050
35000
35080
35020
35010

22020
22030
N164
N165
N24
N12
N12
N137
N171
N157
N12
N176
A84

56280
56010
56110
56270
56030
56360
56020
56050
56300
56130
56230
56040
56200
56120
56240
56180
56090
56080
56430
56100
56160
56140
56150

44210
44320
44250 44170
44150
44070
44160
44340
44270
44040
44020
44240
44230
44190
44300
44180
44100
44050
44130

N165
N162
N162
N182
N149
A11
A87

35090
35040 35050

s on this map are featured on pages 17-73 of the guide.
se refer to the numerical index (page 562) for exact campsite page references.

539

Normandy - Map 2

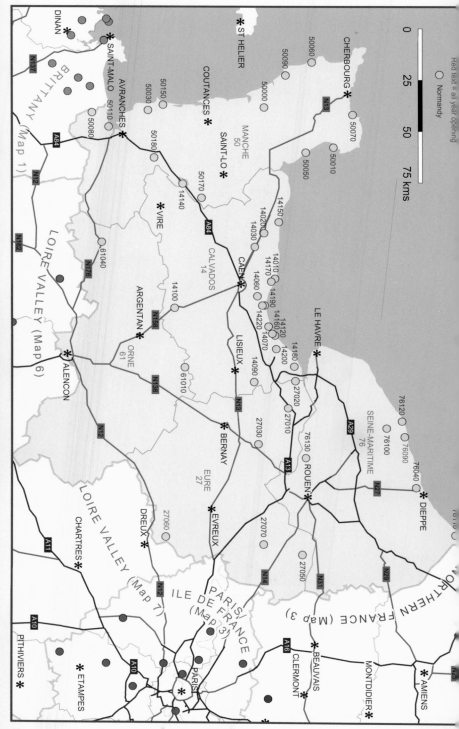

Sites on this map are featured on pages 75-94 of the guide.
Please refer to the numerical index (page 562) for exact campsite page references.

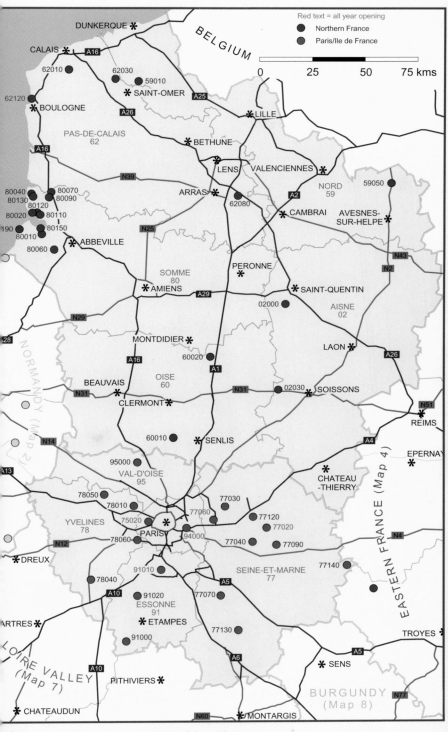

Red text = all year opening

● Northern France
● Paris/Ile de France

0   25   50   75 kms

DUNKERQUE

BELGIUM

CALAIS   A16

62010   62030   59010
62120   SAINT-OMER   A25
BOULOGNE   A26   LILLE
PAS-DE-CALAIS
62   BETHUNE
A16   LENS   VALENCIENNES
N39   NORD   59050
80040   80070   ARRAS   59
80130   80090   62080   A2
80120   CAMBRAI   AVESNES-
80020   80110   SUR-HELPE
190   80150   N25   N43
80010   ABBEVILLE   N2
80060   SOMME   PERONNE
80   SAINT-QUENTIN
AMIENS   A29   AISNE
02000   02
N29
28   MONTDIDIER   LAON
A16   60020   A26
OISE   A1
BEAUVAIS   60   02030   SOISSONS
N31   CLERMONT   N31   N51
REIMS
N14   60010   SENLIS   EPERNAY
13   95000   A4
78050   VAL-D'OISE   CHATEAU
78010   95   -THIERRY
75020   77030
A13   78060   77060   N4
PARIS   77120
N12   94000   77020
78040   77040   77090
DREUX   SEINE-ET-MARNE   77140
91010   77   A5
A10   91020   77070
ESSONNE   A5
ARTRES   91   77130   TROYES
ETAMPES
91000   A6
A10   SENS
LOIRE   PITHIVIERS   N77
VALLEY   BURGUNDY
(Map 7)   (Map 8)
CHATEAUDUN   N60   MONTARGIS

NORMANDY (Map 2)

EASTERN FRANCE (Map 4)

s on this map are featured on pages 95-115 of the guide.
se refer to the numerical index (page 562) for exact campsite page references.

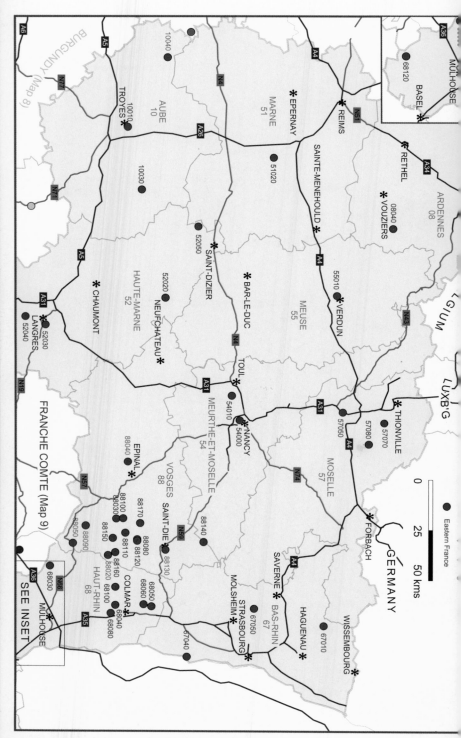

Sites on this map are featured on pages 106-132 of the guide.
Please refer to the numerical index (page 562) for exact campsite page references.

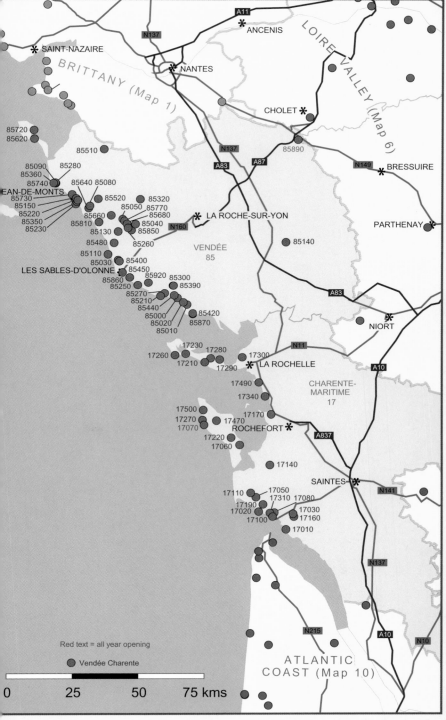

A11
ANCENIS ✳

N137

SAINT-NAZAIRE ✳

BRITTANY (Map 1)

NANTES ✳

LOIRE VALLEY (Map 6)

CHOLET ✳

85720
85620

85510

85890

N137

A83 **A87**

N149 **BRESSUIRE** ✳

85090 85280
85360
85740
EAN-DE-MONTS
85730
85150   85640 85080
85220   85520   85320
85350   85050 85770
85230   85660   85680   **LA ROCHE-SUR-YON** ✳
85810   85040
85130   85850   **N160**
85480   85260
85110
85030   85400   **VENDÉE**
LES SABLES-D'OLONNE   85450   **85**
85860   85920   85300
85250   85390
85270
85210
85440
85000   85420
85020   85870
85010

85140

PARTHENAY ✳

A83

NIORT ✳

17230
17260   17280
17210   17300   **N11**
17290   **LA ROCHELLE** ✳   **A10**

17490

17340   **CHARENTE-**
MARITIME
17500   17170   **17**
17270   17470
17070
17220
17060

17140

17110   17050
17190   17310   17080
17020   17030
17100   17160
17010

ROCHEFORT ✳

A837

SAINTES ✳

N141

N137

N215

A10   **N10**

Red text = all year opening

⬤ Vendée Charente

0   25   50   75 kms

ATLANTIC
COAST (Map 10)

on this map are featured on pages 133-167 of the guide.
e refer to the numerical index (page 562) for exact campsite page references.

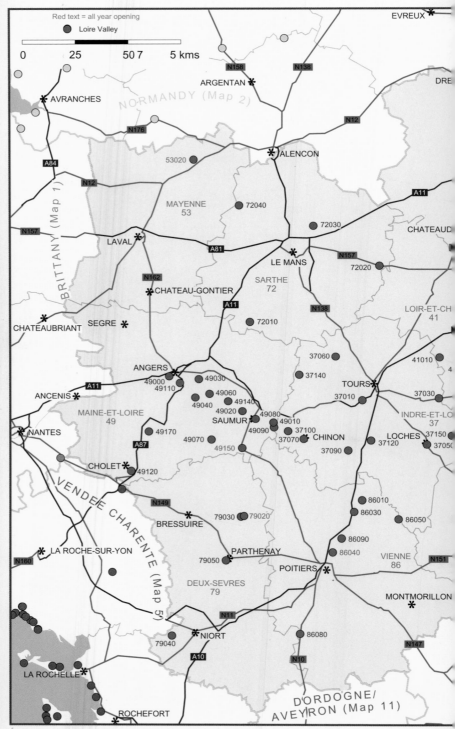

Red text = all year opening
● Loire Valley

0   25   50 7   5 kms

EVREUX ✳

DRE

N158   N138

ARGENTAN ✳

NORMANDY (Map 2)

AVRANCHES ✳

N12

N176

A84

ALENCON ✳

N12

53020 ●

A11

MAYENNE
53

72040 ●

72030 ●

CHATEAUD

N157

A81

N157

LAVAL ✳

72020 ●

LE MANS ✳

N162

SARTHE
72

CHATEAU-GONTIER ✳

A11

N138

LOIR-ET-CH
41

CHATEAUBRIANT ✳

SEGRE ✳

72010 ●

37060 ●

41010 ●

ANGERS ✳

37140 ●

TOURS ✳

37030 ●

A11

49000
49110

49030 ●

ANCENIS ✳

49040 ●

49060 ●

49140 ●

37010 ●

MAINE-ET-LOIRE
49

49020

49080 ●

INDRE-ET-LO
37

NANTES ✳

49170 ●

SAUMUR

49010

37150 ●

A87

49070 ●

49090

37100 ●

CHINON

LOCHES

37050

37070 ●

37120 ●

49150 ●

37090 ●

CHOLET ✳

49120 ●

VENDEE

N149

86010 ●

86030 ●

86050 ●

BRESSUIRE ✳

79030 ● 79020

CHARENTE (Map 5)

86090 ●

LA ROCHE-SUR-YON ✳

PARTHENAY ✳

86040 ●

VIENNE
86

N151

N160

79050 ●

POITIERS ✳

DEUX-SEVRES
79

MONTMORILLON ✳

N11

NIORT ✳

86080 ●

79040 ●

N147

A10

N10

LA ROCHELLE ✳

D'ORDOGNE/
AVEYRON (Map 11)

ROCHEFORT ✳

Sites on these maps are featured on pages 169-193 of the guide.
Please refer to the numerical index (page 562) for exact campsite page references.

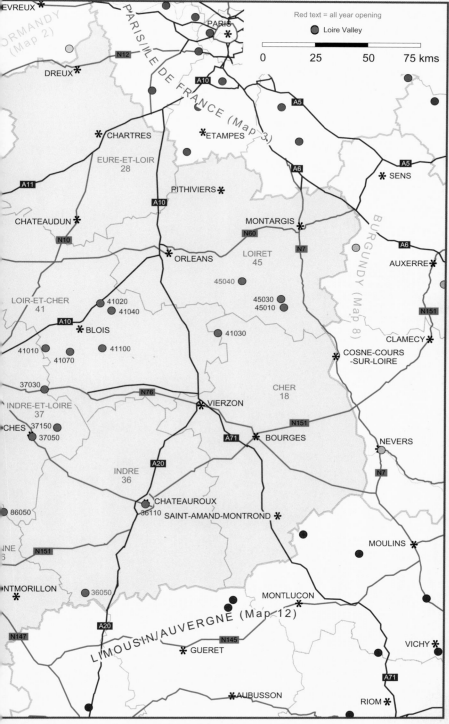

EVREUX

NORMANDY (Map 2)

PARIS/ILE DE FRANCE (Map 3)

N12

DREUX

PARIS

Red text = all year opening

Loire Valley

0   25   50   75 kms

A10

A5

CHARTRES

ETAMPES

EURE-ET-LOIR 28

A11

A6

SENS

PITHIVIERS

A10

MONTARGIS

CHATEAUDUN

N60

N10

N7

A6

AUXERRE

ORLEANS

LOIRET 45

BURGUNDY (Map 8)

45040

N151

LOIR-ET-CHER 41

41020

45030

41040

45010

A10

BLOIS

41030

CLAMECY

41010

41100

COSNE-COURS -SUR-LOIRE

41070

37030

CHER 18

N76

INDRE-ET-LOIRE 37

VIERZON

CHES

37150

N151

NEVERS

37050

A71

BOURGES

A20

N7

INDRE 36

86050

CHATEAUROUX

36110

SAINT-AMAND-MONTROND

NE 6

N151

MOULINS

NTMORILLON

36050

MONTLUCON

N147

A20

LIMOUSIN/AUVERGNE (Map 12)

N145

VICHY

N147

GUERET

A71

AUBUSSON

RIOM

on these maps are featured on pages 169-193 of the guide.

e refer to the numerical index (page 562) for exact campsite page references.

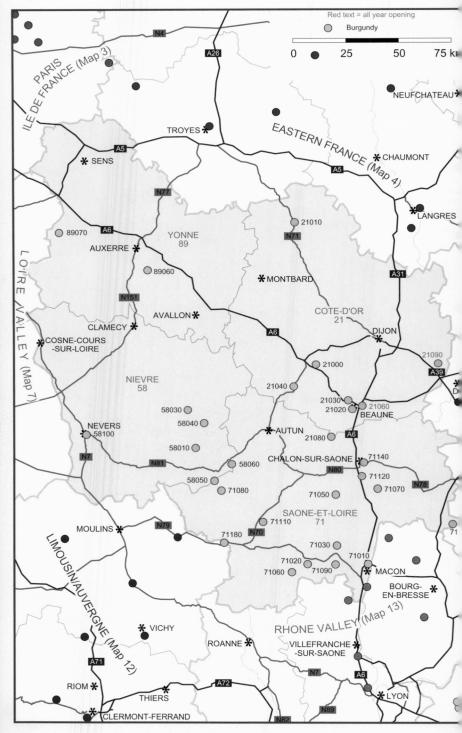

Burgundy

0   25   50   75 k

N4
A26
A5

PARIS
ILE DE FRANCE (Map 3)

NEUFCHATEAU

TROYES

EASTERN FRANCE (Map 4)

✱ SENS

✱ CHAUMONT
A5

N77

LANGRES

89070   A6

YONNE
89

21010
N71

AUXERRE ✱

89060

✱ MONTBARD

A31

N151

AVALLON ✱

COTE-D'OR
21

DIJON

CLAMECY ✱

21090
A39

✱ COSNE-COURS
-SUR-LOIRE

LOIRE VALLEY (Map 7)

21000

NIEVRE
58

21040

21030
21020   21060
BEAUNE

58030
58040

21080   A6

58010

✱ AUTUN

NEVERS
58100

58060

CHALON-SUR-SAONE   71140
N80

N7

N81

58050

71120   N78
71070

71080

71050

MOULINS ✱   N79

71180   N70

71110

SAONE-ET-LOIRE
71

71

71030

71010

71020   71090

MACON ✱

71060

LIMOUSIN/AUVERGNE (Map 12)

✱ VICHY

BOURG-
EN-BRESSE ✱

A71

RHONE VALLEY (Map 13)

ROANNE ✱

VILLEFRANCHE ✱
-SUR-SAONE

N7   A6

RIOM ✱

A72

THIERS ✱

✱ LYON

CLERMONT-FERRAND

N82   N89

Sites on these maps are featured on pages 194-206 of the guide.
Please refer to the numerical index (page 562) for exact campsite page references.

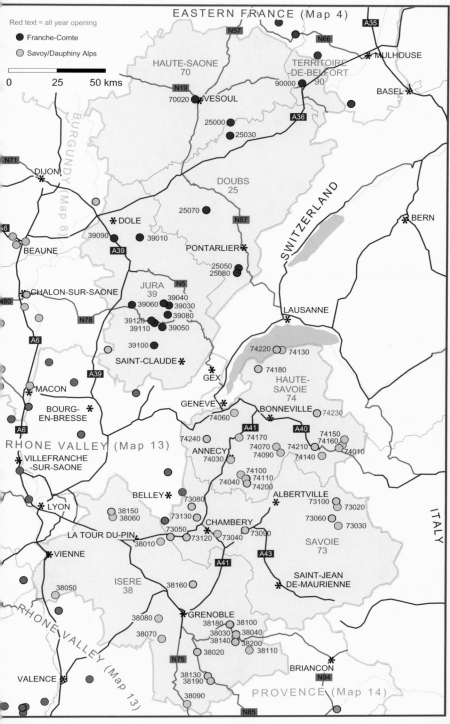

Red text = all year opening
● Franche-Comte
○ Savoy/Dauphiny Alps

0   25   50 kms

EASTERN FRANCE (Map 4)

N57

N66

A35

HAUTE-SAONE
70

TERRITOIRE
-DE-BELFORT
90

*MULHOUSE

90000

N19

N19

70020 VESOUL

BASEL *

25000

A36

25030

BURGUNDY (Map 8)

N71

DIJON *

DOUBS
25

25070

*BERN

A6

*DOLE

SWITZERLAND

39090

A39

39010

BEAUNE

PONTARLIER *

25050
25080

*CHALON-SUR-SAONE

JURA
39

N5

39040

39060 39030

N78

39120 39080

39110 39050

LAUSANNE
*

A6

39100

A39

SAINT-CLAUDE *

74220 ○○ 74130

*MACON

GEX

74180

HAUTE-
SAVOIE
74

BOURG-
EN-BRESSE *

GENEVE *

BONNEVILLE

74230

74060

74240

A41

A40

74150
74160

RHONE VALLEY (Map 13)

74170

74070   74210

74010

*VILLEFRANCHE
-SUR-SAONE

ANNECY

74090   74140

74030

74100
74110
74200

*LYON

74040

38150
38060

BELLEY *

73080

73130

ALBERTVILLE

LA TOUR DU-PIN *

73050

73100   73020

73060   73030

73120   73040   73090

38010

CHAMBERY

*VIENNE

A41

SAVOIE
73

ITALY

ISERE
38

38160

A43

SAINT-JEAN
DE-MAURIENNE *

38050

38080

*GRENOBLE

38070

38180   38100

38030   38040

38140   38200

38020   38110

N75

BRIANCON *

VALENCE *

38130
38190

N94

38090

PROVENCE (Map 14)

RHONE VALLEY (Map 13)

N85

tes on these maps are featured on pages 207-235 of the guide.
ease refer to the numerical index (page 562) for exact campsite page references.

Franche-Comté, Savoy & Dauphiny - Map 9

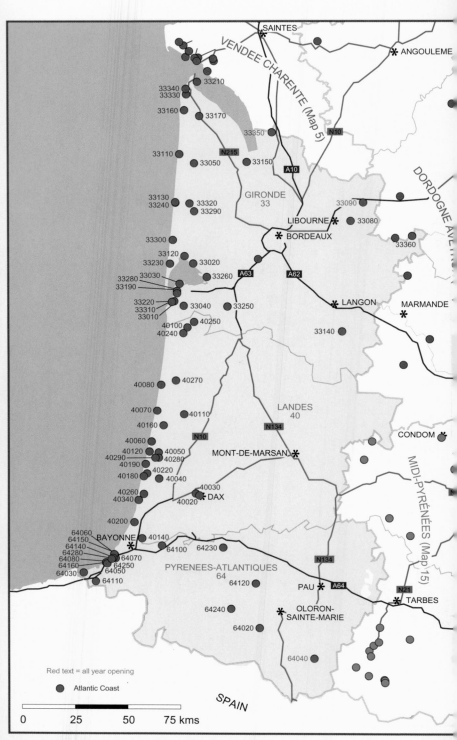

SAINTES

VENDEE CHARENTE (Map 5)

ANGOULEME

33210

33340
33330

33160   33170

33350   N10

33110   N215

33050   33150   A10

GIRONDE
33

33130   33320   33090
33240   33290

LIBOURNE   33080
BORDEAUX   33360

33300

33120
33230   33020

33280 33030   A63   A62
33190

33220   33260
33310   33040   33250   LANGON   MARMANDE
33010

40100   40250   33140
40240

40080   40270

40070
40110

40160   LANDES
40

40060   N10   N134   CONDOM
40120   40050
40290   40280   MONT-DE-MARSAN
40190
40180   40220
40040   MIDI-PYRÉNÉES (Map 15)

40260   40030
40340   DAX
40020

40200

64060
64150   40140
64140   BAYONNE
64280   64100   64230
64080   64070
64160   64250   PYRENEES-ATLANTIQUES
64030   64050   64
64110   64120   PAU   A64   N21   TARBES

64240   OLORON-
SAINTE-MARIE

64020

64040

Red text = all year opening

● Atlantic Coast

SPAIN

0   25   50   75 kms

Sites on these maps are featured on pages 236-271 of the guide.
Please refer to the numerical index (page 562) for exact campsite page references.

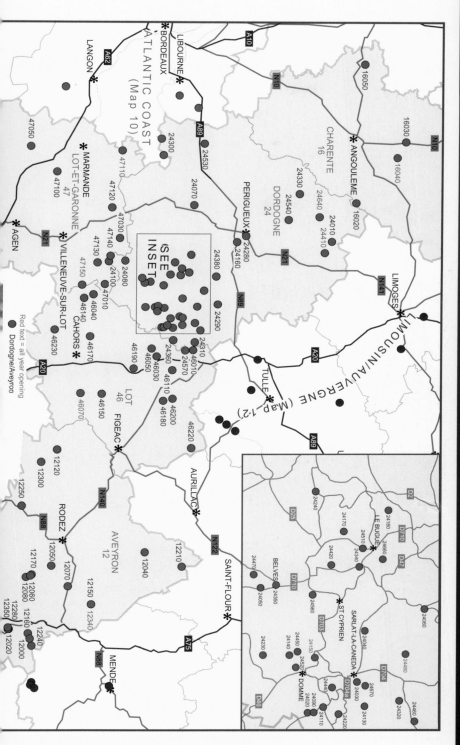

n these maps are featured on pages 272-316 of the guide.
refer to the numerical index (page 562) for exact campsite page references.

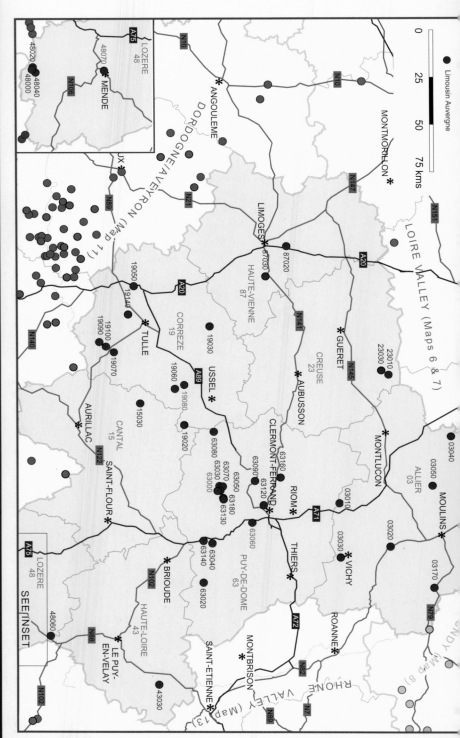

Limousin & Auvergne - Map 12

Sites on these maps are featured on pages 317-335 of the guide.
Please refer to the numerical index (page 562) for exact campsite page references.

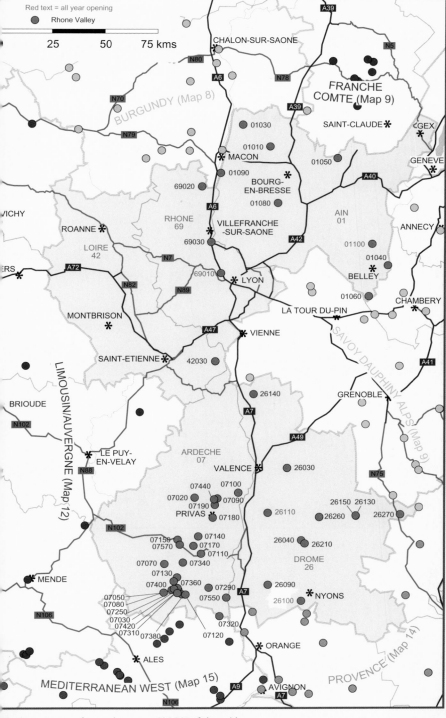

Red text = all year opening
● Rhone Valley

25   50   75 kms

CHALON-SUR-SAONE

N80
A6
N78
N70
BURGUNDY (Map 8)
N79

FRANCHE COMTE (Map 9)
SAINT-CLAUDE ✳
GEX

A39
01030
01010
MACON ✳
01050
GENEVE ✳
01090
69020
BOURG-EN-BRESSE
A40
A6
01080
AIN 01
ANNECY
RHONE 69
VILLEFRANCHE -SUR-SAONE
01100
VICHY
ROANNE ✳
LOIRE 42
69030
A42
01040
BELLEY ✳
N7
69010
LYON ✳
01060
CHAMBERY ✳
N82
N89
LA TOUR DU-PIN
MONTBRISON ✳
A47
VIENNE ✳
SAINT-ETIENNE ✳
42030
BRIOUDE
26140
GRENOBLE ✳
A7
N102
A49
26030
LE PUY-EN-VELAY ✳
ARDECHE 07
N75
N88
VALENCE ✳
07440 07100
07020 07190 07090
PRIVAS 07180
26150 26130
26110 26260 26270
07150 07140
07570 07170
07110
26040 26210
07070 07340
DROME 26
07130
07400 07360
07290
26090
07050 07550
A7
26100 ✳ NYONS
07080
07250
07030 07320
07420
07310 07380 07120
MENDE ✳
N106
ORANGE ✳
ALES ✳
PROVENCE (Map 14)
MEDITERRANEAN WEST (Map 15)
A9
AVIGNON ✳
N106
A7

LIMOUSIN/AUVERGNE (Map 12)
SAVOY DAUPHINY ALPS (Map 9)

on these maps are featured on pages 336-361 of the guide.
e refer to the numerical index (page 562) for exact campsite page references.

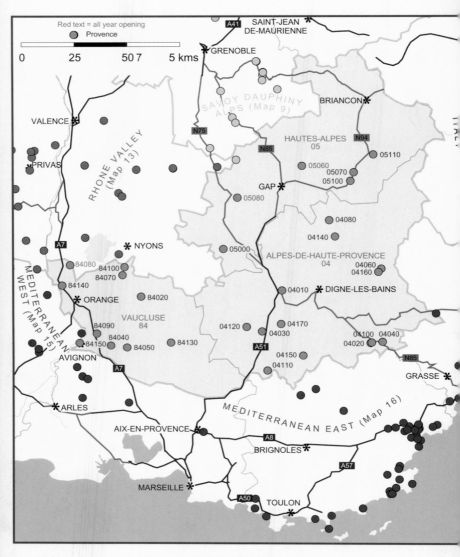

Red text = all year opening
Provence

0   25   50 7   5 kms

SAINT-JEAN DE-MAURIENNE
A41
GRENOBLE
BRIANCON
SAVOY DAUPHINY Alps (Map 9)
VALENCE
N75
HAUTES-ALPES 05
N94
PRIVAS
RHONE VALLEY (Map 13)
N85
05060
05110
05070
05100
GAP
05080
04080
04140
A7
NYONS
05000
ALPES-DE-HAUTE-PROVENCE 04
04060
04160
MEDITERRANEAN WEST (Map 15)
84080
84100
84070
84140
04010
DIGNE-LES-BAINS
ORANGE
84020
VAUCLUSE 84
04120
04170
04030
04100 04040
04020
84090
84040
84150
84050
84130
A51
04150
04110
N85
AVIGNON
A7
GRASSE
ARLES
MEDITERRANEAN EAST (Map 16)
AIX-EN-PROVENCE
A8
BRIGNOLES
A57
MARSEILLE
A50
TOULON

Sites on these maps are featured on pages 362-377 of the guide.
Please refer to the numerical index (page 562) for exact campsite page references.

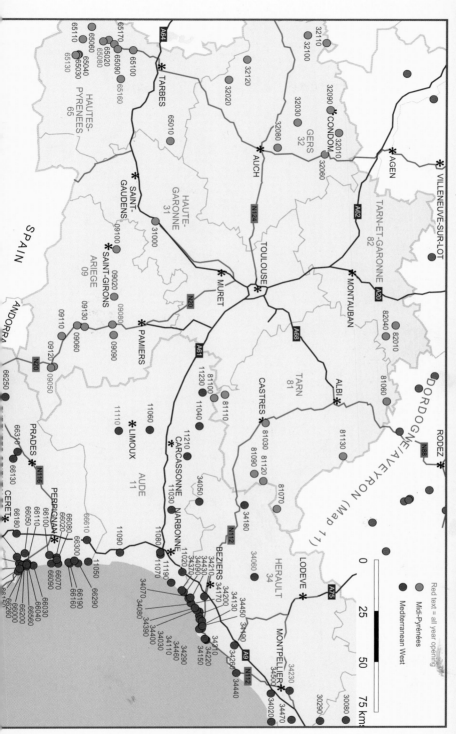

on these maps are featured on pages 378-440 of the guide.
se refer to the numerical index (page 562) for exact campsite page references.

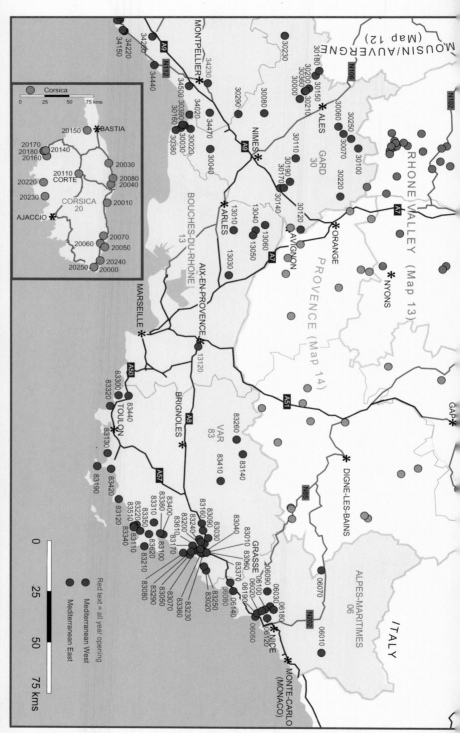

Sites on these maps are featured on pages 441-479 of the guide.
Please refer to the numerical index (page 562) for exact campsite page references.

Town and Village Index

Index - town and village

A

Acotz	266
Agde	418, 420, 427
Agos Vidalos	388
Aigues-Mortes	401
Airvault	170
Aix En Provence	449
Alèria	477
Alet-les-Bains	398
Allas-les-Mines	305
Allègre	402
Allègre-Les Fumades	403
Allés-sur-Dordogne	292
Amiens	100
Amphion-les-Bains	220
Andelys	83
Andernos-les-Bains	237
Anduze	401, 408, 410, 412
Angers	182
Angles	393
Angoulins-Sur-Mer	146
Annecy	216
Anneyron	356
Anse	361
Antonne et Trigonant	298
Aramits	264
Arcachon	237
Arès	239
Argelès-Gazost	386, 388
Argelès-sur-Mer	426, 428, 432-438
Argentat	323-324
Aries-Espenan	386
Arnay le Duc	196
Arpaillargues	404
Arradon	61
Arrayade	390
Ars-en-Ré	143
Artemare	338
Ascou	381
Aston	381
Atur	293
Aubazine	325
Aubenas	346, 353
Auberville	78
Audenge	247
Aureilhan	263
Autrans	228
Auxonne	197
Avignon	375
Azur	252

B

Badefols-sur-Dordogne	294
Baden	65
Bagnères-de-Bigorre	389
Bagnols sur Cèze	409
Baguer-Pican	46
Ballan-Miré	172
Bannalec	35
Barbothan les Thermes	384
Barjac	405
Barneville-Carteret	88
Bayeux	76
Bazas	242
Beaune	195
Beauvezer	370
Bédoin	373
Beg-Meil	36
Belfort	214
Belle-Hutte	124
Bellerive-sur-Allier	319
Belmont Tramonet	233
Belvès	285, 297, 300
Bénodet	27, 41, 44
Bénouville	77
Berny-Riviere	96
Bidart	265-266, 269, 271
Biron	288
Biscarrosse	254, 260
Boiry-Notre-Dame	100
Bois de Céné	161
Boisset-et-Gaujac	401
Boisson	403
Bollène	374
Bonifacio	474-476
Bonnac-la-Côte	327
Bonnal	208
Bormes-les-Mimosas	456
Bort les Orgues	320
Bouge-Chambalud	227
Bouillancourt-sous-Miannay	101
Bourdeaux	358
Bourg	132
Bourg d'Arud	230
Bourg de la Canéda	299
Bourg-d'Oisans	225-226, 229, 231
Bourg-St Maurice	232
Bourg-St-Andeol	350
Boussac	325
Boussac-Bourg	326
Bout-du-Lac	216
Brain-sur-l'Authion	184
Braize	319
Brantôme	304
Bravone	477
Brem sur Mer	150, 160
Bressuire	170
Breville-sur-Mer	91
Brignogan-Plages	40
Brissac	185
Brousses et Villaret	396
Burtoncourt	119
Bussang	125
Buysscheure	96
Buzancy	130

C

Cagnes-sur-Mer	445
Calenzana	478
Calvi	478-479
Calviac en Périgord	293
Calviac-Sousceyrac	312
Camaret sur Mer	32
Campagne	296
Candé-sur-Beuvron	181
Canet-de-Salars	278
Canet-en-Roussillon	427-431
Cany-Barville	93
Cap d'Agde	422
Carantec	27
Carnac	63, 66, 70
Caroual Village	24
Carqueiranne	458
Carsac-Aillac	291
Castellane	364, 366
Castelnaud la Chapelle	300
Castelnaudary	401
Castelnau-Magnoac	386
Castera Verduzan	382
Castres	390
Caudon par Montfort	289
Caurel	19
Cauterets	389
Cavalaire-sur-Mer	456, 465, 467, 472
Cayeux sue Mer	105
Cazaux La Teste de Buch	238
Celles-sur-Plaine	128
Cesseras-en-Minervois	416
Chabeuil	354
Chaillac	172
Challes-les-Eaux	233
Chalon sur-Saône	202
Châlons-en-Champagne	118
Chambon sur Lac	330
Chamonix	216, 220-221
Champagnat	205
Champigny-sur-Marne	113
Charchigne	171
Charleville-Mezieres	129
Charny	206
Châteaulin	40
Châteauroux	172
Châteauroux-Les-Alpes	372
Châtelaillon-Plage	145
Châtellerault	192
Chatillon	212
Chatillon en Diois	357
Châtillon-sur-Seine	195
Chavannes-sur-Reyssouze	338
Chemille	189
Chemillé-sur-Indrois	177
Cheverny	183
Chigy	199
Chinon	175

Cholet	187
Clairvaux-les-Lacs	211, 214
Clapiers	416
Clisson	50
Clohars-Carnoët	36
Cluny	201
Coëx	149, 157
Cognac	283
Cogolin	466
Coiroux	325
Combrit	42
Concarneau	35, 37, 45
Concourson-sur-Layon	186
Condat	315
Contamine Sarzin	224
Contis Plage	254
Corbés-Thoiras	410
Corcieux	126-127
Cormoranche-sur-Saone	340
Cornet	170
Corte	477
Couderc	292
Couhé	193
Coulon	170
Courtils	88
Coutures	184
Coux-et-Bigaroque	299
Crayssac	311
Crécy-la-Chapelle	111
Crespian	404
Crèvecoeur-en-Brie	109
Creysse	308
Crozon	32
Cuguen	45

D

Daglan	294
Darbres	349
Dardilly	361
Dax	251
Dienville	130
Digoin	206
Dol-de-Bretagne	46-47
Domfront	92
Domme	302
Dompierre-les-Ormes	200
Dompierre-sur-Besbre	320
Donzenac	322
Doucier	210
Doussard	216, 220, 222
Douville	285
Dunes de Ste Marguerite	34
Duras	314
Duravel	309

E

Ebreuil	318
Eclaron	132
Eguisheim	122

Embrun	373
Eperlecques	99
Epiniac	47
Equemauville	80
Erdeven	71
Erquy	19, 24-27
Esplanade St Vorles	195
Esquieze Sere	387
Estaing	387
Estang	385
Etables-sur-Mer	21
Eymouthiers	283

F

Falaise	78
Faubourg St Antoine	477
Ferme de Rhodes	401
Feunteun Vilian	42
Fiquefleur-Equainville	82
Fleurie	360
Fleury	397, 400
Foix	380
Fontmolines	372
Font-Romeu	435
Forcalquier	367-368
Fort-Mahon-Plage	102
Fouesnant	36, 39
Fouras	139
Francueil-Chenonceaux	173
Frangy	224
Fréjus	449, 454, 462, 467-468
Fresne-sur-Authie	103
Frontignan-Plage	425
Fuilla	440
Fumel	315

G

Gallician	403
Gassin	470
Gaubazon	384
Gaugeac	287
Gennes	188
Ger	390
Gérardmer	128
Ghisonaccia	476
Gibles	201
Gien	178-179
Gigny-sur-Saône	202
Givrand	164
Gluiras	340
Gondrin	384
Grande Dune du Pyla	249
Grâne	356
Granges-sur-Vologne	127
Graveson en Provence	448
Grayan et l'Hopital	240
Gréoux Les Bains	368
Grève du Man	43

Grignan	358
Grimaud	454, 460, 469
Groire	334
Groisy	221
Groléjac-en-Perigord	287
Guégon-Josselin	68
Guemene-Penfao	54
Guérande	56, 60
Guillestre	373
Guines	98

H

Haute-Greyere	369
Hautot-sur-Mer	92
Hendaye	264
Honfleur	80
Houlgate	77
Hourtin	238
Hourtin-Plage	240
Huanne-Montmartin	208
Hyères	461
Hyeres les Palmiers	468

I

Ile d'Offard	186
Ile de la Barthelasse	375
Ile de Nieres	318
Ile de Noirmoutier	161
Ile de Ré	141, 143
Ingrandes-sur-Vienne	190
Issoire	332
Issy-l`Évêque	204

J

Jablines	109
Jard-sur-Mer	153, 156
Jassat	331
Jugon-les Lacs	23
Jumieges	93

K

Kerandouaron	18
Kerguistin	24
Kerisole	38
Kerleven	28
Kermerour	35
Kervel	43
Kervourdon	18

L

L'Isle sur la Sorgue	374
L'Ayguade	468
L'Houmeau	144
La Bastide-de-Sérou	379
La Baule	54
La Bernerie en Retz	51
La Bresse	124
La Cadière d'Azur	472
La Cerclière	112

La Chapelle	26	
La Chapelle-aux-Filtzméens	49	
La Chapelle-devant-Bruyères	129	
La Chapelle-Hermier	163	
La Clapière	373	
La Clusaz	218	
La Colle-sur-Loup	442, 444	
la Couarde-sur-Mer	141	
La Croix Patron	186	
La Croix Valmer Plage	468	
La Flèche	189	
La Flotte-en-Ré	144-145	
La Forêt-Fouesnant	28, 38	
La Fouasse	134	
La Gaillarde-Plage	452	
La Galinée	20	
La Glière	224	
La Grande Grève	27	
La Grande Motte	413	
La Grouinière	149	
la Guérinière	161	
La Guyonnière	155	
La Josephtrie	139	
La Jousselinière	146	
La Lie	360	
La Mothe-Achard	148	
La Nautique	398	
La Passe	141	
La Petite Beauce	107	
La Plaine-sur-Mer	52, 55	
La Pointe du Bile	67	
La Pyla-sur-Mer	237	
La Roche Bernard	64	
La Roche-Posay	192	
La Romieu	383	
La Salle en Beaumont	231	
La Tranche-sur-Mer	148, 159, 166	
La Trinité-sur-Mer	62, 64, 69	
La Tuillière	337	
La Turballe	50, 61	
La Vallée Gatorge	49	
Labenne-Océan	262	
Lac Chambon	332	
Lac de la Raviège	392	
Lac de Laffrey	225	
Lac de Laives	205	
Lac de Leon	252	
Lac de Naussac	329	
Lac de Pareloup	275-276, 278	
Lac de Rillé	177	
Lac de Vouglans	214	
Lac du Jaunay	163	
Lac du Laouzas	391	
Lac Rive Ouest	235	
Lacanau-Lac	248	
Lacanau-Océan	243, 246-247	
Laives	205	
Lalley	228	
Lamontélarié	392	

Land Rosted	34	
Landéda	34	
Landevieille	152	
Landrellec	22	
Landry	233	
Langogne	329	
Langres	131-132	
Lanloup	24	
Lansargues	422	
Lapalme	400	
Largentière	342	
Larnas	348	
Laruns	265	
Lathuile	222	
Lattes	424	
Lau-Balagnas	388	
Laurens	416	
Le Bar sur Loup	444	
Le Barcarès	436-437	
Le Bec-Hellouin	82	
Le Bois-Plage-en-Ré	140	
Le Bos Rouge	300	
Le Bouil	159	
Le Boulou	434	
Le Bourg-d'Oisans	232	
Le Bourget du Lac	235	
Le Brévedent	78	
Le Bugue	292, 301, 304	
Le Cannet	445	
Le Chambon	340	
Le Château d'Olonne	166	
Le Château-d'Oléron	136, 142	
Le Croisic	56, 59	
Le Crotoy	104	
Le Faouët	72	
Le Fourneau	205	
Le Grand-Bornand	217	
Le Grau du Roi	402, 408, 412	
Le Guen	27	
Le Guilvinec	33	
Le Lac Chambon	330	
Le Logis	49	
Le Mas du Plan	229	
Le Muy	456, 460	
Le Poët Célard	354	
Le Porge	248	
Le Porteau	154	
Le Poujol	295	
le Pouldu	36	
Le Raisse	305	
Le Rocher	69	
le Tallud	171	
Le Tholy	125	
Le Thor	374	
Le Tréport	94	
Le Tuilier Gudas	380	
Le Vau Madec	21	
Le Verdon-sur-Mer	244	
Le Vigan	308	

Le Vigan	411	
Lectoure	383	
Lège-Cap Ferret	244	
Léon	263-264	
Les Abrets	224	
Les Issambres	452	
Les Mathes	134	
Les Mathes-La Palmyre	138	
Les Ollières-sur-Eyrieux	341	
	347, 353	
Les Pieux	86	
Les Ponts-de-Cé	186	
Les Sables d'Olonne	159	
Lesconil	39	
Lézignan-Corbières	397	
Lit-et-Mixe	256	
Loches en Touraine	174	
Locunolé	29	
Longeville-sur-Mer	147-148, 159	
Lons-le-Saunier	212	
Louan Villegruis Fontaine	112	
Lourdes	388	
Luc-sur-Mer	80	
Lus la Croix Haute	360	
Lussac	239	
Lussas	346	
Luz St Sauveur	387, 389	
Luzy	199	
Lyon	361	
Lyons la Foret	83	
M		
Maché	157	
Mâcon	200	
Maisod	214	
Maisons-Laffitte	113	
Malbuisson	209	
Mandelieu-la-Napoule	443	
Mansle	282	
Marciac	382	
Marcillac St Quentin	301	
Marcilly-sur-Eure	84	
Marigny	211	
Marseillan Plage	418, 421	
Martragny	76	
Martres-Tolosane	386	
Masevaux	121	
Massignieu-de-Rives	337	
Matafelon-Granges	338	
Matignon	26	
Maubeuge	97	
Mauleon-Licharre	271	
Maupertus-sur-Mer	87	
Mauriac	321	
Maussane	447	
Médis	138, 140	
Melun	110	
Mende	330	
Menglon	357	

Mercus-Garrabet	382
Merville-Franceville	80-81
Mesland	182
Mesnois	213
Mesquer	59
Messanges	258-259
Metz	119
Meyrueis	328-329
Méze	421
Mézos	256
Millau	274, 280-281
Mimizan	253
Mirandol-Bourgnounac	390
Moliets-Plage	258
Monceaux-sur-Dordogne	323-324
Monflanquin	316
Monnerville	107
Monpazier	287
Montbron	283
Montcabrier	306
Montclar	366
Montclar	396
Montignac	290, 295
Montjoie - Audinac	381
Montmarault	320
Montmeyan	464
Montpon Ménestérol	302
Montreuil Bellay	188
Montrevel-en-Bresse	337
Montsabert	184
Montsoreau	187
Moriani-Plage	476
Mornas	377
Mostuéjouls	279
Mousterlin	39
Moyenneville	101
Muides-sur-Loire	180
Munster	124
Murol	331-332, 334
Murs-et-Gélignieux	340

N

Nages	391
Nampont-St Martin	103
Nant-d'Aveyron	273
Narbonne	398-399
Naucelle	280
Naussannes	292
Navarrenx	268
Nébouzat	333
Nesles-la-Vallée	113
Neuvic	322
Nevers	200
Névez	32, 42
Neydens	217
Neyrac les Bains	353
Niozelles	367
Noirmoutier en L'Ile	163
Nonette	334

Nontron	302
Notre-Dame-de-Riez	160
Noyal-Muzillac	73

O

Oberbronn	120
Olonne-sur-Mer	149, 158
Olonzac	416
Orcet	332
Ornans	209
Orouet	151
Orpierre	371
Orvillers-Sorel	97
Ounans	210

P

Padirac	311
Paimpol	25
Palau del Vidre	430
Palinges	205
Palisse	324
Parcey	213
Paris	108
Parthenay	171
Passy	223
Patornay	214
Pauillac	240
Paulhiac	316
Payrac-en-Quercy	306
Peigney	131
Peisey-Nancroix	232
Pelussin	359
Pénestin-sur-Mer	67, 70
Penmarc'h	38
Périgueux	293-294
Perros Guirec	20
Peyratel	312
Pierrefitte-sur-Sauldre	179
Pineuilh	250
Piriac-sur-Mer	52, 55
Plaisance du Gers	385
Pleubian	22
Pleumeur-Bodou	22
Plobannalec-Lesconil	34
Plonevez-Porzay	43
Plouézec	23
Plouézoc'h	44
Plougoulm	37
Ploumanach	20
Plozévet	40
Poilly	178-179
Pommeuse	108
Pont Audemer	82
Pont Aven	34
Pont de Vaux	338
Pont de-Salars	275
Pont Farcy	79
Pont Kereon	35
Pont l'Evêque	78

Pont St Mamet	285
Pont Ste Marie	130
Pontchâteau	53
Pontorson	89
Pordic	21
Pornic	51, 56, 60
Port Camargue	402
Port Cassafières	419
Port de Vire	309
Port en Bessin	79
Port Leucate	396
Portiragnes Plage	419, 423
Porto	475
Porto-Vecchio	474, 479
Poullan-sur-Mer	31
Pradons	344, 352
Privas	347
Puget-sur-Argens	450, 470
Puget-Theniers	444
Puimichel	369
Pyla-sur-Mer	244-246, 249

Q

Quelmer 47	
Quiberon	72
Quimper	30

R

Raguenèz	42
Ramatuelle	462
Rambouillet	114
Ravenoville-Plage	84
Régusse	460
Rehaupal	126
Remoulins	406-407
Rhinau	120
Ribeauvillé	122
Riez la Romaine	370
Rillé	177
Riquewihr	123
Rives	312
Rivière-sur-Tarn	273, 277
Rochefort-en-Terre	65
Rochegude	410
Rochetaillée	229, 231
Roquebrune-sur-Argens	453, 457, 462-463
Roquelaure	384
Rostrenen	18
Rouffignac St Cernin	298
Rougemont	208
Royan	137
Royan-Pontaillac	138
Royat	335
Ruoms	342, 344, 348, 351

S

Sagone	475
Salies de Béarn	271

Salignac-Eyvigues	300	
Salles	246	
Salles	316	
Salles-Curan	275-276	
Salon-de-Provence	448	
Salses-le Château	440	
Salvinsac	329	
Samoëns	224	
Sampzon	341-342, 352	
Sanary-sur-Mer	466	
Sanchey	125	
Sanguinet	260	
San-Nicolao	476	
Santenay	197	
Sarlat-la-Canéda	284, 288-291, 299-303, 305	
Sarzeau	68, 71, 73	
Saulxures-sur-Moselotte	126	
Saumur	185-186	
Sauveterre-la-Lemance	313	
Savigny-en-Véron	176	
Savigny-les-Beaune	196	
Sazeret	320	
Sazos	389	
Scaer	38	
Séez	234	
Seignosse	257, 262	
Séniergues	310	
Seppois-Le-Bas	124	
Seraucourt-le-Grand	96	
Sérignac-Péboudou	316	
Sérignan	414	
Sérignan Plage	414, 422	
Sévérac-l`Eglise	276	
Seyne les Alpes	369	
Sillé le Guillaume	190	
Sillé-le-Philippe	190	
Singles	333	
Sommieres	411	
Sonzay	174	
Soréze	392	
Sorgeat	380	
Sospel	442	
Souillac-sur-Dordogne	307	
Soulac-sur-Mer	242, 249	
St Alban de Montbel	235	
St Alban-Auriolles	342	
St Amans des Cots	274	
St Angeau	282	
St Antoine de Breuilh	296	
St Antonin Noble Val	393	
St Arnoult	81	
St Aubin des Préaux	87	
St Aubin sur Mer	76	
St Augustin sur Mer	141	
St Aulaye de Breuilh	296	
St Avit de Vialard	292	
St Aygulf	452, 458	
St Aygulf Plage	464	

St Boil	201	
St Brévin les Pins	58, 60	
St Briac-sur-Mer	49	
St Brieuc	18	
St Calais	189	
St Cast le Guildo	19-20, 26	
St Chéron	107	
St Cirq	304	
St Cirq Lapopie	308, 310	
St Clair du Rhône	230	
St Crépin Carlucet	295	
St Croix en Plaine	123	
St Cybranet	291	
St Cyprien	305	
St Cyprien Plage	428	
St Cyr	193	
St Cyr-sur-Mer	466	
St Denis d'Oleron	147	
St Dié de -Vosges	128	
St Emilion	238	
St Firmin	104	
St Florent	478	
St Foy de Belvès	285	
St Geniès en Périgord	297	
St Geniez d'Olt	277, 282	
St Georges d'Oléron	137, 142, 146	
St Georges de Didonne	134	
St Georges les Baillargeaux	191	
St Germain l'Herm	330	
St Gervais les Bains	219	
St Girons	381	
St Hilaire de Riez	150, 154, 157, 162	
St Hilaire la Foret	156, 158	
St Hilaire sous Romilly	131	
St Hilaire-St Florent	185	
St Honoré les Bains	198	
St Jean de Chevelu	234	
St Jean de Luz	266, 270	
St Jean de Monts	150-151, 154, 156, 158, 164-165	
St Jean du Gard	405, 407	
St Jorioz	218	
St Jouan des Guerets	48	
St Julien de Lampon	298	
St Julien des Landes	165	
St Julien en Born	254	
St Julien Plage	72	
St Julien-des-Landes	148, 155	
St Julien-en-Genevois	217	
St Just Luzac	139	
St Laurent de la Prée	139	
St Laurent du Pape	344	
St Laurent en Beaumont	230	
St Laurent sur Sèvre	152	
St Léger de Fougeret	199	
St Léger les Mélèzes	371	
St Léonard-de-Noblat	328	

St Léon-sur-Vézère	290	
St Leu d`Esserent	115	
St Lunaire	46, 48	
St Malo	47-48	
St Marcel	202	
St Martial de Valette	302	
St Martial Entrayguis	323	
St Martin d'Ardèche	350	
St Martin de Seignanx	257	
St Martin-Lars en Ste Hermine	152	
St Maure-de-Touraine	176	
St Maurice d'Ardèche	351	
St Nectaire	335	
St Nic	41	
St Ours	334	
St Pair sur Mer	87	
St Palais	250	
St Palais sur Mer	136	
St Pantaléon	312	
St Pardoux	286	
St Paul de Varax	339	
St Paul lès Dax	251	
St Père sur Loire	180	
St Pereuse en Morvan	198	
St Pierre d'Albig	234	
St Pierre de Chartreuse	231	
St Pierre la Mer	400	
St Point	204	
St Point Lac	208	
St Pol de Léon	28, 43	
St Pons de Thomières	419	
St Privat de Champclos	405	
St Quay Portrieux	24	
St Quentin en Tourmont	100	
St Raphaël	464	
St Raphaël-Agay	450	
St Rémy de Provence	447-448	
St Révérend	162	
St Romain en Viennois	376	
St Rome de Tarn	281	
St Salvadou	278	
St Saturnin les Apt	376	
St Sauveur de Montagut	340	
St Symphorien le Valois	85	
St Théoffrey	225	
St Ustre	190	
St Vaast La Hougue	86	
St Valery en Caux	92	
St Valéry sur Somme	99, 105	
Ste Catherine de Fierbois	176	
Ste Foy la Grande	250	
Ste Lucie de Porto-Vecchio	474	
Ste Marie la Mer	431	
Ste Marine	42	
Ste Mère Eglise	84	
Ste Nathalène	284, 303	
Ste Reine de Bretagne	53	
Ste Sigolène	327	

Suare	478
Suartone	475
Suèvres	178
T	
Taden	20
Talmont-St-Hilaire	154, 167
Tarascon-sur-Ariege	379
Taupont	69
Tazilly	199
Telgruc-sur-Mer	31
Terre Rouge	316
Thégra	310
Therondels	279
Thonnance-les-Moulins	132
Thonon-les-Bains	223
Tonneins	315
Torcy	110
Torigni sur Vire	90
Torreilles-Plage	433-434
Touquin	111
Tourettes-sur-Loup	446
Toutainville	82
Trébas	392
Tredrez-Locquémeau	18
Treignac	321
Trélévern	22
Trept	226
Trogues	175
U	
Ucel	346
Urrugne	267
Urt	268
Uzès	404

V	
Vaison-la-Romaine	375
Vallée du Céou	300
Vallée du Fournel	457
Vallée du Tarn	392
Vallon Pont d'Arc	345, 349, 352
Valras Plage	418, 424-425
Vandenesse-en-Auxois	195
Vannes-Meucon/Monterblanc	66
Varennes-sur-Allier	318
Varennes-sur-Loire	183
Varilhes	380
Vaubarlet	327
Vauvert	403
Vaux-sur-Mer	144
Vedene	377
Vence	442, 446
Veneux-Les-Sablons	112
Venosc	230
Vensac	242
Ventoulou	310
Vercheny	359
Verdun	119
Verdun en Lauragais	401
Vernet-les-Bains	432
Verneuil-sur-Seine	114
Versailles	115
Vers-Pont-du-Gard	409
Vesoul-Vaivre	210
Veulettes sur Mer	94
Veynes	372
Vézac	290
Vias-Plage	413, 417, 420
Vias-sur-Mer	426
Vielle-St Girons	250, 252, 256

Vieux-Mareuil	297
Vignoles	196
Villard de Lans	227
Villars-Colmars	366
Villecroze - Les Grottes	469
Villediieu les Poêles	90
Villefranche-de-Queyran	314
Villefranche-de-Rouergue	276
Villegly-En-Minervois	400
Villeneuve-de-Berg	343
Villeneuve-les-Béziers	420
Villeneuve-lez-Avignon	406
Villeneuve-Loubet	446
Villeneuve-Loubet-Plage	443
Villeréal	312
Villers les Nancy	118
Villers-sur-Authie	102
Villers-sur-Mer	78-79
Villey-le-Sec	118
Villiers-sur-Orge	107
Vimoutiers	91
Vincelles	206
Vinsobres	355
Vitrac	289
Vogüé Gare	351
Volonne	363
Volstroff	120
Wasselonne	121
Wimereux	98
X	
Xonrupt-Longemer	129

Widely regarded as the 'Bible' by site owners and readers alike, there is no better guide when it comes to forming an independent view of a campsite's quality. When you need to be confident in your choice of campsite, you need the Alan Rogers Guide.

✓ Sites only included on merit

✓ Sites cannot pay to be included

✓ Independently inspected, rigorously assessed

✓ Impartial reviews

✓ 40 years of expertise

FR01010 - 09130

FR01010	Plaine Tonique	337
FR01030	Ripettes	338
FR01040	Lit Du Roi	337
FR01050	Gorges de l'Oignin	338
FR01060	Ile de la Comtesse	340
FR01080	Etang du Moulin	339
FR01090	Pierre Thorion	340
FR01100	Vaugrais	338
FR02000	Vivier aux Carpes	96
FR02030	Croix du Vieux Pont	96
FR03010	Filature	318
FR03020	Chazeuil	318
FR03030	Beau Rivage	319
FR03040	Champ de la Chapelle	319
FR03050	Petite Valette	320
FR03170	Dompierre-sur-Besbre	320
FR04010	Hippocampe	363
FR04020	Verdon	364
FR04030	Moulin de Ventre	367
FR04040	Collines	366
FR04060	Haut-Verdon	366
FR04080	Etoile des Neiges	366
FR04100	International	364
FR04110	Verdon Parc	368
FR04120	Forcalquier	368
FR04140	Prairies	369
FR04150	Rose de Provence	370
FR04160	Relarguiers	370
FR04170	Matherons	369
FR05000	Princes d'Orange	371
FR05060	Pause	371
FR05070	Cariamas	372
FR05080	Solaire	372
FR05100	Vieille Ferme	373
FR05110	Rochette	373
FR06010	Ste-Madeleine	442
FR06020	Vallon Rouge	442
FR06030	Bergerie	442
FR06050	Vieille Ferme	443
FR06070	Origan (Naturiste)	444
FR06080	Cigales	443
FR06090	Gorges du Loup	444
FR06100	Pinèdes	444
FR06120	Green Park	445
FR06140	Ranch	445
FR06180	Rives du Loup	446
FR06190	St-James Sourire	446
FR07020	Ardéchois	340
FR07030	Soleil Vivarais	341
FR07050	Ranc Davaine	342
FR07070	Ranchisses	342
FR07080	Bastide	342
FR07090	Plantas	341
FR07100	Garenne	344
FR07110	Pommier	343
FR07120	Ardéchois	345
FR07130	Coudoulets	344
FR07140	Lavandes	349
FR07150	Gil	346
FR07170	Ludocamping	346
FR07180	Ardèche	347
FR07190	Chambourlas	347
FR07250	Plaine	348
FR07290	Imbours	348
FR07310	Roubine	349
FR07320	Gorges	350
FR07340	Cros d'Auzon	351
FR07360	Petit Bois	351
FR07380	Provençal	352

FR07400	Riviera	352
FR07420	Pont (Pradons)	352
FR07440	Mas de Champel	353
FR07550	Lion	350
FR07570	Plage (Neyrac)	353
FR08010	Mont Olympe	129
FR08040	Samaritaine	130
FR09020	Arize	379
FR09050	Prade (Sorgeat)	380
FR09060	Pré Lombard	379
FR09080	Lac (Foix)	380
FR09090	Millfleurs (Naturiste)	380
FR09100	Audinac les Bains	381
FR09110	Pas de l'Ours	381
FR09120	Ascou la Forge	381
FR09130	Lac (Mercus-Garrabet)	382

FR10010 - 19140

FR10010	Troyes	130
FR10030	Tertre	130
FR10040	Noue des Rois	131
FR11020	Hamacs	397
FR11030	Mun. la Pinède	397
FR11040	Martinet Rouge	396
FR11050	Rives des Corbières	396
FR11060	Arnauteille	396
FR11070	Mimosas	399
FR11080	Nautique	398
FR11090	Clapotis (Naturiste)	400
FR11110	Val d'Aleth	398
FR11190	Grande Cosse Naturiste	400
FR11210	Moulin de Sainte-Anne	400
FR11230	Bout du Monde	401
FR12000	Peyrelade	273
FR12010	Val de Cantobre	273
FR12020	Rivages	274
FR12040	Tours	274
FR12050	Terrasses du Lac	275
FR12060	Beau Rivage	275
FR12070	Grange de Monteillac	276
FR12080	Genêts	276
FR12120	Rouergue	276
FR12150	Marmotel	277
FR12160	Peupliers	277
FR12170	Caussanel	278
FR12210	Source	279
FR12240	Saint Pal	279
FR12250	Lac de Bonnefon	280
FR12280	Viaduc	280
FR12300	Muret	278
FR12310	Cascade	281
FR12340	Clédelles le Colombier	282
FR12350	Côté Sud	281
FR13010	Romarins	447
FR13030	Nostradamus	448
FR13040	Monplaisir	447
FR13050	Mas de Nicolas	448
FR13060	Micocouliers	448
FR13120	Chantecler	449
FR14010	Côte de Nacre	76
FR14020	Bayeux	76
FR14030	Martragny	76
FR14060	Hautes Coutures	77
FR14070	Vallée	77
FR14090	Brévedent	78
FR14100	Mun. du Château	78
FR14120	Ammonites	78
FR14140	Mun. Pont Farcy	79
FR14150	Port'land	79
FR14160	Bellevue	79

FR14170	Capricieuse	80
FR14180	Briquerie	80
FR14190	Peupliers	80
FR14200	Vallée de Deauville	81
FR14220	Ariane	81
FR15030	Val Saint Jean	321
FR16020	Gorges du Chambon	283
FR16030	Champion	282
FR16040	Devezeau	282
FR16050	Cognac	283
FR17010	Bois Soleil	134
FR17020	Puits de l'Auture	136
FR17030	Bois Roland	138
FR17050	Orée du Bois	134
FR17060	Airotel Oléron	136
FR17070	Gros Joncs	137
FR17080	Royan	137
FR17100	Clairefontaine	138
FR17110	Monplaisir	138
FR17140	Sequoia Parc	139
FR17160	Clos Fleuri	140
FR17170	Charmilles	139
FR17190	Logis du Breuil	141
FR17210	Interlude	140
FR17220	Brande	142
FR17230	Océan	141
FR17260	Cormoran (Ré)	143
FR17270	Anse des Pins	142
FR17280	Grainetière	145
FR17290	Peupliers	144
FR17300	Port de l'Houmeau	144
FR17310	Val Vert	144
FR17340	Port Punay	145
FR17470	Domaine d'Oléron	146
FR17490	Chirats	146
FR17500	Seulières	147
FR19020	Aubazines	320
FR19030	Plage (Treignac)	321
FR19050	Rivière	322
FR19060	Mialaret	322
FR19070	Chateau de Gibanel	323
FR19080	Vianon	324
FR19090	Vaurette	323
FR19100	Soleil d'Oc	324
FR19140	Coiroux	325

FR20000 - 29520

FR20000	Pertamina Village	474
FR20010	Arinella Bianca	476
FR20030	Merendella	476
FR20040	Riva Bella	477
FR20050	Chiappa (Naturiste)	479
FR20060	Vetta	474
FR20070	Santa Lucia	474
FR20080	Bagheera	477
FR20110	Restonica	477
FR20140	Dolce-Vita	478
FR20150	Olzo	478
FR20160	Paradella	478
FR20170	Paduella	479
FR20180	Pinède	479
FR20220	Oliviers	475
FR20230	Sagone	475
FR20240	Rondinara	475
FR20250	Liccia	476
FR21000	Panthier	195
FR21010	Louis Rigoly	195
FR21020	Mun. les Cent Vignes	195
FR21030	Premier Pres	196
FR21040	Fouché	196

FR21060	Bouleaux	196
FR21080	Sources	197
FR21090	Arquebuse	197
FR22000	Vallées	18
FR22010	Capucines	18
FR22020	Fleur de Bretagne	18
FR22030	Nautic International	19
FR22040	Châtelet	19
FR22050	Vieux Moulin	19
FR22060	Mun. la Hallerais	20
FR22080	Ranolien	20
FR22090	Galinée	20
FR22100	Abri Côtier	21
FR22110	Madières	21
FR22120	Port (Pleumeur-Bodou)	22
FR22130	Port l'Epine	22
FR22140	Port La Chaine	22
FR22150	Launay	23
FR22160	Neptune	24
FR22190	Roches	24
FR22200	Bocage	23
FR22210	Bellevue	25
FR22230	Bellevue	24
FR22250	Mun. de Cruckin	25
FR22260	Vallon aux Merlettes	26
FR22270	Blés d'Or	26
FR22280	Hautes Grées	26
FR22360	Pins (Erquy)	27
FR23010	Château de Poinsouze	326
FR23030	Creuse Natuisme	325
FR24010	Verdoyer	286
FR24020	Granges	287
FR24030	Périères	288
FR24040	Moulin du Roch	284
FR24050	Hauts de Ratebout	285
FR24060	Paradis	290
FR24070	Lestaubière	285
FR24080	Moulin de David	287
FR24090	Soleil Plage	289
FR24100	Moulinal	288
FR24110	Aqua Viva	291
FR24130	Grottes de Roffy	284
FR24140	Bel Ombrage	291
FR24150	Deux Vallées	290
FR24160	Grand Dague	293
FR24170	Port de Limeuil	292
FR24180	St-Avit Loisirs	292
FR24190	Couderc (Naturiste)	292
FR24220	Chênes Verts	293
FR24230	Moulin de Paulhiac	294
FR24240	Bo-Bains	294
FR24280	Barnabé	294
FR24290	Moulin du Bleufond	295
FR24300	Rivière Fleurie	296
FR24310	Bouquerie	297
FR24320	Peneyrals	295
FR24330	Etang Bleu	297
FR24340	Val de la Marquise	296
FR24350	Moulin de la Pique	297
FR24360	Mondou	298
FR24380	BleuSoleil	298
FR24410	Bois du Coderc	298
FR24420	Valades	299
FR24440	Acacias	299
FR24450	Maisonneuve	300
FR24460	Temps de Vivre	300
FR24470	Nauves	300
FR24480	Tailladis	301
FR24510	Trois Caupain	301
FR24520	Perpetuum	302

FR24530	Port Vieux	302
FR24540	Peyrelevade	304
FR24560	Cro Magnon	305
FR24570	Palombière	303
FR24640	Nontron	302
FR24660	Brin d'Amour	304
FR24670	Terrasses du Périgord	305
FR25000	Val de Bonnal	208
FR25030	Bois de Reveuge	208
FR25050	St-Point-Lac	208
FR25070	Chanet	209
FR25080	Fuvettes	209
FR26030	Grand Lierne	354
FR26040	Couspeau	354
FR26090	Truffières	358
FR26100	Sagittaire	355
FR26110	4 Saisons	356
FR26130	Hirondelle	357
FR26140	Chataigneraie	356
FR26150	Lac Bleu	357
FR26210	Bois du Chatelas	358
FR26260	Acacias	359
FR26270	Champ la Chèvre	360
FR27010	Etangs Risle-Seine	82
FR27020	Catinière	82
FR27030	Saint-Nicolas	82
FR27050	Mun. St-Paul	83
FR27060	Marcilly	84
FR27070	l'Isle des Trois Rois	83
FR29000	Mouettes	27
FR29010	Ty-Nadan	29
FR29020	Saint-Laurent	28
FR29030	Letty	27
FR29040	Ar Kleguer	28
FR29050	Orangerie de Lanniron	30
FR29060	Pil-Koad	31
FR29070	Plage de Trez Rouz	32
FR29080	Panoramic	31
FR29090	Raguenès-Plage	32
FR29110	Plage (Le Guilvinec)	33
FR29120	Manoir de Kerlut	34
FR29130	Abers	34
FR29140	Kerlann	34
FR29150	Sables Blancs	35
FR29160	Genets d'Or	35
FR29170	Piscine	36
FR29180	Embruns	36
FR29190	Prés Verts	37
FR29210	Mun. Bois de la Palud	37
FR29220	Mun. de Kerisole	38
FR29240	Kéranterec	38
FR29260	Genêts	38
FR29270	Dunes (Lesconil)	39
FR29280	Pointe Superbe	40
FR29290	Grand Large	39
FR29330	Corniche	40
FR29340	Côte des Légendes	40
FR29380	Port de Plaisance	41
FR29410	Ker Ys	41
FR29450	Helles	42
FR29470	Deux Fontaines	42
FR29480	Kervel	43
FR29490	Trologot	43
FR29500	Plage (Bénodet)	44
FR29510	Baie de Térénez	44
FR29520	Cabellou Plage	45

FR30000 - 39120

FR30000	Gaujac	401
FR30020	Petite Camargue	401
FR30030	Abri de Camargue	402
FR30040	Mas de Mourgues	403
FR30060	Fumades	402
FR30070	Boisson	403
FR30080	Mas de Reilhe	404
FR30100	Sablière (Naturiste)	405
FR30110	Mas de Rey	404
FR30120	Ile des Papes	406
FR30140	Soubeyranne	407
FR30150	Sources	405
FR30160	Boucanet	408
FR30170	Sousta	406
FR30180	Mas de la Cam	407
FR30190	Gorges du Gardon	409
FR30200	Cévennes-Provence	410
FR30210	Arche	408
FR30220	Gênets d'Or	409
FR30230	Val de l'Arre	411
FR30250	Universal	410
FR30290	Massereau	411
FR30360	Castel Rose	412
FR30380	Secrets de Camargue	412
FR30390	Petits Camarguais	412
FR31000	Moulin	386
FR32010	Florence	383
FR32020	Lac (Marciac)	382
FR32030	Verduzan	382
FR32060	Trois Vallées	383
FR32080	Talouch	384
FR32090	Pardaillan	384
FR32100	Lacs de Courtés	385
FR32110	Lac de l'Uby	384
FR32120	Arros	385
FR33010	Dune	237
FR33020	Fontaine-Vieille	237
FR33030	Club d'Arcachon	237
FR33040	Pinèda	238
FR33050	Ourmes	238
FR33080	Barbanne	238
FR33090	Pressoir	239
FR33110	Côte d'Argent	240
FR33120	Cigale	239
FR33130	Grands Pins	243
FR33140	Grand Pré	242
FR33150	Gabarreys	240
FR33160	Euronat	240
FR33170	Acasias	242
FR33190	Pyla	244
FR33210	Pointe du Medoc	244
FR33220	Petit Nice	245
FR33230	Truc Vert	244
FR33240	Océan	246
FR33250	Val de l'Eyre	246
FR33260	Braou	247
FR33280	Forêt	246
FR33290	Tedey	248
FR33300	Jenny (Naturiste)	248
FR33310	Panorama	249
FR33320	Talaris	247
FR33330	Lilhan	242
FR33340	Sables d'Argent	249
FR33350	Chez Gendron	250
FR33360	Bastide	250
FR34020	Garden	413
FR34030	Napoléon	413
FR34050	Mas de Lignières (Naturiste)	416
FR34060	Oliveraie	416
FR34070	Sérignan Plage	414
FR34080	Sérignan Plage Nature	414
FR34090	Yole	418
FR34110	Club Farret	417

FR34130	Neptune	418		**FR40020 - 49170**		
FR34150	Méditerranées	418		FR40020	Chênes	251
FR34170	Mimosas	419		FR40030	Pins du Soleil	251
FR34180	Borio de Roque	419		FR40040	Paillotte	252
FR34190	Champs Blancs	420		FR40050	Col-Vert	252
FR34200	Californie Plage	420		FR40060	Eurosol	250
FR34210	Berges du Canal	420		FR40070	Lous Seurrots	254
FR34220	Creole	421		FR40080	Marina-Landes	253
FR34230	Chênes	416		FR40100	Rive	254
FR34260	Beau Rivage	421		FR40110	Sen Yan	256
FR34290	Mer Et Soleil	422		FR40120	Arnaoutchot (Naturiste)	256
FR34370	Blue Bayou	424		FR40140	Lou P'tit Poun	257
FR34390	Aloha	422		FR40160	Vignes	256
FR34400	Sablons	423		FR40180	Vieux Port	259
FR34430	Occitanie	425		FR40190	Saint Martin	258
FR34440	Tamaris	425		FR40200	Sylvamar	262
FR34450	La Dragonnière	426		FR40220	Acacias	258
FR34460	Int de l'Hérault	427		FR40240	Mayotte Vacances	260
FR34470	Fou du Roi	422		FR40250	Grands Pins	260
FR34500	Oasis Palavasienne	424		FR40260	Chevreuils	262
FR35000	Vieux Chêne	46		FR40270	Saint James Eurolac	263
FR35010	Bois Coudrais	45		FR40280	Lou Puntaou	263
FR35020	Ormes	47		FR40290	Punta Lago	264
FR35040	P'tit Bois	48		FR40340	Océliances	257
FR35050	Ville Huchet	47		FR41010	Val de Loire	182
FR35060	Touesse	46		FR41020	Grenouillère	178
FR35070	Longchamp	48		FR41030	Alicourts	179
FR35080	Logis	49		FR41040	Marais	180
FR35090	Pont de Laurin	49		FR41070	Grande Tortue	181
FR36050	Vieux Chênes	172		FR41100	Saules	183
FR36110	Rochat Belle-Isle	172		FR42030	Bel' Epoque du Pilat	359
FR37010	Mignardière	172		FR43030	Vaubarlet	327
FR37030	Moulin Fort	173		FR44020	Mun. du Moulin	50
FR37050	Citadelle	174		FR44040	Sainte Brigitte	50
FR37060	Arada Parc	174		FR44050	Ecureuils	51
FR37070	Ile Auger	175		FR44070	Guibel	52
FR37090	Rolandière	175		FR44090	Deffay	53
FR37100	Fritillaire	176		FR44100	Patisseau	51
FR37120	Fierbois	176		FR44130	Hermitage	54
FR37140	Rillé	177		FR44150	Tabardière	52
FR37150	Coteaux du Lac	177		FR44160	Armor-Héol	55
FR38010	Coin Tranquille	224		FR44170	Ajoncs d'Or	54
FR38020	Ser Sirant	225		FR44180	Boutinardière	56
FR38030	Cascade	225		FR44190	Fief	58
FR38040	Rencontre du Soleil	226		FR44210	Ocean	56
FR38050	Temps Libre	227		FR44220	Léveno	56
FR38060	Trois Lacs (Trept)	226		FR44230	EléoVic	60
FR38070	Oursière	227		FR44240	Ranch	55
FR38080	Au Joyeux Réveil	228		FR44250	Trémondec	60
FR38090	Belle Roche	228		FR44270	Château du Petit Bois	59
FR38100	Belledonne	229		FR44300	Pierres Couchées	60
FR38110	Champ du Moulin	230		FR44320	Pierre Longue	59
FR38130	Belvédère de l'Obiou	230		FR44340	Falaise	61
FR38140	Colporteur	229		FR45010	Bois du Bardelet	178
FR38150	Daxia	230		FR45030	Gien	179
FR38160	Martinière	231		FR45040	Hortus	180
FR38180	Château de Bourg d'Oisans	231		FR46010	Paille Basse	307
FR38190	Champ Long	231		FR46030	Pins	306
FR38200	Ferme Noémie	232		FR46040	Moulin de Laborde	306
FR39010	Plage Blanche	210		FR46050	Rêve	308
FR39030	Chalain	210		FR46070	Plage (St Cirq-Lapopie)	308
FR39040	Pergola	211		FR46110	Port (Creysse)	308
FR39050	Fayolan	211		FR46140	Duravel	309
FR39060	Marjorie	212		FR46150	Truffière	310
FR39080	Epinette	212		FR46170	Reflets du Quercy	311
FR39090	Bords de Loue	213		FR46180	Ventoulou	310
FR39100	Trélachaume	214		FR46190	Faurie	310
FR39110	Moulin	214		FR46200	Chênes	311
FR39120	Beauregard	213		FR46220	3 Sources	312
				FR46230	Arcades	312

FR47010	Moulin du Périé	313
FR47030	Fonrives	312
FR47050	Moulin de Campech	314
FR47100	Mun. Le Robinson	315
FR47110	Cabri	314
FR47120	Vallée de Gardeleau	316
FR47130	Des Bastides	316
FR47140	Laborde (Naturiste)	316
FR47150	Guillalmes	315
FR48000	Champ d'Ayres	328
FR48020	Capelan	329
FR48040	Cascade	329
FR48060	Lac de Naussac	329
FR48070	Tivoli	330
FR49000	Lac de Maine	182
FR49010	Etang de la Brèche	183
FR49020	Chantepie	185
FR49030	Caroline	184
FR49040	Etang	185
FR49060	Montsabert	184
FR49070	Vallée des Vignes	186
FR49080	Ile d'Offard	186
FR49090	Isle Verte	187
FR49120	Lac de Ribou	187
FR49140	Au Bord de Loire	188
FR49150	Thouet	188
FR49170	Coulvée	189

FR50000 - 59050

FR50000	Etang des Haizes	85
FR50010	Gallouette	86
FR50030	Lez-Eaux	87
FR50050	Cormoran	84
FR50060	Grand Large	86
FR50070	Anse du Brick	87
FR50080	Haliotis	89
FR50090	Gerfleur	88
FR50110	St-Michel	88
FR50150	Route Blanche	91
FR50170	Charmilles	90
FR50180	Chevaliers	90
FR51020	Mun. Champagne	118
FR52020	Forge de Ste Marie	132
FR52030	Lac de la Liez	131
FR52040	Croix d'Arles	132
FR52050	Champagne	132
FR53020	Malidor	171
FR54000	Brabois	118
FR54010	Villey-le-Sec	118
FR55010	Breuils	119
FR56010	Grande Métairie	63
FR56020	Plage (Trinité-sur-Mer)	62
FR56030	Baie (La Trinité-sur-Mer)	62
FR56040	Penboch	61
FR56050	Kervilor	64
FR56080	Mun. le Pâtis	64
FR56100	Moulin Neuf	65
FR56110	Moustoir	66
FR56120	Iles	67
FR56130	Mané Guernehué	65
FR56140	Mun. du Bas de la Lande	68
FR56150	Haras	66
FR56160	Vallée du Ninian	69
FR56180	Cénic	67
FR56200	Lann Hoedic	68
FR56230	Plijadur Park	69
FR56240	Inly	70
FR56250	Bohat	71
FR56270	Menhirs	70
FR56280	Sept Saints	71

FR56300	An Trest	73
FR56310	Mun. Beg Er Roch	72
FR56360	Do Mi Si La Mi	72
FR56430	Moulin de Cadillac	73
FR57050	Mun. Metz-Plage	119
FR57070	Centre de Loisirs	120
FR57080	Croix du Bois Sacker	119
FR58010	Bains	198
FR58030	Bezolle	198
FR58040	Etang Fougeraie	199
FR58050	Château De Chigy	199
FR58060	Gagère (Naturiste)	199
FR58100	Nevers	200
FR59010	Chaumière	96
FR59050	Mun. du Clair de Lune	97

FR60010 - 69030

FR60010	Campix	115
FR60020	Sorel	97
FR61010	Campière	91
FR61040	Champ Passais	92
FR62010	Bien-Assise	98
FR62030	Château de Gandspette	99
FR62080	Paille-Haute	100
FR62120	Eté Indien	98
FR63000	Chalets du Hameau du Lac	330
FR63020	St-Eloy	330
FR63030	Europe	331
FR63040	Grange Fort	332
FR63050	Ribeyre	331
FR63060	Clos Auroy	332
FR63070	Pré Bas	332
FR63080	Moulin de Serre	333
FR63090	Domes	333
FR63120	Royat	335
FR63130	Repos du Baladin	334
FR63140	Loges	334
FR63160	Bel-Air	334
FR63180	Vallée Verte	335
FR64020	Barétous-Pyrénées	264
FR64030	Ametza	264
FR64040	Gaves	265
FR64050	Itsas Mendi	266
FR64060	Pavillon Royal	265
FR64070	Ruisseau	266
FR64080	Tamaris Plage	266
FR64100	Etche Zahar	268
FR64110	Col d'Ibardin	267
FR64120	Beau Rivage	268
FR64140	Berrua	269
FR64150	Residence des Pins	269
FR64160	Merko-Lacarra	270
FR64230	Mun. Mosqueros	271
FR64240	Uhaitza le Saison	271
FR64250	Atlantica	270
FR64280	Ur-Onea	271
FR65010	Eglantière (Naturiste)	386
FR65020	Trois Vallées	386
FR65030	Pyrénées	387
FR65040	International	387
FR65060	Pyrenees Natura	387
FR65080	Lavedan	388
FR65090	Soleil du Pibeste	388
FR65100	Moulin du Monge	388
FR65110	Cabaliros	389
FR65130	Pyrenevasion	389
FR65160	Monlôo	389
FR65170	Arrayade	390
FR66000	Pujol	426
FR66020	Ma Prairie	430

FR66030	Cala Gogo	428
FR66040	Soleil	428
FR66050	Haras	430
FR66070	Brasilia	431
FR66080	Fontaines	430
FR66090	Mar Estang	427
FR66100	Pergola	431
FR66110	Dauphin	432
FR66130	Eau Vive	432
FR66150	Criques de Porteils	434
FR66160	Palmeraie	433
FR66180	Mas Llinas	434
FR66190	Tropiques	434
FR66200	Marsouins	437
FR66220	Stade	435
FR66230	Romarin	433
FR66250	Font-Romeu	435
FR66260	Massane	436
FR66290	Floride et l'Embouchure	436
FR66300	Pré Catalan	437
FR66310	Rotja	440
FR66560	Sirène	438
FR66570	Hippocampe	438
FR66590	Bois du Valmarie	438
FR66610	Bois de Pins	440
FR67010	Oasis	120
FR67040	Ferme des Tuileries	120
FR67050	Wasselonne	121
FR68030	Masevaux	121
FR68040	Trois Châteaux	122
FR68050	Pierre De Coubertin	122
FR68060	Riquewihr	123
FR68080	Clair Vacances	123
FR68100	Fecht	124
FR68120	Lupins	124
FR69010	Lyon	361
FR69020	Mun. la Grappe Fleurie	360
FR69030	Portes du Beaujolais	361

FR70020 - 79050

FR70020	Lac Vesoul	210
FR71010	Mun. Mâcon	200
FR71020	Meuniers	200
FR71030	Mun. St-Vital	201
FR71050	Moulin de Collonge	201
FR71060	Montrouant	201
FR71070	Epervière	202
FR71080	Etang Neuf	204
FR71090	Lac de St-Point	204
FR71110	Lac (Palinges)	205
FR71120	Heronniere	205
FR71140	Pont de Bourgogne	202
FR71170	Louvarel	205
FR71180	Chevrette	206
FR72010	Route d'Or	189
FR72020	Mun. du Lac	189
FR72030	Chanteloup	190
FR72040	Des Molières	190
FR73020	Versoyen	232
FR73030	Lanchettes	232
FR73040	Mun. le Savoy	233
FR73050	Trois Lacs	233
FR73060	Eden	233
FR73080	Lacs de Chevelu	234
FR73090	Lac de Carouge	234
FR73100	Reclus	234
FR73120	Sougey	235
FR73130	Mun. Int. l'île aux Cygnes	235
FR74010	Deux Glaciers	216
FR74030	Belvédère	216
FR74040	Ravoire	216
FR74060	Colombière	217
FR74070	Escale	217
FR74090	Plan du Fernuy	218
FR74100	Europa	218
FR74110	Taillefer	220
FR74130	Plage (Amphion-les-Bains)	220
FR74140	Dômes de Miage	219
FR74150	Mer de Glace	220
FR74160	Ile des Barrats	221
FR74170	Moulin de Dollay	221
FR74180	Lac Bleu	222
FR74200	Idéal	222
FR74210	Iles de Passy	223
FR74220	Saint Disdille	223
FR74230	Giffre	224
FR74240	Chamaloup	224
FR75020	Bois de Boulogne	108
FR76040	Source	92
FR76090	Mun. Etennemare	92
FR76100	Cany-Barville	93
FR76110	Mun. Boucaniers	94
FR76120	Mun. Veulettes sur Mer	94
FR76130	Forêt	93
FR77020	Chêne Gris	108
FR77030	Jablines	109
FR77040	4 Vents	109
FR77060	Colline	110
FR77070	Belle Etoile	110
FR77090	Etangs Fleuris	111
FR77120	Soleil De Crécy	111
FR77130	Courtilles du Lido	112
FR77140	Paris/Ile-de-France	112
FR78010	International	113
FR78040	Rambouillet	114
FR78050	Val de Seine	114
FR78060	Versailles	115
FR79020	Courte Vallée	170
FR79030	Puy Rond	170
FR79040	Venise Verte	170
FR79050	Bois Vert	171

FR80010 - 89070

FR80010	Drancourt	99
FR80020	Champ Neuf	100
FR80040	Royon	102
FR80060	Val de Trie	101
FR80070	Ferme des Aulnes	103
FR80090	Val d'Authie	102
FR80100	Cygnes	100
FR80110	Ridin	104
FR80120	Aubépines	104
FR80130	Vertes Feuilles	104
FR80150	Walric	105
FR80190	Galets de la Mollière	105
FR81030	Mun. de Gourjade	390
FR81060	Clots	390
FR81070	Rieu Montagné	391
FR81090	Manoir de Boutaric	393
FR81100	Rigole	391
FR81110	Saint Martin	392
FR81120	Rouquié	392
FR81130	Amitié	392
FR82010	Trois Cantons	393
FR82040	Gorges de l'Aveyron	393
FR83010	Pins Parasol	449
FR83020	Esterel	450
FR83030	Leï Suves	453
FR83040	Bastiane	450
FR83050	Résidence du Campeur	452

FR83060	Baume	454
FR83070	Etoile d'Argens	458
FR83080	Au Paradis	452
FR83090	Noguière	456
FR83100	Plage (Grimaud)	454
FR83110	Baie (Cavalaire-sur-Mer)	456
FR83120	Domaine	456
FR83130	Beau Vezé	458
FR83140	Lacs du Verdon	460
FR83160	Cigales	460
FR83170	Bergerie	457
FR83190	Presqu'île de Giens	461
FR83200	Pêcheurs	463
FR83210	Tournels	462
FR83220	Cros de Mouton	465
FR83230	Colombier	462
FR83240	Moulin des Iscles	462
FR83250	Douce Quiétude	464
FR83260	Eouvière	464
FR83290	Saint Aygulf	464
FR83300	Clos Ste-Thérèse	466
FR83310	Argentière	466
FR83320	Mogador	466
FR83340	Bonporteau	467
FR83350	Sélection	468
FR83360	Pierre Verte	467
FR83370	Fréjus	468
FR83380	Prairies de la Mer	460
FR83400	Holiday Marina	469
FR83410	Ruou	469
FR83420	Parc Et Plage	468
FR83440	Malissonne	472
FR83510	Pinède	472
FR83610	Saint James Oasis	470
FR83620	Saint James Gassin	470
FR84020	Bélézy (Naturiste)	373
FR84040	Jantou	374
FR84050	Sorguette	374
FR84070	Carpe Diem	375
FR84080	Simioune	374
FR84090	Pont d'Avignon	375
FR84100	Soleil de Provence	376
FR84130	Chênes Blancs	376
FR84140	Beauregard	377
FR84150	Flory	377
FR85000	Petit Rocher	148
FR85010	Zagarella	147
FR85020	Jard	148
FR85030	Loubine	149
FR85040	Garangeoire	148
FR85050	Village de Florine	149
FR85080	Puerta del Sol	150
FR85090	Abri des Pins	150
FR85110	Océan	150
FR85130	Pong	152
FR85140	Colombier (Naturiste)	152
FR85150	Yole	151
FR85210	Ecureuils	153
FR85220	Acapulco	154
FR85230	Ecureuils	154
FR85250	Littoral	154
FR85260	Guyonnière	155

FR85270	Oceano d'Or	156
FR85280	Places Dorées	156
FR85300	Grand' Métairie	156
FR85320	Val de Vie	157
FR85350	Ningle	157
FR85360	Forêt	158
FR85390	Batardières	158
FR85400	Bois Soleil	158
FR85420	Bel	159
FR85440	Brunelles	159
FR85450	Roses	159
FR85480	Chaponnet	160
FR85510	Bois Joli	161
FR85520	Renardieres	160
FR85620	Caravan'ile	161
FR85640	Chouans	162
FR85660	Pont Rouge	162
FR85680	Pin Parasol	163
FR85720	Noirmoutier	163
FR85730	Jardins de l'Atlantique	164
FR85740	Aux Coeurs Vendéens	165
FR85770	Ferme du Latois	157
FR85810	Dauphins Bleus	164
FR85850	Bretonnière	165
FR85860	Fosses Rouges	166
FR85870	Baie d'Aunis	166
FR85890	Rouge-Gorge	152
FR85920	Loyada	167
FR86010	Petit Trianon	190
FR86030	Relais du Miel	192
FR86040	Futuriste	191
FR86050	Riveau	192
FR86080	Peupliers	193
FR86090	Saint Cyr	193
FR87020	Leychoisier	327
FR87030	Beaufort	328
FR88020	Belle Hutte	124
FR88030	Noirrupt	125
FR88040	Lac de Bouzey	125
FR88050	Champé	125
FR88080	Bans	126
FR88090	Lac de la Moselotte	126
FR88100	Barba	126
FR88110	Sténiole	127
FR88120	Clos de la Chaume	127
FR88130	Vanne de Pierre	128
FR88140	Lacs (Celles-sur-Plaine)	128
FR88150	Ramberchamp	128
FR88160	Jonquilles	129
FR88170	Pinasses	129
FR89060	Ceriselles	206
FR89070	Platanes	206

FR90000 - 95000

FR90000	Etang des Forges	214
FR91000	Bois de la Justice	107
FR91010	Beau Village	107
FR91020	Parc Des Roches	107
FR94000	Tremblay	113
FR95000	Séjour Etang	113

Brittany

FR29130	Abers	34
FR22100	Abri Côtier	21
FR44170	Ajoncs d'Or	54
FR56300	An Trest	73
FR29040	Ar Kleguer	28
FR44160	Armor-Héol	55
FR56030	Baie (La Trinité-sur-Mer)	62
FR29510	Baie de Térénez	44
FR22230	Bellevue (St Quay-Portrieux)	24
FR22210	Bellevue (Erquy)	25
FR22270	Blés d'Or	26
FR22200	Bocage	23
FR56250	Bohat	71
FR35010	Bois Coudrais	45
FR44180	Boutinardière	56
FR29520	Cabellou Plage	45
FR22010	Capucines	18
FR56180	Cénic	67
FR44270	Château du Petit Bois	59
FR22040	Châtelet	19
FR29330	Corniche	40
FR29340	Côte des Légendes	40
FR44090	Deffay	53
FR29470	Deux Fontaines	42
FR56360	Do Mi Si La Mi	72
FR29270	Dunes (Lesconil)	39
FR44050	Ecureuils	51
FR44230	EléoVic	60
FR29180	Embruns	36
FR44340	Falaise	61
FR44190	Fief	58
FR22020	Fleur de Bretagne	18
FR22090	Galinée	20
FR29260	Genêts	38
FR29160	Genets d'Or	35
FR29290	Grand Large	39
FR56010	Grande Métairie	63
FR44070	Guibel	52
FR56150	Haras	66
FR22280	Hautes Grées	26
FR29450	Helles	42
FR44130	Hermitage	54
FR56120	Iles	67
FR56240	Inly	70
FR29410	Ker Ys	41
FR29240	Kéranterec	38
FR29140	Kerlann	34
FR29480	Kervel	43
FR56050	Kervilor	64
FR56200	Lann Hoedic	68
FR22150	Launay	23
FR29030	Letty	27
FR44220	Léveno	56
FR35080	Logis	49
FR35070	Longchamp	48
FR22110	Madières	21
FR56130	Mané Guernehué	65
FR29120	Manoir de Kerlut	34
FR56270	Menhirs	70
FR29000	Mouettes	27
FR56430	Moulin de Cadillac	73

FR56100	Moulin Neuf	65
FR56110	Moustoir	66
FR56310	Mun. Beg Er Roch	72
FR29210	Mun. Bois de la Palud	37
FR22250	Mun. de Cruckin	25
FR29220	Mun. de Kerisole	38
FR56140	Mun. du Bas de la Lande	68
FR44020	Mun. du Moulin	50
FR22060	Mun. la Hallerais	20
FR56080	Mun. le Pâtis	64
FR22030	Nautic International	19
FR22160	Neptune	24
FR44210	Ocean	56
FR29050	Orangerie de Lanniron	30
FR35020	Ormes	47
FR35040	P'tit Bois	48
FR29080	Panoramic	31
FR44100	Patisseau	51
FR56040	Penboch	61
FR44320	Pierre Longue	59
FR44300	Pierres Couchées	60
FR29060	Pil-Koad	31
FR22360	Pins (Erquy)	27
FR29170	Piscine	36
FR29500	Plage (Bénodet)	44
FR29110	Plage (Le Guilvinec)	33
FR56020	Plage (Trinité-sur-Mer)	62
FR29070	Plage de Trez Rouz	32
FR56230	Plijadur Park	69
FR29280	Pointe Superbe	40
FR35090	Pont de Laurin	49
FR22120	Port (Pleumeur-Bodou)	22
FR29380	Port de Plaisance	41
FR22130	Port l'Epine	22
FR22140	Port La Chaine	22
FR29190	Prés Verts	37
FR29090	Raguenès-Plage	32
FR44240	Ranch	55
FR22080	Ranolien	20
FR22190	Roches	24
FR29150	Sables Blancs	35
FR44040	Sainte-Brigitte	50
FR29020	Saint-Laurent	28
FR56280	Sept Saints	71
FR44150	Tabardière	52
FR35060	Touesse	46
FR44250	Trémondec	60
FR29490	Trologot	43
FR29010	Ty-Nadan	29
FR56160	Vallée du Ninian	69
FR22000	Vallées	18
FR22260	Vallon aux Merlettes	26
FR35000	Vieux Chêne	46
FR22050	Vieux Moulin	19
FR35050	Ville Huchet	47

Normandy

FR14120	Ammonites	78
FR50070	Anse du Brick	87
FR14220	Ariane	81
FR14020	Bayeux	76
FR14160	Bellevue	79

FR14090	Brévedent	78
FR14180	Briquerie	80
FR61010	Campière	91
FR76100	Cany-Barville	93
FR14170	Capricieuse	80
FR27020	Catinière	82
FR61040	Champ Passais	92
FR50170	Charmilles	90
FR50180	Chevaliers	90
FR50050	Cormoran	84
FR14010	Côte de Nacre	76
FR50000	Etang des Haizes	85
FR27010	Etangs Risle-Seine	82
FR76130	Forêt	93
FR50010	Gallouette	86
FR50090	Gerfleur	88
FR50060	Grand Large	86
FR50080	Haliotis	89
FR14060	Hautes Coutures	77
FR27070	l'Isle des Trois Rois	83
FR50030	Lez-Eaux	87
FR27060	Marcilly	84
FR14030	Martragny	76
FR76110	Mun. Boucaniers	94
FR14100	Mun. du Château	78
FR76090	Mun. Etennemare	92
FR14140	Mun. Pont Farcy	79
FR27050	Mun. St-Paul	83
FR76120	Mun. Veulettes sur Mer	94
FR14190	Peupliers	80
FR14150	Port'land	79
FR50150	Route Blanche	91
FR27030	Saint Nicolas	82
FR76040	Source	92
FR50110	Saint Michel	88
FR14070	Vallée	77
FR14200	Vallée de Deauville	81

Northern France

FR80120	Aubépines	104
FR62010	Bien-Assise	98
FR60010	Campix	115
FR80020	Champ Neuf	100
FR62030	Château de Gandspette	99
FR59010	Chaumière	96
FR02030	Croix du Vieux Pont	96
FR80100	Cygnes	100
FR80010	Drancourt	99
FR62120	Eté Indien	98
FR80070	Ferme des Aulnes	103
FR80190	Galets de la Mollière	105
FR59050	Mun. du Clair de Lune	97
FR62080	Paille-Haute	100
FR80110	Ridin	104
FR80040	Royon	102
FR60020	Sorel	97
FR80090	Val d'Authie	102
FR80060	Val de Trie	101
FR80130	Vertes Feuilles	104
FR02000	Vivier aux Carpes	96
FR80150	Walric	105

Paris & Ile de France

FR77040	4 Vents	109
FR91010	Beau Village	107
FR77070	Belle Etoile	110
FR75020	Bois de Boulogne	108
FR91000	Bois de la Justice	107
FR77020	Chêne Gris	108
FR77060	Colline	110
FR77130	Courtilles du Lido	112
FR77090	Etangs Fleuris	111
FR78010	International	113
FR77030	Jablines	109
FR91020	Parc Des Roches	107
FR77140	Paris/Ile-de-France	112
FR78040	Rambouillet	114
FR95000	Séjour Etang	113
FR77120	Soleil De Crécy	111
FR94000	Tremblay	113
FR78050	Val de Seine	114
FR78060	Versailles	115

Eastern France

FR88080	Bans	126
FR88100	Barba	126
FR88020	Belle Hutte	124
FR54000	Brabois	118
FR55010	Breuils	119
FR57070	Centre de Loisirs	120
FR52050	Champagne	132
FR88050	Champé	125
FR68080	Clair Vacances	123
FR88120	Clos de la Chaume	127
FR52040	Croix d'Arles	132
FR57080	Croix du Bois Sacker	119
FR68100	Fecht	124
FR67040	Ferme des Tuileries	120
FR52020	Forge de Ste Marie	132
FR88160	Jonquilles	129
FR88040	Lac de Bouzey	125
FR52030	Lac de la Liez	131
FR88090	Lac de la Moselotte	126
FR88140	Lacs (Celles-Sur-Plaine)	128
FR68120	Lupins	124
FR68030	Masevaux	121
FR08010	Mont Olympe	129
FR51020	Mun. Champagne	118
FR57050	Mun. Metz-Plage	119
FR88030	Noirrupt	125
FR10040	Noue des Rois	131
FR67010	Oasis	120
FR68050	Pierre de Coubertin	122
FR88170	Pinasses	129
FR88150	Ramberchamp	128
FR68060	Riquewihr	123
FR08040	Samaritaine	130
FR88110	Sténiole	127
FR10030	Tertre	130
FR68040	Trois Châteaux	122
FR10010	Troyes	130
FR88130	Vanne de Pierre	128
FR54010	Villey-le-Sec	118
FR67050	Wasselonne	121

Vendée & Charente

FR85090	Abri des Pins	150
FR85220	Acapulco	154
FR17060	Airotel Oléron	136
FR17270	Anse des Pins	142
FR85740	Aux Coeurs Vendéens	165
FR85870	Baie d'Aunis	166
FR85390	Batardières	158
FR85420	Bel	159
FR85510	Bois Joli	161
FR17030	Bois Roland	138
FR17010	Bois Soleil (St Georges)	134
FR85400	Bois Soleil (Olonne-sur-Mer)	158
FR17220	Brande	142
FR85850	Bretonnière	165
FR85440	Brunelles	159
FR85620	Caravan'ile	161
FR85480	Chaponnet	160
FR17170	Charmilles	139
FR17490	Chirats	146
FR85640	Chouans	162
FR17100	Clairefontaine	138
FR17160	Clos Fleuri	140
FR85140	Colombier (Naturiste)	152
FR17260	Cormoran (Ré)	143
FR85810	Dauphins Bleus	164
FR17470	Domaine d'Oléron	146
FR85210	Ecureuils (Jard-sur-Mer)	153
FR85230	Ecureuils (St Hilaire-de-Riez)	154
FR85770	Ferme du Latois	157
FR85360	Forêt	158
FR85860	Fosses Rouges	166
FR85040	Garangeoire	148
FR17280	Grainetière	145
FR85300	Grand' Métairie	156
FR17070	Gros Joncs	137
FR85260	Guyonnière	155
FR17210	Interlude	140
FR85020	Jard	148
FR85730	Jardins de L'Atlantique	164
FR85250	Littoral	154
FR17190	Logis du Breuil	141
FR85030	Loubine	149
FR85920	Loyada	167
FR17110	Monplaisir	138
FR85350	Ningle	157
FR85720	Noirmoutier	163
FR17230	Océan (Ile de Ré)	141
FR85110	Océan (Brem sur Mer)	150
FR85270	Oceano d'Or	156
FR17050	Orée du Bois	134
FR85000	Petit Rocher	148
FR17290	Peupliers	144
FR85680	Pin Parasol	163
FR85280	Places Dorées	156
FR85130	Pong	152
FR85660	Pont Rouge	162
FR17300	Port de l'Houmeau	144
FR17340	Port Punay	145
FR85080	Puerta del Sol	150
FR17020	Puits de l'Auture	136
FR85520	Renardieres	160

FR85450	Roses	159
FR85890	Rouge-Gorge	152
FR17080	Royan	137
FR17140	Sequoia Parc	139
FR17500	Seulières	147
FR85320	Val de Vie	157
FR17310	Val Vert	144
FR85050	Village de Florine	149
FR85150	Yole	151
FR85010	Zagarella	147

Loire Valley

FR41030	Alicourts	179
FR37060	Arada Parc	174
FR49140	Au Bord de Loire	188
FR45010	Bois du Bardelet	178
FR79050	Bois Vert	171
FR49030	Caroline	184
FR72030	Chanteloup	190
FR49020	Chantepie	185
FR37050	Citadelle	174
FR37150	Coteaux du Lac	177
FR49170	Coulvée	189
FR79020	Courte Vallée	170
FR72040	Des Molières	190
FR49040	Etang	185
FR49010	Etang de la Brèche	183
FR37120	Fierbois	176
FR37100	Fritillaire	176
FR86040	Futuriste	191
FR45030	Gien	179
FR41070	Grande Tortue	181
FR41020	Grenouillère	178
FR45040	Hortus	180
FR37070	Ile Auger	175
FR49080	Ile d'Offard	186
FR49090	Isle Verte	187
FR49000	Lac de Maine	182
FR49120	Lac de Ribou	187
FR53020	Malidor	171
FR41040	Marais	180
FR37010	Mignardière	172
FR49060	Montsabert	184
FR37030	Moulin Fort	173
FR72020	Mun. du Lac	189
FR86010	Petit Trianon	190
FR86080	Peupliers	193
FR79030	Puy Rond	170
FR86030	Relais du Miel	192
FR37140	Rillé	177
FR86050	Riveau	192
FR36110	Rochat Belle-Isle	172
FR37090	Rolandière	175
FR72010	Route d'Or	189
FR41100	Saules	183
FR86090	Saint Cyr	193
FR49150	Thouet	188
FR41010	Val de Loire	182
FR49070	Vallée des Vignes	186
FR79040	Venise Verte	170
FR36050	Vieux Chênes	172

Burgundy

FR21090	Arquebuse	197
FR58010	Bains	198
FR58030	Bezolle	198
FR21060	Bouleaux	196
FR89060	Ceriselles	206
FR58050	Château de Chigy	199
FR71180	Chevrette	206
FR71070	Epervière	202
FR58040	Etang Fougeraie	199
FR71080	Etang Neuf	204
FR21040	Fouché	196
FR58060	Gagère (Naturiste)	199
FR71120	Heronniere	205
FR71110	Lac (Palinges)	205
FR71090	Lac de Saint Point	204
FR21010	Louis Rigoly	195
FR71170	Louvarel	205
FR71020	Meuniers	200
FR71060	Montrouant	201
FR71050	Moulin de Collonge	201
FR21020	Mun. les Cent Vignes	195
FR71010	Mun. Mâcon	200
FR71030	Mun. St-Vital	201
FR58100	Nevers	200
FR21000	Panthier	195
FR89070	Platanes	206
FR71140	Pont de Bourgogne	202
FR21030	Premier Pres	196
FR21080	Sources	197

Franche-Comté

FR39120	Beauregard	213
FR25030	Bois de Reveuge	208
FR39090	Bords de Loue	213
FR39030	Chalain	210
FR25070	Chanet	209
FR39080	Epinette	212
FR90000	Etang des Forges	214
FR39050	Fayolan	211
FR25080	Fuvettes	209
FR70020	Lac Vesoul	210
FR39060	Marjorie	212
FR39110	Moulin	214
FR39040	Pergola	211
FR39010	Plage Blanche	210
FR25050	Saint Point-Lac	208
FR39100	Trélachaume	214
FR25000	Val de Bonnal	208

Savoy & Dauphiny Alps

FR38080	Au Joyeux Réveil	228
FR38090	Belle Roche	228
FR38100	Belledonne	229
FR74030	Belvédère	216
FR38130	Belvédère de l'Obiou	230
FR38030	Cascade	225
FR74240	Chamaloup	224
FR38110	Champ du Moulin	230
FR38190	Champ Long	231
FR38180	Château de Bourg d'Oisans	231

FR38010	Coin Tranquille	224
FR74060	Colombière	217
FR38140	Colporteur	229
FR38150	Daxia	230
FR74010	Deux Glaciers	216
FR74140	Dômes de Miage	219
FR73060	Eden	233
FR74070	Escale	217
FR74100	Europa	218
FR38200	Ferme Noémie	232
FR74230	Giffre	224
FR74200	Idéal	222
FR74160	Ile des Barrats	221
FR74210	Iles de Passy	223
FR74180	Lac Bleu	222
FR73090	Lac de Carouge	234
FR73080	Lacs de Chevelu	234
FR73030	Lanchettes	232
FR38160	Martinière	231
FR74150	Mer de Glace	220
FR74170	Moulin de Dollay	221
FR73130	Mun. Int. l'île aux Cygnes	235
FR73040	Mun. le Savoy	233
FR38070	Oursière	227
FR74130	Plage (Amphion-les-Bains)	220
FR74090	Plan du Fernuy	218
FR74040	Ravoire	216
FR73100	Reclus	234
FR38040	Rencontre du Soleil	226
FR38020	Ser Sirant	225
FR73120	Sougey	235
FR74220	St-Disdille	223
FR74110	Taillefer	220
FR38050	Temps Libre	227
FR73050	Trois Lacs	233
FR38060	Trois Lacs (Trept)	226
FR73020	Versoyen	232

Atlantic Coast

FR40220	Acacias	258
FR33170	Acasias	242
FR64030	Ametza	264
FR40120	Arnaoutchot (Naturiste)	256
FR64250	Atlantica	270
FR33080	Barbanne	238
FR64020	Barétous-Pyrénées	264
FR33360	Bastide	250
FR64120	Beau Rivage	268
FR64140	Berrua	269
FR33260	Braou	247
FR40020	Chênes	251
FR40260	Chevreuils	262
FR33350	Chez Gendron	250
FR33120	Cigale	239
FR33030	Club d'Arcachon	237
FR64110	Col d'Ibardin	267
FR40050	Col-Vert	252
FR33110	Côte d'Argent	240
FR33010	Dune	237
FR64100	Etche Zahar	268
FR33160	Euronat	240
FR40060	Eurosol	250

FR33020	Fontaine-Vieille	237
FR33280	Forêt	246
FR33150	Gabarreys	240
FR64040	Gaves	265
FR33140	Grand Pré	242
FR33130	Grands Pins (Lacanau-Océan)	243
FR40250	Grands Pins (Sanguinet)	260
FR64050	Itsas Mendi	266
FR33300	Jenny (Naturiste)	248
FR33330	Lilhan	242
FR40140	Lou P'tit Poun	257
FR40280	Lou Puntaou	263
FR40070	Lous Seurrots	254
FR40080	Marina-Landes	253
FR40240	Mayotte Vacances	260
FR64160	Merko-Lacarra	270
FR64230	Mun. Mosqueros	271
FR33240	Océan	246
FR40340	Océliances	257
FR33050	Ourmes	238
FR40040	Paillotte	252
FR33310	Panorama	249
FR64060	Pavillon Royal	265
FR33220	Petit Nice	245
FR33040	Pinèda	238
FR40030	Pins du Soleil	251
FR33210	Pointe du Medoc	244
FR33090	Pressoir	239
FR40290	Punta Lago	264
FR33190	Pyla	244
FR64150	Residence des Pins	269
FR40100	Rive	254
FR64070	Ruisseau	266
FR33340	Sables d'Argent	249
FR40110	Sen Yan	256
FR40270	Saint James Eurolac	263
FR40190	Saint Martin	258
FR40200	Sylvamar	262
FR33320	Talaris	247
FR64080	Tamaris Plage	266
FR33290	Tedey	248
FR33230	Truc Vert	244
FR64240	Uhaitza le Saison	271
FR64280	Ur-Onea	271
FR33250	Val de l'Eyre	246
FR40180	Vieux Port	259
FR40160	Vignes	256

Dordogne & Averyron

FR46220	3 Sources	312
FR24440	Acacias	299
FR24110	Aqua Viva	291
FR46230	Arcades	312
FR24280	Barnabé	294
FR12060	Beau Rivage	275
FR24140	Bel Ombrage	291
FR24380	BleuSoleil	298
FR24240	Bo-Bains	294
FR24410	Bois du Coderc	298
FR24310	Bouquerie	297
FR24660	Brin d'Amour	304
FR47110	Cabri	314

FR12310	Cascade	281
FR12170	Caussanel	278
FR16030	Champion	282
FR46200	Chênes	311
FR24220	Chênes Verts	293
FR12340	Clédelles le Colombier	282
FR16050	Cognac	283
FR12350	Côté Sud	281
FR24190	Couderc (Naturiste)	292
FR24560	Cro Magnon	305
FR47130	Des Bastides	316
FR24150	Deux Vallées	290
FR16040	Devezeau	282
FR46140	Duravel	309
FR24330	Etang Bleu	297
FR46190	Faurie	310
FR47030	Fonrives	312
FR12080	Genêts	276
FR16020	Gorges du Chambon	283
FR24160	Grand Dague	293
FR12070	Grange de Monteillac	276
FR24020	Granges	287
FR24130	Grottes de Roffy	284
FR47150	Guillalmes	315
FR24050	Hauts de Ratebout	285
FR47140	Laborde (Naturiste)	316
FR12250	Lac de Bonnefon	280
FR24070	Lestaubière	285
FR24450	Maisonneuve	300
FR12150	Marmotel	277
FR24360	Mondou	298
FR47050	Moulin de Campech	314
FR24080	Moulin de David	287
FR24350	Moulin de la Pique	297
FR46040	Moulin de Laborde	306
FR24230	Moulin de Paulhiac	294
FR24290	Moulin du Bleufond	295
FR47010	Moulin du Périé	313
FR24040	Moulin du Roch	284
FR24100	Moulinal	288
FR47100	Mun. Le Robinson	315
FR12300	Muret	278
FR24470	Nauves	300
FR24640	Nontron	302
FR46010	Paille Basse	307
FR24570	Palombière	303
FR24060	Paradis	290
FR24320	Peneyrals	295
FR24030	Périères	288
FR24520	Perpetuum	302
FR12160	Peupliers	277
FR12000	Peyrelade	273
FR24540	Peyrelevade	304
FR46030	Pins	306
FR46070	Plage (St Cirq-Lapopie)	308
FR46110	Port (Creysse)	308
FR24170	Port de Limeuil	292
FR24530	Port Vieux	302
FR46170	Reflets du Quercy	311
FR46050	Rêve	308
FR12020	Rivages	274
FR24300	Rivière Fleurie	296

FR12120	Rouergue	276
FR24090	Soleil Plage	289
FR12210	Source	279
FR24180	Saint Avit Loisirs	292
FR12240	Saint Pal	279
FR24480	Tailladis	301
FR24460	Temps de Vivre	300
FR12050	Terrasses du Lac	275
FR24670	Terrasses du Périgord	305
FR12040	Tours	274
FR24510	Trois Caupain	301
FR46150	Truffière	310
FR12010	Val de Cantobre	273
FR24340	Val de la Marquise	296
FR24420	Valades	299
FR47120	Vallée de Gardeleau	316
FR46180	Ventoulou	310
FR24010	Verdoyer	286
FR12280	Viaduc	280

Limousin & Auvergne

FR19020	Aubazines	320
FR03030	Beau Rivage	319
FR87030	Beaufort	328
FR63160	Bel-Air	334
FR48020	Capelan	329
FR48040	Cascade	329
FR63000	Chalets du Hameau du Lac	330
FR48000	Champ d'Ayres	328
FR03040	Champ de la Chapelle	319
FR19070	Chateau de Gibanel	323
FR23010	Château de Poinsouze	326
FR03020	Chazeuil	318
FR63060	Clos Auroy	332
FR19140	Coiroux	325
FR23030	Creuse Natuisme	325
FR63090	Domes	333
FR03170	Dompierre-sur-Besbre	320
FR63030	Europe	331
FR03010	Filature	318
FR63040	Grange Fort	332
FR48060	Lac de Naussac	329
FR87020	Leychoisier	327
FR63140	Loges	334
FR19060	Mialaret	322
FR63080	Moulin de Serre	333
FR03050	Petite Valette	320
FR19030	Plage (Treignac)	321
FR63070	Pré Bas	332
FR63130	Repos du Baladin	334
FR63050	Ribeyre	331
FR19050	Rivière	322
FR63120	Royat	335
FR19100	Soleil d'Oc	324
FR63020	Saint Eloy	330
FR48070	Tivoli	330
FR15030	Val Saint Jean	321
FR63180	Vallée Verte	335
FR43030	Vaubarlet	327
FR19090	Vaurette	323
FR19080	Vianon	324

Rhône Valley

FR26110	4 Saisons	356
FR26260	Acacias	359
FR07180	Ardèche	347
FR07020	Ardéchois	340
FR07120	Ardéchois	345
FR07080	Bastide	342
FR42030	Bel' Epoque du Pilat	359
FR26210	Bois du Chatelas	358
FR07190	Chambourlas	347
FR26270	Champ la Chèvre	360
FR26140	Chataigneraie	356
FR07130	Coudoulets	344
FR26040	Couspeau	354
FR07340	Cros d'Auzon	351
FR01080	Etang du Moulin	339
FR07100	Garenne	344
FR07150	Gil	346
FR07320	Gorges	350
FR01050	Gorges de l'Oignin	338
FR26030	Grand Lierne	354
FR26130	Hirondelle	357
FR01060	Ile de la Comtesse	340
FR07290	Imbours	348
FR26150	Lac Bleu	357
FR07140	Lavandes	349
FR07550	Lion	350
FR01040	Lit Du Roi	337
FR07170	Ludocamping	346
FR69010	Lyon	361
FR07440	Mas de Champel	353
FR69020	Mun. la Grappe Fleurie	360
FR07360	Petit Bois	351
FR01090	Pierre Thorion	340
FR07570	Plage (Neyrac)	353
FR07250	Plaine	348
FR01010	Plaine Tonique	337
FR07090	Plantas	341
FR07110	Pommier	343
FR07420	Pont (Pradons)	352
FR69030	Portes du Beaujolais	361
FR07380	Provençal	352
FR07050	Ranc Davaine	342
FR07070	Ranchisses	342
FR01030	Ripettes	338
FR07400	Riviera	352
FR07310	Roubine	349
FR26100	Sagittaire	355
FR07030	Soleil Vivarais	341
FR26090	Truffières	358
FR01100	Vaugrais	338

Provence

FR84140	Beauregard	377
FR84020	Bélézy (Naturiste)	373
FR05070	Cariamas	372
FR84070	Carpe Diem	375
FR84130	Chênes Blancs	376
FR04040	Collines	366
FR04080	Etoile des Neiges	366
FR84150	Flory	377
FR04120	Forcalquier	368

FR04060	Haut-Verdon	366
FR04010	Hippocampe	363
FR04100	International	364
FR84040	Jantou	374
FR04170	Matherons	369
FR04030	Moulin de Ventre	367
FR05060	Pause	371
FR84090	Pont d'Avignon	375
FR04140	Prairies	369
FR05000	Princes d'Orange	371
FR04160	Relarguiers	370
FR05110	Rochette	373
FR04150	Rose de Provence	370
FR84080	Simioune	374
FR05080	Solaire	372
FR84100	Soleil de Provence	376
FR84050	Sorguette	374
FR04020	Verdon	364
FR04110	Verdon Parc	368
FR05100	Vieille Ferme	373

Midi-Pyrénées

FR81130	Amitié	392
FR09020	Arize	379
FR65170	Arrayade	390
FR32120	Arros	385
FR09120	Ascou la Forge	381
FR09100	Audinac les Bains	381
FR65110	Cabaliros	389
FR81060	Clots	390
FR65010	Eglantière (Naturiste)	386
FR32010	Florence	383
FR82040	Gorges de l'Aveyron	393
FR65040	International	387
FR09080	Lac (Foix)	380
FR32020	Lac (Marciac)	382
FR09130	Lac (Mercus-Garrabet)	382
FR32110	Lac de l'Uby	384
FR32100	Lacs de Courtés	385
FR65080	Lavedan	388
FR81090	Manoir de Boutaric	393
FR09090	Millfleurs (Naturiste)	380
FR65160	Monlôo	389
FR31000	Moulin	386
FR65100	Moulin du Monge	388
FR81030	Mun. de Gourjade	390
FR32090	Pardaillan	384
FR09110	Pas de l'Ours	381
FR09050	Prade (Sorgeat)	380
FR09060	Pré Lombard	379
FR65030	Pyrénées	387
FR65060	Pyrenees Natura	387
FR65130	Pyrenevasion	389
FR81070	Rieu Montagné	391
FR81100	Rigole	391
FR81120	Rouquié	392
FR65090	Soleil du Pibeste	388
FR81110	St-Martin	392
FR32080	Talouch	384
FR82010	Trois Cantons	393
FR32060	Trois Vallées	383
FR65020	Trois Vallées	386
FR32030	Verduzan	382

Mediterranean West

FR30030	Abri de Camargue	402
FR34390	Aloha	422
FR30210	Arche	408
FR11060	Arnauteille	396
FR34260	Beau Rivage	421
FR34210	Berges du Canal	420
FR34370	Blue Bayou	424
FR66610	Bois de Pins	440
FR66590	Bois du Valmarie	438
FR30070	Boisson	403
FR34180	Borio de Roque	419
FR30160	Boucanet	408
FR11230	Bout du Monde	401
FR66070	Brasilia	431
FR66030	Cala Gogo	428
FR34200	Californie Plage	420
FR30360	Castel Rose	412
FR30200	Cévennes-Provence	410
FR34190	Champs Blancs	420
FR34230	Chênes	416
FR11090	Clapotis (Naturiste)	400
FR34110	Club Farret	417
FR34220	Creole	421
FR66150	Criques de Porteils	434
FR66110	Dauphin	432
FR66130	Eau Vive	432
FR66290	Floride et l'Embouchure	436
FR66080	Fontaines	430
FR66250	Font-Romeu	435
FR34470	Fou du Roi	422
FR30060	Fumades	402
FR34020	Garden	413
FR30000	Gaujac	401
FR30220	Gênets d'Or	409
FR30190	Gorges du Gardon	409
FR11190	Grande Cosse Naturiste	400
FR11020	Hamacs	397
FR66050	Haras	430
FR66570	Hippocampe	438
FR34460	Int de l'Hérault	427
FR34450	La Dragonnière	426
FR30120	Ile des Papes	406
FR66020	Ma Prairie	430
FR66090	Mar Estang	427
FR66200	Marsouins	437
FR11040	Martinet Rouge	396
FR30180	Mas de la Cam	407
FR34050	Mas de Lignières (Naturiste)	416
FR30040	Mas de Mourgues	403
FR30080	Mas de Reilhe	404
FR30110	Mas de Rey	404
FR66180	Mas Llinas	434
FR66260	Massane	436
FR30290	Massereau	411
FR34150	Méditerranées	418
FR34290	Mer Et Soleil	422
FR11070	Mimosas	399
FR34170	Mimosas	419
FR11210	Moulin de Sainte-Anne	400
FR11030	Mun. la Pinède	397
FR34030	Napoléon	413
FR11080	Nautique	398

FR34130	Neptune	418
FR34500	Oasis Palavasienne	424
FR34430	Occitanie	425
FR34060	Oliveraie	416
FR66160	Palmeraie	433
FR66100	Pergola	431
FR30020	Petite Camargue	401
FR30390	Petits Camarguais	412
FR66300	Pré Catalan	437
FR66000	Pujol	426
FR11050	Rives des Corbières	396
FR66230	Romarin	433
FR66310	Rotja	440
FR30100	Sablière (Naturiste)	405
FR34400	Sablons	423
FR30380	Secrets de Camargue	412
FR34070	Sérignan Plage	414
FR34080	Sérignan Plage Nature	414
FR66560	Sirène	438
FR66040	Soleil	428
FR30140	Soubeyranne	407
FR30150	Sources	405
FR30170	Sousta	406
FR66220	Stade	435
FR34440	Tamaris	425
FR66190	Tropiques	434
FR30250	Universal	410
FR11110	Val d'Aleth	398
FR30230	Val de l'Arre	411
FR34090	Yole	418

Mediterranean East

FR83310	Argentière	466
FR83080	Au Paradis	452
FR83110	Baie (Cavalaire-sur-Mer)	456
FR83040	Bastiane	450
FR83060	Baume	454
FR83130	Beau Vezé	458
FR06030	Bergerie	442
FR83170	Bergerie	457
FR83340	Bonporteau	467
FR13120	Chantecler	449
FR06080	Cigales (Mandelieu-la-Napoule)	443
FR83160	Cigales (Le Muy)	460
FR83300	Clos Ste-Thérèse	466
FR83230	Colombier	462
FR83220	Cros de Mouton	465
FR83120	Domaine	456
FR83250	Douce Quiétude	464
FR83260	Eouvière	464
FR83020	Esterel	450
FR83070	Etoile d'Argens	458
FR83370	Fréjus	468
FR06090	Gorges du Loup	444
FR06120	Green Park	445
FR83400	Holiday Marina	469
FR83140	Lacs du Verdon	460
FR83030	Leï Suves	453
FR83440	Malissonne	472
FR13050	Mas de Nicolas	448
FR13060	Micocouliers	448
FR83320	Mogador	466

FR13040	Monplaisir	447
FR83240	Moulin des Iscles	462
FR83090	Noguière	456
FR13030	Nostradamus	448
FR06070	Origan (Naturiste)	444
FR83420	Parc Et Plage	468
FR83200	Pêcheurs	463
FR83360	Pierre Verte	467
FR83510	Pinède	472
FR06100	Pinèdes	444
FR83010	Pins Parasol	449
FR83100	Plage (Grimaud)	454
FR83380	Prairies de la Mer	460
FR83190	Presqu'île de Giens	461
FR06140	Ranch	445
FR83050	Résidence du Campeur	452
FR83610	Rives du Loup	446
FR13010	Romarins	447
FR83410	Ruou	469
FR83350	Sélection	468
FR83290	Saint Aygulf	464
FR83620	Saint James Gassin	470
FR83610	Saint James Oasis	470
FR06190	Saint James Sourire	446
FR06010	Sainte Madeleine	442
FR83210	Tournels	462
FR06020	Vallon Rouge	442
FR06050	Vieille Ferme	443

Corsica

FR20010	Arinella Bianca	476
FR20080	Bagheera	477
FR20050	Chiappa (Naturiste)	479
FR20140	Dolce-Vita	478
FR20250	Liccia	476
FR20030	Merendella	476
FR20220	Oliviers	475
FR20150	Olzo	478
FR20170	Paduella	479
FR20160	Paradella	478
FR20000	Pertamina Village	474
FR20180	Pinède	479
FR20110	Restonica	477
FR20040	Riva Bella	477
FR20240	Rondinara	475
FR20230	Sagone	475
FR20070	Santa Lucia	474
FR20060	Vetta	474

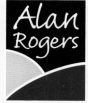